Reader's Digest

SECRETS OF BETTER COOKING

The Reader's Digest Association, Inc.
Pleasantville, New York Montreal Sydney

Photo Credits:

James Viles: Facing page 1; 28, 74, 98, 162, 260, 538, 578, 642

Teubner Studio: 216, 408, 470, 618, 680 (Germany)

Våra Bilder: 328 / Kjell Nilsson: 366 (Sweden)

Drawings by Lucy Durnford Etienne

Library of Congress Catalog Card No. 72-91833

Printed in the United States of America

Fifth Printing

Introduction

Secrets of Better Cooking is designed to help you make nutritious and exciting meals a regular part of your family's life-style without breaking your budget. In these pages you will find the basic techniques of good cooking, the fundamentals on which all good cooks must rely. You will learn, for example, how to read and understand a recipe, and how that recipe can serve as the starting point for dozens of variations of your own. You will also learn what ingredients can be mixed with what others, and in what quantities. This kind of practical knowledge, the basis of the artistry of cooking, will help you extend your culinary repertoire and make your cooking more fun.

For the beginner, *Secrets of Better Cooking* is a complete book of kitchen knowledge that can make cooking easier and less expensive. It begins with the basics and explains the nature and chemistry of foods to assure good nutrition for your family. It also details the techniques of good shopping and the kitchen tools you will need to do the job the easy way.

For the experienced cook, this book offers more than 600 time-tested recipes and more than 40 pages of clear information on herbs and spices plus an up-to-the-minute chapter on frozen foods. In addition, there is a knowledgeable discussion on wines along with 56 pages of helpful information on entertaining.

And as a bonus to beginners and experts alike, the key symbol O━ you will find throughout the book identifies the hundreds of simple secrets expert cooks use to produce gourmet dishes quickly and easily.

A good meal is a compliment to those who share it and a tribute to the care and expertise of the cook. With the help of *Secrets of Better Cooking,* you can discover the real joy and genuine satisfaction that are the rewards of truly good cooking.

Contents

«1»

Nutrition: The Key to Health

Proteins, carbohydrates, fats, vitamins, minerals and why you need them • The seven basic food groups • How to economize on food purchases • Why calories are important • How to regulate calorie intake • How to lose weight • How to gain weight • Calorie table • Pros and cons of organic foods • Recommended daily dietary allowances for maintaining good nutrition

Chemical analysis of foods was relatively unknown before the beginning of the 20th century. At first, foods were analyzed only for their calories and their fat, protein and carbohydrate content. Later work led to the discovery of other food ingredients—vitamins, minerals and amino acids—which play an important role in growth and the maintenance of health.

A healthy body is the basic requirement for a good life as well as a long one. In this chapter you will find some information on basic nutrition. You will feel more energetic when your body is provided with the dietary materials it needs: proteins (amino acids), carbohydrates (starches and sugars), fats, minerals, vitamins and water. All of these nutrients are interdependent and interact with one another. Proteins are the building blocks that we use for growth and repair; they also help form antibodies to fight infection. Carbohydrates supply us with the fuel we need. Fats store certain essential vitamins and minerals in the body until they can be used. In addition, we need to ensure that the foods we eat also provide vitamins and minerals to help the body function successfully. Some foods are more valuable contributors of vitamins and minerals than others.

PROTEIN

By absorbing and using protein, the body creates bones, muscles, nerves, skin, hair and much more. In fact, almost half of the solid matter of the body is protein.

Plants manufacture protein by combining the energy of the sun with the nitrogen and moisture of the soil and the carbon dioxide in the air. Cud-chewing animals, called ruminants, can create protein from the plants they eat. The human body, however, cannot manufacture protein, but must acquire it from digested foods. Once taken in, these proteins are broken down into smaller units and rearranged to form the special and distinct proteins the body needs. Proteins are the chief structural units of the body and yield energy. Although some surplus protein may be converted to fat, protein is not stored and needs to be replaced regularly.

Because of its similarity to human protein, animal protein—found in lean meat, fish, poultry, eggs, milk and cheese—is of more value to us than the vegetable proteins in flours, cereals, beans, peas and peanut butter. By themselves, these poorer proteins cannot be used for repair or growth. It is important to eat some animal protein daily to enable the body to utilize other foods.

Protein needs alter throughout life: an older person —one who no longer grows but who merely repairs existing tissues—needs less than children, adolescents, pregnant women and nursing mothers.

When planning meals for your family, remember that fish and the cheaper cuts of meat provide as much protein as more expensive cuts of meat. All cheeses except cream cheese are high in protein.

CARBOHYDRATES

Starches and sugars comprise the food group known as carbohydrates. There are smaller amounts of carbohydrates in fruits, vegetables and milk, but the major portion of carbohydrate intake comes from bread and other baked goods, cereals, rice, macaroni and highly sweetened foods. In the body, large molecules of carbohydrates are split into simple sugars.

Sugar, a pure carbohydrate, is our poorest food, containing only its energy value and no proteins, vitamins or minerals at all. Sugar supplies us only with calories, and we usually obtain enough of these from other, more nutritious foods, so we cannot afford to overindulge in highly sweetened items.

Our bodies need carbohydrates not just for their energy value but also in order to use fats efficiently. Also, carbohydrates are components of nerve fibers. Some diseases, such as diabetes, develop when the body is unable to handle carbohydrates.

FATS

Is fat needed in daily diet? Very much so. High in calories, fat is the body's most concentrated source of energy. It is necessary for the utilization of proteins and carbohydrates and is the storehouse for certain fat-soluble vitamins.

Many claims have been made in recent years about

the benefits of polyunsaturated fats and oils. An unsaturated fat is one that has some of its molecular "arms" free to join with other materials in the body. Unsaturated fats are more readily absorbed and can carry around other nutrients more easily than can saturated fats, which have no free "arms." Vegetable oils, such as sesame and peanut oils, are lower in saturated fat than are animal fats such as butter and lard. However, our knowledge about this is still limited; some researchers claim our salvation lies in never eating butter; others insist that butter is a good food for human nutrition.

Foods high in *saturated* fats include meats, egg yolk, whole milk, cream and cheeses made from whole milk and cream, ice cream, butter, some margarines, solid shortenings, chocolate, coconut. Foods high in *unsaturated* fats include fish and seafood, liquid vegetable oils and margarines made from such oils, nuts (except coconut) and nut butters. Chicken and turkey have equal amounts of both fats. Some medical authorities believe that eating fewer foods with saturated fats will reduce the amount of cholesterol in the blood, but we do not know whether or not that is an important goal for humans. Research is continuing, and someday we will know more.

Beware of "hidden" fats in foods. Recognizable fat —that found on meat, or in the form of butter, lard, drippings or shortening—is not the only fat we eat. A glass of whole milk contains 148 calories, of which 70 are fat. Of the 226 calories in 2 ounces of Cheddar cheese, 160 come from fat. Only about 25 percent of our total calorie consumption should come from fats, yet in the United States this figure is now about 44 percent.

VITAMINS

Vitamins are organic substances contained in food. They do not provide energy, nor do they serve as building material the way proteins do. They are necessary, however, to keep the body's metabolic "equation" balanced. Some vitamins are produced in the body, but we must acquire the major portion from the foods we eat. These are the most important ones, and their sources:

Vitamin A

Keeps skin and mucous membranes healthy and resistant to infection; protects against night blindness. Vitamin A can be stored in the body.

BEST SOURCES: liver, yellow vegetables and fruits, green vegetables (the darker the color the better), whole or homogenized milk, cream, butter, margarine, eggs, cheese (except cottage or skim-milk cheeses).

Vitamin B_1 (thiamine)

Maintains normal appetite and digestion and a healthy nervous system; helps change food substances into energy for work and heat. This is a water-soluble vitamin and cannot be stored; therefore, some foods rich in thiamine should be eaten regularly.

BEST SOURCES: whole-grain cereals, wheat germ, lean pork, liver, kidney, heart, potatoes, peas, green lima beans, asparagus.

Vitamin B_2 (riboflavin)

Helps cells use oxygen, keeps vision clear and skin smooth. Like thiamine, this water-soluble vitamin cannot be stored.

BEST SOURCES: milk, eggs, liver, heart, kidney, spinach, mushrooms; other fruits, vegetables and meats add smaller amounts.

Niacin

This is usually considered part of the B-complex vitamins. Like B_1 and B_2, this is water-soluble and cannot be stored.

BEST SOURCES: meats, shellfish, nuts (especially peanuts), enriched breads and whole grains.

Vitamin C (ascorbic acid)

Helps cement body cells together and strengthens the walls of blood vessels; helps resist infection and aids healing. Vitamin C cannot be stored in the body, so it is important to eat at least one food rich in vitamin C every day.

BEST SOURCES: Of the foods rich in this essential, each of the following will supply an equal amount of the vitamin: 1 orange; ½ grapefruit; 4 ounces orange or grapefruit juice (fresh, frozen, canned); 4 ounces vitaminized apple juice; 8 ounces tomato juice, or fresh or canned tomatoes; 1 serving of cantaloupe, strawberries, raspberries, or raw cabbage salad. Vitamin C is also found in green peppers, broccoli and some other fruits and vegetables.

Vitamin D Assists the absorption of calcium and phosphorus and builds strong bones. Lack of this vitamin results in rickets, a disease characterized by stunted growth, soft bones and poorly developed and defective teeth. Vitamin D can be stored in the body, and excessive amounts can be harmful, but it is a vitamin that does not occur naturally in our foods in useful amounts.

BEST SOURCES: The only common foods that are naturally high in vitamin D are salmon, sardines, tuna and herring. Some milk and margarine is fortified with vitamin D, and this information will be stated on the label. During the summer months our bodies can absorb some vitamin D from the direct rays of the sun.

Other vitamins Some other vitamins have been discovered and labeled E, F, G, K and so on. Research on these and their essential roles in human nutrition is still continuing. We do not know the minimum daily requirements of these vitamins.

Vitamins in the diet

An insufficiency of a particular vitamin in the human diet can lead to poor health; in extreme cases, to deficiency diseases or death. Remember the old adage, "An ounce of prevention is worth a pound of cure." If you provide well-balanced meals for your family, you will usually supply an adequate amount of vitamins. While synthetic vitamins can be administered, the natural ones in foods are more readily used by the body, especially in the case of fat-soluble vitamins A and D. Also an overdose of vitamins in pill form should be guarded against. This is particularly important with vitamin D, for the concentrated medicinal vitamin can have toxic effects. Actually, a normal healthy person eating a well-balanced diet and getting sunshine and fresh air does not need supplementary vitamins.

MINERALS

Minerals are chemical elements that are necessary constituents of all body cells and fluids. Their most obvious function is to provide strength and rigidity to bones and teeth. In addition, they participate in muscle contraction, nerve responses and other processes. In addition to the vitamin and calorie content of the foods we eat, we ought to know which foods supply the most essential minerals—iron, iodine, calcium, phosphorus. If your diet is well balanced, the other minerals will likely be present in sufficient quantity.

Iron

Maintains the red-cell count in blood. Hemoglobin, an iron-containing protein pigment in the red blood cells, helps move oxygen from the lungs to other parts of the body. Too little hemoglobin leads to low vitality and poor health.

BEST SOURCES: liver, kidney, heart, red meat, poultry, eggs, enriched white flour or bread, whole-grain and special baby cereals, fruits and vegetables (particularly cooked greens), peas and mature beans.

Iodine

Regulates growth and rate of metabolism.

BEST SOURCES: Seafoods are high in iodine content, and people who live in coastal regions may get small amounts from locally grown produce. If you live inland, iodized table salt will probably be the only kind available to you. The amount of salt normally used will suppy the body's requirement.

Calcium

Helps maintain muscular tissues and builds bones and teeth; helps blood to clot and nerves and muscles to act and react normally.

BEST SOURCES: milk, cheese, leafy vegetables, dried legumes, fruits, meats.

Phosphorus

Builds bones and teeth; without phosphorus the body is unable to utilize calcium properly.

BEST SOURCES: meats, fish, poultry, dried legumes, eggs, nuts, root vegetables.

Other minerals

Other minerals are found in small quantities in foods, and research on their place in human nutrition is still being explored. They include *copper,* which works with iron to form hemoglobin; *fluorine,* part of teeth and bones; *magnesium,* needed for the utilization of amino acids; *potassium,* necessary for good functioning of nerves and muscles, including the heart muscle, and for the utilization of carbohydrates; *sodium,* related to the water balance of the body. Some of these others are needed in extremely small amounts.

WATER

Of course, water is not a nutrient, but it is necessary for the maintenance of all body functions and helps to move all the nutrients through the system.

THE FOUR BASIC FOOD GROUPS

Dietitians group foods according to the nutrients they provide. The "Basic Four," prepared by the Agricultural Research Service of the United States Government, can be a helpful guide to planning meals for balanced nutrition.

I. Meat group

Foods in this group are valued for their protein, which is needed for growth and repair of body tissues—muscle, organs, blood, skin and hair. These foods also provide iron, thiamin, riboflavin and niacin.

These foods include beef; veal; lamb; pork; variety meats, such as liver, heart, kidney; poultry and eggs; fish and shellfish. Alternates are dry beans, dry peas, lentils, nuts, peanuts, peanut butter.

Choose 2 or more servings every day. Count as a serving: 2 to 3 ounces (not including bone weight) cooked lean meat, poultry or fish. Count as alternates for ½ serving of meat or fish: 1 egg; ½ cup cooked dry beans, dry peas or lentils; or 2 tablespoons peanut butter.

II. Milk group

Milk is our leading source of calcium, which is needed for bones and teeth. It also provides high-quality protein, riboflavin, vitamin A and many other nutrients.

Foods in this group are milk (fluid whole, evaporated, skim, dry, buttermilk); cheese (cottage, cream, cheddar-type—natural or processed); ice cream.

Everyone should drink milk daily. Below are recommended amounts in terms of 8-ounce cups of whole fluid milk:

Children under 9	2 to 3
Children 9 to 12	3 or more
Teen-agers	4 or more
Adults	2 or more
Pregnant women	3 or more
Nursing mothers	4 or more

Part or all of the milk may be fluid skim milk, buttermilk, evaporated milk or dry milk.

Cheese and ice cream may replace part of the milk. The amount of either it will take to replace a given amount of milk is figured on the basis of calcium content. Common portions of various kinds of cheese and of ice cream and their milk equivalents in calcium are: 1-inch cube cheddar-type cheese equals ½ cup milk; ½ cup cottage cheese equals ⅓ cup milk; 2 tablespoons cream cheese equals 1 tablespoon milk; ½ cup ice cream or ice milk equals ⅓ cup milk.

III. Vegetable-fruit group

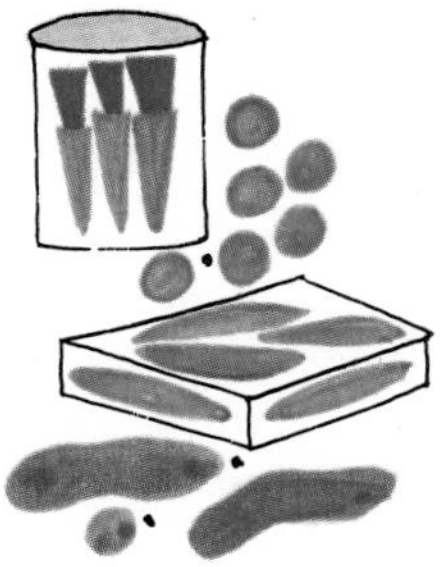

Fruits and vegetables are valuable chiefly because of the vitamins and minerals they contain. In this plan, this group is counted on to supply nearly all the vitamin C needed and more than half of the vitamin A.

Vitamin C is needed for healthy gums and body tissues. Vitamin A is needed for growth, normal vision, and healthy condition of the skin and other body surfaces.

These foods include all vegetables and fruits. This guide emphasizes those rich in vitamin C and vitamin A.

Good sources of vitamin C are grapefruit or grapefruit juice, oranges or orange juice, cantaloupes, guavas, mangoes, papayas, raw strawberries, broccoli, brussels sprouts, green peppers and sweet red peppers.

Good sources of vitamin A are dark-green and deep-yellow vegetables and a few fruits, such as apricots, broccoli, cantaloupes, carrots, chard, collards, pumpkins, spinach, sweet potatoes, turnip greens and other dark-green leaves, winter squash.

Choose 4 or more servings every day, including: 1 serving of a good source of vitamin C; 1 serving, at least every other day, of a good source of vitamin A. If the food chosen for vitamin C is also a good source of vitamin A, the additional serving of a vitamin A food may be omitted.

The remaining 1 to 3 or more servings may be of any vegetable or fruit, including those that are valuable for vitamin C and vitamin A.

Count as 1 serving: ½ cup of vegetable or fruit; or a portion as ordinarily served, such as 1 medium apple, banana, orange or potato; half a medium grapefruit or cantaloupe; or the juice of 1 lemon.

IV. Bread-cereal group

Foods in this group furnish worthwhile amounts of protein, iron, several of the B vitamins and food energy. All whole-grain, enriched, or restored breads and cereals are included.

Choose 4 servings or more daily. Or, if no cereals are chosen, have an extra serving of breads or baked goods, which will make at least 5 servings from this group daily.

Count as 1 serving: 1 slice of bread; 1 ounce ready-to-eat cereal; ½ to ¾ cup cooked cereal, cornmeal, grits, macaroni, noodles, rice or spaghetti.

Other foods

To round out meals and meet energy needs, almost everyone will use some foods not specified in the four food groups. Such foods include unenriched, refined breads, cereals, flours; sugars; butter, margarine, other fats. Try to include some vegetable oil among the fats used.

HOW TO ECONOMIZE

Use the listing of the four food groups to plan which foods you can serve together in an interesting fashion without stinting on essential nutrition. With a little ingenuity you will be able to balance the more expensive against the less expensive. With a little experience you will be able to economize on your food costs. Here are a few elementary examples:

In Group I (meat, poultry, fish): if you can't provide prime ribs of beef or sirloin steak, buy cheaper cuts to braise or stew. Meat is relatively the most expensive of the basic foods, but a good rule is to allot no more than a quarter of your food budget to meat products.

In Group II (milk, cheese and ice cream): buy buttermilk and nonfat dried skim milk. Both are more economical to use than whole milk.

In Group III (fruits and vegetables): make use of tomatoes in the summer when they are cheaper, but use canned tomatoes at other times of the year. Buy citrus and the other fruits when they are priced at their lowest. Make the most use of potatoes, cabbage, carrots, turnips, parsnips and squash during the winter months.

CALORIES: WHY THEY ARE IMPORTANT

A calorie is a unit of measurement used by scientists to designate the energy potential of a food when it is used up—or "burned" by the body. Scientists describe a calorie as the amount of heat (energy) required to raise the temperature of 1 gram of water 1 degree centigrade. In the laboratory, the number of calories in a food is determined by placing a measured sampling of the food in an oxygen-filled capsule which is surrounded by water. The food is electrically ignited, and because it is enveloped in pure oxygen, it burns quickly and completely. The resulting heat is measured by recording the rise in the temperature of the water surrounding the capsule.

The calorie content of a food is important to nutrition because it tells you the energy-producing value of various foods. The number of calories in foods depends upon their protein, carbohydrate and fat content. Every gram of protein or carbohydrate yields 4 calories; every gram of fat supplies 9 calories. Calculated in ounces, there are 115 calories per ounce of protein or carbohydrate, and 255 calories per ounce of fat.

The number of calories you need depends on your age and how active you are. When more calories are consumed than the body can convert into energy, the excess calories are stored by your body in the form of fatty tissue. Children and teenagers, who lead active lives and whose bodies are constantly growing, seldom experience overweight problems caused by excessive calorie intake. Adults, however, often consume more calories than their bodies can burn. Desk jobs, automobiles and easy living keep most adults from getting sufficient exercise to burn up their daily calorie intake. Also, today's foods tend to be high in calorie content. As a result, being overweight is a serious modern health problem leading toward such diseases as diabetes, gallstones, heart trouble, high blood pressure and stroke. Doctors recommend that we regulate our diets carefully, paying close attention to the ratio between the exercise we get and the calories we consume.

REGULATING CALORIE INTAKE

There are a number of helpful formulas available to help you coordinate your daily calorie intake with your body's energy requirement. One suggestion from nutritionists is that your ideal weight at age 22 should be the guideline for your weight throughout life.

Ideal weight is determined by scientific weight charts that relate height to weight to body frame. These charts are available in most medical guides, or, if you cannot find such a chart, consult with your doctor to determine your ideal weight.

Use the ideal weight figure as a base for calculating your body's calorie requirement. If you are a woman, multiply the ideal weight by 16; for a man, multiply by 18. Subtract 10 for each year of age beyond 22. The resulting figure tells you what your daily calorie intake should be.

Consume more calories per day than the calculated figure and you will gain weight; consume fewer calories and you will lose weight. Bear in mind, however, that calorie intake is only one aspect of good nutrition. It is possible that in adjusting your diet to reduce or increase calorie intake, you may deprive yourself of other important nutrients. Avoid this by using a reliable calorie chart to help you in food planning, and do not make any drastic changes in your diet without first seeking your doctor's advice.

The following menu suggestions vary the amounts for overweight and underweight conditions without omitting the nutritional value of the important food groups.

Normal meal pattern

Breakfast: citrus fruit or juice; whole-grain cereal with milk; other protein food, if desired; toast with butter or fortified margarine; beverage (milk for children).

Lunch (or supper): cheese, egg or other protein food; vegetable; bread with butter or fortified margarine; dessert; beverage—milk.

Dinner: meat, fish or poultry; potato; other vegetable(s); bread (if desired); fruit or fruit dessert; beverage (milk for children).

To lose weight

Follow the normal pattern, but

For breakfast

OMIT: sugar and cream on cereal and in beverages; cereal, or eat only a small serving (have a soft-cooked egg instead); bread alternates such as pancakes and doughnuts; jam, jelly, syrup, marmalade.

For lunch (or supper)

USE: clear soups instead of cream soups; skim-milk cheeses (they are labeled as such); lemon juice or vinegar on salads instead of salad dressing; fresh fruits for dessert instead of rich puddings, pies, cakes, sundaes; skim milk or buttermilk.

OMIT: fried foods; rich creamed dishes; gravy; cookies and cake.

DO NOT: take large servings or second helpings; eat between meals; omit any meal (three regular meals should still be taken); take soft drinks, beer, liquor.

For dinner

USE: lean meats and fish; fresh fruits instead of canned or dried fruits.

OMIT: gravy; cream and sugar.

To gain weight

For breakfast

USE: sugar and cream on cereals; bacon or extra protein food; extra bread and butter; jam, jelly, syrup or marmalade; cream in beverage.

For lunch (or supper)

USE: richer main dishes (creamed dishes, extra butter, etc.); mayonnaise or French dressings on salads; extra bread and butter; richer desserts; beverage of half milk and half cream.

DO: take generous servings; eat between meals as long as it does not spoil appetite at mealtimes.

For dinner

USE: cream soup if desired; bread and butter; gravy or butter on potatoes; butter on vegetables; cookies or cake with the fruit dessert; milk as a beverage.

CALORIE COUNTER

The following calorie table will help in planning well-balanced meals. The figures are based on data published by the United States Department of Agriculture. You may write the USDA for more calorie and nutrient information. Ask for Home and Garden Bulletin No. 72, *Nutritive Value of Foods*.

Meats*

FOOD	AMOUNT	WEIGHT IN GRAMS	CALORIES
Beef			
chipped beef	2 ounces	57	115
corned beef	3 ounces	85	185
cuts broiled (steaks)	3 ounces	85	330
cuts cooked with liquid	3 ounces	85	245
cuts cooked without liquid (roasts)	3 ounces	85	375
frankfurter, broiled	1 frank-furter	56	170
hamburger, broiled	3 ounces	85	245
heart, braised	3 ounces	85	160
kidney, braised	3 ounces	85	215
liver, fried	3 ounces	85	195
tongue, braised	3 ounces	85	210
Veal			
calf's liver, fried	3 ounces	85	220
cutlet without bone, broiled	3 ounces	85	185
kidney, braised	3 ounces	85	140
roast	3 ounces	85	230
Lamb			
chop with bone, broiled	1 chop	89	360
kidney, broiled	3 ounces	85	120
leg, roast	3 ounces	85	235
shoulder, roast	3 ounces	85	285
Pork, cured			
bacon, broiled	2 slices	15	85
Canadian bacon, broiled	2 slices	21	60
ham, baked	3 ounces	85	245
sausage	1 link	13	60
Pork, fresh			
chop with bone, broiled	1 chop	78	305
cuts cooked with liquid	3 ounces	85	320
cuts cooked without liquid	3 ounces	85	310

*The measured portions of meat are similar to those the average shopper would buy; they contain both lean and fat. To reduce the calories further, trim each portion.

	FOOD	AMOUNT	WEIGHT IN GRAMS	CALORIES
Poultry	chicken			
	boneless and skinless,			
	(broiled)	3 ounces	85	115
	breast, fried	3 ounces	85	160
	canned, boneless	3 ounces	85	170
	leg, fried (drumstick)	1 ounce	85	90
	liver, cooked with liquid	3 ounces	85	140
	duck, roast	3 ounces	85	345
	goose, roast	3 ounces	85	360
	Rock Cornish game hen	3 ounces	85	250
	squab, roast	3 ounces	85	240
	turkey, roast	2 slices	85	170
Fish				
	bluefish, broiled	3 ounces	85	135
	cod, broiled	3 ounces	85	145
	flounder, baked	3 ounces	85	170
	haddock, fried	3 ounces	85	140
	halibut, broiled	3 ounces	85	145
	herring, kippered	3 ounces	85	180
	mackerel, broiled	3 ounces	85	200
	perch, breaded and fried	3 ounces	85	195
	red snapper, broiled	3 ounces	85	110
	salmon, baked	3 ounces	85	155
	salmon, canned	3 ounces	85	120
	sardines, canned in oil	3 ounces	85	175
	shad, baked	3 ounces	85	170
	swordfish, broiled	3 ounces	85	150
	tuna, canned in oil	3 ounces	85	170
Shellfish				
	clams, canned	3 ounces	85	45
	clams, raw	3 ounces	85	65
	crab meat, canned	1 cup	135	135
	lobster, fresh, cooked	3 ounces	85	80
	mussels, raw	3 ounces	85	80
	oysters, canned	3 ounces	85	65
	oysters (selects), raw	1 cup	240	160
	shrimps, poached	3 ounces	85	100

Vegetables—leafy, green, yellow

FOOD	AMOUNT	WEIGHT IN GRAMS	CALORIES
asparagus, green, cut	1 cup	145	30
beans, green	1 cup	125	30
beans, lima	1 cup	170	190
broccoli	1 cup	155	40
brussels sprouts	1 cup	155	55
cabbage, green (cooked)	1 cup	145	30
carrots, raw	1 carrot	81	30
raw, grated	1 cup	110	45
cooked	1 cup	155	50
collards	1 cup	190	65
dandelion greens (cooked)	1 cup	105	35
kale	1 cup	110	45
lettuce, loose-leaf types	1 cup	55	10
peas, green	1 cup	160	115
peppers, green	1 pod	73	15
peppers, red	1 pod	60	20
pimientos	1 pod	38	10
pumpkin	1 cup	245	80
spinach	1 cup	180	40
squash, winter	1 cup	205	130
sweet potatoes			
baked, peeled	1 potato	114	160
boiled, peeled	1 potato	151	170
candied	1 piece	105	175
canned, mashed	1 cup	255	275

Citrus fruits and vegetables rich in vitamin C

FOOD	AMOUNT	WEIGHT IN GRAMS	CALORIES
cabbage, raw	1 cup	90	20
cantaloupes	½ melon	447	80
cauliflower, raw, chopped	1 cup	115	30
endive, curly	1 cup	50	10
escarole	1 cup	50	10
grapefruit juice	1 cup	246	95
grapefruit sections	1 cup	200	80
grapefruits, pink or red	½ grapefruit	277	60
grapefruits, white	½ grapefruit	241	45
lemon juice	1 cup	244	60
	1 tablespoon	15	5

FOOD	AMOUNT	WEIGHT IN GRAMS	CALORIES
lemons	1 lemon	110	20
lime juice	1 cup	246	65
orange juice*	1 cup	248	110
oranges, California	1 orange	206	70
oranges, Florida	1 orange	204	70
parsley, chopped	1 tablespoon	4	1
peppers, green, raw	1 pod	90	15
pineapples, raw, diced	1 cup	155	80
potatoes, new, peeled, boiled	3 small potatoes	135	90
spinach, raw	1 cup	55	15
strawberries	1 cup	149	55
tangerine juice	1 cup	247	105
tangerines	1 tangerine	116	40
tomato juice	1 cup	243	45
tomatoes, canned	1 cup	241	50
tomatoes, raw	1 tomato	135	25
turnips, raw, diced (rutabagas)	1 cup	140	65
watercress, whole sprigs	1 cup	35	7

Potatoes and other vegetables

FOOD	AMOUNT	WEIGHT IN GRAMS	CALORIES
potatoes			
baked, peeled	1 potato	156	145
boiled, peeled	1 potato	150	105
French fried	10 pieces	50	135
mashed, with milk and butter	1 cup	210	195
peeled, boiled	1 potato	135	90
potato chips	10 chips	20	115
bean sprouts (mung)	1 cup	105	35
beets, diced	1 cup	170	55
cabbage, white, cooked, drained	1 cup	170	30
cauliflower, cooked, drained	1 cup	125	30
celery	1 rib	40	5

* Oranges vary in calories according to the season and origin of the fruit. Florida oranges have more vitamin A, California oranges more vitamin C. The difference is reflected in the juice too, of course; this figure is for juice from a late-season Florida Valencia orange.

FOOD	AMOUNT	WEIGHT IN GRAMS	CALORIES
celery, diced, raw	1 cup	120	20
corn, canned, wet-pack, drained	1 cup	165	140
corn, sweet	1 ear	140	70
cucumbers, raw, with peel	6-8 small slices	28	5
eggplant, diced, boiled	1 cup	200	40
lettuce, Boston types	1 head	220	25
lettuce, Iceberg types	1 head	567	70
mushrooms, canned	3 ounces	85	15
mushrooms, fresh, raw	1 cup	70	20
okra, cooked	10 pods	106	30
onions, cooked	1 cup	210	60
onions, green (scallions)	6 scallions	30	15
onions, raw, chopped	1 cup	170	65
parsnips, diced	1 cup	155	100
radishes	4 radishes	32	5
sauerkraut	1 cup	235	40
squash, summer, diced	1 cup	210	30
turnips (rutabagas), diced	1 cup	155	35
turnips (white)	1 cup	155	35

Fruits other than citrus fruits

FOOD	AMOUNT	WEIGHT IN GRAMS	CALORIES
apple juice	1 cup	248	115
apples	1 apple	150	80
applesauce, sweetened	1 cup	255	230
apricots	3 apricots	114	55
apricots, canned with syrup	1 cup	258	220
apricots, dried	1 cup	130	340
avocados	½ avocado	125	190
bananas	1 banana	175	100
blackberries	1 cup	144	85
blueberries	1 cup	145	90
cherries, sour, canned, water pack	1 cup	244	105
cherries, sweet	10 cherries	75	45

	FOOD	AMOUNT	WEIGHT IN GRAMS	CALORIES
	cranberry-juice cocktail	1 cup	253	165
	cranberries, raw	½ pound	227	100
	dates, pitted	10 dates	80	220
	figs, dried	1 fig	21	60
	figs, fresh, raw	3 figs	114	90
	grapes, adhering skins	1 cup	160	105
	grapes, slip skins	1 cup	153	70
	peaches, canned in syrup	1 cup	256	200
	peaches, dried	1 cup	160	420
	peaches, fresh	1 peach	100	40
	peaches, fresh, sliced	1 cup	170	65
	pears, canned	1 cup	255	195
	pears, fresh, Bartlett	1 pear	164	100
	pineapple juice	1 cup	250	140
	pineapple, canned, crushed	1 cup	255	190
	plums, canned with syrup	1 cup	272	215
	plums, fresh	1 plum	70	30
	prunes, dried	5 prunes	38	80
	raisins	1 cup	145	420
	raspberries, red	1 cup	123	70
	rhubarb, cooked, sweetened	1 cup	270	380
	watermelon	1 wedge	926	110
Dried legumes	blackeye peas, dry, cooked	1 cup	250	190
	kidney or red beans, dry, cooked	1 cup	255	230
	lima beans, cooked, drained	1 cup	190	260
	navy or pea beans, cooked, drained	1 cup	190	225
	peas, split, dry, cooked	1 cup	200	230
Shelled nuts	almonds	1 cup	142	850
	Brazil nuts	1 cup	140	915
	cashews	1 cup	140	785
	coconut, dried, sweetened	1 cup	62	340
	coconut, fresh	1 cup	80	275
	hazelnuts	1 cup	135	856

FOOD	AMOUNT	WEIGHT IN GRAMS	CALORIES
peanut butter	1 table-spoon	16	95
peanuts, chopped	1 table-spoon	9	50
peanuts, roasted, salted	1 cup	144	840
pecans, chopped	1 table-spoon	7½	50
pecans, halves	1 cup	118	810
walnuts, black, chopped	1 cup	125	785
walnuts, English, chopped	1 table-spoon	8	50
walnuts, English, halves	1 cup	120	780

Dairy products

FOOD	AMOUNT	WEIGHT IN GRAMS	CALORIES
cheese			
blue types	1 counce	28	105
Cheddar types	1-inch cube	17	70
grafted	1 cup	113	455
cottage, creamed, large curd	1 cup	225	235
cottage, uncreamed	1 cup	145	125
cream	1 ounce	28	100
Swiss types	1 ounce	28	105
cream			
heavy (whipping cream)	1 cup	238	820
	1 table-spoon	15	80
light (coffee cream)	1 cup	240	470
	1 table-spoon	15	30
ice cream	1 cup	133	270
ice milk	1 cup	131	185
milk			
buttermilk	1 cup	245	100
condensed, sweetened, undiluted	1 cup	306	980
evaporated, unsweetened, undiluted	1 cup	252	340
skim, dry	1 cup	68	245
skim, fluid	1 cup	245	85
whole, dry	1 cup	128	645
whole, fluid	1 cup	244	150

FOOD	AMOUNT	WEIGHT IN GRAMS	CALORIES
Eggs			
cooked, boiled	1 egg	50	80
raw, whole	1 egg	50	80
white only	1 white	33	15
yolk only	1 yolk	17	65
scrambled with butter	1 egg	64	95
Bread, flour, cereals			
Boston brown bread	1 slice	45	95
cracked-wheat bread	1 slice	25	65
French bread	1-pound loaf	454	1,315
Italian bread	1-pound loaf	454	1,250
rye bread	1 slice	25	60
white bread	1 slice	25	70
whole-wheat bread	1 slice	28	65
bread crumbs, dry	1 cup	100	390
biscuits	1 biscuit	28	105
graham crackers	4 small crackers	14	55
muffins, plain	1 muffin	40	120
pancakes	1 pancake	27	60
rolls, nonsweet	1 roll	35	120
rolls, sweet	1 roll	43	135
rye wafers	2 wafers	13	45
saltines	4 crackers	11	50
waffles	1 waffle	75	210
barley, uncooked	1 cup	200	700
bran flakes, enriched	1 cup	35	105
corn cereals, cold	1 ounce	25	95
corn grits (hominy), cooked	1 cup	245	125
cornmeal, whole ground	1 cup	122	435
oat cereals, cold	1 ounce	28	110
oats, oatmeal, cooked	1 cup	240	130
rice, cooked, instant	1 cup	165	180
rice cereals, cold	1 cup	14 to 30	55 to 115
wheat flour, all-purpose	1 cup	125	455
wheat flour, whole-wheat	1 cup	120	400

Fats, oils, sweets

FOOD	AMOUNT	WEIGHT IN GRAMS	CALORIES
wheat germ, toasted	1 tablespoon	6	25
wheat cereals, cold	1 ounce	28	about 100
butter	1 stick	113	815
	1 tablespoon	14	100
margarine	1 stick	113	815
	1 tablespoon	14	100
chocolate, unsweetened	1 ounce	28	145
chocolate syrup	2 tablespoon	38	90
corn oil	1 tablespoon	14	120
corn syrup	1 tablespoon	21	60
French dressing	1 tablespoon	16	65
honey	1 tablespoon	21	65
jams, preserves, jellies	1 tablespoon	20	55
lard	1 cup	205	1,850
	1 tablespoon	13	115
mayonnaise	1 tablespoon	14	100
molasses	1 tablespoon	20	50
olive oil	1 tablespoon	14	120
sugar, brown, packed	1 cup	220	820
	1 tablespoon	14	50
sugar, confectioners'	1 cup	120	460
	1 tablespoon	8	30
sugar, granulated	1 cup	200	770
	1 tablespoon	12	45
vegetable fat	1 cup	200	1,770
	1 tablespoon	12½	110

ORGANIC FOODS

In recent years there has been an enormous growth in the popularity of so-called organic foods. Stores that specialize in these foods have multiplied in urban and suburban areas, and many supermarkets now stock at least a small selection. Just what are organic foods, and what are their advantages and disadvantages?

No government standard stipulates exactly what the word "organic" on a food label is supposed to mean. (This is an objection cited by many people who believe the foods are a passing fad.) But there is general agreement on what constitutes organic foods.

Organic fruits and vegetables are grown without the use of any chemical pesticides or fertilizers. The soil in which organic vegetables are cultivated is treated with natural animal manure and with humus—decomposed organic waste matter that serves as a natural fertilizer. The composting process that produces humus, familiar to most gardeners, utilizes materials that might otherwise be burned or carted away, such as leaves, grass cuttings, straw and weeds, which are heaped up in layers and left to stand until they molder into humus. Understandably, this is a slow process, and the amount of natural fertilizer available for the growth of organic foods severely limits their supply.

The organic gardener or farmer faces an even more challenging problem when dealing with insect pests. But there are solutions. Natural insect predators such as ladybugs and praying mantises, which can be purchased in large lots from suppliers, are effective in destroying many plant pests. And farmers have found that they can destroy plant-eating slugs by setting out pans of warm beer. Attracted by the odor of the beer, the slugs crawl into the pans and drown.

Organic meats, like organic vegetables, are naturally pure and free of any artificial chemical substances. Cattle, chickens and other organically raised animals receive no special hormones (used to promote growth in most commercially raised animals) and are not treated with antibiotics. Nor are they allowed to graze in areas treated with chemical pesticides or to consume feed that contains artificial additives or preservatives. Similarly, organic foods are not subject to chemical processing and contain no preservatives. Because these conditions are difficult to meet, the supply of organic food falls far short of the demand, and prices are generally high.

What is behind the growing popularity of organic foods? Its enthusiasts seem to fall into four main categories. First, there are those who simply think that organic foods—particularly fruits and vegetables—taste better. Picked at their peak, they are rushed to nearby organic food stores and into the consumers' homes when they are fresh and tender, rather than being subjected to lengthy refrigeration and storage before reaching the table.

A second group encourages the wider use of organic foods because of concern about the environment. Ecologists approve of treating the soil with humus rather than chemical fertilizers; the organic farmer's method improves the structure and aeration of the soil, reduces water runoff and erosion, and encourages the development of helpful organisms in the soil. More and more groups object to the use of chemical fertilizers and pesticides because of their damaging effects on water and wildlife. Related indirectly to the environmentalists are those who embrace the use of organic foods as representative of a new and better way of life—one closer to nature and diametrically opposed to the technological culture they have come to distrust.

By far the largest group of enthusiasts is composed of people who think organic foods really are better for you: that by eating organic meat and produce you will become a healthier, more vital, more attractive person. There is considerable disagreement about this. Every day more books and periodicals explore the subject with varying degrees of responsibility, some of them setting forth extreme claims for the nutritional or even curative powers of certain organic health foods, others deriding them. Magazines and newspapers blossom with articles as experts on both sides of the controversy clash.

Bluntly, there is no proof one way or the other.

The attitude of the Department of Agriculture is that there is no harm in organically grown foods. The department recognizes that if these foods are produced closer to where they are sold, they will be fresher and have a more vine- or tree-ripened flavor than some that are shipped cross-country. Foods in their more natural, pure state do not violate any government regulations (except for raw milk). But organic foods should not be chosen with the avowed purpose of getting a more nutritious diet. The greater cost of the food claimed to be organically grown may buy certain desirable characteristics not always found in the usual food market—but greater nutritive value is not one of them.

Opponents of organic foods claim that many dealers are dishonest, buying produce from regular commercial wholesalers and then representing it as organic, at a markup of as much as 100 percent above the supermarket price. Critics argue further that old people with limited incomes are among those who are most susceptible to misleading claims about the special virtues of organic food, and that by paying higher prices than necessary these people are dangerously cutting into their nutrition budget. Less serious, but equally worth considering, is the objection of many housewives that organic foods simply are too inconvenient to prepare on a regular basis—particularly the grain foods.

On the plus side, however, the family that decides in favor of organic foods automatically cuts out of its diet almost all of the so-called empty-calorie snack foods and beverages of little or no nutritive value. These are largely carbohydrates in one form or another that tend to force more nutritionally valuable foods out of the diet. Thus, while a head of organic lettuce may be no more nutritional than a head of commercial lettuce, an overall diet based largely or exclusively on organic foods—fresh fruits and vegetables, proteins, nuts and grains—might tend to improve a family's general nutritional balance.

The cook herself must ultimately decide to what extent she wants to use organic foods in her kitchen. Such foods provide good nutrition, they are unadulterated and their growth is ecologically beneficial. Often the fruits and vegetables are fresher and better tasting. There is a pleasure in working with nature's pure product, and a challenge in fitting these foods into the family diet. Often this provides more than enough satisfaction to offset the high cost and occasional inconvenience of organic foods.

Daily allowances for good nutrition

The following chart summarizes the daily dietary allowances for normally active persons in a temperate

Recommended daily dietary allowances

		INFANTS		CHILDREN		
AGE	Years	0.0-0.5	0.5-1.0	1-3	4-6	7-10
WEIGHT	Kilograms	6	9	13	20	30
	Pounds	14	20	28	44	66
HEIGHT	Centimeters	60	71	86	110	135
	Inches	24	28	34	44	54
ENERGY	Calories	kgx117	kgx108	1,300	1,800	2,400
PROTEIN	Grams	kgx2.2	kgx2.0	23	30	36
FAT-SOLUBLE VITAMINS	Vitamin A Activity (IU)[1]	1,400	2,000	2,000	2,500	3,300
	Vitamin D (IU)[1]	400	400	400	400	400
	Vitamin E Activity (IU)[1]	4	5	7	9	10
WATER-SOLUBLE VITAMINS	Ascorbic Acid (mg)	35	35	40	40	40
	Folacin (μg)[2]	50	50	100	200	300
	Niacin (mg)	5	8	9	12	16
	Riboflavin (mg)	0.4	0.6	0.8	1.1	1.2
	Thiamin (mg)	0.3	0.5	0.7	0.9	1.2
	Vitamin B_6 (mg)	0.3	0.4	0.6	0.9	1.2
	Vitamin B_{12} (μg)[2]	0.3	0.3	1.0	1.5	2.0
MINERALS	Calcium (mg)	360	540	800	800	800
	Phosphorus (mg)	240	400	800	800	800
	Iodine (μg)[2]	35	45	60	80	110
	Iron (mg)	10	15	15	10	10
	Magnesium (mg)	60	70	150	200	250
	Zinc (mg)	3	5	10	10	10

[1]International Units [2]Micrograms

climate. The figures in this chart are designed for the maintenance of *good,* not minimum, nutrition. The figures that follow for the age ranges are designed for the age that is the midpoint between the two extremes, so an adjustment can be made up or down from that point.

MALES					FEMALES					PREG-NANT	LAC-TATING
11-14	15-18	19-22	23-50	51+	11-14	15-18	19-22	23-50	51+		
44	61	67	70	70	44	54	58	58	58		
97	134	147	154	154	97	119	128	128	128		
158	172	172	172	172	155	162	162	162	162		
63	69	69	69	69	62	65	65	65	65		
2,800	3,000	3,000	2,700	2,400	2,400	2,100	2,100	2,000	1,800	+300	+500
44	54	54	56	56	44	48	46	46	46	+30	+20
5,000	5,000	5,000	5,000	5,000	4,000	4,000	4,000	4,000	4,000	5,000	6,000
400	400	400			400	400	400			400	400
12	15	15	15	15	12	12	12	12	12	15	15
45	45	45	45	45	45	45	45	45	45	60	80
400	400	400	400	400	400	400	400	400	400	800	600
18	20	20	18	16	16	14	14	13	12	+2	+4
1.5	1.8	1.8	1.6	1.5	1.3	1.4	1.4	1.2	1.1	+0.3	+0.5
1.4	1.5	1.5	1.4	1.2	1.2	1.1	1.1	1.0	1.0	+0.3	+0.3
1.6	2.0	2.0	2.0	2.0	1.6	2.0	2.0	2.0	2.0	2.5	2.5
3.0	3.0	3.0	3.0	3.0	3.0	3.0	3.0	3.0	3.0	4.0	4.0
1,200	1,200	800	800	800	1,200	1,200	800	800	800	1,200	1,200
1,200	1,200	800	800	800	1,200	1,200	800	800	800	1,200	1,200
130	150	140	130	110	115	115	100	100	80	125	150
18	18	10	10	10	18	18	18	18	10	18+	18
350	400	350	350	350	300	300	300	300	300	450	450
15	15	15	15	15	15	15	15	15	15	20	25

Source: *Recommended Dietary Allowances* (1974), National Academy of Sciences

GIANT SIZE
WHOLE BEETS
YELLOW CAKE MIX
CRACKERS
ALL PURPOSE Flour
GRANULATED SUGAR
TOMATO JUICE
SALT
MILK
NATURE'S MOST NEARLY PERFECT FOOD
LARGE WHITE EGGS
SLICED BACON

«2»

Good Shopping Comes First

Why food costs vary · Making a pattern for your daily meals · Some suggestions for meal planning · Fitting nutrition requirements into your budget · Weekly food plans for low, moderate and liberal budgets · Where to shop · How to buy convenience foods, meat, poultry, fish, cheese, butter, milk, fresh fruits and vegetables · Buying guide—food weight and equivalent servings

Preparing meals begins with planning. As a beginner, you may discover that meal planning is difficult, but do not be discouraged. It may cheer you to learn that homemakers who have shopped and cooked for decades are always learning new tricks.

In this chapter you will find many helpful ways to plan weekly menus that will provide variety and proper nutrition, while saving you money. Three charts, organized around low, moderate and liberal budgets, will show you how much of each kind of food is required for each member of your family. A buying guide will give you the weight of a food item with the corresponding number of servings it yields. With this chart you should find it as easy to prepare meals for fifty as it is for two.

You will also learn how to purchase every type of food from meat, poultry, fish and dairy products to fruits, vegetables and processed foods. This chapter is a shopping "education" that will teach you how to correct your expensive buying habits and get through the check-out counter with money saved.

FACTORS THAT CONTRIBUTE TO VARIATIONS IN FOOD COSTS

AGE AND OCCUPATION. Naturally those who do manual labor or frequently participate in very active athletics will burn up more energy and require more food than those with sedentary jobs and less active hobbies. Younger children eat less than adolescents, older people less than young people or middle-age adults, and after the age of twelve girls eat less than boys.

FAMILY SIZE. "Average" figures for food budgeting are based on a family with three to five persons. If the family is larger than this, food costs per person drop about 10 percent because more foods can be bought in quantity and greater savings result. For one person living alone, a rule-of-thumb adjustment is to increase the per-person food costs 20 to 35 percent; for a family of two, costs rise 10 percent above the per-person average.

WEATHER. Produce grown outdoors is at the mercy of the elements. A bumper crop can lower prices, while a drought or unseasonable cold spell can raise them. Processed as well as fresh foods are affected by such climatic conditions, because the producers who can and pack foods must also obtain them from the farmer who grows them.

GEOGRAPHY. Where you live influences how much you pay for certain foods; locally produced food is less expensive than foods that are transported great distances.

HIDDEN COSTS. Often more than half of the retail price of a food goes not for the actual object but for some service that adds to its cost: processing, packaging, transportation, advertising, wholesalers' and retailers' profits.

CONSUMER DEMAND. Homemakers want and purchase new foods and more convenient packaging. The price we pay for these foods also pays the cost of creating, developing and testing new recipes and new products.

Your bills may be higher than you would like, but remember that not all the money you spend in the supermarket pays for foods. Fifteen to 20 percent of your supermarket bill may go for such nonfood items as paper goods, cleaning materials, health and beauty aids.

MAKE A PATTERN FOR YOUR DAILY MEALS

Make a menu pattern that will suit the tastes and habits of your family while keeping in mind nutrition and budget considerations. Here is an example.

BREAKFAST	fruit or juice; eggs or cereal; bacon or other meat; bread; beverage
LUNCH	meat or cheese dish with bread and vegetable; dessert; beverage
DINNER	meat, poultry or fish; potatoes or other starch; vegetable other than potatoes; bread; dessert; beverage

This skeleton structure can be a help to you. Once the pattern for your meals is well established, proceed in the following manner with breakfast first:

Fruits. List the fruits or juices that will be needed for

the week. Then consider if some will be used also at lunch or for the lunch box. Be aware of the fruits that are in season and buy these rather than rare, exotic ones; do this and you will pay less and still have variety.

Eggs. Decide how many will be needed each morning for a week's breakfasts; how many for lunch or lunch box; how many for cooking and baking. When you have worked out the quantity that you need, add three to six more eggs to be kept on hand for unexpected uses.

Bacon. Determine whether it is more economical to use bacon only once or twice a week for breakfast, or whether it will be practical to use it perhaps two more times a week as part of a lunch or light dinner menu. This will depend on your own particular food budget and the eating habits of your family. Then work out the amount needed for the week.

Cereal. A slow-cooking cereal is tastier and also costs less. When prepared the night before, the morning work of reheating is simple. Also, the nourishment is more than in uncooked cereals. O━ Add 2 to 4 teaspoons of nonfat dry skim milk to each cup of water used for cooking dry cereals. This will add nourishment without altering the flavor. Keep uncooked cereal for busy days. Plan to use some of each every week.

Bread and beverage. The use of both bread and beverage varies from one family to the next. Consider your own family's tastes here, but do not forget that a family that has a large proportion of bread in the diet must get a large proportion of nutrition from it, so try to use whole-grain or enriched breads as much as possible.

O━ And remember—always serve a hearty breakfast; it can be the cheapest meal of the day, but it should be no less nutritious than the more expensive meals. This meal, which follows a long fast, has to make up for the hours without food and must sustain you until lunch.

We have been talking seriously about food value,

food quality and price, but also remember that you and your family must derive a certain amount of pleasure from the food you put on the table. Therefore, guard against slipping into a food rut. You are in a rut when you buy the same food week after week and cook and serve it with little or no variation. This is a deadly habit to acquire. You spend good money on good food and use valuable time preparing it, but find that it all adds up to little. It is especially easy to fall into this routine if you use too many packaged, canned or frozen items. Packers must maintain uniform standards. While this gives good quality to the foods, it also results in a sameness of flavor and style. Using seasonal foods will help you avoid this monotony. Another way is to use a different herb or spice to accent a familiar food in a new way. You will find many helpful suggestions later on in the chapter on herbs and spices. You do not need to buy expensive items; learn to make interesting, tasty dishes from inexpensive ingredients.

Some suggestions for planning menus

O━ Review the menus you have planned and try to use less costly foods to supply your family's nutritional needs.

O━ Avoid waste and leftovers. If there are six members in the family, do not cook enough for seven. A five-year-old boy does not eat as much as an adult, so plan accordingly.

O━ If your family is large enough so that substantial savings can result from buying in quantity, you should try to freeze or can fresh fruits and vegetables at home.

O━ Entertain more simply if you find that lavish hospitality destroys your food budget. Plan a dessert party or a light supper rather than an elaborate sit-down dinner.

O━ Casserole meals may save work and fuel, but check the cost of the ingredients; sometimes the extras called for can raise the price per serving to that of a steak dinner.

O━ Margarine and butter have the same nutrient value, except that some margarine is currently enriched with vitamin D. Some brands of margarine are much less expensive than butter. However, margarine is slightly more caloric than butter.

O┳ Skim-milk powder reconstituted to fluid skim milk will reduce the milk bill by approximately two thirds. The nutritional value of this milk is almost exactly that of whole milk; the loss of vitamin A (from the lower fat content of skim milk) can be made up by serving more green and yellow vegetables or other foods rich in vitamin A such as yellow fruits, liver or eggs. If your family does not enjoy the flavor of skim milk as a beverage, try mixing it with whole milk to economize.

FITTING NUTRITION REQUIREMENTS INTO YOUR BUDGET

Naturally you are concerned not only with the amount you spend on food but also with the value you get. Merely spending a great deal on food does not mean that your family is well nourished. Price is not necessarily the most important factor when shopping. Some foods are cheap at almost any reasonable price because they supply so much nutrition, whereas some "cheap" foods may not be worth the price spent on them.

One example of good value for your shopping dollar is dairy products. A group of city families spent 14 percent of their food money on milk, cheese and ice cream. This bought approximately 15 percent of the calories, 22 percent of the protein, 65 percent of the calcium and 44 percent of the riboflavin (vitamin B_2) needed for good human nutrition. It is a real bargain to obtain for 14 percent of your food money much more than 14 percent of your requirements for some of the essential nutrients.

Plan carefully to ensure that your food money is well spent. It is not sufficient merely to understand, after reading the nutrition section, that our bodies need certain foods; it is also important to know specifically the amount of each item you must purchase. To assist you, three charts beginning on page 36 show you how much of each kind of food is required by different groups, male and female. The three are organized around low, moderate and liberal budgets.

Because of the variables in determining food costs

at any given time for any given family, it is impossible to predict whether a family should use the low, moderate or liberal food plan. Only you can decide, after a few weeks of carefully examining your food expenditures, which plan best suits your budget. Try the moderate plan, and if after a few weeks you realize that you can afford to spend more on food, organize your meals around the liberal plan. If you have been spending more than you can afford, switch to the low-cost plan. In this way you can reduce the quantities of higher-priced protein and fruits on your shopping list.

In order to adapt the food plan of your choice to your family, simply list the quantities necessary for the types that fit the members of your household, and determine, according to the food plan you have selected, how much of each food your family needs for one week. Remember, these plans are proposals, not rules. If anyone in your family is allergic to eggs, this part of your plan must be altered. Perhaps you are concerned about cholesterol. You will want to reduce the number of eggs and be particular about your choice of fats and oils. The person who has to limit calcium intake will reduce his amount of milk and cheese. Without going into a long medical discussion, you can see that adjustments should be made. And adjust for personal tastes, too. Some foods may not appeal to you, so you will need to supply these nutrients in another way. Also, the amounts are for persons of "average" weight and height. To adjust quantities for children who are growing more rapidly than their age group, the amounts for the next higher age group may be used.

The next step is to plan your week's menus, deciding which foods you want to purchase in each category. The season of the year, the amount of time you have for food preparation and your family's preferences will influence your decisions, as will the choice of your food plan. For example, the low-cost plan allows less for fruits, so fruit desserts cannot be served to your family often. But grain products can be the basis for dessert—such as rice or bread pudding or shortcake—with a little fruit added for contrasting texture and flavor.

Weekly food plans for low-cost budgets

Family members	Milk, cheese, ice cream	Meat, poultry, fish		Dry beans, peas, nuts		Flour, cereal, baked goods	
	Qt.	Lb.	Oz.	Lb.	Oz.	Lb.	Oz.
CHILDREN:							
Under 1 year	5½	1	0	0	0	0	12
1-3 years	5½	1	4	0	1	1	4
4-6 years	5½	1	8	0	2	2	0
7-9 years	5½	2	0	0	4	2	4
10-12 years	6½	2	4	0	6	3	0
GIRLS:							
13-15 years	7	2	8	0	4	3	0
16-19 years	7	2	8	0	4	2	12
BOYS:							
13-15 years	7	2	8	0	6	4	4
16-19 years	7	3	4	0	8	5	4
WOMEN:							
20-34 years	3½	2	8	0	4	2	8
35-54 years	3½	2	8	0	4	2	8
55-74 years	3½	2	8	0	4	2	4
75 years and over	3½	2	8	0	4	2	0
Pregnant	7	2	8	0	4	2	8
Lactating	10	3	4	0	4	3	0
MEN:							
20-34 years	3½	3	12	0	6	4	4
35-54 years	3½	3	8	0	6	3	12
55-74 years	3½	3	4	0	4	3	8
75 years and over	3½	3	4	0	4	3	4

Eggs	Citrus fruit, tomatoes		Dark-green and deep-yellow vegetables		Potatoes		Other vegetables and fruit		Fats, oils		Sugar, sweets	
No.	Lb.	Oz.	Lb.	Oz.	Lb.	Oz.	Lb.	Oz.	Lb.	Oz.	Lb.	Oz.
5	1	8	0	2	0	8	1	0	0	1	0	2
5	1	8	0	4	0	12	2	4	0	4	0	4
5	1	12	0	4	1	4	3	4	0	6	0	6
6	2	0	0	8	2	0	4	4	0	8	0	10
6	2	4	0	8	2	8	5	0	0	8	0	12
6	2	4	0	12	2	8	5	0	0	10	0	12
6	2	4	0	12	2	4	4	12	0	6	0	10
6	2	8	0	12	3	4	5	4	0	12	0	12
6	2	8	0	12	4	12	5	8	0	14	0	14
5	2	0	0	12	2	0	5	0	0	6	0	10
5	2	0	0	12	1	8	4	8	0	4	0	10
5	2	0	0	12	1	4	3	8	0	4	0	6
5	2	0	0	12	1	4	3	0	0	4	0	6
7	3	8	1	8	2	0	5	0	0	6	0	8
7	4	8	1	8	3	4	5	8	0	8	0	10
6	2	4	0	12	3	4	5	8	0	12	1	0
6	2	4	0	12	3	0	5	0	0	10	0	12
6	2	4	0	12	2	8	4	12	0	10	0	10
6	2	0	0	12	2	4	4	8	0	8	0	10

Weekly food plans for moderate budgets

Family members	Milk, cheese, ice cream Qt.	Meat, poultry, fish Lb. Oz.	Dry beans, peas, nuts Lb. Oz.	Flour, cereal, baked goods Lb. Oz.
CHILDREN:				
Under 1 year	6	1 4	0 0	0 12
1-3 years	6	1 12	0 1	1 0
4-6 years	6	2 4	0 1	1 12
7-9 years	6	3 0	0 2	2 0
10-12 years	6½	4 0	0 4	2 12
GIRLS:				
13-15 years	7	4 8	0 2	2 12
16-19 years	7	4 4	0 2	2 8
BOYS:				
13-15 years	7	4 12	0 4	4 0
16-19 years	7	5 8	0 6	5 0
WOMEN:				
20-34 years	3½	4 4	0 2	2 4
35-54 years	3½	4 4	0 2	2 0
55-74 years	3½	4 4	0 2	1 12
75 years and over	3½	3 12	0 2	1 12
Pregnant	7	4 4	0 2	2 4
Lactating	10	5 0	0 2	2 12
MEN:				
20-34 years	3½	5 8	0 4	4 0
35-54 years	3½	5 4	0 4	3 8
55-74 years	3½	5 0	0 2	3 4
75 years and over	3½	5 0	0 2	2 12

Eggs	Citrus fruit, tomatoes		Dark-green and deep-yellow vegetables		Potatoes		Other vegetables and fruit		Fats, oils		Sugar, sweets	
No.	Lb.	Oz.	Lb.	Oz.	Lb.	Oz.	Lb.	Oz.	Lb.	Oz.	Lb.	Oz.
6	1	8	0	2	0	8	1	8	0	1	0	2
6	1	8	0	4	0	12	2	12	0	4	0	4
6	2	0	0	4	1	0	4	0	0	6	0	10
7	2	4	0	8	1	12	4	12	0	10	0	14
7	2	8	0	12	2	4	5	8	0	10	0	14
7	2	8	0	12	2	4	5	12	0	12	0	14
7	2	8	0	12	2	0	5	8	0	10	0	12
7	2	12	0	12	3	0	6	0	0	14	1	0
7	3	0	0	12	4	4	6	4	1	2	1	2
6	2	8	0	12	1	8	5	12	0	8	0	14
6	2	8	0	12	1	4	5	4	0	8	0	12
6	2	4	0	12	1	4	4	4	0	6	0	8
6	2	4	0	12	1	0	3	12	0	6	0	8
7	3	8	1	8	1	8	5	12	0	8	0	12
7	5	0	1	8	2	12	6	4	0	12	0	12
7	2	12	0	12	3	0	6	8	1	0	1	4
7	2	12	0	12	2	8	5	12	0	14	1	0
7	2	12	0	12	2	4	5	8	0	12	0	14
7	2	8	0	12	2	0	5	4	0	10	0	12

Weekly food plans for liberal budgets

Family members	Milk, cheese, ice cream	Meat, poultry, fish		Dry beans, peas, nuts		Flour, cereal, baked goods	
	Qt.	Lb.	Oz.	Lb.	Oz.	Lb.	Oz.
CHILDREN:							
Under 1 year	6	1	4	0	0	0	12
1-3 years	6	2	4	0	1	1	0
4-6 years	6	3	0	0	1	1	8
7-9 years	6	3	12	0	2	1	12
10-12 years	6½	4	12	0	4	2	12
GIRLS:							
13-15 years	7	5	8	0	2	2	8
16-19 years	7	5	4	0	2	2	4
BOYS:							
13-15 years	7	5	8	0	4	4	0
16-19 years	7	6	4	0	6	5	0
WOMEN:							
20-34 years	4	4	12	0	1	2	0
35-54 years	4	4	12	0	1	1	12
55-74 years	4	4	12	0	1	1	8
75 years and over	4	4	4	0	1	1	8
Pregnant	7	4	12	0	1	2	0
Lactating	10	5	12	0	2	2	12
MEN:							
20-34 years	4	6	0	0	4	3	12
35-54 years	4	5	8	0	4	3	8
55-74 years	4	5	4	0	2	3	4
75 years and over	4	5	4	0	2	2	12

Eggs	Citrus fruit, tomatoes	Dark-green and deep-yellow vegetables	Potatoes	Other vegetables and fruit	Fats, oils	Sugar, sweets
No.	Lb. Oz.	Lb. Oz.	Lb. Oz.	Lb. Oz.	Lb. Oz.	Lb. Oz.
7	1 12	0 2	0 8	1 8	0 2	0 2
7	1 12	0 4	0 12	2 12	0 4	0 4
7	2 4	0 8	0 12	4 8	0 8	0 12
7	2 12	0 8	1 8	5 4	0 10	1 0
7	3 0	0 12	2 4	6 0	0 10	1 0
7	3 0	0 12	2 4	6 0	0 12	1 2
7	3 0	0 12	1 12	5 12	0 10	1 0
7	3 4	0 12	3 0	6 8	0 14	1 4
7	3 8	0 12	4 4	7 4	1 4	1 2
6	3 0	0 12	1 4	6 4	0 8	1 2
6	3 0	0 12	1 0	6 0	0 8	1 0
6	3 0	0 12	1 0	4 8	0 6	0 12
6	3 0	0 12	0 12	4 0	0 6	0 10
7	4 8	1 8	1 4	6 4	0 8	1 0
7	5 8	1 8	2 8	6 4	0 12	1 2
7	3 0	0 12	2 12	7 12	1 0	1 8
7	3 0	0 12	2 4	6 8	0 14	1 4
7	3 0	0 12	2 0	6 0	0 12	1 2
7	2 12	0 12	1 12	5 12	0 10	1 0

WHERE SHOULD YOU SHOP?

Many families shop at one or two stores only. This habit is largely influenced by proximity and convenience. Actually you will broaden your experience considerably by shopping around and comparing prices, quality of food, types of service.

If you are the type of person who likes to ask questions and get suggestions, you should search out a store that will best satisfy you on these two counts. This may not apply to all your shopping, but there may be certain foods, like cheeses or breads, about which you do want special information.

You may prefer to shop in a store where prices and weights are well displayed and easily readable. You will probably find self-service quicker and more convenient. If you want assistance from sales clerks, self-service stores will just frustrate you and make marketing a chore. Generally speaking, you will find the lowest prices in self-service stores, since trained clerks who give customers individual assistance cost the management more, and these higher operating costs are added on to the price of food. Self-service does leave you free to study and reflect on the information on labels and the weights and prices of different cuts of meat. Another point in favor of self-service supermarkets is that they enable you to make many shopping decisions at home since many of these stores have detailed newspaper advertisements featuring their best buys and specials just before the important shopping days.

Do not be a lazy shopper. Be curious about all foods, their origins, their uses. Take time occasionally to visit specialty shops where you can look and learn. You will get many interesting ideas and discover exciting foods you can bring to your table.

Shopping suggestions

🔑 Learn how to recognize good quality in fresh foods. Before picking up a "bargain" in fresh fruits or vegetables, check their condition carefully. Perfect produce would not be reduced to "seconds." Make sure that vegetables have not dried out. Buy spotted or bruised fruits only if you know you can use them soon after purchase so that they will neither spoil nor lose their food value. Buy fresh produce in season. The food will be lower in price, more plentiful and better flavored.

O┳ Memorize the different grades of canned fruits, vegetables and meats. Learn which foods retain good nutritive value, color and flavor when canned. Fancy packaging adds to food costs. Choose simple containers over elaborate jars and reusable canisters, unless the price per unit for the same quality is the same or lower for the special package. Avoid items offering premiums such as towels and dishes.

O┳ Suit the style of food to your purposes. Standard canned goods, government graded, are just as nutritious as the more expensive Fancy fruits and vegetables, and should be used when uniform appearance is not important. For instance, low-grade sliced peaches are good for pie, even if not attractive as a plate of fruit. Broken olives are fine when used in salads, sandwiches or sauces, even if they are not appealing as appetizers.

O┳ By reading food labels and through observation, study and learn the different forms in which some foods are available. Find out the difference in price, quantity and cost between fresh, frozen and canned products of the same variety.

O┳ Study labels on bread before you buy. Choose bread for weight and food value, not by size of loaf. Look for bread that contains milk and is whole-grain or enriched.

O┳ Buy packaged cereals or any other packaged food by weight, not by the size of the package. To compare prices, first look for the weights listed on the labels, and note the prices. Then figure cost for an ounce or a pound.

O┳ Ready-to-serve cereals in multipacks of small boxes may cost two or three times more per ounce than the same cereal in a larger box. Sugar-coated ready-to-serve cereals cost more per ounce than many common unsweetened ones, and furnish more calories but less food value.

O┳ Dried fruits give eight or more servings per pound; canned fruits, which contain more water, may give fewer servings. Compare costs per portion.

O┳ Day-old pastries and bread may be a good

buy, especially if your bread supply is never consumed in one day. Buying day-old baked goods and freezing them until you use them may lower your bread costs as much as 50 percent. Usually a supermarket has day-old bakery products available in the morning.

- Buy in quantity if you pay a lower price per unit, if you have adequate storage space for the food and if you can use all you buy before it can spoil or lose some of its nutritive value. For instance, you may be able to buy a large piece of meat at a lower price per pound. If you can cut this up and store what you do not need immediately, this may be economical. In this case, a freezer can be a help.
- The high cost of national advertising, packaging and promotion often makes brand-name products much more expensive than the same foods marketed under the store's own brands. Usually, markets will feature their own labels at prices below those of comparable national brands. Watch for the best values at moderate or low cost. Study food advertisements and compare.
- Trading stamps, games and contests cost you money, unless you are sure the prices at stores which offer them are no higher than at stores without such gimmicks.
- Learn and remember your family's own preferences in food. A supermarket bargain may turn out to be a waste if no one in the family will eat it.
- Snack foods are expensive for the food value they provide. Low-calorie fresh fruits and vegetables are more practical "nibbles." Remember that pure fruit juices give better nutritional value per dollar than soft drinks. Spend money on those foods that provide the most nutrition at the lowest cost; then, if money permits, buy the extras.
- If you have a low food budget, choose foods with little or no waste, or make sure the waste you pay for can be put to use in some way. For instance, the bones in meat can be used to make a substantial soup for the main course of another meal. When used in this way, bones cease to be a waste. But a lot of fat or gristle that has to be discarded is waste, and this could make your meat costs far too high. Judge your

purchases by the cost per serving rather than the cost per pound.

0━ Keep a pad and pencil in the kitchen. They are your best insurance against forgetting some staple you may need. Always know how much you need. It is troublesome to buy too much or too little of an item; the buying guide on pages 70 to 73 can help you. When you get to the market, stick to the shopping list. Avoid impulse buying unless you see something you need at a real reduction from its regular price.

0━ Ask questions frequently. Be sure to ask the clerks in charge for information when you are not sure of what you are buying. Of course they may not know any more than you do, but if you persist you may reach the buyer for that department. People who do know are often pleased to share information.

0━ Maintain records of your food purchases, both the amount you buy and the price you pay. Study your notes after three or four weeks and look for areas where you have done exceptionally well. You will be able to use these findings in future buying and they will prove invaluable. Eventually these steps to good shopping will become so automatic that this record keeping can be discontinued.

CONVENIENCE FOODS

These are foods that come to us either partly or fully prepared: baked, canned, dehydrated, frozen. Certainly they are very often a help to the homemaker, but you must pay for this service. For this reason these foods are relatively the most expensive to buy.

When the budget is limited, it is not wise to depend on convenience foods too often. However, study them from the point of view of prices, portions and flavors as well as the servings they supply. It will then be simpler to decide which you can afford on your budget and how often they should be purchased.

There is probably not a woman on this continent who does not take advantage of one or more of these foods every day of the year. For example, breakfast usually includes one or more of the following: fruit juice—grapefruit, tomato, orange—which someone else has squeezed, from frozen concentrate, carton or dehydrated powder; pancakes from a mix; rolls or coffee cake that just need warming up; instant coffee.

And what about lunch? Canned soups, beans, fish of various kinds, macaroni or spaghetti with sauce are usual items.

Dinner possibilities are too numerous to mention. One can put together a menu composed of favorite convenience foods, or simply put a TV dinner into the oven.

Convenience foods are not new. Some of them have been around for years—canned and dehydrated soups; canned fruits, vegetables, fish and meats; ready-baked beans; packaged baked cookies, breads and cakes. Today we have foods prepared by the newer methods such as freezing, dehydrating, freeze-drying. These foods resemble freshly prepared ones far more than the older products do, and this has increased the use of such foods tremendously.

Convenience foods save you time. All the preparation, cooking and much of the washing of pots and pans has been done for you. For example, a beef stew that would take 30 minutes to prepare and perhaps hours to simmer while you watched over it, takes only a few minutes to remove from a can and heat on the stove.

These foods are also easier to carry home from the market, usually less bulky and easier to store. At times this is important. Generally, fresh produce must be purchased in greater quantity than processed foods because of the inedible parts, such as peels and husks.

Some convenience foods are actually cheaper than fresh foods because they are more compact to ship and store and they have a longer shelf life.

Your food budget must strike a balance between time and energy on one hand and money on the other. You will need to compare the time, work and space saved with the time and work you would spend if you made the whole dish or the whole dinner. But you must also compare the quality, quantity and flavor of the prepared food with the food you could cook at home with imagination. Perhaps you can afford to use convenience foods for certain occasions, but a diet solely or in large part of these foods would be very dull fare indeed.

HOW TO BUY MEAT

A large proportion of the money spent for food is for meat. Because of its richness of flavor, meat seems to satisfy the appetite best. Appetites seem most demanding during long periods of cold weather.

A few generations ago a housewife bought large roasts that provided cold meat for several other meals. Even people of moderate means had a "Sunday roast" that was stretched out for as many days as possible. A few decades ago the average housewife could have afforded this cut of meat, but the price of meat today makes this extravagant, and such a diet could be very monotonous.

Different ways to prepare the same cut, or new combinations of meat with vegetables and seasonings, can provide almost limitless variety. Far too many home cooks let habit and prejudice keep them in a rut. For instance, muscle meats, the most popular, are a poor source of several important vitamins. This is not true of organ meats—heart, kidney, sweetbreads and, especially, liver. Yet, ironically, organ meats are most often spurned by the home cook. Also, a reluctance to buy tougher meats, because of the supposed difficulty in cooking them, makes too many shoppers purchase only tender cuts. Unfortunately, tender cuts make up only a small proportion of the beef carcass, so demand increases the cost. Any kind of meat can be made tender if correctly prepared. Sometimes the "difficult" cooking of less tender cuts amounts to little more than starting the oven a few hours sooner.

Meat is not the only item in your menu. You need to complement the meat you serve with foods that will furnish carbohydrates, vitamins, cellulose and minerals. You will have no shortage of protein if you provide one serving of meat per day to each member of your family. If you cannot do this, provide other protein-rich foods such as fish or cheese.

Beef

Wholesale cuts of beef graded by the United States Department of Agriculture (USDA) are marked with a shield-shaped imprint containing the letters USDA and the name of the grade, such as prime, choice and good. All graded meat is wholesome and has been processed in a sanitary plant. The purple mark will be found on all meat sold in interstate commerce. *Prime* is the most tender, juicy and flavorful, and the cuts will be well marbled. *Choice* is also good, but slightly less marbled. *Good* is less juicy, less flavorful, less marbled, and is usually lean. *Standard,* lean with little fat, is usually cut from young animals and lacks flavor. *Commercial* is cut from mature animals and has good marbling and flavor, but will need long, slow cooking since it is less tender. Other beef grades are sold only to wholesalers, and neither standard nor commercial can be found in most markets.

Inspection for wholesomeness is another service of the USDA, and this is required for all meats sold across state lines. The inspection mark tells you that the meat is clean, wholesome and has been processed in an inspected plant. It will not tell you if the meat is tender; for that you must look for the grading shield. If you cannot find the inspection mark, you can be sure that any graded meat has been inspected.

Veal and lamb

Veal grades are similar to those for beef: *prime, choice, good, standard.* Lamb is graded *prime, choice, good.* Veal is baby beef, or calf, brought to market at six weeks to two months. The fat should be an ivory-white color. The meat should be pinkish-white. This coloring indicates that it is milk-fed veal and this, of course, is the very best.

Pork

The federal grades for pork are numbers 1, 2, 3, 4, but these are not widely used since pork is sold differently from other meats. In addition to fresh pork, there are many cuts of smoked or cured pork besides the familiar ham and bacon.

WHOLE HAMS. A whole ham weighs between 10 and 16 pounds, but is often cut into portions. Shank halves contain part of the leg bone. Although they cost less per pound than the butt, they nevertheless have a higher proportion of meat. The butt end actually has more bone in proportion to lean meat, but the meat is a little more tender than the shank end and more expensive.

HAM SLICES. The best slices are cut out of the center of a whole ham in varying thicknesses of 1 to 3 inches. Ham slices, particularly thick ones, are expensive unless you want just a few portions. For a less expensive way to buy ham slices, have one or two slices cut off when you are buying a half ham.

CURED SHOULDER. The picnic ham, available in 4- to 8-pound pieces, is cut from the shoulder. The shoulder roll, or butt, weighs from 2 to 4 pounds. Depending on the use you wish to make of them, both of these cuts are economical to buy, but both are rather fatty.

COUNTRY-STYLE HAMS. These are usually not available at supermarkets. Specialty butcher shops often have dark-brown, crusted, maple-smoked hams, or hams that have been smoked many times. These are especially delicious and are as easy to cook as any other ham, but preparation does take time. People sometimes find them too smoky and too hard because most commercial hams are mild-cured and have added moisture. Be sure to ask your butcher about the ham you buy and whether it needs extra soaking.

Ham can be generally divided into two groups: those that must be cooked before eating, and those that are fully cooked. Cook-before-eating ham includes regular hams, whole, shank and butt halves, and slices. Of course, other cuts of cured pork of this type are available.

Fully cooked hams include whole hams, leg bone in, weighing 8 to 12 pounds, and rolled boneless ham. Fully cooked ham is usually considered just that, and no cooking whatever is needed. But even these can be improved by cooking, as you will see later.

When buying any cured pork, it is important to find out how much cooking is required. Read the labels or tags, or ask your butcher to be sure what you are buying. Even if you are entirely familiar with the cut, you cannot guess at the packer's style of processing.

Internal and processed meats

Other types of meat include internal meats—liver, kidney, heart, tongue, tripe, sweetbreads and brains. There are no bones in any of these except for a few small ones at the base of the tongue. Tripe comes only from beef; sweetbreads from veal and lamb. These are generally good buys because there is no waste, and if well prepared they are delicious.

Processed meats include dried meats (such as chipped beef); pickled meats (such as corned beef); canned meats; and ground or chopped meats, fresh and cured. The last group includes hamburger and ground veal or lamb and all kinds of sausages. Frankfurters, liver sausage, bologna and dried sausages are ready to eat, but most other sausages need cooking.

When you decide on the kind of meat that you plan to buy, remember to look for the inspection stamp and the grading shield. Choose a cut and grade appropriate for the cooking method you plan to use. For instance, cuts for oven roasting or broiling should be *prime* or *choice*. You will not find too much prime meat in stores; most of it is sold wholesale to restaurants and hotels. Steaks from the loin are so tender that even when graded *good* they will be delicious broiled. Plan to braise, pot-roast or poach the less tender grades.

How much meat should you buy?

In general, 1 pound of meat provides three servings, but when there is little bone and little or no other waste, 1 pound can serve four. When buying meat for stew or meat pie, 1 pound of meat can be sufficient for four or five servings if the dish contains vegetables as well. Use the following as a buying guideline:

1 pound beef round steak	=	3 or 4 servings
1 pound liver	=	4 or 5 servings
6 pounds leg of lamb	=	6 to 8 servings
1 pound lamb or veal chops	=	about 3 chops, usually 3 servings
2 pounds beef pot roast	=	8 servings
2 pounds pork spareribs	=	4 servings
2 pounds ham	=	6 to 8 servings

How to save money on meat purchases

O━ Avoid meat containing high proportions of fat and bone unless you can make use of what otherwise would be waste. For example, bones can be used to make stocks; rendered meat fats can often be used for cooking instead of commercial fats.

However, keep in mind that some meats, although they may not appear to be wasteful, may contain fat in large quantities. It takes about 10 slices of crisp side bacon to equal the protein in a serving of cooked ground beef, because bacon is largely fat.

Ground shoulder of beef (chuck) is better to buy than the slightly cheaper and considerably fattier ground meat sold as "hamburger." The fattier meat is more expensive per serving because of shrinkage due to the fat.

Learn how to estimate the cost per pound of the meat actually eaten as compared to the price paid per pound for the whole piece of meat including the wasted part. A higher-priced cut may be less costly to serve than a cheaper one, depending upon the percentage of fat, bone and gristle in each. Meaty, less tender cuts from the shoulder and flank of beef, lamb and pork are usually good buys, but beef short ribs, lamb neck and pigs' feet, unless sold very cheaply, are usually uneconomical.

Meats such as liver, heart and kidney are economical because of the high nutritive value and total absence of waste. Beef, chicken and pork liver cost much less than calf's liver and have similar food value. Buy these organ meats frequently.

Meat prices depend mostly on supply and demand. Beef is available all year and is the most popular meat in America since it provides so many different cuts at a wide range of prices. Pork is most plentiful and therefore most economical to buy in the fall and winter, veal in the spring and lamb from September to December.

Some meats that are usually bought sliced may be more economical to buy in a large piece and slice at home. Bacon is an example, although this is not easy to slice at home. Some butchers will slice it for you without additional charge, but not all will do this.

Bologna bought in bulk and sliced at home is less expensive than sliced bologna. For lunch-box sandwiches, an inexpensive roast of beef cooked at home, chilled and sliced thin may make more economical sandwiches than store-bought sliced luncheon meats.

In addition, it provides good nourishment with much less fat than the prepared meats.

🗝 To save money, prepare combination dishes of meat mixed with other ingredients in preparations such as stews, meat pies and meat with pasta. These are especially successful with ground meat. The "meat extenders"—rice, macaroni, spaghetti, nonfat dry milk powder, bread crumbs—not only stretch the expensive meat ingredient but also add food value other than protein and improve the texture of the finished dish. One of the following is the usual amount of extender per pound of ground meat:

½ cup nonfat dry milk powder	1 cup fresh bread crumbs
	¾ cup rolled oats
½ cup dry bread crumbs	½ cup cornmeal

🗝 Leftover meat will go further as a sandwich filling when it is ground and combined with chopped raw cabbage, onions, carrots or celery.

🗝 You can prepare successful dishes with tough cuts of meat if you learn how to cook in a Dutch oven or a casserole. Long, slow cooking is the secret way to tenderize. You can accomplish the same objective in less time in a pressure cooker.

🗝 If you serve eggs as a meat substitute, remember that it takes three medium-size eggs to replace the amount of protein in a good serving of meat.

🗝 When you buy a large roast, be sure to plan dinner menus for the week ahead to make use of the roast by varying your cooking and cutting methods.

For further information, write to the Superintendent of Documents, U.S. Government Printing Office, Washington, D.C., and ask for leaflets on meat published by the U.S. Department of Agriculture, Consumer and Marketing Service; or to the National Live Stock and Meat Board, 36 South Wabash Ave., Chicago, Ill. 60603.

HOW TO BUY POULTRY

Poultry includes chicken, capon, turkey, duck, goose, squab, Rock Cornish game hen, pheasant and guinea hen. Occasionally wild birds or game birds may come your way. When planning your meals, consider these as you would domestic poultry.

Birds are usually labeled according to their age, which determines tenderness. Young chickens may be labeled young chicken, broiler, fryer, roaster, capon. Young turkeys may be labeled young turkey, fryer-roaster, young hen, young tom. Young ducks may be labeled duckling, young duckling, broiler duckling, fryer duckling, roaster duckling. Mature, less tender birds also have a variety of labels. Chickens may be labeled mature chicken, old chicken, hen, stewing chicken, fowl. Turkeys can be labeled mature turkey, yearling turkey, old turkey. Ducks, geese and guineas may be labeled mature or old.

Like meat, poultry handled in interstate commerce must be federally inspected for wholesomeness. Chicken, turkey, duck, goose and guineas are also graded. Grade A birds are fully fleshed and meaty, and attractive in appearance. Grade B is less meaty and attractive. If you do not find an A mark on the shield, you can safely assume the bird is poorer in quality. Whole birds will have the inspection stamp, and often the grade shield and the class of bird, such as "frying chicken."

Broilers (about 3 months old)	1 to 2 pounds
Fryers (3 to 6 months old)	2½ to 3½ pounds
Roasters	3½ to 5 pounds
Fowls or hens	4 to 5 pounds
Capons	6 to 9 pounds
Turkeys	8 to 20 pounds (12 to 14 pounds best size)

From 50 to 60 percent of the live weight of poultry is edible meat. This makes poultry more expensive per pound than it appears from the purchase price per pound. Nevertheless, poultry is a good buy for protein, and it is often a bargain. As a general rule, "broiler-fryers" (chickens weighing 1½ to 3½ pounds whole) are as cheap a source of protein as fairly lean ground beef when the price per pound of the chicken is three quarters or less the price of beef. Instead of buying cut-up chicken, save a few cents per pound by cutting up whole poultry at home.

When buying poultry watch for special sales. When the supply of any given poultry is at its highest peak, the price is the lowest. However, chickens are plentiful all year—whole, quartered, cut up, and as separate parts, including packages of gizzards and backs.

All poultry is perishable. Buy only what you know you can cook within two days. If you have purchased frozen poultry, keep it solidly frozen until time to thaw it for cooking.

As with meat, choose the bird that is best adapted to the use you plan for it. Use tender birds for roasting, broiling, barbecuing, sautéing. Use less tender birds for moist cooking—braising, poaching, stewing. An average broiler will make two generous servings; an average fryer will make four servings; a fat roaster will make at least six servings. If the poultry is mixed with other ingredients such as vegetables, it can make more servings.

HOW TO BUY FISH

Fish is one of the oldest foods used by man. With our country's long coastline and many lakes and rivers, we have enough fish available to offer an abundant source of food. The chief nutrient in fish is protein—a complete protein—which makes fish interchangeable with meat in the diet.

In some parts of the country fresh fish is an extremely economical food, but its price varies with the distance from the source of supply and with the seasons. Today, large portions of the catch are frozen, but well-organized transportation makes it possible for fresh fish to be marketed in excellent condition at great distances from the source of supply. Fresh fish is the most delicious. Because it is a seasonal food, you will find considerable variety from month to month even though the familiar fillets of white-fleshed fish—flounder, halibut, so-called sole—can be found in most markets all year long. Take advantage of this food as a means of varying your family's diet. And do not overlook the fact that fish is not only a good health food but is quick to prepare.

When you are shopping for fresh fish, look for fish that are plump for their type, bright-eyed, red-gilled, smooth-skinned, with all their scales adhering to firm flesh, and the overall color shimmering and clear. Take a good look at the eyes. They should be bright, full and clear. If they have a hazy white look, the fish are not fresh.

O━ If you are able to touch the flesh of a scaled fish with your fingers and no impression remains, this is a sign of freshness. A truly fresh fish has no unpleasant odor; odor develops with age. Also, a fresh fish is never slimy but an older one is.

If you are not buying whole fish, it is far more difficult to judge freshness. Often much of the supposedly fresh fish may be frozen and defrosted for sale. Here, too, the fish should have no odor and the flesh should be firm, not mushy. There should be very little liquid in the package; excess liquid indicates that the fish has been frozen and thawed.

Frozen fish should still be solidly frozen. It should also be well balanced in the package; if not, it has probably thawed out and been refrozen. Whole fish, especially trout, are extremely good frozen. Also available are steaks, fillets, large pieces. Many prepared fish dishes are also available. As with other convenience foods, these usually cost more than plain fish, and often the preparation is one you could complete quickly and easily.

You will find it to your advantage to search for a fish dealer in your community. Even though your supermarket may sell fish—usually a limited selection—a man whose business is fish will know much more, will help you understand how to buy and often will give you good cooking suggestions.

Fish servings are generally based on 1/3 to 1/2 pound of cooked fish per person. To provide this amount, buy 1/3 pound per person of fillets, sticks or steaks; 1/2 pound per person dressed fish; and 1 pound of whole fish. This rule applies whether the fish is fresh or frozen. Since fillets are 100 percent edible, steaks 85 percent edible and dressed fish 45 percent edible, it is often cheapest to buy fillets, though the price may be higher per pound. If you are using the fish in chowders or stews, a smaller amount may be enough.

Shellfish

These foods are seldom inexpensive, but they are very nutritious and low in calories. If you purchase them already shelled, they will be even more expensive but there will be no waste. Very good canned and frozen shellfish are available; shrimp are particularly good if flash-frozen. However, some canned shellfish are far more salty than the fresh or frozen product. Since the taste of these foods is distinctive, often a small amount can be stretched to make more servings by adding other blander ingredients.

In general, a pound of completely shelled and cleaned shellfish will provide four to six servings. If you are buying them uncooked and still in their shells, you must allow more. For an average six servings:

4 to 6 pounds live lobster (about six small lobsters) or 1 to 2 pounds shelled cooked lobster meat

1½ pounds scallops (these are completely shelled and there is no waste)

2 pounds uncooked, unshelled shrimp

1 to 1½ pounds cooked crab meat

HOW TO BUY CHEESE, BUTTER, MILK

Cheese is one of the oldest known prepared foods. The refrigerators of supermarkets are full of many general-purpose processed cheeses. These come in any number of types, bearing as many different labels. They are generally rindless, precut, sliced, prepackaged. Learning about these is only the beginning of your cheese education. The same refrigerator, along with specialized cheese shops or counters in delicatessens, offers a wide variety of natural cheeses from all over the world. With such a wide range of types from which to choose, a little daring is all you need to discover several that will please you and your family.

Cheese contains high concentrations of protein and fat; in food value, 1 pound equals approximately 1 gallon of milk. Cheese can be a staple diet article rather than merely an addition to apple pie, or a last course after a meal.

Generally speaking, cheese can be divided into three classes: soft, semisoft or semihard, hard. Each class contains hundreds of different cheeses. The best way to learn about them is to buy a small quantity of a cheese that is new to you. Find out where it comes from and what type it is. Make a note of the name.

Read the label, and ask the cheese man for more detailed information. Note the shape, flavor, texture. Most of all, watch your family's reaction.

In general, buy only as much fresh cheese (cream cheese, cottage cheese) as you expect to eat in about 10 days. Hard cheese (Parmesan and other grating cheeses) will keep for a very long time. The storage life of the cheeses in between depend on their stage of ripeness when you buy them. If possible, taste a tiny piece before buying to test for ripeness.

The most popular cheeses in North America are descendants of the famous English Cheddar. In the United States, the USDA offers voluntary inspection and grading of Cheddar. The flavor, texture and color all count, and they result from the milk quality, curing process and packaging. The grades are AA and A. Grade A is good cheese, but AA is better in all ways. Also noted on labels is the kind of cure—*mild, mellow-aged, sharp*. The longer a cheese is ripened, the more distinctive, or sharp, the flavor will be.

Soft small cheeses such as Liederkranz or Camembert usually cannot be sampled. Press the cheese gently—it should be slightly yielding to finger pressure. If it is hard, it will be some time before it is ready to eat; if it is soft, it is probably overripe and past its best stage.

For more about cheeses, see the chapter on Cheese and Nuts.

Butter

Butter is also graded, and the grade should appear on packages. All graded butter has been produced in a sanitary plant approved by the USDA and is sure to be wholesome. The grades are AA, A and B. AA is made from high-quality sweet cream, has good flavor and aroma, is smooth and spreadable and is only lightly salted. Grade A is almost as good. B is made from soured cream and is slightly acid in flavor. Keep butter in the refrigerator, or freeze it if you plan to keep it longer than a week. This is true for salted butter, but crucial for sweet butter.

Today most butter is packed in 1-pound packages of four ¼-pound sticks, although some country markets may still offer so-called "tub butter," in a chunk cut from a large tub. Most stores will sell as little as 1/4 pound; for a small household this can be an advantage.

Both sweet and salted butter can absorb flavors in your refrigerator, so be sure to wrap butter carefully in foil, plastic wrap or wax paper if you remove it from its carton.

Milk

In many societies, milk is infant food and no child over five years and certainly no adult would think of drinking it. In America, however, we have a marvelous dairy industry, and milk is considered a suitable food for everyone. Goats' milk is also sold. For some individuals it may be more digestible than cows' milk.

LIQUID WHOLE MILK is milk as it comes from the cow. All whole milk for general sale is pasteurized. In pasteurization, milk is heated to a high temperature, but less than boiling (212° F. or 100° C.), and kept at that temperature for some minutes. This degree of heat is enough to destroy pathogenic organisms without significantly altering the chemical composition of the milk. Most milk sold today is also homogenized, that is, the fat globules and other solids in the milk are broken up into very tiny particles evenly dispersed throughout the liquid. In milk that is not homogenized, the butterfat rises to the top when the milk is left to stand for even a short while. Most milk has vitamin D added; it is the chief source of this vitamin in our diet.

Raw milk for commercial use is produced in a few carefully managed dairies, but in some states a doctor's prescription is necessary to buy it.

LIQUID SKIM MILK is made by removing the butterfat from whole milk. It is also pasteurized.

BUTTERMILK is the liquid that remains after butterfat has been extracted from cream. Commercial buttermilk is "cultured" by addition of organisms to sweet milk. This too is pasteurized.

EVAPORATED MILK is whole milk with part of the water content removed so that it is about half the original volume. No sweetening is added. By adding an equal amount of water, you obtain a product similar to whole milk.

CONDENSED MILK is whole milk that has been sweetened, then evaporated. Both condensed and evaporated milks are especially rich in calcium and vitamin A. Since they are canned, they have been processed at higher heat than pasteurized milk and their flavor is definitely different from that of fresh milk.

DRIED MILK can be *dried whole milk* or *nonfat dried skim milk.* Most dried milks are pasteurized, but this is not indicated on every package. The liquid from the milk is removed until only 2½ to 4 percent of moisture remains. Nonfat dried skim milk is extremely nutritious, nonfattening and, because of its ability to reabsorb moisture, is an important ingredient in cooking, especially in baking.

The USDA inspects and grades nonfat dried skim milk. Skim milk labeled U.S. Extra Grade must be pasteurized, have a pleasant flavor and natural color. This dried milk must also dissolve instantly when mixed with water.

Packages of dried milk should be kept in a cool dry place, but not at freezing temperatures. After reconstituting, refrigerate it just like fresh milk. Unopened packages will keep for several months. When a quart of fresh whole milk costs 32 cents and enough dried milk to reconstitute a quart costs 14 cents or less, you can see how economical this is. Do not forget, however, that it is very low in vitamin A, so this must be supplemented in your family's diet by some other food.

HOW TO BUY FRESH FRUITS AND VEGETABLES

If you have had the advantage of gathering fruits and vegetables from your own garden when they were at their peak, you may never find any in stores that will suit you perfectly. But as a shopper you have the advantage of knowing what perfect produce should look like. The city housewife has to learn this, and she may make some unfortunate purchases while learning. These few suggestions may help to prevent mistakes.

First, remember that fresh produce bought in its proper season is cheaper because more is available, and it is also more nutritious. Tomatoes vine-ripened outdoors in the summer sun have twice as much vitamin C as winter hothouse tomatoes. If you can buy local produce, so much the better. Local fruits and vegetables have traveled less and are less likely to have suffered bruising and drying with their consequent loss of vitamins. And, of course, if you do not have to pay for trucking and packing as well, you will inevitably save money.

In general, avoid fruits or vegetables that have cracks, bruises and soft spots, and those that appear to be drippy or mushy. Good fruits are heavy for their size, and firm. Leafy vegetables should be crisp and glossy, with their green color fresh and bright. Root vegetables such as carrots, beets and parsnips should be crisp and have green leaves. If the leaves are limp and droopy, you can be sure the roots have been out of the ground for some time and there has been some drying out. Be sure vegetables inside plastic bags do not look wet, for even one bad carrot, potato or onion can spoil the rest.

"Firm" does not mean the rock hardness of green unripe fruits or vegetables. Unripe produce has already suffered vitamin loss because it has been picked too soon. Then transportation may harm it still further. There is a point at which tomatoes, melons, avocados, and so on may be picked and still continue to ripen until a satisfactory—if not ideal—state is reached. If picked sooner than this, the fruit may never ripen, but just change color and dry a little. It may be edible, but it will not be luscious. If you are a new shopper, ask your grocery man or produce man to help you. If he wants to keep your trade, it will be to his interest to be honest and take time to help you. Sometimes a green tomato may look perfect, but when it ripens it will develop spoiled areas. Unripe tomatoes or melons will ripen best at room temperature, but not on a hot window sill. If you attempt to ripen tomatoes in the refrigerator they become watery and more subject to decay.

It is possible to buy overripe produce that is not spoiled. In the case of melons, you may hear the seeds and liquid moving around in the center. With some vegetables, such as squash and pumpkins, the skin will be very hard, almost too hard to pierce with a knife, and there will be some loss of weight through drying in the center. You will seldom hear seeds move, however; they are too firmly netted.

You have heard many jokes about the shopper pinching the apples or pears. Of course you should not pinch them, but press gently with a finger. A ripe peach, pear, plum, melon, tomato or avocado should yield a little to gentle pressure while still feeling firm. You can recognize ripeness in tree fruits and melons by their smell. Only fully ripe fruits have the particular fragrance that gives us added pleasure when eating and serving them.

Peas and beans and such must have good color and crispness. Pea pods should not be split. If the seeds inside snap beans are very developed, the pods will be dry and tough. Unless you plan to cook only the seeds, do not buy them.

All produce that comes from far away will be more costly than locally grown fruits and vegetables. If you live in northern states, for instance, citrus fruits will be quite expensive. However, this food is cheap at any price, because it is the best source of vitamin C. To equal the vitamin C in one orange, you would have to eat several fresh tomatoes or a great deal of cabbage. Sometimes crops are very small because of weather and plant pests. In those years the amount available will be small and the price higher.

There is limited grading of fresh produce by the USDA. If you find such labels you can be sure the item is of good quality. The top grade for fruits or vegetables is U.S. No. 1 or U.S. Fancy.

Another suggestion for shoppers: buy only what you need. Fruits are perishable, although citrus fruits with their thick tough skins last longer than others. Green vegetables should be used within a week, but root vegetables can be stored for several weeks, some far longer (potatoes, for instance). Winter squash and onions will keep for several weeks.

Do not buy produce because it is the biggest or most gorgeous in appearance; it could be tasteless. Remember what you plan to do with the food; small bumpy apples can make good applesauce, enormous potatoes might be wasteful because no one can eat so much, very large beets might be hard and woody in the center. Iceberg lettuce, the most popular, is often very expensive in the winter months; smaller heads of Boston lettuce may offer better flavor and texture at a lower price.

Fruits and their seasons

Apples—Early apples come into the market in late summer and continue all through fall. Cold-storage fruit is available through winter and spring. *Eating apples:* Delicious, McIntosh, Stayman, Golden Delicious, Jonathan, Winesap. *Applesauce and pie apples:* Gravenstein, Grimes Golden, Jonathan, Newtown. *Baking apples:* Rome Beauty, Rhode Island Greening, Winesap, York Imperial. There is an additional grade for apples, U.S. Extra Fancy.

Apricots—Domestic apricots come into the market in June and July; imported fruit in December and January.

Avocados—Available all year; the crop comes from California and Florida. The skin should be green, just beginning to darken. If brown and spotted, the fruit is overripe, perhaps spoiled.

Bananas—Available all year; ripeness is indicated by the yellow skin color. Never store bananas at temperatures below 55° F.

Blueberries—These come into the market May through September. Large berries are cultivated, smaller berries come from wild bushes.

Cherries—Sweet cherries come into the market May through August. Sour cherries seldom appear; you may need to harvest your own.

Cranberries—These come into the market September through January.

Grapefruit—Available all year, but most abundant January through May. Some have seeds and others do not; this should be indicated in the store. Both white and pink fruits can be found.

Grapes—Available late summer and fall; some varieties appear in specialty shops at other times but are usually more expensive. Native American grapes (slipskins) are Concord, Delaware and Catawba. Other grapes, mostly grown in California, are Thompson seedless (green), Tokay and Cardinal (bright red), Emperor (dark red).

Lemons—Available all year; fruits should be heavy for their size or they may have thick rind and little juice.

Limes—Available sporadically all year. There are two kind: the green Persian lime and the smaller, yellower Key lime.

Melons—These fruits, relatives of cucumbers and squash, include cantaloupe, casaba, Crenshaw, honey ball, honeydew, Persian, watermelon. In melons with a rough netted surface (cantaloupe, Persian), the netting should be thick and the color in the spaces in between should be yellowish; the scent of ripeness should be discernible. In smooth melons, the surface should yield to slight pressure at the blossom end. Casaba and Crenshaw should be golden yellow; honeydew and honey ball should be yellowish-white to creamy with no hard spots. Watermelons should be smooth, well rounded, with creamy rind underneath. Cantaloupes come into the market May through September; casaba, July to November; Crenshaw, July through October; honey ball and honeydew, July through October, although some are available all year long; Persian, August and September; watermelons, June through September.

Nectarines—These come into the market June through September.

Oranges—Available all year; state regulations ensure that the fruits are matured before shipment, but be sure to buy fruits that are heavy for their size, and firm. Navel oranges, good for eating, are available November to May; Valencia, good for juice or salads, April through October; Temple, December to March; pineapple orange, good for eating, November through March.

Peaches—These come into the market in late summer and early fall. Clingstones are good for cooking, but freestones are easier to eat.

Pears—Bartlett pears come into the market August through November; winter pears—Anjou, Bosc, Winter Nellis, Comice—November to May. All should be firm but not rock hard. The color depends on the variety: yellow for Bartlett, green for Anjou and Comice, russet for Bosc, light green for Winter Nellis.

Pineapples—Available all year, but best supply April and May. You can easily pull out a leaf from the top of a ripe pineapple. The odor should be fragrant.

Plums—These come into the market June through September. Italian blue plums, also called prune plums, are found August through October.

Raspberries and other berries—Summer fruits, delicious but perishable, with short seasons.

Rhubarb—Available January to June.

Strawberries—Best supply in markets in May and June, although some appear earlier and later. Ripe berries are red and shiny.

Tangerines—Available November to March. They should be bright-colored with no soft spots.

Vegetables and their seasons

Artichokes—Available most of the year, but the largest crop comes to the market in April and May.

Asparagus—These come to the market mid-February through June, western asparagus earlier, the New Jersey crop later.

Beans—Green snap beans are available all year; yellow wax beans in summer and fall.

Beets—Available all year.

Broccoli—Available all year, but not as good in hot months.

Brussels sprouts—Available about 10 months of the year, but best supplies October through December.

Cabbage—Available all year. Fresh cabbage ("new") has good color and retains its outside leaves. Storage cabbage ("old") usually is very pale and has been trimmed of all outer leaves.

Carrots—Available all year.

Cauliflower—Available all year, but best season is September through January. At other times of the year these can be very expensive.

Celery—Available all year.

Corn—Most plentiful from May to mid-September. For best flavor and nutrition, buy local corn picked the same day.

Cucumbers—Available all year, but most plentiful in summer months. In many markets they are coated with a waxy substance that keeps them looking more green and shiny than their true condition; be sure to peel such coated vegetables. Recently some other vegetables and fruits, apples especially, have been appearing with this same wax coating. If you must buy these, be sure to wash thoroughly or peel.

Eggplant—Available all year, but most plentiful in late summer.

Greens—Available according to kind: spinach all year; kale in fall and winter; dandelions in spring; broccoli leaves and Swiss chard in summer and fall.

Mushrooms—Available all year.

Okra—Available in summer and fall.

Onions—Dried (cured) onions are usually available all year, but are most plentiful in summer, fall and winter. Spanish onions are available in fall and winter. Fresh onions—green onions or scallions, shallots, leeks—are most plentiful in spring and summer, but some leeks and dried shallots can usually be found all year.

Parsley—Flat-leaved and curly-leaved are both available all year.

Parsnips—Available in fall and winter, but have best flavor in late winter.

Peppers—Available all year, but best in late summer. Fully ripe peppers, which are red, are usually found in fall and early winter.

Potatoes—Available all year. New potatoes are available in later winter and early spring.

Radishes—Available all year, but most plentiful May through July.

Salad greens—Chicory and escarole are most plentiful in winter and spring. Belgian endive is chiefly available in winter and spring. Iceberg lettuce, Boston lettuce, Bibb lettuce and Romaine are available all year long, but winter lettuces can be very expensive. Leaf lettuces with loose heads are usually found in local markets in summer and fall. Watercress can be purchased all year, but it is more perishable than other salad greens, so plan to eat it within a few days.

Squash—Summer squash is at its best during late summer and early fall, but some varieties are available all year. Winter squash, which is fully matured and has firm to hard skin, can be stored; these are most plentiful from early fall to late winter. Acorn squash is available all year.

Sweet potatoes—Available all year. Moist sweets are now more popular than the dry sweets. These are perishable; look for firm potatoes with no spots. Do not store in the refrigerator.

Tomatoes—Hot-house tomatoes or those picked green are available all year, but only locally grown tomatoes picked when nearly ripe are really luscious. Usually these good ripe specimens are available in late summer and fall. Do not store tomatoes in the refrigerator until fully ripened.

Turnips—White turnips are available all year. Yellow turnips or rutabagas are available in fall and winter.

HOW TO BUY DRIED, CANNED, FROZEN PRODUCE

These processed foods are often among the best buys for shoppers. The Consumer and Marketing Service of the USDA has established grades of quality for many of the dried, canned and frozen foods, and they are used as standards by many producers. U.S. Grade A or Fancy have best color, flavor and tenderness, and usually all the pieces are the same size. U.S. Grade B or Extra Standard are slightly more mature produce, not so tender, and less well matched for color and size. U.S. Grade C or Standard are not uniform in color or flavor and are often not matched in size, but they can be a good buy if you are using them for soup or purée. The legend "Packed under continuous inspection of the U.S. Department of Agriculture" may appear with or without the grade name. This assumes a wholesome product, and even without a grade name indicates a basically good product. Many packers use the grades without "U.S.," and they must match the standard set by the USDA.

The commonly dried foods are legumes—beans, peas, lentils and chick-peas. They should be bright in color, uniform in size, with no cracked or broken seeds and no foreign materials (stems, leaves, little pebbles). The grades are U.S. No. 1 for dry whole or split peas, lentils and blackeye peas; U.S. No. 1 Choice Handpicked for Great Northern beans, pinto beans and pea beans; U.S. Extra No. 1 for lima beans. The carton or transparent bag must state the name and net weight, and may often give some cooking information.

Cans and packages are required to state the exact weight, the name of the product and a description of the way it is prepared (whole, sliced, chopped). Often the number of servings is given (based on ½ cup for an adult serving).

INDUSTRY NAME	WEIGHT IN OUNCES	APPROXIMATE CUP CONTENTS
8 ounces	8	1
Picnic	10½ to 12	1¼ to 1½
No. 300	14	1¾
No. 303	16 to 17	2
No. 1 tall	16	2
No. 2	20	2½
No. 2½	29	3½
No. 3	32	4
No. 3 Special	46	5¾
No. 10	96 to 104	12 to 13

When buying canned foods, be sure the can is solid with no cracks, leaks or bulges. Dents are less dangerous, but the food in damaged cans can be considered spoiled without further investigation and might be dangerous to eat. Even if such cans are for sale at reduced prices, it is not economical to buy them. If the freshness code (below) indicates that the can has been around for a long time, look for a newer one. While canned food does keep its quality a long time, inevitably there is loss of flavor and nutrients in long-stored cans, especially if they have been stored improperly (at too high heat or allowed to freeze). The USDA shields can only indicate the condition of the contents at the time the can was filled.

When buying frozen foods, you should look for firm packages with the contents evenly balanced inside. If the food is shoved to one end, you can be sure the package has been defrosted and refrozen. While the food might be safe to eat, it will have lost some of its color, flavor and nutrients in the process. Packages that you purchase should not be leaky, dripping, torn or damaged in any way.

Some fruits and vegetables are frozen without additional liquid in a loose or dry pack. It is possible to remove a part of these contents and return the rest to the freezer. In such cases, you might save money by buying large packages which are often in transparent bags so you can see the quality of the food. However, in general it is better to buy frozen foods in packages just large enough for your purpose. You should cook the whole contents as soon as it has thawed and eat it without delay.

Frozen foods are usually packed in containers holding 8, 9, 10, 12, 16, 24 or 32 ounces. However, this is an expanding industry and new packaging is constantly appearing on the market. Freeze-drying, a technique of removing water from frozen foods, is still only experimental, so there is no established size for packages of such foods.

Freshness codes

Some large food chains have freshness codes on all their produce—a set of numbers including dates. These numbers can be the date the item was packaged, the date after which it should not be used or the date after which it is removed from sale. Other numbers in the set may indicate a U.S. grade or information on temperature of storage or time for safe storage by the buyer. Information on these freshness codes is usually available to customers, and a smart shopper can learn a lot about good storage and care of all foods from company information leaflets on this subject.

BUYING GUIDE

By learning to compare the weight of an item as purchased with the number of servings it will yield, you will find it is as easy to cook for 50 as it is to cook for 2. It is merely a matter of adding and subtracting. Check the items on your shopping list against the items in this buying guide. Jot down next to the items any information you believe important for you to know.

FOOD	NUMBER OF SERVINGS	EQUIVALENTS & COMMENTS
Almonds, shelled, 1 lb.	20 (12 nuts each serving)	6 oz. whole almonds = 1 cup
Almonds, in shell, 1 lb.	8 servings	6 to 8 oz. nutmeats
Apples, fresh, 1 lb.	3 (1 whole apple each serving)	3 cups pared and sliced 2½ cups cubed
Apples, dried, 8 oz.	18 servings	2 cups uncooked 5 cups cooked
Apricots, fresh, 1 lb.	5 (2 apricots each serving)	8 to 12 apricots
Apricots, dried, 1 lb.	16 servings	3 cups uncooked 5 cups cooked
Asparagus, fresh, 1 lb.	3 (5 to 6 stalks each serving)	16 to 20 stalks
Asparagus, canned, 20 oz.	5 to 7 servings	
Bacon, 1 lb.	8 (3 slices each serving)	25 thin slices
Bananas, 1 lb.	3 servings	3 bananas
Bananas, 1 lb. sliced	5 servings	2½ cups
Bananas, 1 lb. mashed		2 cups
Barley, pearl, 1 lb.	8 servings	6 cups cooked
Barley, whole, 1 lb.	8 servings	6 cups cooked
Beans, dried, 1 lb.	8 servings	6 cups cooked

FOOD	NUMBER OF SERVINGS	EQUIVALENTS & COMMENTS
Beans, fresh, 1 lb.	4 servings	2 to 3 cups, diced or slivered
Beef, ground, 1 lb.	4 servings	5 servings with stretcher added
Beef, porterhouse, 1 lb.	2 servings	
Beef, round, 1 lb.	4 to 5 servings	
Beef, sirloin, 1 lb.	2 servings	
Beef, stewing, 1 lb.	4 servings	
Beets, 1 lb.	4 servings	3 to 5 beets, 2 cups diced
Blueberries, 1 pint	4 servings	
Brazil nuts, in shell, 1 lb.	12 to 15 (10 nuts each serving)	½ lb. nutmeats
Bread, 1 lb.	6 to 8 servings	12 to 16 slices
Bread stuffing, 8 oz.		3 cups, enough to stuff 5-lb. chicken
Broccoli, 1 lb.	3 servings	
Brussels sprouts, 1 lb.	5 servings	
Butter, 1 lb.	48 (⅓-oz. square each serving)	2 cups (¼ lb. = ½ cup)
Cabbage, raw, 1 lb.	10 to 12 servings	4 cups shredded
Cabbage, cooked (1 lb. raw)	4 (½ cup each serving)	
Carrots, 1 lb.	5 (½ cup each serving)	2½ cups diced or shredded
Cauliflower, 1 lb.	4 servings	
Celery, 1 lb.	4 servings	1 medium-size head, or 2 cups diced
Cheese, Cheddar, 1 lb.	20 (1-inch cube each serving)	8 oz. = 2 cups grated
Cheese, cottage, 1 lb.	4 (½ cup each serving)	2 cups
Cherries, 1 lb.	4 servings	2 cups pitted
Chicken, small broiler	2 servings	
Chicken, large broiler	4 servings	
Chicken, roaster or capon, per lb.	2 servings	

FOOD	NUMBER OF SERVINGS	EQUIVALENTS & COMMENTS
Chinese cabbage, 1 lb.	10 to 12 servings	4 cups shredded
Chinese cabbage, cooked (1 lb. raw)	4 (½ cup each serving)	
Chocolate, unsweetened, 8 oz.		8 squares, 1 oz. each
Chocolate, unsweetened, grated		1 square grated = ½ cup
Cocoa, unsweetened, 8 oz.	30 (1 cup hot cocoa each serving)	2 cups
Coconut, 3½ oz.		1⅓ cups
Coffee, ground, all types, 1 lb.	40 to 45 servings	5 cups
Coffee, instant, 2 oz.	25 servings	1 cup
Corn, ears, 12 medium	5 to 6 servings	3 cups cut kernels
Cornflakes, 15 oz.	18 (1 cup each serving)	16 to 20 cups, average volume
Crackers, graham, 1 lb.		66 crackers; 15 crackers crushed = 1 cup
Crackers, soda, 3½ oz.		33 crackers; 22 crackers crushed = 1 cup
Cranberries, fresh, 1 lb.	4 to 6 servings	4¾ cups = 3 to 3½ cups cooked
Cream, light, 2 cups	15 to 18 for coffee	
Currants, dried, 11 oz.		2 cups
Dates, 1 lb.		2⅔ cups
Eggplant, medium-size	5 to 6 servings	2 to 2½ cups diced
Figs, dried, 1 lb.	7 servings	2¾ cups cut up
Filberts, shelled, 1 lb.	25 (10 nuts each serving)	
Fish (any type), boneless, 1 lb.	3 servings	
Flour, all-purpose, 1 lb.		4 cups sifted
Flour, cake, 1 lb.		4½ cups sifted

FOOD	NUMBER OF SERVINGS	EQUIVALENTS & COMMENTS
Flour, whole-wheat		3½ cups, unsifted
Fruit peels, candied, mixed, 1 lb.		2½ cups
Gelatin, unflavored, 1 envelope		1 tablespoon (approx.), enough to set 2 cups liquid
Grapefruit, 1 medium-size	2 servings	1 lb.
Grapefruit juice		¾ cup per grapefruit
Grapefruit sections		1¼ cups per grapefruit
Grapes, 1 lb.		1 qt. whole 2¾ cups halved and seeded
Ham, cooked, 1 lb.	4 (1 slice each serving)	
Honey, 1 lb.		1½ cups
Ice cream, 1 quart	6 to 8 servings	
Lemons, juice from 1 lemon		3 tablespoons juice
Lemons, grated rind of 1 lemon		2 tablespoons rind
Liver, 1 lb.	4 to 5 servings	4 to 5 slices
Macaroni, 1 lb.	6 to 8 servings	1 cup uncooked = 2 cups cooked
Marshmallows		10 miniature = 1 large ¼ lb. = 16 large
Molasses, 1 lb.		1⅓ cups
Mushrooms, fresh, ½ lb.	2 to 3 servings	15 to 20 small mushrooms
Noodles, 1 lb.	4 to 6 servings	
Onions, 1 lb.	3 to 4 servings	3 large onions
Oranges, juice from 1 orange		½ cup juice
Oranges, grated rind of 1 orange		3 tablespoons rind

FOOD	NUMBER OF SERVINGS	EQUIVALENTS & COMMENTS
Parsnips, 1 lb.	4 servings	4 medium-size parsnips
Peaches, fresh, 1 lb.	3 to 4 servings	3 to 4 peaches
Peanuts in shell, 1 lb.	25 (10 nuts each serving)	⅔ lb. nutmeats
Pears, fresh, 1 lb.	3 servings	3 large pears
Pecans, in shell, 1 lb.	20 (10 nuts each serving)	½ lb. nutmeats = 2 cups
Plums, blue (prune plums), 1 lb.	5 (4 plums each serving)	20 plums
Plums, red or green, 1 lb.	5 servings	5 plums
Potatoes, sweet, 1 lb.	3 to 4 servings	2 to 3 large potatoes
Potatoes, white, 1 lb.	3 to 4 servings	3 large or 6 to 8 small potatoes
Prunes, dried, 1 lb.	12 servings	2½ cups uncooked 4 cups cooked
Raisins, 11 oz.		2 cups
Rice, 1 lb.	10 to 12 portions	6 cups cooked rice
Spaghetti, 1 lb.	4 to 6 servings	
Spinach, fresh, 1 lb.	2 servings	
Sugar, brown, 1 lb.		2¼ cups packed
Sugar, confectioners', 1 lb.		4 to 4½ cups sifted
Sugar, granulated, 1 lb.		2¼ cups
Sugar, superfine, 1 lb.		2⅓ cups
Tea, loose, ¼ lb.	75 cups	1 teaspoon per cup
Tomatoes, 1 lb.	3 servings	2 to 3 medium-size tomatoes
Turnips, 1 lb.	4 servings	3 cups mashed 2 to 2½ cups diced
Walnuts, in shell, 1 lb.	15 to 18 (10 nuts each serving)	½ lb. nutmeats

10
SPEEDS

«3»

The Kitchen: Where The Action Is

Kinds of pots and pans, top-of-stove, oven and broiler utensils • What to do if the pan or mold is the wrong size • Kinds of knives • Starter set of knives • Other essential tools • Small appliances • Luxuries • Refrigerator and freezer • How long to keep foods on the pantry shelf • Weights and measures • Efficient refrigerator use • Stocking your pantry • Grams and ounces • Equivalent measures • Difficult fractions • Measurement conversion table

A kitchen is not just a room in which you prepare daily meals. Often it is where the children entertain their friends, and the family gathers to talk and "see what's cooking." Although your kitchen must be efficient, it should also be a pleasant room to work in, a place for informality and hospitality.

Color is important—your kitchen need not be sterile white or look like an industrial laboratory. Use bright, washable wallpaper or paint. Decorate the walls with pictures. Furniture should be comfortable and attractive. Good lighting is a must. Add a few green plants, perhaps some potted herbs, a flowering plant in spring. You will be surprised how these touches brighten your attitude toward daily tasks.

The success of everything you cook or prepare depends to a great extent on the kind of equipment you have in your kitchen. Proper tools and utensils will give better results and cut down on preparation time. It is wise to invest in the best you can afford.

A well-equipped, convenient kitchen requires thoughtful planning. You need ample storage space for canned, bottled and packaged foods as well as utensils, dishes and seasonings. Nonessentials that clutter kitchen drawers and cabinets often make it difficult to find the important things. Discard equipment you never use. Save time and energy by storing articles and tools close to the place where you will use them. Electrical appliances, for example, should be near an electric outlet; your chopping block should be handy to the sink and to your garbage disposal. Decide where things should be placed or stored for your greatest convenience. After some rearranging you will arrive at the storage system best for you.

If you are a new homemaker, the following lists may seem impossibly long, and equipping your kitchen may seem expensive. But you do not need to purchase everything at once. Start with the essentials, then add those things which would be convenient; later, treat yourself to a few luxuries.

Pots and pans

One common mistake many people make, especially the young bride or bride-to-be, is to equip a kitchen with matched sets of uniform pots and pans. Actually, most women soon discover that a variety of different types is much more useful. Get acquainted with the different kinds of kitchenware on the market and find out which are best for you.

Stainless steel

This is expensive, but it is practically indestructible and is easy to clean and shine. Some stainless-steel pans have attractive copper bottoms, although they require work to keep clean. It may be better for you to buy pans with laminated aluminum bottoms. Either kind helps distribute the heat evenly. Use stainless-steel pots for vegetables, soups, stews and fruits.

Aluminum

This is the best material for all-around use. Buy substantial pans because the thinner ones tend to warp and dent with use. Aluminum does require care to keep clean and shiny. Regular use of a steel-wool soap pad is the best as well as the easiest cleaning method. Just give your pan a little buff every time it is washed. A heavy-duty aluminum frying pan is excellent for pan-cooking and sautéing foods, because it gives even heat distribution.

Enamelware

This term may be applied to a lightweight pan made of a thin layer of enamel fused onto metal. Such pans tend to crack, chip and discolor easily, and the heat distribution is very uneven. However, the nonmetallic coating makes enamelware useful for marinating, or for cooking foods that would discolor aluminum pots.

Porcelain enamelware

This is made of porcelain enamel applied over cast iron. It combines bright colors, sturdiness and control of heat for foods that require long, slow cooking. The best type has porcelain applied both inside and outside the cast iron. Good-quality wares of this type are rather expensive, like stainless steel, but with careful handling they will last a lifetime. The use of this heavy ware is the secret of many of the great recipes of classic cuisines. It is perfect for casserole cooking.

Many attractive casserole dishes are available that can be brought from the stove to the table.

Cast iron

This is still the dependable, low-price, sturdy ware that our ancestors used. Because cast-iron pots and pans have no wooden or composition parts, they can be used on top of the stove and in the oven. This is perfect ware for pan-broiling steaks and chops and for cooking such things as bacon, pancakes and eggs.

A new cast-iron pan must be seasoned before using. Spread a light coat of melted lard, shortening or salad oil on the inside of the utensil and cover. Then place it on a sheet of heavy aluminum foil in a 200° F. oven for three hours, brushing the sides and cover occasionally with more fat. Turn off the heat. When the utensil has cooled, wipe off the excess fat with paper towels. Wash the pot in warm water with no soap, and put it back in the warm oven to dry thoroughly. Follow this procedure for used pots that have rusted. Wash them well before seasoning. Each time a utensil is washed, dry it over low heat or in a warm oven before storing. Do not cover tightly when storing; humidity trapped inside may cause rusting.

Copper

All copper utensils are expensive and difficult to keep clean. Also, the tin lining must be renewed from time to time. However, these splendid pans are a real treasure to own because they are attractive, light to handle and conduct heat quickly. The indispensable luxury, if soufflés and meringues are on your list of accomplishments, is a large copper bowl for beating egg whites.

Teflon

This is a nonstick coating applied to the inside of cookware that makes it possible to cook without fat. Although very easy to clean, its delicate surface must be protected against scratches. Steel-wool or scratchy cleaners should not be used on the Teflon coating, and plastic utensils or wooden spoons are best when turning or stirring anything in one of these pans. This type of cookware excels as bread and cake pans, cookie sheets and omelet pans.

Pyrex
Watching the pot boil or the cake bake became possible with this heatproof, flameproof glass. It is especially good for preparations that may need careful attention. For instance, you can tell if a crust is getting too brown on the bottom and adjust oven heat accordingly. Pyrex is fragile and cannot be moved from hot to cold with safety.

Pyroceram
This is a wonder of the modern world. It is a special ceramic that can be removed from the freezer or refrigerator and immediately put in a hot oven or on top of the stove. When the food is ready, it can be carried from the stove to the table. This ware is available in a large range of shapes and sizes. It is most useful for all types of slow cooking.

Earthenware
This ancient type of red clay cooking ware was once used almost universally. It is still made and extensively used in France in special sizes and shapes for each purpose. It is especially fragile and can be used for stove-top cooking only with the greatest care. If you plan to cook certain classics of the provincial French cuisine, such as *cassoulet* or *tian,* an earthenware pot of the right shape is a good choice. For top-of-the-stove cooking, however, it is better to choose a less fragile ware. Recently a renewed interest in earthenware cookery has produced a new type of unglazed earthenware to use on top of the stove and in the oven.

Top-of-stove utensils

If you find it hard to determine what size or type pan you should purchase, check the following list. Remember, you do not need to buy all of these utensils at once; purchase only those that will be most useful to you.

1 large covered pan. Six- to 10-quart size, for meat, soup, spaghetti or food for a large party.

1 double boiler. The 2-quart size is best, but they come smaller or larger. Either part can be used separately as a saucepan.

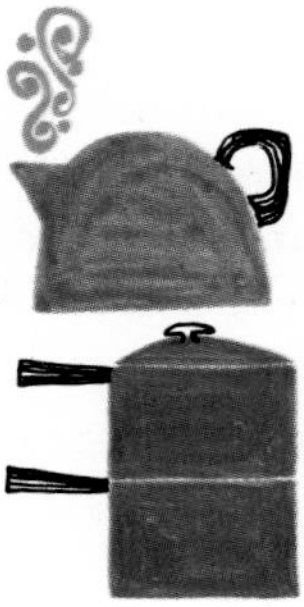

2 saucepans. The 1-quart size is used most frequently for all types of small jobs. At least one should be stainless steel and the other whatever you choose.

1 saucepan. Two-quart size of stainless steel or porcelain enamelware.

2 frying pans. Ten-inch pan with a cover, in porcelain enamelware or heavy aluminum. This type pan is often called a *sauteuse*—a pan for sautéing (frying in very little fat). For the second pan, choose the 7- or 8-inch size in cast iron, porcelain enamel, or metal with nonstick coating.

1 cast-iron Dutch oven or a 2-quart saucepan of porcelain enamelware with a cover.

1 tea kettle. Choose the 2- or 3-quart size that can be cleaned inside (you may prefer an electric tea kettle).

1 or 2 teapots if you are a tea drinker. Choose two sizes, one small or medium, the other large. Teapots should either be earthenware or the more elegant porcelain, but do not make tea in a metal pot; metal changes the fine, delicate flavor.

1 or 2 coffee makers if you are coffee drinkers. Drip coffee made in a filter coffeepot is the most digestible. Coffee makers come in all sizes and types. If you have retained the good habit of making coffee from ground coffee rather than instant, choose a 2- to 3-cup size to suit small daily needs and a larger size for the entire family or for guests. Whatever your choice, you can find something that pleases you.

3 or 4 assorted pieces of heatproof ceramic with covers in different sizes to suit your needs. They can be used in oven or broiler.

Oven and broiler utensils

1 large shallow roasting pan without a cover. Select sizes 12 to 15 inches long by 10 to 12 inches wide and 2 to 3 inches deep. In porcelain enamelware or, as a second choice, stainless steel. It is possible to roast in any sturdy shallow pan.

1 broiler pan with a rack. Ovens are often equipped with these, but a small-size one as a second is very practical.

1 porcelain enamelware casserole in the 2-quart size. Choose one attractive enough to bring to the table. This can be most useful, but is not essential as a starter unless you have a large family. However, it is an ideal utensil for braising a large piece of meat. You can use this on top of the stove and in the oven.

2 cookie sheets or baking sheets. At least one should have a nonstick coating.

2 pie pans. One 8-inch and the other 9-inch, or both 9-inch. Aluminum or heatproof glass are the usual materials.

2 square cake pans, 8 × 8 × 2 inches, plain or with nonstick coating.

3 round cake pans, 8 × 1½ inches, with nonstick coating.

2 loaf pans, 9 × 5 × 3 inches. Bread and cake baked in heatproof glass, ceramic or aluminum with nonstick coating are easier to turn out after baking, but plain aluminum will do.

4 loaf pans, 5 × 3 × 2 inches, for breads and cakes.

1 jelly-roll pan, 11 × 7 × 2 inches, or 12 × 8 × 2 inches, with nonstick coating.

2 cake racks, a large one and a small one.

1 tube pan. The most practical size is 10 × 4 inches. Nonstick coating is very useful.

1 muffin or cupcake pan. These come with cups of 1½, 2½ and 3 inches in diameter. The 2½-inch size is the most practical size, but choose whichever you prefer. Nonstick coating is recommended for muffins or cupcakes because they unmold so easily.

6 custard cups. These come in different sizes, but the 6-ounce size is the most practical. You will use them for many things other than custard.

1 springform pan. This consists of a rim and a flat-bottom inset with a clamp or spring to open the rim. They are also available with a tube inset. The usual size is 9 × 3 inches. These are very useful for *Torten,* angel food cake, cheesecake and other fancy desserts.

Oven-to-table servers. The number and size will depend upon your preferences and needs.

Assorted small fancy molds. The number and size will depend upon your need.

Ring molds. Capacity ranges from 3⅓ to 11 cups, or 1- to 3-quart sizes. The size is usually marked on the molds. Use these for molded desserts, jellied foods, and cakes. Choose according to your requirements.

For special items such as omelet pans and soufflé dishes, see the chapter on eggs.

If the pan or mold is the wrong size

Often a recipe will call for a mold or a pan size you do not have. The following suggestions will help you solve this problem.

O━ If the recipe calls for a 3-cup mold or for a 2-quart casserole, you can use any other container of another shape as long as it will hold the same volume. To determine the volume, fill the pan with water, using a standard 8-ounce measuring cup. As an example, a pan holding 4 cups of water will be equivalent to a 1-quart casserole.

O━ If a baking recipe specifies a pan 13 × 9 × 2 inches, the surface area is important and not the shape. Measure the width and length of the pan you have available and multiply these two figures to determine the area in square inches. Do the same for the measurements given in the recipe. A pan 13 × 9 inches will have a surface area of 117 square inches. A pan 12 × 10 inches may look quite different, but its surface area is almost the same—120 square inches. If you have only small pans, use two or more to get the same surface area. Determining the specified 2-inch depth is not as important; the pan can be deeper, but not shallower. It is the surface area that counts.

Here is still another way to solve the problem. O━ Cake batters should never fill a pan more than two thirds full. If you do not have a pan large enough to hold all the batter at this level, make cupcakes with the remainder.

O━ When the recipe calls for a 9- or 10-inch tube pan, bake the batter in a flat pan 13 × 9 × 2 inches.

If you do not know the size of your pie pan, measure from the inside edge to the opposite side with a ruler. For depth, measure perpendicularly, not along the sloping sides. The volume of a pie pan or any other baking pan can be measured by filling with water, as described on page 82. A 9-inch pie pan 1½ to 2 inches deep holds about 1 quart (4 cups) of filling; an 8-inch pie pan, about 3 cups.

O╥ Whenever a recipe calls for a casserole with a cover, use any heavy baking pan that is the right size and make a cover of heavy-duty foil.

Knives

These are among the most neglected tools in the kitchen, although they are used constantly. They are often poor in quality, not well sharpened or not the proper type for the work they are expected to do. There is a knife for every job. The variety is endless, but you can get a perfect starter set of six knives. If you are not able to pay for a good-quality set, buy one good knife at a time as the need arises. Cheap knives are a waste of money.

A good-quality knife made of hard steel is expensive but, if well cared for, will last a lifetime. Wash and dry your steel knives promptly after use to prevent rust or stain.

Stainless-steel knives have become very popular in recent years. They are far easier to care for than the old-fashioned steel knives but will never keep as sharp an edge.

A new type of knife with a scalloped edge is fast gaining in popularity with practical cooks. Originally designed for slicing crumbly bread and cake, it is now made in many sizes and shapes for use in general work such as paring, cutting and even carving. Do not let anyone tell you, however, that these knives will last a lifetime without being sharpened. Although they stay sharp much longer than knives with straight-edged blades, the teeth that project beyond the cutting edge wear down. This knife requires occasional sharpening with a butcher's steel on the flat side of the blade, and will eventually need regrinding by an expert.

It is a good idea to have a long butcher's steel for sharpening knives. These are easy to find; any store that sells quality knives will have them. Keep your knives sharp by frequent honing on the steel. To do this, press the knife edge against the steel at a 20° angle. Starting with the heel of the blade at the top of the steel, draw the blade across and down to the bottom of the steel, in a swinging motion. Do this several times, then repeat on the other side.

The most important advice: store your knives in a knife rack or on a magnetic bar; do not jumble them carelessly with other kitchen tools. This will keep the blades keen longer, and you will never cut yourself when reaching for a kitchen tool.

Starter set of knives

Chef's knife. This is called a French chef's knife, a butcher knife or a general-purpose knife. It is used to chop, mince and cut. The blade size ranges from 7 to 14 inches. The best for an average kitchen is the 10-inch size; it can do the work of a small or large knife and is easy to manipulate.

Carving knife. The best kind has a straight blade 8½ to 9 inches long with a plain or scalloped edge.

Bread knife. The scalloped-edged types can slice a loaf of bread wafer-thin, but those with serrated edges tend to tear rather than cut.

If you do not know the difference between a scalloped edge and a serrated edge, ask a sales clerk to show you the next time you go shopping. Scalloped-edged knives are made from a high-carbon steel formula and are heat tempered. This makes them more expensive, but they are worth the money.

Small slicing and scraping knife. The most useful size has a 4-inch blade with a slightly scalloped edge.

Slicer. Usually 4½ to 5 inches long, this can have a straight blade with a straight or slightly turned-up point. A scalloped edge is very practical for cutting tomatoes, citrus fruits, hard-cooked eggs or cucumbers into thin even slices.

Utility knife. This usually has a 5-inch blade, plain or scalloped, with a concave ground edge. Use this to peel and pare vegetables and fruits and to slice tough-skinned vegetables.

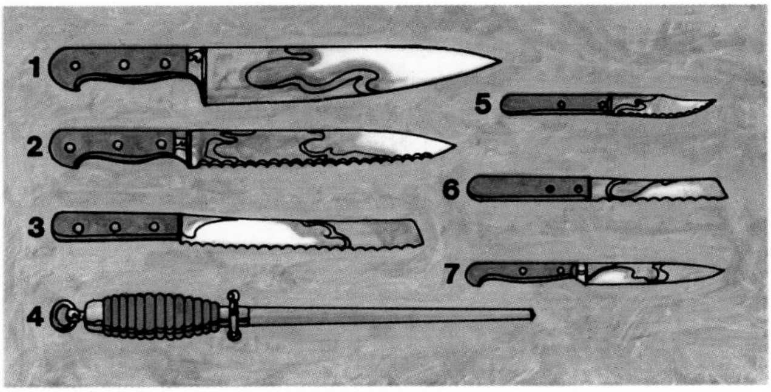

1. Chef's knife
2. Carving knife
3. Bread knife
4. Butcher's steel
5. Small slicing and scraping knife
6. Slicer
7. Utility knife

Other essential tools

In addition to pots, pans and knives, there are other small tools you will need. Do not try to economize by buying cheap ones. They will prove to be a poor investment; they may bend, break, rust or come apart at the joint of blade and handle. Cheap tools are always a waste of money.

1 set of large sturdy salt and pepper shakers.

1 set of wooden spoons. Buy three or four in graduated sizes. Usually made of birch, these are indispensable and do not scratch the bottoms of your pots and pans.

1 large 2-pronged fork. Select stainless steel with a sturdy handle.

1 slotted spoon. This is used to remove cooked vegetables, soft-cooked eggs or any food that may have released sandy particles in the cooking liquid, such as spinach or fresh mussels.

1 vegetable peeler. Even one of good quality is inexpensive. Indispensable.

2 metal spatulas. Choose a short wide spatula with a flexible blade as a butter and sandwich spreader, and a long narrow one for lifting cookies from a baking sheet and for many other uses.

1 pancake turner. The short wide type is best. One with nonstick coating can play a double role since it can be used on nonstick pans as well. This is stiffer than a spatula; you will also turn fish cakes, eggplant slices and the like with it.

1 set of canisters. Buy airtight ones for storing such staples as flour, salt, sugar.

1 set of measuring spoons. Choose good quality for accurate measurement.

2 sets of measuring cups. For dry ingredients, buy four graduated metal cups that fit inside each other. When using these, fill to the brim. Buy glass measuring cups for liquid ingredients. The rims of these are higher than the measuring line to prevent spilling. To measure accurately, hold the measuring line at eye level. Cups come in ¼-, ⅓-, ½-, and 1-cup sizes, also in 2- and 4-cup sizes. The 1- and 2-cup sizes are the most useful for liquids. There are usually lines on the 1- and 2-cup sizes indicating thirds and fourths.

1 set of mixing bowls. Buy either stainless steel, which is expensive but will last a lifetime, or a good-quality plastic or polyethylene, which is light in weight and easy to wash. Pottery bowls can be used too. They are often handsome and easy to hold, but breakable.

2 or 3 rubber scrapers. These are useful for scraping any mixture out of a bowl because they bend around the inside and collect every bit of the mixture.

1 pair of metal tongs to turn steak and other meats.

1 set of skewers for foods *en brochette.*

1 larding needle for inserting strips of fat into meat to give it juiciness and flavor.

1 trussing needle for tying poultry, game or meat to keep its shape while cooking.

1 set of stainless-steel nails. Used with string, they close the opening in poultry or in any stuffed food, such as a whole fish or stuffed veal breast.

1 potato masher. Stainless steel is best. Use for mashing potatoes and other vegetables, apples and cranberries for sauces, and fruits for jams and jellies.

2 French wire whisks, whips or beaters. A medium-size and a large one. Use for making hollandaise, mayonnaise, meringues, even for blending the ingredients of a simple salad dressing. The wooden-handled type with a double row of piano wires is the best.

1 egg beater. Purchase a top-quality beater with smooth heavy-duty bearings and stainless-steel blades. Cheap beaters do not last and never work efficiently.

1 soup ladle. A small sauce ladle is also very useful.

2 cutting boards. A large one for meat and a small one for cheese or vegetables.

1 pair of kitchen scissors or shears. These will help you in countless ways—cutting herbs, especially chives and parsley; cutting up dried fruits such as dates or figs; opening plastic bags of food; cutting pizza.

1 apple corer.

1 set of graters. The best have three grater sizes. If your grater is metal, get a small ceramic one for grating citrus rinds.

2 strainers. Choose one for tea and the other large enough to double as a small colander. Later you may want other sizes of strainers and a large collander.

2 funnels. Get a small one and a medium-size one.

1 corkscrew for bottles sealed with corks. Choose one that really works; many on the market are worthless.

1 bottle opener for bottles sealed with metal caps. Get one with a sturdy handle.

1 punch opener for cans.

1 meat thermometer. This is important if you are a new cook; it will help you prepare successful roasts from the start. Also, it is essential if you plan to cook frozen meats.

1 candy (frying) thermometer. This is important if you make candy or often deep fry. Also, you can test the temperature of liquids to be mixed with yeast in bread making.

When you start to bake, you will need to add a few more items.

1 flour sifter. These are used less and less because of the no-sifting flour now available, but you will need regular flour for many recipes. A 1-cup sifter should be adequate. Place it over the measuring cup when sifting to save time.

1 rolling pin made of wood or coated with nonstick coating.

1 pastry brush. A small paint brush, 1 inch wide, is perfect, but brushes especially designed for cookery are available.

Pastry bag with various tips for icings and meringues.

Storage equipment for freezing is described in Chapter 15 on Freezing Foods.

Small appliances

Some small appliances can be invaluable because they save so much time and labor. They can be hand-operated or electrically powered.

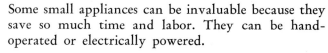

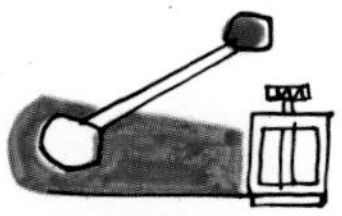

A can opener. Quality is essential. The hand-operated type should have a sturdy handle, or get a good-quality hand-operated wall type. A can opener should be cleaned often and oiled occasionally. There are electric can openers too.

A fruit juicer. Choose a good reamer that fits over a cup to catch the juice. A hand reamer can be just as effective as any electric juicer unless you squeeze large quantities of juice daily.

A food mill. A medium-size mill is a most useful kitchen tool to purée vegetables for soups or fruits for sauces. There are also larger and smaller mills. A similar appliance is a ricer, but the mill is easier and quicker to operate for a variety of vegetables and fruits.

An electric hand mixer. If you do not have a large electric mixer with a stand, this will serve well, although it is heavy to hold for a long period of time. A large electric mixer is very useful if you make cakes or stir heavy mixtures.

A food grinder. Some electric mixers have a grinder attachment. This will grind meat, vegetables, nuts—

almost anything. An old-fashioned hand grinder is equally effective, but not as easy to use.

Scales. These are handy, especially if you enjoy making international dishes or if you are a dieter who must measure food by weight. There are several types and sizes. Some weigh up to 4 ounces, others to 25 pounds. Those marked with kilograms as well as ounces and pounds will make it possible for you to use recipes from English and European cookbooks.

Luxuries

The following items do not belong on a master list of essentials. However, if you have graduated from the beginner class and have developed a genuine interest in cooking, you may want some of them. Study their uses before you buy. It would be foolish to spend the money and clutter up your cupboard for some elaborate, expensive equipment that is seldom used.

Boxwood spatula and spoons. French boxwood spatulas and spoons are light and smooth. Their flexibility lets you feel the consistency and texture of the ingredients you stir. One of these spatulas is good for mixing bread dough.

Chopping block (butcher's block). Larger and thicker than the cutting boards listed previously. It can be used like a cutting board, but the block is much sturdier. Price varies according to size and quality. You do not need the biggest or best, but make sure that the wood is thick and the board heavy so that it will not slide around when used.

Meat hammer. This is a double-headed hammer made of metal or hard plastic with blunt teeth on one side and grooves on the other. Pounding meat with it breaks up the fibers while spreading out the meat into a thin layer. You prepare *scaloppini* or *schnitzel* in this manner.

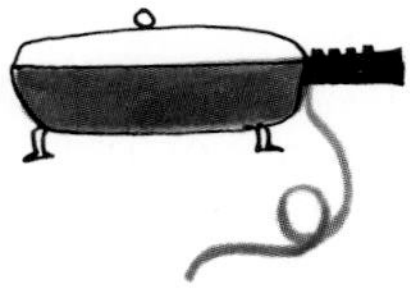

Electric frying pan. Many cooks never use this appliance; others say they would not be without one and use it several times a week. Whether or not this item would be useful depends on the sort of cooking you do. Some women find it convenient as a thermostatically controlled utensil for cooking at the table, or as a chafing dish.

Electric coffee grinder. This item will be classed as a luxury if you drink instant coffee most of the time. But if you make fresh coffee every day, it could be considered an essential. A cup of coffee is at its best only when made with freshly ground beans. Keep your grinder clean; use it every day and you will relish every cup of coffee you make.

Blender. This may come with two speeds or with several. An electric blender is certainly not essential, but it is a great joy to use because it can do so many things quickly and efficiently. A good blender is expensive but well worth the price if used for more than the preparation of fancy drinks.

Electric hot tray. A hot tray of good quality will keep food hot for two or three hours and can be a tremendous help when entertaining. You can set food on the tray long before guests or family arrive for dinner.

Portable food heater. These butane-fueled table heaters with adjustable flame have become very popular. They are wonderful for a fondue party.

A garbage-disposal unit in the sink may be a convenience for you if the location of your home and your plumbing arrangements make it practical.

Refrigerator and freezer

When you shop for a refrigerator or freezer, save yourself time and money by first deciding what you want and need. Consider the following points:

How much storage space do you need? This is determined by how large your family is, how often you shop and the kind of food you buy. Since no one has ever had too much refrigerator space, get one as large as room and budget will allow.

What types are available? Refrigerators with single doors include conventional types, refrigerators without freezers and compact refrigerators. Two-door combinations include those with a separate freezer at the top, at the bottom or at the side. When deciding which you want, consider the convenience of use and the freezer-refrigerator proportion that will work best for you.

What features do you want? Shelf arrangement: shelves vary in flexibility. They may adjust up or down in a great variety of combinations, or they may slide, glide or even swing out.

Special storage areas: look for an abundance of compartmentalized storage areas if you want ease in organizing. Superchilled drawers are great for more-than-one-day storage of fresh meats. Some of them can be converted to an extra crisper drawer. Doors may have compartmentalized storage, adjustable shelves, even a vegetable crisper.

Freezer storage features are important too. Think of the frozen foods you use most. Can you store these within easy reach?

Ice making: some refrigerator-freezer combinations now include automatic ice makers. Other refrigerators have trays with ice-removal features.

"Fast cold recovery" will let you maintain a uniform cold temperature inside, no matter how often the door is opened.

Refrigerators are available in greens, reds, blue, copper tones, beiges, brushed chrome and wood grains. Trim, square lines give a built-in look, and you can get wood-grained finishes to match your cabinets.

What size? Measure the kitchen space available so you can choose a refrigerator of the correct size. The different types of refrigerators are available in many dimensions; even the side-by-side combination comes as narrow as 33 inches and as wide as 48 inches.

Do not overlook the compact refreshment refrigerators or freezers; they are a wonderful convenience for the family room or den.

When you buy a freezer for the first time, it will not be easy to judge the best size. As with a refrigerator, the larger, the better. Once you have a freezer, it will be only a few weeks before you realize what frustration can be caused by a freezer that is too small for your needs. On the other hand, if you use a freezer only to make meal planning a little easier by storing just enough frozen food for two or three days and keeping a few emergency items, it is more economical to buy a large refrigerator with a good frozen-food compartment. The investment in a freezer is not economical under such circumstances.

For more about freezers and how to use them, see Chapter 15 on Freezing Foods.

Efficient refrigerator use

Since a refrigerator is a large investment, you will want to get the best use from it. It also is one appliance that is always plugged in, so savings on power costs are worth considering. Here are some helpful ideas:

1. Place the refrigerator in the coolest part of your kitchen. Air should be able to circulate around it freely.
2. Be sure the outside door, hinges and door catch work properly; otherwise warm air can enter.
3. Do not open your refrigerator more often or longer than necessary.
4. Avoid quick freezing (by turning your freezer control to the coolest position) if you want to save on power costs.
5. Turn your control down to "low" or "economy" if you go away for several days.
6. Defrost the refrigerator when frost around the freezing unit is ¼ inch thick. The coils will then continue to work at maximum efficiency.
7. Maintain circulation of air inside the refrigerator. Do not line the shelves with wax paper or foil to avoid drips. Air circulates best through the open grid of the shelves. Lining them reduces the efficiency of the cooling mechanism.
8. Do not use your refrigerator as pantry space. Chill canned goods only if you want them cold for serving.
9. Always cover liquids or moist foods. The refrigerator will dry them out, and their moisture will freeze on the refrigerator coils.
10. Do not put hot food or dishes into the refrigerator. Allow them to cool to room temperature first or, if speed is essential, set the dish in a bowl of ice cubes.

As you continue to use your kitchen you will think of other pieces of equipment that you will want. Your family's food tastes and customs will determine whether the new utensil is an extravagance or a useful work saver. Remember that you need electrical outlets for new electrical appliances, and that for any new item you will need convenient storage space.

Pantry

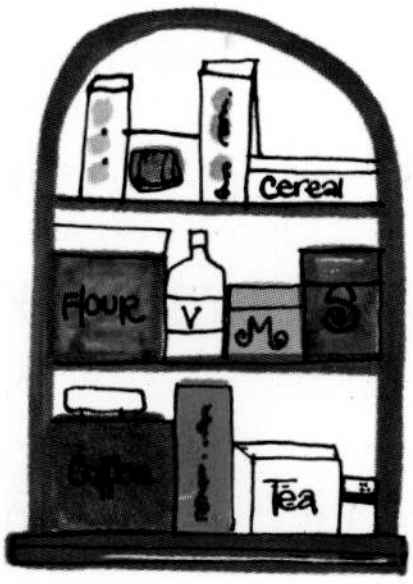

A properly stocked pantry is essential to every cook. Even in the smallest kitchen there must be some food storage area. Adjust the lists below to your space limitations.

Study the suggestions and then look at your own pantry. Remove all those things you will never use. Add only those you know you will need. Make sure necessary items are replenished quickly.

Flour and leavening. NECESSARY: all-purpose flour, biscuit mix, cornstarch, baking powder, baking soda, cream of tartar.

USEFUL BUT NOT BASICALLY NECESSARY: other flours, piecrust mix, potato starch, arrowroot, active dry yeast.

Cereals. NECESSARY: rice, noodles, macaroni, spaghetti, small pasta for soup, rolled oats, farina, your favorite cold cereal.

USEFUL BUT NOT BASICALLY NECESSARY: cornmeal, fine bread crumbs (it is cheaper to make your own), barley.

Sugar. NECESSARY: granulated white sugar, dark and light brown sugar or your choice of one, confectioners' sugar, molasses, corn syrup.

USEFUL BUT NOT BASICALLY NECESSARY: maple syrup or maple blend, maple sugar, superfine sugar, honey.

Beverages. NECESSARY: coffee, instant coffee powder, tea, dry skim milk, cocoa, instant cocoa powder.

USEFUL BUT NOT BASICALLY NECESSARY: coffee beans in the freezer, choice tea, evaporated milk, condensed milk.

Chocolate. NECESSARY: chips, unsweetened, semisweet.

USEFUL BUT NOT BASICALLY NECESSARY: sweet chocolate, fancy imported chocolate, Dutch process cocoa.

Extracts and flavorings. NECESSARY: vanilla, almond and maple extracts, bouillon cubes, ketchup, prepared mustard, Worcestershire sauce.

USEFUL BUT NOT BASICALLY NECESSARY: other extracts, soy sauce, chili sauce, condiment sauces, hot-pepper sauce, fancy mustards.

Fats and shortening. NECESSARY: salad oil, vegetable shortening, pure lard.

USEFUL BUT NOT BASICALLY NECESSARY: olive oil, peanut oil.

Vinegar. NECESSARY: white vinegar, cider vinegar.

USEFUL BUT NOT BASICALLY NECESSARY: malt vinegar, wine vinegar, herb vinegar.

Herbs, spices and seasonings. NECESSARY: Basic spices: ground allspice; ground cinnamon; cloves, whole and ground; ground ginger; dry mustard; grated nutmeg; paprika; pepper, black, whole and ground. Basic dried herbs: basil, bay leaves, marjoram, oregano, sage, savory, thyme. Also coarse salt, fine table salt, monosodium glutamate.

USEFUL BUT NOT BASICALLY NECESSARY: Spices: whole allspice, cardamom pods, cinnamon sticks, coriander berries, mace blades, whole nutmeg, white pepper. Herbs: dried chives, powdered garlic, powdered onion, dried parsley, dried tarragon. Also seasoned salt.

Dried fruits, legumes and nuts. NECESSARY: apricots, dates, prunes, seedless raisins; navy beans, split peas, yellow peas; coconut, walnuts.

USEFUL BUT NOT BASICALLY NECESSARY: almonds, Brazil nuts, pecans; currants, maraschino cherries, candied fruits, muscatel raisins.

Miscellaneous: unflavored gelatin, flavored gelatin, food coloring, grated cheese, olives, pimientos, tomato paste, tomato sauce; a few cans of cream soups to be used as sauces or in casseroles (celery, mushroom, tomato).

There are many other items you may need, but buy them only as they are required for a recipe. An overstocked cupboard can become a mess and requires a lot of attention. Do not clutter valuable space with items you rarely use. This applies even to the preceding list. If there are items here you are sure you will never use, then by all means omit them. The list is only a guide to get you started. Do not plan to buy them all at once, but perhaps each week you could add another staple or spice.

How long to keep most-used foods on the pantry shelf

FOOD	TIME
Baking powder, baking soda, cream of tartar	8 to 12 months
Cake, biscuit, pancake, piecrust mixes:	
opened	2 to 3 months
unopened	6 to 8 months
*Canned foods (kept in a cool dry place)	1 year
Cereals (dry) and flours	2 to 3 months
Chocolate, cocoa, instant cocoa	1 year
Coconut, unopened can	6 to 8 months
Coconut, opened can	1 week
Instant coffee powder	6 to 8 months
Tea, unopened box	3 to 4 months
Tea, opened box	2 weeks
Instant tea	6 to 8 months
Potato chips	7 to 10 days
Dry bread crumbs in covered container	6 weeks
Dried fruits and dry legumes	6 to 8 months
Extracts, flavorings	8 to 12 months
Herbs, spices, seasoning salts	8 to 12 months
Macaroni, noodles, spaghetti, etc.	3 to 6 months
Milk, dry (discard it if it gets lumpy)	1 year
Nuts, in shell	1 year
Nuts, shelled	2 to 3 months
Shortening, lard, salad oil	3 to 4 months
**Sugar, syrups	1 year

*Canned baby foods should be used within 6 months because of vitamin deterioration, even in the unopened can or jar. Evaporated milk and condensed milk should be used within 3 months.

**Maple syrup, when opened, should be transferred to a glass bottle. It should be refrigerated if kept for longer than 10 days. Under refrigeration it will keep for 6 to 8 months.

WEIGHTS AND MEASURES

Spoons, cups and saucepans are designed according to ancient patterns. There is no particular reason a cup should hold 8 ounces or 16 tablespoons, but it does.

You will notice that there are two kinds of pints and quarts, Canadian (or Imperial) and U.S. While the cup is the same standard 8-ounce measure, the pint and quart in Canada and other Commonwealth countries hold more cups than the U.S. pint and quart. For recipes from a Canadian or British source, use the Imperial measure; for U.S. recipes, use the 2-cup pint and the 4-cup quart.

One of the problems for those cooks who use French cookbooks is that the French have dispensed with odd measures such as ounces and pounds and cook according to the metric system. A complete comparison of these measures would require a large book, so in the tables that follow you will only find a short summary as a guide and reference.

Grams and ounces

1 gram	=	.035 oz.
10 grams	=	.35 oz.
100 grams	=	3.5 oz. or 7 tblsp.
200 grams	=	7 oz. or 14 tblsp. or 7/8 cup
1 cup	=	about 229 grams
1 oz.	=	31.103 grams
16 oz. (dry measure)	=	1 pound
16 oz. (liquid measure)	=	1 pint (U. S.) or 2 cups

Equivalent measures

a few grains	=	less than 1/16 tsp.
a pinch	=	less than 1/8 tsp.
1/2 tblsp.	=	1 1/2 tsp.
1 tblsp.	=	3 tsp. or 1/2 oz.
1/8 cup	=	2 tblsp. or 1 oz.
1/4 cup	=	4 tblsp. or 2 oz.
1/3 cup	=	5 tblsp. plus 1 tsp.
1/2 cup	=	8 tblsp. or 4 oz.
2/3 cup	=	10 tblsp. plus 2 tsp.
3/4 cup	=	12 tblsp. or 6 oz.
1 cup	=	16 tblsp. or 8 oz.
2 cups (8 oz. each)	=	1 pint (U. S.)
2 pints (16 oz. each)		1 quart, liquid (U.S.) or 4 cups
1 imperial pint (Canadian)	=	2 1/2 cups
1 imperial quart (Canadian)	=	5 cups
4 quarts, liquid (U.S.)	=	1 gallon
8 quarts, dry (U.S.)	=	1 peck
4 pecks	=	1 bushel

Some difficult fractions

one third of 1/4 cup	=	1 tblsp. plus 1 tsp.
one third of 5 tblsp.	=	1 tblsp. plus 2 tsp.
one third of 1/3 cup	=	1 tblsp. plus 2 1/3 tsp.
one third of 1/2 cup	=	2 tblsp. plus 2 tsp.
one half of 3/4 cup	=	6 tblsp.

Measurement conversion table

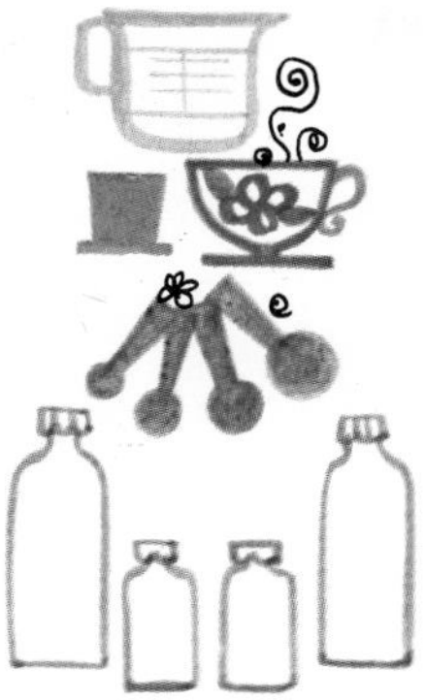

(approximate equivalents)

	U.S.—CANADIAN	ENGLISH	FRENCH
Apples, sliced	2½ cups	1 pound	480 grams
Onions, sliced	4 cups	1 pound	480 grams
grated	4 tblsp.	3 oz.	90 grams
Strawberries, fresh, whole	3 cups	1 pound	480 grams
Tomatoes, fresh, peeled and quartered	1 cup	5 oz.	150 grams
Bacon fat	1 cup	6 oz.	180 grams
Butter	2 cups	1 pound	480 grams
	2 tblsp.	1 ounce	30 grams
Cottage cheese	2 cups	1 pound	480 grams
Shortening	1 cup	8 oz.	240 grams
Suet, chopped	½ cup	4 oz.	120 grams
Barley	1 cup	6½ oz.	195 grams
Bread crumbs	1 cup	4 oz.	120 grams
Cracker crumbs	1 cup	2 oz.	60 grams
Cocoa	1 cup	4 oz.	120 grams
Flour, all-purpose	1 cup	4 oz.	120 grams
Walnuts	1 cup	4 oz.	120 grams
	4 cups	16 oz.	480 grams
Baking powder	8 tsp.	1 oz.	30 grams
Cream of tartar	3 tblsp.	1 oz.	30 grams
Molasses	1 cup	12 oz.	370 grams
Sugar	1 cup	8 oz.	240 grams
	2 cups	16 oz.	480 grams (½ kilo)
Yeast, active dry	2½ tsp.	¼ oz.	8 grams
Candied peels	1 cup	3 oz.	90 grams
Celery seeds	4 tblsp.	1 oz.	30 grams
Cinnamon, ground	4 tblsp.	1 oz.	30 grams
Curry powder	4 tblsp.	1 oz.	30 grams
Lemon rind, grated	3 tblsp.	1 oz.	30 grams
Mustard, dry	4 tblsp.	1 oz.	30 grams
prepared	1 tblsp.	½ oz.	15 grams

NOTE: Whenever grams are required in a European recipe, you can easily convert them into ounces by dividing by 31; e.g., 500 grams divided by 31 = 16 ounces approximately.

Sugar
SALT

«4»

Science and Seasoning

How to mix, blend, whisk, incorporate, fold, beat, grind, mash and cut • The effect of heat on food • How to apply heat • Kinds of acids used in cooking • Using acids • What happens when salt is added to food • Using salt • Types of sugar • How seasonings work • What monosodium glutamate does to food

You may wonder why you need information on chemistry when all you want to know is how to cook. To understand the basic mechanics of cooking, you should know something about what causes the changes that take place as you transform your raw materials into a finished dish. It would take years to learn all about food chemistry. You may not realize it, but you are dealing in chemistry—a secret art in the Middle Ages, a science today—every time you apply heat to food, or add salt, sugar, lemon juice, baking powder or yeast, or mix diverse elements to make a new food entity. If you understand what happens when you add an acid or a sweet to food, or how heat changes meat fibers and egg protein, you will be a better cook. The art of cooking requires theoretical knowledge as well as practical experience. One reinforces the other.

You will not find here a long lecture about these subjects. Instead, there are bits of information all through the chapters that follow. For instance, the effect of heat on eggs is discussed in the egg chapter, and the process of emulsion—mixing oil and water—is described in the chapter on sauces. In this chapter you will learn only the indispensable basic techniques such as mixing, folding and cutting, and the simplest information about the effect of heat on food and what happens when you add acid, salt and sugar.

MECHANICS OF COOKING

Before foods are cooked, and often after they are cooked, they are subjected to a variety of procedures: washing, scraping, peeling, cutting, chopping, grinding, mashing, whisking, stirring, folding, kneading, rolling, shaping. All of these processes and many more comprise the mechanics of cooking. Without a fair understanding of most of these terms, cooking could remain a mystery forever, since all of them are used in cookbooks. And without some practical experience in these mechanics, cooking will be a chore. Even as simple a task as slicing a vegetable is not easy at first try.

Mixing

This process consists of stirring two or more ingredients in a cup, a bowl or a saucepan, by moving them

around with a spoon or fork. Sometimes a spoon will mash the ingredients while a fork can give a lighter mixture.

Blending

Blending consists of mixing thoroughly, but without beating, by stirring until all the ingredients are well mixed, with all the particles evenly distributed throughout the mixture. A wooden spoon of the proper size is the best tool. First stir to mix, then move the mass in the shape of a figure 8 to reach all areas.

This term is also used to describe the action of an electric blender, although that process is different. In an electric blender the ingredients are broken into much smaller particles at tremendously high speed.

Whisking or whipping

This operation consists of agitating with a light rapid motion, using an instrument that will froth such ingredients as eggs and creams, by incorporating as much air as possible. Nothing can replace the French wire whisk for this operation. It is perfect to aerate a single food, like egg white or whipping cream. It is the only utensil that will incorporate enough air bubbles to produce a perfect meringue and a full-bodied whipped cream. It is also the only tool that will make it possible to keep beaten egg whites perfect for 10 to 15 minutes, and whipped cream fluffy for a few hours.

Incorporating

This process consists of forming a light ingredient and a heavy ingredient into one body. A good illustration is the emulsifying action that takes place in making hollandaise sauce or mayonnaise. In hollandaise, butter is slowly incorporated in the egg yolks; in mayonnaise, oil is incorporated. The nature of the mixture determines the best tool to use, but here too the French wire whisk is ideal. In this process the lighter ingredient must be added a little at a time and fully mixed before adding the next lot.

Folding

This term describes the process of combining air-filled ingredients, such as beaten egg whites or cream, with a heavier mass such as a batter. This must be done in such a way that none of the air is lost; the lightness or leavening action of the air-filled ingredient is what gives the mixture its character. Angel food cake is an example; the egg whites act as leavening. A more vigorous method such as beating would break down the air bubbles.

An orangewood or rubber spatula or paddle of suitable size is the best utensil. Slide the lighter mixture on top of the heavier. Then, tilt the bowl and draw the paddle or the spatula through the ingredients in a clockwise direction from bottom to top of the bowl and round again, using as few strokes as possible. A gentle up and down rhythmic motion as you cut in is also very important. The rhythm must continue without stopping until the incorporation is complete. It is not necessary to make a mixture that is as homogeneous as a mayonnaise. For instance, when folding beaten egg whites into batters or sauces, a few flecks of white may remain on top.

Beating

This means to strike, or to crush. In its original meaning we use this term for flattening meats such as pieces of veal for making *scaloppini,* or sometimes for pounding to tenderize. We also use it for the kind of mixing in which ingredients are completely blended together so that each of them loses its individual identity to become part of a whole.

The usual utensil is a rotary hand beater, which takes vigorous 2-handed action, one hand firmly holding the beater and the other turning the handle steadily and rapidly. This can also be done with an electric mixer and in an electric blender.

Grinding

This is one of the most ancient ways to process food. For thousands of years wheat has been ground to make flour for bread. When we grind peppercorns or other spices in a small mortar with a pestle, we are following the same method. However, most grinding is done in some kind of machine. The food grinder grinds meat to make hamburger or peanuts to make peanut butter; or the electric grinder grinds coffee beans. An electric blender can also be used to grind coffee beans and some kinds of food.

Mashing

Generally, mashing applies to cooked foods such as potatoes, but we also use this term for crushing a garlic clove with the flat side of a knife to release the garlic flavor more quickly in cooking.

Cutting

All kinds of foods are cut up to make them smaller for cooking or eating. We use various terms for this. When a chicken is "cut up" this usually means that it has been disjointed and cut into 8 pieces. Vegetables are cut into chunks. We use many other terms which describe the size or shape of the pieces we make. Meats can be sliced, fruits diced, herbs minced, but vegetables are cut up most often.

Some cutting is best done with scissors; a good example is cutting chives. Marshmallows and sticky dried fruits—dates, figs, apricots—are easier to cut with scissors dipped into hot water first.

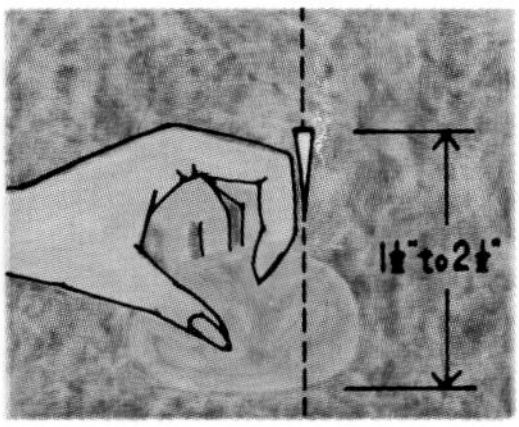

How to hold a vegetable when cutting

Practice the position of both hands: first, arranging your fingers on the holding hand, second, raising the knife with your other hand to just the correct height.

As you can see by the illustration, the holding hand must be placed on the food so that the first two fingers present a vertical guard wall to the side face of the knife. Be sure the fingertips are well tucked underneath out of the way. The fingers then form a right angle with the cutting board so that the face of the knife leans against them as it moves up and down. Never lift the knife higher than the height of your finger guard wall.

For quick, easy work, a 10-inch chef's knife is best. Never use a curved-edge knife; the straight edge must meet the cutting board on the down stroke to cut through the whole vegetable.

To slice

This is a vertical, straight cutting action used on tender or fleshy vegetables which do not have hard fibers.

To slice a mushroom, hold the mushroom as shown in the illustration, and cut straight through in ¼-inch slices, starting from the outer rim. When you reach the center, turn the mushroom around and slice the other half from outer rim to center. Some other tender or fleshy vegetables commonly sliced are asparagus, cucumbers, eggplant, onions, tomatoes and zucchini.

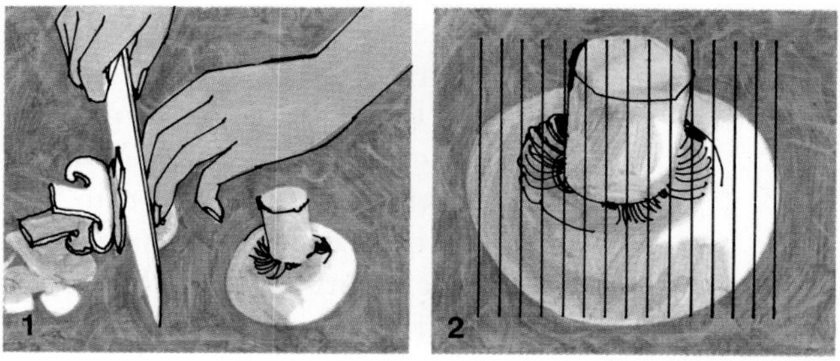

1. Fingertips tucked out of the way act as a guard to the knife.

2. From the outer rim, slice straight through in ¼-inch slices.

To julienne

Vegetables, such as carrots, potatoes or turnips, cut into long thin strips are called julienne. First scrape or peel. Then cut a thin strip off one side of the vegetable to make it lie flat. Place the flat side down on the cutting board and cut the vegetable into very thin lengthwise slices. Cut each thin slice into narrow long strips. A tablespoon of these julienne vegetables, perfectly cooked by steaming, makes a beautiful and tasteful garnish for consommé or any other clear soup.

If you cut the long thin strips crosswise, you can make very short narrow strips like matchsticks.

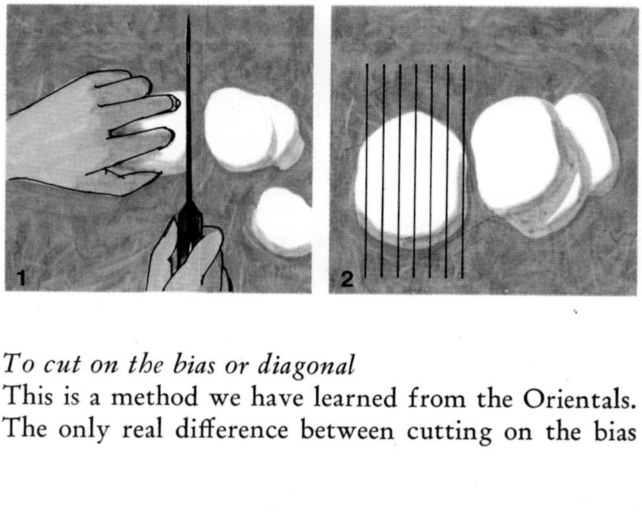

1. Cut a thin strip off one side to make the vegetable lie flat, then cut the vegetable into thin slices.

2. Cut each slice into strips.

To cut on the bias or diagonal

This is a method we have learned from the Orientals. The only real difference between cutting on the bias

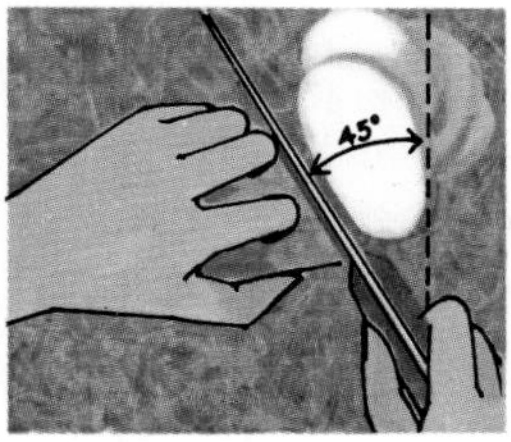

and straight slicing is the angle at which you hold your finger guard. Cut at a 45° angle to the vegetable to make the slices.

To sliver

This is done by cutting on the bias. The advantage of this method is that the vegetables cook very fast because the heat can penetrate evenly.

First make a diagonal cut at one end of the vegetable. Then cut the whole vegetable parallel to the first cut, always on the bias, into long slivers as thin as possible. With a good sharp knife and a bit of experience, you will soon be able to do this very quickly.

To dice

Diced vegetables are cut into cubes of about ⅜ inch to make them look their best in a dish and to help them cook quickly in a short time. Practice on a peeled cucumber because it is soft, and then you will be able to dice any vegetable.

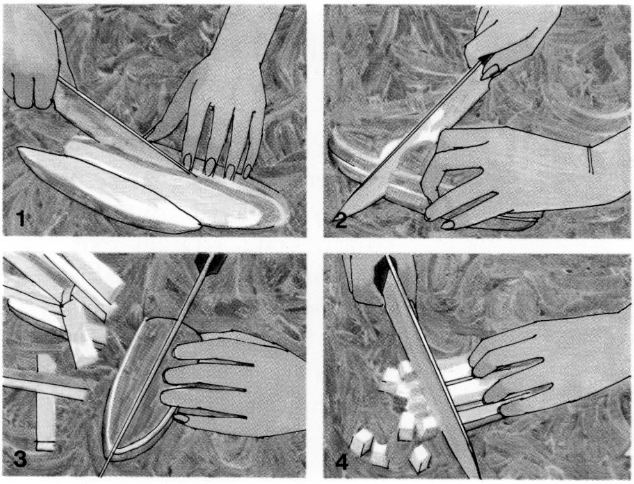

1. Quarter the vegetable lengthwise.
2. Cut each quarter into halves.
3. Julienne each piece.
4. Gather the strips together and cut into uniform cubes.

Cut the vegetable lengthwise into quarters. If it is seedy, remove the seeds. Now cut the quarter section into halves crosswise and line up 4 halves in a row. Holding them down with your hand, slice these lengthwise to make julienne strips. Then place the strips in a small bundle and cut them crosswise to dice them into uniform cubes.

To cut into chiffonade

Usually a chiffonade is made with leafy greens such as spinach and lettuce. Place 6 to 8 washed leaves one over the other, then cut them into long thin shreds. Blanched chiffonade vegetables make a flavorful garnish for consommé.

To shred

This kind of vegetable preparation is well known because of coleslaw. The preparation is almost the same as chiffonade, except that the vegetable used is coarse and hard. To be really perfect, the shreds must be very fine. Use a thin-bladed sharp knife.

To mince

First, gather what you wish to mince—whole nuts, mushrooms, parsley—into a small heap; then chop them with the chef's knife, using an up-and-down motion, until they are cut into coarse pieces. Heap the pieces together again. Grip the back of the knife blade near the handle with one hand and the tip with the other. Chop with short, rapid, up-and-down strokes, pushing the food back into a heap occasionally. Continue until the food is cut into very small pieces.

To curl vegetables

Vegetables are usually curled to serve as decorations, or to be passed around as an hors d'oeuvre or appetizer. Long, straight root vegetables are the best for curling. With a vegetable peeler, slice a thin strip off one side of a peeled carrot, turnip or parsnip. Curl each strip around a finger as tightly as possible. If necessary keep the strip curled by pinning it with toothpicks. Place the curls in a bowl of ice water.

1. Slice a thin, flat lengthwise strip from the vegetable.

2. Roll up into a tight curl and fasten with a toothpick.

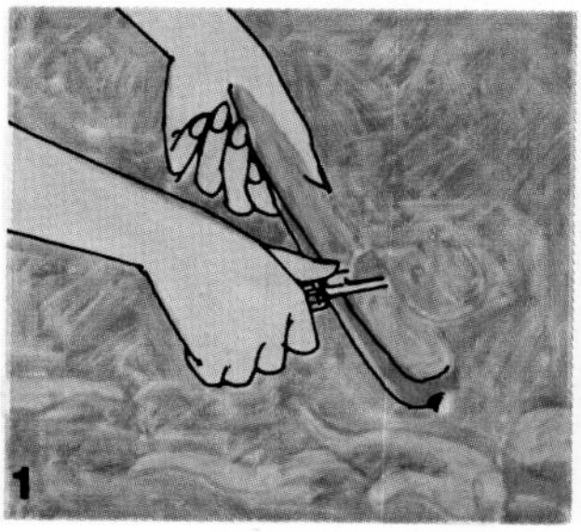

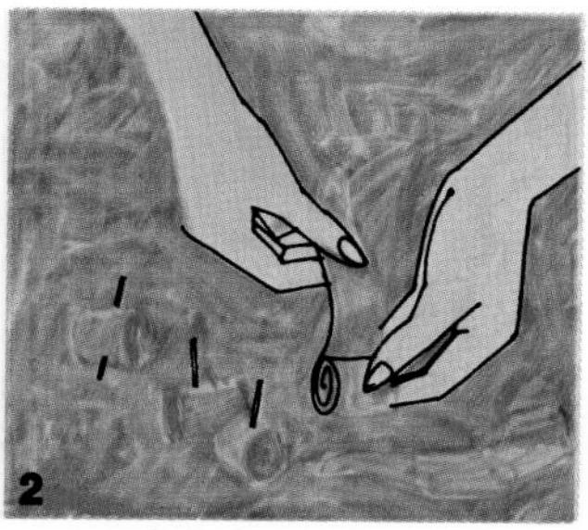

There will be vitamin loss from soaking, but these are mainly for decoration, not nutrition. Refrigerate for 4 to 5 hours. Remove the toothpicks from the vegetable curls before serving.

Celery is an example of a different kind of curly garnish. To make this, slice the celery ribs vertically. Make several long cuts at the end of each piece. Place sliced ends in ice water to curl.

CHEMISTRY OF COOKING

The effect of heat on food

By submitting food to heat we are able to change its form, color, texture and flavor. Meat as it cooks in the oven shrinks and its contour changes. It goes from deep red to reddish brown. The soft texture of the uncooked fibers hardens and then tenderizes and the flavor changes. The proteins coagulate, as they do in eggs, but much more slowly. Fats in the tissues melt. You will notice that some fat escapes into the pan from even the best-trimmed piece of meat. When meat is cooked properly, the fat and juices are dispersed among the fibers to make the meat tender. Overcooked meat has lost too much juice and liquified fat. Undercooked meat will retain its juices, but the proteins will not be sufficiently cooked and the muscle will be tough.

Some foods when heated together become completely changed and form something quite different from the original. White sauce is an example; the butter, flour and liquid, which originally had individual identities, are joined into one by heat. Slow gentle heat makes the flour swell and absorb liquid, but this will not happen if the heat is too high.

The same processes take place in vegetables and fruits; the harder fibers are softened and the starchy elements absorb liquid. Overcooking a fruit makes the fibers so soft that it loses its shape and becomes mushy. If it is the fruit juices you want, as in jelly making, then the fruit should be cooked until it is completely shapeless.

Some vegetables, such as spinach, contain so much liquid that no additional liquid is necessary for cooking. More starchy vegetables need some liquid to make their starches swell and soften.

How we apply heat

Heat can be applied in many ways.

HOT LIQUID, as in boiling, simmering, blanching, poaching, scalding.

HOT FAT, as in frying in shallow fat, or in deep fat where foods such as fritters are immersed in it.

HOT METAL, as when a steak is panbroiled, or any food is cooked in greaseless pans.

RADIATION, which is heat given off by the red-hot coil of an electric stove unit or the flame of the gas stove or the glowing charcoals of a barbecue.

TRAPPED HEAT, which is the heat in ovens of various kinds. This combines two basic principles: part of the baking is done by the heat coming from the hot metals walls and grill of the oven and is therefore radiated heat; the other part of the baking is done by the trapped heat, the heated air. 🗝 When the oven door is opened, part of the heated air escapes and the oven temperature is reduced. This explains why oven doors should be opened as little as possible when a delicate food such as a soufflé or a cake is baking. Any food cooked by trapped or oven heat, even if not delicate, should be submitted as rarely as possible to cold air currents, which enter the moment the door is opened. As an example, a roast that is constantly basted will shrink more than one that has not been disturbed. The cold air striking the hot meat does part of the shrinking.

On the subject of heat adjustment, it is important to know that heat controls in and on top of gas and electric stoves are slightly different. Gas, for instance, is very easily controlled; the degree of heat is increased or decreased almost instantly by the turn of the knob. The heat of electric units takes some time to be increased or decreased. This makes a significant difference when cooking food that requires varied amounts of heat at different stages. 🗝 If you are cooking on an electric stove, it is better to use two burners; when a change of heat is required, simply move the cooking vessel from one unit to the other.

ROOM TEMPERATURE HEAT is another kind that we tend to ignore. This will warm up cold food from the refrigerator, such as fruits, cheese, cooked meat. As with cooked food, it is the heat that brings out the best in the food. Refrigerators should be used to store food and to keep it fresh. They also give the shopper an opportunity to save time by shopping only once a week. However, too many foods are served without being brought back to perfection by returning them to room temperature. O-ᴛ Melons or peaches, for example, even the very best, lose most of their quality when served cold. O-ᴛ Any cheese served cold would be better not served at all. Cold cheese has practically no smell or taste and it is hard so that its natural texture is impossible to appreciate. Brought to room temperature, the flavor and texture return and cheese becomes a joy to eat. O-ᴛ Cold roast beef should be kept refrigerated, but return it to room temperature for 2 to 3 hours before serving it. It makes a world of difference in flavor.

This should not be construed as unnecessary fussiness. The human palate has very definite and well-defined sensations: first, the sense of taste, combined with the sense of smell; secondly, the feel of texture in food, whether soft, hard, brittle or crisp; thirdly, the temperature, hot or cold; and fourthly, the inner sense of taste, which is the real pleasure derived from food.

Understanding the action of heat and cold on food is most important, because they affect all of these sensations.

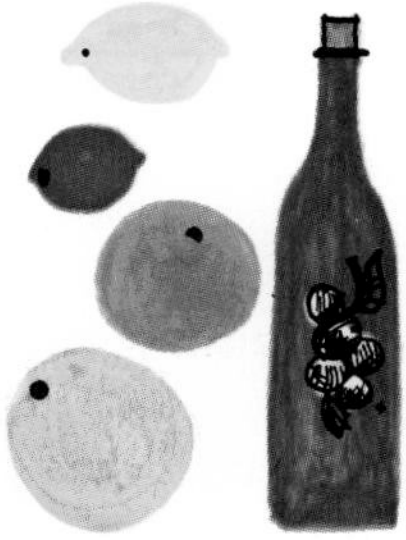

ACIDS

Acids used in cooking are lemon or lime juice, orange or grapefruit juice, vinegar and wine. Acid gives a clean taste to food, brings a feeling of freshness to the palate, and saves any dish, cooked or uncooked, from monotony.

There is a difference between the acid of vinegar and the acid of citrus fruits. Vinegar, whether wine, cider, malt or herb vinegar, has an aromatic flavor of its own.

O-ᴛ Citrus fruits are essentially acid and play a role in enlarging and refreshing flavor, but if an aromatic is needed, the grated rind must be added because it contains the aromatic oil. Here is an example: squeeze the juice of a wedge of lemon over a piece of fried fish and it will add freshness to the flavor. But add the grated rind of the lemon to the butter or cream sauce served with the fish. The freshness and aroma are combined, because the intense lemon flavor carried in the oil of the rind is more lasting.

A knowledge of the action of acids can be very important to people on salt-free diets, because acids can give life to foods that would otherwise be dull.

How much acid to use in food, and how to use it, is a matter of taste. In order of decreasing sharpness, cooking acids can be classified as follows: wine vinegar, cider vinegar, malt vinegar, lemon juice, lime juice, orange juice, grapefruit juice, and dry red or white wine. You can use any one of them, depending on the acidity you desire. Taste and add as you please.

When a recipe calls for wine, such as ½ cup white or red wine, it can be replaced by half water and half of another chosen acid, or by ½ cup apple juice accentuated with 1 tablespoon of a chosen acid. The second substitution will give a milder flavor than the first one, but it is sometimes preferred. For another possible substitution, 1 cup of red or white wine can be replaced by 3 tablespoons cider or wine vinegar, or the juice of 1 lemon, plus enough water to make 1 cup. Or you can use 1 cup of orange juice.

If a recipe calls for 3 tablespoons lemon juice, use the juice of a medium-size lemon without measuring. In the same way, you can assume that ½ cup orange juice is the amount of juice from 1 medium-size orange.

Using acids

Vegetables

All cooked vegetables respond to an acid. Cooked spinach is a different dish when seasoned with wine or cider vinegar, a little grated lemon rind and a pinch of grated nutmeg. Cooked potatoes improve with a seasoning of lemon juice and grated rind mixed with minced parsley. 🔑 Add 1 teaspoon of vinegar or lemon juice to the water of boiling potatoes to make them mealy.

Fruits

When preparing any type of stewed fruit, add fresh lemon or lime juice to the syrup, usually the juice of

½ lemon or lime for each 2 cups syrup. When putting any type of dried fruit through the food chopper, for such things as fruitcake, sprinkle the fruits with lemon or orange juice, so they do not stick to the blades of the chopper.

Add a little lemon juice to jams and jellies when they have finished cooking. It deepens the color and accentuates the flavor of the fresh fruits; most of all it helps them to jell. Good proportions are the juice of ½ lemon to each 4 cups of fruit being cooked.

Lemon juice or cider vinegar added to the bowl of water in which sliced fruits stand before cooking acts as a bleach and prevents discoloration of the fruits. Fruits that are to be served uncooked may also discolor when exposed to the air after peeling or slicing. Sliced apples, avocados, bananas, peaches and pears will not turn brown if they are dipped in water mixed with lemon juice, or if they are brushed with lemon juice on the cut surfaces.

A small amount of lemon, lime, orange or grapefruit juice added to a fruit cup accentuates the flavor.

Meats

To help tenderize meat and poultry and to keep seafood firm and white, soak in a marinade before cooking. The marinade: use 2 to 4 tablespoons, depending on the strength, of dry red or white wine, lemon juice, cider or wine vinegar for each 4 cups of oil.

Any protein food that is to be fried, such as fish, chicken liver, eggplant, ham steak, should be brushed first with lemon or lime rind. This cuts the fat used in frying and protects the natural flavor.

Sauces

Butter sauce is improved by the addition of 1 tablespoon of lemon or other citrus juice per ¼ cup melted or soft butter. White sauce for fish or white meat is enhanced by lemon or lime juice and its grated rind. To gravy for veal, chicken or liver, add lemon or lime juice or red-wine vinegar.

Milk and cream

To sour one cup of fresh milk or cream, add two teaspoons of lemon juice or vinegar. In place of milk or cream you may stir together ½ cup evaporated milk, ½ cup water, 1 tablespoon vinegar. Let stand for 5 minutes and you will have sour milk. Mix 1 tablespoon of vinegar in 1 cup undiluted evaporated milk and in 5 minutes you will have sour cream.

When whipping well-chilled cream, sprinkle the cream with a few drops of lemon juice before whipping. It speeds up the work and gives the final product more body. It is just as important to add fresh lemon juice to evaporated milk or to nonfat dry milk when either is being whipped, because it will increase the stability of the protein foam that results when these milks are whipped.

Sugar cookery

Acid added to ordinary sugar (sucrose) while it cooks speeds up the process of changing the sucrose to glucose and fructose, or invert sugar. This change helps to keep the sugar from returning to crystals, which would be a disaster in making jams and jellies. Even in syrups and sauces the acid keeps the sugar from being grainy. Use a few drops of lemon juice or a pinch of cream of tartar for a cup of sugar.

Meringues

Acid, usually cream of tartar, is important in these preparations. See the chapter on eggs. Another way to add acid to the meringue is to rub the inside of your copper bowl with vinegar just before you put in the egg whites and start to beat them.

Pastry

An acid, lemon juice or vinegar, is sometimes added to pastry mixtures to soften the gluten in the flour. This helps the dough to stretch; it is especially important in such preparations as strudel. Use it in tarts and pies where the pastry has to be fitted into shaped pans. But too much would make the dough too soft. About 1 tablespoon of one of these acids to 4 cups flour is a usual proportion.

SALT

When food chemists prepare blends of different ingredients for seasoning, they refer to salt as a "bloom"

because it does not flavor, taste or bite like spices; it simply causes all the other ingredients to "bloom" into a perfect union. You may be served a very good soup, but a lack of salt will give the impression that it is flat. When you add the required amount of salt to taste, you will find that every flavor in the soup will come alive.

Salt is neither an herb nor spice but a mineral, and one that is essential to life. It is contained naturally in most foods. Salt, like sugar and acid, increases the flow of saliva. When used in the right proportion, it opens the taste buds. These two actions stimulate the appetite. Remember, the role of salt is not to give a special taste of its own to food, but to intensify a natural flavor or to bring several flavors into one blended perfection. For this reason, a bit of salt in sweet dishes helps to sharpen the sweetness. Both salt and sugar act best when a small amount of one is added to the predominant use of the other.

Just as salt in the mouth makes saliva flow, it will release juices in foods in the same way. For this reason, do not add salt to most vegetables before cooking; you want the juices to remain in the food. However, salt can be used deliberately to release bitter juices. It helps give aroma to foods by this very action of releasing juices.

There are several types of salt: coarse or kosher salt; rock salt, used with a grinder; fine sea salt, usually found at health-food stores; plain and iodized salt. You may wonder why you should spend time looking in various stores for a special kind of salt, but a good salty salt has a most satisfying taste and is worth the trouble.

Many recipes read "salt to taste" and very often the inexperienced cook panics. How much salt is "to taste"? Too much may spoil the dish, and too little will make it tasteless. Just stop and realize that this is no more mysterious an operation than adding sugar to your coffee, or pepper to your steak. You simply add to taste in these instances, and in cooking you do the same. Of course, the amount that is "to taste" varies with the individual. The right amount is that which gives the food a certain authority to your particular taste, or makes a flavorful whole of the food.

This is the best way to salt to taste: Put in a little salt and taste. If necessary, add a little more, then taste again. O┳ After the second time the taste buds become dull and the palate does not respond; therefore, if you must add salt a third time, wait about 10 to 15 minutes before tasting.

Salt always improves a sweet dish; that is why it is added to cakes, cookies and fruit desserts. O┳ Do not double the salt when doubling a recipe; use the same amount as in the original recipe. A pinch of sugar added to salted dishes, such as tomato sauce or vegetables, perks up flavor and color.

A touch, a pinch, a bit of salt, if you must have accurate measurements, is about 1/16 teaspoon.

If you are adding salt at an early stage of the preparation, when you cannot really "taste" the mixture, add about 1/2 teaspoon for 1 liquid quart, or follow the suggestions in the following paragraphs.

Using salt

Meats

When you have all meat and no bones, use 1 teaspoon of salt per pound of meat. Cut the quantity in proportion when there are many bones.

Use no salt with corned beef, ham, bacon or dried beef until the meats are fully cooked; then add salt to taste if necessary.

Poultry

Use about 1 teaspoon salt for a 3-pound broiler-fryer; 1 1/2 teaspoons in the water in which you poach a chicken; 1/4 teaspoon for 2 drumsticks or 6 wings.

Fish

Except for smoked fish, salt cod, and shellfish, which are naturally salty, use 1/2 teaspoon per pound.

Macaroni, noodles, etc.

Use 1 tablespoon salt for 3 quarts water for boiling macaroni or noodles.

Rice

Use 1 teaspoon salt for 1 cup raw rice and 2 to 3 cups water.

Salads

For a bowl of salad to serve 4 persons, use ½ teaspoon salt.

Vegetables

Only potatoes are salted while cooking; use 1 teaspoon salt for each quart of water. Salt other vegetables after they are cooked.

Fats

When substituting lard or shortening in a recipe calling for butter, add ⅛ teaspoon salt per cup of fat.

Yeast doughs

Excess salt will inhibit the action of yeast. Remember that salt was our first preservative and has some antibacterial powers. However, salt also makes the gluten in flour firm. Follow baking recipes carefully for best proportions.

SUGAR

Food texture and color are affected in different ways depending on the type of sweetening agent used. What all sweetening agents have in common is their appeal to our sweet taste buds. And, like salt and acid, sugars can draw out flavor. On the other hand, if a chemical action is needed to hold ingredients together as in meringue, or to give texture in cakes, sugars are added to produce a new combination. It is important to know that most foods have some kind of hidden sugar such as fructose in fruits, lactose in milk, maltose in grains and dextrose in grapes. This fact may make many dieters despair, but remember that the hidden sugar is Nature's unique contribution to the taste of the whole, to give each food a special appeal.

Types of sugar

GRANULATED SUGAR: When a recipe does not specify a particular type of sugar, this is the type to use. It comes in two forms, granulated and fine granulated. Use ordinary granulated sugar for jams and jellies.

Granulated sugar gets lumpy when moisture in the container melts the granules and causes them to stick together. Sift this sugar before using it in a recipe.

SUPERFINE SUGAR: This is referred to under various names, such as berry sugar, veri-sugar, ultra-fine sugar and fruit sugar. In England it is called castor sugar. In this book it will be called superfine sugar.

Its virtues are numerous. Much finer than fine granulated sugar, it dissolves quickly in cold beverages, such as lemonade, when sugar syrup is not available. It should be used in caramelizing or glazing since it melts easily, for fruit cups, or on top of raw fruits such as grapefruit and strawberries. 🔑 Whenever sugar is called for in beaten egg whites, superfine sugar will give the best results, as its fineness interferes less with the air bubbles of the beaten eggs.

BROWN SUGAR: In English cookbooks the dark brown is referred to as Demerara and the light as moist sugar. The light brown sugar has less flavor than the dark. Brown sugar is considered more nutritious than white sugar.

Brown sugar hardens as it loses moisture. Keep it in a heavy transparent plastic bag, well closed, or in a tightly covered glass jar. Brown sugar should never be kept in anything made of metal because its acid will eat the metal. When only a few lumps are present, smooth them out with a rolling pin. If a large quantity has hardened, place the sugar in a heatproof pan in a 200° F. oven for a few minutes to soften, then roll.

Light brown sugar is good to sweeten fruits, raw or cooked, because it gives syrup and fruits additional flavor.

When substituting brown sugar for white, measure as follows: Pack the brown sugar into a measuring cup so firmly that it will hold its shape when turned out. You will then get the right amount to equal a cup of granulated sugar.

To substitute white sugar for brown sugar, measure 1 cup white sugar, take out 2 tablespoons (this leaves 7/8 cup of white sugar), add 1/4 cup molasses and let stand for 1 hour before using.

There is a new type of brown sugar on the market which is dry and pours as freely as granulated white sugar. It does not have the same texture or rich moistness as the old-fashioned brown, but it is useful because it is so quick and easy to measure. It does not pack down or dry out and is not as sweet as ordinary brown sugar.

CONFECTIONERS' SUGAR: This also has a variety of names. U.S. recipes refer to it as confectioners' sugar, sometimes adding one to three Xs after the name, which indicate fine, finer, finest. English recipes refer to it as icing sugar. Canadian recipes call it both icing sugar and powdered sugar. In this book it will be called confectioners' sugar.

This is an extremely fine powdered sugar with cornstarch added. For this reason it should not be used in drinks. You can see why hot liquid is usually recommended when this sugar is used for frostings; the hot liquid absorbs the starchy flavor of the cornstarch. In spite of the added cornstarch, confectioners' sugar lumps readily. It should always be sifted before using. Like brown sugar, it absorbs a great deal of humidity and should be kept well covered.

HONEY: In a sense honey is more than a sweet sugar, because it consists of dextrose and fructose as well as sucrose, plus small amounts of aromatic oils and traces of acids. Only bees can make honey. Humans have tried, but its complicated constitution has eluded all synthesis. There are many different types with different kinds of perfume, depending on the particular blossoms used for their nectar.

In cooking, honey should be used with caution, and it cannot replace sugar quantity for quantity. You can substitute it for half of the sugar called for in desserts and jellies. As an example: 1 cup sugar can be replaced by ½ cup honey and ½ cup sugar. For each cup of honey reduce the amount of liquid in the recipe by 3½ tablespoons and add ¼ teaspoon baking soda. Or substitute corn syrup in fudge or other candies with honey, for more flavor and smoothness.

O┳ A little honey as well as sugar will bring out the flavor much more than salt. In the summer, when garden-fresh tomatoes are around, cut a tomato at room temperature into thick slices, spread them lightly with honey, and sprinkle generously with minced chives and freshly ground pepper. Eat with cottage cheese and freshly baked bread.

MOLASSES: This is a thick syrup resulting from the processing of sugarcane into sugar. It will not crystallize. It is called treacle in English cookery. It is used more often as a flavoring than as a sweetener. In Indian, Chinese and other Oriental cuisines, molasses in small amounts is used as a seasoning for meats to give color and to enhance the soy sauce. Molasses has an alkaline reaction which makes it contribute to leavening in baking, especially when combined with baking soda.

MAPLE SYRUP: This is the concentrated sap of an American tree, *Acer saccharum*. When the liquid is evaporated further *maple sugar* is formed. Both these delicious sweets are widely used, but the strong maple taste makes them less versatile than sugar.

CORN SYRUP: This transparent thick syrup is made from cornstarch and contains dextrins, maltose and dextrose. There is a light syrup, almost as colorless as water, and a dark syrup that resembles molasses in appearance and texture although the taste is entirely different. Both are used in baking and confectionery for smoothness. Compared to sugar, corn syrup does not taste very sweet, but it does enhance the sweetness of other sugars in preparations like pecan pie.

SORGHUM SYRUP: This is sometimes called sorghum molasses, but it has nothing to do with sugarcane. Instead, it is made from the stalks of a plant like corn that is used for animal fodder. The juices are extracted and then boiled down like the sap of the maple to make a very sweet syrup used like maple syrup or molasses. The grain is grown in the South and the syrup is scarcely known in other sections of the country.

HOW SEASONINGS WORK

Now that we have learned about the use of the three basic kinds of seasonings—salts, acids, sugars—it is important to understand the role they play in the preparation of all foods.

Remember, different tastes or seasonings do not stimulate reactions at the same speed. To prove this, taste different seasonings. Close your eyes and concentrate on the taste. The most pronounced, which you taste first, is the acid. This is followed by the most usual and natural, salt, and after this the sweet taste. Although the sweet taste buds, at the tip of the tongue, are the first part of the tongue to receive the food, their reaction is the slowest.

O┳ When you sweeten fruits, take a drop of syrup on the tip of your tongue and keep it there for 10 to 12 seconds. Because the sweet taste buds are so slow to react you must allow enough time to be sure you do not add too much sweetening.

When seasoning any type of food, you should not rely on measuring spoons alone. It is a truly personal matter. Many dishes have been saved by perfect seasoning because something special was added in just the right quantity. If you become familiar with the effects of salt, acid and sugar and learn about herbs and spices, and then if you use them cautiously to begin with and learn to really taste them, you will soon acquire a true wisdom about seasoning.

Although the two words, seasonings and condiments, are often used interchangeably, there is a subtle difference. To season a food means to add a substance at some point during the cooking to improve or enhance the flavor. Of course, additional seasoning can be added to the completed dish, as one adds salt and pepper at table. A condiment is a prepared pungent mixture, sometimes complex, which is served with food after it has been prepared and usually added by an individual diner at the table. Chutney and ketchup are examples.

Monosodium glutamate (MSG)

This seasoning accentuates the natural flavor of foods to which it is added. Although MSG cannot replace salt in food, it increases the saltiness of salt. It cannot replace sugar either, but it does accentuate the natural sweetness of such vegetables as carrots and squash. It enhances the flavor of meat. On the other hand, inherent sourness in food is slightly reduced by MSG, and it removes the bitterness from spinach and liver. It blends aromas, makes food smell better, and is the only ingredient capable of spreading taste rapidly in the mouth while sending a fully blended odor to the nose. It is particularly well suited to Oriental foods. Too much monosodium glutamate, however, is detrimental to foods and may even be a health hazard. Use it cautiously.

草菇老抽
MUSHROOM SOY
Salt

«5»

Herbs and Spices

Kinds of herbs • Recipes using herbs • Some herbs that you can grow: borage, chervil, chives, lemon balm, lemon thyme, lemon verbena, lovage, marigold, marjoram, nasturtium, rosemary • Other herbal seasonings • Kinds of spices • Recipes using spices

The basic difference between the herb and spice families is that herbs grow in temperate climates while spices come from the tropics. The leaves of herbs usually provide the seasonings, but the leaves of spice plants are seldom used for this purpose. Herbs and spices accent and complement food, and offer an endless source of pleasure to all good cooks.

Use herbs and spices cautiously so that the flavor is subtle; most foods have distinct flavors of their own, which should not be overpowered.

Since the strength of herbs and spices varies so much, it is difficult to state exact quantities to be used. To begin with, use only a tiny amount: ½ teaspoon of mild herbs and ¼ teaspoon or less of strong herbs or spices. Taste and experiment, changing the amount of each to suit your own taste and the particular dish.

Essential oils are the source of the characteristic aroma and flavor of all herbs and spices. These oils are released either by grinding, as with a pestle in a mortar, or by fine chopping. This is one reason herbs and spices that are bought already ground or powdered lose their character more quickly than whole leaves or seeds. Replace them as soon as they lose their scent, for they will have lost most of their flavor too. 🗝 Keep herbs and spices away from the light by using metal containers or bottles that are nearly completely covered by wrap-around labels. Otherwise they will lose their color and flavor.

HERBS

Some herbs are so popular or easy to grow that they can always be bought—parsley, for instance. Others appear fresh seasonally but may be available dried or ground all year round. The first herbs described below are familiar and available almost everywhere. The next group is different: if you want these fresh, you must grow them yourself, and even if you want them dried you may need to grow them, for they are not for sale everywhere.

Why not grow herbs of your own? It is not necessary to plant them in a special herb garden. You can easily grow them intermingled with flowers or vegetables. Their charm, fragrance and grace will be an asset to your garden. You can also plant them in tubs or boxes in the backyard, or in a window box. Herbs will grow well in pots indoors if they get sufficient sunlight.

Parsley *Petroselinum crispum*
This is the most familiar of all herbs, with its crinkly green leaves and fresh smell. It is sold fresh all year round, and dried flakes are always available. Flakes also come mixed with other herbs in various seasoning mixtures. Parsley grows easily outdoors in temperate zones, or in pots indoors so you can have it fresh all year long.

Whole fresh sprigs serve as a decorative garnish; finely chopped parsley adds flavor, aroma and color to many foods. Parsley stems, which are usually discarded when the herb is used as a garnish, are actually more flavorful than the leaves. Use these in your herb bouquet, or add directly to any liquid sauce, soup or stew that is to be strained before serving.

Italian parsley, a variety with coarser leaves that are not curled, is more flavorful. If you want flavor rather than appearance, choose this plain herb.

Herb bouquet

Chop ¼ cup fresh parsley with 2 green onions. Add 2 crumbled bay leaves and ½ teaspoon basil, either fresh or dried. Chop all of this together for a few seconds. It does not have to be tied in a bag. Use it to flavor soups, sauces and stews, especially beef or lamb stew. Or sprinkle some over a tomato salad.

Basil *Ocimum basilicum*
There is an aura of magic about basil. In India it is sacred to Krishna and Vishnu (deities worshiped in the Hindu religion), and is regarded as the protecting spirit of the family. Basil is an easily grown garden annual, and makes a fine pot plant as well. In late summer, bunches of fresh basil will be for sale in markets in Italian neighborhoods. Crumbled dried leaves are available wherever herbs are sold, but if you grow your own basil you can tie it in bunches and hang in a cool, airy place to dry or freeze it for winter use. There are both green and purple basil. The purple has a more intense flavor.

Basil can be used to flavor soups, sauces, sausages, liver, salads and *fines herbes* mixtures. It is excellent in fish sauces, and is always found in Italian tomato dishes—even on top of canned tomatoes and tomato paste. Try a pinch in canned tomato soup, or with scrambled eggs. 🗝 Basil can be a subtle addition to any recipe for cheese soufflé; add ¼ to ½ teaspoon minced basil to the grated cheese.

Baked tomatoes with mushrooms and basil

- 3 tablespoons peanut oil
- 1 garlic clove, crushed
- 1 teaspoon minced fresh basil
- 1 tablespoon butter
- ½ pound fresh mushrooms, chopped
- Salt and pepper
- 4 large tomatoes, ripe but firm
- 2 teaspoons sugar
- ½ cup fine dry bread crumbs

Heat 1 tablespoon of the oil. Add garlic and basil to the hot oil, stirring over low heat until garlic starts to brown lightly. Add the butter; when hot, pour in mushrooms. Stir quickly over high heat for 2 minutes, then remove from heat. Add salt and pepper to taste.

Cut tomatoes into halves. Sprinkle each half with ¼ teaspoon sugar and lots of pepper, but no salt. Mix bread crumbs with remaining 2 tablespoons oil and spread on the cut surfaces of the tomatoes. Bake in a 425° F. oven for 20 minutes. Pour the mushroom mixture over the tomatoes. Makes 4 servings.

Bay leaf *Laurus nobilis*

Fresh bay leaves are dark green, shiny and from 2 to 3 inches long. These smooth-edged leaves are sold dried, though they lose some of their color when dried. In general, the greenest leaves are the best. They are almost indispensable in cooking. Bay leaves grown in California have a more intense flavor than any others, and, used in excess, may overpower the other flavors of your dish.

A bay leaf is always a part of the *bouquet garni,* which is a combination of herbs tied together with string, or put into a cotton bag, and used to flavor soups, sauces and various meat and fish dishes. The whole little bundle or bag of herbs is lifted out and discarded when the dish is cooked.

Simple bouquet garni

Sprinkle a pinch of thyme on a few dried celery ribs. Add 1 bay leaf, and tie in a small cotton bag. If you use fresh herbs, they can simply be tied together in a small bundle and added to the food you are cooking. If you wish to elaborate on this, add ½ carrot, a piece of leek or onion and a few celery leaves.

In the summertime the French always use fresh chervil as part of a *bouquet garni.*

In Wales, a bay leaf is simmered with the milk that is used to make custard. A bay leaf is the proper decoration for the top of a meat loaf or a baked pâté or terrine.

Dill *Anethum graveolens*

Dill is a hardy annual of the parsley family, and is easy to grow. Fresh dill leaves are available in late summer and early fall. Dried and ground dill and dill seeds are sold, and many flavoring mixtures include ground dill.

The flavor of dill is sharply aromatic, with a faint lemony taste. It is delicious in lentil, bean or pea soup, especially when the soup is combined with tomatoes. It is good in all egg dishes. Try it also in a white sauce that you serve with boiled cauliflower. Add a few dill seeds when you are boiling cabbage. Fresh dill leaves are perfect to flavor the liquid used to poach fresh fish. Use also with all kinds of smoked or pickled fish. Make dill vinegar for use with cucumbers, beets and canned fish salad: add a few sprigs of fresh dill to cider vinegar and let stand. Try a few dill seeds in apple pie for an unusual taste.

Dill sauce for poached lamb

- ¼ cup minced fresh dill, *or* 1 tablespoon dillweed, *or* 1 teaspoon dill seeds
- 1 tablespoon plain or dill-flavored cider vinegar
- 1 tablespoon butter
- 2 tablespoons flour
- 1 cup lamb broth
- ½ cup light cream
- Salt
- White pepper

Put the fresh dill or dillweed or dill seeds in a bowl. Add vinegar and stir well. Let stand until the lamb is cooked. Then make a sauce with the butter, flour, 1 cup of the broth in which the lamb was cooked and ½ cup cream. When smooth and creamy, season to taste and stir in the dill-vinegar mixture. Simmer for 1 or 2 minutes. Makes about 1⅔ cups.

Mint *Mentha*

This large family of herbs has many members; among them are spearmint, curlymint, applemint, orangemint and peppermint. Mints are used to flavor sauces, vegetables, jelly, fruits and alcoholic beverages, as well as tea and candy.

Mint is not available fresh all year, but the dried flakes retain their flavor quite well. Mint is easily grown in the garden; it is a perennial, and a well-established bed of it will be a permanent addition. This herb is much too tall and scraggy to make a good pot plant.

Mint sauce is generally served with roast lamb. Chop fresh mint leaves fine, then pour 1 to 2 tablespoons boiling water over them before adding the other ingredients. This releases the full flavor. Recipe on p. 202.

Here are some additional uses for mint. When boiling green peas or new potatoes, add a few sprigs of fresh mint. Add chopped fresh mint to canned green-pea soup, seafood salad, potato salad, fruit salad and applesauce. Add 1 tablespoon chopped fresh mint or 1 teaspoon dried mint to cabbage while it is boiling. Put a few sprigs of mint in cider or wine vinegar to mix with oil for a salad dressing. Mash several mint leaves with soft butter and cream cheese for an unusual tea sandwich.

Mint lemonade

- ¼ cup boiling water
- 1 cup chopped mint leaves
- Juice of 6 lemons
- Grated rind of 1 lemon
- Juice of 3 oranges
- 1 cup superfine sugar

Pour boiling water on the mint leaves. Add lemon juice, grated lemon rind and orange juice. Stir in sugar. Refrigerate in a tightly capped bottle. Pour enough of the liquid into a glass to make it one fourth or one third full; then add ice water, soda or ginger ale. Add the ice. The mint syrup will keep well in the refrigerator for as long as two weeks. Makes about 4 cups.

Spearmint *Mentha spicata, var. viridis*
Spearmint is available in some parts of the country, but in the North it must be grown at home. It is an easy perennial to grow.

The ancient Greeks and Romans used it to scent their baths. In combination with aniseed and cumin-seed, they also used it to flavor food, especially lamb. Since the 14th century, spearmint has been the commonest flavor in toothpowder and toothpaste.

It is also excellent with cream cheese; in fruit salads, lentil soup and fresh green peas; or added to stuffing for broiled chicken. In any recipe that calls for mint, spearmint can be substituted.

Applesauce with spearmint or lemon verbena

Wash 20 to 30 apples; do not peel them, but cut into coarse pieces. It is not necessary to remove pits or cores. Place the pieces in a large saucepan with enough cold water to reach to about the middle of the apples. Add a generous handful of either spearmint or lemon verbena and bury this in the middle. Cover and cook over medium heat for 20 to 30 minutes, stirring once or twice, until the apples are mushy.

Put 2 to 3 cups sugar in a large bowl. Pour the apples into a food mill or strainer and stir over the bowl of sugar until all the apples have been strained. Stir until the sugar is completely dissolved. Taste; add more sugar for more sweetness, but remember that the applesauce will be sweeter and thicker when cold. In the bottom of plastic containers, place a few fresh leaves of spearmint or lemon verbena, pour in the sauce and close. Cool and serve or freeze. Makes 3 to 4 quarts.

Oregano *Origanum vulgare*
This herb has become a favorite in recent years because of the increased popularity of Italian cooking. It can always be found dried in stores; it may be sold fresh in Italian neighborhoods. Oregano, an attractive small plant, is an easy perennial to grow.

This is a natural sprinkled on top of pizza, used in sauces for pasta, or added to any Italian dish with tomato or cheese. It is also delicious on broiled chicken or in stuffing for mushrooms or eggplant. However, it is a strong herb, and can perfume the whole house while you are cooking with it, so use it with caution.

Italian seasoning

2 teaspoons dried oregano
2 teaspoons dried purple basil
½ teaspoon ground sage
½ teaspoon dried rosemary
½ teaspoon dried savory
2 teaspoons dried grated lemon rind

Mix together all ingredients. If you are adding this to a liquid mixture that will be cooked, mix the ingredients with an equal amount of minced dried onions. Use for all Italian-style dishes. Try sprinkling it on veal or pork before cooking. Makes about ½ ounce.

Sage *Salvia officinalis*
Sage, a woody plant, is an easily grown garden perennial. A single plant will supply all the leaves you need. Dried sage is available as whole leaves or ground leaves, also called "rubbed sage."

This is a powerful assertive herb requiring care in its use. It is familiar to us in the traditional sage and onion stuffing for pork, duck and turkey. A pinch will also give a racy tang to braised meats, soups, croquettes and stews.

To make an excellent cheese spread, blend sage to taste with a mixture of half cream cheese and half grated Cheddar. Another good-tasting spread, a sweet one to use on tea sandwiches, can be made by adding ½ teaspoon crumbled dried sage, or minced fresh sage, to the grated rind of 1 lemon in 1 cup of honey.

Sage tea

This is inspired by the famous Moroccan mint tea.

1 teaspoon green tea leaves
½ teaspoon minced fresh sage
2 teaspoons minced fresh mint
3 tablespoons sugar
3 cups boiling water
Lemon slices

In an earthenware teapot place the tea leaves, sage, mint and sugar. Stir until sugar is well blended. Pour in the boiling water. Stir again for a few seconds, then cover to keep warm. Allow to brew 5 to 10 minutes, then serve in small glasses or demitasse cups, with a plate of lemon slices on the side. Makes enough for 4 to 5 teacups, or 6 demitasse cups.

Savory *Satureia*

There is a summer savory (S. *hortensis*) and a winter savory (S. *montana*). The summer variety, an annual, is the more popular of the two. Winter savory, a perennial, has a slightly coarser and more pungent flavor. Both are used in the same manner.

Savory has a warm, aromatic, spicy, peppery quality. It resembles both thyme and marjoram, and the three can be interchanged successfully. In Germany, savory is referred to as "bean herbs." It is always added to the water when cooking fresh green or wax beans. It is equally good to flavor dressing for a bean salad. In Denmark, a pinch of savory is added to horseradish sauce to be served with boiled beef or tongue.

Add some minced savory and grated lemon rind to the bread crumb coating used on veal and fish.

Split-pea soup is always delicious when flavored with a pinch or so of savory.

Herb-flavored vegetable soup

1 teaspoon minced savory
½ teaspoon dill seeds
¼ teaspoon minced marjoram
2½ cups (one 20-ounce can) stewed tomatoes
1 teaspoon sugar
1 garlic clove, crushed
2 quarts water
4 cups chopped or diced vegetables
⅔ cup uncooked long-grain rice
Salt and pepper

Mix the herbs and add them to the tomatoes along with the sugar and garlic. Mix well, cover and let stand in the refrigerator overnight. The next day, add the water and vegetables. Bring all to a boil. Reduce heat, cover and simmer over very low heat for 3 hours. Add the rice and cook for 20 minutes more. Season with salt and pepper to taste. Makes 8 to 10 cups.

Tarragon *Artemisia dracunculus*

Tarragon was described by the herbalists as "highly cordial and friend to head, heart and liver." Its distinctive flavor is like a combination of licorice and anise, with a sweet and aromatic scent. Dried tarragon is available wherever herbs are sold. Tarragon plants are difficult to grow from seeds and are usually started by root cuttings, although small plants are often available from nurseries in early spring. It is a perennial, but where winters are cold, you may need to start with new plants in the spring.

Tarragon, which is much used in French cooking, is the herb used to flavor béarnaise sauce. 🗝 Tarragon vinegar, which is excellent served with poached salmon, is very easy to make when you have fresh tarragon. Add a sprig or two to a pint of good-quality cider or white-wine vinegar and let it stand. As it ages it gets better and better. Tarragon vinegar can be mixed with dry mustard or added to tartar sauce.

Blanched tarragon leaves are usually part of the decoration on aspic-coated foods.

Tarragon butter

Make this for grilled steak or fish fillets by simply mashing 1 teaspoon crushed dried tarragon leaves with ½ cup butter. Refrigerate 30 to 40 minutes. Shape into little balls, then roll each in minced chives or parsley. Place on a sheet of foil, cover and refrigerate. These will keep refrigerated for 2 weeks. Simply place them on top of the hot grilled steak or fish when it is served. The heat of the food will slowly melt the butter balls.

Thyme *Thymus vulgaris*

Thyme is one of the oldest herbs in use. The Romans and Egyptians found that it stimulated their appetites and helped them digest rich, fat foods. Because bees love thyme, it strongly influences the flavor of the famous Greek honey from Mount Hymettus, where the hills are covered with thyme. It is also the important ingredient of Benedictine liqueur.

Thyme is easily grown outdoors or in pots indoors. However, dried and ground thyme can be found in all markets.

Because both the flavor and odor of thyme are penetrating and very distinctive, you must exercise care when using it. A small pinch adds flavor to all types of meats, vegetables and soups. Combine it with parsley to flavor chicken or veal stuffing. Thyme is also excellent in cheese sauce and meat loaves. This herb can be combined with savory to give an interesting flavor to roast-beef or corned-beef hash.

Thyme and lemon dressing

This dressing can be for salads of fresh or canned fish and mixed vegetables.

1 lemon
¼ teaspoon dried crumbled thyme
Pinch of sugar
3 peppercorns
½ cup olive oil
1 teaspoon salt
¼ teaspoon curry powder

Grate the rind of the lemon into a small bowl. Extract the juice from the lemon and set it aside. Add the thyme and sugar to the grated rind and mix well. Crush the peppercorns in a mortar with a pestle until broken into coarse pieces. Blend these with the rest of the mixture.

Place the reserved lemon juice, olive oil, salt and curry powder in a bottle. Cap the bottle and shake well. Add the mixture containing the thyme and shake again.

This dressing will keep in a cool place for a month. If it becomes cloudy, bring it to room temperature and it will clear. Shake the mixture well each time before using. Makes about ¾ cup.

GROW YOUR OWN HERBS

The following herbs must be grown if you want them fresh, although a few of them, rosemary for instance, can be bought in dried form. All of them are decorative and well worth growing for their appearance as well as savor.

Borage *Borago officinalis*

The mild and refreshing borage is said to be one of the four cardinal flowers of the ancient herbalists. Whenever borage grows among flowers, bees seem to be around in much greater profusion. Borage is an easily grown garden annual. It will seed itself, and the next year you will have little plants without having to purchase new seeds.

In Victorian times the sky-blue, five-point flowers were candied and used as a delicate decoration on top of compotes or cakes. Borage is the distinctive flavor of the world-famous "Pimm's No. 1," and this drink is sometimes served with a borage leaf floating in it.

O━ The young borage leaves chopped up make a

pleasant addition to a green salad because they give the flavor of fresh cucumber.

Sugared borage flowers

To have a supply of borage flowers all winter to garnish birthday cakes, decorate Easter eggs, or top fruit salads, preserve them in sugar. They are lovely to look at and are also quite tasty.

To preserve them, pick the blue flowers when they are in fresh, full bloom, each one with a bit of stem. Spread them on a clean towel and shake each one gently to be sure it is free of any garden pest. Place the flower on a fine-mesh cake rack or a piece of screening, passing each stem through so that each flower will sit on top of the screen. With a small camel's-hair paintbrush, coat each flower carefully with egg whites that have been beaten just enough to lose their slippery texture. Then sprinkle the flower gently with superfine sugar through a shaker or a fine sieve. The flowers should dry in a cool place for 48 hours. After this, examine them; if any part of the flower is uncovered, repeat the process. They will keep longer when treated twice. When the flowers are thoroughly dried, set them, one next to the other, on cotton wadding in a shallow box. Cover the box with transparent plastic wrap and over this place the lid of the box. In a cool place, these will last for 4 to 6 months.

Chervil *Anthriscus cerefolium*
Chervil, a small annual herb with delicate feathery leaves, slightly resembles parsley in appearance, although its flavor is not the same. It has a mild pleasant taste of anise. Dried chervil can sometimes be found in stores that have a large herb supply.

In many parts of England sweet cicely is referred to as chervil. Sweet cicely (*Myrrhis odorata*) is a beautiful herb plant that grows 2 to 3 feet high and has large leaves of an unusual light-green color. Its only resemblance to chervil is its taste, which is like anise but much milder.

🗝 Cream soups and creamy sauces flavored with fresh chervil are a gourmet's treat. The French relish it as part of the *fines herbes* used in omelets, and they use it as part of a *bouquet garni* during the summer.

🗝 Chopped fine and mixed with grated lemon rind, chervil gives a subtle, pleasant flavor to fried fish.

Chervil butter

Chervil is delicious with barbecued chicken or trout. Cream a few tablespoons of unsalted butter, then add fine-grated lemon rind and enough chopped chervil to make a green butter. When cooled, shape the butter into little balls, then wrap them in foil and refrigerate. When the chicken or trout is ready to serve, pop a ball of chervil butter on top of each serving.

Chives *Allium schoenoprasum*
Chives take a long time to grow, but you can buy a small pot at your market when spring is around the corner and plant the bulblets in your garden. They will grow all summer. If you snip off the tops, new shoots will appear. The bulblets will put forth new shoots in the spring. When the clump becomes too thick, dig them up and separate the bulbs.

Chives are often called the most ladylike member of the onion family, since they have such a gracious way of mixing with other herbs. They are the crowning glory of an omelet or scrambled eggs, but they equally enhance cucumbers, tossed green salad, fresh seafood salad, vichyssoise, jellied or hot consommé, and especially consommé madrilene. Chives are perfect with poached white fish too. In all of the above, chives may be used delicately or lavishly according to taste.

Fines herbes with chives

This herb mixture is used with countless dishes. It can be made with fresh herbs or a mixture of fresh and dried ones. Start with an equal amount of chives and fresh parsley chopped fine, then add one of the following, in dried or fresh form:

½ teaspoon minced chervil and ¼ teaspoon minced tarragon;
½ teaspoon minced basil and ¼ teaspoon minced thyme;
2 tablespoons grated lemon rind.

Lemon balm *Melissa officinalis*
This herb is both refreshing and soothing. It has the fragrance of lemon without the sharpness. The pretty

leaves make it a decorative plant for the garden. It is a perennial and will grow in any temperate climate. In the 1600s it was the "in" thing to have a glass of Canary wine (sherry) topped with a few leaves of balm because it was said to "renew youth, strengthen the brain, relieve languishing nature and prevent baldness." We realize today that it is not the miracle herb it was then supposed to be, but it does add a fresh flavor, which can perk up practically any sort of drink. 0→ Lemon balm is an interesting addition to gin and tonic. 0→ Try one or two crushed leaves with new carrots or small new potatoes. 0→ Add some finely chopped leaves, to suit your taste, to your next fruit salad, or stir some into the sugar of the next raspberry pie you make.

Lemon-balm iced tea

12 leaves of lemon balm
2 teaspoons sugar
Juice of ½ lemon
1 whole clove
4 tablespoons green tea or English breakfast tea
4 to 5 cups boiling water

Crush the lemon balm leaves with the sugar, lemon juice and clove to make a thoroughly blended green paste. Add the tea leaves and pour the boiling water on top. Stir, cover and refrigerate. To serve, strain the mixture and serve it with a bowl of ice, a small dish of lemon balm leaves and a jar of honey. Each guest may flavor and sweeten to taste. Makes enough for 6 teacups.

Lemon thyme *Thymus serpyllum, var. citriodora*
A plant related to thyme, the stems and leaves of lemon thyme are filled with an aromatic volatile oil that makes up one percent of the total plant. The lemon flavor is very strong, but extremely pleasant. This easily grown perennial is a low creeping plant especially suited to wall gardens and rock gardens. Lemon thyme is one of the best fresh herbs to flavor any type of salad. The uses of thyme apply to lemon thyme.

Lemon verbena *Lippia citriodora*
Lemon verbena is a fragrant herb with long, delicate, yellow-green leaves. When the leaves are lightly

rubbed with the fingertips, they can perfume the whole hand. This low-growing tender shrub must be brought inside in cold winter weather.

The Spanish conquerors of South America first brought lemon verbena to Europe. It was an exciting find that would make a tea to prevent digestive ailments. Even today, it is still a favorite tea all over Europe. 🗝 Measure 1 teaspoon of fresh or dried leaves per cup and pour boiling water on top. Let the leaves steep for 5 minutes, then serve with honey and very thin lemon slices.

🗝 Try the lemon verbena leaves chopped and sprinkled over a green salad or a tomato salad. 🗝 It is excellent to flavor a white sauce for serving over fish. To make this, start with 2 cups medium white sauce and add the juice of ½ lemon and 5 or 6 chopped verbena leaves.

Herb potpourri with verbena

This can be used to perfume a room, the linen closet or a clothes closet. If a jar with a perforated top is filled with herb potpourri and placed on the fireplace shelf, the heat of the fire will cause the potpourri to fill the room with its pleasant fragrance. Use thoroughly dried leaves and blend them with a pestle in a mortar.

- 2 cups lemon verbena leaves
- 1 cup thyme leaves
- 1 cup marjoram leaves
- 1 cup sage leaves
- 2 cups lavender flowers
- 2 cups green or purple basil
- 2 tablespoons allspice berries
- 20 whole cloves
- 2 tablespoons dried lemon rind
- 2 tablespoons powdered orrisroot

Thoroughly mix all the ingredients and put them into a small jar. Make a few holes in the cover and place it wherever you please. If you are the proud owner of any of those beautiful English potpourri jars of perforated porcelain, you should use them, by all means.

Note: To dry the lemon rind, simply grate into coarse shreds, spread on wax paper and leave in a warm dark place for 2 or 3 days. The orrisroot can be purchased at most drugstores.

Lovage *Levisticum officinale*
Lovage is a perennial plant with ribbed stalks resembling celery. An aromatic scent pervades this plant. The flowers grow in yellow umbels. 🗝 When these plants dry in the autumn, the seeds can be gathered to be used during the winter to give a celery flavor to stews and soups. 🗝 The young leaves are very tasty when chopped and added to lettuce.

Plant lovage seeds along a fence; they will start to grow early in the spring and will last well into the autumn. The plants grow to 5 or 6 feet and live for years.

Lovage cordial

In Europe, a pleasant cordial is made with the fresh seeds gathered before the plants dry.

½ cup fresh lovage seeds	1 cup sugar
3 to 4 cups brandy	¼ cup water

Steep the seeds in the brandy for a week. Then make a syrup with the sugar and water and boil it for 10 minutes. Add this to the brandy and lovage seeds. Let stand for a month. Then strain to remove the seeds, and the cordial is ready. Makes about 1 quart.

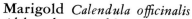

Marigold *Calendula officinalis*
Although marigolds are not familiar to us in cooking now, they are a very old potherb of the past. Marigold petals were used for coloring instead of the costlier saffron, and today in Mexico and Italy they are still used for this. In the old days they were often referred to as "herb of the sun" or "marsh gold" because of their bright golden color.

Marigold is a hardy annual, easy to cultivate, and will bloom all season until frost. In the South it will bloom all year long.

The flavor of marigold is mild, pleasant and slightly peppery. The dried petals improve dried pea and bean soups, stews, chowders, roast pork or veal, fried liver, rice and noodles. 🗝 If you like to bake bread, add 1 tablespoon of dried petals to your next batch when you add the flour. It will give the bread a beautiful pale-yellow color and add immeasurably to the flavor. 🗝 You can also add 1 teaspoon of dried or fresh marigold leaves to a pound cake.

Marigold has more flavor when it is gathered in fine weather, early in the morning, as soon as the dew has dried.

Marigold in a salad

Brown 1 cup diced bread cubes lightly in butter. Place them on a plate and sprinkle with 1 tablespoon marigold petals, fresh or dried. Cover with wax paper and let stand at room temperature for a few hours. Make a green salad with French dressing and pour the marigold croutons on top. Toss the salad again at the table when ready to serve.

Marjoram *Majorana hortensis*

Marjoram is a perennial of the mint family; however, it is so tender that it must be treated like an annual except in those states where winter temperatures do not go below freezing. It is one of the sweetest and most adaptable herbs in cooking. It smells and tastes both sweet and spicy and is moderately pungent. You may detect a suggestion of mint or cloves in the flavor.

Use marjoram with veal and pork roasts, with sausages and frankfurters, with hamburgers, mushrooms, meat soups and omelets. It is excellent combined with basil in a spaghetti sauce. Marjoram can also be used to replace oregano, although marjoram has a more delicate taste.

Tomato salad with marjoram

2 or 3 ripe firm tomatoes, unpeeled
Salt and pepper
Sugar
1 green onion, minced, *or* 1 tablespoon minced chives
1 tablespoon minced fresh or dried marjoram
2 or 3 tablespoons olive oil
Lettuce
1 small cucumber, peeled

Wash unpeeled tomatoes and cut into ½-inch-thick slices. Place these in a shallow dish and sprinkle with salt and freshly ground pepper to taste, along with a few pinches of sugar. Do not mix. In a bowl, mash together the onion or chives and the marjoram. Stir in the olive oil. When well mixed, pour a spoonful at a time over the tomatoes. Again do not mix. Cover and refrigerate 2 to 3 hours.

To serve, shred some lettuce and grate the cucumber. Make a row of the lettuce all around the dish surrounding the tomatoes. Inside the lettuce row make a row of grated cucumber. Serve with toast spread with cream cheese. This makes a perfect summer luncheon.

Nasturtium *Tropaeolum majus* or *minus*
The beautiful nasturtium with its many gorgeous colors originated in Peru. There are dwarf nasturtiums and climbers; the brilliance of these flowers makes them attractive plants in a border or window box. Nasturtium, an annual, is easy to grow in a sunny place, but the plants will collapse at the first frost.

These flowers and leaves have a light peppery flavor somewhat like cress, and are as delightful to the taste as they are to the sight. The name is derived from Latin words meaning "to twist the nose," no doubt a reference to its peppery quality. The Indians used to call it Indian cress.

Nasturtium is rarely used in cooking, but its flowers, leaves and seeds can be used. 🗝 In France, a summer salad often has the leaves and flowers of nasturtiums added to it; they are chopped fine and used as parsley would be. After the salad has been tossed, a few whole flowers are used to decorate it.

🗝 In Italy, the flowers are usually dipped into either crêpe or fritter batter, then fried in deep fat. When sprinkled with sugar, they are crunchy and full of flavor as well as quite colorful.

🗝 To give a new flavor to cottage cheese, add a few chopped nasturtium leaves. 🗝 Mix in some chopped leaves and flowers with creamed butter, salt lightly, and spread on brown bread to make tea sandwiches. 🗝 To make a relish similar to capers, pickle nasturtium seeds by pouring hot vinegar on top of them. Add 1 teaspoon sugar to each cup vinegar. Cover and let the seeds ripen for 1 month before using.

Nasturtium and green-bean salad

Cook the green beans, keeping them a bit firm. Rinse under cold water as soon as they are cooked and drain thoroughly. Place in a salad bowl and add 2 green onions, chopped fine, plus 6 to 8 nasturtium flowers, also chopped. Toss with French dressing and serve.

Rosemary *Rosmarinus officinalis*
Rosemary, the herb of friendship and remembrance, has appeared at weddings and funerals for centuries. It is very difficult to grow outside of hot or mild areas. Usually small pots can be found in nurseries in the spring. If you bring them into the house for the winter months and repot the plants as they grow larger, you may succeed in getting large, handsome, rather woody plants. One will provide all the rosemary you will ever need. Dried leaves are available in markets, but it is very easy to dry your own. Rosemary is strongly individualistic, with a spicy pungent flavor.

O━ Use a few sprigs to flavor roast chicken. O━ To flavor roast veal, mix a few sprigs with garlic and lemon juice and brush the mixture over the roast or insert in openings made in the meat. O━ A pinch of rosemary crushed almost to a powder can be added to ½ cup prepared horseradish. O━ For delicious roast or braised lamb, insert rosemary leaves and garlic cloves into slits all over the outside of the meat. Rosemary is a particularly good flavoring for lamb.

In a sense, rosemary may be called the Italian herb, since it grows wild all over Italy and is used a great deal there. Basil is another favorite Italian herb. Together these make a most happy flavoring combination with pork or lamb.

OTHER HERBAL SEASONINGS

All the herbs listed so far are called leaf herbs, although more than the leaves are used. We use seeds of dill and nasturtium and flowers of borage and marigold. We use chiefly the seeds of other plants, and some we value for the bulb, like garlic, or for the root, like horseradish. Here is some information about a few of these other herbs. While some are garden plants, which could be grown in the home garden, the development of special strains for maximum production of the desired part results in a better commercial product than could be grown at home. This is especially true for the seed herbs.

Anise *Pimpinella anisum*
Aniseed is the dried ripe fruit of an easy-to-grow garden annual. It is native to Egypt and has been

planted in the gardens of Central Europe since the Middle Ages.

Anise is highly aromatic and has a sweetish scent and flavor. It is different from caraway, which is more peppery. Aniseeds are greenish gray, oval and tapered to a point. Whole seeds are sold. Anisette, the liqueur, is known around the world. Anisette sugar is available commercially and is a nice addition sprinkled on sweet rolls and pastries.

This herb can be used in recipes for sweet puddings, pancakes, breads, buns and cakes, but its flavor is penetrating and powerful, so use discretion. 🗝 If you are interested in tisane, or herb tea, aniseed makes one of the tastiest. Just pour 1 cup boiling water over ½ teaspoon aniseeds. Let stand for 5 minutes.

Capers *Capparis spinosa*

Capers are the flower buds of a shrub extensively grown in France, Spain and Italy. French capers are very small compared to the Spanish and Italian types, and the flavor is a little different. The buds are a dark greenish brown, sometimes mottled with bright green or pale gray.

Capers are often sold pickled in vinegar. The vinegar is full of flavor and can be used in sauces or on salads. Capers are also available packed in salt; they must be rinsed before being added to recipes. Capers are used most commonly in caper sauce for boiled meat, especially lamb. Another familiar use is as part of an Italian antipasto. However, they can serve as a garnish and piquant flavoring for any nonsweet salad or vegetable dish, and they are particularly good with tomatoes or in potato salad.

Caraway *Carum carvi*

Caraway seeds are the dried ripe fruits of a biennial garden plant similar to other umbelliferous plants such as anise, fennel, cumin and dill. If you lack seeds of one of these, you can always replace them with one of the others. Although there are differences in the flavors, substituting one for another does not spoil the finished dish.

Caraway seeds are dark brown, slightly curved and tapered toward the ends. The flavor is warm and aromatic, with a slight undertone of eucalyptus and mint. Whole seeds are sold. Kümmel, a popular liqueur in Eastern Europe and Germany, is flavored with caraway seeds.

We often see caraway seeds on top of certain dark breads and in sugar biscuits and pound cakes, but they have many more uses. For instance, caraway seeds are a natural as a flavoring for many vegetables. O┳ Sprinkle a generous pinch on sauerkraut while it cooks, and stir some of the seeds into the butter you pour over boiled cabbage. O┳ Spiced or buttered beets, or beets cooked any way, are improved with a pinch of caraway. Sprinkle it over French fries too, when they are served with fish. Try it with boiled new potatoes.

You can use caraway with pork, liver, kidneys, goose and duck. Toss a pinch into soups and stews. O┳ For a quick appetizer, cut cubes of Cheddar cheese and dip them into a bowl of caraway seeds. O┳ Add a few caraway seeds to spice or ginger cakes.

If you grow the plants in your garden, you can use the leaves to flavor soups, salads, vegetables, and the same meats that are enhanced by the seeds.

Celery seed *Apium graveolens*
The celery seeds used as flavoring are not the product of the cultivated celery plant but come from a wild form of this plant, and the seeds have a more pronounced flavor. Most of them are imported, and the best come from France. They are sold as ground seeds or packed in salt. They have a distinctive flavor and are strongly aromatic.

Tomatoes—broiled, stewed, in salads or soups—are always improved with the addition of a few celery seeds. O┳ Potato salad as well as tomato aspic, coleslaw and tossed green salad will all take on new allure when flavored with celery seeds. Also try a pinch in meat loaves, stews and pot roasts. O┳ Mix celery seeds with sandwich fillings of ham, cheese, egg or tuna. They are also a treat sprinkled over the ketchup or mustard spread on a frankfurter. Scrambled eggs and omelets are improved by celery seeds. O┳ Add a pinch of the seeds to the water used to poach fish and shellfish.

Everybody knows the value of celery seeds in homemade pickles, but they can also be used with fruits. ⊶ Mix a few with a fruit salad dressing for a new taste.

Cumin *Cuminum cyminum*
Cuminseeds are the dried ripe fruit of an annual plant much like fennel. The seeds are small, light brown and about the same size as caraway seeds. They also resemble caraway seeds in flavor, but have a harsher taste and a bitter undertone. Cumin is an important ingredient in curry powder, so it is often considered a spice rather than an herb. The Bible says that these seeds, ground with bread and wine, were often taken for their stimulating and digestive qualities. Whole seeds and ground seeds are available.

⊶ Cuminseeds can be crushed and sprinkled over vegetable salads or added to salad dressings. ⊶ Toss the seeds in a little butter over medium heat, then roll bits of cheese in the butter and serve as appetizers.

You will find Dutch, Scandinavian and Swiss cheeses with cuminseeds in them.

Cumin combines nicely with fennel and juniper berries, or it can be used combined with orange rind. This seed, because of its strength and aroma, is always successful when added to rich foods.

Fennel *Foeniculum vulgare*
Fennel is a yellow-flowered perennial plant closely related to dill. The leaves and seeds have a distinctively fragrant aroma.

The feathery leaves, which are generally available in summer months, can be used in the same way as dill. Sprinkle them on salad, or mix them with cream cheese. Fennel is often thought of as the "fish flavor," and rightly so: dried seeds or fresh leaves are good with any type of fish; either cook fish with the seeds or sprinkle minced leaves on top like parsley. The slight acidity of the fennel sets off the flavor of fish in much the same way lemon juice does. Fennel and lemon juice or lemon rind make an excellent combination.

Fennel seeds are available whole or ground. The seeds are light green; if they have lost the color, they will also have lost their taste. ⊶ Use fennel seeds with split-pea or fresh green-pea soup and with tomato soup or borscht. Try them in lamb stew and sprinkled on roast lamb. Sprinkle a few seeds on the top crust of an apple pie before baking. Add to sweet buns and quick breads, and throw in a teaspoonful when making your next fruitcake.

Fennel bulbs and stalks are used as a vegetable. See the vegetable chapter for more about this.

Garlic *Allium sativum*

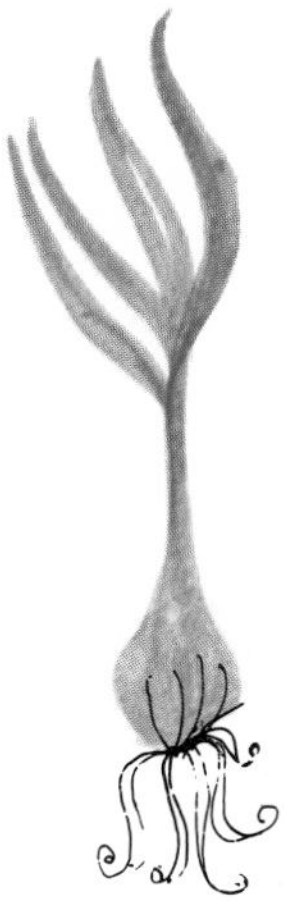

Like onions, leeks, shallots and chives, garlic is an herb that belongs to the lily family. It is so ancient that its origins have become obscured, but many believe that it came originally from southwest Siberia.

The part we use is a bulb, which is like a lily bulb, and is sometimes called a head. The bulb is made of many little sections called cloves. Each garlic clove has a separate skin or peel that is usually removed before using. A garlic clove can be pushed through a special garlic press, and only the pulp on the press used. Garlic is strong and racy and has a pronounced odor, but it is not coarse, vulgar or offensive. Because of its high sulphur content it is an excellent aid to digestion. As for garlic breath, you can eliminate that by chewing a few cardamom or coriander seeds.

Garlic can be used to give character to all kinds of savory dishes. It can be combined with other flavorings and used sparingly or lavishly as one chooses. When lightly fried in oil or butter, it loses quite a bit of its potency.

Garlic can also be bought as garlic salt or garlic powder. These can be used to season foods to be cooked, and the salt can be sprinkled on foods that are served uncooked. Liquid extract of garlic is also available. However, none of these is as strong as fresh garlic. To keep garlic at its best, store in the refrigerator. It will not release its odor until peeled and cut.

Horseradish *Armoracia lapathifolia*

Horseradish is a long thick root with a peppery, pungent taste. It stimulates the appetite and aids digestion. Its main role is as a condiment, either freshly grated or commercially prepared.

Horseradish can be grown in the home garden, but it may get out of bounds; it is a vigorous plant. Fresh roots are usually sold in the late autumn or early winter. The roots have to be peeled and grated, and that is easier said than done. The person who grates the root almost needs a gas mask, and will finish his job with streaming eyes. After that it is surprising how mild and almost sweet the grated shreds taste.

🗝 Fresh horseradish is delicious added to a cream sauce to be served with boiled beef or tongue, or blended with whipped cream to be served with roast beef. Fresh horseradish and melted butter are the Scandinavian accompaniment to poached fresh cod. You will find this a perfect sauce for any bland fish.

Horseradish is also sold in a powdered form that can be added to recipes or mixed with water or mustard to serve as a condiment. The commercial preparations of this plant are usually mixed with vinegar and hardly resemble the delicious flavor of the fresh root.

Mustard *Brassica*

This plant grows in temperate as well as tropical areas, so it is an herb as well as a spice. The leaves are used as a vegetable; the seeds are used whole in pickling and are ground to make all the various forms of the familiar condiment. It is available ground, and is usually called dry mustard. The flavor must be developed by adding the crushed seeds or the dry mustard to a liquid—water, vinegar, wine, a marinating mixture, a stew.

There are many types of prepared mustards on the market; each type is different and will produce different results.

Mild yellow mustard is a mixture of dry mustard, ground turmeric, vinegars, glucose and salt. It is the all-purpose mustard.

Horseradish mustard is a mixture of the familiar yellow mustard, above, with freshly grated horseradish. It has a little more snap.

English mustard is a mixture of dry mustard and water. A little salt can be added if you wish. Use when a sharp pungent mustard is required. This kind you can prepare for yourself. Allow at least 20 minutes for the flavor to develop.

French mustard is often referred to as Dijon mustard. This contains dry mustard, sugar, herbs, flour, spices and white wine. It has a pungent but very smooth flavor and is available in mild and strong forms.

Dutch mustard contains dry mustard, sugar, vinegar, herbs and spices. It is pleasantly sharp and especially good as an ingredient in cooking.

German mustard is made from various ingredients very much like those of Dutch mustard, but the flavor differs somewhat. It is good with cold cuts and spicy dishes.

Bahamian mustard is not as readily available as the others. It contains dry mustard, wine vinegar, sugar, herbs, flour and many spices. It is very hot but most pleasant, especially with roasted meat and game.

Homemade Dijon-style mustard

- 2 large onions, sliced
- 2 garlic cloves, chopped
- 2 cups white- or red-wine vinegar
- ¼ teaspoon cayenne pepper *or* hot-pepper sauce
- 2 teaspoons salt
- 1 cup dry English mustard
- 1 tablespoon olive oil
- 2 tablespoons honey

Place onion slices and chopped garlic cloves in a glass jar. Add wine vinegar (the mustard is darker with red wine). Cover and let stand on a kitchen counter for 24 hours. Then strain through filter paper or a double layer of cheesecloth and reserve.

In a bowl combine the cayenne pepper or hot-pepper sauce, salt, dry mustard and ½ cup of the reserved strained vinegar mixture. Bring remaining strained vinegar to a boil in a stainless-steel or enameled cast-iron saucepan. Gradually add the mustard mixture. After all of it has been added, simmer over low heat for 5 minutes, stirring constantly. Cool with the saucepan covered.

Stir in olive oil and honey and beat together with an electric mixer for 3 minutes. Store in small, tightly covered jars or bottles. Makes about 3 cups.

Juniper berries *Juniperus*

Juniper berries are the fruits of the juniper evergreen, which grows wild in many parts of the American continent and is also well known in Europe. The berries are strongly aromatic and clearly astringent.

Gin owes most of its perfume to juniper berries. In Sweden, the berries are used to make a good-tasting beer. In France, especially in the north, the berries are crushed and soaked in distilled water, producing a refreshing drink.

Juniper is the perfect flavor to add to veal and lamb kidneys, and is also good with all types of wild birds. The berries are excellent when mixed with an equal quantity of coriander, both crushed, to flavor beef or lamb stew. When roasting duck, quail or venison, flavor the gravy by adding 8 to 10 crushed juniper berries that have been soaked in 1/4 cup of gin for 12 to 24 hours.

Poppy seeds *Papaver somniferum*

These tiny slate-colored seeds, which are readily available at herb counters or specialty shops, give a delectable nutty flavor to many foods. In case you are wondering about their narcotic effect, rest assured that commercial poppy seeds have positively no narcotic properties.

Poppy seeds are usually thought of in or on top of cakes, cookies and breads, especially in the delicious poppy-seed strudel, but there are many other uses. O━ Add a tablespoonful to pie pastry when adding the flour. O━ For a quick tart or cake filling, make a pastelike mixture of poppy seeds, honey and a little lemon juice. Toss a spoonful in your next bread pudding. O━ Shower some poppy seeds over hot buttered noodles and discover that they are not only colorful but crunchy as well. Do the same over carrots, potatoes and turnips. O━ Mix poppy seeds to taste with cream cheese and a little sour cream for a dip to serve with potato chips.

Do not assume that these are all the herbs in the world—there are several not even mentioned here. Every country has some special favorites. For example, Indonesian cooking has been introduced recently to America, and we have learned of many new leaves and roots. If you develop an interest in herbs, all types of reference books are available.

SPICES

Spices have stimulated some of the most dramatic chapters of human history. An important ingredient used in the Middle Ages, spices did not simply enhance the taste of food. In an era without refrigeration or quick transportation, they were necessary in order to make food edible. In those days, Venice held a monopoly on European sales through its control of the Mediterranean and its trading contacts with the East. The Portuguese, followed by the Dutch, Spanish, French and English, decided to break in on a trade with fabulous possibilities. In doing so, they sparked some of the greatest discoveries and some of the worst international rivalries man has known.

True spices come from tropical plants. They are the seeds of the fruits, the fleshy covering of the fruits, the unopened flower buds, the roots, barks or berries. Spices can be sweet, like nutmeg and cinnamon, or peppery, like black pepper, ginger and cloves. In cooking with spices, the nose plays almost as important a role as the taste buds in determining the exact amount required in a recipe. For this reason it is not necessary to follow exactly the dictates of a recipe when spices are involved. Your personal taste should decide whether you prefer cinnamon to nutmeg, or feel happier with only ¼ teaspoon spice rather than ½ teaspoon. Changes such as these do not affect the texture of the food nor the finished recipe.

Grinding spices is a sensible procedure for the interested cook because whole spices, ground when needed, are much more full-flavored than already ground spices in containers. The latter have sometimes been standing for months waiting to be used. Our grandmothers always had their own nutmeg graters as well as their own mortars and pestles. If they did not possess a mortar, they crushed spices against the bottom of a flat iron by using a hammer. In those days, no spices came ground up in little boxes, ready for immediate use.

Allspice

Allspice is the fruit of a tropical tree, *Pimenta dioica,* of the myrtle family. The berry is picked green and then sun-dried. The flavor is a mixture of cloves, cinnamon and nutmeg, with the clove flavor predominating. Allspice can be purchased ground or whole. 🗝 The berries are easy to crush in a mortar and are at their best when used in dishes prepared by long, slow cooking or in marinating mixtures. Tie the berries, whole or crushed, in a square of cheesecloth so they can be retrieved easily before serving.

Allspice combines well with lemon or orange rind. It also makes an excellent combination with lime rind or juice. No pumpkin pie should be without allspice. Mixed with a little lemon rind and mace, it is also a delicious addition to blueberry pie.

Cardamom

Cardamom is the dried ripe fruit of a large perennial herb, *Elettaria cardamomum,* native to India. The spice is used extensively there. Perhaps its most important use is in making curry powder. After saffron, cardamom is the most expensive spice, because every delicate seed pod has to be snipped off the plant by hand, and the yield is relatively low. An acre usually yields about 250 pounds.

The cardamom fruit or pod is a small, bleached, white capsule that contains 10 to 12 little black seeds the size of small grape pips. Usually the seeds alone are used, but the pod will dissolve if cooked in liquid mixtures (such as stews) for any length of time. The taste is clean, flowery and slightly sweet.

While the Indians use cardamom for curry, the Scandinavians would be unable to make many of their sweet breads and pastries without it. Swedish and Finnish cooks also use cardamom to flavor the meat for their famous cold table, their meatballs and the stuffing for their cabbage rolls, which are served with a milk gravy also flavored with cardamom. It is an Arabic custom to offer a bowl of cardamom seeds to add to the taste of sweet black coffee.

🗝 Combined with cloves and cinnamon, cardamom makes an excellent seasoning for fried rice. 🗝 Try a few crushed seeds in mashed sweet potatoes. 🗝 The perfumed spiciness of cardamom is sometimes combined with almonds or lemon rind to make a delicious pound cake. 🗝 Try it, sometimes combined with coriander seeds, to flavor apple or pear pies. Cardamom is also good in gingerbread and in spicy pickles.

Because the seeds have a warm flavor and scent, they are often used as a pleasant way to sweeten the breath. Or chew a few cardamom seeds to relieve mild indigestion.

Cardamom can be bought ground or in pods. The pods are best because the easily detached capsule keeps the essential oil in the seeds from evaporating, and the seeds are very easy to grind or crush in a mortar.

Cinnamon

Cinnamon is the bark of a handsome evergreen, *Cinnamomum*, which somewhat resembles a birch tree because of its loose bark. The bark is peeled from the trees, rolled into quills and dried. Ground spice is available, and it is easier to use for some preparations.

Cassia is a variety of cinnamon. Actually it is cassia that we usually have on our shelves, stronger in both color and flavor than cinnamon itself. This all-time favorite spice can be used in cookery from soup to nuts, and lends itself very well to experimentation.

When cooking anything that contains chocolate, add a pinch or more of ground cinnamon. You may not always detect its flavor as a separate ingredient, but it constantly does its bit to improve and intrigue.

Put a small cinnamon stick in the winter compote of dried or fresh fruits. Simmer a cinnamon stick and a blade of mace in the milk used for plain custards or rice puddings. O━ Roll a cube of sugar in cinnamon, then in grated orange rind, and place it in the middle of a plain muffin before baking. O━ Peel and slice an orange and sprinkle with a mixture of cinnamon and sugar, or maple syrup and cinnamon.

Cinnamon is delicious in applesauce, but use only a little. It is also good combined with grated lemon rind. A cinnamon stick in a bread sauce makes it much tastier. O━ If you enjoy a glass of hot milk before going to bed, sweeten it lightly with honey and add a sprinkle of cinnamon on top.

Cloves

Cloves are the dried unopened flower buds of a large evergreen tree, *Eugenia caryophyllata*. They are small,

dark brown and look something like a small nail. (Their name is derived from the Latin word for nail.) When the bud of the clove has separated from the little stem, the bud is sometimes confused with an allspice berry. To be certain, look and see that the clove has tiny overlapping dried petals, whereas the allspice berry has a single wrinkled skin. Ground cloves are also available, but the ground spice does not keep its flavor very long.

Because cloves have a high proportion of essential oil, they are very aromatic, warming and astringent. The flavor is penetrating and powerful, so use them with discretion. When you want a subtle flavor, take a few of the round buds from the top of their nail-like bases and crush the buds in a mortar with a pestle or with a wooden mallet.

Studding a ham with cloves is the most common use for this spice, but there are several others. O┳ Sprinkle a dash of cloves into cold cranberry juice or iced tea. This spice is always good with boiled onions and on baked apples. O┳ When you make apple jelly, place a clove in the glass before pouring in the jelly. O┳ Put a couple of cloves in the jar of any type of commercial pickles. Beets, sweet potatoes and squash are much tastier with a pinch of cloves. O┳ Combine 1 or 2 cloves with a small piece of cinnamon bark in baked rice pudding.

Coriander

Coriander seeds are the dried aromatic fruits of a small annual herb, *Coriandrum sativum*. The Hindus credit it with being one of the most ancient spices. The seeds are round and pale brown and can be bought whole or ground. As they are so easily crushed, it is better to buy them whole, because they will retain their flavor much longer. The seeds have the unique quality of increasing their aroma with age, which is another reason for buying them whole and keeping them until you are ready to use them. Although coriander has a faint licorice taste, the general impression it leaves is pleasantly flowery, with a faint hint of orange.

Coriander is one of the flavoring agents used in making gin. This spice is also used a great deal in the

East as one of the principal ingredients in curry powder.

The fresh coriander leaves called *cilantro* or Chinese parsley are used extensively by Indians and Italians, by many Central Europeans and by Mexicans. The plant grows very well in most gardens, but people do not like growing it because of its unpleasant smell. However, the chopped leaves over fruits are very tasty.

Experiment with a little coriander in soups, stews, sauces, duck and game. It is particularly good to flavor goose or pork dressing. If you ever plan to make homemade sausage, you'll discover that coriander is a necessary flavoring. It is also perfect in apple pie. O━ Combine it with grated lemon or with orange rind to flavor custards and fruit salads or any type of creamy dessert.

Ginger

Ginger is native to China and is one of the most important seasonings, along with soy sauce, in Chinese cuisine. The root of the ginger plant, *Zingiber officinale,* is what is used. The root is peeled and dried to make a spice that is aromatic, hot and biting, giving a full and pungent flavor. Because it is both heartening and warming, it has long been used as a stimulant as well as an aid to digestion. It is available fresh, dried, preserved, crystallized and ground to a powder.

Fresh gingerroot can be bought in Chinese grocery stores, or at times in Chinese restaurants. To know the full, delicate, pungent flavor of ginger, it must be tasted fresh. To use the fresh root (or rhizome, to be exact), simply peel it, taking off the thinnest possible layer of peel, and grate or slice or chop fine, whichever best suits your recipe. You will seldom use all of the fresh root at once. O━ There are several ways to keep gingerroot for long periods. One method is to place it in a plastic container and freeze it. It can be kept frozen, in perfect condition, for as long as two years. To use, simply cut off a piece; then peel, and grate or slice without even thawing it out. Another method is to peel the root and place it in a glass jar, cover with sherry, and keep refrigerated. The sherry will be flavored with the ginger after a while and can be used as an extract to flavor sauces, custards, stews and so on. Gingerroot will keep its potency and flavor for 10 to 12 months if preserved with sherry.

To preserve fresh gingerroot to use either as a dessert or in a dessert, make a thick syrup with 1 cup sugar and 1/4 cup water. Add 1/2 to 1 cup sliced peeled gingerroot, cover and simmer over low heat for 40 minutes. Pour into a clean glass jar. Keep refrigerated or in a cool place. It will keep for 12 to 14 months. The ginger-flavored syrup can be used too.

The fresh roots, wrapped in foil and refrigerated, will keep for a few days, but if you do not plan to use them within this time, it is better to freeze them, preserve them, or cover them with sherry.

O━ When a gingerbread recipe calls for 1 or 2 teaspoons of ground ginger, grate 1 teaspoon of fresh gingerroot to replace it. Use with all Chinese foods, of course. Ginger is particularly good with any bland or delicate food, such as fruit salad. Try it first by adding 1/2 teaspoon or so of grated fresh gingerroot to a can of fruit salad or sliced peaches. Cover and let stand for a few hours.

A pinch or two of grated fresh gingerroot or the ground spice will give body and warmth to meats or other foods. O━ This is also excellent with oxtail soup, creamed or buttered carrots, or white sauce for cod or salmon. For a sweet white sauce to be used on a pudding, flavor with the ginger syrup, above, to taste. O━ Grated fresh gingerroot or ground ginger mixed with a few tablespoons of sugar is delicious; this is a rare treat sprinkled over cantaloupe and other melons. O━ A quick and simple dessert sauce can be made by beating together 1/2 cup maple or corn syrup, 1 tablespoon butter and 1 teaspoon grated fresh gingerroot.

Remember, ground ginger loses its flavor and pungency easily when exposed to air, so be sure to keep ginger jars closed tightly.

Mace

Mace is the bright scarlet aril that covers a hard brown kernel. The nutmeg seed is found inside this brown kernel. When ripe, the nutmeg fruit splits open to reveal one of nature's most beautiful combinations of colors as well as one of its most fascinating patterns.

The first layer of fresh nutmeg is a vivid green, the next a bright orange; the third layer is the bright scarlet aril that protects the nutmeg kernel. It is this covering that is dried to become mace. Of course it tastes something like nutmeg, but mace is more delicate. Mace and nutmeg can often be interchanged in a recipe. Mace is best used with fish, meat, cheese, soups and vegetables. It is good also in a dessert or with fruit. O┳ Add a pinch or 1/4 teaspoon to mashed potatoes when adding the butter and milk.

The best way to obtain a delicate mace flavor is to use what are referred to as "blades of mace," although the spice can be used ground. The "blades" are the fibers of the scarlet aril, which changes to a pinkish beige color when dried.

Nutmeg

Nutmeg is the dried seed from the fruit of a sturdy evergreen tree, *Myristica fragrans,* with leaves resembling the rhododendron and a fifty-year yield of fruits. The spice has a straight, sweet, aromatic quality. It differs from other spices by appealing to different taste buds, because it is both sweet and bitter at the same time.

Nutmeg blends well; it adds richness and warmth to bland foods such as custard, milk pudding, eggnog, pears and tapioca. O┳ To a French chef, nutmeg is a must with fresh spinach. O┳ For a pleasant surprise you might try it in scrambled eggs, but use it with discretion.

Nutmeg is usually purchased already ground, but this spice should be freshly grated just before using; it makes a great difference in the flavor. Use a nutmeg grater for best results. You will also find that a small jar of whole nutmegs goes much farther than a box of ground nutmeg. On the average, one nutmeg will give you a large tablespoon of grated spice.

Pepper

Pepper, the berry of a beautiful vine of the Tropics, *Piper nigrum,* is perhaps the most important spice of all. It is taken for granted by most people today, but it has more than 5000 years of history behind it, and a peppery history it has been. This spice is in no way

related to *Capsicum* peppers in spite of the similarity of the names.

O┳ One important thing to remember about pepper is that much of the biting quality it possesses is lost during cooking, so add it after cooking.

Pepper stimulates the gastric juices, enhances the flavor of food and stimulates the digestive processes. It does not make food as "hot" as most people believe; cayenne pepper and various kinds of *Capsicum* peppers are much hotter. Pepper has the marvelous ability to bring out and strengthen the inherent flavor of any food to which it is added. It never camouflages the natural flavor of meat and vegetables. It will not mask a bad dish, but it will bring out the best in a good one.

Both black and white pepper come from the same vine. When first harvested, pepper seeds are red, odorless and tasteless. When dried in the sun they become black and spicy. White pepper is made from berries that are allowed to ripen longer; the berries are soaked or fermented to remove the outer coating. They are less spicy than the black berries.

In order to achieve the best results with pepper, buy it as whole peppercorns, which you grind in a pepper mill as needed. A good pepper mill is not only a status symbol (a minor one, but one that indicates a knowledgeable cook), but it is also a truly useful utensil. You can have a more flavorful spice this way, and you can also adjust the grind from coarse to very fine to suit your recipe. Ground pepper loses much of its quality in a short time.

There is often a question about the difference in cost between ground pepper and peppercorns. There are many types of peppers, and they are grown in different parts of the world. They are produced in such places as Java, Johore and Penang in Malaya, Trang in Thailand, Saigon in Vietnam, Singapore (which produces a superb smoked pepper) and Malabar in India, where Tellicherry pepper comes from. These areas sometimes have two or three different types each. The price varies according to the quality of the berries. When you buy peppercorns, you will buy one kind only, and they will be of uniform size. Naturally, they will be more expensive than ground pepper, which can be made from a mixture of various kinds and sizes, perhaps even mixed with less flavorful seeds of similar spices. In this case, the more expensive product is definitely superior. Once you have become acquainted with fresh-ground pepper of a kind you like, you will never want to go back to any commercial ground pepper.

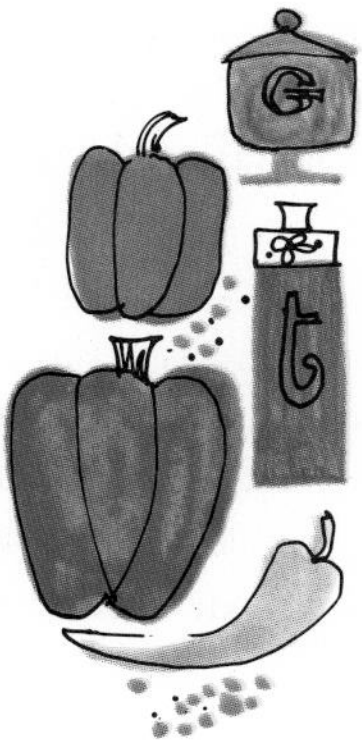

Capsicum peppers

These peppers are the fruits of a large plant genus, generally the product of subtropical and tropical countries, but some species grow in temperate zones. The genus includes chili peppers, cayenne peppers, paprika peppers, pimientos, bell peppers and others. Each has individual qualities of its own, as well as characteristics shared with the others.

Sweet bell peppers are a familiar garden plant. Their fruits are used as vegetables, usually when they are still immature and green in color. Fully ripe peppers are red. They are delicious at either stage.

Chili peppers

These are peppers of a small pungent species, usually eaten dried. They are red or green, sometimes yellowish, with a shiny lacquered surface. They are bitingly hot, so use them with caution. The hotness increases with prolonged cooking, as in spaghetti sauce. They are used in curry and other mixes to give pungency.

Cayenne peppers

These are the ripe fruits of another *Capsicum* species. The long twisted pods are dried, and usually they are sold as ground spice. Salt and other spices in varying quantities are often added to commercial varieties of ground cayenne pepper to vary the taste.

Cayenne pepper is biting and pungent, with a most pronounced flavor. Always use it sparingly. It is easy to add more if you find you have not used enough, but try taking it out!

Tabasco peppers

These are very slender small peppers that grow in the South, especially Louisiana, and in Central America. This pepper is used most familiarly in a fiery-hot liquid sauce.

Pimientos

These are the shiny red fruits of another *Capsicum* species. Sweet and mild, they leave an acid aftertaste. They are used a great deal in Spanish and Mexican cooking. We usually get them peeled and canned. Pimientos are used as a vegetable or garnish rather than a spice. They make a useful addition to the larder in the winter when other red vegetables are not available, and they combine well with salad ingredients, eggs, potatoes, rice and shellfish (especially clams) to give color contrast and flavor.

Paprika

This spice is made by grinding the dried stemless pods of a mild *Capsicum* pepper. Because of its use in Hungarian cuisine, it has earned a universal reputation.

There are marked differences in paprika. The everyday type that is found, bearing no identification, on the shelves of markets everywhere is fine to sprinkle here and there for color and a pleasant garnish. However, more attentive care should be exercised in choosing paprika that is to flavor a dish.

Hungarian paprika, with its distinctive warm flavor and beautiful deep-red color, comes in a range of tastes from very mild to very pungent. The most famous is "Noble Rose," a rather sweet-tasting superior spice. Spanish paprika is harsher and does not have such a splendid color. Use a mixture of sweet and sharp paprika on meats; first brush the meat with oil to help release flavor. 🗝 Add paprika to the flour used to coat fish before frying. 🗝 Sprinkle paprika on hashed brown potatoes at the start of cooking to help them brown faster and taste better.

Saffron

Saffron is made from the dried stigmas of the flowers of the saffron crocus, *Crocus sativus*. Its cultivation in the East goes back to antiquity. Because an enormous number of stigmas is needed to produce a pound of the spice (some estimates say 60,000, others go as high as 200,000), the cost is always high. However, a few stigmas or a pinch of ground saffron will serve to flavor and color a dish. Its mildly aromatic flavor has a slight aftertaste of iodine. It will give a beautiful light orange color when mixed in food. Saffron is available as dried stigmas, looking like dark red pieces of thread, and as ground spice. It is found in seasoning mixtures such as "Spanish seasoning." Usually it is best to soak the stigmas in some of the liquid used for the recipe in order to be sure the color is mixed well with all the ingredients.

A taste for saffron must be acquired; some people do not care for it. Try a pinch and find out for yourself. O╤ Add saffron to chicken consommé, or to rice while it is boiling. Saffron is an essential flavoring ingredient in the famous French bouillabaisse and the Spanish paella, which indicates that in almost any type of fish cookery saffron has a secure place. It is also used in breads, such as English saffron buns.

Curried eggs with saffron rice

1 cup long-grained rice
1/8 teaspoon ground saffron
4 1/2 cups chicken stock
3 tablespoons butter
1 small onion, minced
1 teaspoon curry powder
3 tablespoons flour
1 1/2 cups milk
6 hard-cooked eggs, quartered
Minced fresh parsley
Juice of 1 lime

Simmer the rice with the saffron in 3 cups of chicken stock. Salt may not be needed if there is salt in the stock, but taste a kernel of rice after 10 minutes and add salt if necessary. When the rice is cooked and all the stock is absorbed (about 20 minutes), stir in 1 tablespoon of butter with a fork.

Fry the onion in remaining 2 tablespoons butter. Add curry powder. Cook until curry powder is completely dissolved in the butter and beginning to give off its distinctive odor. Add flour and stir until well mixed. Add milk and remaining chicken stock. Cook until smooth and creamy. Season to taste. Add the eggs.

Mound rice in the center of a warm platter, then pour the egg sauce around it. Sprinkle the sauce with parsley. Pour lime juice over the rice. Makes 6 servings.

Sesame

Sesame seeds, also called benne seeds in some parts of the world, are the dried fruits of a beautiful tropical herb, *Sesamum indicum*. In many parts of the world

this herb is cultivated on a large scale. It is also the basis of the famous Middle East sweet, halva.

Sesame oil is used for cooking in the Far East and Near East. Many Chinese dishes are prepared with a dark, heavy sesame oil, in contrast to some Indian curries, which are prepared with a pale, light sesame oil. Today, diet-conscious people highly value sesame oil as one of the best kinds of polyunsaturated fat.

The cream-colored little sesame seeds have a warm, nutty flavor that resembles the flavor of toasted almonds. When toasted to a golden brown, either in butter or spread on a baking sheet in a 300° F. oven, the flavor is accentuated. The seeds can be used as a substitute for nuts.

⊶ A generous sprinkling of sesame seeds over a chicken, fish, noodle or vegetable casserole can take the place of buttered crumbs to give a crunchy topping. Add toasted sesame seeds to rice dishes, or sprinkle some on top of baked potatoes. ⊶ Plain or toasted sesame seeds make an interesting garnish for hot cream soups and a pleasant addition to salads. Cakes and cookies, biscuits and crackers, are improved with a sprinkling of sesame seeds. The seeds also make a delicious and very healthful candy. Simply use them to replace the nuts in any nut brittle candy recipe.

Bahamian benne cakes

½ pound sharp Cheddar cheese
½ cup butter
1 cup all-purpose flour
Cayenne pepper
1½ to 2 ounces sesame seeds

Shred or grate the cheese while it is cold, then let it and the butter reach room temperature; they should be quite soft. Mix cheese, butter and flour. Add about half a shake of cayenne, or more to taste. Roll the dough into marble-size balls, then roll them in the sesame seeds. Place the balls on a cookie sheet and refrigerate until firm; then pack in a container and freeze.

About 2 hours before serving, remove the balls from the freezer to defrost. Bake in a 400° F. oven for 10 to 15 minutes, or until slightly brown. These are delicious with drinks or soup, or as an accompaniment to salad. Makes 50 to 60.

Turmeric

Turmeric belongs to the ginger family. The rootstalk of the plant, *Curcuma longa,* is the part used; this is dried and ground to a powder. It was used as a yellow dye centuries before Christ, and still is so used today by women in the East.

Most people know turmeric only as an ingredient for coloring mustard pickles or prepared mustard, but it is a spice of great character and certainly deserves more usage. It is aromatic, with warm, rather musky overtones. Turmeric is one of the basic ingredients of curry powder, and gives this its familiar color. The light-colored Madras turmeric, usually sold in small airtight cans, is the best. This is one spice that does not appear whole in our markets. There is a great variation in color, depending upon the origin of the different kinds. Color alone is not a reliable guide to quality.

🗝 If you have a good Madras turmeric, combine it with ginger and cardamom in the quantity you prefer and you will have a quickly mixed curry powder. Often a pinch or two of turmeric is added to a dish merely to give it color. 🗝 An oven-fried cut-up chicken or a barbecued chicken, rolled in turmeric mixed with a little flour before cooking, will not only have a beautiful gold color when cooked but will also possess an added pleasant flavor. 🗝 Turmeric can always replace saffron in a recipe for the color, but the flavor will differ, of course.

Vanilla

This familiar flavoring comes from the fruit of an orchid, *Vanilla planifolia,* native to Mexico. Its exquisitely fragrant blossom lasts for only a day and then gives way to a cluster of long green pods, which are the vanilla beans. After Cortes brought it to Europe from Mexico, where he had tasted it as a flavoring for chocolate, everybody began drinking hot chocolate flavored with vanilla. Only much later was it adapted to other uses.

Without doubt vanilla has remained one of the most popular flavorings in the world. Most people use it in the form of extract, but the dried pods, or beans, are also available. Use the beans rather than the extract to combine quality with economy.

Because vanilla trees must be pollinated by hand, harvested by experts and cured by a lengthy, demanding process requiring many months, the perfect vanilla bean is always expensive. It is a long, thin, shriveled brown bean, soft and pliable, usually 6 to 10 inches long. The best and the most flavor is trapped in the pod, so the cost becomes relative when we learn how to use it and get the most out of it. One fact is certain: the flavor can never be imitated.

Uses of the whole bean

For rice or other puddings, custards or even packaged puddings, add the whole bean to the milk and simmer. Place the bean in the syrup you make to poach fruits. Bury it in a bread pudding.

You can also keep vanilla beans buried in a jar of granulated, superfine or confectioners' sugar. After a week, the entire jar of sugar becomes flavored with vanilla. European cooks know how good vanilla sugar is when sprinkled on fruits or on top of cookies, or in making a cake. As you use the sugar, keep replacing it, but keep the jar tightly closed. The beans buried in sugar will keep soft for a long time.

After a vanilla bean is used, it can be washed and dried and used over and over again. Just rinse under cold running water and dry on wax paper. These beans are good to the very last bit.

After many uses, when the bean really dries out, grate it for flavoring such foods as fruits, custard and cakes.

Uses of the split bean

For a special dish, or when additional flavor is required, or when you wish the flavor to be released more quickly, cut a 1- to 4-inch piece of the bean and split it open. Sometimes only the tiny black seeds, like specks, are used. Scrape the split pod with a knife to get out the seeds, and then add them to the food. Do not discard the split pod, however; simply bury it once more in sugar.

In places such as the West Indies and Martinique, it is the custom to keep two or three pods of vanilla in a tall narrow bottle filled with rum or brandy. In a few months time this becomes a perfect vanilla extract. It is more economical for us, though, to buy and use the commercial extract.

Bread and butter pudding

- 4 to 5 thin slices day-old white bread, trimmed of crusts
- 2 tablespoons soft butter
- ¼ cup raisins
- 2 cups milk
- ½ inch vanilla bean
- ½ cup sugar
- 2 whole eggs and 1 egg yolk, beaten

Preheat oven to 350° F. Butter bread and cut each slice into 4 squares. Arrange squares in a buttered baking dish. Sprinkle raisins over bread. Scald milk with vanilla bean and sugar. Remove bean. Gradually pour mixture into eggs, stirring vigorously. Pour over bread. Bake 25 minutes or until knife inserted near center comes out clean. Serve warm. Makes 4 servings.

Curry powder

Curry powder is a mixture of spices pounded together and used as a seasoning. There are many brands on the market; try several to discover which you prefer. In India, where curry is like salt and pepper to us, each woman grinds or pounds on stone her own favorite mixture, often from seeds she gathers herself. Here is a recipe for mild curry powder. You can adjust the ingredients to suit your own taste.

- 3 tablespoons black peppercorns
- 4 tablespoons coriander seeds
- 2 tablespoons caraway seeds
- 1 tablespoon cuminseeds
- 1 tablespoon whole cloves
- 2 tablespoons cardamom seeds
- 1 tablespoon cinnamon
- ¼ teaspoon ground hot chili pepper

Use an electric blender, or mix and grind as needed in a mortar with a pestle. Be careful if you are using the mortar. These spices release volatile oils and dusts that can be very irritating to eyes and mucous membranes. When the curry powder is mixed, store in a tightly covered jar and keep in a dark place.

In India, women sprinkle a pinch or two on top of all foods. It is a pleasant change on boiled potatoes and cabbage. For a curried dish, you might like to add some grated fresh gingerroot, some ground turmeric and some crushed garlic in amounts to suit your taste.

«6»

Marinades and Stocks

Uses for marinades • Marinades for fish, chicken, duck, venison, beef, lamb, pork, vegetables and fruit • Stocks for soups and sauces: basic bone, brown, beef, veal, white, chicken, turkey, fish, and vegetable • Stocks for aspic • Clarifying stock for aspic • Adding gelatin to stock for aspic

MARINADES

A marinade is a liquid that seasons and tenderizes foods soaked in it. Originally it was used by sailors to preserve fish. The word comes from the French, meaning "to pickle in brine." Before marinades were used as preservatives, salt alone was used.

A marinade also can be used to flavor bland-tasting food. This makes it possible to serve uninteresting foods that might not be eaten otherwise. A marinade can give a zesty new flavor to leftovers. It is a great asset in barbecuing for sharpening the flavor of meat, fish or fowl and for supplying fat to meats (through oil penetration) that are lacking in natural oils. Certain meats such as spareribs, shoulder pork or lamb chops, or short ribs can be tenderized by the acid penetration of the marinade, thus shortening the cooking time. Marinade can also be used as a flavorful basting sauce, applied with a brush or spoon.

Basically, a marinade is a combination of oil and wine with vinegar, lemon juice or consommé, spices and herbs, and often garlic and/or onions. The acid breaks down the fibers, allowing the oil to enter. The oil carries with it the flavors of the seasonings.

Marinades can be made with olive oil or salad oil. You can use any of the different types of vinegar, or any white or red wine. There are also dozens of different herbs and spices, fresh or dried, to season a marinade to your personal taste.

Meat, fish, poultry, vegetables and fruits can be marinated. However, where fruits are concerned, the word "macerate" is more accurate. The purpose of maceration is the same as that of marination.

When meat is marinated, it is not necessary to cover it with the marinade. It can be placed in a lesser amount of liquid and turned frequently during the time it is marinating. With other foods it is usually better to cover them with the liquid. When working with meat, place it in a glass, enamelware or ceramic container and pour on the marinade. Turn the meat frequently. Most foods require only two to six hours at room temperature, but large or tough cuts of meat should be kept in the refrigerator for a few days and covered tightly to prevent their strong seasoning odors from reaching other foods.

O┳ One trick is to place the meat with a relatively small amount of marinade in a plastic freezer bag, tightly tied.

After using a marinade, it will keep for two to three weeks if it is well covered and refrigerated. Drain the liquid from the food, strain it and store for future use.

Sometimes a marinade is used in the following cooking process. A piece of marinated meat is drained, wiped dry, browned on all sides and then pot-roasted, with the strained marinade used as part of the cooking liquid.

Most of the following recipes are for uncooked liquid marinades, that is, the ingredients are mixed cold or at room temperature and the marinade is poured over the food without any further preparation. Marinades can also be cooked, like a *court bouillon,* before pouring over the food. A dry mixture can be called a marinade.

If you have a very large amount of food to marinate, you may want to double or triple the amounts of the ingredients.

Basic marinade

Use 2 parts oil, 1 part vinegar, 1 minced onion or 1 crushed garlic clove, and salt, pepper, herbs and spices to taste. Following this rule, you can make many variations for specific foods.

Marinade for fish

6 tablespoons salad oil
3 tablespoons vinegar
6 parsley sprigs, chopped
⅛ teaspoon ground thyme
1 teaspoon salt
½ teaspoon crushed peppercorns
Juice and rind of 1 lemon
Few green onions, chopped

Combine the ingredients and place in a shallow dish. Add fish fillets, fish steaks or whole fish. Makes about ¾ cup.

Soy marinade for fish and shellfish

6 tablespoons soy sauce
6 tablespoons water
2 garlic cloves, crushed
Fresh lime juice

Mix soy sauce, water and garlic. Add the fish or shellfish. Use lime juice to baste the food while cooking. Makes ¾ cup.

Beer marinade for shrimp

2 cups beer
½ cup vegetable oil
1 medium-size onion, thinly sliced
2 tablespoons lemon juice
¼ teaspoon pepper
1 garlic clove, halved
1½ teaspoons salt

Mix ingredients and add to shrimp. Marinate in refrigerator 1 to 3 hours. Makes about 2 cups.

Marinade for chicken

This is an example of a "dry" marinade. It has very little liquid and is brushed on the chicken rather than poured over it.

1 or 2 garlic cloves, crushed
½ teaspoon curry powder *or* 1 teaspoon crushed cuminseeds
½ teaspoon dried tarragon or basil
1 teaspoon salt
1 tablespoon salad oil
Juice of 1 lime or 1 lemon *or* 2 tablespoons brandy
½ teaspoon crushed peppercorns

Mix all ingredients thoroughly. Place chicken in a shallow dish and brush chicken with the mixture. Cover and refrigerate overnight.

Tarragon marinade for chicken

½ cup olive oil
¼ cup tarragon-flavored white-wine vinegar or dry vermouth
½ teaspoon crumbled dried thyme
2 teaspoons minced fresh tarragon *or* 1 teaspoon dried tarragon
2 tablespoons minced parsley

Mix all the ingredients and pour over two frying chickens cut into pieces, or pour over a large, whole roasting chicken. Turn the pieces or the bird often. Marinate in a cold place for about 3 hours. If you plan to use the marinade as a basting sauce when cooking the chicken, use the dry vermouth rather than the vinegar or the tarragon flavor may be overpowering. Makes about 1 cup.

Italian marinade for chicken and fish

6 tablespoons sweet (Italian) vermouth
¼ teaspoon crushed dried rosemary
¼ teaspoon crushed dried basil
6 tablespoons olive oil

Mix all ingredients. You can add more of either herb if you like, but try it this way first because both rosemary and basil are pungent. If you use this with chicken, add about 1 teaspoon salt for about 3 pounds of chicken. Omit salt with fish; it will cause the fish to lose too much liquid. Makes ¾ cup.

Butter and wine marinade for duck

½ cup dry red wine
¼ cup melted butter
¼ teaspoon crushed dried rosemary
Grated rind of 1 lemon
¼ to ½ teaspoon ground sage
¼ cup chopped celery leaves

Mix together and use for pieces of duck *without skin* that are to be broiled or barbecued. (Duck skin has enough fat in it so that no extra fat would be needed.) Marinate at room temperature (to keep the butter liquid) for about 5 hours. Makes 1 cup.

Orange marinade for duck and game

½ cup orange juice
¼ cup sweet vermouth, red wine or lime juice
1 thick onion slice
10 juniper berries, crushed
Handful of parsley
½ teaspoon aniseeds

Mix, pour over the pieces of duck or game and refrigerate for 2 to 6 hours. Makes ¾ cup.

Marinade for venison

3 cups dry white wine
1¼ cups olive oil
2 onions, sliced
2 carrots, sliced
2 garlic cloves, mashed
1 teaspoon salt
1 bay leaf
2 tablespoons chopped parsley
¼ teaspoon thyme
8 peppercorns
1 clove
6 coriander seeds
6 juniper berries, crushed

Mix ingredients and pour into bowl just large enough to hold the meat. Marinate in refrigerator at least overnight, but preferably for a few days, turning occasionally. Makes over 1 quart.

Garlic butter marinade

Add 1 sliced garlic clove to ½ cup salad oil or melted butter. Cover and let stand overnight. Remove the garlic with a fork and use the oil as a marinade for chicken or for dry cuts of meat such as chuck steak. Use also as a basting sauce.

If you use melted butter instead of salad oil, brush

this onto the meat or poultry. Some can be scraped off when you are ready to broil or barbecue, but the remainder will help form a delicious crust on the meat.

Oriental marinade

- ¼ cup soy sauce
- ¼ cup sweet vermouth, sake or consommé
- ½ teaspoon grated fresh gingerroot or ground ginger
- 1 teaspoon cider vinegar
- 1 garlic clove, crushed
- 1 teaspoon MSG (monosodium glutamate)

Mix all ingredients. Use for meats and poultry. Makes ½ cup.

Marinade for steak

- ½ cup olive oil
- 3 tablespoons red-wine vinegar
- 1 tablespoon paprika (medium hot)
- 1 teaspoon garlic salt
- 1 teaspoon MSG (monosodium glutamate)

Mix all together and pour over a thick steak to be broiled or barbecued. Marinate at room temperature for about 2 hours. Drain. Pat the meat dry with paper towels. Use a little of the marinade to baste the steak while barbecuing, if necessary. If you are cooking inside, you will probably not need to baste at all. Makes about ¾ cup.

Wine marinade for meat

- ½ cup salad oil
- ½ cup dry red wine
- ½ teaspoon dry mustard
- 1 bay leaf
- 1 teaspoon crushed peppercorns

Mix the ingredients and place in a dish just large enough to hold the meat. In this way a small amount of liquid can cover a large piece of meat. Marinate in the refrigerator for 2 to 10 hours. Makes 1 cup.

Sherry marinade for meat

- ½ cup dry sherry
- ¼ cup vegetable oil
- ¼ cup olive oil
- 1 medium-size onion, finely chopped
- 1 garlic clove, finely chopped
- 1 tablespoon chopped parsley
- 1 teaspoon salt

Mix the ingredients and pour over meat. Marinate in the refrigerator 2 to 10 hours. Makes about 1½ cups.

Start "Cheating" Tonight!

Free Recipe From Weight Watchers®

CHOCOLATE CRUNCH BARS

Time: Prep 5 minutes; Cook 5 minutes

6 cups cocoa crisp rice cereal

1 1/2 tablespoons margarine

1 1/2 tablespoons reduced-fat peanut butter

1/2 (16-ounce) package large marshmallows

1/3 cup reduced-fat semisweet chocolate morsels

Vegetable cooking spray

Place rice cereal in a large bowl; set aside. Combine margarine, peanut butter, and marshmallows in a medium saucepan; cook, stirring constantly, over low heat until marshmallows are melted and mixture is smooth. Pour marshmallow mixture over cereal, stirring until cereal is well coated. Stir in chocolate morsels. Press mixture into a 13- x 9- x 2-inch pan coated with cooking spray using a rubber spatula coated with cooking spray. Let cool completely. Cut into 24 bars. **Yield:** 2 dozen.

Each Bar Provides: 67 optional calories
Per Bar: 96 Calories, 19.0g Carbohydrate, 2.2g Fat (1.1g saturated), 0g Fiber, 1.1g Protein, 0mg Cholesterol, 90mg Sodium, 1mg Calcium, 0.5mg Iron

Turn over for your FREE GIFT!

Shallot and dill marinade for lamb

½ cup olive oil
2 tablespoons minced shallots
¼ cup red-wine vinegar
1 teaspoon dill seeds, crushed

Mix all ingredients. Use for any cut of lamb to be broiled or barbecued. This is also good for tougher cuts to be braised or pot-roasted. Add the shallots and some of the marinade to the liquid for pot-roasting, but do not add all of the marinade because it would make the meat too oily. Makes ¾ cup.

Honey mint marinade for lamb

½ cup water
1 tablespoon cider vinegar
1 cup honey
¼ to ½ cup minced fresh mint

Bring water and cider vinegar to a boil. Add honey and stir until dissolved. Remove this mixture from heat and stir in the fresh mint. Marinate lamb to be broiled or barbecued for 4 to 6 hours. Use the marinade for basting while the lamb is cooking. Makes about 2 cups.

Dry marinade for pork

2 teaspoons salt
2 garlic cloves, peeled
1 teaspoon crumbled dried thyme
6 peppercorns, crushed
3 bay leaves, crumbled
2 tablespoons grated lemon rind

Crush the garlic with the salt until the garlic is almost a purée and the salt has absorbed all of the garlic oil. Add the other ingredients and mash together. Rub the mixture by hand all over any cut of fresh pork to be roasted. The meat will be more flavorful if several shallow slits have been cut in the surface in different places and the marinade rubbed into the slits. Place the pork in a covered bowl. Let the meat rest in a cool place for about 4 hours. Makes about 4 tablespoons.

Marinade for pork chops

¾ cup wine vinegar
3 tablespoons olive oil
2 garlic cloves, mashed
½ teaspoon marjoram
1 bay leaf
2 tablespoons chopped parsley
1½ teaspoons salt
¼ teaspoon pepper

Mix ingredients and pour over chops. Marinate for 1 hour. Makes almost 1 cup.

Marinade for spareribs

- 1 garlic clove, finely chopped
- ½ cup chopped onion
- 2 teaspoons salt
- ½ teaspoon pepper
- 2 teaspoons dry mustard
- 3 tablespoons brown sugar
- ½ cup ketchup
- ½ cup chili sauce
- ½ cup cider vinegar
- 1 tablespoon Worcestershire sauce
- 2 tablespoons lemon juice

Mix ingredients and pour over spareribs. Marinate for 2 to 3 hours. Makes about 2 cups.

Cooked marinade

- 3 cups water
- 1 cup red-wine vinegar
- 2 onions, chopped
- 1 carrot, chopped
- 2 celery stalks, chopped
- 3 tablespoons chopped parsley stems
- 2 sprigs of fresh thyme *or* ½ teaspoon dried thyme
- 4 juniper berries, crushed
- 6 peppercorns, crushed
- 1 teaspoon salt

Put all ingredients in an enamelware pot and bring to a boil. Simmer for about 1 hour. Cool thoroughly before using. Especially good for game, but also for beef, pork and lamb. Discard the marinade at cooking time and pat the meat dry before roasting or braising. Makes about 3 cups.

Marinade for vegetables

- ¼ cup wine or cider vinegar
- ⅔ cup salad oil
- ¼ teaspoon prepared Dijon-style mustard
- ¼ teaspoon sugar
- ½ teaspoon dried herb of your choice
- ½ teaspoon salt
- ¼ teaspoon pepper

Place mixture in a bottle, shake well and pour over cooked vegetables. Refrigerate for 3 to 4 hours. Drain vegetables before serving. Makes about 1 cup.

Variations

Any of the liquid marinades can be varied by adding or substituting different ingredients. For example, add any of the following:

- 1 garlic clove, crushed
- 1 teaspoon toasted sesame seeds
- 1 tablespoon capers
- 1 fresh tomato, peeled and diced
- 2 hard-cooked eggs, chopped

You can also replace the vinegar with an equal amount of fresh lemon juice, dry vermouth or cider.

Marinade for fruits

½ cup orange juice or any other fruit juice
Grated rind and juice of ½ lemon
¼ cup maple or corn syrup
1 vanilla bean *or* 5 or 6 coriander seeds, crushed *or* ¼ teaspoon aniseeds
¼ cup brandy or liqueur (optional)

Thoroughly mix the ingredients. Pour over fresh fruits that have been peeled and then sliced, diced or quartered. Gently mix all together well. Cover and refrigerate for 4 to 6 hours. Makes 1 cup.

STOCKS FOR SOUPS AND SAUCES

A stock is a liquid made by cooking various foods in water long enough to extract the flavor and nutrients from the solid particles. The liquid becomes flavorful and nutritious, and the remaining solid particles are discarded. Stocks must be seasoned and flavored cautiously because they will be concentrated when they are finished and probably reduced even further when used as ingredients in other preparations.

Stocks made with calf's feet or other veal bones, and well reduced, can be clarified to make aspic jelly. When additional seasoning is added, a clarified stock can be served as a clear soup, but it is usually an ingredient in a soup. Stock can be used in recipes instead of other liquids to give added nutritional value to the dish. A good stock is the secret of a delicious sauce.

Stock can be an extremely economical ingredient, since it is usually made from foods often thrown away and thus wasted. Whenever your butcher removes any bones from meat you purchase, make sure he includes them in your parcel. These, as well as bones left over from cooked meats and poultry, can be used in stock. You can also use vegetables, herbs and bits of meat.

Bones used in stock should be cracked, if possible, to release minerals, especially calcium, and the vitamins in the marrow, because they are then cooked in the liquid and add to the nutritional value.

Stock can be made in a pressure cooker, but it is more delicious made in the conventional way. Fill the cooker three quarters full with bits and pieces of vegetables, meat and bones. Then add liquid to about the halfway mark in the cooker. Toss in a bay leaf, a few peppercorns and a pinch of salt. Cover and cook for 20 minutes. Remove from the heat and let the pressure reduce. Once the pan is cooled, remove the cover and strain the contents. This makes a very tasty stock that turns into a thick, clear jelly when refrigerated.

A good general measure for stock is 2 cups of water and 2 cups of soup greens for each pound of bones.

Basic bone stock

- 2 pounds of bones
- 4 cups cold water
- 1 to 2 cups cooked or uncooked vegetables
- 1 small onion, sliced
- 2 slices of parsnip (optional)
- Few parsley sprigs
- 10 peppercorns
- 1 teaspoon coarse salt
- 1 teaspoon dry mustard
- 1 bay leaf

Cut any bits of meat away from the bones and place the meat in a large, heavy, heated saucepan. Sear the meat over high heat until brown; this gives the stock flavor. Remove pan from heat and add the cracked bones, cold water, vegetables and seasonings. Bring to a fast rolling boil. Cover very tightly and simmer over low heat for 2 hours. Pour the stock through a large colander to remove the bones. Then strain again through a fine sieve. For a very clear stock, line the sieve with two layers of cheesecloth. Cool, uncovered. Store the strained stock in a covered glass jar in the refrigerator. Before using, remove any fat that has accumulated on top. This stock will keep refrigerated for 8 to 10 days. Makes about 3 cups.

Brown stock

- 3 pounds beef bones with meat
- 2 pounds veal bones with meat
- 2 carrots
- 2 onions
- 3 celery ribs with leaves
- 4 tablespoons chopped parsley stems
- 3 peppercorns, crushed
- *Bouquet garni*

Use low-priced but flavorful cuts of meat. Usually cross cuts of beef shin are available in markets. These are especially good because the bones do not need to be cracked. You can use bones with less meat on them, but a stock made with too little meat has a thin flavor.

Roast meats, carrots and onions in a large roasting pan at 400° F. until well browned, usually about 45 minutes. Transfer to your largest pot and add celery, parsley, peppercorns and *bouquet garni.*

Pour 2 or 3 cups of water into the roasting pan and bring the water to a boil on top of the stove. Stir to deglaze the pan, then pour over the meat and vegetables. Add about 4 quarts of cold water. Bring to a boil and remove the scum that rises to the top. Boil and continue to skim for about 10 minutes. Then reduce heat to a simmer and cook for at least 4 hours. Add more water if necessary to keep the bones covered. The longer you cook the stock, the more flavor you will extract.

At the end of cooking, strain as for Basic Stock, cool uncovered, then store in the refrigerator. To freeze, remove the hardened layer of fat and reduce the stock further (to save freezer space). Cool and pour into freezer containers. Do not forget to label: all frozen stocks look alike. Makes about 2 quarts.

Beef stock

Follow the same method as for Brown Stock, but use only the beef bones. Veal bones release large amounts of gelatin—this stock without them will not jell as firmly as Brown Stock, above. You can alter the vegetables and add other seasoning, but remember flavors are greatly concentrated after long cooking.

Veal stock

Follow the same method as for Brown Stock but use only the veal bones. Try to find veal shanks and a veal knuckle. If you have bones with very little meat, add about 1 pound of the least expensive veal in your market. Add 2 or 3 leeks, washed very carefully, and the celery. This stock will be lighter in color than Brown Stock, and the flavor will be more delicate. For this reason it may be more useful because it can be used with many different foods.

Beef consommé

- 2 quarts cold strained Brown or Beef Stock
- ½ pound lean beef, with no fat
- 1 carrot, chopped
- 2 leeks, cleaned and chopped
- 2 egg whites, lightly beaten
- Salt

Remove the layer of fat and put the stock in a large pot. *Chop* the beef; do not grind it. *Do not use* commercial hamburger; it is too fatty. Add beef to the stock with vegetables and egg whites. Bring slowly to a boil while stirring. Reduce heat as much as possible and simmer the stock, covered, for 50 minutes. Remove from the heat. With a skimmer, remove and discard the particles that have risen to the top. Strain through a sieve lined with several layers of cheesecloth. Add salt to taste.

Bring the consommé to a boil and serve in bouillon cups or soup plates, garnished with slivers of vegetable, chopped herbs such as parsley or chives, or tiny croutons. Makes 6 servings.

White stock

- 3 pounds veal bones with meat
- 3 pounds chicken pieces and carcasses
- 1 carrot
- 4 leeks
- 2 white peppercorns, crushed
- *Bouquet garni*
- 1 onion
- 1 bay leaf

Use veal shank and knuckle, if possible. The chicken pieces can be necks, backs, wings, gizzards or bones of birds you have cooked. (These carcasses and bony pieces can be stored in your freezer until stock-making day.) Put the meat and bones in a large pot, cover with water and bring to a boil. Boil for a few minutes and drain. Rinse the meat and bones and return to the pot. Add the other ingredients and about 5 quarts of cold water. Bring to a boil and simmer for about 5 hours. If necessary, add more water during the cooking.

At the end of cooking, strain as for Basic Stock. Cool, uncovered, and store in the refrigerator. This stock will be pale because the meats were not browned. Makes about 2 quarts.

White veal stock

Follow the recipe for White Stock, but use only veal. Omit the peppercorns if you want a delicate flavor.

Chicken stock

Follow the recipe for White Stock, but use only the chicken pieces. Also add 1 tablespoon salt and some chopped parsley stems.

🗝 To make a simple chicken stock when you need only a few cups, buy chicken wings and cook them in water. For 1 pound of wings, use 6 cups water and 1 teaspoon salt. Simmer for 1 to 2 hours. (You can save the bits of meat from the thicker part of the wing and use them for sandwich filling or a small salad.) This stock will keep in the refrigerator for at least a week, and can be frozen. Makes about 3 cups.

🗝 Whenever you poach chicken for a salad, serve boneless chicken breasts or cook chicken and debone it for pies or casseroles, you will have a lot of bones, skin and fat left. Return these to the cooking liquid. Add more water if necessary to cover well, and simmer for 1 hour or longer. If you have boned raw chicken, add water to cover. This is an economical stock because you would normally discard all of the ingredients. The skin and fat add flavor, and they are discarded at the end of the cooking along with the bones. If you are cooking something in your oven, you can simmer this in the oven at the same time.

Simple chicken soup

- 4 cups Chicken Stock
- 1 large carrot, sliced or grated
- 3 tablespoons minced fennel leaves or parsley
- 2 tablespoons tiny soup pasta
- Salt

Scrape the layer of fat from the cold stock. Your stock will be jellied underneath, making it easy to remove the fat (but it will never be as firm as beef fat). Put stock in a saucepan with remaining ingredients. Add salt to taste as soon as the stock has melted enough to taste. Simmer for 10 minutes. The pasta should be done, the herbs still green and the carrot crunchy. Makes 4 servings.

Chicken consommé

Follow the recipe for Beef Consommé, but instead of the beef and carrot, use ½ pound raw chicken and 2 celery stalks. Garnish as you prefer: sliced mushrooms, a few green peas, a spoonful of salted whipped cream—any of these makes a good garnish for this delicate soup. You can also flavor the soup with 4 to 6 tablespoons dry Madeira or sherry and put 2 or 3 salted almonds in each soup cup.

Turkey stock

Make this just as you do Chicken Stock. The flavor is more pronounced than chicken, but it can be used in all the same ways. 0┳ Frozen turkey wings, cut from very large birds, are often available at quite low cost. These can be used to make a quick stock, and there is enough turkey in 2 large wings to make 2 servings for dinner. Although usually not tender, they are more flavorful and well suited to stock making. Cook these about twice as long as chicken wings.

Stocks from lamb, pork, game

Lamb and pork are too strong-flavored for stock except for a recipe using the same meat. Pork meat has so much fat that it does not make a very good stock. Broth can be made with pork and lamb neck bones following the procedure of the Chicken Stock recipe made with wings.

Game stock can be made from carcasses and bony portions such as backs of birds or wing tips. For a brown game stock, follow the procedure for Brown Stock; for a white game stock (usually made with birds or small game like rabbits) follow the procedure for White Stock. Game stock can be clarified and used for soup. It is usually improved by a dash of Madeira.

Fish stock

Fish stock is the easiest of all stocks to make because it can be ready in an hour. The chief ingredient can usually be gathered at your fish store for nothing. Fish heads, tails and trimmings from filleting are discarded by the bucketful every day. Take your own covered container and ask. The more trimmings you get, the stronger the stock.

Often recipes will suggest clam juice as a substitute for fish stock. If you have no choice, it will do, but it is much saltier than stock and the pronounced flavor might overpower delicate preparations.

- 2 to 3 pounds fish trimmings (such as heads and tails)
- 1 bay leaf
- 1 small carrot, chopped
- 1 celery rib
- ½ teaspoon salt
- ¼ teaspoon pepper
- 4 cups cold water
- ¼ cup dry white wine (optional)

Place all ingredients except the wine in a large saucepan. Bring to a fast rolling boil. Cover tightly and simmer for 30 to 40 minutes, or until the flesh drops from the bones. Strain as for Basic Stock.

If you use the wine, pour the strained fish stock back into a clean saucepan, add the wine and bring to a boil. Remove from heat and cool. Refrigerate, covered, until ready to use. The stock will keep for 6 to 8 days. Makes about 3 cups.

Red-wine fish stock

Use the recipe for Fish Stock but substitute red wine for the white wine. This is useful for some fish stews.

You can make this in larger quantities if you have room to store it. Increase the proportion of wine if you choose, but if you do, add it with the water so the taste of raw wine does not overpower the stock.

Vegetable broth

A meatless vegetable broth can be an extremely tasty stock, full of vitamins. Add it to soups and sauces and use when cooking meats that require liquid, such as pot roast. It is an economical stock because it is made with several foods that are usually thrown away.

- 1½ cups chopped celery tops
- ½ cup chopped parsley stems and leaves
- 1¼ cups chopped spinach leaves
- ¼ cup chopped green onions or leek tops
- 1 cup chopped carrots
- 2 cups shredded outer leaves of salad greens
- 1 teaspoon salt
- Pinch of dried thyme
- 6 peppercorns
- 5 cups water

Place all ingredients in a saucepan and bring slowly to a simmer. Cook for 25 minutes. Strain as for Basic Stock, cool uncovered and store in the refrigerator. Makes 4 cups.

For a simple, nutritious soup, serve vegetable broth with a poached egg in it, or garnish with chopped watercress, or sprinkle with grated cheese.

Almost any vegetable can be used for this broth except beets. A small amount of tomato will give the broth a faintly rosy color, but beets will make the broth too red.

Mushroom broth

Make this when you have mushroom stems and peelings. It will keep refrigerated for 2 weeks and frozen for 6 months. Use it to dilute canned cream of mushroom soup, or as the liquid in chicken or veal gravy. It can replace chicken stock or consommé in any mushroom recipe, or part of the liquid when cooking meat, poultry or fish.

3 cups water
¼ teaspoon salt
1 small onion, halved
1 cup mushroom peelings and stems

Bring the water to a boil with the salt and onion. Add the mushroom peelings and stems. Cover and simmer for 30 minutes. Strain through a fine sieve. Makes about 2½ cups.

Note: If you add 1 or 2 dried mushrooms to the peelings and stems the flavor will be greatly enhanced.

Cream of mushroom soup

5 tablespoons butter
4 tablespoons flour
2 cups mushroom broth
2 cups light cream
Dash of white pepper
Salt
6 mushroom caps, sliced

Melt 4 tablespoons of the butter and stir in the flour until well mixed. Then add the liquids and the pepper. Stir over low heat until the soup is thickened and smooth. Season with salt to taste. Sauté the mushroom slices quickly in the remaining tablespoon of butter. Serve the soup in cream soup bowls, garnished with mushroom slices. Makes 6 servings.

STOCKS FOR ASPIC

Any stock can be used for aspic; choose the one that agrees with the dish. However, the obvious choice may not be the best. For instance, fish stock can be overpowering even with fish, whereas chicken stock or white stock, because of the delicate flavor, might be more adaptable even to a fish dish.

Flavor the stock, then clarify it. Add gelatin if needed and chill until syrupy. For ways to use aspic, see the chapter on Cold Cookery.

Flavoring stocks for aspic

For a rosy-colored aspic, add ¼ cup tomato purée or 2 tablespoons tomato paste to 4 cups stock.

For wine-flavored stock, substitute dry red wine for part of the liquid in a brown stock, or dry white wine for part of the liquid in a white stock. Use 2 cups wine for the basic recipes, and add it near the end of the cooking period. If the recipe requires a more intense flavor, use a fortified wine—Madeira, port or sherry. Use ½ cup wine for 4 cups strained stock, or more to your taste. Add a fortified wine after the stock has been strained.

For herb-flavored aspic, use one sprig of fresh herb or ¼ teaspoon of dried herb for each cup of stock. Either simmer in the entire amount of liquid, or make a strong infusion in about 1 cup stock and then strain it into the balance of the stock. Tarragon, rosemary, dill and mint are some herbs that can be used.

Season the stock before clarifying—the addition of even salt might cloud the aspic. Remember not to overwhelm the aspic stock with any flavor or seasoning because the transparent aspic is designed to enhance a food, not overpower it.

Clarifying stock for aspic

Put 4 cups strained stock, with all fat removed, in a large saucepan and add 2 egg whites, well beaten but not stiff. Stir the egg whites into the stock and very slowly bring to a boil, stirring constantly. When the liquid reaches the boiling point, lower the heat to keep the stock at a steady simmer and cook without stirring for 30 minutes. Then strain through a cloth-lined sieve. All particles will cling to the egg whites, making the liquid perfectly clear and sparkling. Do not hurry this process, but let the aspic drip through until only solids remain in the sieve.

Adding gelatin

If the stock was made with veal bones or calf's feet, it may jell completely without any additional gelatin. To be sure, test it by placing a few spoonfuls in a saucer and chilling. The sample should be firm in about 20 minutes. If it does not jell, add unflavored gelatin. Measure 1 envelope gelatin for 2 cups liquid, or use half that amount if the stock is half jelled. Do not be tempted to add too much gelatin; this would make a rubbery aspic with tough edges. Soften the gelatin in 3 tablespoons cold water, then stir it into the hot stock until completely dissolved.

«7»

Sauces and Salad Dressings

How to thicken a sauce • Three basic hot sauces: white sauce, velouté and brown sauce and their variations • Hot emulsified sauces: hollandaise and its variations • Chefs' secrets for using hollandaise • Cold emulsified sauces: mayonnaise and its variations • More tasty sauces • Salad dressings • Dessert sauces

There is almost no limit to the number of ingredients, both cooked and uncooked, that can be mixed together to create delicious sauces. Once you have mastered the best-known classic sauces, some methods of preparing them and the basic ingredients, you will be able to use your imagination to develop other variations.

The perfect sauce enhances both the appearance and the flavor of the food with which it is served. Sauces perform other important functions as well. They bolster the flavor of a dish that would otherwise be too bland. They bind several different kinds of food together into a unified whole, as does white sauce used in making croquettes. Those made with aspic, such as jellied mayonnaise, keep foods from drying out while on the buffet table. Other sauces, such as mayonnaise and vinaigrette, offer a contrast in flavor and texture to the salads or vegetables they dress. A sauce should contribute to the dish for which it is designed and should possess its own special flavor as well.

Even in preparing the great classic sauces, a good chef may develop some new trick to make a better sauce or to simplify the preparation. You can do the same. There is no need to become a slave to a recipe. Both seasoning and flavoring are matters of taste. Herbs, extracts, spices and salt do not change the basic recipe; using more or less than is called for will not change the texture of your sauce. When you begin, add only a part of the flavoring and seasoning ingredients and taste as you proceed. You may then add a little more of an ingredient to adjust the sauce for the particular dish. The consistency can be made thicker or thinner, too.

To determine the amount of sauce you require, use this as a general guide: 7 tablespoons is the equivalent of one portion. If the sauce happens to be particularly rich, you may reduce each portion to 3 tablespoons. However, there are occasions when you will want no more than 1 tablespoon per portion of a particular sauce.

HOW TO THICKEN A SAUCE

A teaspoon of a liqueur or a tablespoon of thin cream poured over food could be considered a sauce, but a true sauce is thick enough to have body and to adhere to the food. There are various ways to achieve this thickening.

Reducing a sauce

A sauce is reduced to give it a more concentrated flavor, as well as to thicken it. Boil the sauce, uncovered, over low heat, stirring frequently, until the desired quantity is obtained. You may boil it down only a little or by half or more. Sauces that are to be reduced must be seasoned cautiously because the seasoning will also be concentrated. Often this procedure will result in an adequate thickening.

Roux

This is a mixture of flour and fat cooked together at the very start of the recipe before any liquid is added. This cooking eliminates the raw flour taste and allows the flour particles to absorb the liquid added later. If the roux is cooked until just smooth and bubbling, you will get a natural-colored or pale sauce. By browning the mixture over medium heat, stirring constantly, you will produce a darker ivory-colored sauce. If you continue browning the roux, the result will be a darker brown, richer-looking sauce. Only after you have browned the roux to the desired color do you add liquid to finish the sauce. Flour and fat must be cooked together first before any liquid is added. As a general rule, use 1 tablespoon fat and 2 teaspoons flour for each ½ cup liquid, but these proportions vary according to the recipe.

Beurre manié

This is a mixture of flour and butter added at the end of the cooking process rather than at the beginning. Blend together an equal amount of soft butter and flour to make soft balls. Add quickly to hot stock or gravy but do not boil. Beat with a wire whisk until smooth and creamy.

Another method is to mix 1 part butter and 2 parts flour to make a drier, more crumbly mix. You can store it in the refrigerator indefinitely. Add a little at a time to a simmering sauce and whisk until smooth after each addition. Repeat until the desired thickness has been obtained.

Flour or other starch with cold liquid

The liquid can be cold water, milk or consommé, and the starch can be any flour such as wheat or potato flour, cornstarch or fine tapioca. Each kind will give a slightly different texture to the finished sauce. Whichever liquid you use, add the starch, stir to a smooth cream or thin paste, then add to boiling stock or gravy. Beat with a wire whisk. Remember, the liquid must be cold when you mix it with the starch. To obtain a smooth, creamy texture free from any starchy flavor, boil the mixture for 3 to 4 minutes as you beat it with the whisk.

The usual proportion of flour to liquid for a flour-thickened sauce is 2 teaspoons flour to ½ cup liquid, although some recipes call for different amounts. To substitute another starch for the 2 teaspoons wheat flour, use any one of the following: 1 teaspoon cornstarch, 1⅔ teaspoons rice flour, ⅔ teaspoon potato flour or arrowroot.

Egg yolks

Some of the great classic sauces are thickened with egg yolk only; no flour is used. Examples are hollandaise and béarnaise and the best-known cold sauce, mayonnaise. In a sauce such as Mornay, where egg yolks are used, the amount of flour is reduced. Later in this chapter you will find another way to make these egg-thickened sauces.

Any mixture enriched or thickened with egg yolks must never be allowed to boil, because this could cause the sauce to curdle. Low heat is essential. If the sauce is too hot, even if it is not boiling, the egg may cook into little hard lumps before it can expand and mix completely with the other ingredients. Remember, it takes only seconds to cook an egg once it is out of its shell.

Egg yolks and cream

This mixture, called a *liaison* in classic terminology, is used to thicken the rich, delicious velouté sauce and its variations. The yolks and cream are well mixed, and a little hot velouté is stirred in to warm the yolks and allow gradual expansion. Then the *liaison* is stirred into the sauce and everything is brought to a boil. In this case, the egg yolks can be brought to a boil because a *liaison* is used to enrich sauces made with starch of some kind, and this combination needs to be cooked at a higher heat than sauces that are emulsions.

Butter and cream

Butter plays its part in thickening emulsified sauces such as hollandaise, but it is used by itself for some special sauces such as the white butter sauce served with fish in France. Butter and cream cooked over very low heat will thicken a sauce. Whipped cream and sour cream also are used, for example in *velouté Chantilly* described later on, but both these creams are used especially in dessert sauces. You will find examples in the section on dessert sauces.

Cheese and bread crumbs

Grated cheese is used to thicken cheese and Mornay sauces. Bread crumbs thicken *sauce polonaise,* so often served with cauliflower. They are also the thickener as well as the chief ingredient for bread sauce, which the English serve with roast chicken. A recipe for this can be found on page 201.

Purées

The best-known purée for a sauce is onion, which makes *sauce soubise,* but other purées of vegetables, nuts or fruits can be used to thicken sauces. Your imagination will give you many ideas along these lines.

Finishing a sauce

The French chef's method of finishing a sauce is to remove it from the source of heat when ready to serve, then add butter and stir until melted. The heat of the completed sauce melts the butter; it is not necessary to return it to heat. This is called "buttering a sauce"; it gives both gloss and richness. If you want a light and fluffy sauce, omit the butter and stir in 3 tablespoons of whipped cream instead.

BASIC SAUCES

There are three basic hot sauces you should know: white sauce, or *sauce béchamel; sauce velouté;* and brown sauce. Once you learn these, you will be able to experiment with hundreds of variations.

Sauce béchamel

The basic ingredients of béchamel are fat, flour and liquid. The classic béchamel is made with butter, flour and veal stock, but for a béchamel-type sauce there are other possibilities.

The fat can be butter, oil, drippings or melted meat fat. You can also mix different types of fat such as half oil with half butter.

Flour is the usual thickening agent, but you can substitute such starches as arrowroot, potato flour and cornstarch.

For the liquid use plain or flavored milk, wine, light or heavy cream, water, tomato juice, beef consommé, homemade or canned chicken or veal stock. A béchamel can be made in two ways: by making a roux and then adding the liquid, or by simmering the liquid with the flavoring ingredients first, then adding *beurre manié*. The following recipe describes the second method.

2 cups milk
  or 1 cup milk and
  1 cup light cream
½ teaspoon salt
⅛ teaspoon grated
  nutmeg
1 bay leaf
1 piece of celery leaf
1 or 2 inches of leek
  (optional)
4 tablespoons butter
4 tablespoons flour

In a saucepan place the milk (or milk and cream), salt, nutmeg, bay leaf, celery leaf and leek. Cover and simmer over low heat for 30 minutes. If you wish a smooth sauce, strain through a fine sieve and return the liquid to the saucepan.

Make a *beurre manié* using the butter and flour. Add it to the hot flavored milk. Beat with a wire whisk over medium heat until smooth and creamy. Taste for seasoning, adding more salt if necessary.

When the sauce is ready to serve, remove from the heat, add cold butter—1 to 3 teaspoons according to your taste—and stir until butter is melted; or fold a few spoonfuls of whipped cream into the sauce. Makes about 2 cups.

Variations

There are several possible variations of *sauce béchamel*. Here are a few. The extra ingredients listed are just enough for the quantity of sauce in the basic recipe.

If you want a larger amount, *all* the ingredients must be increased proportionally.

Instead of making *beurre manié* with the butter and flour, use the mixture to make a roux. If you prefer, use half butter and half oil for the fat part of the roux. When it is cooked, add the strained flavored milk. Cook and stir over low heat until the sauce is thickened and hot.

Sauce Aurore (for eggs and all poultry dishes)
Add 1 tablespoon tomato paste or mild paprika to the finished sauce.

Sauce Mornay (for fish, eggs, vegetables, or gratiné topping)
Use only 3 tablespoons flour when making the roux. The sauce will seem thin until the eggs and cheese are added. Beat 2 egg yolks with ½ cup grated cheese and 1 tablespoon water. Add a little of the sauce to the egg and cheese mixture, stirring constantly, then return the mixture to the rest of the sauce. Stir until the sauce reaches the boiling point. Do not let it boil because the cheese will become lumpy.

Sauce soubise (for eggs, roast pork, chicken, pasta casseroles)
Slice 4 large onions. Sauté the slices in 1 tablespoon butter and 2 tablespoons salad oil in a large frying pan. Cook over low heat until the onions are soft but not browned, about 20 to 30 minutes.

For the classic sauce, pass the onions through a food mill or blender to make a smooth purée. Omit this step if you prefer to have the onions apparent in the sauce.

Make a basic béchamel, starting with a roux. Use a chicken or veal stock as the liquid instead of milk, and flavor with nutmeg only. When the sauce is smooth and creamy, add the puréed or sliced onions. Taste for seasoning.

Dill sauce (for boiled or poached fish or meat)
Make the sauce with butter and flour, and use veal, chicken or fish stock instead of milk. Choose the stock according to the dish to be sauced. Just before serving

add 1 tablespoon chopped fresh dill mixed with 2 tablespoons cider or wine vinegar, and ½ teaspoon sugar. Season to taste.

Caper sauce
Add 3 tablespoons capers to basic béchamel made with 1 cup milk and 1 cup stock instead of 2 cups milk. When ready to serve, add the juice of ½ lemon.

Curry sauce
This is a basic curry sauce to serve with soufflés, vegetables or poultry. It can be used for a simple or elaborate dish.

Mix 2 to 3 teaspoons of a good curry powder with 1 teaspoon ground turmeric, the grated rind of ½ lemon and 3 tablespoons brandy or whisky. Add this mixture to the basic béchamel made with milk or chicken stock.

Egg sauce (for boiled or poached fish or other seafood)
When the béchamel is ready to serve, add 2 chopped hard-cooked eggs and 3 to 4 tablespoons minced parsley.

Mushroom sauce
Finely chop 2 green onions and enough mushrooms to make 1 cup. Melt 1 tablespoon butter in a frying pan, add the mushrooms and onions, and stir over medium heat for 10 minutes. Add to the basic béchamel made with milk. Season with salt and pepper to taste.

Mustard sauce (for fish, egg dishes, boiled meats, ham)
To the flavored milk add 2 tablespoons prepared mustard, 1 teaspoon dry mustard and a 1-inch strip of lemon rind. Beat with a wire whisk until the mustard is well incorporated. Different varieties of mustard will make subtle changes in the color and flavor of the sauce. Strain the milk into the roux and finish the sauce in the usual way.

White-wine sauce
Use 1 cup light cream and 1 cup dry white wine instead of 2 cups milk in the basic béchamel recipe.

When ready to serve, add 3 tablespoons heavy cream whipped until thick.

Sauce fines herbes
Add to the white-wine sauce (above) ¼ cup minced fresh parsley, ¼ teaspoon crumbled dried tarragon or ½ teaspoon minced fresh tarragon, and 1 minced shallot.

Sauce velouté

One difference between velouté and béchamel is that in velouté the liquid from the cooked food to be served is used in the sauce. This is not necessary with béchamel, because the sauce is made separately from the food. Also, the velouté is finished off with egg yolk and cream to make it more "velvety," which is what the name means.

There are two basic types of velouté. The first is white-meat velouté, for chicken and veal; the second is fish velouté, for fish or other seafood.

The cooking liquid, called a *fumet,* must be well flavored. When 2 cups of liquid are required and the liquid from the cooked food falls short of that amount, the difference may be made up with milk, cream, white wine or stock; for fish velouté make up the difference with fish stock.

3 to 4 tablespoons butter
3 to 4 tablespoons flour
2 cups liquid from cooking
1 egg yolk
¼ cup light cream

Make a roux with the butter and flour. Add the liquid. Cook and stir over low heat until smooth and thickened.

To finish a velouté, blend the egg yolk and the cream together to make a *liaison.* Spoon some of the thickened hot sauce into the *liaison* to warm the eggs, then turn all this into the balance of the sauce. Bring to a boil, beating constantly with a wire whisk. The moment the sauce reaches the boiling point, remove immediately from the heat and continue to whisk it for a minute longer. 🔑 For a perfect velvety sauce, do not stop beating as the sauce is brought to a boil, and keep stirring for a few minutes when you take it off the heat. Makes about 2½ cups.

Variations

The number of possible variations is enormous, since the *fumet* can be made with so many foods—meats, fish and shellfish, vegetables—and there is a wide choice of herbs or other flavorings.

Sauce Bercy (for fish and meat)
Mince 3 shallots and cook them in the butter required for the sauce until they are soft but not browned. Add the flour, cook it, then add 1 tablespoon minced parsley and the cooking liquid. When the sauce is to be used with seafood, use fish stock to make up any deficiency in the liquid. When it is to be used with meat, use white wine or chicken stock.

Sauce bretonne (for eggs, fish, white meats, poultry)
Mince 2 celery ribs, the white part of 1 leek, 1 small onion and 6 mushrooms. Melt the butter needed for the sauce and add the vegetables. Stir until well covered with the butter. Cover the saucepan and simmer over low heat until well softened, but do not brown. Add the flour and cook. Then add the cooking liquid of the fish, meat or poultry. Add white wine if necessary to bring the quantity to 2 cups. Simmer, covered, for 20 minutes. Correct the seasoning and stir in a tablespoon of butter.

Sauce diplomate (for fish and other seafood)
Make velouté with part seafood cooking liquid and part clam juice. Flavor with brandy and cayenne to taste. You can also add about ¼ cup of diced lobster or chopped truffle for an elegant, rich sauce.

Sauce suprême (for chicken and other poultry)
Make the velouté with good chicken stock mixed with about ½ cup mushroom broth. Correct the seasoning. When ready to serve, fold in 3 to 4 tablespoons heavy cream, whipped until thick.

Sauce poulette (for braised white meat, vegetables or seafood)
Melt the butter needed for the sauce and add ¼ pound of minced mushrooms. Cook until they begin to brown. Then add the flour and cook. Add the

cooking liquid. If there is not enough cooking liquid to make up the 2 cups, make up the difference by adding light cream.

Beat the egg yolk with only 2 tablespoons cream and the juice of ½ lemon. When the sauce is ready, stir a little of it into the egg, lemon and cream mixture (the *liaison*) to warm the eggs, then turn into the balance of the sauce. Simmer for 2 minutes, stirring constantly. Taste the sauce for seasoning, adding salt if necessary.

Velouté Chantilly (for eggs, poultry, sweetbreads, brains)
This sauce should be thick, so add 1 more tablespoon of flour to the basic recipe. When ready to serve, stir in ½ cup heavy cream whipped until thick, or 1 cup commercial sour cream. Beat with a wire whisk while warming, and serve immediately.

Brown sauce

½ cup chopped celery
½ cup chopped carrot
½ cup chopped onion
¼ teaspoon dried thyme
1 bay leaf
¼ teaspoon dried marjoram, savory or tarragon
3 tablespoons fat
4 tablespoons flour
2 cups brown stock

First prepare the vegetables, then add the herbs. The choice of fat is important; unsalted fresh pork fatback is exactly right in flavor, but beef or veal drippings or even oil are acceptable. Melt the fat and then stir in the vegetables with a wooden spoon. Cook over low heat, uncovered, until they are soft, translucent and a light golden color, but do not allow them to brown. Stir frequently.

Make the roux: sprinkle the softened vegetables with the flour and stir over medium heat until the flour completely disappears. Keep stirring until the whole mixture turns light brown. 🔑 It is this operation that gives the color to the sauce, but if anything is allowed to stick or burn, the sauce will have a bitter taste. Lower the heat if the vegetables or the flour appear to be overcooking.

The next step is to add the liquid. While the classic choice is brown stock, the sauce is particularly good if the liquid is made in part from the juices of a roast with red wine added. Measure the liquid you wish to use and let it cool. 🗝 Add only a cold liquid to a hot roux. Or, if you prefer, a hot liquid can be added to a cold roux. The important thing is the difference in the temperature of the two—one hot, the other cold. Stir the mixture of roux and liquid over medium heat until smooth and creamy. Cover and simmer on top of the stove or in a 200° F. oven for 1 hour.

Strain through a fine sieve, or through a sieve lined with cheesecloth. At this point season to taste. This makes an excellent brown sauce that keeps well in the refrigerator and can be used for many dishes. Makes about 2 cups.

🗝 To save time and trouble, prepare 12 cups brown stock. Make a roux with enough vegetables for 6 recipes. When this is ready, pour it into a large casserole, add the stock, cover it tightly and cook the sauce in a 200° F. oven for 3 hours. Strain the finished sauce, pour into small containers and refrigerate. Store 1 or 2 containers in the refrigerator; the sauce will keep for 2 weeks. Freeze the balance for later use. It will keep frozen for 6 months.

Variations

Sauce madère or *Madeira sauce* (for all roasted meats and for boiled tongue and ham)
Add ¼ cup Madeira to the 2 cups liquid, or substitute ½ cup Madeira for ½ cup of the liquid.

Sauce espagnole
Add 2 minced garlic cloves and a generous amount of freshly ground pepper to the vegetables. When the vegetables are soft and translucent, add 2 tablespoons tomato paste. Finish the sauce in the usual fashion.

Sauce Robert (for roasted pork, or to warm up beef and root vegetables)
Instead of the 3 vegetables, use only 4 chopped onions. Flavor with ¼ teaspoon dried thyme and the grated rind of 1 lemon. Use ½ cup white wine to replace ½ cup of the liquid. When the sauce is finished, flavor it with 1 teaspoon of Dijon-style mustard.

Sauce piquante (for roasted veal, all pork dishes and all chops)
Instead of the vegetables use only onions, as in sauce Robert. Flavor with 1 bay leaf and 1/4 teaspoon salt. Replace 1/4 cup of the liquid with 1/4 cup cider vinegar, and add 1 teaspoon sugar. When the sauce is finished, add 4 tablespoons thinly sliced baby gherkins.

Sauce diable (for meat and poultry)
Chop 2 shallots or 1 small onion and place in a saucepan with 1/2 cup wine or cider vinegar, 8 crushed peppercorns, 1 bay leaf, 1/2 teaspoon dry mustard, 1/2 teaspoon paprika and 1/2 teaspoon salt. Simmer until the mixture is reduced by half. Strain and add to cooked brown sauce.

EMULSIFIED SAUCES

An emulsion is the combination of two basically incompatible liquids such as oil and water. To combine them, an emulsifying agent such as an egg yolk is necessary. When making a hot emulsified sauce such as hollandaise, the egg yolk binds together the melted butter (oil) with the lemon juice (water). As the oil is beaten, it is broken down into tiny globules that spread evenly through the water. By adding the egg yolk as an emulsifying agent, the two are combined. This principle applies to both hot and cold emulsified sauces.

An emulsified mixture separates easily without such an agent. For instance, French dressing will separate as soon as one stops stirring it, because there is nothing in it to bind the ingredients together. In a hollandaise or any of its variants, which contain egg yolk, the emulsion will remain in suspension if not overbeaten. If you master the art of making emulsified sauces, you will be able to serve elegantly sauced dishes for sophisticated menus.

Hot emulsified sauces, hollandaise, variants

Hollandaise is the basic sauce of the hot emulsified type, and it is a classic in itself. Other well-known related sauces are *béarnaise, Choron, maltaise, mousseline, muscovite* and *Bordeaux hollandaise*. Each sauce is distinctive. These sauces are used to complement such foods as artichokes, asparagus, broccoli, chicken, meat, eggs and fish.

The wonder of hollandaise lies in its simplicity. The ingredients are few: egg yolks, lemon juice, butter and salt. The egg yolks contain the liquid that gives the sauce its base while the protein acts as a thickening agent and gives the sauce its texture. Lecithin, the emulsifying agent, binds the lemon juice and the liquid of the egg yolks with the oil of the butter. The acid of the lemon juice also plays a role in blending the eggs with the butter. The combination of heat and constant stirring brings about the emulsion; little heat is required, however.

There are three easy ways of making hollandaise: the chef's method, the hot-water method and the blender method. The double-boiler method is not reliable and is also more complicated.

Only the simplest equipment is required. First, you need a heat-resistant nonmetallic bowl; the best are made of heavy crockery, glass or enameled cast iron. Do not use an aluminum or stainless steel bowl; either may affect the flavor and texture of the sauce. For stirring the sauce, a wire whisk is best, but almost any nonmechanical hand beater that will fit the curves of the bowl will do—a wire spoon, a Scandinavian twig beater, a wooden spoon or a plastic spatula.

If a hollandaise separates during cooking, too much heat has been applied. When this happens, beat the sauce vigorously while simultaneously adding one of the following: an ice cube, a few drops of thick cream or a few drops of boiling water. Any one of these three should bind the sauce, but if one fails, immediately follow through with the next, until one or all three have achieved the desired effect.

If the sauce turns out to be too thin, this means that it has not been cooked enough. Return it to low heat and stir until thickened.

Do not be discouraged if you experience either of these apparent failures. Only a few degrees too much heat or a few minutes too little cooking time will affect the sauce. Practice.

To reheat the sauce, place the sauce container over hot water or over very low heat and beat vigorously until warm. Hollandaise is served warm, not hot.

Hollandaise can be kept refrigerated in a covered bowl for 2 to 3 days, or in the freezer for 2 to 3 months. Before reheating a frozen sauce, thaw it in the covered freezer container.

Chef's hollandaise

This is one of the best ways to make hollandaise. Once made, it can be kept warm for up to an hour in a container set over warm water or on a hot tray set at a low temperature.

- 2 egg yolks
- ⅓ cup cold butter, in 3 pieces
- 1 to 4 tablespoons lemon juice
- ½ teaspoon salt

Place the egg yolks in a bowl and break them up lightly with a fork. Top with the 3 pieces of cold butter. Pour in the lemon juice to taste and sprinkle with the salt. Place the bowl over direct low heat and stir until all the butter has melted.

At no time should the bowl get too hot, because excess heat will curdle the sauce. To test the temperature, lift the bowl occasionally from the source of heat and touch the bottom. If it is too hot to be comfortable to the touch, remove it from the heat for a few seconds, but continue to stir constantly.

When the butter has melted, continue stirring and testing the temperature of the bowl until the sauce is smooth and creamy. Once you have removed the bowl from the heat, continue to stir for another 40 to 50 seconds because the heat of the container will continue to cook the sauce. The entire procedure takes no more than 5 or 10 minutes. Makes 1 cup.

Hot-water hollandaise

This recipe produces a fluffier sauce that can be blended with mayonnaise and is economical because the yield is greater. It is especially good served on heavier foods such as hard-cooked eggs.

- 3 egg yolks
- ¼ cup hot water
- 1 to 3 tablespoons lemon juice
- Cayenne (added to taste) *or* ½ teaspoon salt
- ½ cup cold butter

Place the egg yolks in a bowl and beat vigorously over low heat. At the same time, add the hot water slowly. When well mixed, remove from the heat and add the remaining ingredients. Return to low heat and proceed as for Chef's Hollandaise. Makes 1 ½ cups.

Blender hollandaise

Using the hot-water hollandaise recipe, proceed in the following manner: rinse the blender container with hot water. Place the egg yolks, hot water, lemon juice and seasoning in the container.

Melt the butter over medium heat.

Cover the blender container and whirl at high speed for 3 seconds. Remove the cover, but keep the blender turned on as you pour in the hot melted butter. As soon as all the butter has been added, the hollandaise is ready. Since the egg yolks are cooked only by the hot butter, this has a slightly different flavor from the others, but is the easiest to make.

Sauce béarnaise

Serve with baked or fried fish, beef tenderloin, sautéed *tournedos,* as well as egg dishes and cheese soufflés.

Prepare a hollandaise, but substitute the following mixture for the lemon juice.

4 tablespoons cider or wine vinegar
1 shallot, minced
1 teaspoon minced fresh tarragon or dried tarragon
4 peppercorns, freshly ground

Reduce the vinegar, tarragon, shallot and pepper to 2 tablespoons (this is an infusion). Add this to the hollandaise mixture instead of the lemon juice.

Variations

Bordeaux hollandaise (for fish, poached chicken, mixed vegetables)
Make a chef's hollandaise or hot-water hollandaise, but replace the lemon juice, or the hot water and lemon juice, with an equal amount of white wine or white-wine vinegar. Add minced fresh tarragon, chives, parsley or dill to taste immediately before serving.

Sauce mousseline (for fish, boiled vegetables, soufflés)
Whip ¼ to ½ cup heavy cream until very thick. Immediately before serving, beat the whipped cream into 1 cup of Chef's Hollandaise.

Light mousseline sauce
Beat until stiff any egg whites left over from making the hollandaise. Add these to the sauce immediately before serving. This mousseline can be served either hot or cold.

Sauce choron (for beef tenderloin, roast veal, meat loaf, fried fish)
Add 2 tablespoons tomato paste to a recipe for hollandaise or béarnaise.

Sauce maltaise (for asparagus, artichokes, herring dishes)
Make a hot-water hollandaise, but replace the hot water with hot orange juice. Add 1 tablespoon grated orange rind to the sauce immediately before serving.

Sauce muscovite (for poached salmon, Dover sole, poached eggs, fish soufflés)
To Chef's Hollandaise add 2 tablespoons heavy cream, 2 to 3 tablespoons black caviar and the grated rind of ½ lemon or lime.

Chef's secrets

O╥ Add 2 to 3 tablespoons of cold or hot hollandaise to 1 cup of white sauce when you want it smoother and richer.

O╥ Add ¼ cup cold hollandaise or any of its variants to 1 cup whipped cream to serve over cold poached meat or fish. This is particularly delicious with steamed chicken breasts or salmon steak.

O╥ Immediately before serving a casserole, pour ¼ cup hollandaise over it and brown under the broiler for a few seconds.

Cold emulsified sauces, mayonnaise and its variants

Mayonnaise is the typical cold emulsified sauce. It is simple to make and is well worth the trouble because there is a world of difference between the homemade mayonnaise and the best of the commercial types.

Use the best ingredients and have them close at hand before you begin. The better the oil, the better the mayonnaise. Use a good brand at room temperature. The eggs you use should be the freshest; they are the strongest emulsifying agents. The mustard also contributes to the emulsifying action. You will need a 1-quart mixing bowl and a wire whisk. The whole process of emulsifying a mayonnaise will take from 20 to 25 minutes once your ingredients and utensils are assembled.

Mayonnaise

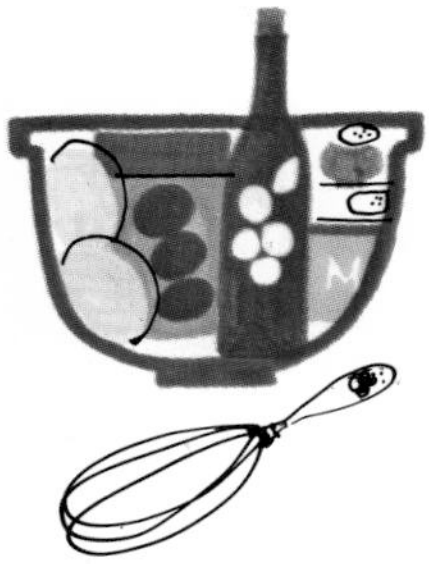

- 2 egg yolks
- ½ teaspoon dry mustard
- 2 to 4 tablespoons cider vinegar, white wine or fresh lemon juice
- 1 cup olive oil or salad oil
- 1 teaspoon salt

Place the egg yolks, dry mustard and 2 tablespoons of the vinegar, wine or lemon juice in the bowl. Mix well with a wire whisk, then add the oil. O━ The way the oil is added is the secret of making mayonnaise successfully. Add it almost drop by drop, beating vigorously and constantly with the wire whisk until the mixture is emulsified. You will know when this takes place because the texture will become smooth and creamy. Once this happens the oil may be dribbled in a little more quickly, but never too much at one time. Make certain the oil has been completely beaten in before adding more. The more slowly the oil is combined in the beginning, the firmer the mayonnaise will be. A perfect mayonnaise should have the consistency of thick whipped cream. Beat in the salt toward the end, and taste to be sure the seasoning is just right.

If the oil is added too quickly, the mayonnaise will separate and no amount of beating will bind it together again. If this happens, make a fresh start with a clean bowl. Place in the bowl 1 teaspoon of dry mustard and mix it into a thin cream with a few drops of water. Then, beating vigorously, start adding the separated mayonnaise, drop by drop, as with the oil when you began. As you proceed, you may speed up the process as it reemulsifies.

If you want a mayonnaise with a tart flavor, beat in an additional tablespoonful or two of cider vinegar or fresh lemon juice once the mixture has thickened.

O━ Remember the secret of a perfect mayonnaise: add the oil slowly and beat with a wire whisk.

Mayonnaise can be stored in a well-covered glass jar and kept in a cool place. Do not freeze or keep in an extremely cold part of the refrigerator. The oil will solidify at too cold a temperature, and in all probability the emulsion will break down.

Variations

Swedish mayonnaise (for cold boiled ham and meat salads)
To 1 cup mayonnaise add 1 tablespoon well-drained prepared horseradish, 1 tablespoon prepared German-style mustard, 3 tablespoons applesauce. Mix well.

Russian mayonnaise (for cold or jellied fish or other seafood)
To 1 cup mayonnaise add 2 tablespoons black caviar, 1 teaspoon prepared Dijon-style mustard, ½ teaspoon crumbled dried tarragon. Mix well.

Green mayonnaise or *Sauce verte I* (for cold chicken, aspics, salmon, jellied vegetables)
Finely chop 1 well-packed cup of fresh spinach. Mince ¼ cup parsley leaves. Place both in a bowl and add ¼ to ½ cup boiling water; the leaves should be covered. Let stand for 3 minutes. Strain through cheesecloth into a bowl, allowing the water to drain for 1 hour. *Reserve the liquid.* Add the reserved liquid to 1 cup mayonnaise. The soaking and draining are necessary to give extra deep color to the mayonnaise.

If you have a blender, place the mayonnaise mixed with the water into the blender and add the drained chopped spinach and parsley. Cover and blend for 2 seconds. If you do not have a blender, mix well in a bowl. The mayonnaise will turn a beautiful green.

Green mayonnaise or *Sauce verte II*
Here is another version. Chop ½ cup green onion tops or chives, ½ cup green-pepper pieces, ¼ cup parsley leaves and ½ cup uncooked spinach leaves. Place them in a blender with 2 tablespoons lemon juice. Cover and blend until the mixture turns to a mush, but leave some small bits in it. Add to 1 cup mayonnaise and mix well.

Without a blender, chop the ingredients very fine

and mix into the mayonnaise, crushing them to give as much color as possible to the sauce.

Horseradish mayonnaise (for cold ham, meat and fish salads, cabbage, potato salad)
Whip ½ cup heavy cream. Fold in 3 tablespoons well-drained prepared horseradish. Fold the mixture into 1 cup mayonnaise.

Tartar sauce (for all fried or broiled fish and other seafood)
Mince ½ cup sweet pickles. Thinly slice 2 small sour gherkins. Mince 2 tablespoons chives or parsley. Add all to 1 cup mayonnaise with 1 tablespoon capers. Mix well.

Mayonnaise cressonière or *Watercress mayonnaise* (for cold meat, mild fish, vegetables, eggs)
Grate 1 hard-cooked egg. Chop the leaves of 1 bunch of watercress; there should be ½ to ¾ cup chopped leaves. Add these to 1 cup mayonnaise with 1 teaspoon anchovy paste. Mix well.

Mayonnaise dijonnaise or *Mustard mayonnaise* (for hors d'oeuvres, fish, salads of all types)
Grate 1 hard-cooked egg. Add 1 to 2 tablespoons prepared Dijon-style mustard to the grated egg and blend together until creamy. Add the mixture to 1 cup mayonnaise made with lemon juice rather than vinegar (or at least with half lemon juice and half vinegar). Mix well.

Mayonnaise indienne or *Curry mayonnaise* (for eggs, chicken, seafood, vegetables)
Mix together 1 teaspoon curry powder, ½ teaspoon ground turmeric and 1 teaspoon brandy, sherry or lemon juice. Add to 1 cup mayonnaise with chives or parsley to taste. Mix well.

Mayonnaise niçoise or *Pimiento mayonnaise* (for salads, tomatoes, fish)
Mix together 1 finely chopped red pimiento, 1 teaspoon tomato paste and ½ teaspoon crumbled dried tarragon. Add to 1 cup mayonnaise. Mix well.

MORE TASTY SAUCES

In addition to the preceding basic sauces that can be varied in so many different ways, here are some secondary sauces.

English bread sauce

Serve with roast chicken or broiled or roasted game birds.

1 medium-size onion, peeled
6 whole cloves
1 ½ cups milk
2-inch piece of lemon rind
¾ cup soft white bread crumbs, crusts removed (from fresh bread)
2 tablespoons butter
Salt and pepper

Stud the peeled onion with the cloves and place in the top part of a double boiler with the milk and lemon rind. Heat over boiling water, covered, for 30 minutes. Do not let the milk boil. Remove and discard the onion and the lemon rind.

To the milk add the soft bread crumbs. All trace of crust should be removed before making the crumbs; crusts would discolor the white sauce. Add 1 tablespoon of the butter. Cook, beating with a wire whisk or hand beater, until the sauce is smooth and creamy and has absorbed all the crumbs. Add salt and pepper to taste. Add the second tablespoon of butter and stir until it has melted. Serve immediately; the sauce will turn yellow if kept standing. Makes about 2 cups.

Mustard cream sauce

Serve with charcoal-broiled lamb, veal kidneys, beef.

2 egg yolks
½ teaspoon dry mustard
½ teaspoon tomato paste
1 tablespoon tarragon vinegar
Salt
Cayenne pepper
4 tablespoons light cream
¼ pound (½ cup) butter, cut into pieces

In a bowl place the egg yolks, mustard, tomato paste, tarragon vinegar, and salt and cayenne to taste. Beat with a wire whisk until smooth. Add 1 tablespoon of the cream and mix in. Place the bowl over hot water and beat until the sauce thickens. Beat in the butter, piece by piece. Thin the sauce by adding some or all of the remaining cream, 1 teaspoon at a time, until you have achieved the desired consistency. This is also an emulsified sauce, related to hollandaise. Makes about 1 cup.

Mint sauce

Serve with all lamb dishes.

¾ cup minced fresh mint
1 teaspoon salt
¼ cup cider or white-wine vinegar
1 tablespoon sugar
¼ teaspoon ground ginger
1 teaspoon lemon juice

Put all the ingredients in a screw-top jar and shake hard for a few seconds. Refrigerate for 6 to 12 hours before using. Makes about ½ cup.

Scandinavian egg sauce

Serve with poached poultry, white meat or fish.

4 hard-cooked eggs
2 tablespoons butter
1 tablespoon flour
2 cups chicken stock
⅛ teaspoon ground savory
¼ cup minced parsley
Salt and pepper
Capers (optional)

Remove the egg whites from the yolks. Mash the yolks with the butter and flour until well blended. Stir in the chicken stock and simmer for 5 to 7 minutes, stirring occasionally. Remove from the heat and add the savory and parsley plus salt and pepper to taste. Shred the egg whites and add them and the capers. Stir. Makes about 2 cups.

Raisin sauce

1 cup dark raisins
1 cup port
Grated rind of 1 orange
Juice of 2 oranges (about 1 cup)
1 tablespoon prepared Dijon-style mustard
Pinch of salt
2 tablespoons cornstarch
4 tablespoons cold water

Soak the raisins in the port for several hours or overnight. Transfer raisins and wine to a saucepan and add the orange rind and juice, mustard and salt. Slowly bring to a boil, stirring to mix. Mix cornstarch with water and stir into the simmering sauce. Simmer until smooth and thickened. Especially good with tongue and ham. Makes about 2 cups.

Tomato sauce I

Serve this good, fresh-tasting tomato sauce with meat, eggs or fish. It freezes very well. When tomatoes are in full season, make the sauce in quantities and store in the freezer to use throughout the year.

- 3 tablespoons butter
- 1 ½ tablespoons flour
- ½ teaspoon salt
- Pinch of cayenne pepper
- 2 tablespoons tomato paste
- 1 small garlic clove, crushed
- ½ teaspoon minced fresh basil
- 2 large tomatoes, peeled and sliced
- 1 teaspoon honey
- 1 ½ cups water
- ¼ cup minced fresh parsley (optional)

Melt 2 tablespoons of the butter and blend in the flour, salt, cayenne, tomato paste and garlic. Stir until well blended. Add basil, tomatoes, honey and water. Stir over medium heat until the sauce comes to a boil. Simmer over reduced heat for 10 to 15 minutes. Immediately before serving, add the remaining tablespoon of butter. Taste for seasoning. If you wish, you can add ¼ cup of minced fresh parsley at this point. Makes about 2 cups.

Tomato sauce II

This sauce is thicker and richer and is flavored differently from the sauce above. Since it is puréed, it has a velvety texture.

- 5 tablespoons unsalted butter
- 1 onion, minced
- 1 tablespoon all-purpose flour
- 6 large fresh tomatoes
- 1 tablespoon sugar
- ½ teaspoon dried thyme
- Pinch of grated nutmeg
- Salt and pepper
- 1 tablespoon tomato paste

Melt 4 tablespoons of the butter and add the onion. Cook together over low heat until the onion is soft but not brown, stirring occasionally. Sprinkle the flour on top and blend thoroughly.

Chop the unpeeled tomatoes into small pieces and add them to the onion with the sugar, thyme, nutmeg, and salt and pepper to taste. Bring to a boil, stirring constantly. Cover the mixture and cook over low heat for 15 minutes.

Remove from heat and pass the sauce through a coarse strainer to remove the seeds and peels, then purée it in a blender or food mill, or push through a fine strainer. Add the tomato paste and the remaining 1 tablespoon butter to the purée. Stir until the butter is melted. Taste, adding more seasoning if necessary. Makes about 4 cups.

Verona spaghetti sauce

Very few Italian sauces for pasta can be prepared in 30 minutes, but this is one of them. Not only is it delicious, but its texture is excellent and it has the added attraction of being easily digestible.

- 7 tablespoons butter
- 1 pound chicken livers
- 2 garlic cloves, crushed
- 2 large onions, finely chopped
- ¼ pound mushrooms, finely chopped
- Salt and pepper
- Pinch of dry mustard
- 5 tomatoes, peeled and chopped into large pieces
- 1 tablespoon flour
- 3 tablespoons tomato paste
- 1 cup canned condensed consommé, undiluted
- 1 teaspoon dried basil
- ½ teaspoon dried marjoram
- ¼ teaspoon dried rosemary

Heat a large frying pan. Place 2 tablespoons of the butter in the heated pan and just before it turns brown, add the chicken livers. Cook over high heat until the livers are well browned. Remove the livers. Place 2 more tablespoons of the butter into the same pan to melt. Add the crushed garlic and cook for 1 minute. Add the onions and cook quickly until they begin to brown. Add the mushrooms, lower the heat and cook slowly for another 5 or 6 minutes. Use more butter if necessary to keep mushrooms from sticking. Season with salt and pepper and the mustard. Add the tomato pieces and cook for 2 minutes.

Remove the pan from the heat and blend in the flour and tomato paste. When these are blended, pour in the consommé. Return to the heat and stir constantly until the mixture comes to a boil. Simmer for about 10 minutes. Chop the chicken livers and add them plus the basil, marjoram and rosemary to the sauce. Simmer for 5 minutes. Stir in the remaining butter just before serving. Makes enough sauce for 1 pound of spaghetti.

Lemon basting sauce

- ¾ cup butter
- 2 teaspoons paprika
- 1 teaspoon sugar
- 1 teaspoon salt
- ½ teaspoon pepper
- ¼ teaspoon dry mustard
- Pinch of cayenne
- ½ cup lemon juice
- ½ cup hot water

Melt the butter, but be careful not to brown it. Add the paprika, sugar, salt, pepper, mustard and cayenne. Stir until thoroughly blended. Then add the lemon juice and hot water. Beat until well mixed. Use as a basting sauce for chicken, fish, pork or hamburgers that are being broiled or barbecued. The sauce keeps refrigerated for 2 to 3 weeks. Warm before using. Makes 1½ cups.

Honey basting sauce

Mix ¼ cup liquid honey, ¼ cup prepared mustard and 1 teaspoon curry powder. Use for chicken or lamb that is being broiled or barbecued. Makes ½ cup.

Butter and chive sauce

- 1 cup butter
- 2 tablespoons lemon juice
- ¼ teaspoon salt
- ¼ teaspoon paprika
- ⅛ teaspoon pepper
- ¼ cup chopped parsley
- 3 tablespoons chopped chives

In a small saucepan heat the butter, lemon juice, salt, paprika and pepper. Do not let the butter brown. Add the parsley and chives and serve. Use for broiled or barbecued seafood. One way to serve it is to give each guest a small bowl of the sauce. The seafood can be dipped into it.

Butter and mustard sauce

- 2 hard-cooked egg yolks
- 2 teaspoons dry mustard
- 2 tablespoons tarragon vinegar
- 2 teaspoons minced herbs
- 1 cup butter
- Salt and pepper

Mash the egg yolks to a smooth paste and stir in the mustard, then the vinegar; the mixture will thicken. Choose the herbs according to the dish you are serving; they should be minced as small as possible. Melt the butter over very low heat and stir in the mustard paste until well mixed. Add salt and pepper to taste. Serve with broiled or barbecued beef or lamb, plain roast chicken, baked whole fish or fish steaks, asparagus or broccoli. Reduce the amount of mustard if you prefer a milder flavor. Makes 1¼ cups.

Other hot butter sauces

Hot butter sauces can be made following the method in Butter and Chive Sauce by adding all kinds of herbs or flavorings to sweet or salted butter. Another method is similar to preparing mayonnaise. Unmelted butter is beaten into the flavoring mixture to make a thick sauce. This kind of sauce is served warm rather than hot.

Shallot butter sauce

6 tablespoons white wine	2 white peppercorns
4 to 6 shallots	¾ cup softened butter

Put the wine in a small saucepan. Mince the shallots; there should be about 3 tablespoons. Crush the peppercorns very fine in a mortar. Cook the shallots and pepper in the wine until the wine has almost boiled away, but do not let it brown or burn.

Set the pan in a warm place and start beating in the butter, a little at a time, the way oil is beaten into mayonnaise. Do not let the pan get cold; the butter should expand and soften, but it should not melt. Serve with fish and shellfish. Makes about 1 cup.

Cold butter sauces

Cold butter sauces, related to the familiar hard sauce, can be made by beating various herbs or seasonings into butter, which is then refrigerated. These sauces are served cold, often on hot food, where they melt and release the flavors of the seasonings. In classic terms these are called *compound butters.* Some of these butter sauces are described in the chapter on herbs and spices.

These butters will keep for 2 weeks or longer in the refrigerator, or they can be frozen. In addition to serving them as simple sauces on their own, you can also add them to other sauces to give extra flavor and richness. You could use a tablespoon of one of these instead of the butter called for to finish a sauce.

Parsley butter

Mince enough parsley leaves to measure 3 tablespoons. Be sure to mince them very fine. Add 1 teaspoon lemon juice and beat into ½ cup butter (at room temperature) until thoroughly mixed. Roll into a ball and wrap in plastic, or pack small balls in a jar, and refrigerate. Serve on vegetables such as new potatoes, blanched green or yellow snap beans and broiled fish steaks or fillets.

Curry butter

Melt 2 tablespoons butter in a small pan and cook 1 small onion, minced, until wilted. Add 4 teaspoons curry powder and continue to cook until the onion is almost soft and the curry begins to give off its characteristic smell. Cool the onion-curry mixture. Then beat it into ½ cup butter (at room temperature) until thoroughly mixed. Serve on cauliflower, broccoli, broiled chicken, lamb chops, broiled swordfish.

Other cold sauces

Sour cream cucumber sauce

3 green onions	2 cups commercial sour cream
1 large cucumber	Salt and pepper
2 tablespoons lemon juice	

Mince the onions. Peel and chop the cucumber. Mix both with the lemon juice and fold into the sour cream. Season to taste. Serve with poached salmon or any broiled or barbecued fish. Makes about 3 cups.

Sour cream walnut sauce

½ cup walnut pieces	1 tablespoon soy sauce
1 tablespoon walnut oil	2 cups commercial sour cream
1 teaspoon ground ginger	

Chop or grind the walnuts until they are quite small. Then sauté them in the walnut oil until the nuts are light brown. Stir in ginger and soy sauce and cook for 2 minutes longer. Cool, then stir into the sour cream. Add more soy sauce if you like. You may not need any salt because the soy sauce itself is salty. Serve with cold chicken and cold ham. Makes about 2½ cups.

SALAD DRESSINGS

Salad dressings are sauces too. You have already had an example of a sauce often used for salads—mayonnaise. While we most often use these cold sauces to dress lettuce leaves or other greens, they are also used to dress vegetables such as asparagus with vinaigrette sauce. The sauce that the French call *vinaigrette* is almost the same as what we call French dressing. And French dressing can have endless variations.

The best-known and simplest salad dressing is prepared by mixing 1 part vinegar with 2 to 3 parts oil and adding salt and pepper to taste. The flavor and color of this dressing can vary, however, depending upon several factors: whether you use French, Italian, Spanish or Greek olive oil, or corn oil, and whether you use a white, cider or malt vinegar, or a white- or red-wine vinegar, or a tarragon-flavored vinegar or one flavored with garlic or basil. You might also use lemon juice instead of vinegar, or freshly ground white pepper instead of black.

If you want to be an accomplished cook, you will vary the ingredients in your salad dressing to suit the salad it is intended to enhance. Experiment to discover what combinations you like best.

⊶ With tomatoes, use white vinegar with basil and an Italian or Greek olive oil. ⊶ With cold salmon, use lemon juice with French olive oil. ⊶ With rice and fresh vegetables use cider vinegar and corn oil. ⊶ With an everyday salad fresh lemon juice is best. ⊶ With a French or Spanish olive oil, use freshly ground black pepper and coarse salt crushed in the bottom of the bowl before the vegetables are put into the salad.

No dressing is ever as good after it has been stored or refrigerated. ⊶ Freshly made dressing is the true secret of a good salad.

French dressing

- 2 tablespoons fresh lemon juice
- 2 tablespoons cider vinegar
- ¾ cup salad oil
- 1 teaspoon salt
- ¼ teaspoon pepper
- 1 teaspoon Worcestershire sauce
- ½ teaspoon paprika
- ¼ teaspoon garlic powder
- ½ teaspoon sugar

Mix all the ingredients in a blender, shake in a glass jar or beat with a rotary beater. This dressing keeps 2 to 3 weeks. Shake hard before using. Makes about 1 cup.

Chiffonade dressing

To 1 cup French dressing add 2 tablespoons minced parsley, 2 teaspoons each of diced green pepper and pimiento, 2 minced green onions and 1 grated hard-cooked egg. Add salt to taste. Blend, shake or beat.

Danish dressing

This can serve as a year-round recipe for those who like a piquant dressing. It is delicious on sliced or diced cucumbers and perfect on cold chicken broiled or barbecued.

- 4 ounces Danish blue cheese
- ½ cup salad oil
- 1 tablespoon Worcestershire or HP Sauce
- 1 tablespoon lemon juice
- 1 tablespoon vinegar
- ¼ teaspoon dried basil

Mash the cheese with a few tablespoons of the oil. Add the rest of the oil and the remaining ingredients. Beat thoroughly. The dressing will keep, covered and refrigerated, for a few weeks. Shake well before using. If the oil is thick and opaque, leave at room temperature for 15 to 25 minutes. Makes about 1½ cups.

English dressing

- ½ cup tarragon vinegar
- 1 cup olive oil
- 1 teaspoon dry mustard
- ½ teaspoon Worcestershire sauce
- ½ teaspoon salt
- ½ teaspoon pepper
- ¼ teaspoon celery seeds
- 2 ice cubes

Place the vinegar in a bowl and gradually beat in the oil. Then add the dry mustard, Worcestershire, salt, pepper and celery seeds, one ingredient at a time, beating well after each addition. Add the ice cubes and beat for 3 to 4 seconds. Refrigerate for 30 minutes. Stir well before using. Makes about 1⅔ cups.

American salad dressing

- 1 cup salad oil
- ¼ cup malt vinegar
- 1½ tablespoons ketchup
- 1 teaspoon sugar
- ½ teaspoon paprika
- 1 teaspoon salt
- ½ teaspoon dry mustard
- 1 teaspoon grated onion
- 1 egg white, unbeaten

Place all the ingredients in a bowl and beat with a hand beater or electric beater until well blended. Keep refrigerated. Shake well before using. Makes about 1½ cups.

Madras dressing

- ½ cup walnut oil
- 3 tablespoons fresh lime juice
- ½ teaspoon salt
- ¼ teaspoon ground coriander
- ¼ teaspoon ground cuminseed

Mix all the ingredients just before you plan to serve the salad. This does not keep its fresh taste after storage. Use for fish salads, especially for plain poached shrimps, and for vegetable salads. The walnut oil has a special flavor; if you like it you may want to try this on an ordinary salad of greens. Makes 3/4 cup.

Roquefort dressing

4 ounces Roquefort cheese
1/4 teaspoon salt
1/4 teaspoon paprika
6 tablespoons cider vinegar or port wine
6 to 8 tablespoons olive oil

Crush the cheese in a bowl with a fork. Add the salt, paprika, vinegar or wine and oil. Beat with a wire whisk until the mixture is smooth and creamy. If you prefer, this dressing can be forced through a fine sieve. Store in a closed jar in the refrigerator. Makes about 2 cups.

Honey dressing

3 tablespoons honey
1 tablespoon lemon juice
1 cup heavy cream
Pinch of salt

Mix the honey and lemon juice together. Whip the cream and add to the mixture along with the salt, folding it in gradually. Use for fruit salads. Makes 2 cups.

Poppy-seed dressing

1/3 cup heavy or light cream
1/2 teaspoon salt
1/3 cup honey
1 1/2 teaspoons poppy seeds
1/3 cup lemon juice

Combine all the ingredients and shake hard. The lemon juice will thicken the cream. Use for fruit salads. Makes about 1 cup.

Apricot dressing

6 to 8 very ripe apricots (about 1 cup mashed)
Juice of 1 fresh lime
3 tablespoons sugar
2 tablespoons mayonnaise
1 cup heavy cream, whipped
Few drops of yellow coloring

Halve the apricots and remove the pits. Whirl in a blender for 3 seconds, or force through a sieve to make a purée. Add the lime juice and sugar; stir until well blended. (If you wish, freeze it at this point.)

Add the mayonnaise and fold mixture into the whipped cream. Color to taste. Pile on fruit salad. For a sophisticated garnish, top with a few green pistachios. Makes 2 ½ cups.

DESSERT SAUCES

Sauces are also used with desserts of all kinds. A sauce can transform something simple into a party dessert. Here are a few examples.

Custard sauce

This light but rich custard sauce can be served hot or cold with fruits, cakes, puddings, soufflés.

2 cups light cream
  or 1 cup light cream
  and 1 cup milk
¼ cup sugar
½ vanilla bean
½ cup cold milk
4 egg yolks
1 tablespoon cornstarch
¼ teaspoon salt
2 tablespoons butter

In a saucepan place the cream (or the cream and milk), the sugar and the vanilla bean. Heat slowly over low heat. Beat together the cold milk and the egg yolks. Add the cornstarch and salt. Pour milk mixture into the hot cream, beating as you pour, and continue to beat with a wire whisk until blended. Add the butter. Continue to cook over low heat, stirring all the time, until the mixture will coat a spoon.

Remove the vanilla bean. Serve the custard at once if it is to be used as a hot sauce. If the sauce is to be served cold, remove the vanilla bean only after the sauce has cooled. Makes about 3 ½ cups.

Mocha sauce

Perfect for light-colored puddings, for chocolate, coffee or vanilla soufflés, for custards or ice cream.

2 cups water
½ cup sugar
⅓ cup powdered cocoa
  (use only pure cocoa)
1 ½ tablespoons
  cornstarch
Pinch of salt
2 teaspoons instant
  coffee powder
½ teaspoon vanilla
  extract

Bring 1 ½ cups of water to a boil and add the sugar. Stir until the sugar is dissolved, then boil for 5 minutes. Remove from heat.

Blend together the cocoa, cornstarch, salt and remaining ½ cup cold water. When smooth, add to the hot syrup. Stir over medium heat until creamy, then simmer over low heat for 3 minutes. Add the instant coffee powder and the vanilla. Stir until the coffee is blended. Serve hot or cold. Makes about 2 cups.

Vanilla brandy sauce

This is an uncooked sauce.

- ⅓ cup unsalted butter
- 1¾ cups sifted confectioners' sugar
- 2 eggs, separated
- 3 tablespoons brandy
- 2 teaspoons vanilla extract
- 1 cup heavy cream

Cream the butter with the sifted sugar until fluffy and smooth. Beat the egg yolks with the brandy and vanilla. Add to the butter mixture. Beat with a rotary beater or whisk until well blended. Then fold in the egg whites beaten stiff. Refrigerate until ready to serve, then whip the cream. Stir the sauce and fold in the whipped cream. Makes about 3 cups.

Whipped cream and chocolate

It is easy to whip heavy (or whipping) cream with a rotary hand beater or with an electric beater. But if you do not have heavy cream on hand and want to make a sauce that calls for whipped cream, you can use nonfat dry milk or evaporated milk instead.

To whip nonfat dry milk
Combine ½ cup nonfat dry milk and ½ cup ice water in a bowl. Whip 3 to 4 minutes, using an electric or hand beater, until soft peaks form. Add 2 tablespoons lemon juice. Continue whipping for another 3 to 4 minutes until stiff peaks form. Gradually add ¼ cup confectioners' sugar. Makes 2½ cups.

To whip evaporated milk
Place 1 can (6 ounces) evaporated milk in the refrigerator until it is quite cold, or put it in the freezer for 1 hour. Pour the undiluted contents into a cold bowl and whip for 2 to 3 minutes. Add 2 tablespoons fresh lemon juice. Continue to whip for another 3 to 4 minutes until stiff peaks form. Gradually add confectioners' sugar to taste. Makes 2 cups.

Chocolate is another ingredient sometimes called

for in dessert sauces. If you do not have any, you can replace 1 ounce (1 square) unsweetened chocolate with 3 tablespoons powdered cocoa and 1 tablespoon butter. To replace the same amount of semisweet chocolate, use the same amount of cocoa and butter plus ½ teaspoon fine granulated sugar.

Chocolate sauce

Serve hot over cold ice cream, poached pears, meringues, pound cake.

- 4 ounces (4 squares) unsweetened chocolate
- 2 tablespoons butter
- 1 cup sifted confectioners' sugar
- 1 cup light cream
- Pinch of salt
- 3 tablespoons dark rum

Melt the chocolate (or use 4 one-ounce packages of premelted chocolate) and butter over low heat or in the top part of a double boiler. Add sugar, cream and salt. Cook over low heat, stirring constantly, until the sauce reaches the boiling point. Cook for a few minutes longer over very low heat, then stir in the rum. Leave over heat for 1 minute longer. Serve this sauce hot. If you need to wait, keep it over hot water. Makes about 3 cups.

Fruit sauce

To make and freeze fruit sauces, see Chapter 15. These are delicious when defrosted and served hot or cold. For even more flavor, add 2 to 4 tablespoons brandy, rum or an appropriate liqueur to each cup of defrosted sauce.

Whipped-cream apricot sauce

Defrost a pint container of frozen sweetened apricot purée (see Chapter 15); or cook and purée fresh or dried apricots to make 2 cups purée. If the purée is thin, cook it over *very low heat* until reduced. Stir constantly because this burns easily. When the purée is thick, stir in 3 tablespoons lemon juice and 2 drops of almond extract. Cool the purée, then fold in ¾ cup heavy cream, whipped until stiff. (Or use whipped nonfat dry milk or evaporated milk.)

This same recipe can be used for any fruit purée. It is particularly delicious with strawberry or raspberry purée. When the fresh fruits are not in season, frozen fruits can be used.

Orange and green sauce

Serve over vanilla ice cream, plain steamed or baked puddings, meringues, plain cake, spice cake.

3 large oranges
Salt
1 cup sugar
3 egg yolks, beaten
2 tablespoons orange-flavored liqueur or brandy
2 tablespoons sweet butter
3 tablespoons shelled green pistachios

Peel the oranges with a swivel peeler or very sharp knife, removing only the outer orange part of the skin (called the zest). Cut the zest into slivers and blanch in 3 cups of water with a pinch of salt for about 5 minutes. Drain and spread out on paper towels to dry.

Remove all the white part of the orange rind. Cut the fruit into chunks over a plate to catch the juices. Whirl the fruit and juice in a blender for a few seconds until chopped into bits. (You can squeeze the oranges, but the sauce texture will be different.) Strain through a coarse sieve to remove the seeds and any thick pieces of membrane. Put juice and pulp into a large saucepan and add the sugar and a pinch of salt. Cook until the mixture is thick and syrupy, about 200° F. on a candy thermometer. Stir occasionally, making sure it does not burn.

Pour a little of the hot syrup into the beaten yolks, then turn the yolks into the rest of the syrup and cook until thickened (it will not be smooth). Add the liqueur, butter and blanched orange zest. Stir in the pistachios. (If you cannot get pistachios, use chopped angelica or 2 or 3 cooked greengage plums cut into tiny pieces. Or just serve orange sauce without the green ingredients.) Serve at room temperature or warm. Makes about 2 cups.

Caramel sauce

For steamed pudding, ice cream, plain baked apples.

1 ¼ cups brown sugar
⅔ cup corn syrup or maple syrup
¼ cup boiling water
¾ cup light cream
Grated nutmeg or vanilla extract (optional)

Put brown sugar, corn or maple syrup and boiling water in a saucepan. Stir over low heat until the sugar is dissolved. Add the light cream and cook until smooth. Stir frequently. 🗝 Long cooking over low heat makes this sauce smooth and velvety. It is good just as it is, but it can be flavored with a dash of grated nutmeg or a teaspoon of vanilla extract. Makes about 3 cups.

Molasses and lemon sauce

For pudding or plain cake, and especially good with pancakes.

1 ½ tablespoons cornstarch
½ cup sugar
Pinch of salt
¾ cup water
½ cup molasses
Grated rind of 2 lemons
2 tablespoons butter

In a saucepan mix together the cornstarch, sugar and salt. Add water and molasses. Cook over low heat until clear and thickened, stirring constantly. Stir in the lemon rind and butter. Serve hot. This can be made a day ahead. Makes about 1 ½ cups.

Honey butter

For vanilla ice cream, French toast, waffles, pancakes, toasted homemade English muffins.

½ cup unsalted butter
¼ cup cream honey
½ cup heavy cream

With an electric mixer, cream the butter until soft, then add honey. Beat until the honey is well blended into the butter. Add the cream, beating until smooth and fluffy. Refrigerate covered until ready to use. Makes about 1 ½ cups.

Maple pecan sauce

For ice cream, plain custard, pumpkin pudding.

2 tablespoons butter
¼ cup water
3 tablespoons maple syrup
¾ cup brown sugar
¼ cup light cream
½ cup pecans, chopped or whole

Melt the butter. Add water, maple syrup and brown sugar. Boil until the mixture forms a soft ball when a small amount is dropped into cold water, about 235° F. on a candy thermometer. Remove from heat. Slowly beat in the light cream and pecans. Beat for a few seconds. Serve the sauce hot or cold. Makes about 2 cups.

«8»

Eggs and Egg Dishes

Grades of eggs • How to store eggs • Basic methods of cooking eggs • What kind of omelet pan to use • How to make the classic omelet and its variations, dessert omelets and soufflés • How to make the base for the soufflé • The best soufflé dish to use • How to bake the soufflé • How to serve the soufflé • Common errors in making soufflés • How to make meringues, eggnogs and custards

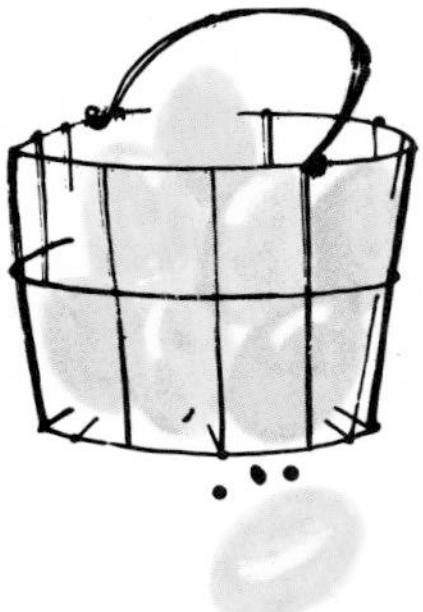

There is no doubt that the egg is one of the most useful and most used foods. It can be served around the clock, as a nutritious and basic part of a healthy breakfast or as a decorative flourish to a midnight snack; it has no special season or time of day. One of the advantages of an egg is that it can be prepared quickly in a variety of ways. For this reason it can be classified as one of the most ancient of instant foods, used from soup to dessert in one form or another, and eaten by infants as well as the aged.

Eggs are handsome to look at too, and they can make a most attractive centerpiece. Let them suggest a true country atmosphere when their whiteness gleams in a nest of real straw placed in a wicker basket on the breakfast or luncheon table; or enhance a dinner table in a more sophisticated manner with eggs arranged on a pewter dish with avocados and large lemon leaves.

If you are a typical busy woman with many duties, learn to cook a variety of egg dishes. Their speed and ease of preparation will prove a definite advantage, and you can be sure of providing nutritionally sound meals as well.

In the first part of this chapter you will find information about dishes in which eggs are served as eggs, but of course this remarkable package of food is used in many other preparations in which it is no longer identifiable, but has been beaten or cooked or mixed with additional ingredients to form some other kind of dish. In some of these the egg is the significant part—for instance, hollandaise sauces and mayonnaise, or desserts such as custards and soufflés. For the use of the egg in emulsified sauces and in egg-thickened dessert sauces, see Chapter 7.

Soufflé recipes begin on page 237; meringue recipes on page 246. Information on storage of fresh eggs is on the next page. To store cooked or uncooked eggs by freezing, see p. 605.

Grading

Eggs in the shell are sold by grade throughout the United States. The grade and size are marked on egg cartons on a shield of the United States Department of Agriculture. The grade is an indication of freshness and quality and has nothing to do with size. Within any one grade there can be several sizes.

Grade AA (Fresh Fancy) and Grade A eggs are good for all uses where appearance and flavor are important. Grade B eggs are good for general cooking and baking. Grade C and cracked eggs are generally available only for the wholesale market. Within the same grade, the price will vary according to size.

How to store eggs

Eggs are perishable and quickly lose their prime quality unless kept in a cool place, preferably the refrigerator. Never place them uncovered in the refrigerator as they absorb surrounding odors very easily and lose moisture. Keep them in their container, which is designed for their best storage. Store them with the narrow end down to keep the egg yolk centered.

Leftover egg yolks should be stored in a clean glass jar. Pour a thin layer of cold water over the eggs in the jar and cover. Leftover egg whites should also be covered and stored in a clean glass jar. Do not keep separated unshelled parts for more than 2 or 3 days.

BASIC METHODS OF COOKING EGGS

There are hundreds of ways of serving eggs, but all are derived from a few basic methods. Learn each method so that you can do it perfectly. Then apply the classic variations, or create your own. No other food offers more scope for the creative ability of a good cook.

Eggs in the shell, soft-cooked

Cold-water methods

Place the eggs in cold water and *slowly* bring the water to a boil, uncovered.

For coddled eggs, with creamy whites, remove the

eggs from the water as soon as it comes to a full rolling boil.

For 3- to 5-minute eggs, remove the pan from the heat as soon as the water comes to a boil. Cover it and let the eggs stand for 3 to 5 minutes.

Hot-water methods

Put enough water in a saucepan to cover the eggs completely. 🗝 To prevent cracking, put the eggs in warm water first, or let them come to room temperature before cooking. Bring the water to a full rolling boil. Then place the egg on a spoon and gently slip it into the water. Lower the heat and cook for 3 to 4 minutes, according to taste. In 3½ minutes the white will be almost set, the yolk still runny. From this you can calculate the time needed to cook to your taste.

Another method is to remove the pan of boiling water from the heat, cover, and let the eggs stand for 6 to 8 minutes.

As soon as cooking time has elapsed, remove the eggs from the water. 🗝 To make the eggs easier to handle and also to stop the cooking, run cold water over them for several seconds.

If cooked eggs in the shell must be kept for a few minutes before serving, place them in a bowl of tepid water.

French method
In classic French cuisine, *oeufs mollets* are soft-cooked eggs that are shelled, left whole and used in the same manner as poached eggs, although the final taste and appearance is totally different from poached eggs.

Follow the hot-water method above. Cook the egg for *exactly* 6 minutes. Remove the egg and place it in a bowl of ice-cold water. Gently crack the shell with the back of a spoon, then put the egg back in the hot water for a few seconds. Remove from the water. Start peeling by holding the egg in the middle of your hand and gently pulling away the shell.

A perfect *oeuf mollet* consists of a cooked wall of egg white with a semirunny yolk inside. Keep the shelled egg in tepid water until ready to use.

Oeufs mollets pour déjeuner

- 6 *oeufs mollets*
- 3 leeks
- 4 carrots
- ½ cup chicken stock
- ½ teaspoon salt
- 1¼ cups mustard sauce (p. 188)
- ¾ cup fine fresh bread crumbs
- 3 tablespoons butter

Cook the *oeufs mollets,* peel and put in a bowl of tepid water. Wash the leeks very carefully, then slice. Scrape and grate the carrots. Put the leeks, carrots, stock and salt in a covered pan and cook over low heat until the vegetables are tender and the stock almost absorbed. Divide the vegetables among 6 individual baking dishes (miniature soufflé dishes). Place an egg in each and spoon about 3 tablespoons mustard sauce over each one. Sprinkle each with 2 tablespoons bread crumbs and dot with ½ tablespoon butter. Bake the eggs in a 400° F. oven for about 6 minutes, or until the crumbs are browned.

This makes a perfect main dish for a small luncheon, or a good first course for a more elaborate meal. You can make this with other kinds of vegetables and sauces.

Eggs in the shell, hard-cooked

An egg is hard-cooked when the temperature in the center of the yolk is the same as that of the surrounding water. If it is overcooked, a dark green line will form between the white and yolk; this is caused by a combination of the sulphide from the white with iron from the yolk. Although harmless, this is not very attractive.

O‑‑ If the eggs are taken cold from the refrigerator, prick a small hole in the blunt end of each shell with a pin to minimize the risk of the shells cracking. Should an egg crack, immediately add a pinch of salt or a few drops of vinegar to the boiling water, and this will prevent the escape of the white from the crack in the shell.

To hard-cook more than four eggs, follow the cold-water method (p. 219). When the water boils, cover the saucepan, lower the heat and cook for 20 minutes; the heat should be low enough so that the water barely moves.

For one to four eggs, remove the saucepan from the heat when the water boils and let the egg or eggs stand in it for 20 minutes.

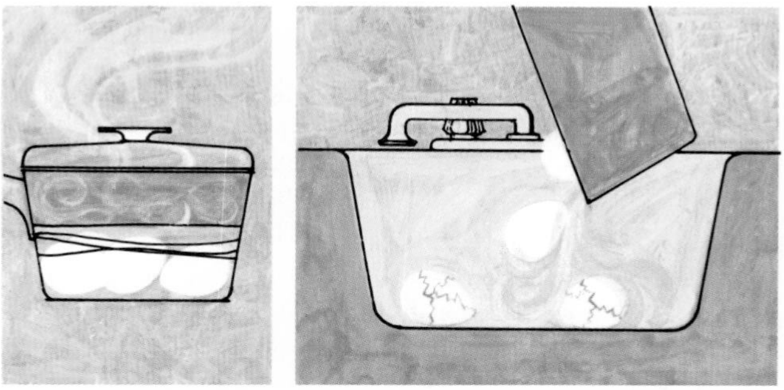

When the eggs are ready, pour both the eggs and water into the sink. This will crack the shells. O‑‑ Then place the eggs in a bowl of cold water and let them stand for 5 to 6 minutes. The water will seep through the cracked shells and make them easy to peel.

When peeled, hard-cooked eggs are best kept refrigerated. It is important to cover the eggs to prevent them from drying out.

🗝 To store unshelled hard-cooked eggs that will be easy to peel, crack the cooked shell all over by tapping the egg gently on the kitchen counter; then place, unpeeled, in a bowl and cover completely with water. They are easy to peel even after three or four days when stored in this manner.

Stuffed eggs

A favorite party and picnic dish is stuffed eggs. To make these, halve hard-cooked eggs lengthwise and lift out the yolks. Mash the yolks and mix with mustard, mayonnaise and seasoning. Be creative. Mix the yolks with minced anchovies, fish roe, chopped shrimps or crab meat, mushrooms, herbs and other seasonings.

Other ways to cut the eggs are into halves crosswise, at angles or with zigzags.

Stuffed eggs are great for picnics, buffet suppers and lunches, and they can be fine hors d'oeuvres for informal dinners or small cocktail parties.

Poached eggs

A poached egg is an egg cooked without its shell. Eggs must be absolutely fresh to ensure success.

Use a pan at least 2 inches deep. Fill it with salted water, add ½ teaspoon vinegar, and bring to a simmer. Break the egg into a *cup*. Then, placing the cup at the edge of the saucepan, slip the egg gently into the *simmering* water. Cover the saucepan and cook the egg over very low heat for 3 to 5 minutes. Lift it out of the water with a slotted spoon.

For softer poached eggs, grease the frying pan with butter or margarine. Bring the water to the simmering point, as above, but do not boil. Break egg into a *saucer* and lower the saucer almost into the water in the frying pan, then quickly slip the egg into the simmering water. *Cover* the frying pan and turn off the heat but do not remove the pan from the source of heat. Let the pan stand for 3 to 7 minutes, depending on how well cooked you desire the egg. Lift the egg from the water with a slotted spoon. Drain well, then serve.

Any number of eggs can be cooked in this manner, but when learning, it is better to cook only one egg at a time.

If you care about the appearance of your egg, you can swirl the water with a wooden spoon, place the egg in the center of the pan and keep the water moving in a circle around the egg. This will keep the white in a compact circle and help to center the yolk. Or you can trim the cooked egg if appearance is crucial.

There are special pans for poaching eggs, but the egg looks stiff and is often leathery at the bottom. Also, the individual depression or mold is often hard to clean. The old-fashioned method is really the best.

Eggs Benedict

This classic dish using poached eggs is an excellent choice for a luncheon, brunch or supper. It is prepared by putting a slice of ham on an English muffin half, covering the ham with a poached egg, then spooning hollandaise sauce over all. You can do exactly this if you choose, but why not vary it? Invent a name of your own, and use sautéed slices of Polish sausage under the egg and mustard sauce on top; or crisp bacon underneath and tomato sauce on top; or sautéed mushroom slices underneath and cheese sauce on top. Even if you prefer the ham, the sauce can be different, and a beautiful garnish of a sautéed vegetable gives the dish elegance.

Eggs en cocottes

An egg *en cocotte,* or a molded egg, is also called a poached egg *à la française.* Cocottes are small individual dishes of earthenware, glass or china, with or without covers. They must be deep enough to take at least one egg; some English china egg cups with silver covers can hold two eggs.

There are many variations of this recipe which can be served for breakfast or as an entrée. Basically, a piece of butter or a small amount of cream is placed in the bottom of the cocotte, then one raw egg is broken on top. Salt and pepper to taste is sprinkled on the egg. It is then cooked in the dish. The cocotte can be covered or left uncovered. The advantage of the cover is that it keeps the egg hot longer once it is cooked.

To cook, place the cocotte in a saucepan with enough hot, not boiling, water to reach within ½ inch of the brim. Cover the saucepan and simmer over low heat until the white is set and the yolk is to your taste. This will take 6 to 9 minutes.

The cocotte can also be baked in a preheated 400° F. oven. Place it in an oven pan with hot water, as for top-of-the-stove cooking. This is a more practical method when six or more eggs are being cooked.

Shirred eggs

These eggs are cooked in flameproof dishes, usually of pottery, especially designed for *oeufs sur le plat,* as the French call them. In fact, we call these shirred-egg dishes even when cooking something else in them. They are different from cocottes, for they are flat and shallow. The finished egg is always served in the dish it was cooked in, while the molded egg is often turned out of the cocotte for serving.

Put 1 teaspoon melted butter in the dish and tip it back and forth to distribute the butter over the bottom. Sprinkle salt and pepper on the butter and break an egg into the dish. Bake in a preheated 350° F. oven for 1 minute, until the white begins to solidify. Then spoon another teaspoon of butter over the top and finish cooking for 3 minutes, or until the whites are milky and the yolks shiny and glazed. Be careful not to overcook, for they can become hard and tough. Remember the dish itself is hot, retains heat and continues to cook the egg even when removed from the source of heat. These eggs are never covered during cooking.

Shirred-egg dishes come in more than one size. A fine luncheon dish can be made in one large enough to hold two eggs and a garnish of tomatoes, ham, cheese or any other flavorful ingredient. Put part of the garnish in the bottom of the dish before breaking the egg on top; then arrange the remaining garnish around the edge of the dish when the egg has been cooked and is ready to serve.

Scrambled eggs

Lots of practice is required to learn how to make perfect scrambled eggs that are both soft and creamy.

Break the eggs, usually two per person, into a bowl. 🗝 Season to taste and then beat with a fork or wire whisk until the white and yolk are well mixed. Do not use a rotary beater or you will overbeat the eggs and affect the creaminess of the finished product.

Cook with 1 tablespoon butter for each two or three

eggs. This is twice as much butter as the amount used for an omelet. Why so much butter? Because here the butter is not used to prevent the eggs from sticking to the pan, but as the necessary liquid which must be incorporated into the eggs to give them a rich texture and flavor.

Always cook over gentle heat. If the heat is too high, a wheylike liquid is released from the eggs. The heat has forced the coagulated mass to yield up a liquor it should naturally have retained.

Place the frying pan over medium heat, melt the butter, then pour in the whisked eggs. Let them sit for a few seconds, then stir *with a fork,* without stopping, making no attempt to retain any kind of shape. 🗝 The constant moving of the eggs is the secret in making creamy scrambled eggs. The easiest way is to stir them by lifting the cooked eggs underneath so that uncooked eggs on top can flow to the bottom of the frying pan. Give one stir all around, then repeat the first operation, and keep repeating these two operations until the eggs are *almost set* but still appear shiny and a bit underdone. At this point, remove immediately from the heat.

🗝 Add one teaspoon cold light cream or milk for each four eggs, and stir fast for a second. This is to stop the cooking, which would otherwise continue for a few minutes because of the internal heat retained by the eggs. Without this last step, the eggs would be overcooked and dry. Turn out on a warm plate and serve. The whole operation should take only a few minutes.

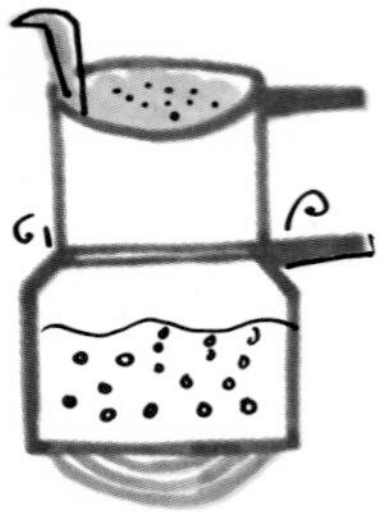

Double-boiler method to scramble eggs

Advantages of this method over the frying-pan procedure are that the eggs require less care, for they can be cooked practically unattended, and they can be kept waiting for a few minutes before being served.

To succeed, however, you must observe one important precaution: *at no point should the water boil in the bottom of the double boiler.* Start the cooking over hot water and finish over simmering water. This is easily controlled if the water is checked three or four times during the cooking period by lifting the top part of the double boiler. Or use a heatproof glass double boiler so you can see what is happening in the bottom.

Melt the required amount of butter in the top part of the double boiler over *hot water*. Tilt the top part until the butter coats the sides and bottom. Pour in the eggs and let them set for a few seconds, then stir in the same way as in the frying pan.

Serve the eggs as soon as they are ready, if possible. If you have to keep the eggs waiting for a few minutes, it is best to remove the double boiler from the heat while the eggs are still slightly uncooked, keeping them over the hot water. Stir once when they are ready to serve.

Fried eggs

To obtain the best results in frying eggs, use a heavy metal 8-inch frying pan; the best is the enameled cast-iron type.

Over high heat, melt the fat you prefer: butter, bacon fat, olive or salad oil. Use about 1 tablespoon for every two eggs. When the fat has reached the smoking point but is not too brown, add the eggs and reduce the heat to low.

The easiest way to add the eggs is to break them, one at a time, into a saucer and lower the saucer almost onto the hot fat. Tip the saucer sideways with the edge touching the bottom of the pan, allowing the uncooked egg to slip in slowly. When all the eggs are added, cook gently over low heat, basting the eggs with some of the hot fat.

For a leaner egg, cover the frying pan for 2 to 4 minutes after the heat has been lowered, and do not baste with the fat.

For a completely fat-free fried egg, break the eggs into a cold frying pan lined with nonstick coating. Cover and cook over low heat for 3 to 5 minutes.

For crisp lacy edges on the white, pour each egg from a saucer into very hot oil or butter, then quickly tip the frying pan, which will cause the egg to slide where the oil is the deepest. Quickly spoon the white over and on top of the yolk with a wooden paddle or a silver knife. Fry only one egg at a time to get these results.

If you like "eggs over easy," proceed the same as for plain fried eggs, but just before they are done to your taste, turn each egg over swiftly with a well-oiled wide spatula; then cook the egg for half a minute or so, to your taste.

OMELETS

Omelets are made of lightly beaten eggs that become a soft blanket of coagulated eggs as they are cooked. A perfect omelet should be plump, fluffy and light, with a glossy top. Overcooking will make it flat, leathery and dull-looking. There are three fundamental points to master in making omelets. Only practice, while applying these points, will teach you how to make a perfect one.

1. Although low-heat cooking is usually best for eggs, most omelets should be cooked over brisk heat. If the omelet seems to cook too fast, simply lift the pan off the heat for a few seconds.

2. Use the proper amount of butter or other fat.

3. Beat the eggs briskly, for 30 to 40 seconds. This is all the omelet needs in the way of beating. If eggs are beaten with a wire whisk or a fork, count 30 to 40 beatings. Eggs that are not sufficiently beaten will not mix properly. When beaten too much, the eggs get thin and watery, and this changes the texture of the omelet. ○━ Beat the eggs just before you pour them into the hot butter in the pan; otherwise they lose their liveliness.

Omelet pan

No egg cookery is easy; you must practice to reach perfection. Eggs can be cooked in all types of frying pans. It is a fallacy to believe that an unwashed pan or a special omelet pan is an absolute necessity for making the perfect omelet. ○━ What is important is that the pan be of thick cast aluminum or iron, but not too heavy for you to handle easily with either hand. A good omelet pan should have a perfectly flat bottom and curving sides, which help in sliding the omelet onto a platter.

For low-fat or fat-free diets, a pan with nonstick coating can be used, but the heat must be lowered.

No matter what metal an omelet pan is made of, a new pan must be seasoned, unless it is already a nonstick pan. Wash and dry the pan, then fill it with vegetable oil and heat very slowly until the oil seems to move at the bottom; this may take from 20 to 30 minutes, as the heat must be kept very low. Turn off the heat and let the oil cool in the pan. Drain from the pan when cool. (Do not throw the oil away; use it for cooking.) Wipe the pan thoroughly with absorbent paper. The inside of the pan should be perfectly smooth, with a slightly greasy feeling. Never use scouring powder on an omelet pan. After you have made an omelet, simply wipe the pan with a paper towel. If anything sticks, throw in a spoonful of coarse salt and rub with a paper towel. Or, if you prefer, rinse it under running hot water and wipe dry.

The size of an omelet pan is important. An omelet made with two or three eggs requires a pan 7 to 8 inches in diameter. A six-egg omelet takes a 10-inch pan. Any omelet made with more than six eggs is rarely perfect; it is better to make two omelets in that case. In fact, even a six-egg omelet will be less than ideal, for the pan will be heavy to handle.

A two-egg omelet will yield one or two portions, depending on appetites. A single egg yolk added to two whole eggs will make a bit more.

Another piece of equipment needed for omelets is either a wire whisk, the very best, or a plain table fork. For some types of omelets a rotary beater may be used.

Classic or French omelet

Practice the following steps one by one.

1. Warm the prepared frying pan over low heat just until you can touch the bottom of the pan quickly with the tips of your fingers without getting burned.

2. Place a well-rounded tablespoon of butter in the hot pan. (Unsalted butter gives a perfect creamy flavor, but salted butter can be used.) Let the butter melt.

3. While the butter is melting over low heat, break three eggs into a bowl; add salt and pepper to taste and 1 tablespoon cold water. Beat the eggs briskly, as previously explained, for no more than 40 seconds. For six eggs, add 2 tablespoons water.

4. Turn the heat high under the frying pan. When

the butter has a deep golden color (after a few seconds), pour the eggs into it. Wait 10 seconds.

5. Take the handle of the pan in your left hand and a fork in your right hand. With the fork, gently push the eggs from the side to the middle, going around and around the pan. Do this as quickly as possible, shaking the pan gently to keep the eggs from sticking to the bottom of the pan. Continue to push the eggs from the outside edge to the middle, using the fork to lift the part that has set and allowing the liquid to run under it. This operation should not take more than 1 to 1½ minutes.

6. Now quickly transfer the omelet to a warm plate or dish. (Never allow an omelet to wait in the pan after being cooked.) Transfer the omelet by lifting the edge of the omelet that is nearer to you and folding the omelet in half, tilting the pan as the folding proceeds. Tilt the pan still further and let the omelet slide onto the plate. Use a large spatula at the beginning. With experience, this folding and slipping will take only 10 seconds to accomplish. If the omelet does not slide freely onto the plate, you can free it with the spatula and also slip a little piece of butter underneath to act as lubrication.

If you prefer an omelet folded in three, fold over the edge that is nearer to you and let the top third flip over as you tip the pan. The folded side should be underneath as the omelet tilts onto the plate.

Variations

The following variations are based on a three-egg omelet, made according to the steps for Classic or French omelet.

Tomato omelet

Dice an unpeeled tomato. 0┳ Remove the seeds as you cut, for they have a tendency to give an acid taste to the omelet. Add salt and pepper to taste, sprinkle with ¼ teaspoon sugar, and add a pinch of dried basil or curry powder, or 1 tablespoon chopped fresh parsley.

Melt the butter. Add the tomato to the melted butter. Cook over brisk heat for 1 minute. Add the three-egg mixture, cook and serve. This will make a moist omelet.

Chives omelet

Add 1 tablespoon fine-cut chives, cut with kitchen shears, to the beaten three-egg omelet mixture. Cook and serve.

Fines-herbes omelet

Dried herbs can be used, but always try to use fresh parsley, chives or dill with the dried herbs.

Use 2 tablespoons minced parsley, 1 teaspoon minced chives, and a pinch of basil or 1 teaspoon minced fresh chervil. Or if you have leeks, mince about ½ inch of the white and add to the herbs; in this case chives can be omitted.

Melt the butter, remove the pan from the heat, add the herbs, and stir once. (Herbs are added to the butter first to bring out their full flavor.) Add the three-egg omelet mixture. Put the pan containing the mixture back on the heat. Cook and serve.

For a nice addition, sprinkle 2 to 3 tablespoons of grated Swiss cheese over the finished omelet.

Bercy omelet

Cut a sausage into five or six pieces. Brown over low heat in the omelet pan. Pour off the fat. Add butter and 1 tablespoon minced parsley or ¼ teaspoon minced marjoram. Pour in the three-egg omelet mixture. Cook. Top with 2 tablespoons tomato sauce.

Raw-potato omelet

Peel a raw potato and slice as thin as possible. Melt 2 tablespoons butter and add 1 teaspoon salad oil. Add the potato. Cook over medium heat, turning a few times, until the potato slices are cooked and slightly browned, about 10 to 15 minutes. Add a thick slice of onion broken into rings. Cook for a few minutes with the potato. Beat the three eggs with 1 tablespoon grated cheese. Pour over the potato, cook and serve.

Mushroom omelet

Thinly slice two or three medium-size fresh mushrooms. Add a green onion or one inch of white leek, minced. Pepper generously. Melt 1 tablespoon butter until light brown. Add the mushroom mixture. Stir constantly over high heat for 30 seconds. Pour the three-egg omelet mixture on top. Cook and serve.

German omelet

This type of omelet is a cross between a very light pancake and a French omelet. It can be used as a dessert omelet as well as a main-course dish.

1. Measure 2 tablespoons all-purpose flour into a bowl.

2. Add three eggs, one at a time, beating well at each addition, preferably with a wire whisk.

3. Add ½ cup light cream or milk, a few pinches of salt, a dash of pepper and a pinch of grated nutmeg. Mix thoroughly.

4. Refrigerate the mixture for about 30 minutes.

5. Cook as two thin omelets, which would be the classic way, or as one thicker omelet.

To cook two omelets, heat the omelet pan and add 1 teaspoon butter. When the butter is hot, pour in half of the egg mixture and quickly spread it out by moving the pan back and forth to make a very thin omelet. Cook over medium-low heat. When the omelet is brown on one side, turn and brown the other side. This should only take about a minute.

For a single thick omelet, cook all the mixture at once, but allow a longer time for it to cook.

6. When the omelet is cooked, turn it onto a hot plate and roll up tightly in the shape of a cigar.

To stuff a German omelet, simply spread with hot ingredients before rolling. This type of omelet is sometimes cut into strips after being rolled, whether it is stuffed or plain.

Variations

Any of the omelet variations can be used, but everything must be chopped fine and warmed before being rolled into the omelet just after it is cooked.

Italian omelet (frittata)

The difference between a *frittata* and a basic omelet is that the filling is mixed with the eggs before they are poured into the pan. A *frittata* is always served flat, not rolled. Often it is broiled under direct heat for 1 or 2 seconds, especially when the top has been sprinkled with grated cheese.

This is the perfect omelet to make with leftovers, whether they are fish or meat, vegetables or fruits.

Follow the steps for making a plain or French omelet. However, when the eggs are beaten, add ½ to 1 cup of whatever filling ingredients you choose. Then proceed to cook, but do not fold; simply slip onto the plate flat.

Variations

Use any of the combinations for the basic omelet. Cook the fillings if necessary, or heat them, then add them to the beaten eggs. Cook according to the rule for *frittata.*

Spanish omelet (tortilla)

The true Spanish omelets are the *tortillas redondas,* or flat omelets. They are made with one to six eggs and are always cooked very quickly in olive oil or lard, the way that most omelets are cooked in Spain.

They are nice for a party, as each can be cooked into a little omelet in 40 to 60 seconds and can be served piping hot with different garnishes. No liquid is added to a *tortilla.* A one-egg omelet must be cooked in a 4- or 5-inch frying pan.

1. Beat three whole eggs with a pinch of salt, just long enough to mix the yolks and whites of the eggs.

2. Heat 1 teaspoon olive oil or lard in a frying pan. When it is very hot, lower the heat and pour in the eggs.

3. Let the bottom set for 1 second, then lift the pan from the heat for 1 second. Then, with the flat side of a fork, start spreading the eggs over the bottom and slightly up the sides of the pan for another second, keeping the pan on low heat. Turn the omelet in a flip movement, or turn it onto a plate and slip the uncooked side back into the pan by touching the bottom of the pan with the edge of the plate and turning the plate upside down with one quick movement. Cook for 1 second and serve.

Pipérade Basque

This omelet might appear to be similar to a Spanish omelet, but it has little relation to Spain's *tortilla.* A *pipérade* is still a center of heated discussion; there are some who say it is an omelet and others who insist that it is scrambled eggs. Call it whatever you like, but do try it.

1 small green pepper
1 small onion
1 small garlic clove
2 tomatoes
1 tablespoon salad oil
1 tablespoon butter
½ teaspoon sugar

Few drops of hot-pepper sauce
or pinch of cayenne
Salt
4 to 6 eggs
Pepper

Cut green pepper into long thin shreds. Finely chop onion and garlic clove. Peel, seed and chop tomatoes. Set all these aside.

Heat salad oil and butter. When hot, add the green pepper, onion and garlic. Stir over high heat for 30 to 40 seconds. Add the tomatoes and stir. Remove the pan and mixture from the heat. Sprinkle with sugar, hot-pepper sauce or cayenne, and salt to taste. Stir and put back over low heat.

Beat four to six eggs with salt and pepper to taste, just as you beat eggs for an omelet. No water is added to the eggs, as the cooked tomato replaces it in this instance. Pour the eggs over the simmering vegetables. Over high heat, stir the eggs vigorously into the vegetables, cooking them as quickly as possible. O━ The secret of a perfect *pipérade* is speed, which is easily achieved if everything is ready when the omelet starts to cook. When possible, serve directly from the pan.

DESSERT OMELETS

These great continental favorites are spectacular yet easy to make. They can be cooked in the kitchen or at the table. Guests enjoy watching them in preparation and the hostess has the pleasure of joining the party while cooking.

The dessert omelet is always fluffier than the basic omelet. It can be served plain or filled. Either way, it is always sprinkled with sugar just before serving.

The French chef usually marks or glazes the sugar with a red-hot poker, which gives the omelet a professional finish with little effort. However, that step can only be performed in the kitchen.

Basic dessert omelet

Allow one egg per person. Follow these steps:

1. Separate two eggs and keep the separated parts at room temperature for 1 hour.

2. To the yolks, add 2 teaspoons sugar and ½ teaspoon vanilla extract, or use 2 teaspoons vanilla sugar and omit the extract. Beat with a wire whisk or rotary beater until very light and fluffy. O━ This beating is very important as it dissolves the sugar, which then will be less apt to burn; in addition, it introduces air into the eggs, which will give lightness to the cooked omelet.

3. To the egg whites, add a pinch of salt and 1 teaspoon water. Beat until stiff.

4. Carefully fold the whites into the yolks. Up to this point the work can be done in the kitchen; the bowl of egg mixture can be brought to the table when you are ready to cook.

5. Heat the frying pan hotter than for an entrée omelet and add 1 teaspoon butter. Make sure it is spread all over the pan and becomes light brown. Then carefully add the egg mixture. Tilt the pan back and forth so the eggs will be evenly distributed. Smooth the top with a spatula if necessary.

6. A sweet omelet is never stirred during the cooking period, so that the lightness may be preserved. Because of this, the cooking is done over low heat from beginning to end. If you are using an electric stove, move the pan from the unit on which you heated the butter to another unit set at low heat the instant you are ready to pour in the egg mixture. It takes too long for the hotter electric unit to reach the lower temperature, and the eggs would be overcooked on the bottom. The omelet is cooked when the eggs are lightly brown and the top, in the middle, still a bit uncooked. The inner heat of the omelet will finish cooking the middle while it is being folded.

7. Run a spatula all around the edges to loosen the omelet. Tilt the pan, holding it with your left hand. With the help of the spatula, fold the omelet in half. Tilt the pan further over a warm plate or platter, and turn the omelet onto it.

8. Sprinkle the top with 3 tablespoons confectioners' sugar. Serve plain, or glaze the top. If you add filling, do so just before folding the omelet.

Sour-cream omelet

This type of sweet omelet is completely different from the preceding one. Cook it first over direct heat, then finish in the oven. This omelet is never folded; it is cut into wedges like a pie and served with fruits and sour cream.

1. Beat five egg yolks until thick and lemon-colored. This will take about 5 minutes with a hand beater, or 3 minutes with an electric beater.

2. Add ½ cup commercial sour cream and ½ teaspoon salt. Beat until well mixed.

3. Beat five egg whites until stiff. Fold into yolks.

4. Melt 2 tablespoons butter in a 10-inch frying pan; use one with a heatproof handle that can go into the oven. Pour in the omelet mixture, leveling it gently with a spatula.

5. Cook the omelet over very low heat until the bottom is lightly browned. Lift here and there to check. It usually takes 8 to 10 minutes.

6. Set the omelet in a preheated 325° F. oven. Bake until it is puffed and dry on the top, 15 to 20 minutes. After you have made this omelet once, you can adjust the baking time to suit your taste: if baked longer it will be drier; if baked for a shorter time it will still be a little moist in the middle.

Serve the omelet as soon as it is baked, for like a soufflé it will not stay puffed up if it has to wait. Pull it into wedges with two forks; a knife would mash it down. Garnish each wedge to taste with sliced or whole sugared fresh fruits, whipped cream or sour cream.

Variations

Berry omelet

Slice 1 cup fresh strawberries, or use fresh, whole raspberries. Mix with 3 tablespoons superfine sugar and the juice of ½ lemon *or* 1 teaspoon vanilla extract *or* 1 tablespoon orange liqueur. Let stand for 30 to 40 minutes.

Make a three-egg sweet omelet. Surround with the berries, or place them in the middle before folding. Glaze or flame, or serve with whipped cream.

Marmalade omelet

Make a three-egg sweet omelet. Warm ¼ cup marmalade over low heat before cooking the omelet. Fill the omelet with the hot marmalade and fold. Serve with the hot juice of 1 orange mixed with 2 tablespoons confectioners' sugar, or sprinkle the omelet with sugar and flame with rum.

Macaroon omelet

Crush 2 large dry almond macaroons. Melt the butter for the eggs and add the macaroons. Stir with a fork over medium heat for 2 or 3 seconds. Pour a three-egg sweet omelet on top. Cook. Fill with 2 tablespoons currant or apricot jam before folding. Sprinkle with confectioners' sugar. Glaze and serve.

SOUFFLÉS

No dessert is more spectacular than a perfect soufflé. And soufflés can be prepared for hors d'oeuvres or entrées as well. They would be served more often if they did not have the reputation of being so difficult to make. Actually, a soufflé is as simple to make as cream sauce plus eggs.

A soufflé is composed of three parts: The first part is the thick sauce, the base; the second part, the egg yolks and added ingredients; the third part, the beaten egg whites. The first and second parts can be prepared ahead of time, carefully covered and kept on the kitchen counter. The third part, the beaten egg whites, is added when you are ready to bake the soufflé. Keep the egg whites in a bowl next to the sauce, with the wire whisk or hand beater nearby, ready to beat them and fold them in. It is only a 3- to 4-minute operation when the time comes to add the egg whites.

Soufflé base

The base of a soufflé is a sauce composed of butter, flour and liquid. Unsalted butter is used for sweet soufflés, salted butter for the others. The sauce must be perfectly smooth, as lumps will affect the texture and interfere with the uniform rising of the soufflé during the baking. Constant stirring of the sauce while it cooks prevents the formation of lumps. 🗝 If you beat the sauce with a wire whisk rather than with a spoon, it will never lump.

The various ingredients added to a soufflé sauce, such as onions, chicken, cheese or fish, should be grated or chopped very fine, then incorporated into the sauce.

🗝 While the cooked sauce base is cooling for 10 minutes before the egg yolks are added, cover it with wax paper or plastic film, pushing the paper onto the sauce. This will prevent formation of a skin on top, which can cause unpleasant lumps when the sauce is stirred.

The egg

The main ingredient—and the most important to understand in a soufflé—is the egg, which rules the play and makes or breaks the rising of the soufflé.

The eggs should be fresh, of good quality and

Grade A or Grade AA large. They should be at room temperature when you are ready to start the soufflé. 0━ Eggs can be more easily separated when cold, but the whites will beat up to more volume when they have reached room temperature. Therefore, separate the eggs when they are cold, then cover them and keep on the kitchen counter.

Egg yolks
Egg yolks, slightly beaten, are always added to the hot base after it has cooled for 10 minutes; then the mixture is thoroughly stirred together. Do not put the base back on the heat to cook further. There is a preliminary cooking of the eggs by their contact with the hot sauce; the cooking is finished when the soufflé is baked. The sauce with the incorporated egg yolks serves to stabilize the airy mixture that results when the beaten egg whites are added. Egg yolks also add lightness and thickening power.

Cover the sauce again if you are not going to finish the soufflé at once.

Egg whites
In all soufflés, an added egg white—for example, with two yolks use three whites—gives extra lightness.

To obtain fluffy air-filled whites, beat with a wire whisk; failing this, use a hand beater. Do not use an electric beater, for it beats too fast and not enough air is incorporated into the whites. The amount of air beaten into the egg whites determines the high rise of the soufflé during the baking. For more details on the changes in egg whites as they are beaten, and information on the technique of beating, see the section on meringues (p. 246). Egg whites should be beaten *stiff but not dry.* This point is reached when the whip or beaters are lifted and the egg whites stand high, but bend a little. If the shiny look disappears and the peaks stand straight up, or if the beaten whites slide out of the bowl, then the whites have been overbeaten, or beaten until dry.

Folding
Beaten egg whites must be folded *by hand* into the soufflé base, not beaten in. They are folded in the fol-

lowing manner: move a rubber spatula around the side of the bowl, clockwise from left to right. Then go underneath the mixture in the bowl and back on top. The whole movement must be done slowly without lifting the spatula. When one movement is complete, start again. Repeat until all the egg whites are blended. Fold in half of the beaten egg whites thoroughly, then fold in the remaining half gently, even leaving an occasional white spot of egg.

Soufflé dish

The classic soufflé dish is round with perfectly straight sides, usually highly glazed, with the bottom slightly raised in the middle. It is made of ovenproof glass or pottery. The straight-sided dish permits the soufflé to rise straight up to its maximum height. A dish with sloping sides can be used, but the soufflé will rise higher in the middle with a round shape or mound in the middle. To obtain the highest soufflé, the dish is not greased (that is why these dishes are highly glazed). However, there is a possible exception: for some soufflés the dish is buttered, bottom and sides, then sprinkled generously with fine dry crumbs and/or grated cheese, for entrée or hors-d'oeuvre soufflés; or with sugar for dessert soufflés. This gives the finished dish a delicate crust.

A four-egg soufflé requires a 4-cup (1-quart) soufflé dish with a 2- to 3-inch collar tied around it; without a collar, use a 6-cup (1½-quart) dish. A six-egg soufflé needs an 8-cup (2-quart) dish.

When using a regular casserole dish, fill only three quarters full and do not use a collar.

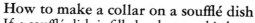

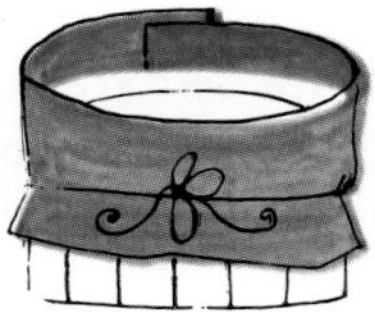

How to make a collar on a soufflé dish

If a soufflé dish is filled only two thirds to three quarters full, a collar is not necessary, as the soufflé will rise above the dish without a collar. When the soufflé dish is filled to the top, the collar is needed, for then it guides the high rise of the soufflé.

To make a collar, cut a wide strip of foil or wax paper long enough to go around the dish, usually about 22 to 24 inches long. Fold it in two or three lengthwise folds (this gives it greater stiffness) to make a piece large enough to overlap the top edge of the dish about 2 inches below the rim and to extend 1½ to 2 inches above the rim all around. Butter or oil the side of the folded foil or paper that will touch the food. Place it around the rim of the dish and tie it on securely with string, or fasten it with paper clips. When the soufflé is baked, remove the collar carefully, so as not to break the surface of the soufflé.

Always prepare the baking dish before starting the sauce.

How to make a hat on a soufflé

A hat is the chef's touch to a soufflé. Before the soufflé is baked, after it has been poured into the baking dish, run the smooth handle of a table knife around the mixture about 1½ inches from the outside edge and about 1 to 2 inches deep. Hold the knife straight up and run it around in a complete circle. When the soufflé is baked, it will rise more in the center than on the sides, creating the hat or crown effect. What you are doing is breaking some of the air bubbles with the knife so that the mixture cannot rise as much in the part you dented.

Baking the soufflé

A French-type soufflé is baked in a preheated 400° F. oven, which makes it brown and rise quickly, leaving the center very moist.

Most of our soufflés are cooked in a preheated 375° F. oven for a longer period. The soufflé is cooked throughout and does not rise quite so high, but does not collapse as quickly as the French type. Those are the basic temperatures, depending on the soufflé made. There can be slight variations. Be sure your oven is accurate.

O┳ Do not open the oven door until five minutes before the end of the specified baking time. This is important: opening the door admits cool air and disturbs the expansion of the soufflé. If cold air touches the soufflé before it is sufficiently firm, the cells will contract and the soufflé will fall. Open the door slowly and do not let it slam shut. The soufflé is done when the top is golden brown with a very light crust.

To bake a moist soufflé with a liquid center, set the soufflé dish directly on the center shelf of the preheated oven. To bake a soufflé evenly cooked throughout, set the dish in a shallow pan of hot water, and put that on the bottom shelf of the preheated oven.

O┳ When necessary, a soufflé can be prepared in its dish, all ready to be baked, 1 hour before baking. Keep the dish *covered* until ready to place it in the preheated oven. Uncovered, the soufflé will fall or form water in the bottom.

O┳ Still another way to deal with a soufflé if the guests are not ready is to reduce the heat of the oven to 250° F. The soufflé will then wait for an extra 20 minutes without spoiling or falling. If it is not ready when you wish to serve it, increase the heat to 450° F. It will then take 10 to 15 minutes less to cook. But, of course, the ideal situation is to have the guests ready for the soufflé the minute it is perfectly done.

Serving the soufflé

A hot soufflé must be served at the peak of its perfection, and that is as soon as it is out of the oven. Make sure the plates and silver are set before presenting the soufflé.

A soufflé is cut into portions with a fork, or with two forks if you find it easier (although one fork does less damage to the structure of the soufflé). As each portion is cut, spoon it onto a warm plate.

Common errors in making soufflés

1. Egg whites are beaten in a plastic bowl, or a bowl with even a small trace of fat or grease (see more about this under meringues, p. 246).
2. Egg whites are too cold to beat to high volume.
3. Egg whites are beaten dry, breaking into flecks.
4. Egg whites are beaten with an electric beater, which does not incorporate enough air into the mixture.
5. Egg whites are overstirred when added to the sauce, instead of being gently folded in; this results in a loss of trapped air.
6. Sauce is lumpy, or the added ingredients are not cut into small enough pieces.
7. Egg yolks are added to a sauce that is too hot, or are added too quickly, resulting in cooked hard particles.
8. Too much or too little baking, or oven temperature too high or too low.

Cheese soufflé

A cheese soufflé can be served as an hors d'oeuvre, a luncheon dish or a main course at a light supper. It can be baked in individual dishes or in a single large dish. Many types of cheese can be used; two or three different types can even be mixed.

Have ready a 4-cup soufflé dish, ungreased.

2 tablespoons butter
2 tablespoons flour
¾ cup cold milk
½ teaspoon salt
¼ teaspoon dry mustard
Pinch of cayenne
or few drops of hot-pepper sauce
1½ cups grated sharp Cheddar or other cheese
4 egg yolks
5 egg whites

FIRST PART: Make the sauce: Melt the butter. Add flour, remove from heat and stir until flour and butter are thoroughly mixed. Put back over low heat. Stir and cook for 1 minute. Remove from heat and add cold milk all at once. Stir until well mixed. The mixture will appear lumpy and hopeless, but all will be right once it starts to heat. Put back over medium heat and beat *constantly* with a wire whisk or spoon until the sauce is smooth and creamy.

SECOND PART: Add to the sauce the salt, mustard, cayenne or hot-pepper sauce and Cheddar, or any other grated cheese or combination of cheeses. Stir until thoroughly mixed. Remove from heat. Cover the sauce with paper and let cool for 10 minutes.

Beat yolks slightly. Gradually beat them into the cooled sauce, briskly stirring the sauce.

THIRD PART: Beat whites until stiff but not dry. Fold gently into the cheese sauce.

Pour the mixture into the prepared soufflé dish. Bake in a preheated 450° F. oven for 25 to 30 minutes (the French way), or in a preheated 375° F. oven for 50 to 60 minutes. Makes 4 servings.

For a six-serving cheese soufflé

Use ¼ cup butter, ¼ cup flour, 1½ cups milk, 1 teaspoon salt, ½ teaspoon dry mustard, hot-pepper sauce to taste, 2 cups cheese, 6 egg yolks, 7 or 8 egg whites. Bake in a 2-quart (8-cup) soufflé dish at 375° F. for 1¼ hours, or at 400° F. for 40 to 50 minutes.

Chicken soufflé

A cup of leftover chicken or turkey can be used. Part of the liquid can be a concentrated chicken stock or sherry.

Make a collar on an ungreased 4-cup soufflé dish.

- 3 tablespoons butter
- 3 tablespoons flour
- ¾ cup milk
- ½ cup concentrated chicken stock or sherry
- ¼ teaspoon dry mustard
- 1 teaspoon salt (or less)
- ¼ teaspoon pepper
- ½ teaspoon ground tarragon
- 1 cup cooked chicken or turkey
- 4 egg yolks
- 6 egg whites

FIRST PART: Make the sauce with the butter, flour, milk and concentrated chicken stock or sherry.

SECOND PART: Add to the sauce dry mustard, 1 teaspoon salt (use less if the chicken stock is very salty), pepper, ground tarragon and cooked chicken or turkey that has been passed through a meat grinder or chopped very fine. Mix thoroughly. Cool, covered, for 10 minutes. Add egg yolks, slightly beaten.

THIRD PART: Beat egg whites. Fold gently into the sauce mixture.

Pour the mixture into the prepared dish. Bake in a preheated 375° F. oven for 40 to 45 minutes. Makes 4 servings.

Mushroom soufflé

Only ¾ cup of liquid is used for the sauce, which will be thick to start with. It will eventually obtain its proper texture from the liquid released by the mushrooms during baking.

- 3 tablespoons chicken fat or butter
- 3 tablespoons flour
- ¾ cup milk
- ½ teaspoon salt
- ¼ teaspoon curry powder
- ½ pound mushrooms, thinly sliced
- 1 tablespoon melted butter
- 2 tablespoons grated Parmesan cheese
- 4 egg yolks
- 5 egg whites

FIRST PART: Make a sauce with the chicken fat or butter, flour and milk.

SECOND PART: Add salt and curry powder. Quickly sear sliced mushrooms in 1 tablespoon melted butter over high heat. Add mushrooms and grated cheese to the sauce. Cover and cool for 10 minutes. Gradually add slightly beaten egg yolks, stirring briskly.

THIRD PART: Beat egg whites. Fold gently into sauce mixture.

Pour into a 1½-quart (6-cup) soufflé dish. Bake in a preheated 375° F. oven for 30 to 40 minutes. Makes 4 to 6 servings.

Seafood soufflé

This basic seafood soufflé can be made with cooked shrimp, chopped lobster, crab meat or a mixture of two, such as shrimp and crab meat.

O━ To give the necessary lightness to a seafood soufflé, only 1 tablespoon flour is used. The rest of the needed starch is replaced by ½ cup cooked rice. If you prefer, the rice can be omitted and the flour replaced with 2 tablespoons cornstarch. Rice gives a lighter and more attractive texture to the soufflé.

- 2 tablespoons butter
- 2 green onions, finely chopped
- 1 or 2 teaspoons curry powder
- 1 tablespoon flour
- 1 cup milk
- ½ teaspoon salt
- ¼ teaspoon pepper
- ½ cup cooked rice
- 1 cup cooked seafood, finely chopped
- 4 egg yolks
- 5 egg whites

FIRST PART: Melt butter in a saucepan without browning. Add green onions and stir over low heat for about 2 minutes. Add curry powder and flour. Stir until thoroughly blended. Add 1 cup milk. Cook and stir over medium heat until creamy.

SECOND PART: To the sauce add salt, pepper, cooked rice and finely chopped cooked seafood of your choice. Stir until well mixed. Cover and let cool for 10 minutes. Then add slightly beaten egg yolks, stirring briskly.

THIRD PART: Beat egg whites until stiff but not dry. Fold gently into the sauce. Pour into a 1½-quart (6-cup) soufflé dish. Bake in a preheated 350° F. oven for 45 to 50 minutes. Makes 4 to 6 servings.

Liqueur soufflé

This dessert soufflé is an example of a custard-base type; it can be made with any sweet liqueur, or a mixture of liqueur and brandy. The sauce is actually a stirred custard, quite different from the usual soufflé.

PREPARING THE SOUFFLÉ DISH: Butter a 1½-pint (3-cup) soufflé dish and dust with sugar. Refrigerate until ready to use.

¼ cup sugar
¼ cup flour
Pinch of salt
3 egg yolks
1 cup hot light cream
2 to 4 tablespoons liqueur
4 egg whites

FIRST PART: In the top part of a double boiler blend sugar, flour and salt. Add egg yolks, well beaten. Mix thoroughly with the first ingredients. While stirring, slowly add hot light cream. Cook over hot water, stirring constantly, until sauce is smooth and thickened like a custard. Remove from heat.

SECOND PART: Add liqueur of your choice. Stir until well mixed. Cover and cool for 15 minutes.

THIRD PART: Beat egg whites until stiff but not dry. Fold gently but thoroughly into the cooled custard. Pour into the prepared dish. Bake in a preheated 350° F. oven for 20 to 25 minutes. Makes 6 servings.

Chocolate soufflé

In this soufflé the semisweet chocolate, or any other sweet chocolate, provides most of the sweetening. Two 4-ounce fancy European chocolate blocks can replace the semisweet chocolate. No butter is used in a rich chocolate soufflé because of the fat contained in the chocolate.

PREPARING THE SOUFFLÉ DISH: Butter a 1-quart (4-cup) soufflé dish and sprinkle with sugar. Refrigerate until ready to use.

4 tablespoons sugar
4 tablespoons flour
¼ teaspoon salt
1 cup milk
4 egg yolks
4 ounces (4 squares) semisweet or sweet chocolate, melted
6 egg whites

FIRST PART: Place sugar, flour and salt in a saucepan. Stir until well mixed. Add milk and stir well. Cook over low heat, stirring constantly, until the sauce is thick and creamy.

SECOND PART: Remove sauce from heat, cover and cool for 10 minutes. Add slightly beaten egg yolks, stirring briskly. Stir in melted semisweet or sweet chocolate until thoroughly mixed (or use 4 ounces premelted chocolate).

THIRD PART: Beat egg whites until stiff but not dry. Fold gently into the sauce. Pour into the prepared soufflé dish. Bake in a preheated 375° F. oven for 25 minutes if you want a moist soufflé, 35 minutes if you prefer it well cooked. Makes 6 servings.

MERINGUES

Here is another preparation based on eggs, but this one uses only the egg whites. A meringue can be a soft spreading cream, a spongy white topping, a crunchy shell of hard-baked foam. Meringue can be folded into other preparations to give height and pride. And of course it is the finishing touch for pies.

For any kind of meringue you must learn to beat air into the egg whites and add sugar or any other ingredient at just the right moment. To get this timing perfect, learn to recognize the stages the egg whites go through. As they are beaten, they undergo transformation, increasing in bulk because of the air you are beating into them.

FIRST STAGE: Beat the egg white into a *soft foam.* At this point *only,* add 1 teaspoon of sugar.

SECOND STAGE: Continue to beat the egg white, adding 1 tablespoon of sugar at a time, until a *thick foam* is formed.

THIRD STAGE: While the last of the sugar is being added and the beating continues, the meringue in this third stage will be glossy and soft, and *rounded peaks* will form when the whisk or beater is lifted gently from the mixture.

FOURTH STAGE: Finally, the whites become stiff, the mass is moist and smooth, and *pointed peaks* stand up when the whisk is withdrawn.

O┳ Be sure to separate the whites from the yolks while the yolks are still firm, just as you take them from the refrigerator. Cover the yolks and return them to the refrigerator. O┳ Leave the whites out to reach room temperature; egg whites beat to a greater volume at room temperature rather than when cold.

O┳ The best beater to use for meringue is the French wire whisk. *Nothing* can replace the whisk, because it incorporates a great deal more air in the egg whites than any other type of beater. If you do not have a wire whisk, use a hand beater. *Do not use an electric beater or mixer,* unless you are making a specific type of meringue that requires this kind of beating.

Next in importance is the type of bowl in which to beat the meringue. French chefs insist that only large copper bowls will give satisfactory results. They are very good, but expensive and not always readily available. However, a large metal bowl proportioned to the number of egg whites being beaten is the kind to use: for example, medium to large round-bottomed stainless-steel bowls. The bowl must be non-porous, which excludes certain plastics, and you must make absolutely certain that there is no hidden grease on it. This does not necessarily mean that the bowl is dirty, but minute particles, invisible to the naked eye, can spell trouble. Even a spot of fat cuts the volume of the egg whites being beaten. To make sure of the cleanliness of the bowl, fill it with cold salted water. If you use a wire whisk, wash it also in the salted water, then rinse both whisk and bowl under running cold water and do not dry. Another method is to rub both whisk and bowl with absorbent paper dipped into vinegar.

Use superfine sugar for meringue, whenever this is available. A sugar that is too coarse will make the meringue weep. Too much sugar of *any* kind will also make it weep.

Salt in meringue helps increase the volume, but too much will decrease it. Use 1/4 teaspoon salt for each cup of egg whites.

Cream of tartar is often added to meringue. It is a stabilizing agent that keeps the whites firm so that they will not reach that dry, overbeaten stage. Folding becomes easier if cream of tartar has been added, because it keeps the beaten whites in a soft well-beaten mass. Use 1/8 teaspoon cream of tartar for each egg white; never use more than this.

To help you in measuring, seven or eight whites of large eggs or eight or nine whites of medium-size eggs will fill 1 cup. You will need four or five to fill 1/2 cup.

There are many variations and uses of meringues, but only three basic types: hard meringue, soft meringue, cold-water meringue.

Hard meringue

For best results, choose a cool dry day to make this type. To be perfect, it must be crisp but tender and of the palest shade of beige. This kind can be made in small individual meringues or in a large shell that can be filled with sweetened fruits, whipped cream, ice cream or any other filling you prefer. It will keep in a metal box in a cool dry place for 3 weeks, but *do not refrigerate.*

2 egg whites
Pinch of salt
¼ teaspoon cream of tartar
½ cup superfine sugar
¼ teaspoon extract of your choice

Beat egg whites with salt and cream of tartar to a soft foam. Sprinkle 1 teaspoon of the sugar over the surface and beat until completely incorporated. Continue adding sugar, 1 tablespoon at a time, until all the sugar is added. *Beat in* the flavoring and continue to beat until the mass holds its shape.

Prepare a baking sheet by sprinkling it with flour or covering with freezer paper or parchment (this can be found in department stores at kitchen and freezer counters).

To shape small to medium meringues, use a spoon or a pastry bag and drop the meringues onto the prepared baking sheet, leaving ½ inch between the shaped meringues.

To make a shell, shape meringue into a round 8 to 10 inches in diameter directly on baking sheet, or in an 8-, 9- or 10-inch pie plate; gently flatten the middle with the back of a spoon.

Bake in a preheated 300° F. oven until the meringues reach a delicate pale brown, 20 to 60 minutes depending upon their size and shape.

Soft meringue

Soft meringue is fine grained, easier to cut than the hard variety and has no tendency to shrink or weep. This is the type used for baked Alaska; the air beaten into the egg whites acts as an insulating agent to prevent the melting of the ice cream. The differences between hard and soft meringues result from differences in baking time and oven temperature.

This meringue covers an 8-inch pie.

2 egg whites
¼ teaspoon cream of tartar
Pinch of salt
4 tablespoons superfine sugar
¼ teaspoon extract of your choice

Beat as for hard meringue (opposite page).

Spread the meringue over pies, puddings and so on while they are still warm, but not hot. Make sure the filling is completely covered. Meringue acts as an insulating agent so that the filling underneath will not be overcooked. Bake immediately in a preheated 425° F. oven for 5 to 6 minutes.

If you are used to baking a soft meringue topping on a pie in a slow oven, you will be pleased with this hot-oven technique. For best results, pile the meringue on the pie or pudding shortly before serving. This is easy to arrange. Soft meringue will hold up for 1 hour, refrigerated, before baking. This is the only type that can be refrigerated in this fashion. But never refrigerate it after baking.

🗝 A soft meringue on a pie is more easily cut if you first dip the knife into hot water, or rub it with butter.

Cold-water meringue

This one belongs to French classic cuisine. It never shrinks, weeps or falls. It is slow cooking and can be successfully beaten with a hand rotary beater or with a hand electric beater at slow speed.

The beating method and sugar content are quite different from the other types of basic meringues.

1¾ tablespoons cold water
2 egg whites
Pinch of salt
⅛ teaspoon cream of tartar
¼ teaspoon extract of your choice
2 tablespoons superfine sugar

Add the water to the egg whites and beat with a hand rotary beater until a soft foam is formed. Add the salt, cream of tartar and extract. Continue to beat until stiff. Add the sugar and continue to beat until the meringue is stiff enough to form peaks.

Pile on pies, tarts or cakes. Bake in a 325° F. oven for 12 to 20 minutes, or until pale brown.

Electric-mixer meringue

To make this, an electric mixer is essential, contrary to the usual rule that prohibits an electric mixer with meringue. This meringue is sometimes referred to as Swiss meringue.

½ cup egg whites (from about 4 large eggs)	1 cup granulated sugar
	½ teaspoon salt

Place the egg whites in the top part of a double boiler. With an electric hand beater set at medium speed, beat until bubbly or to the soft-foam stage (first stage). Then place over *lukewarm* water and stir until the egg whites are *lukewarm.* Do not let the water boil in the bottom of the double boiler. Remove from heat. Add the sugar and salt all at once. Beat again with the electric hand beater for *10 minutes,* or until stiff enough for the meringue to hold its shape. (At this stage the meringue can be poured into the bowl of an electric mixer for the 10-minute beating period if you do not wish to hold the beater by hand for that length of time.)

This meringue can be used as a topping without being baked; it is an uncooked meringue. Or, if you prefer to have a browned meringue, place it in a preheated 425° F. oven for 5 minutes.

These ingredients make enough meringue to fill and top two 8-inch layer cakes, or to top two 9-inch pies. Any unused portion can be refrigerated, for use within 24 hours.

Meringue buttercream

This soft, creamy meringue is mostly used to garnish French pastry, but it is also very nice with sponge cake.

1 cup granulated sugar	3 egg whites
½ cup water	1 cup unsalted butter
1 tablespoon corn syrup	Flavoring

Place ⅔ cup of the sugar, the water and corn syrup in a saucepan. Stir over *low heat* until the

sugar is completely dissolved. Raise the heat to medium and boil the syrup without stirring until it forms a soft ball when dropped into cold water, or registers 238° F. on a candy thermometer.

While the syrup is cooking, beat the egg whites until they form soft peaks. Gradually add the remaining 1/3 cup sugar, 1 teaspoon at a time, beating hard after each addition. Beat until you have a firm meringue. 0— Pour the boiling syrup into the egg whites in a fine stream, *beating constantly*. This can be done with the electric mixer at medium speed. After all the syrup is added, continue to beat until the meringue is very smooth and very stiff. Cool completely. It will take an hour or more.

Cream the butter until soft and fluffy. Then beat the cold meringue mixture into the butter. Flavor to taste with any of these: 1 tablespoon instant coffee powder, 3 tablespoons brandy or rum, 2 tablespoons powdered Dutch cocoa, 1 tablespoon vanilla or almond extract.

Italian meringue

This type of cooked meringue is the ancestor of our seven-minute icing. It is much smoother and very thick, with a creamy light texture. It is the perfect meringue to top angel food cake, chiffon pie or sweet dessert omelets.

2 cups granulated sugar
1 cup water
5 egg whites
1 teaspoon extract of your choice

Boil the sugar and water until the mixture forms a firm ball when dropped into cold water (242° F. on a candy thermometer). Beat egg whites with a wire whisk until stiff. Gradually add the hot syrup you have just made, beating constantly with a wire whisk; or place the beaten egg whites in the bowl of an electric mixer and add the syrup while beating at medium speed.

Set the bowl over a bowl of ice water, add the extract and fold over and over for 5 minutes with a rubber spatula. Cover and let stand for 15 minutes, then use as topping.

If you want to make individual meringues to be filled with whipped cream or ice cream, shape with a spoon or pastry bag on a buttered baking sheet dusted with cornstarch. Bake at 300° F. for 30 minutes.

To halve this recipe, use three egg whites and half of the other ingredients.

American pie meringue

Lemon juice and boiling water added to this meringue make it different from the classic types. It is perfect to use on pies.

2 egg whites
3 tablespoons granulated sugar
½ teaspoon lemon juice
2 teaspoons boiling water

Beat the egg whites with an electric hand beater or a wire whisk until stiff. Add the sugar, 1 tablespoon at a time, beating hard with each addition. Add the lemon juice with the last tablespoon of sugar. Beat until the meringue is smooth and glossy. Beat in the boiling water. Spread on pie and brown in a 425° F. oven for 5 to 8 minutes.

Meringue pie

Instead of a pastry-dough crust, make a meringue pie shell. The filling can be topped with sweetened fresh berries or whipped cream. Or try filling with scoops of ice cream or with sweetened berries topped with whipped cream or ice cream.

MERINGUE PIE SHELL

4 egg whites (½ cup)
¼ teaspoon salt
1 teaspoon lemon juice or vinegar
1 cup sugar

Beat egg whites until fluffy. Add salt and lemon juice or vinegar. Beat until the eggs are stiff. Add sugar, 1 tablespoon at a time, beating hard after each addition. Butter an 8-inch pie plate. Fill with the meringue, pushing it up on the sides and hollowing the center lightly. Bake in a 275° F. oven for 1 hour and 15 minutes.

LEMON FILLING

4 egg yolks
⅔ cup sugar
2 teaspoons grated lemon rind
½ cup lemon juice

Beat egg yolks until thick and lemon-colored. Continue to beat and gradually add sugar, grated lemon rind and lemon juice. Cook in the top part of a double boiler over simmering water, stirring constantly, for approximately 5 minutes or until thickened. Pour into the cooled baked meringue shell. Makes 6 servings.

French crêpe meringue

The basic idea is a filled French crêpe with frangipane cream, rolled, and garnished with meringue. In the summer use sweetened berries for filling; in the winter use apricot or other jams. The crêpes can be cooked in the early morning to be served later in the day or at night, with only the meringue topping to be added at the last minute.

CRÊPES

1 cup all-purpose flour	1 cup milk
½ teaspoon salt	2 eggs

Stir together flour, salt and milk. Beat in eggs until thoroughly mixed. Let this batter rest for 30 minutes.

Grease and heat a 5-inch frying pan. Pour in just enough batter to cover the pan with a very thin layer. Tilt the pan to spread the batter evenly. Cook to a light brown on one side, then set on a cloth with the cooked side on the bottom. If the crêpe batter seems too thick, beat in about 1 tablespoon of water. Continue until all the batter is used, cooking the crêpes only on one side. This will make 18 to 20 crêpes.

FRANGIPANE CREAM

1 cup sugar	2 tablespoons butter
½ cup all-purpose flour	1 teaspoon vanilla extract *or* 3 almond macaroons, crushed
Pinch of salt	Grated rind of ½ lemon
3 cups milk	
3 egg yolks	

Mix together sugar, flour and salt. Add milk and stir over medium heat until creamy and smooth. Slowly add slightly beaten egg yolks, beating with a wire whisk or hand beater. Cook and beat for 3 minutes. Add butter and vanilla extract (or crushed macaroons) and the fine-grated lemon rind. Cool.

PREPARE a recipe of Italian meringue (p. 251).

TO ASSEMBLE CRÊPES, spread each crêpe with fruit or jam to taste and top with a portion of frangipane cream. Roll. Place the rolls in a shallow baking dish, the folded sides on the bottom. Top with the meringue. Sprinkle with 2 tablespoons of superfine sugar and bake in a 400° F. oven for 15 minutes. Serve hot, about two crêpes for a serving.

EGGNOGS

Eggnogs should be made with the freshest and best-quality eggs available, for they beat up to a greater volume and are more delicious. In addition to the eggs, a liquid is used. This can be milk, light or heavy cream, orange juice, cider, white wine, or a fortified wine such as port, sherry or Madeira. Usually eggnogs are sweetened, but the amount of sugar can be adjusted to your taste. It can be ordinary granulated sugar, brown sugar, confectioners' sugar, honey or a flavored sugar. The proportions of egg to liquid can be altered—the more eggs, the thicker and richer the drink. Or you can flavor the mixture with vanilla or other extract. For parties, rum and/or brandy or other liquors can be added.

If you want a smooth mixture, beat whole eggs and the liquid together. For richer mixtures beat the yolks and liquid together and beat the whites separately—with part of the sugar if you like—and fold this meringuelike fluff into the finished drink. If you are using cream, that too can be beaten separately and folded in at the end to make a thicker nog.

While the traditional flavoring is nutmeg, you can use whatever you like—cinnamon, cloves, anise. Or you can omit spice altogether if you prefer.

O┳ After you have beaten the egg mixture, strain it to remove the small lumps of thickened albumen.

Eggnog can be made in advance and allowed to mellow, but remember that mixtures like this need to be refrigerated.

Basic eggnog

1 egg
½ cup milk
1 teaspoon sugar
Grated nutmeg or anisette sugar

Beat egg with milk and sugar. Strain into a glass. Sprinkle the top of the drink with a little grated nutmeg or anisette sugar. Makes 1 serving.

Orange eggnog

1 egg
½ cup orange juice
1 teaspoon sugar
¼ teaspoon grated lemon rind
Sliver of candied orange rind

Beat together egg, orange juice, sugar and grated lemon rind. Decorate with candied orange rind. This is especially good for a health drink. Makes 1 serving.

Beef and rum eggnog

3 egg yolks
1 cup seasoned beef stock or consommé
2 dashes of orange bitters
2 to 3 ounces very dry rum or vodka

Beat the egg yolks with the broth. Strain through a fine sieve into another bowl. Add bitters and liquor. Stir to mix and serve as the drink and soup course combined at Sunday night supper. This is a nutritious drink. Makes 2 servings.

Jersey nog

12 eggs
1 cup sugar
2 quarts light cream
¼ cup 151-proof rum
Fifth of applejack
Grated nutmeg or ground cinnamon

Separate the eggs while cold, then let the yolks rest at room temperature for at least 30 minutes. Beat the yolks, sugar and cream until frothy and the sugar dissolves; the eggnog should not be grainy. Beat in the rum and applejack. If the nog does not seem sweet enough, add a little warm honey or sugar syrup. Do not add more sugar; the beating required to dissolve the sugar would overbeat the mixture.

Just before serving, beat the egg whites until they are thick, foamy and almost stiff. Fold them into the nog in a large bowl. Sprinkle the top with nutmeg or a little cinnamon. Makes about 4 quarts.

CUSTARD

A custard is a mixture like an eggnog except that it is cooked; the eggs are solidified by heat and thicken the mixture. How firm or solid a custard will be depends on the amount of heat and the nature of other ingredients mixed with the eggs. 🗝 Do not overbeat the ingredients. Too much air will spoil the texture.

🗝 As with all egg cookery, the heat is critical.

Use steady low heat for stirred custards and low oven heat for baked custards. Custards are often baked in larger containers of hot water for more even heat control. Do not pour egg yolks into hot liquid. They will cook at once and will not mix with the liquid. Instead, pour the hot liquid into the eggs gradually. Beat constantly to heat the eggs slowly and to expand them.

Custard Sauce (p. 211) is actually a soft or stirred custard, whereas Timbale Colombière (recipe on next page) is a baked custard. In Spanish-speaking countries a flan is not a shallow pastry tart but a baked flat custard, usually coated with caramel.

Flavor custards with fruit essences, liqueurs, chocolate or coffee. Custard dishes that are not desserts can be mixed with shellfish, vegetables and herbs. Custards can be used for pie and cake fillings.

Simple custard

3 eggs	¼ teaspoon salt
6 tablespoons vanilla sugar (p. 160)	2 cups milk

Put all ingredients into a saucepan and beat until well mixed. Cook over low heat until the mixture is thickened and coats a metal spoon. Stir *gently* until the custard is smooth and thickened. Or cook it in the top part of a double boiler over simmering water for about 10 minutes. Serve hot or cold as a simple sauce, or cold as a soft custard dessert. This is good cold topped with whipped cream and fresh strawberries or raspberries. Makes about 2½ cups sauce, or 6 servings.

If you prefer, make the custard with plain sugar and add other flavoring.

Keviona dip or sandwich

1 tablespoon butter	2 hard-cooked eggs, chopped
1 tablespoon flour	3 pimientos, chopped
1 tablespoon sugar	1 tablespoon minced onion
½ cup milk or light cream	Cayenne pepper
1 egg, beaten	Salt
2 tablespoons vinegar	
3 ounces cream cheese	

Mix butter, flour, sugar, milk or cream, beaten egg

and vinegar in a saucepan. Cook over low heat until the mixture is thickened and coats a metal spoon. Remove the saucepan from the heat. Add the cheese, softened or cut into chunks, and stir until well mixed. Add the chopped eggs, pimientos and onion. Season with cayenne pepper and salt to taste. Cool. Use for a dip with simple crackers, or as a spread for tea or cocktail sandwiches. Makes 1½ cups.

Timbale colombière

Serve this delicate mushroom custard in individual custard cups (*petits pots*) as an entrée at a luncheon, or as an accompaniment with roast chicken or veal.

- 1 cup chicken consommé
- ½ cup heavy cream
- 4 eggs
- ½ teaspoon salt
- Dash of pepper
- ¼ teaspoon minced tarragon
- ⅛ teaspoon grated nutmeg
- 2 tablespoons butter
- ½ pound mushrooms, finely chopped
- 2 tablespoons minced parsley

Place the consommé, cream, eggs, salt, pepper, tarragon and nutmeg in a bowl. Beat with a whisk until well blended. Melt the butter in a large frying pan and add the mushrooms. Stir over high heat until lightly browned and dry. Add the mushrooms and parsley to the egg mixture. Stir well. Pour into buttered individual molds or *petits pots*. Set the molds in a pan of hot water. Bake in a 350° F. oven for 30 to 35 minutes, or until the custard is set. Serve hot. Makes about 6 servings.

Brunch pie

- Pie pastry for 1-crust 9-inch pie
- ½ pound bacon
- ¼ cup chutney
- ½ teaspoon curry powder
- 1 tablespoon brandy or dry sherry
- 6 eggs
- ⅔ cup light cream or milk
- Salt and pepper

Line a 9-inch pie plate with the pastry; make a fluted edge. Fry the bacon until crisp. Remove the pieces from the fat, drain and crumble over the bottom of the pastry. Blend the chutney (cut up any large pieces), curry powder, and brandy or sherry. Beat the eggs lightly with the cream or milk. Add salt and pepper to taste, stir in the chutney mixture and pour over the bacon. Bake in a 400° F. oven for 15 minutes, then reduce the heat to 350° F. and bake for another 35 to 45 minutes, or until the top custard is set and lightly browned. Serve hot in the winter, or at room temperature in the summer. This is good with tomato slices sprinkled with fresh chives and basil, and with crisp watercress. Makes 6 servings.

Flan

¾ cup light brown sugar
¼ cup orange juice
1 piece of vanilla bean (4 inches)
2 cups milk
5 eggs
½ cup granulated sugar

Place brown sugar and orange juice in a heavy pan and bring to a boil, stirring. Reduce heat and continue to stir until the mixture becomes thick, syrupy and dark brown. Do not let it burn or it will be bitter. Pour the caramel into six individual soufflé dishes or small-size shirred-egg dishes. Swirl the caramel to coat the inside and let the dishes cool.

Drop the vanilla bean into the milk in a saucepan. Beat eggs with granulated sugar until well mixed. Stir eggs into the milk. Warm slowly over low heat until hot to your finger, then strain into the caramel-lined dishes. Set the dishes in a large pan filled with hot water and bake in a 350° F. oven for about 45 minutes. Cool. Unmold to serve. The liquid caramel serves as a sauce.

A true Spanish flan is served with guava jelly, quince paste or fresh pineapple. Makes 6 servings.

Crème caramel renversée aux pêches

This elegant dessert can be prepared two days ahead. In the summer make it with poached fresh peaches; in the winter use canned peaches.

2 cups heavy cream
1 cup milk
1 piece of vanilla bean (4 inches)
3 whole eggs
2 extra egg yolks
1½ cups sugar
½ cup water
12 peach halves, poached
Candied cherries
Pistachios

Scald 1 cup of the cream and the milk with the vanilla bean. Thoroughly beat together the whole eggs, egg yolks and ½ cup of the sugar. Remove the vanilla bean from the hot cream and milk and gradually pour the hot liquid into the egg mixture, stirring vigorously.

MAKE A CARAMEL: Heat the remaining 1 cup sugar in a heavy frying pan until it is melted. Gradually stir in the water and cook the syrup until it becomes caramel-colored. Pour the syrup into a 1-quart ring mold and tilt the mold in all directions until the bottom and sides are well coated. Let the caramel set.

Pour the custard into the mold. Set the mold in a pan of hot water and bake in a 350° F. oven about 45 minutes, or until a knife inserted into the center comes out clean. Cool. When ready to serve, unmold onto a serving dish.

Whip the remaining cream and sweeten to taste. Flavor with vanilla extract or another flavoring if you wish. Fill the center of the mold with the poached peaches and cover the peaches with the whipped cream piled high in the middle. Decorate the cream with candied cherries and pistachios. Makes 6 servings.

Crème brûlée

- 4 cups light cream
- 4 tablespoons sugar
- 2 teaspoons vanilla extract
- 8 egg yolks, well beaten
- Brown sugar

Scald the cream. Remove from the heat, add the sugar and vanilla and mix well. Pour slowly over the egg yolks, beating constantly. Pour through a fine sieve into a shallow, flameproof, buttered baking dish. Bake in a 300° F. oven for 1 hour and 15 minutes, or until set. Remove from the oven, cool and chill.

Shortly before serving, when the custard is cold, cover the top with a ¼-inch layer of brown sugar. Place the baking dish under the broiler long enough to caramelize the sugar. Watch carefully to be sure the sugar does not burn; the whole process takes only seconds. The sugar will become very hard.

To serve, tap the hard sugar layer with a spoon to crack it. You can do this ahead of time and refrigerate it, but the sugar tends to soften and sink into the custard. The flavor is still the same but the appearance is different. Makes 8 or more servings.

«9»

Meat and Meat Cookery

How to buy meat · Basic techniques for cooking meat · Timetables for cooking meat · Roasting, braising and pot-roasting, broiling, panbroiling, barbecuing · How to sauté · Coatings for sautéed and panfried foods · How to panfry · The best pan for deep-frying · Fats for deep-frying · Temperatures for frying · Coatings for fried foods · How to deep-fry · How to stew, poach, fricassee · Cooking internal meats

Meat is among our most important foods. It contains proteins necessary for the constant rebuilding of cells throughout our bodies. In the form of game, it was the main food available to our early colonists. As the land was settled, however, other edibles were cultivated and individual meat consumption decreased. A well-balanced agriculture provided a variety of foods, resulting in a better-balanced diet. Because of this the importance of meat as our principal food has diminished somewhat, but it has by no means disappeared. We are healthier, stronger, more resistant to disease when meat plays its proper role in our diet.

BUYING MEAT

Good cooking begins at the market, and this is particularly true with meat.

Butchers and general meat merchants are well aware that the average shopper can identify only a few of the more familiar cuts. If you rely on a butcher's advice, you must realize that he may suggest an unnecessarily expensive cut. Of course, all butchers are not waiting to pounce unscrupulously on gullible and unwary customers, but they are human beings in business to make a profit. Your ignorance can cost you money, so it is worthwhile to inform yourself.

A supermarket where the meat is on display, pre-cut and packaged in clear plastic, with the price, weight and name of the cut on the label, may seem the answer. However, it provides only part of the answer, for you are still left with the problem of which cut to choose for your particular need.

Learn to recognize the various cuts of meat. On pages 320 to 327 you will find charts illustrating the principal cuts of beef, veal, lamb and pork. Knowledge of the wholesale cuts can be important if you plan to buy large portions of meat for freezing. Retail cuts are shown with an indication of the part of the animal from which each piece is cut.

You may buy a cut that is suitable for the purpose you have in mind; or you may decide on your cooking method after you have made your purchase of the cut that suits your pocketbook and family size. Any cut of meat can be made tender by proper cooking, but it is obviously unwise to buy sirloin steak to make boiled beef, or to plan on roasting a relatively tough cut like the brisket. Bones give the meat flavor, especially when it is being cooked by moist heat, but they present difficulties in carving.

Ground beef, veal and lamb are widely available. Ground pork is usually made into sausage or luncheon meats but is also used with veal and beef for meat loaf and similar dishes. Since ground meats have been processed—even grinding takes time and labor—they are not always as cheap as they may seem at first glance. Also, unless your butcher indicates that they are "lean" or ground from the round or sirloin, they tend to be somewhat fatty. Veal is the least fatty because it comes from a young animal that has not lived long enough to develop a heavy layer of fat.

Tenderness

Here is a simple explanation that may help you to remember which cuts are more tender and which are less so.

The legs and neck of an animal carry weight, work hard and move a great deal. As a result, these parts develop strong muscles and become tough and gristly. Careful, slow cooking with moisture for long periods is required to soften and tenderize such cuts. Since these particular cuts come mostly from mature animals, they are usually flavorful and are by far the best for making stews and casseroles. They are also much cheaper than cuts used for roasting and frying because they are not nearly so much in demand. Many shoppers prefer meat that can be cooked quickly.

The middle of the animal—the loin, and the internal parts such as kidneys—are protected by the back of the animal, are carried around and do little work. These cuts are the less muscular and will be tender without lengthy simmering or other lengthy cooking. Because these are the cuts in greatest demand, the price tends to be high.

BASIC TECHNIQUES OF COOKING MEAT

Once you have mastered the art of buying and cooking meat you will be able to transform economy cuts into tasty, interesting dishes. First learn the cooking techniques applicable to the various cuts of meat. When you master the art of roasting a piece of meat of one kind, you will be able to apply the same technique to other roasts. You will likewise discover that braising a piece of beef is much like braising a piece of veal or lamb, and so on.

These cooking methods, each related to a specific type of heat, are all familiar to American cooks.

COOKING METHOD	TYPE OF HEAT USED
Roasting	Trapped heat, in an oven
Broiling or grilling	Radiation, usually from an overhead broiler
Barbecuing	Radiation, direct or indirect, usually from a barbecue below the meat
Panbroiling	Contact with hot metal, usually in a heavy metal frying pan
Panfrying	Contact with hot fat in a heavy metal pan
Sautéing	Contact with very little fat in a hot metal pan
Braising and pot-roasting	Contact with hot fat, then with moist heat in a closed cooking pot
Stewing	Immersion in hot liquid
Poaching or simmering	Cooking in more or less liquid
Fricasseeing	Contact with hot fat, then with liquid or sauce

ROASTING

Here are four methods of roasting meat. You will no doubt find that one of these will suit your need better than another at various times and with different types of meat. No matter which method you use, follow these general rules:

Place any cut of meat in a shallow roasting pan.
Do not put flour on top of the meat.
Do not cover the roasting pan.
Do not baste while roasting.

Timetable for roasting beef

FIRST METHOD, beef roast with bones

Weight in pounds	Oven temperature	Interior temp. on therm.	Approx. total min. per pound
6 to 8	450°F. for 15 minutes, then reduce to 325°F. for balance of roasting time.		
rare		140°F.	15 to 18
medium		160°F.	20 to 22
well done		170°F.	25 to 27

NOTE: For rolled roasts or other roasts without bones, add 10 minutes per pound.

SECOND METHOD, beef roast with bones

6 to 8	325°F. for 15 minutes, then raise to 450°F. for balance of roasting time.		
rare		140°F.	15 to 18
medium		160°F.	20 to 22
well done		170°F.	25 to 27

NOTE: For rolled roasts or other roasts without bones, add 10 minutes per pound.

THIRD METHOD, beef roast with bones

rare	6 to 8	325°F.	140°F.	15 to 18
medium			160°F.	20 to 22
well done			170°F.	25 to 27

rolled roast or other roasts without bones

rare	6 to 8	325°F.	140°F.	25 to 30
medium			160°F.	33 to 35
well done			170°F.	40 to 45

FOURTH METHOD, beef roast with bones

rare	6 to 8	350°F.	130°F.	10 to 13
medium			140° to 150°F.	15 to 17
well done			160° to 170°F.	20 to 22

rolled roast or other roasts without bones

rare	6 to 8	350°F.	140°F.	20 to 25
medium			160°F.	28 to 30
well done			170°F.	35 to 40

First method
Preheat oven to 450° F.; this will take about 15 minutes. Make sure there is a natural coating of fat on top of the roast. Add a thin layer of chopped fat if the meat is lean. Roast for exactly 15 minutes to seal the outside pores of the meat and preserve the natural juices. Reduce temperature to 325° F. for the balance of required time.

Second method
Reverse the above temperatures by preheating the oven to 325° F., roasting the meat for 15 minutes, then raising the temperature to 450° F. This method is the best to use with fatty cuts of meat.

Third method
Preheat oven to 325° F. Roast at this temperature for the entire time. The fat on top will not get as crusty brown as with either the first or second method. To brown the surface fat, at the end of the cooking period add an extra 10 minutes with the oven heat raised to 425° F. This is the most economical of the methods because there is less meat shrinkage. However, the top of the roast lacks crustiness.

Fourth method
Preheat oven to 350° F. and roast the meat at this temperature for the entire time. This is the easiest method. The shrinkage, as in the third method, is less than the first or second; the meat is always tender and the top is crusty brown.

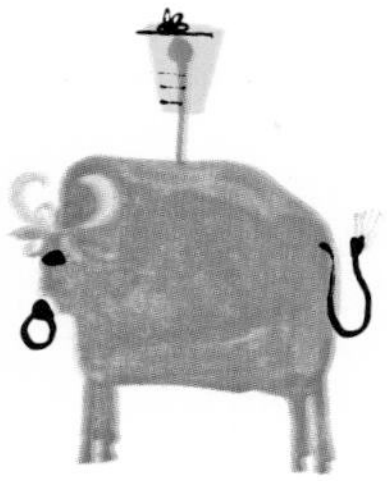

Meat thermometer
To roast any type of meat exactly as one wishes without the help of a meat thermometer requires a great deal of experience and a complete understanding of one's oven. Only a meat thermometer can give an accurate measurement of the degree to which a roasted meat is done. When this is coupled with a reliable roasting timetable, it is always possible to get good results. When the meat reaches the interior temperature indicated on the timetable, it is done to the degree indicated.

A good meat thermometer is designed with the reading gauge on the top, for easy visibility, and the tip is of pointed stainless steel, so that it can be inserted easily into the meat.

For the best results, and to make things easier for yourself, make a hole in the center of the thickest part of the roast with a metal skewer. Then insert the thermometer until the tip reaches the center of the meat. Be sure it is not in contact with the bone or heavy fat. This is easy to determine because you will feel the bone instantly and the softer fat will allow an easier penetration of the tip than the muscle part of the meat.

Kitchen scales will help you to find the accurate weight of the meat or poultry you cook. Not that the weight given on the package is inaccurate, but many changes occur in a piece of meat from the time it is originally cut and weighed to the time it is ready for roasting.

Cuts for roasting

When you choose a cut of meat to roast, evaluate its cost in relation to its bone and fat content. The fat, incidentally, is not to be scorned, because it adds juiciness and flavor. When you are looking for a steak or a fine roast, therefore, make sure to choose a cut with streaks of fat running through the lean. The butcher refers to a meat thus fatted as "well marbled," or maybe simply "marbled." 🔑 Remember, a good covering of fat is an indication that you are getting high-quality meat.

Beef

Beef has 2 hindquarters and 2 forequarters. Any cut from the hindquarters is more expensive than one from the forequarters.

The roasting pieces from the hindquarters are as follows:

ROUND. A 4-inch steak from the top round can be successfully roasted by the Third Method. You can identify the cut by the small round bone through the center. It is a semieconomical cut.

SIRLOIN TIP. This is a thick, triangular wedge of boneless meat which is the tip of the round. This is a tender and economical cut. It can be roasted successfully by the Third Method.

RUMP. A superb roast for flavor, this is a large even piece of meat, found just above the round. The whole rump weighs from 10 to 15 pounds. It is expensive as a whole roast unless many portions are required. It is generally cut into smaller roasts, and sold either with or without the bones. It is best when cooked by either the First or the Fourth Method.

LOIN. A large section of the beef, located between the ribs at one end and the round at the other. The loin end can be recognized by its wedge-shaped bone. The T-bone of the short loin provides the choice cuts: the sirloin roast, the porterhouse roast and the tenderloin. All of these are luxury cuts and should be roasted by either the First or Fourth Method.

FLANK. This is coarse grained, boneless and almost fat free. It adjoins the short loin of the beef. It is often overlooked, but it should not be, since it is tender and tasty and economical as well. Cook it to perfection by the Third Method.

The roasting pieces of the forequarter are as follows:

RIB. You have a choice between a standing rib roast and a rolled rib roast. The standing rib has more flavor because of the bones. The rolled rib is more economical in a top-quality piece, because it is boneless. The term "prime rib" refers to grade or quality of meat. The best piece is cut from the section nearest the loin and is referred to as "first rib roast."

A 3-rib piece, weighing 5 to 7 pounds, is more economical than a 2-rib piece and will roast better. Use the First or Third Method.

Veal

The loin with kidney attached is the most delicate and delicious cut to roast, but it is the least economical because there are so many bones. Roast by either the First or Fourth Method for Beef (p. 265).

The rib is also a good cut. To roast, use the Timetable for Veal (p. 269).

The leg, either whole or half, is also excellent. You will find it easy to carve and full of meat. To roast, use the Timetable for Veal.

The shoulder, either rolled or in a cushion shape, is an economical cut, tasty and full of meat. To roast, use the Timetable for Veal.

Regardless of the cut, veal, because of its blandness, requires more seasoning than other meats. Garlic, onion, or herbs such as tarragon, thyme or bay leaf, help greatly to bring out the very fine flavor.

When roasting veal by the First, Second or Fourth Method, use the same minutes per pound and temperatures as for beef. Specifications for the Third Method are shown below.

Timetable for roasting veal, third method

	Weight in pounds	Constant oven temp.	Interior temp. on therm.	Approx. total min. per pound
Leg with bones in	5 to 8	325°F.	170°F.	20 to 25
Leg, boned and rolled	4 to 6	325°F.	170°F.	35 to 40
Loin	4 to 6	325°F.	170°F.	25 to 30
Ribs	3 to 5	325°F.	170°F.	25 to 30
Shoulder	5 to 8	325°F.	170°F.	20 to 25

Lamb

Because almost all lamb in the United States comes from young animals, rarely over two years old, all cuts except perhaps the shank are tender. Genuine spring lamb is only two to three months old. Although more tender than the 1- or 2-year-old lamb, the spring lamb is less flavorful.

People sometimes hesitate to roast lamb because it is supposed to have a strong unpleasant flavor and odor. This is the result of overcooking. Lamb is a red meat and should be roasted in the same ways as beef.

The choice cuts of lamb for roasting are the leg and the loin. These are best roasted by the First or Fourth Method (p. 265).

An economical boned and rolled lamb shoulder is tender and makes an excellent roast. Unless the bones are removed, however, it is not a successful roast because carving is difficult. The best methods of cooking the unrolled shoulder are broiling or poaching. For roasting rolled shoulder use the Third Method.

For roasting lamb by the First, Second and Fourth Methods, use the same minutes per pound as for beef. The interior temperatures should read the same as given in the table on page 270 for the Third Method.

Timetable for roasting lamb, third method

	Weight in pounds	Constant oven temp.	Interior temp. on therm.	Approx. total min. per pound
Leg and loin	5 to 8	325°F.		
medium rare			140° to 150°F.	15 to 20
well done			175° to 180°F.	25 to 30
Boned rolled roast	3 to 5	325°F.		
medium rare			140° to 150°F.	20 to 25
well done			175° to 180°F.	30 to 35
Shoulder	4 to 6	325°F.		
medium rare			140° to 150°F.	15 to 20
well done			175° to 180°F.	25 to 30

Mutton seldom appears in our markets, although this meat is a favorite in England and in some European countries. Mutton is cut from older animals and consequently is stronger in flavor and much fattier than lamb. Nevertheless, when properly cooked it can be very good. Remember to allow for the extra fat just as you do when cooking a fatty piece of pork.

Pork, fresh

Pork is rich, fat and succulent when well done. For a top-quality roast choose a cut with fine-grained flesh, firm white fat and bones that are pinkish in color.

As with veal, the best cut for roasting is the loin. Pork loin is more economical than veal because pork has more meat in relation to the bones.

Timetable for roasting pork, fourth method

	Weight in pounds	Constant oven temp.	Interior temp. on therm.	Approx. total min. per pound
Whole pork leg	10 to 12	350°F.	185°F.	30 to 35
Loin				
center with tenderloin	3 to 5	350°F.	185°F.	35 to 40
half of loin	5 to 7	350°F.	185°F.	40 to 45
Shoulder				
boned and rolled	4 to 6	350°F.	185°F.	40 to 45
cushion	3 to 5	350°F.	185°F.	35 to 40

The loin of pork with the attached tenderloin is more expensive than the loin without the tenderloin, but both are choice pieces. If you buy the loin with the tenderloin, you can detach the tenderloin from the roast before cooking and use it for a separate meal. Of course, there is no bone in the tenderloin, so it is easy to serve.

A fresh pork leg (called a ham when it is smoked), either whole or half, is economical to roast and easy to carve.

Roast all cuts of pork by the Fourth Method only.

Pork, cured

Ham is the kind of cured pork we use most often for roasting, although we usually call it "baking" when we speak of ham. There is relatively little you need know about this because it will cook without being watched. A simple glaze will give it a certain glamour and enhance the flavor, but the ham can be equally delicious without it.

Whole hams, halves—either butt or shank end—and ham slices can be roasted, as can the shoulder butt or picnic shoulder.

Timetable for baking ham at 325°F.

Type	Weight in pounds	Internal temp.	Approx. baking time in hours
FULLY COOKED HAM			
bone-in whole ham	8 to 12	140° F.	2½ to 3
bone-in whole ham	14 to 18	140° F.	3 to 3½
bone-in half ham	6 to 8	140° F.	2¼ to 2¾
boneless whole ham	8 to 10	140° F.	2½ to 3½
boneless quarter or half ham	2½ to 5	140° F.	1½ to 2
picnic shoulder, bone-in	3 to 5	140° F.	1½ to 2½
picnic shoulder, bone-in	7 to 9	140° F.	2½ to 3½
COOK-BEFORE-EATING HAM			
bone-in whole ham	8 to 12	160° F.	2¾ to 3½
bone-in whole ham	14 to 18	160° F.	4 to 5
bone-in half ham	6 to 8	160° F.	2¼ to 3
picnic shoulder, bone-in	4 to 6	170° F.	2¼ to 3
picnic shoulder, bone-in	8 to 10	170° F.	4½ to 5½

Put the meat, fat side up, on a rack in an open roasting pan. Insert a meat thermometer into the center of the thickest part. Make a gash in the thick skin to facilitate penetration. Do not let the thermometer touch the bone. Do not cover the meat; do not wrap in foil; do not add water. Bake in a 325° F. oven for the length of time indicated on the timetable.

Even fully cooked ham is improved by baking. If you allow 20 minutes per pound in a 325° F. oven, you will greatly improve both the flavor and the texture. This really requires little effort. The ham will also keep better when refrigerated if treated in this way. If you want to give it a beautiful appearance, glaze it (pp. 282 and 283).

Standing rib roast with Yorkshire pudding

A 3-rib standing roast usually weighs 5 to 7 pounds. Do not use a boned and rolled piece of the ribs for this recipe.

5 to 7 pounds standing ribs of beef	Salt and freshly ground pepper
1 teaspoon dry mustard	3 tablespoons chopped beef fat

Remove the roast from the refrigerator an hour or two before roasting. Place the meat in a 2- to 4-inch-deep roasting pan (enameled cast iron is the best) with bones down, fat on top. Do not use a rack.

Rub the mustard on the red part of the meat. Sprinkle with salt and pepper. Then spread the chopped beef fat around the meat. Do not add water; the meat prepared in this manner is self-basting. Do not cover; this would steam the meat instead of roasting it.

Insert a meat thermometer to the center of the thickest portion of the meat, but avoid touching bone or fat. Roast according to the Second Method. The roast is cooked, rare, when the thermometer registers 140° F., medium at 160° F., and well done at 170° F. Makes 6 to 8 servings.

YORKSHIRE PUDDING

1 cup flour	1 cup milk
½ teaspoon salt	2 eggs

Sift flour and salt together in a bowl. Add the milk, and beat the mixture with a wire whisk or a hand beater until it is about as thick as cream. Beat the eggs until thick and pale yellow. Combine with the flour mixture and beat hard for another 2 to 3 minutes.

To cook the Yorkshire pudding in the roasting pan, in the English way, remove ½ cup of the drippings (for the gravy) before the heat is raised to 450° F. Set this aside. Pour the pudding mixture around the roast, then raise the heat to 450° F. and cook for 15 minutes. Lower heat to 350° F. and bake for another 10 minutes.

The Yorkshire pudding should be well browned and crusty around the edges. It should also be puffed up and slightly moist in the center.

Of course, you can bake Yorkshire pudding in a separate pan, or in muffin pans. If you prefer, you can use butter instead of the drippings from the roast to grease the pans. Makes 6 servings.

BROWN GRAVY WITH FLOUR

½ cup drippings (from the roasting pan)
3 tablespoons flour
1 to 1½ cups water, beef stock or vegetable cooking liquid
Salt and pepper
¼ teaspoon ground thyme, *or* 2 tablespoons Madeira wine, *or* 1 tablespoon HP Sauce or Worcestershire, *or* 2 tablespoons minced chutney

Heat the drippings in a cast-iron frying pan and add the flour. Stir constantly until smooth and well blended and lightly browned. Add the liquid and simmer for at least 5 minutes, stirring most of the time. For a velvety smooth sauce, beat it with a wire whisk. Taste, and add salt and pepper. Also add whichever seasoning you prefer. Simmer for 2 minutes and serve.

Roast rolled ribs of beef

2 flat beef rib bones
4½ to 5 pounds rolled rib roast
1 garlic clove (optional)
⅓ cup melted butter or salad oil
1 teaspoon salt
½ teaspoon pepper
¼ teaspoon dry mustard
½ teaspoon sugar
1 tablespoon brown gravy maker or soy sauce
6 to 9 medium-size potatoes

Place the flat beef bones (which you can obtain from your butcher) in the bottom of the roasting pan. Set the meat, with the fattest side up, on top of the bones. Cut the garlic clove in two. With a pointed knife make slits at each end of the meat and push the garlic into the slits.

Mix together the butter or oil, the salt, pepper, mustard, sugar and gravy maker or soy sauce. Rub all over the meat.

Insert the meat thermometer. Roast, following the Fourth Method, until the interior temperature registers 140° or 160° or 170° F., according to whether you want the meat rare, medium or well done. Makes about 8 servings.

PAN-BROWNED POTATOES

Place peeled whole medium-size potatoes in a bowl and pour boiling water over them. Cover and allow to stand for about 20 minutes. Drain and place around the roast after the roast has been in the oven about 25 minutes. Roll the potatoes in the drippings. Continue roasting the meat, and during this time turn the potatoes once or twice more in the drippings.

Make gravy just as you would for a standing rib roast.

Roast tenderloin of beef with Madeira sauce

- 2 flat beef bones
- 1 whole beef tenderloin (4½ to 6 pounds)
- 1 teaspoon salt
- ½ teaspoon coarse-ground pepper
- ¼ teaspoon dry mustard
- 2 tablespoons chutney, minced
- 4 tablespoons soft butter
- 1 cup thinly sliced fresh mushrooms
- ½ cup canned condensed beef consommé, undiluted
- 3 tablespoons Madeira wine

The technique for roasting this costly cut of beef is different from that used for other beef roasts. The tenderness, lack of fat and long narrow shape of the tenderloin make it necessary for it to be cooked quickly at a high temperature.

Use a shallow roasting pan 1½ to 2 inches deep when roasting beef tenderloin. Place the meat on 2 flat beef bones. Placing the meat on the bones is important because the meat should not touch the metal.

Mix together the salt, pepper, mustard, chutney and 2 tablespoons of the butter. Rub the top of the tenderloin with this mixture.

Preheat the oven to 450° F. Insert the thermometer in the meat. Roast for 20 to 40 minutes, or until the thermometer registers 140° F. (rare) or 160° F. (medium). Never change the oven temperature. The meat is at its best when the thermometer registers 140° F., because beef tenderloin should be served rare. 🔑 A thermometer is indispensable for consistently good results with beef tenderloin. When the roast is ready, remove it to a hot platter. Keep on a hot tray or in a warm place until ready to serve.

Add the sliced mushrooms and consommé to the drippings in the roasting pan. Stir over high heat, scraping the bottom of the roasting pan to loosen all the flavorful bits—these are meat juices. Boil for 1 minute. Then add the Madeira and the remaining 2 tablespoons butter. Simmer for about ½ minute. Pour into a warm sauceboat. Makes 8 servings.

Rolled chuck roast

A low-cost cut used for this recipe can be tasty and tender when cooked with the proper technique. Choose a roast that will be 5 to 6 inches thick at the end of the meat roll.

4 to 5 pounds rolled chuck
2 flat beef bones
1 teaspoon meat tenderizer
Juice of 1 lemon
6 medium-size potatoes
12 medium-size carrots
½ teaspoon crumbled dried savory or sage

Place the meat on the bones in a shallow roasting pan. Thoroughly moisten each side of the meat, patting cold water on it with your fingers. Mix together the meat tenderizer and lemon juice. Pierce the meat deeply with a sharp fork at ½-inch intervals. Pour the lemon-juice mixture over the meat and pierce a second time. Cover the roast with wax paper and allow to stand for 1 hour. Remove the paper. Roast, following the Third Method, for 25 minutes per pound, or until the thermometer registers 140° F. for rare or 160° F. for medium rare.

While the roast is cooking, peel the potatoes and carrots and place them in a bowl. Pour rapidly boiling water over the vegetables and allow them to soak for 30 to 40 minutes. Drain, then distribute them around the roast about 1 hour before you expect it to be done. Sprinkle the vegetables with the savory or sage, and baste two or three times with the drippings.

To serve, remove the roast from the pan and place on a platter with the vegetables around it. Make gravy, according to your taste. Makes 8 servings.

Baked meat loaf

The usual mixture for meat loaf includes beef, veal and pork, but all beef can be used. However, the veal adds flavor, and the pork, because it is fatter, adds juiciness. The proportions can be varied.

- 1½ pounds ground beef (hamburger, ground chuck or round)
- ¼ pound ground veal
- ¼ pound ground pork
- 1 teaspoon salt
- ½ teaspoon pepper
- ½ cup chopped parsley
- ¼ cup minced onion
- ¼ to ½ cup tomato purée
- 2 eggs
- 2 bay leaves

The meat must be well mixed. Have your butcher grind the meat together if you can. Spread it around the sides of a mixing bowl and sprinkle with salt and pepper. Add parsley and onion, tomato purée and eggs, and mix well to distribute all the seasonings evenly. Form the mixture with your hands into a loaf shape and put it in a baking dish that is at least an inch larger all-around than the loaf. Press the bay leaves into the top. Bake the loaf in a 350° F. oven for 1 to 1¼ hours. If the meat loaf does contain raw pork, be sure the interior temperature reaches 185° F. As the loaf bakes, fat and juices will escape and fill the baking dish. (Meat loaves made with bread crumbs or other starchy fillings will not do this.) Once or twice baste the loaf with some of the pan juices. Serve hot meat loaf with baked potatoes (baked in the oven with the loaf) and a green vegetable. Return leftover meat loaf to the baking dish and let it cool. The fatty layer that rises to the top can be removed, and the rest of the juices will be absorbed by the loaf. This will keep it juicy until the last slice is eaten. Meat loaf is very good served cold or in sandwiches. Makes at least 8 servings.

Roast loin of veal

This is a luxury cut greatly appreciated by French chefs, who refer to it as *la rogonnade,* which means the loin of veal with the kidney and its fat attached.

2 tablespoons salad oil
1 medium-size onion, diced
1 carrot, grated
1 celery rib, diced
4- to 5-pound loin of veal with kidney attached
1½ teaspoons salt
½ teaspoon pepper
½ teaspoon crumbled dried thyme
1 teaspoon paprika
4 tablespoons soft butter
1 can (10½ ounces) condensed beef consommé, undiluted

Heat salad oil in a frying pan. Add onion, carrot and celery. Stir over low heat for 8 to 10 minutes. Place in the bottom of the roasting pan. Put the meat, kidney side down, on the vegetables. Mix together salt, pepper, thyme, paprika and soft butter. Spread over top of the meat. Roast by the Fourth Method for Beef (p. 265) until the thermometer registers 170° F., or for 20 minutes per pound.

Add the consommé to the roasting pan and boil hard for 2 minutes. Pass the mixture through a strainer, or whirl in the blender, to have as much of the puréed vegetables as possible. Serve with pan-browned potatoes and buttered green peas and mushrooms. Makes 8 servings.

Leg of veal Italiano

Certain fish, such as tuna and anchovies, go well with veal, and the Italian chefs are best at preparing veal with these fish.

6- to 8-pound leg of veal
½ cup salad oil
½ cup diced celery
1 medium-size onion, diced
1 can (7 ounces) white tuna, chopped
8 flat anchovy fillets, diced
1 cup chicken consommé
Salt and pepper
3 tablespoons capers

Pat the veal as dry as possible with absorbent paper. Heat the oil in a large frying pan over medium heat and brown the meat all over. Place the meat in a roasting pan with celery, onion, tuna and anchovies. Add the consommé. Sprinkle the meat lightly with salt and pepper. Then cover the roasting pan with aluminum foil. Roast by the Third Method for Veal (p. 269) until the thermometer registers 170° F., or for about 25 minutes per pound. When done, remove the meat, strain the sauce and add the capers to it.

To serve cold, place the meat in a deep dish and pour the caper gravy on top; it will jell as it cools. Cover and refrigerate for 24 hours before serving.

This easy-to-carve roast is especially good served cold for a buffet dinner. Makes 10 or more servings.

Glazed roast leg of lamb

Lamb is enhanced by glazes and sauces even as ham is.

4- to 5-pound leg of lamb
1 teaspoon crumbled dried basil
1 teaspoon salt
¼ teaspoon pepper
¼ cup Dijon- or German-style mustard
¼ cup honey
2 tablespoons soft butter
1 cup canned condensed beef consommé, undiluted

Rub the leg of lamb with basil, salt and pepper. Place on a rack in a shallow roasting pan. Roast medium rare, using the Third Method (p. 265), or until thermometer registers 150° F. (approximately 15 to 20 minutes per pound), or cook until well done if that is your preference.

Combine the mustard, honey and soft butter. Spread on the meat about 20 minutes before it is done. Raise heat to 400° F. and continue to roast until the meat is nicely glazed, basting a few times. It should take 15 to 20 minutes.

To make the sauce, remove the meat to a platter and place the roasting pan over direct heat. Add the cold consommé to the drippings and stir, scraping the bottom of the pan. Bring just to a boil and pour into a hot sauceboat.

Serve with baked potatoes, cooked while roasting the lamb. Makes 6 to 8 servings.

Roast rack of lamb à la française

The rack comes just before the loin (see chart p. 324) and consists of all the rib chops in one piece, or the two rib roasts still attached. The French chef always removes the layer of meat that covers the end of the bones. This cut makes a perfect roast, good for special occasions.

1 rack of lamb (about 3 pounds)
1 teaspoon salt
¼ teaspoon pepper
½ teaspoon crumbled dried basil
½ teaspoon paprika
3 tablespoons salad oil

Place the rack standing up on the back bones, directly touching the bottom of the roasting pan. Sprinkle with salt, pepper, basil and paprika. Pour the salad oil on top. Roast by the Second Method for roasting beef (p. 265), until the thermometer registers 160° F., or for 20 minutes per pound.

Serve with boiled potatoes, baked or broiled tomato halves and a green salad. Makes 4 servings.

Baked lamb loaf

2 cups soft crustless bread cubes or shreds
1 cup milk
1 egg, beaten
1½ to 2 pounds ground lamb
½ green pepper, finely chopped
1 cup shredded raw carrot
½ cup diced celery
2 teaspoons Angostura bitters
1 teaspoon minced fresh or dried basil
¼ teaspoon pepper
1½ teaspoons salt
3 tablespoons butter

Place bread cubes or shreds in a bowl and cover with milk. Mash into a paste with the fingertips. When blended, add beaten egg and ground lamb; mix. Add green pepper, carrot and celery; mix thoroughly. Add bitters, basil, pepper and salt. Mix with your hands until blended. Shape into a loaf and put in a loaf pan (9 × 5 × 3 inches). Dot with butter. Bake in a 300° F. oven for 1 hour. Serve hot or cold. Makes 6 to 8 servings.

Rolled shoulder of lamb, Texas style

The tart sauce used on this lamb shoulder need not be limited to this cut. Use it with winter lamb, which is somewhat drier and heavier than the spring lamb.

3- to 4-pound lamb shoulder, boned and rolled
½ cup butter or bacon fat
½ cup cider vinegar or lemon juice
1 teaspoon salt
½ teaspoon pepper
½ teaspoon crumbled dried thyme, basil or rosemary
½ teaspoon dry mustard

Place the meat on a rack in a shallow roasting pan. The meat can be stuffed with a few pieces of garlic to taste. Roast by the Third Method for roasting lamb (p. 270) for 2 hours, or until the thermometer registers 170° F., or for 35 minutes per pound.

Bring to a boil the butter or fat, vinegar or lemon juice, salt and pepper, the herb of your choice, and the mustard. Use to baste the roast every 15 minutes. When the sauce is used up, continue to baste with the juices in the pan until the meat is cooked. Serve with baked potatoes, glazed onions or buttered lima beans, and a tart-flavored sauce made with pan juices. Makes 8 servings.

Roast pork Auvergne

This dish comes from a farm in Ambert, a town in the Auvergne.

- 4- to 5-pound loin end roast of pork, boneless or with bones
- Salt and pepper
- ½ teaspoon ground sage
- ½ teaspoon grated nutmeg
- 2 garlic cloves
- 1 onion, chopped
- 1 bay leaf
- ¼ cup chopped parsley
- 2 cups light red wine
- 1 can (10½ ounces) condensed chicken consommé, undiluted

Rub the pork with salt, pepper, sage and nutmeg. Place the meat fatside down in a Dutch oven. Add garlic cloves. Brown the meat on all sides over medium heat. The meat will release enough fat; do not add any. Add onion, bay leaf, parsley and wine. Cook, uncovered, in a 350° F. oven for 30 minutes per pound. Turn the meat a couple of times during the roasting.

Remove meat to a serving platter. Add the consommé to the pan juices and bring to a fast boil while scraping the bottom of the pan. When all the brown bits are well mixed into the liquid, strain the gravy into a gravy bowl. Serve with baked potatoes (baked while cooking the meat) and green beans flavored with orange rind. Makes 6 or more servings.

Roast leg of pork

The leg of pork, or fresh ham as it is sometimes called, can be cooked either boned or with the bone in, the same as with cured ham. It can be roasted whole or halved. The whole leg weighs about 12 pounds and would be too large for most families, but either butt or shank half makes a good roast.

1 half leg of pork (about 6 pounds)
Salt and pepper
1 teaspoon ground sage
1 garlic clove, crushed
2 cups apple juice or strong cider

Rub the roast all over with salt, pepper and sage. Spread the garlic on top. Place on a rack in a roasting pan. Add the apple juice or cider. To roast use the Timetable for Pork (p. 270) until the thermometer reads 185° F., or for 35 minutes per pound. Serve with buttered noodles, coleslaw and applesauce. Makes 8 servings.

Cranberry dressing for pork

This dressing can be used to stuff a crown roast of pork or a boned leg of pork. To serve with a roast loin of pork, bake the dressing separately.

¼ cup butter
1 cup diced celery
1 large onion, diced
2 medium-size apples, peeled and chopped
6 cups diced bread
1 teaspoon ground sage
¼ teaspoon ground marjoram
1 can (8 ounces) whole cranberry sauce
¼ cup brown sugar
1 teaspoon salt
Grated rind of 1 orange
½ cup fresh orange juice

Melt the butter in a frying pan and add the celery, onion and apples. Stir over medium-low heat until softened, but do not brown. Add the diced bread, sage and marjoram. Place the cranberry sauce, brown sugar, salt and orange rind in a saucepan. Stir together over low heat until the sugar is dissolved. Add to the bread mixture. Add the orange juice gradually, continuing to mix until the bread is moistened.

To bake separately, put in a baking dish and bake, covered, at 350° F. for 1 hour. Makes about 2 quarts.

Roast stuffed pork tenderloin

A pork tenderloin is an ideal cut for a small roast.

1¼ to 1½ pounds pork tenderloin
2 cups Cranberry Dressing (above)
½ teaspoon salt
¼ teaspoon pepper
½ teaspoon curry powder

Pound the tenderloin with the flat side of a cleaver to flatten it, then slit open a pocket in the meat and fill with dressing. Tie securely.

Mix the salt, pepper and curry powder. Rub all over the stuffed tenderloin. Place in a well-oiled roasting pan without a rack. Roast by the Fourth Method for Pork (p. 270) until the thermometer registers 185° F., or for 35 minutes to the pound.

Serve with brown potatoes and broccoli with butter and lemon juice. Makes about 4 servings.

Baked ham

While we talk of "roasting" other meats, for some reason we always talk of "baking" ham, although the process is the same. Whole hams, half hams, butt or shank end, ham slices from the center of the ham, smoked shoulder butt, picnic shoulder, smoked loin can all be baked. Follow the timetable on page 271, or read the packer's directions on the ham you buy. Different curing methods may require different treatment, and this should be described on the wrapper. If you buy a whole ham or a piece without the wrapper, be sure to determine whether the ham is fully cooked or tenderized or requires a long cooking time.

Glazing ham

All kinds of ham can be enhanced by glazing. About 30 minutes before the ham is done, take it out of the oven and remove the rind. Cut off the brown top fat and score the remaining fat in an S-shape design with a punch-type can opener, or form crisscross diamonds with a sharp knife.

Choose a glaze; spread it over the ham with a spoon. Return the ham to the oven and bake again at 375° F. until the ham is well glazed. Baste it two or three times.

SIMPLE GLAZE

Spoon honey, maple syrup or corn syrup on the ham and pat brown sugar on top.

CHEF'S FAVORITE

Heat 1 cup apricot jam with the grated rind of 1 orange, or 3 tablespoons rum, or ½ cup finely chopped walnuts. Spoon over ham. Heated jam by itself also makes a good glaze.

AMERICAN FAVORITE

Heat 1 tablespoon prepared mustard with 1 cup red-currant jelly, ½ teaspoon ground cloves, ½ teaspoon ground cinnamon and ½ cup firmly packed brown sugar. Spoon over ham.

HONEY-CITRUS GLAZE

Stir 1 cup honey with the grated rinds of 1 orange and 1 lemon. Spoon over ham.

Rum ham

The combination of rum, oranges and brown sugar makes a delicious glaze. Even though it takes time to cook, it requires little attention, which makes it a good party dish.

1 fully cooked ham, any size	1 cup brown sugar
1 to 2 teaspoons whole cloves	3 oranges, unpeeled
	1½ cups rum

Wrap the ham of your choice in heavy-duty foil and bake in a 300° F. oven. Figure on 35 minutes to the pound. (Any size ham can be baked this way.)

About 1 hour before ham is done, remove from the foil. Remove the rind with a sharp knife and score the fat. Stud with cloves. Pack brown sugar on top. Pour off the fat from the pan. Slice the oranges unpeeled. Arrange slices in the bottom of the baking pan. Set the ham on the bed of oranges. Slowly pour rum over the top. Return the pan to the oven for 1 hour. Baste the ham a few times with the liquid in the pan. A 6-pound boneless ham will make 8 to 10 servings.

BRAISING AND POT-ROASTING

The difference between braising and pot-roasting is in the amount of liquid used. In braising very little liquid is added. Braising vegetables and the natural juices supply most of the moisture. In pot-roasting liquid is added in variable quantities. In both processes the meat is browned first, usually in hot fat, but sometimes by a quick searing in oven or broiler.

The suitable cuts for braising are listed in the timetable on page 284. Smaller pieces of these same cuts can be either panfried or sautéed.

Braised roasts are economical and give you the most

flavor for your meat dollar. Also, a steady diet of oven roasts, steaks and chops, no matter how good, can become dull. A well-braised roast ends up with an accumulation of delicious flavors, with no single flavor predominant. To obtain the best results the meat must be cooked slowly over low heat. However, the roast requires no attention apart from preparation. Braising has an added advantage: it produces its own gravy, which can be served with the roast. With oven-roasted or pot-roasted meats the gravy has to be made by the cook.

A braised roast will also be even more delicious if it is refrigerated overnight. Before serving it the next day, warm it up exactly as it was cooked originally, that is, covered and over very low heat. A word of warning: if the roast is to be left overnight, use a stainless-steel or enameled cast-iron pan. Flameproof glass or ceramic pans are also excellent.

Braising can be done on top of the stove or in the oven, as you will see on the timetable. The oven temperature may range from 250° to 350° F. At the lower temperature it will take longer.

Timetable for braising

(over low heat on top of stove, or in the oven between 250° and 350° F.)

CUT	APPROXIMATE TIME
Beef	
Brisket, chuck, flank, round, rump, sirloin tip, short rib	whole: 2½ to 3½ hours small, or cut small: 1½ to 2½ hours
Veal	
Blade, breast, neck, round, shoulder, flank	whole: 45 minutes to 1½ hours small, or cut small: 45 minutes to 1¼ hours
Pork	
Shoulder chop, tenderloin, cubed shoulder, spareribs	1 to 2 hours
Internal Meats	
All kidneys, sliced thin	10 to 20 minutes
Liver, in one piece (1 to 2 pounds)	45 minutes to 1 hour
Heart, whole	1 to 3 hours

Timetable for braised lamb

	Weight in pounds	Time in hours
Shoulder roast, boned and rolled	3	1¾
	5	2¾
Shank	¾ to 1¼	2
Shoulder chops (½ inch thick)		½
Heart	¼ to ½	1¾
Shoulder, neck (cut into 1½ inch cubes)		2
Breast	1½ to 2	2

Braised chuck roast

This is a versatile recipe. Without liquid it is braised beef; with liquid it becomes a beef pot roast. Cook a large piece because this is excellent to serve cold, in thin slices.

4 tablespoons flour
1 teaspoon salt
½ teaspoon pepper
1 teaspoon paprika
1 teaspoon crumbled dried savory *or* ½ teaspoon crumbled dried thyme
1 teaspoon ground ginger
4 to 5 pounds beef chuck or shoulder
4 tablespoons melted beef fat or oil
2 onions, finely chopped
1 large carrot, grated
½ cup minced celery leaves

Blend together the flour, salt, pepper, paprika, savory or thyme, and ginger. Roll the meat in the flour mixture and pound in as much of the seasoning as you can.

Brown the meat on all sides in the fat or oil over medium heat. When the meat is browned, remove from the pan. Add the onions, carrot and celery leaves to the pan. Stir the vegetables around in the fat until they are well softened. Place the meat on top of the vegetables in the braising pan. Cover and simmer for 2½ to 3 hours over low heat, or in a 300° F. oven, until the meat is tender. Makes about 10 servings.

TO MAKE A POT ROAST, proceed as for braising, but add 1½ cups tomato juice or beef consommé and ½ teaspoon sugar. Simmer until meat is tender. For the last 30 minutes of cooking, add whole or diced carrots and medium-size potatoes.

Braised lamb shanks with Breton beans

- 3 lamb shanks (1 pound each, or larger if you can get them)
- 1 cup dried green flageolet beans
- 1 teaspoon salt
- 4 tablespoons chopped shallots
- 1 tablespoon olive oil
- 2 cups stewed tomatoes, chopped
- 1 cup red wine
- 2 teaspoons grated lemon rind
- 1 teaspoon crumbled dried oregano
- Pepper
- Chopped parsley

Start this recipe a day ahead. If you have a covered casserole or braising pan large enough to hold the lamb shanks without their being cracked, leave them whole. Otherwise ask your butcher to crack them to make 2 pieces of each. Place the shanks in the casserole with no fat, liquid, seasoning or any other additional ingredients. Cover and roast in a 350° to 400° F. oven for about 1½ hours. You can do this while the oven is being used for other cooking. Let the pot cool, then refrigerate it till the next day. Meanwhile, soak beans overnight in water to cover.

Next day drain the beans, cover with fresh water, and add 1 teaspoon salt. Bring to a boil and simmer gently for about 1 hour. Let the beans cool, then drain them. They should not be mushy.

Take the baked lamb shanks from the casserole and separate the meat from the bones; leave it in large chunks. Do not discard the bones. Remove and discard all the fat in the casserole, but leave the browned meat juices. Sauté the shallots in the oil in a frying pan, then add the tomatoes, mix well, and turn all into the casserole. Add the drained beans, wine, lemon rind, oregano and a little black pepper. Stir gently to mix, then put the pieces of meat and the bones into the mixture; the bones add flavor. This will fill a 6-cup casserole to the top.

Bake the casserole in a 350° F. oven for 1 hour. Then retrieve and discard the bones. Sprinkle with parsley and serve from the casserole. Makes 6 servings.

In this recipe the oven baking in the beginning takes the place of browning in fat. The extra liquid is used to finish cooking the beans and will all be absorbed at the end of the cooking period.

Pot-roasted short ribs with lemon

3 tablespoons butter or olive oil
5- to 6-pound piece of short ribs, in one piece
½ cup brandy
1 can (10½ ounces) condensed beef consommé
Salt and pepper
⅓ cup fresh lemon juice
1 teaspoon crumbled dried thyme

Melt butter (or heat olive oil) in a deep heavy kettle. Place the ribs in it and brown the piece all over. Warm the brandy (do not boil), pour half over the meat when browned, ignite, then pour on the other half. When the flame dies add the undiluted consommé. Cover the kettle and bake the meat in a 225° F. oven for 4 to 5 hours, or until fork tender. Do not raise the heat to speed up cooking; this would spoil the quality of the finished dish.

Remove the meat to a hot platter. Add salt to taste and sprinkle with a good portion of pepper. Skim as much fat as possible from the liquid in the pan. Stir in lemon juice and thyme. Simmer for 5 minutes. Pour the gravy into a sauceboat. Serve the meat sliced thin, with the gravy and rice. Makes 6 to 8 servings.

Easter leg of lamb

5- to 6-pound leg of lamb
1 cup water
1 tablespoon butter
1 onion, stuck with 3 cloves
1 large carrot, sliced
2 slices of unpeeled lemon
2 celery ribs, diced
8 to 10 parsley sprigs, chopped
1 teaspoon crumbled dried basil or oregano
1 teaspoon salt
½ teaspoon pepper
1 cup beef or chicken consommé
½ cup red wine
½ cup light or heavy cream
2 tablespoons browned flour (see note)

Place the leg of lamb in a roasting pan with the water. Cover and cook over high heat on top of the stove until the water evaporates. Uncover, add the butter, and still over high heat brown the meat all over. Remove the lamb from the pan and discard all the accumulated fat from the pan.

In the bottom of the pan place the onion, carrot, lemon slices, celery, parsley, and basil or oregano. Stir until well mixed. Place the lamb on top of these vegetables, and add salt and pepper and consommé. Cover and simmer over very low heat for 1½ hours.

Blend together the wine, cream and browned flour. Pour over lamb. Stir around until well mixed with all the ingredients. Cover and simmer for another 30 minutes. Remove the meat to a hot platter. Strain the gravy and serve it separately. Makes 6 to 8 servings.

Note: To brown, stir all-purpose flour constantly over low heat in a dry, heavy skillet until golden brown.

Braised ham steak

Slash the fat around the edges of the steak. Heat 1 to 2 tablespoons butter or salad oil in a large frying pan. Sauté the ham on both sides over high heat until lightly browned here and there. Cover and simmer over very low heat for 20 to 30 minutes, turning the ham once. A 2-pound ham steak should give you 4 to 6 servings.

Variation: After the ham is browned, add ¼ to ½ cup cider, red wine or orange juice. Cover and cook as above.

Lamb chops bergerie style

6 loin lamb chops, *or* 3 pounds lamb shoulder cut into 2-inch squares
2 tablespoons olive oil
1 tablespoon butter
12 small white onions
8 small carrots
Salt and pepper
½ teaspoon crumbled dried thyme
Grated rind of ½ lemon
½ pound mushrooms, sliced
½ cup dry white wine

Brown the lamb chops or pieces of shoulder in the olive oil and butter. Remove to a casserole dish. Add the onions and carrots to the fat remaining in the pan and stir until brown here and there. Add to the lamb. Sprinkle with salt and pepper, the thyme and lemon rind. Top with sliced mushrooms and pour the wine over all. Cover. Simmer on top of the stove over very low heat, or bake in a 350° F., oven, for 50 to 60 minutes, or until the meat is tender. Add more wine if the pot gets dry. Makes 6 servings.

BROILING

To broil or grill, the meat is placed some distance from the source of heat. It is the radiating heat that actually does the cooking.

A certain amount of shrinkage occurs in meat when cooking, no matter what technique is used. It is caused by the natural meat juices seeping through the surface. These juices become part of the cooking liquid or gravy, depending on how the meat is cooked. In broiling, the juices extracted from the meat are evaporated almost immediately by the heat radiating overhead. This evaporation or drying-off process forms a brown crust on the top of the meat being broiled.

Since excess juices falling into the pan under the grill are usually very fat, or overcooked, they are indigestible and should be discarded.

Broiling is used on very tender cuts of meat, which should be cooked quickly to prevent hardening or drying of the muscle. To achieve this, the first heat penetrating the surface of the meat must be quick and hot so that the center of the meat is raised quickly to cooking temperature. This contrast between the degrees of doneness on the inside and outside of the meat distinguishes broiled meats from those cooked by other methods. The outside of the meat is cooked and browned much more than the inside.

To sear the top of the meat, the broiler should be preheated for at least 15 minutes. Rub the meat generously with soft butter or oil and broil as close to the source of heat as can be managed without having the fat catch on fire, from 2 to 4 minutes. This searing speeds the formation of the brown layer on the top and keeps the juices from escaping. Finish the broiling with the meat about 3 to 4 inches away from the source of the heat.

You can tell when steaks and chops are cooked by the appearance of small drops of blood on the *uncooked* side of the meat. At that point turn the meat and wait again for the juice to appear in small droplets, which is the signal that the meat is cooked.

🔑 If yours is a gas broiler, broil with the door closed, because gas flames consume smoke and absorb moisture. 🔑 If your broiler is electric, leave the door slightly ajar during the broiling period, to expel moisture from the oven. Whether your broiler is gas or electric, make sure that you have read the specific directions for your particular stove. There are usually special mechanical adjustments you will have to make to get the best broiling results.

The position of the broiler pan in any type of oven depends on what is being cooked. The following is a list of foods which, after the first few minutes of searing, should be placed so that they are 2 to 3 inches from the source of the heat: meat to be cooked rare; food requiring only brief cooking; food that is to be heated or browned on top. The following should be placed 4 inches or more from the source of heat: thick steaks, after the first minute of searing; steaks and all other meats that are to be well done; foods that require long cooking.

Remember, for best results in broiling it is important to choose tender cuts. Ask for choice or prime grade when buying steaks. Have them cut at least 1 inch thick and not more than 2 inches thick. You will find that steaks less than 1 inch thick are better panbroiled or pangrilled.

O┳ Slash edges of fat on steaks or chops in several places to prevent curling of the meat.

O┳ Brush all foods with oil, soft butter or margarine before broiling. You can also sprinkle with paprika to help browning. For extra flavor, add lemon juice to the oil or butter.

For crispness, roll foods to be broiled in fine bread crumbs—except for steaks and chops.

O┳ Sprinkle with pepper before broiling, but add salt only after broiling. Salt may draw the flavorful juices to the surface and slow the browning.

O┳ Have the meat at room temperature for 1 hour before broiling. This reduces the cooking time and gives a browner top to the meat.

If an emergency requires that you broil frozen or very cold steaks or chops, broil them 4 to 5 inches away from the source of heat (this will therefore be a lower temperature) and for a longer period. Frozen meat needs 25 to 50 percent more cooking time than meat at room temperature.

Always grease the broiler rack before putting the

meat on it. Because the rack will be hot from preheating, use salad oil and spread it on with a brush.

🗝 Do not remove all the fat from steaks or chops when broiling. Fat gives extra flavor to the meat and to some extent helps to hold in the juices.

🗝 Do not use a fork to turn meat. Use tongs, or a wide firm spatula. Meat should not be pricked with the tines of a fork, because juices will be lost that way.

During the last 5 minutes of broiling, you can place on the rack well-oiled and well-seasoned halves of tomatoes, slices of mild onions, and mushrooms cut into thick slices if they are large, or left whole if they are button mushrooms.

Timetable for broiling meat in preheated broiler

TOTAL BROILING TIME IN MINUTES

	Thickness	Rare	Medium	Well done
Steak	1 inch	12	15	20
	1½ inches	15	20	25
	2 inches	25	30	35
Flank steak (London broil)		7	9	12
Lamb chops	1 inch	8	10	12
	1½ inches	12	15	18
Beef patties	1 inch	10	15	20
Liver	¾ to 1 inch	8	10	12
Kidney		8 to 10 minutes in all		
Bacon		2 to 3 minutes on each side		
Pork sausages		3 to 4 minutes on each side		

Cuts for broiling

Beef: Steaks—club, porterhouse, rib, sirloin, T-bone; flank; tenderloin; ground meat patties; beef frankfurters. Veal: steaks; chops; cutlets; calf's liver. Lamb: chops—loin, rib, shoulder; sirloin; ground meat patties; liver; kidneys, split in two. Pork: bacon, sausages, ready-cooked ham slices.

Broiled ham steaks

The 1½- to 2-inch-thick tender center-cut slices of ham are delicious broiled. Before cooking, slash the fat around the edge with a sharp knife to prevent the slice from curling. Brush one side of the ham steak with half of a mixture containing 1 teaspoon each of brown or white sugar and prepared mustard. Then brush with melted butter. Broil according to timetable. Brush the second side with the remaining sugar, mustard and butter.

Timetable for broiling ham steaks

Thickness of slice	Distance from heat	Approx. cooking time per side, minutes
Fully cooked ham		
½ inch	3 inches	3 to 5 (do not turn)
1 to 3 inches	4 inches	5
Cook-before-eating ham		
½ inch	3 inches	5
1 inch	4 inches	10
1½ inches	4 inches	12

If you prefer your meats extremely well done, you may adjust these tables to broil for a longer time.

Perfect broiled sirloin steak

A 1- to 1½-inch sirloin steak is a family-size steak. It includes a large section of tenderloin, a large section of loin and a small amount of bone. It is cut from the loin of the beef, which is the most expensive of major beef cuts and the tenderest.

If the steak has been frozen, it should thaw in the refrigerator for 9½ hours, or on the kitchen counter for 4 hours to reach room temperature.

1 sirloin steak (2 pounds)
3 tablespoons salad oil
1 teaspoon coarse-ground pepper
4 bay leaves

Brush the steak on both sides with the salad oil. Sprinkle with the pepper. Place on the grill of a preheated broiler. Broil 2 inches from the source of heat for 4 minutes, then turn and sear on the other side in the same manner. Continue cooking 3 to 4 inches from the source of heat for 5 minutes on each side for very rare, 6 minutes on each side for rare, and 10 minutes on each side for medium rare. 🗝 Two minutes before the meat is cooked, top with the bay leaves and allow them to scorch on top of the meat.

Serve with chive butter (melted butter and chives) and sliced tomatoes. Makes 4 servings.

Bourbon steak

2-inch-thick porterhouse steak (about 3 pounds)
½ cup Bourbon
6 tablespoons soy sauce
Juice of ½ lemon
2 tablespoons salad oil
1 garlic clove, crushed
½ teaspoon curry powder
½ teaspoon crushed black peppercorns

Place steak on a platter. Combine Bourbon, soy sauce, lemon juice, oil, garlic, curry powder and peppercorns. Mix thoroughly and pour over the steak. Cover and allow to remain in the refrigerator for 4 to 12 hours before broiling.

Remove steak from the marinade mixture. Broil in a preheated broiler 2 inches from the source of heat for 4 minutes on each side. Then move to 5 inches from the source of heat and broil for 10 minutes on each side for rare, or longer if you prefer your steaks well done. This also makes a fine dish to be cooked at an outside barbecue.

To serve, remove the bone and cut the meat into thin slices on the bias. Makes about 6 servings.

Broiled hamburger

Though we usually think of panfrying hamburger, this versatile meat is very good broiled. Since it often contains considerable fat (unless specifically ground from a lean cut with no added fat), broiling is actually a better way to cook it. The meat will be less caloric and more digestible.

Shape the meat into flattened patties about 1 inch thick. You can season the meat first if you wish. You can make 4 patties from 1 pound of meat. Broil about 2 inches from the source of heat according to the timetable (p. 291).

Hamburgers with surprises

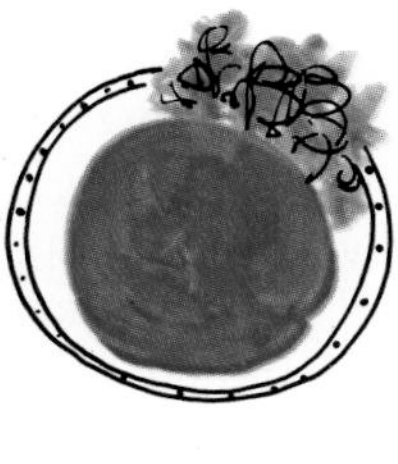

2 pounds hamburger
1 teaspoon salt
½ teaspoon coarse-ground black pepper
1 medium-size onion
1 small green pepper, ribs and seeds removed
6 tablespoons sour cream
3 to 4 ounces blue cheese

Flatten out the hamburger in a large mixing bowl. Sprinkle with salt and pepper. (You can add more salt and less pepper if you prefer, but don't forget the cheese is salty.) Chop or grind the onion and green pepper to make very small bits and sprinkle that over the meat. Add the sour cream. Fold the whole mixture together and mix with the hands only until the additional ingredients are reasonably even throughout. 🔑 Do not handle hamburger more than necessary because it loses juiciness and flavor when overhandled. Shape into 6 large patties about 1½ inches thick. Divide the cheese into 6 portions. Make a hole in each patty and fill with a portion of cheese, then fold the meat over to contain the filling completely.

Broil about 4 inches from the source of heat, but allow about 8 minutes per side for rare because the patties are thick. If the cheese starts to ooze out of the patty, you have cooked it too long. When done, the cheese should be just melted in the middle. Serve with mashed yellow squash and a salad of green beans and red onion rings. Makes 6 servings.

Panbroiling

Panbroiling is cooking in a shallow open container over the heat source, instead of by overhead radiation. Though you use a heavy metal frying pan heated from below, the final result of panbroiling is entirely different from panfrying and much more like oven broiling. Panbroiling is by far the best way to deal with thin slices of meat such as chops or steaks under 1 inch in thickness, or when only small portions are required. To oven broil these cuts would dry them out and they would become hard and be overcooked.

In order to panbroil with success, remember the following points: 🔑 The meat should be dry. Pat it with absorbent paper before cooking. The meat can be marinated or tenderized, but be sure to pat it dry before you start to cook it.

🔑 The pan should be very hot. To check the heat, place a square of newspaper in the middle of the frying pan and wait until it gets brown. When this happens, the pan is ready to use.

A heavy metal electric frying pan, preheated to 400° F., can be used. Keep it at the same temperature throughout the panbroiling period.

When the pan is hot, rub it lightly with the fatty part of a chop or steak, or with a small piece of bacon. Place the meat in the prepared hot pan and cook over high heat until crusty brown on one side. Then turn the meat, sprinkle the cooked side with salt and pepper, and cook the other side. For timing, use the broiling timetable (p. 291) but cut the given time in half. For example, 8 minutes on each side in oven broiling is reduced to 4 minutes on each side in panbroiling.

When chops and steaks are thick and the fat looks pale, turn the meat on end and hold it there to let the fatty sides brown.

O┳ A little secret for crisper, darker rims on chops is to brush them with brown gravy maker and cook 1 to 2 minutes longer.

O┳ Pour off any fat that accumulates in the frying pan as the meat is being cooked. Otherwise you will be frying and not panbroiling.

Barbecuing

Broiling or grilling outdoors over an open fire has become a favorite national pastime in recent decades. All the knowledge you have about indoor broiling will be useful here, but remember that the source of heat is below the food and juices will fall down into the fire unless you take special precautions. Also, the heat is less easy to regulate than in your indoor broiler. All kinds of barbecuing equipment are available, or you can cook without any, as campers and woodsmen do. If you buy any piece of equipment, from a small Japanese *hibachi* to a Mexican black-iron *brasero,* you will get special instructions with it. Familiarize yourself with these directions, and learn which is the best fuel and where to buy it.

The recipes for barbecuing on the following pages can be adapted to the indoor broiler. Any broiling recipe can also be adapted to the barbecue.

Barbecued steak

Marinate the steak for 1 to 12 hours depending on how sharp a flavor you want (see Chapter 6 for marinades). Sprinkle the steak generously with brandy 15 minutes before you start to barbecue. Rub the steak with a piece of suet or brush it with oil to prevent it from sticking to the grill. Place the steak on the grill about 3 inches above the glowing charcoal. Cooking time will depend on the thickness of the meat, temperature of the fire, and how you like your steak done. A basic timing, however, allows 6 minutes for each side. Baste the steak occasionally with soy sauce or HP Sauce while it is cooking. Turn the steak only once during broiling.

O━ Just before removing the steak from the grill, throw a few bay leaves on the charcoal and smoke both sides of the steak over this for a few seconds. At the moment of serving, top each sizzling steak with Seasoned Butter (recipe below).

Barbecue a 1½-inch-thick steak—a porterhouse, sirloin, T-bone or rib steak (about 4 pounds)—3 inches from the glowing coals for 6 to 10 minutes per side.

Barbecue a 1-inch-thick steak, also 3 inches from the coals, for about 4 minutes per side.

Barbecue a cube steak cut from the round or flank 3 inches from the coals for 7 to 8 minutes per side.

SEASONED BUTTER

Blend together 4 tablespoons butter, 1 teaspoon seasoned salt, ½ teaspoon paprika and 1 teaspoon Worcestershire sauce. Form into balls and refrigerate until ready to serve.

Steak can also be served with just salt and pepper and a dab of butter.

Steak can be basted with a special sauce while barbecuing. A simple marinade is made of 1 garlic clove, ½ teaspoon dried thyme and 1 cup salad or olive oil. Let the mixture blend for 12 hours, then dip the steak into the seasoned oil before cooking. More can be brushed on during cooking to keep steak from getting too dry.

Hamburgers or lambburgers

Make 6 large patties with 2 pounds of ground meat. Grill 5 inches from the coals for 4 to 6 minutes on each side.

Barbecued frankfurters

Split the frankfurters or knackwurst and spread with a thin layer of good coarse liverwurst. Top with prepared mustard and minced dill pickle. Then roll each sausage in a slice of boiled ham. Secure with metal skewers. Broil over hot coals until the meat browns.

This is an excellent barbecue to serve at a men's party with a choice of toasted buns or black bread, and really cold beer.

Butterfly leg of lamb

Ask the butcher to bone a 5- to 6-pound leg of lamb. Spread the boned meat out flat so that it resembles the shape of a butterfly. Insert 2 long metal or wooden skewers through the meat in the form of a cross. The skewers keep the meat flat while cooking and they also help in turning it.

Place the meat fat side down on the grill, 3 inches above a medium charcoal fire. Grill for 30 minutes on the first side, then turn and grill on the second side for 30 minutes. This will give you medium-rare lamb. While cooking, brush the meat frequently with Herb Butter (recipe below).

To carve the butterfly lamb, start at one end and cut the meat across the grain into ¼-inch slices. Makes 6 to 8 servings.

HERB BUTTER

Melt 4 tablespoons butter; add the juice of 1 lemon or lime, ½ teaspoon crumbled dried basil, 1 teaspoon crumbled dried savory and 1 teaspoon instant coffee powder.

Lamb chops

Have the lamb chops cut 1 to 1½ inches thick, from the loin, rib or arm. Barbecue them 4 inches from the coals for about 8 minutes per side.

If you like, marinate lamb chops overnight in a basting sauce with fresh mint and dry rosemary. Or you can use Honey Mint Marinade (p. 169). Use the sauce to baste the lamb chops while broiling.

Persian kebab

There are hundreds of ways to make kebabs. These kebabs are prepared with ground lamb, so cheaper cuts of meat can be used.

Mix 2 pounds ground lamb with chopped onion to taste, 1 egg, salt and pepper to taste, 2 tablespoons flour, 1 teaspoon curry powder, and 1 tablespoon chopped fresh mint or 2 tablespoons crushed dried mint. Mix until smooth. Shape into oblong patties about 5 inches long, 1½ inches wide and 1 inch thick. Refrigerate, covered, for a few hours.

Push a skewer through the patty, and add a thick slice of tomato. Barbecue for 10 minutes on each side. Serve on a bed of hot rice sprinkled with fresh mint. Makes 6 servings.

Barbecued ham steak

Use only moist tenderized ham cut 1½ inches to 3 inches thick; a thin slice dries up. Remove any thick rind. Place the ham on the grill over medium-hot coals and cook for 20 to 30 minutes, turning 3 or 4 times, meanwhile basting frequently with the following paste:

2 teaspoons dry mustard
1 cup firmly packed brown sugar
½ cup orange juice, sherry or pineapple juice

A thinner slice of precooked ham can be barbecued 3 inches from the coals for 10 to 12 minutes. Baste the meat often with a mixture of ½ cup commercial sour cream and 1½ to 2 tablespoons of horseradish mustard. This keeps the ham moist and adds flavor.

COOKING IN FAT

To fry foods, we cook them in or with fat. There is quite a difference between the process we call "sautéing," which requires only enough fat to keep the food from sticking to the pan, and deep-frying, which involves immersing the food completely in fat in a deep pan or kettle. The most familiar deep-fried food is probably French fried potatoes, and this method is sometimes called French frying. Another cooking method, called shallow-frying or panfrying, uses fat ½ to 1 inch deep in a shallow frying pan.

For sautéing or panfrying, oil, butter, margarine and all-purpose vegetable shortenings are satisfactory because the foods cook quickly and the fats do not have time to break down and scorch, as they would for longer frying jobs.

In deep-frying, the fat is heated to a much higher temperature and held there for a relatively long time; therefore a high smoking point is important. This eliminates butter, margarine, olive oil, or any fat that will smoke or burn at moderate heat, thus altering the flavor.

Almost any food—meat, poultry, fish, vegetables, fruits, pastries—can be cooked by frying, whether sautéing, panfrying, or deep-frying.

There is some confusion about the terms sautéing and panfrying. Sautéing is a very quick cooking process in which meat is tossed in very little butter or fat in a sauté pan or frying pan over fairly high heat. This method is used for meat that requires high heat and quick cooking. The pan used for this is called a *sautoir* in French. It is a shallow pan, usually fairly large, so the food can be sautéed and quickly turned over.

Panfrying is done in a small amount of fat in a shallow frying pan; this method is used for food that requires a certain amount of cooking after being browned, such as chops.

How to sauté

Use a large frying pan of good quality with a flat bottom because it is important to have even heat distribution.

Beware of using too much fat. The best combination is 1 teaspoon salad oil to 2 teaspoons butter for each pound of meat. 🔑 Always combine butter with oil, since butter alone cannot be heated to the proper high temperature without burning. Make sure the fat is hot enough before adding the meat or other food being sautéed.

Food to be sautéed must be as dry as possible, because dampness will prevent successful browning and searing. This is especially important with fish and meat. 🔑 Wrap these tightly in absorbent paper for 2 minutes before sautéing.

As soon as the fat is hot, the meat should be ready to add immediately. The browning must be done in a matter of minutes. Of course the rest of the meal should be ready to be served. Sautéed foods are instant foods and do not wait.

🔑 One last word of caution: Be very careful not to overcrowd the pan, because insufficient space between the pieces will cause the meat to steam rather than brown and the juices will be lost. This is one of the reasons a large frying pan is recommended for sautéing.

Coatings

Many sautéed or panfried foods are coated to help the browning process. Some of these coatings are flour, egg and bread crumbs, and batter. The pieces of meat or other foods are rolled in or dipped into the coatings.

FLOUR—During the cooking period, the starch bursts and the flour gluten sets, giving a light coating to the food.

EGG AND BREAD CRUMBS—The egg sets with the application of heat and holds the bread crumbs. If you use egg only, you will have a light coating. With bread crumbs added to the egg, the coating is stronger and also enhances the appearance.

BATTER—This is a coating which is used less for sautéing than for deep-frying, although it is often used for sautéing seafood such as scallops and oysters. A batter is composed of flour, milk and eggs. The effect of hot fat on batter is similar to its effect on flour coating.

How to panfry

Use a heavy cast-iron or enameled cast-iron frying pan to panfry successfully.

Use enough fat of your choice to cover the bottom of the frying pan. When the fat is quite hot, add the meat and sear on both sides to brown. This is done over high heat. When the meat is browned, lower the heat to a more moderate level. Do not cover the pan.

Season the meat with pepper but no salt. When herbs are being used, add them at this stage. Cook, usually for 4 to 6 minutes per side, turning only once, after the searing is done. This timing, incidentally, applies not just to meat but to most foods that are panfried.

When the food is done, remove it from the pan and serve immediately. Never leave panfried food standing in the pan, because water will accumulate which will steam the food and give it an unattractive color.

TO MAKE GRAVY: After the meat has been removed from the pan, add to the hot drippings a few spoonfuls of cold water, tea, wine, tomato juice, consommé or cream. Stir this over medium heat, scraping the pan to retrieve any of the brown meat juices which have stuck to it. This takes only a minute or so.

Veal scallops with mustard-wine sauce

If you live in a community where there are people of Italian ancestry, first ask the butcher for *scaloppine* for this dish. If not, ask him to cut thin slices from the leg. All connective tissues should be cut away, making ovals of meat about the size of an orange slice. Pound them, or ask the butcher to do this, to make flat thin slices. There is no end to the ways of seasoning and garnishing these tender morsels; this is only one example.

1½ pounds veal slices, cut from the leg
Flour
3 tablespoons olive oil
2 tablespoons butter
4 tablespoons Dijon-style mustard made with wine
1½ cups dry white wine, at room temperature
Salt and pepper

This much veal will make a surprising number of little slices. They must be sautéed in a single layer, so use a large sauté pan, or several pans, or cook them a few at a time. Sprinkle flour on a sheet of wax paper; press both sides of each veal scallop into the flour. They should retain only the thinnest film of flour; shake off any excess. Heat half of the oil and butter and cook the slices for 2 or 3 minutes on one side; turn. Add the rest of the oil and butter as needed. Mix the mustard with an equal amount of the wine. With a pastry brush spread a little mustard on the cooked side of each of the scallops. Sprinkle with salt and pepper. Cook for 2 minutes on the second side, then turn, brush with mustard, and season. Immediately add the wine; bring it to a boil, and remove the pan from the heat. Transfer the meat to a platter. Put the pan back over heat and stir to retrieve all the meat juices. Add any remaining mustard; heat, and strain the sauce over the meat. Serve with spaghettini sprinkled with cheese, and green peas cooked with mushrooms and white onions. Makes 6 servings.

Super hamburgers

2 pounds round steak
3-inch square of beef suet
1 teaspoon seasoned salt
1 teaspoon plain salt
½ teaspoon freshly ground pepper
3 tablespoons minced parsley
½ teaspoon minced fresh or dried thyme
2 cups red wine
4 tablespoons butter

Have the butcher put the steak and suet through the chopper three times, or do it yourself.

As soon as you get home, put the meat mixture in

a bowl and add the seasoned salt, plain salt, pepper, parsley and thyme. Mix lightly with a fork. Pour the red wine over the meat, but do not mix. Cover and refrigerate all day.

When ready to cook, mix the wine with the meat. Shape into 6 large flat patties. Melt the butter. When it is very hot, brown the patties quickly, then lower the heat and continue to panfry until they are done, about 5 minutes per side. Do not overcook. There is enough suet in the hamburger mixture to keep the butter from burning. Serve with hot French bread and a green salad. Makes 6 servings.

Veal chops Toscanini

This dish was created for the great Maestro at a Paris dinner that followed a Wagner concert he directed in honor of Cosima Wagner, then a very old lady.

4 thick loin veal chops
4 thin slices of bacon
¾ cup grated Swiss cheese
Pepper
5 tablespoons butter
Salt
4 large ripe tomatoes, peeled
½ teaspoon sugar
½ teaspoon crumbled dried thyme
Juice of 1 lemon

Make an incision in the side of each chop large enough to form a small pocket. Dice the bacon. For each chop, mix one fourth of the diced bacon with 1 teaspoon of the grated cheese. Pepper the inside of the pocket and fill with the bacon and cheese mixture.

Melt 3 tablespoons of the butter in a heavy enameled cast-iron frying pan. When butter is light brown, add the chops and brown for 5 minutes on each side, turning only once. Add salt and pepper to taste, cover, and panfry the chops over very low heat for 15 minutes.

In the meantime, place the peeled whole tomatoes in a shallow baking dish and sprinkle with the sugar and thyme. Put dish in a 450° F. oven for 5 minutes. Place a veal chop on each tomato. Pour over the chops any juices accumulated in the pan. Sprinkle the whole with the remaining grated cheese and the rest of the butter cut into tiny dice. Return to the oven until the cheese is melted and chops are crusty brown on top. Remove from the oven and pour the lemon juice on top. Makes 4 servings.

DEEP-FRYING

Pan for deep-frying

The best utensil to use is a narrow deep pan or kettle with straight sides; it must be made of heavy metal. Or use an electric deep fryer with thermostatically controlled heat.

If there is too little fat, food will burn on the bottom. If there is too much fat, it may bubble over and catch on fire. 🗝 If this should happen, douse any flame with a heavy sprinkling of baking soda.

Fats for deep-frying

The very best fat for good flavor and perfect frying is the suet from ribs and kidneys of beef. This has to be rendered over very low heat. Other meat fats, such as lamb fat, can be prepared in the same way.

Lard is pork fat that has already been rendered. It is solid and must be melted before being used in order to gauge the correct amount. The added work is worth it because lard gives a sweet, delicate flavor and a non-greasy finish to food fried in it.

Vegetable oils give a glossy appearance to foods. It is easy to gauge the needed quantity because they are liquid. Peanut oil is best for deep-frying. Many vegetable oils add no flavor of their own to foods, but some, such as sesame-seed oil, give a delicate flavor to foods fried in them.

Vegetable shortening is a vegetable oil that has been treated with hydrogen to make it solid at room temperature and to keep it from spoiling. This gives good results in deep-frying.

Bacon fat and chicken fat are excellent for shallow frying, but they do give foods a flavor of their own. They can be used for deep-frying when mixed with some of the other fats already mentioned.

Whatever fat you choose, you must use one that can be heated to a high temperature without burning. Burning fat smokes and develops an unpleasant flavor which is transmitted to the food being cooked.

Storing used fat

First, never allow the used fat to remain in the fryer. Let it cool. Then, when it is tepid, strain the fat through a sieve lined with several layers of cheesecloth or a double layer of absorbent paper. This operation removes all foreign particles, such as bits of food, batter or coating from the used fat.

Return the strained fat to its container and while it is still warm add 1 cup of fresh fat of the same kind. This prolongs the life of the frying fat. Store in a cool dark place or in the refrigerator.

Temperatures for frying

O━ The secret of success in deep-frying is to heat the fat slowly over medium-low heat until it reaches the correct temperature; then try to maintain that temperature throughout the entire frying period. Fat that is not hot enough soaks into the food and the food overcooks before it browns. Fat that is too hot burns the food on the outside before the interior is well cooked.

A rule of thumb is that almost all foods will fry properly when the fat is at 365° to 375° F., but to be more specific,

> *uncooked foods,* such as doughnuts and fritters that are made of raw fish, will cook best at 365° to 375° F.;
>
> *uncooked foods with a large water content,* such as potatoes and onions, will cook best at 380° to 390° F.;
>
> *cooked foods,* such as croquettes that are made of chopped or ground cooked meat, will cook best at 375° to 385° F.

The old-fashioned method of determining when the fat has reached the correct temperature is to brown a 1-inch cube of bread. The cube should be browned in 60 seconds if the fat is at 365° to 370° F. The bread you use for this must be two or three days old and dry. A frying thermometer is, of course, the most accurate guide.

Coatings for fried foods

While it is possible to fry foods without a coating—potatoes for instance—this does not always result in the crispy golden morsels, cooked throughout but not greasy, that a good coating helps to achieve. The pieces of food can be rolled one at a time in flour or crumbs, or dipped in milk and then rolled in flour or crumbs. The Japanese dip their foods into a batter called tempura batter, and the delicious shrimps prepared this way are a familiar item in Japanese restaurants. The English use a mixture of egg, water and oil, with seasoning; so this kind of coating is called *à l'anglaise.* The foods are coated with bread crumbs after being dipped into the *anglaise* mixture.

Egg and crumb coating is particularly good for deep-frying as well as for other kinds of frying. In the case of mixtures such as croquettes, egg helps to hold the pieces together.

To obtain a chef's result, prepare the food ahead of time, dip it into the egg and crumbs, then refrigerate it for one hour before frying. This allows the egg to dry and any excess liquid in the food to evaporate. The coating will then adhere better.

Basic method to coat food

For 1 to 2 pounds of food, beat 1 egg and 1 tablespoon cold water with a fork, only enough to blend the two. Add ½ teaspoon salt, ½ teaspoon paprika and ¼ teaspoon pepper.

Spread the coating material on a sheet of paper. This coating can be fine bread or cracker crumbs, cornmeal, instant potato powder or flour. Any of these can be combined, and part of the coating can be grated cheese. You will need about 1½ cups of any of these, plain, combined, or with cheese added, for this amount of food.

Dip the prepared food into the coating material. Do this gently; you want only a light coating. Then dip the food into the egg mixture, then a second time into the coating material. Set the dipped pieces on a plate, one piece next to the other. Do not overlap or put one over the other. Refrigerate for at least 20 minutes, or when possible for 1 hour; then the food is ready to be deep-fried.

Batter coating

Almost any batter can be used but thin batters make a thinner layer and a more delicate product. See Index for examples of other batters. Here is a version of the Japanese batter.

Tempura batter

1 cup flour	1 cup water
½ teaspoon salt	2 egg whites
½ teaspoon baking soda	

Sift flour, salt and baking soda together. Mix in water and egg whites and beat with an egg beater till thoroughly mixed. The batter will be thin.

Dip the food into the batter. Let any excess drain off. Chill the food, if time allows, to set the coating.

How to deep-fry

Prepare the food and refrigerate for 1 hour, if possible. Fill the frying kettle half full; it should be deep enough to allow the largest piece of food to be completely immersed. Slowly bring the fat to the correct temperature. When it has reached this point, add the food. The pieces can be added directly to the fat, or they can be lowered into the fat in a frying basket. Be careful not to overcrowd the pan, because this lowers the temperature of the fat. Add only a few pieces at a time, and do it gently to prevent spattering.

Turn deep-fried foods only once. Use a slotted spoon, for a fork or a pointed knife will cause a puncture in the crust and allow the hot fat to soak in.

Remove the finished foods from the fat with a slotted spoon—or lift out the frying basket—and drain on a double layer of absorbent paper placed on a baking sheet or on a thick layer of newspaper.

If additional fat is needed to keep the pan filled to the correct point, add the new fat when the pan does not contain food, and slowly bring the fat back to the correct temperature.

Meats for frying

Tender pieces of meat such as squares of beefsteak, nuggets from lamb chops or steaks, or small pieces of veal cutlets or scallops if they are not cut too thin are best for frying. Coat them, or dip in batter. Cook a test piece for about 3 minutes, then cut it open to see if it is done. If it is not, add another minute or two to the cooking time. Meats are delicious combined with deep-fried pieces of eggplant, green pepper, cauliflower and onion rings. Remember to salt only when you are ready to serve the food.

COOKING IN LIQUID

These next cooking methods are based on the principle of cooking in liquid. In each case the aims are identical: to extract flavor from the vegetables and to tenderize the meat. While this process is going on, the liquid becomes richer as it absorbs the flavors of both meat and vegetables. Meat that is cooked in liquid must never boil. Boiling will toughen even the tenderest piece of meat and make it fibrous. It is the slow cooking, or simmering, that makes the meat tender.

To understand the difference between boiling and simmering, let us look at the thermometer: Water boils when the temperature reaches 212° F. It is at this point that bubbles rise constantly and break at the surface. When water simmers, the thermometer registers between 185° and 190° F.; at this stage bubbles form slowly and collapse below the surface. When they reach the surface and break there, the boiling point has been reached again.

Of course, you do not need to check the water with a thermometer every time you cook food in it. If you watch the water carefully when you put it on to boil, you will easily see the difference between simmering and boiling.

How to stew

For a stew, meat is usually cut into 1- to 2-inch cubes, as uniform in size as possible, not only for the sake of appearance, but to ensure the pieces will be evenly cooked as well.

Roll the meat in seasoned flour. Mix 3 tablespoons flour, 1 teaspoon each of salt and paprika, ½ teaspoon pepper and ¼ teaspoon herb or spice for each pound of meat. Vary the spices and herbs and the finished product will be quite different each time. 🗝 The small quantity of paprika suggested helps the meat to brown and gives a rich brown color to the liquid. It is not used to flavor the meat, since more than this amount would be needed for flavor. Put the mixture on a large plate and roll the meat in it; or put the flour mixture in a paper bag, add the meat and shake until the meat is coated.

Next, brown the meat. Use a Dutch oven, an enameled cast-iron pan or a heavy stainless-steel saucepan.

Use 3 tablespoons fat per pound of meat. You have a choice of bacon fat, meat drippings, margarine, butter, oil, prepared dressing, melted meat fat or diced salt pork. Each will give a different flavor to the finished product. Heat the fat until it is hot, then add the meat, just enough at a time to cover the bottom of the pan. When there is too much, the meat will steam and remain whitish instead of browning. Brown over a fairly high heat. Remove the browned meat to a plate and continue until all the pieces are done. When the browning is completed, return all of the meat to the pan.

However, in some "white" stews the meat is not browned first. See Irish Stew for an example.

Now comes the addition of the liquid. The liquid used can be water, half water and half wine, or all wine; canned tomatoes, tomato juice, vegetable juice or the cooking water from vegetables. You can also use water with the juice and rind of any citrus fruit: 1 cup citrus juice for each 3 cups of water. Again, each chosen liquid will give a different flavor to the stew. O━ The liquid must also sear the meat, so it must be boiling rapidly just before it is poured in.

Now add the vegetables; onion, garlic and all root vegetables can be used. In general, use 2 cups or 1 pound vegetables per pound of meat. The vegetables can be left whole or diced, quartered or cut into thick or thin slices. And have no fear that they will be broken up or will disappear in the sauce if they are cooked for the same length of time as the meat. They will not if you keep the stew at a constant simmer; it is boiling that disintegrates vegetables.

Cover the pan tightly and simmer everything over low heat until the meat is tender. O━ Remember, *do not boil,* because the whole secret of a good stew, or stewing in general, is the long slow cooking in a tightly covered pan.

The meat you use, the spices, the fat and the liquid in turn will each influence the final flavor. So you will be able to make hundreds of different kinds of stews by using your imagination, without having a specific recipe for each one.

For length of cooking time refer to the timetable on page 310 for stewing and poaching.

How to poach

Poaching is a very useful cooking operation. Many cooks overlook, or altogether fail to realize, that the tougher the meat, the more flavorful it is. O┳ The tougher cuts are those that cost less and yet have more flavor than more expensive tender cuts. Fast cooking concentrates the elusive flavor of tender meat; poaching tenderizes and brings out the full flavor of tougher meats.

O┳ The liquids used for poaching are often acidulated with fresh lemon juice, cider vinegar, dry wine or even beer, especially stale beer, which has a tenderizing effect and also gives an added flavor. For example, the world-famous Belgian *carbonnade,* which is a simple beef stew, is poached with beer as part of the liquid. Each acidulated liquid that is used will give a different final flavor to the dish.

Choose the meat, and use the timetable for stewing and poaching for meat cuts that are especially good cooked this way. Stainless-steel, flameproof glass or ceramic, or enameled cast-iron saucepans are the best kinds for poaching. The size is also important; the saucepan or pot must contain the meat comfortably with enough space for the liquid.

In poaching as well as in stewing, the meat can be browned before adding the liquid, especially when there is a need to improve the color and flavor of the meat. Do not coat with seasoned flour as you would do for stew. The type of fat used and the proportions are the same as those that are used in stewing.

When the meat is not browned, you may want to melt the fat over medium heat and roll the meat in it until the meat is well coated. This is done to close the pores of the meat so it will retain most of its natural juice. (However many meats to be poached are simply dropped into the pot and the cold liquid is added.) Then season with salt, pepper, spices and herbs to taste, just as for stewing. Vegetables are also added, whole, sliced or diced, to be served with the poached meat, or to be used as flavoring or as a garnish.

O┳ Cover the meat next with cold liquid, contrary to the method used in stewing where you use boiling liquid. In poaching it is important to use just enough water to barely cover the meat. The greater the volume of water, the less flavorful the taste of the whole. Of course the liquid can be all water or a combination of the other liquids mentioned before. Bring the water to the boiling point over medium-low heat. Do not bring to a fast rolling boil, but just to the point where you see a quivering of the surface of the liquid and the formation of scum around the edge. Remove the scum. Then, turn the heat very low. Cover tightly and simmer very gently until the meat is tender.

At no time during the cooking process should the liquid boil. Also, be careful not to overcook the meat. The timetable that follows will give you a fair idea of the approximate time required for different cuts.

Timetable for stewing and poaching

(on the top of the stove, or in a 250° to 300°F. oven)

CUT	APPROX. TIME
Beef brisket, flank, plate, rump;	3 hours
Beef cut into 1-inch squares: flank, rump, shin, short ribs	2 hours
Veal cut into 1-inch squares: breast, shoulder, flank, neck	1½ to 2 hours
Lamb cut into 1-inch squares: breast, shoulder, flank, neck	1½ to 2 hours
Pork, fresh shoulder, pig's feet or knuckles	2 to 3 hours
Pork, cured smoked ham, 10 to 12 pounds	25 minutes per lb.
over 12 pounds	20 minutes per lb.
half ham	30 minutes per lb.
picnic shoulder	45 minutes per lb.
fully cooked ham	20 minutes per lb.
Variety Meats	
heart	1½ to 2½ hours
tongue	3 hours

Here is a secret which gives poached meat that is to be served cold a perfect flavor, tenderness and juiciness. O‑┳ Cook the meat for 20 to 30 minutes less than you would to serve it hot, and then cool the meat in its own liquid, in a cool place, but not in the refrigerator. The hot liquid will continue the cooking process without the help of the heat from the stove.

To serve hot, remove the meat from its cooking

liquid only when ready to serve, at the end of its full cooking period. This will prevent the meat from drying on top, which happens when meat is exposed to air or stands for any length of time.

Belgian beef carbonnade

This family dish is world renowned. The combination of beer, brown sugar and thyme blends into one delicate, pleasant flavor. Since the stew is twice as good reheated again over low heat, make it for the family in a large quantity. It also freezes exceptionally well.

- 4 tablespoons flour
- 2 teaspoons salt
- 1 teaspoon pepper
- 1 teaspoon paprika
- 3 pounds round steak or chuck, cut into 1-inch cubes
- ½ cup butter or margarine
- 6 large onions, sliced
- 1 garlic clove, halved
- 1 bay leaf
- ¼ teaspoon dried thyme
- ½ cup chopped celery leaves
- ¼ cup chopped parsley
- 3 tablespoons brown sugar
- 2½ cups beer
- 2 tablespoons cider or malt vinegar

Blend together the flour, salt, pepper and paprika. Roll the meat cubes in this mixture until they are well coated. Melt the butter or margarine in a large heavy metal saucepan. Add the onions, and sauté over medium heat until they are softened and tender. Be careful not to brown them. Remove the onions from the pan with a perforated spoon, pressing out as much fat as possible.

Place the same pan over high heat and sear the cubes of meat, a few at a time. This operation will give color to the finished *carbonnade*. Return the onions and meat to the pan, and set it over low heat.

Tie together in a square of cheesecloth the garlic, bay leaf, thyme and celery leaves. Add to the meat, sprinkle the parsley on top, and add the sugar and beer. Bring to a simmer, while stirring, then cover tightly and poach over low heat until the meat is tender, about 1½ hours.

Discard the *bouquet garni,* or cheesecloth bag of seasonings. Add the vinegar. Simmer for 5 minutes. Serve with a dish of boiled potatoes and a beet salad or pickled beets. Makes about 6 servings.

French beef daube

A *daube* is a stew cooked in a pot with an absolutely airtight cover. A French cook would seal the cover to the pot with a ring of flour and water pastry. The food in a *daube* is always cooked over low heat for a long time.

¼ pound fat salt pork
2 to 3 pounds stewing beef (top round or lean short rib), cut into 1-inch cubes
8 to 10 medium-size white onions
½ teaspoon dried thyme
1 bay leaf
2 whole cloves
2 or 3 garlic cloves, crushed or minced
3 tablespoons flour
Salt and pepper
3 cups dry red wine
1 cup beef stock
½ pound fresh mushrooms
2 pounds green peas, shelled and blanched, *or* 1 package (10 ounces) frozen green peas

Cut the salt pork into cubes, and brown the cubes in a Dutch oven. When salt pork is brown, add the beef cubes. Brown on all sides over high heat. Add onions, thyme, bay leaf, cloves, garlic and flour. Sprinkle with a little salt (about 1 teaspoon—remember the pork is salty) and a little pepper. Stir together over medium heat for 2 minutes. Heat the wine and stock, add to the meat, and cover. Simmer over low heat for 2 to 3 hours, or until the meat is tender.

Add fresh mushrooms, cut into thick slices, and peas. Simmer for 20 minutes. Serve with mashed potatoes. Makes 6 to 8 servings.

Poached beef brisket

Fresh brisket can be delicious when poached. When the meat is cold, it should be moist and tasty and you should be able to cut it into paper-thin slices.

3 pounds boneless beef brisket
Salt and pepper
1 teaspoon dry mustard
1 onion, chopped
1 celery rib with leaves, chopped
1 bay leaf
1 teaspoon brown sugar
3 cups cold water

Sprinkle the brisket with salt, pepper and mustard. Spread these all over the meat with your hands. Place the onion, celery, bay leaf and brown sugar in the bottom of a casserole. Add the cold water. Mix well. Place the meat on top. Cover tightly and poach in a

300° F. oven for 3½ hours, or until the meat is tender. Serve with Mustard Sauce (p. 188). Makes about 6 servings.

To serve cold, keep covered, allow to cool, then refrigerate until cold.

Cumberland hot pot

This is a specialty of Cumberland, England; it is usually made with the neck of lamb cut into chops. It makes a most tasty stew-in-a-casserole.

- 2½ to 3 pounds lamb for stew
- 2 tablespoons drippings or butter
- 2 onions, finely chopped
- ½ teaspoon ground thyme
- 6 tomatoes, peeled and chopped, *or* 1 can (20 ounces)
- 1 teaspoon honey or sugar
- 6 potatoes, peeled and diced
- Salt and pepper
- ½ cup beef stock or water
- Chopped parsley

Cut lamb into equal pieces. Remove excess fat. Brown all the pieces in drippings or butter over high heat. Add chopped onions. Stir for a few minutes and put into a casserole. Sprinkle with thyme. Add tomatoes and pour honey or sugar on top. Place potatoes over all, and sprinkle with salt and pepper. Add beef stock or water. Cover and bake in a 350° F. oven for 1½ hours.

At serving time uncover and sprinkle generously with chopped parsley. Serve with any flavorful table sauce. Makes about 6 servings.

Irish stew

- 3 pounds lamb for stew
- 12 medium-size potatoes
- 4 large onions, sliced thick
- Salt and pepper
- ½ teaspoon ground thyme
- 2 cups cold water

The neck is a low-priced cut. Ask your butcher to reserve 3 pounds of lamb neck in advance; it is worth the trouble. But other inexpensive cuts will do.

Remove excess fat from the meat, if necessary, and then cut into sections through the bones. Your butcher can also do this for you, but do not let him remove the bones as they are necessary for flavor.

Peel the potatoes and cut four of them into thin

slices, as for scalloped potatoes. Leave the rest whole.

In the bottom of a heavy metal saucepan or casserole, place the sliced potatoes, then half of the sliced onions, and top this with the pieces of lamb. Season generously with salt and pepper. Sprinkle the rest of the onions with the thyme and place them on top of the lamb. Surround them with the remainder of the potatoes, left whole. Pour the cold water on top. Cover tightly. Cook in a 350° F. oven for 2½ hours, or simmer over very low heat for the same length of time. The sliced potatoes thicken the juice, and the top ones, left whole, will retain their shape. Serve with bowls of capers, good homemade mustard and chopped parsley. Makes 6 servings.

Poached lamb shanks Nice style

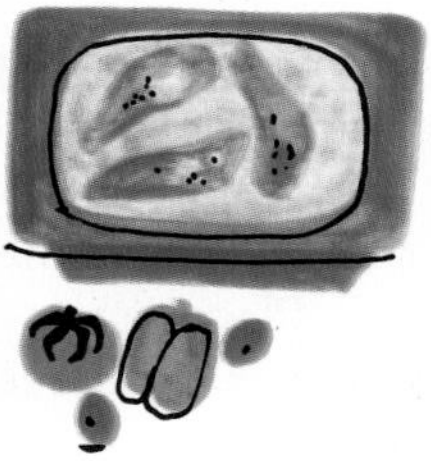

It is too bad that we do not make more use of lamb shanks. They have good flavor and texture, with gelatinous meat. The Indians use them to make superb curry; the Scots poach and braise them; the French poach them with green peppers, olives and tomatoes.

- 4 to 6 meaty lamb shanks
- 2 tablespoons fresh lemon juice
- 1 teaspoon salt
- ¼ teaspoon pepper
- Grated rind of 1 lemon
- 3 tablespoons olive or salad oil
- ½ teaspoon dried basil or rosemary
- 1 garlic clove, minced
- 1 onion, quartered
- 2 green peppers, quartered
- ¼ cup black olives, pitted
- 4 tomatoes, peeled and sliced
- 2 cups hot beef stock, white wine or water

Ask your butcher to give you the whole lamb shanks without cracking the joints. Rub the meat with lemon juice, then roll it in the mixed salt, pepper and lemon rind.

In a large heavy metal saucepan heat the oil and brown the shanks over high heat. Lower the heat and sprinkle the shanks with the basil, or rosemary, and the garlic. If any lemon juice is left, pour it on top. Arrange the onion over the meat. Add the green peppers, olives, tomatoes and the liquid. Bring the whole to a simmer. Cover tightly and poach in a 325° F. oven for 2½ hours, or until the meat is tender. Serve with rice or lentils. Makes 4 to 6 servings.

Boiled ham

The art of boiling ham is almost lost because there are so many precooked or fully cooked hams available. This should really be called "poached ham," because at no time should it boil. Nothing can replace a poached ham for picnic meat, to make sandwiches, or simply to serve as cold cuts on a hot summer day.

This is a good basic recipe which is easily varied. Your imagination will suggest variations once you have tried this recipe. A word of caution: a ready-to-eat ham should not be poached.

- 8 cups cold water
- 8 cups beer, apple juice, red wine or cider
- 3 carrots, quartered
- 4 onions, quartered
- 1 garlic clove, halved
- 4 celery ribs with leaves
- 8 peppercorns
- 1 tablespoon dry mustard
- 6 whole cloves
- 10- to 18-pound cook-before-eating ham

Place all the ingredients, except the ham itself, in a large saucepan. Bring to a fast rolling boil. Lower the heat and simmer for 30 minutes. This flavors the water (like a *court bouillon*).

Lower the ham into the simmering water. Cover and keep simmering over low heat for 25 to 30 minutes per pound—30 minutes per pound when the ham is to be served hot; 25 minutes per pound when it is to be served cold. To serve cold, remove the pan from the heat when the cooking period is up and place it in a cool place. Let the ham cool in the liquid. Remove the skin from the ham while it is hot.

If you want to, a poached ham can be glazed in the same way as ready-to-serve ham.

Without a glaze, the ham, either hot or cold, can be covered with minced parsley. A 10-pound ham will make 12 to 14 servings.

Fricasseeing

Fricasseeing, like braising and stewing, combines two basic techniques: browning, which is contact with hot fat; and cooking in liquid or sauce, which is poaching. In a sense, a fricassee is a thick stew, usually made with pieces of chicken, rabbit, lamb or veal poached in a seasoned liquid. The special difference is that a fricassee is finished in a *sauce velouté* made with the cooking liquid.

Fricassee of veal

The following recipe is a good basic example of a fricasseed meat. Later you will find a recipe for fricassee of chicken (p. 364), which is probably the meat most frequently cooked this way, but the method works well for veal too.

5 tablespoons butter
2 pounds veal, cut into 1-inch cubes
Salt and pepper
Pinch or two of grated nutmeg
1 small onion, minced
1 cup milk
4 tablespoons flour
2 cups veal stock
Mushrooms (optional)
Paprika or minced parsley

Melt 2 tablespoons of the butter in a heavy saucepan and add the cubes of veal. Cook them over medium heat until browned on all sides. Then sprinkle with salt, pepper and the nutmeg, and add the onion. Pour the milk on top. Bring to a simmer, cover tightly, and simmer over low heat, or cook in a 250° F. oven, for 2 hours.

Melt the remainder of the butter and add the flour. Stir and blend together over low heat until the flour is cooked, but do not let the mixture brown. Strain the milk from the veal into the cooked roux and beat with a whisk to blend. Then add the stock, whisking all the time over medium heat until a smooth velvety sauce is formed. Add more seasoning if necessary.

You can add sliced fresh mushrooms to the sauce when you add the stock; the mushrooms will cook in the sauce. Or add drained canned mushrooms at the very last minute.

Pour the sauce over the veal and sprinkle with paprika or minced parsley. Makes about 6 servings.

INTERNAL MEATS

Internal meats, which are often completely overlooked, provide healthy variety in the diet. These include liver, kidneys, heart, sweetbreads, tripe, tongue and brains. They are well worth learning how to prepare and serve, for they can provide many delicious and economical dishes. These meats are sometimes called "variety meats." Each has a distinctive flavor, texture and shape. All are considered delicacies, and yet they can be classified as economical family fare, because they all have special food value and are high in vitamins A, B, C and G. Liver in particular is especially high in iron, vitamin A, riboflavin and niacin. Also, these meats are boneless and waste free. As a general rule, you can count on 4 servings per pound.

Calf's liver brochettes

Brochettes is French for skewers. Cook the skewered liver over direct heat on a covered barbecue.

1 pound calf's liver
¼ cup hot butter
¼ pound sliced bacon
Fine dry bread crumbs
Grated rind of ½ lemon
¼ teaspoon ground thyme

Have the liver cut into ½-inch-thick slices. Cut each slice into 1-inch squares. Heat the butter until it is light brown. Dip the liver pieces in the hot butter just enough to stiffen the meat. Then cut the bacon into squares. Thread the liver squares on skewers alternately with the bacon squares, leaving a small space between each two squares. Blend the fine bread crumbs with the lemon rind and thyme. Roll each *brochette* in this mixture.

Open all dampers in the cover and kettle of the barbecue. Use 30 to 40 briquettes in one layer. It will take 25 to 30 minutes for the fire to be ready. Place the *brochettes* on the cooking grill and barbecue for 4 to 5 minutes. Makes 3 to 5 servings.

Beef and kidney pie

1 cup fat from the kidney, diced
1 beef kidney (about 1 pound), trimmed and diced
1 pound stewing beef, diced
3 onions, chopped
3 cups hot water
1 teaspoon salt
½ teaspoon black pepper
1 teaspoon dry mustard
½ cup browned flour
½ cup cold water
Pie pastry for large 2-crust pie (p. 522)

Melt the kidney fat until the small pieces are crisp and most of the fat released. Add the diced kidney and stewing beef and brown over high heat for 2 minutes. Add the onions and continue to brown over high heat for another 2 minutes. Pour the hot water and seasonings over the meat and onions. Bring to a boil. Cover and simmer over low heat for 2 hours, or until the meats are tender.

Thicken the broth; stir the browned flour into the cold water and stir into the stew. Pour the thickened stew into a pastry-lined casserole. Cover with another layer of pastry, crimp the edges, and make a hole for the steam to escape. Bake in a 400° F. oven until the crust is brown. Serve hot, or cool at room temperature and serve cool. Makes 6 to 8 servings.

Veal kidney limone

- 4 medium-size veal kidneys (about 8 ounces each)
- 3 tablespoons butter
- ¼ teaspoon ground thyme
- 1 unpeeled lemon, sliced thin
- Salt and pepper
- 4 slices of French bread
- Grated rind of 1 lemon
- 1 teaspoon steak sauce
- 2 tablespoons minced parsley
- Watercress

Remove all fat and thin membrane from kidneys. Melt the butter in a cast-iron frying pan and heat to a light-brown color. Add the kidneys and cook over medium heat for 8 minutes on each side, turning only once. Remove to a platter.

Add the thyme and lemon slices to the butter remaining in the pan. Stir around for 3 to 5 minutes. Cut the sautéed kidneys into ½-inch slices. Add to the lemon slices with any of the juice left in the plate. Add salt and pepper to taste. Toss the whole together for a few seconds over very low heat, while you prepare the toast.

Toast the bread. Mix together the lemon rind and steak sauce. Spread a little on each piece of toast. Place on a hot serving platter. Add the parsley to the kidneys. Divide the mixture equally among the pieces of toast, spooning any remaining gravy on top. Garnish with watercress. Makes 4 servings.

Tongue in hot sauces

Simmer fresh tongue in seasoned salted water for about 50 minutes per pound, or until tender. Then remove outer skin and any little bones and pieces of gristle at the root end. Omit salt in cooking smoked tongue, but cook for the same length of time. If you plan to use it at once, slice it. If you plan to use it later, let it cool before slicing, because it is much easier to slice when cold. Make the sauce, and heat the slices in it. Arrange slices overlapping on a serving platter. Spoon remaining sauce over slices. Garnish with parsley sprigs or spiced fruits. Good sauces to use are Madeira Sauce (p. 192), Sauce Robert (p. 192), Sauce Diable (p. 193) or Raisin Sauce (p. 202).

Cold tongue for buffet

A whole tongue can be prepared this way, or slices, which will simplify serving. Cook the tongue, as in the preceding recipe, cool, trim and chill until very cold. Then coat with aspic. Use Basic Aspic (p. 543) made with chicken stock and Madeira. The tongue (whole or sliced) can be decorated with flowers made of herbs or pieces of vegetables or egg white, or with clusters of cooked white or red cherries.

Sweetbreads in Madeira sauce

6 pairs sweetbreads
Lemon juice or vinegar
12 slices of Canadian bacon
4 tablespoons butter
2 cups Madeira Sauce (p. 192)
½ cup slivered blanched almonds
½ cup chopped parsley

Soak sweetbreads in cold water for several hours if you want them absolutely white. Change water several times. Simmer in salted water with a little lemon juice or vinegar for 15 minutes. Remove loose membrane. Flatten sweetbreads between two plates with a weight on top. Each pair has a larger and a smaller lobe. Be sure these are separated and well trimmed.

Sauté the bacon slices in 2 tablespoons of the butter until lightly browned on both sides. Arrange bacon and sweetbreads in a large shallow casserole with a sweetbread on a bacon slice. Pour the Madeira Sauce over, cover the casserole, or use foil, and bake the dish in a 325° F. oven for about 45 minutes.

Meanwhile, in remaining butter, sauté the almonds till golden. Remove the sweetbreads from the oven and take off the cover. Add the parsley to the almonds, stir to mix well and coat the parsley with butter, then spoon almonds and parsley over the sweetbreads. Serve from the casserole, giving each person a large and a small piece of sweetbread and the bacon slices underneath them. Makes 6 servings.

Retail cuts of beef and where they come from

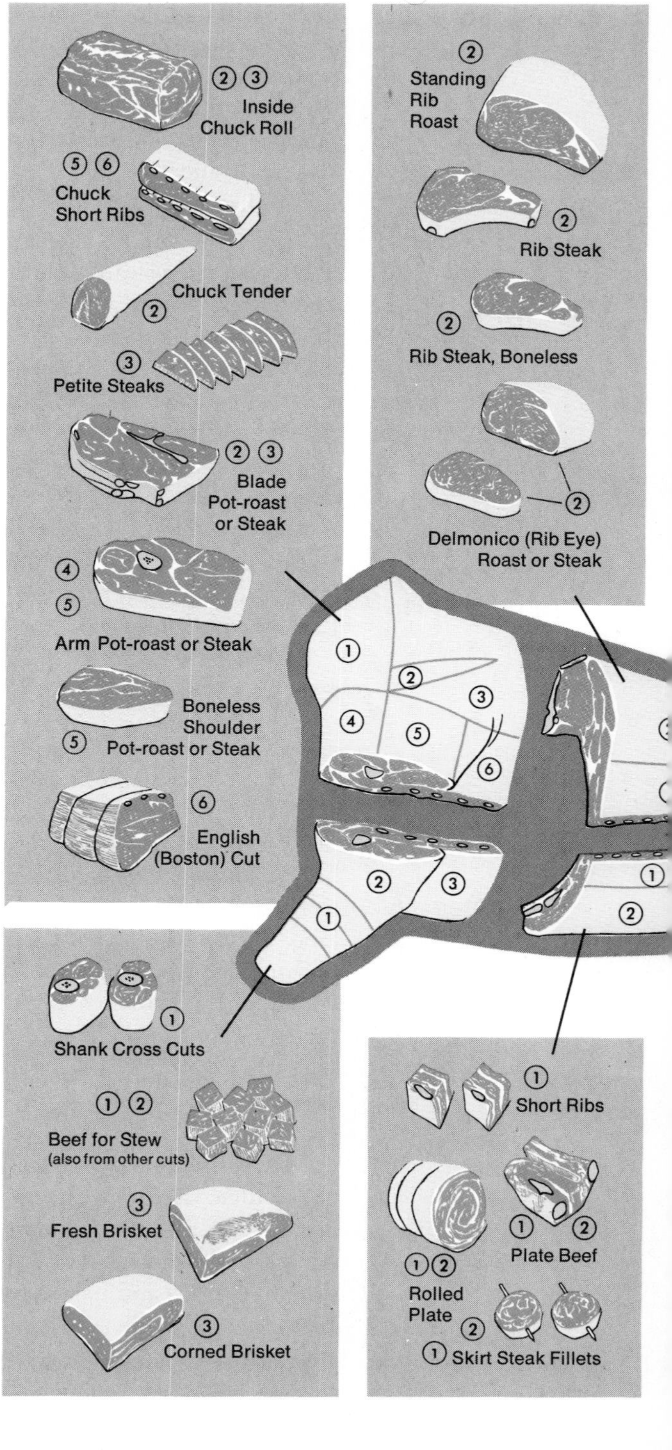

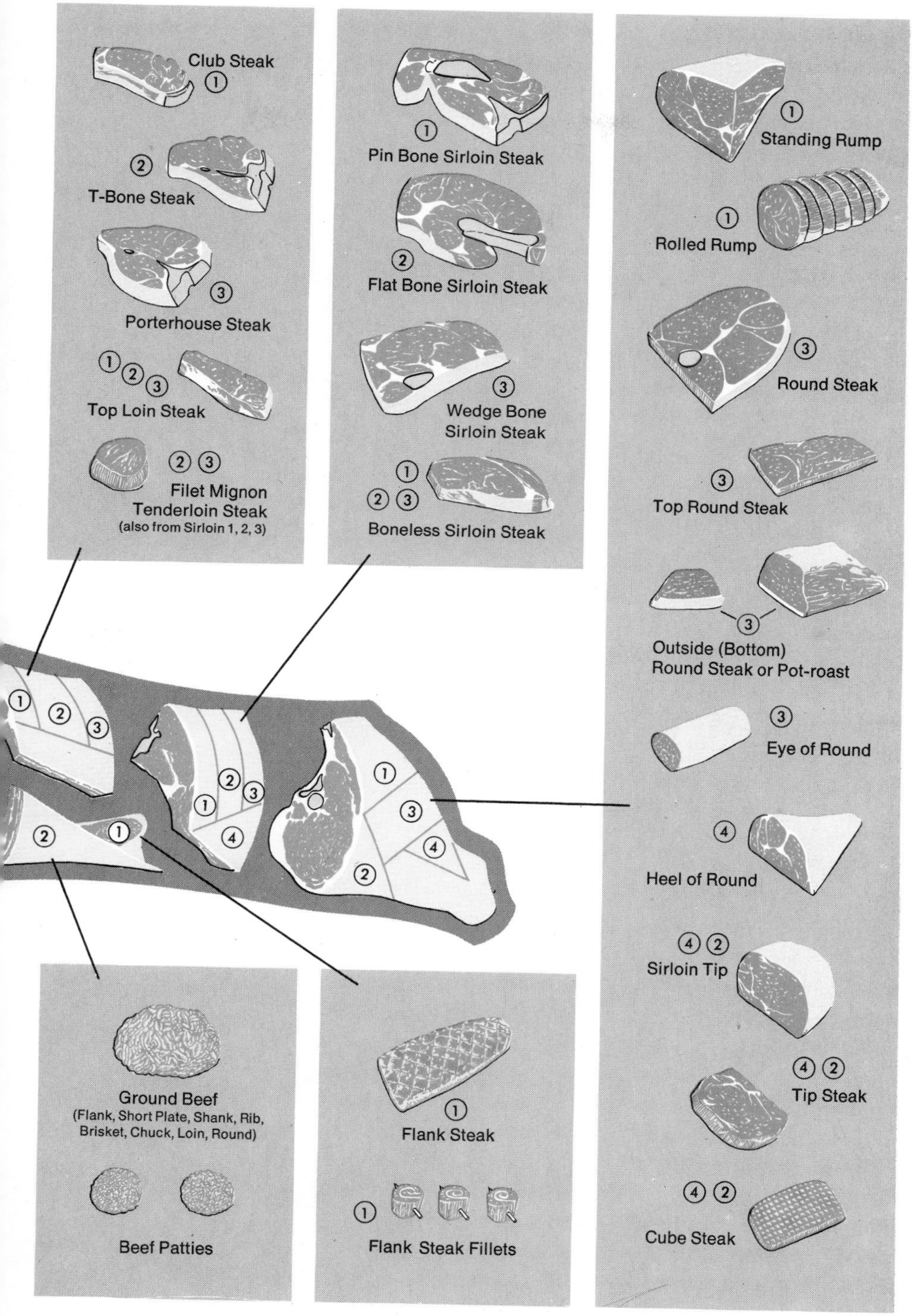
Club Steak ①
② T-Bone Steak
③ Porterhouse Steak
①②③ Top Loin Steak
②③ Filet Mignon Tenderloin Steak (also from Sirloin 1, 2, 3)
① Pin Bone Sirloin Steak
② Flat Bone Sirloin Steak
③ Wedge Bone Sirloin Steak
①②③ Boneless Sirloin Steak
① Standing Rump
① Rolled Rump
③ Round Steak
③ Top Round Steak
③ Outside (Bottom) Round Steak or Pot-roast
③ Eye of Round
④ Heel of Round
④② Sirloin Tip
④② Tip Steak
④② Cube Steak
Ground Beef (Flank, Short Plate, Shank, Rib, Brisket, Chuck, Loin, Round)
Beef Patties
① Flank Steak
① Flank Steak Fillets

Adapted from National Live Stock & Meat Board charts

Retail cuts of veal and where they come from

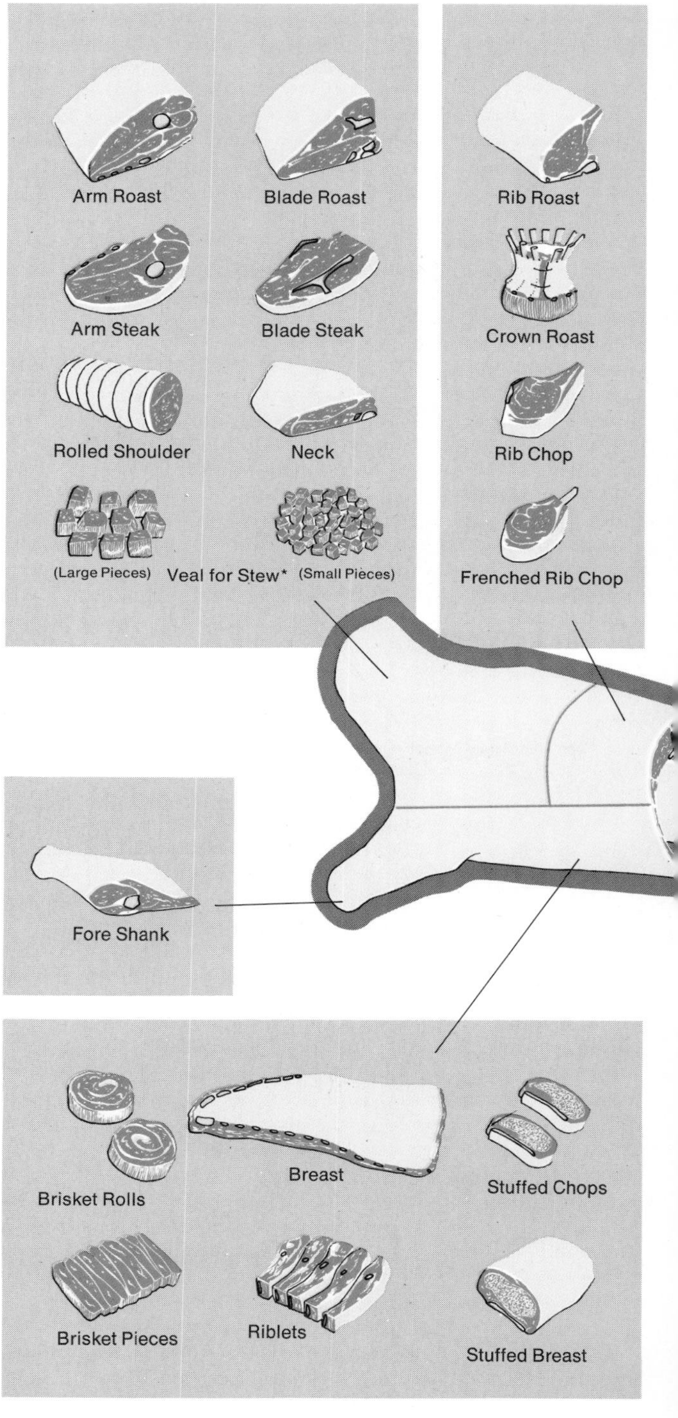

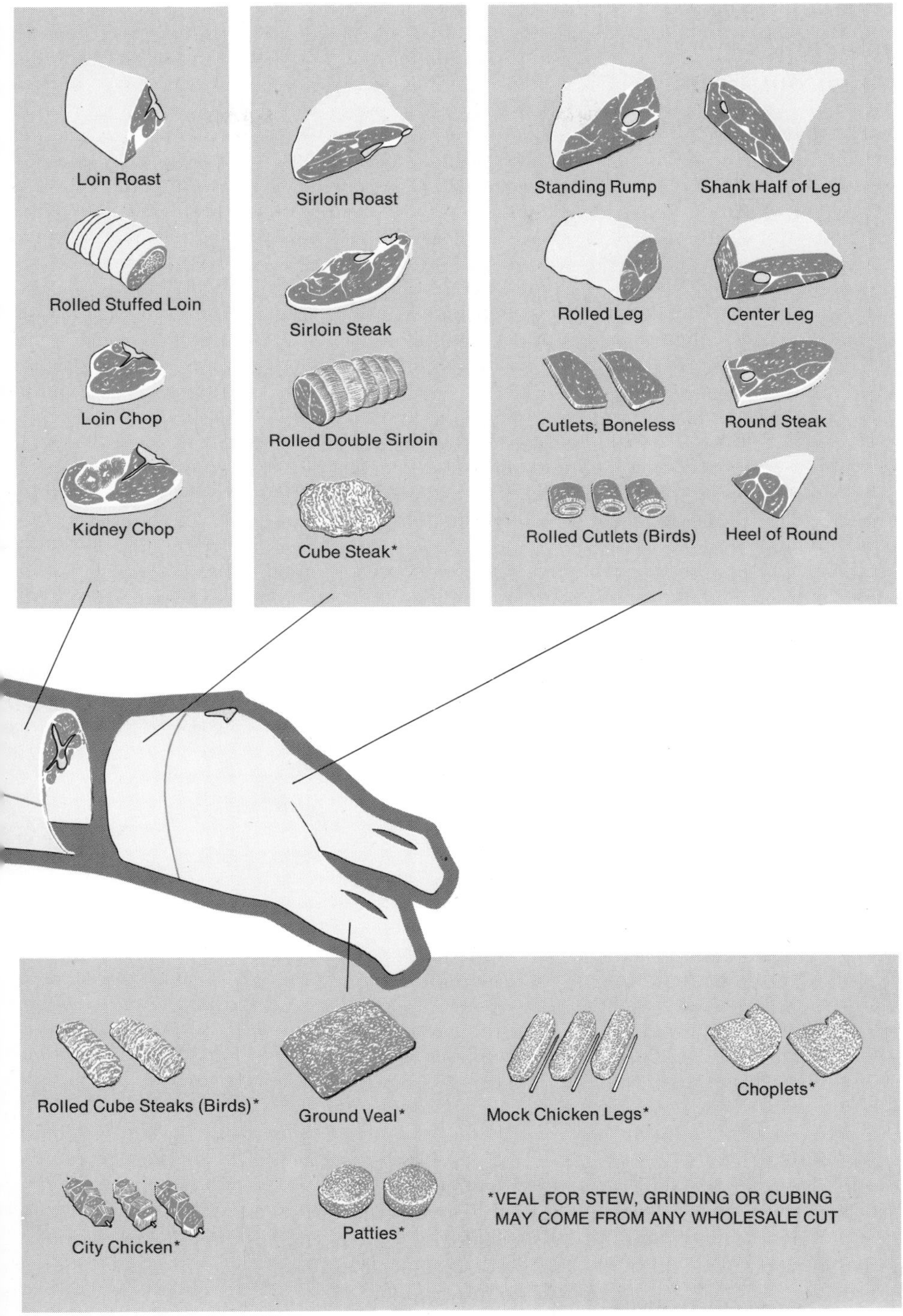

Adapted from National Live Stock & Meat Board charts

Retail cuts of lamb and where they come from

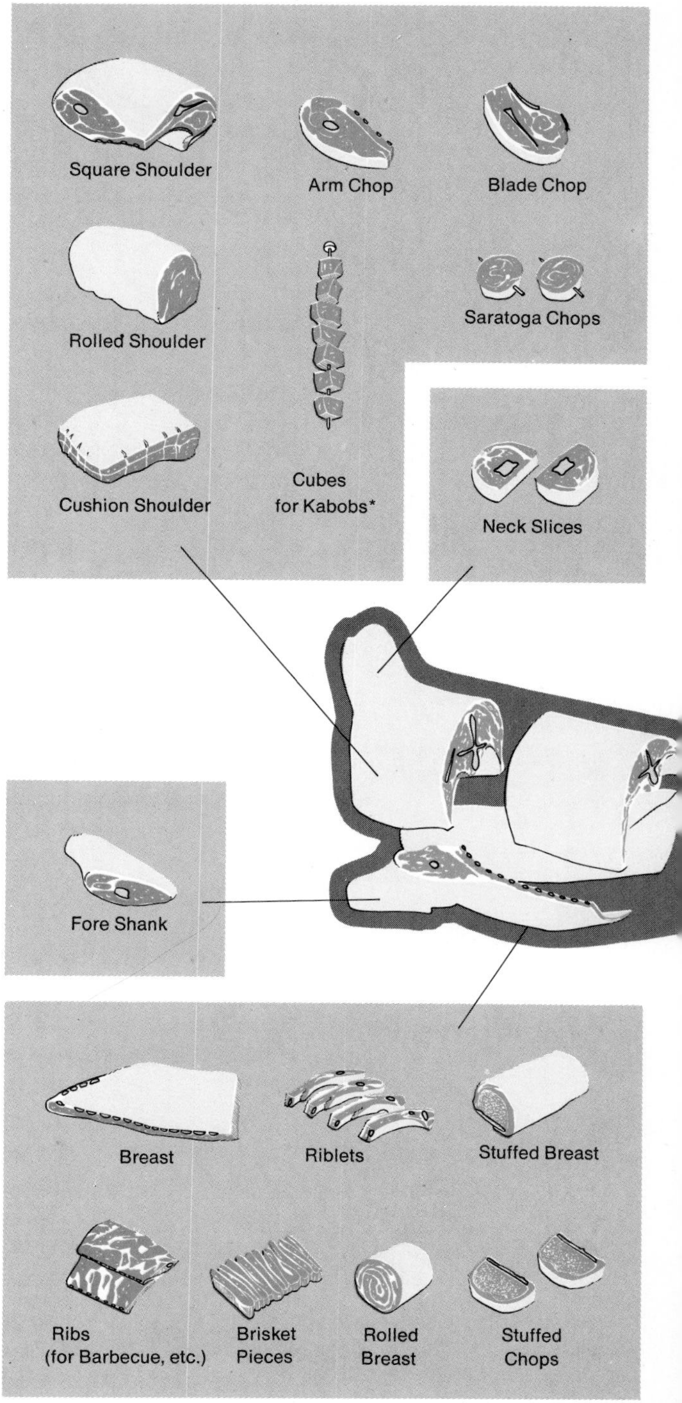

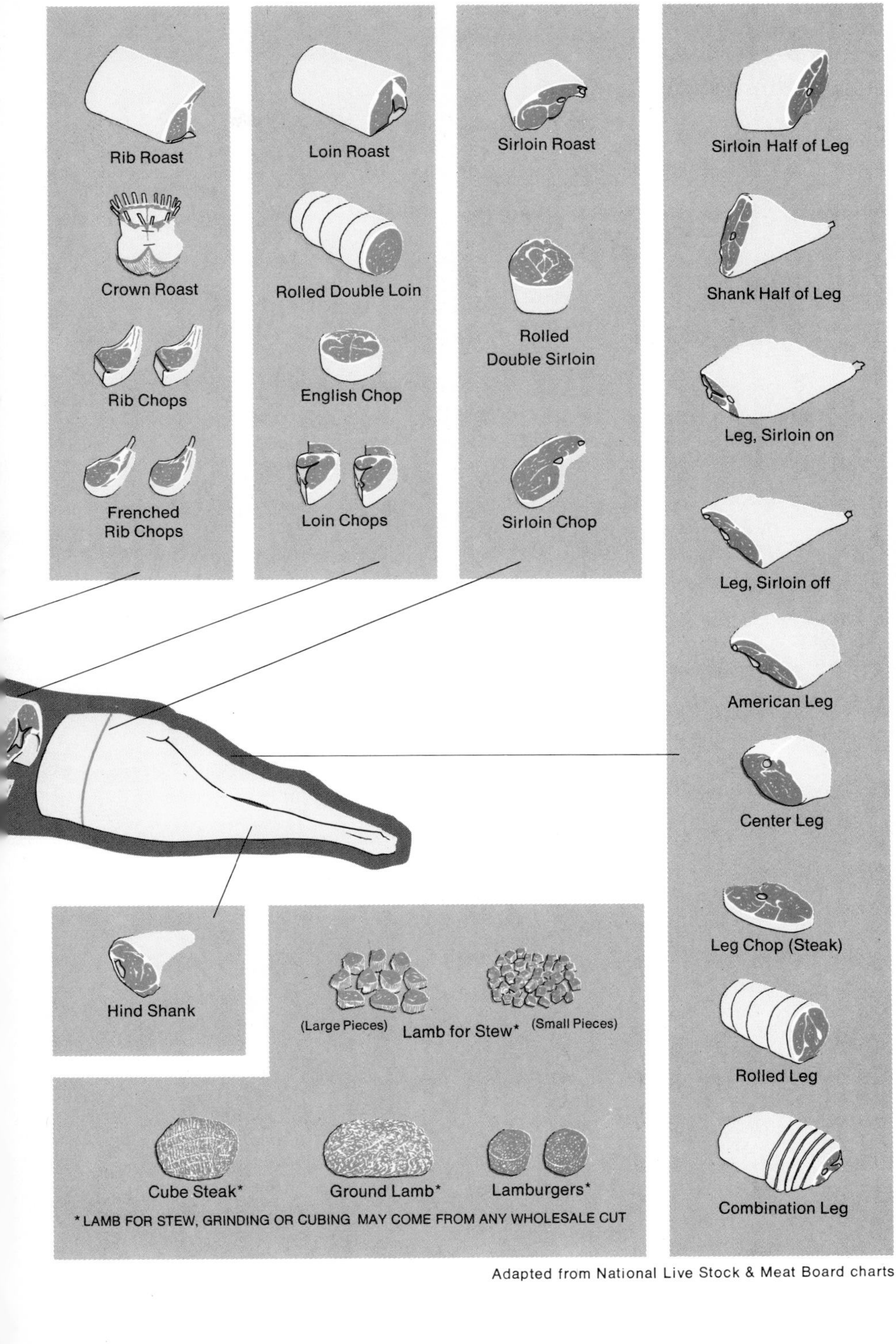

Adapted from National Live Stock & Meat Board charts

Retail cuts of pork and where they come from

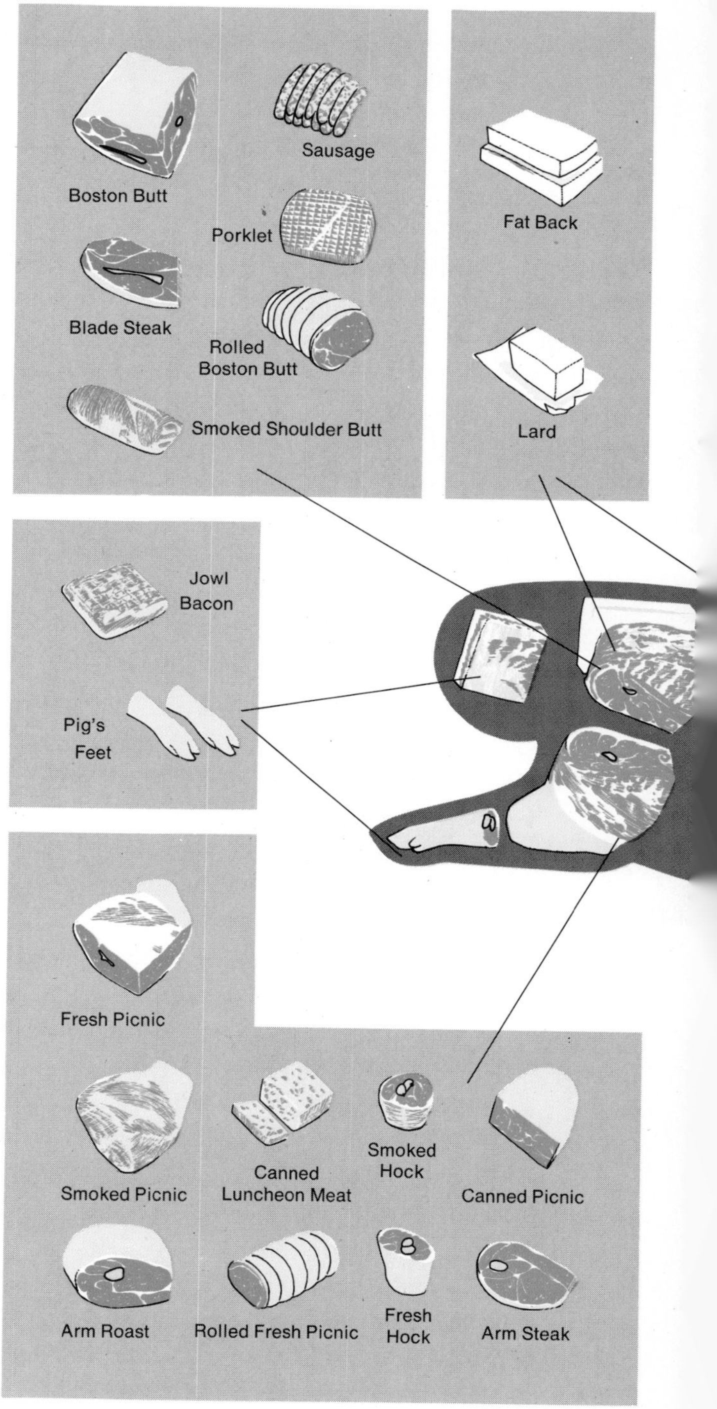

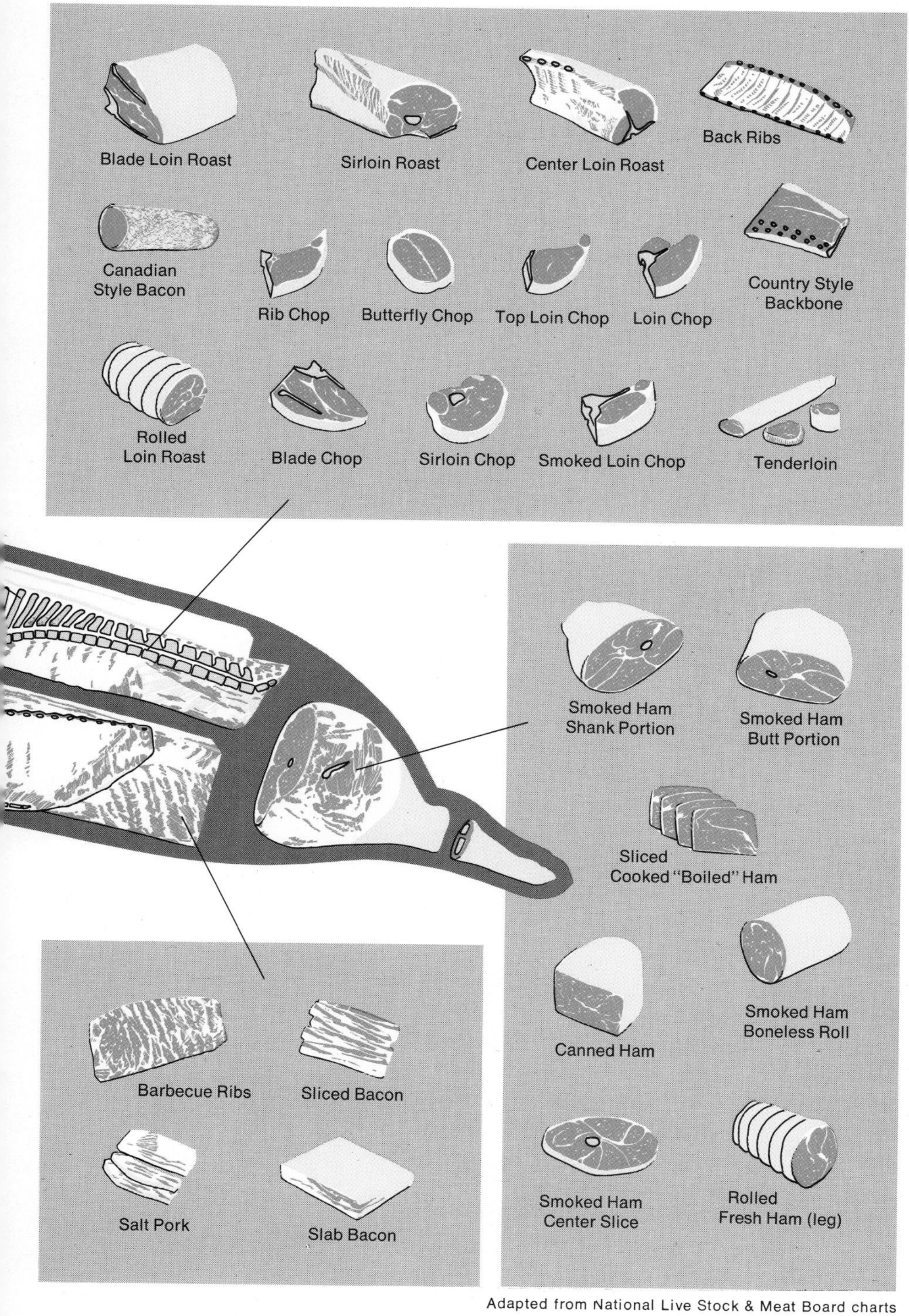

Adapted from National Live Stock & Meat Board charts

«10»

Chicken and Other Poultry

Types of poultry · Basic ways to cook poultry · Preparing poultry for cooking · Stuffing poultry · Flavoring poultry · Trussing a chicken · How to cut up poultry · Roasting chicken · Timetables for roasting chicken and turkey · Roasting turkey · Roasting ducks and geese · Braising and pot-roasting · Broiling and barbecuing · Sautéing and panfrying · Deep-frying · Poaching and stewing

A chicken in every pot is no longer the remote dream it once seemed. Far from it! Chicken is available year-round in most parts of the country, and it is one of the most economical of protein foods. The nutritive value of chicken and other poultry is almost equal to that of red meat, and it can be cooked in countless ways. Because chicken lacks the full-bodied flavor of beef or lamb, the trick is to prepare it so that the bird's appetizing taste is accentuated and it becomes an equally satisfying dish.

O┳ One of the first secrets to learn is how to choose the best bird for the type of cooking you are going to use. Knowing the kind of chicken that responds best to various cooking methods will give you both a more flavorful chicken concoction and a more economical meal. For example, do not purchase a roasting chicken to make soup. This is the same as buying beef tenderloin to make hash. Also, if a 5-pound roasting chicken costs much more per pound than a 3-pound bird, two smaller chickens will be a better buy, in the long run, and will yield more roasted white meat and more favorite pieces than one large bird.

TYPES OF POULTRY

Squab. A young pigeon that has never flown. The flavor is similar to chicken, and a squab is cooked by the same methods. A squab weighs about 1 pound and is served roasted whole, one to a person. Available at specialized dealers, squabs are definitely a luxury item and are usually served only at elaborate dinners.

Rock Cornish game hen. This excellent little bird has almost supplanted squab, and it is usually much less expensive. The weight is ordinarily about 1¼ pounds, but there are slightly larger birds, called "roasters," available in some markets. The small hen will make a generous serving for one or an adequate serving for two. The roaster makes 4 servings. The flavor is similar to chicken.

Broiler-fryer. This is a young, all-purpose chicken, weighing from 2 to 4 pounds. It is called "all-purpose" because it can be roasted, broiled, sautéed, panfried or deep-fried. In some places birds weighing up to 2½ pounds are called *broilers* and those from 2½ to 3½ pounds *fryers*.

Roaster. This is a chicken, male or female, less than a year old, weighing over 3½ pounds. It should be plump and tender, with some fat. The breast bone should still feel flexible. This bird is good roasted, but can be prepared in any other fashion because the meat is tender.

Stewing chicken or fowl. This is a mature female chicken, less tender and less expensive than a roaster but generally heavier. To be at its best a stewing chicken should weigh at least 5 pounds. It is good poached for cold sliced chicken, or for salads or casserole dishes. It can be simmered for soups and stocks. Usually the bird is kept whole during cooking for greater flavor, tenderness and succulence.

Capon. A capon is a castrated cock, usually weighing 6 to 7 pounds. It is good when a large roasting bird is needed. It has a generous amount of white meat; the flavor, however, is somewhat bland compared to that of a fat roasting hen.

Dressed poultry. This is a bird that has been slaughtered and bled, and has had its feathers plucked, but still has its feet, head and viscera. At farmers' markets, fresh poultry is mostly sold dressed.

Eviscerated oven-ready or ready-to-cook poultry. A bird that has been completely cleaned, eviscerated and is ready for the oven. The heart, liver, gizzard and neck are wrapped in paper and returned to the cavity of the bird and are added to the final weight. This evisceration of chickens has contributed greatly to the increase in chicken consumption, since most women rebel at having to do this work themselves.

Turkey. This American native was once plentiful from northern states all the way to Central America. The domestic birds are found in markets all year long, and are generally frozen. The size range is tremendous, from 6 to 20 pounds or even larger. Unfortunately, fresh turkeys seem to be found less frequently. Turkey is less tender than chicken and tends to be drier, especially after freezing.

Duck. This is a water bird and consequently is much more fatty than the other varieties of poultry listed. Because of this it needs special care in cooking. Fresh birds are seldom found, but frozen birds are delicious. A duck usually weighs 4 to 5 pounds. It can be roasted or broiled, and is surprisingly good poached.

Goose. This is another fatty water bird similar to duck. Fresh young geese and frozen birds are on the market at holiday seasons toward the end of the year, but seldom at other times. A goose weighs 5 to 12 pounds. Any cooking method used for duck can be used for goose.

Pheasant and guinea hen. These are raised as domestic birds. Either can be cooked like chicken. Pheasant is less juicy and more stringy than chicken, and the domestic birds are quite different from wild pheasant. Guinea hen is also drier than chicken.

Game birds. These include wild ducks, geese, pheasants, quail, woodcock. If you have a hunter in your family, you will need to discover ways to cook game birds. In general they are cooked like similar domestic birds. Some people enjoy game rare, but this is not a universal taste. Generally wild birds are less tender than domestic fowl and are best adapted to braising or stewing.

BASIC WAYS TO COOK POULTRY

Chicken and all other poultry can be roasted or baked, broiled, barbecued, sautéed, deep-fried, stewed, poached or fricasseed in the same ways meat is cooked. All the rules that apply to meat, regarding each basic method, are applicable to poultry. With some slight differences, the cooking time for most methods can be based on the timetable for roasting chicken.

Because poultry is a protein, the most important rule, as with all meat, is to use the lowest possible heat for the basic method you follow. *Do not overcook.* If you must err, let your chicken be a little underdone rather than overdone. And do not worry about the pink color next to the bone in a completely cooked chicken. This is caused by the same chemical reaction that produces redness in ham. It does not indicate undercooking, nor does it affect the flavor.

PREPARING POULTRY FOR COOKING

Even when a bird is sold dressed or eviscerated, check it for pinfeathers. These can be removed easily with tweezers. Feel the inside of the birds, even if they are supposed to be oven-ready, to make sure the lungs have been removed, and cut out the little oil sac above the tail piece if this has not been done. (Most of the time it will have been removed.)

If you grew up in the tradition of washing poultry before cooking it, start now to follow a different system. Washing does not really clean the bird; certainly it does not sterilize it. To do that you would have to use boiling water, not cold water, and this would change the texture of the meat completely. Most poultry for sale in our markets is carefully packaged and only needs to be wiped off with a damp paper towel, inside and outside. Or use this method: put 2 to 3 tablespoons fresh lemon juice, brandy or whiskey inside the chicken and swish it around with your fingers or with absorbent paper.

Stuffing poultry

A bird can be stuffed with countless fillings. To make the bird look fatter and handsomer, stuff both the neck and body cavities. To do this, first spoon some of the stuffing into the neck part, pushing it in; pull the neck skin over the filling and fasten it under the bird. Spoon the remainder of the stuffing into the body cavity. 🗝 At the opening put a thick slice of dried bread or a piece of crust, lightly buttered and rubbed with onion or garlic, placed buttered side out. The slice of bread acts as a lid, preventing the stuffing from oozing out during the roasting period. The bread becomes crisp and roasted on the outside and soft inside and has a very special flavor. Use a needle and thread to fasten the opening, or fasten with poultry pins laced with string.

Do not stuff any poultry until just before cooking because the stuffing will spoil if allowed to stand.

Flavoring poultry

Whole poultry that is to be roasted or poached should be flavored on the inside. First sprinkle salt and pepper inside the neck and body cavities. Then rub inside and out with the cut side of a lemon. Sprinkle a few pinches of thyme or tarragon into the cavity, then add a sprig or two of parsley and a tablespoon of butter. Then truss the bird.

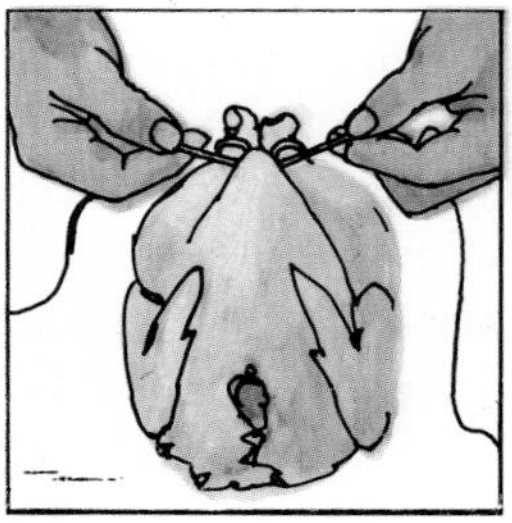

1. Loop string around end of legs and up between legs.

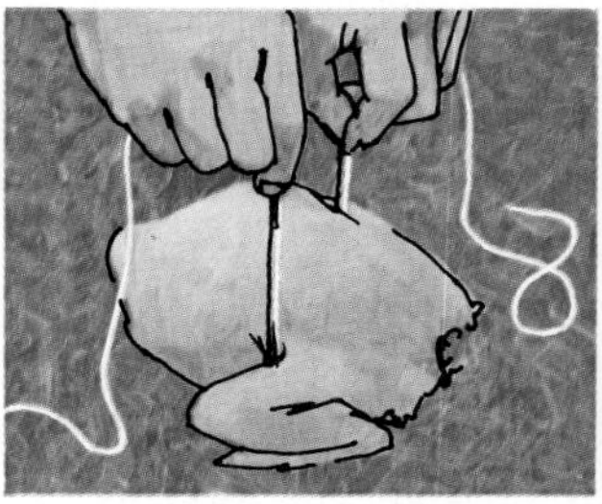

2. Turn chicken over and cross string over back.

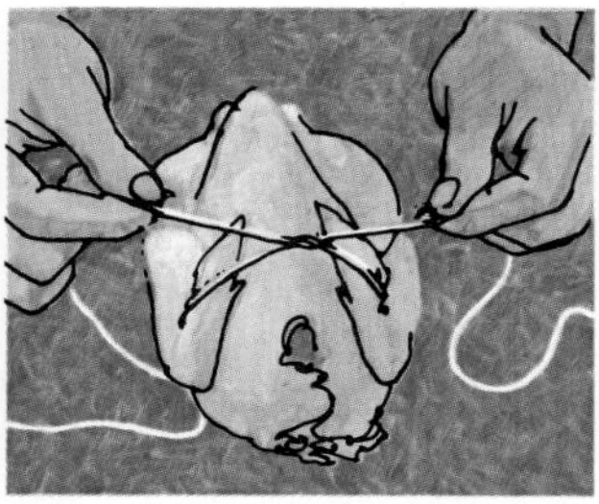

3. Turn chicken on its back. Run string between wings. Tie.

Trussing a chicken

Use soft white string, cut about 20 inches long. Place the chicken on a flat surface, with its feet toward you. Push the legs back close to the body of the chicken. Put the center of the string across the end of the legs and bring it around and up between the legs, forming a figure 8. Then put the string between the legs and the breast, turn the chicken over and put the string through the wings. Make sure the neck skin is pulled over the vent, and tie the string in a bow over it. 🗝 Poultry cooked whole, whether roasted or poached, should always be tied to keep the bird in a neat shape. The same trussing method can be used for other poultry, but you need to adjust to the size of the bird. Ducks and geese are longer and have shorter legs in proportion to the body, so tying with two strings is practical.

How to cut up poultry

While cooking methods other than roasting occasionally use a whole bird, it is more likely that birds will be cut up for other processes. All you need is a sharp knife.

TO REMOVE WINGS (1), pull the wings out from the body and slash the skin between body and wing. Cut around the shoulder joint to separate the wing from the breast, leaving as much white meat on the breast as possible. If you wish, you can cut off the wing tips. (They are bony and can be reserved for making stock.)

TO REMOVE LEGS, DRUMSTICKS AND THIGHS (2), slash the skin between the body and the thigh, then press down and out on the leg until the hip joint pushes out of its socket. Cut through the hip joint, separating the thigh from the body of the bird. If you wish, you can cut the drumstick away from the thigh through the knee joint. Repeat for the other leg.

Note how the "oyster" (fleshy, oyster-shaped piece) pulls away from the spoon-shaped hollow of the backbone of a chicken. In turkeys the thigh tendon must be cut before the oyster will pull away from the backbone.

TO REMOVE NECK AND BACKBONE (3), starting at the tail, cut through the ribs slightly to the right of the backbone, all the way to the neck. Repeat on the left side of the backbone. Remove the backbone and

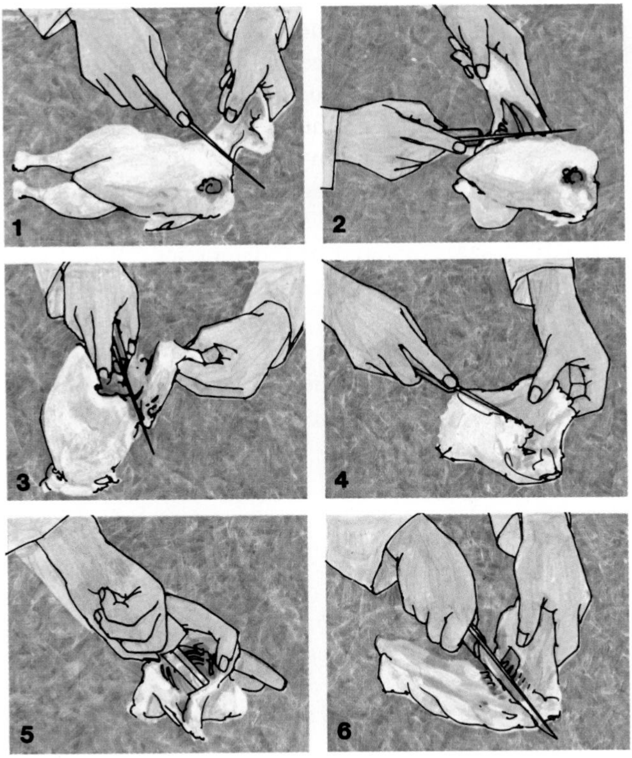

1. Remove the wings.

2. Remove the legs.

3. Remove the neck and backbone.

4. Separate the breast from the back.

5. Cut cartilage next to keel bone.

6. Cut the breast into halves.

neck in one piece by cutting the skin around the neck.

TO SEPARATE BREAST FROM BACK (4), insert your knife in the wing socket and cut through the rib joints to the back of the bird. This separates the back from the breast, leaving part of the ribs on each.

TO DIVIDE THE BREAST (5, 6), spread the bird open and cut the pearllike cartilage on either side of the keel bone in the neck region. Hold the bird firmly and press from underneath, forcing the keel bone to spring up so that it can be removed easily. Cut the breast lengthwise into halves.

TO CUT BROILERS INTO HALVES, remove neck and backbone and divide the breast as described above. FOR QUARTERS, cut each half crosswise into two pieces.

Wipe cut-up birds with a damp cloth; dry thoroughly. Wrap loosely in wax paper and store in the refrigerator until time for cooking.

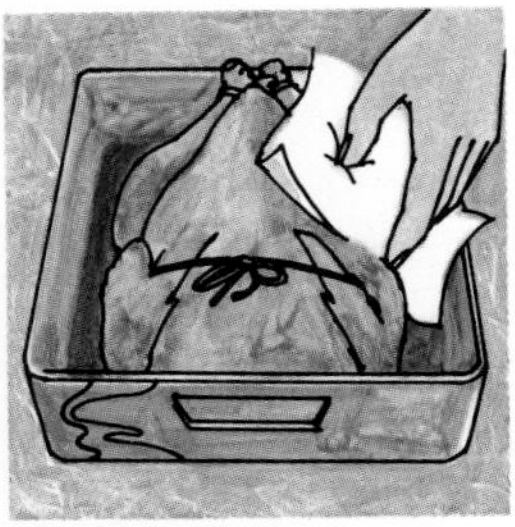

ROASTING CHICKEN

Roast all chickens at an even temperature of 350° F., placing them in a preheated oven. 0━ The chicken should always be at room temperature when it is placed in the oven.

Contrary to the procedure with red meats, a thermometer to test chicken for doneness is not necessary; in any case, it is difficult to insert it far enough into the flesh of a bird without touching a bone.

A satisfactory test that is constantly accurate is to test the drumstick. With a folded piece of cloth to protect your fingers, take hold of the drumstick. The meat should feel soft and the bone should move easily in its socket. Another way is to prick the thickest part of the leg with a fork. Juices should run clear yellow without a trace of pink.

Timetable for roasting chicken

(constant oven temperature at 350°F.)

Ready-to-cook weight	Approximate total cooking time
¾ to 1 pound	30 to 40 minutes
1½ pounds	40 to 50 minutes
3 pounds	50 to 60 minutes
4 pounds	1 hour plus 10 to 20 minutes
4½ pounds	1 hour plus 15 to 30 minutes
5 to 6 pounds	1 hour plus 30 to 45 minutes

Weigh the whole bird with its stuffing, if it has any, to calculate roasting time. If you must put the bird in the oven directly from the refrigerator, remember to allow a little more time for cooking (about 10 minutes for a 3-pound bird).

Two chickens in a pan

It is often more economical to buy two smaller chickens rather than one large one. It is also cheaper to roast two chickens at the same time. If you do roast two, cook them in a pan generous enough for them to have elbowroom. Also use a higher heat than normal, from 360° to 375° F.; otherwise they will stew or poach in their own juices instead of roasting. One bird can be served cold on another day.

French roasted chicken

This is a good, reliable recipe for roasting a chicken, stuffed or unstuffed. It is also a fine way to prepare a bird to serve cold with mayonnaise.

1 chicken (4 to 5 pounds)
1 teaspoon salt
½ teaspoon pepper
Giblets from the chicken
1 small garlic clove
¼ teaspoon ground thyme
2 tablespoons soft butter
1 teaspoon dry mustard
1 cup cold liquid

Remove any extra fat from the chicken. Dice this fat and place it in a little pile in the middle of the roasting pan.

Sprinkle most of the salt inside the chicken, then use the rest to rub on the outside. Sprinkle the pepper inside only. Place the cleaned liver, heart, cut-up gizzard and the garlic and thyme inside the cavity. This gives the chicken a delicious flavor. Another way to flavor the cavity is to fill it with a *big* bunch of unchopped fresh parsley. Truss the chicken.

Blend the soft butter and dry mustard. Spread this mixture on the breast of the chicken. Set the chicken on the little pile of chicken fat.

Do not sear. Do not add water. Do not cover. Roast in a preheated 350° F. oven for 1½ to 2 hours, according to the tenderness of the chicken. To make sure it is cooked, use the drumstick test.

Remove the chicken from the pan. Place the pan

over direct heat. When the pan drippings are bubbling hot, add the cold liquid to the contents; this liquid could be water, chicken stock, white wine, orange juice or cream. Stir, scraping the bottom of the pan. Bring to a boil, strain and serve. This chicken can also be served with English Bread Sauce (p. 201). Makes 6 servings.

Bread and lemon stuffing

- 3 cups soft fine bread crumbs
- 3 tablespoons fresh lemon juice
- Grated rind of ½ lemon
- ¼ cup minced fresh parsley
- ½ teaspoon salt
- ¼ teaspoon pepper

Use only the white part of fresh white bread; cut up fine. Combine all ingredients in a bowl. Mix thoroughly and use to stuff chicken. Makes enough to stuff 1 roasting chicken.

Sausage stuffing

If you plan to serve your roast stuffed chicken cold, remove the stuffing, which comes out in one piece. Cut the stuffing into thin slices and place it around the chicken to serve.

- 2 tablespoons melted chicken fat or butter
- 1 large onion, finely chopped
- ¼ to ½ pound fresh mushrooms, finely chopped
- ½ pound sausage meat
- ½ pound very lean pork, minced
- 5 chicken livers, chopped
- 2 tablespoons chopped parsley
- ¼ teaspoon dried thyme or tarragon
- 2 slices of bread with crusts, diced
- 1 teaspoon salt
- ¼ teaspoon pepper

Heat the chicken fat or butter in a frying pan. Add the onion and mushrooms and stir over medium heat for about 5 minutes. With a slotted spoon press out as much fat as possible and transfer the vegetables to a bowl.

Add the sausage meat and minced pork to the bowl. In the fat left in the frying pan, sauté the chicken livers over high heat for 1 minute. Add to the first mixture, along with the parsley, thyme or tarragon, bread cubes and salt and pepper. Mix thoroughly.

Variation

For a chestnut stuffing, use 2 cups cooked chestnuts broken into coarse pieces instead of the sausage meat. Prepare your own chestnuts, or use the water-packed chestnuts imported from France.

Foil-roasted fowl

The old dry rooster or fowl will be turned into a tender moist chicken when cooked by this method.

1 fowl (4 to 7 pounds)
Salt and pepper
1 onion, quartered
1 teaspoon minced tarragon or basil *or* 2 bay leaves
4 strips of bacon *or* 1 teaspoon soy sauce (optional)

Sprinkle the fowl with salt and pepper inside and out. In the cavity place the quartered onion and minced tarragon or basil or 2 bay leaves. Place bacon strips around the breast and under the wings, or rub with soy sauce. Place the chicken on a large piece of foil set in a roasting pan. Wrap the chicken tightly in the foil, pinching the edges together to seal tightly. Bake in a 350° F. oven for 3 hours without disturbing. The results are always perfect. Unwrap to serve hot, or cool and refrigerate without unwrapping to serve cold. This method leaves plenty of liquid for making sauce or gravy. Makes 6 to 8 servings.

ROASTING TURKEY

Turkeys are usually stuffed, but they need not be. Instead, a mixture of vegetables and herbs can be put in the cavity for flavor. Unless you plan to baste a turkey, coat it with butter, or bard with thin sheets of salt pork, or cover with oil-soaked cheesecloth. It takes so long to cook these birds that the breast can become very dry without these precautions. Truss a turkey as you would a chicken. Place the bird on a greased rack in a shallow roasting pan. If you use a meat thermometer, insert it between the center of the inside of the thigh muscle, but make sure the tip does not touch the bone. Plan to cool the turkey about 20 minutes before you are ready to serve it so the juices will be absorbed; the turkey meat will be moister and the carving will be easier.

Timetable for roasting turkey

(constant oven temperature at 325°F.)
(interior temperature on thermometer 180°F.)

Drawn weight stuffed in pounds	Approximate roasting time in hours
6 to 8	3¾ to 4
8 to 10	4 to 4½
10 to 12	4½ to 5
12 to 14	5 to 5½
14 to 16	5½ to 6
16 to 18	6 to 6½
18 to 20	6½ to 7½
20 to 24	7½ to 9
Over 24	Add 15 minutes additional per pound

NOTE: Without stuffing, deduct 5 minutes per pound from the time given for stuffed turkey above.

Roasted turkey with potato stuffing

1 thick dry crust of bread
¼ small onion
Butter
1 turkey (12 pounds)
1 whole nutmeg
½ lemon
½ cup butter
2 tablespoons dry mustard
1 tablespoon salt
½ teaspoon pepper
3 tablespoons flour
Thin slices of salt pork

Stuff the turkey with Potato Stuffing (next page). Rub the dry crust of bread with the onion, then butter generously. Place inside the opening over the stuffing before sewing up the turkey or closing it with poultry pins. Truss the turkey.

Place the turkey in the roasting pan. Rub the skin all over with nutmeg. Grate the nutmeg occasionally to draw out the oil. Next rub the skin with lemon. Cream together the ½ cup butter, mustard, salt, pepper and flour. Rub this paste over the turkey's breast and legs. Wrap the legs with slices of salt pork. Do not cover or add water. Place in a 325° F. oven and cook for 18 to 20 minutes per pound, or about 4 hours. Do not baste during the cooking period; opening the oven tends to dry out the turkey. The paste coating protects the surface and makes it self-basting.

Transfer the cooked bird to a warm platter and keep warm while you make gravy. The bird will make 10 generous servings.

POTATO STUFFING

Turkey giblets
7 tablespoons butter
3 large onions, minced
1 garlic clove, minced
10 cups cooked potatoes
1½ teaspoons crumbled dried savory
1 tablespoon salt
½ teaspoon pepper
½ teaspoon dry mustard

Grind or mince the turkey heart, liver and gizzard. Melt 4 tablespoons of the butter in a frying pan and add onions and garlic. Stir until well coated with butter, then cover and simmer over low heat until onions are soft. Add minced giblets and stir over high heat until brown. Mash the hot cooked potatoes in a large bowl and add the browned onions, garlic and giblets. Stir until well blended. Then add seasonings and remaining butter, melted.

TURKEY GRAVY

Pan juices from roasting turkey
or turkey or chicken stock
2 cups cold tea
½ cup turkey fat from roasting pan
½ cup flour
1 cup red wine
Salt and pepper

Pour all the pan juices into a small pan and chill quickly to let the fat rise to the top, or remove the juices from the pan with a bulb baster. Measure the defattened juices; if less than 2 cups, add enough turkey or chicken stock to make up the difference.

Meanwhile, put the roasting pan over heat and add the tea. Bring the tea to a boil, stirring constantly to dissolve all the brown bits. Make a roux with the fat and flour and cook to medium brown. Stir in the tea mixture, the pan juices and the wine. Cook over medium heat until thickened. Season to taste. Strain into a gravy boat. Makes about 5 cups.

ROASTING DUCKS AND GEESE

These fatty birds can be stuffed, but it is better to fill the cavities loosely with celery and onions, or with apples. These will add flavor to the birds, and are then discarded after roasting. A bread stuffing might absorb fat and be quite indigestible. Truss the bird. Both ducks and geese are self-basting because of the layer of fat beneath the skin, but basting is sometimes useful to add flavor or to glaze the bird. You will need to pour off fat as it is released in cooking. You can use the fat for other cooking if it has not been burned. Strain it and store in glass jars in the refrigerator. Roast ducks or geese in a 325° F. oven for about 25 minutes per pound. While these birds can be roasted at higher heat, that tends to dry out the flesh and give a slightly burned taste to the skin.

Roast duck with vegetables

1 duck (5 pounds)
3 celery ribs with leaves
2 onions, halved
1 apple, quartered
1 cup dry red wine
4 leeks
2 celery knobs
4 carrots
2 long potatoes
1 pound green beans
4 tablespoons honey or strained orange marmalade
½ cup chopped parsley

If the duck is frozen, let it defrost completely in the refrigerator (about 24 hours). Remove the package of giblets and neck and make about 1 cup of stock with them. (The giblets can be used to make a small salad or sandwiches at another meal.)

Put the celery, onions and apple in the cavity, close the vent with poultry pins and truss the bird. Put the duck breast down on a rack in the roasting pan. Place in a preheated 325° F. oven. Prick the skin with a fork all over to release some of the fat. Roast for 20 minutes, then turn the bird on its side. Prick the skin again and roast for 20 minutes longer. Turn the bird on the other side, prick the skin again and roast once more for 20 minutes. Finally, turn the bird breast up, prick again and roast an additional 20 minutes.

Lift the bird to a platter and pour off all the fat from the pan. (You can do this more than once if you prefer.) Return the bird to the pan and roast, breast up, for about 40 minutes longer. During this part of the cooking, baste the bird about four times with a mixture of the duck stock and the wine.

Meanwhile, wash and trim all the vegetables. Cut the leeks lengthwise into halves, the celery knobs into long thin slices or julienne, the carrots and potatoes into julienne. Leave the beans whole. Wrap each kind of vegetable in cheesecloth and blanch all in the same saucepan. Start with the carrots, then add celery knobs, potatoes, beans and leeks. All the vegetables will be tender in about 15 minutes, but add the last three after the carrots and celery knobs have cooked for 5 minutes. Time the cooking so the vegetables will be cooked just as the duck is finished.

About 10 minutes before the duck is done, spoon the honey or marmalade over it and raise the oven heat to 400° F. to make the skin golden brown. When the duck is done, remove the trussing string and poultry pins, pour off any juices from the cavity into the pan, and discard the celery, onions and apple. Arrange the duck on a large platter and surround the bird with the vegetables. Boil down the pan juices a few minutes, remove the fat from the top or take out the juice with a baster, and spoon some of the juices over both bird and vegetables. Sprinkle with parsley. Makes 4 servings.

Goose with gooseberries

1 goose (8 pounds)
Salt
Pepper
2 large onions
1 clove garlic, crushed
2 teaspoons dried thyme
2 cups dry vermouth
2 cans (1 pound each) gooseberries
2 cups mandarin orange sections

If the goose is frozen, let it defrost completely in the refrigerator (about 2 days). Remove the package of giblets and neck; use them for another meal. Wipe the bird with damp paper towels, then sprinkle the inside with salt and pepper. Put the onions, garlic and thyme in the cavity. Close the vent and truss the bird. Put it breast side down on a rack in the roasting pan and place in a 325° F. oven. Cook this like a duck, turning it over on all sides and pricking well to release the fat (see preceding recipe). Allow about 30 minutes on each side. Then pour off the fat.

Start basting the goose with the vermouth. (This is not to keep the bird from drying out but to add flavor and crisp the skin.) When the vermouth is all used, continue to baste with the pan juices. About 30 minutes before the goose is done, drain off the syrup from the gooseberries. Baste the goose with the syrup. Mix the berries with the orange sections. Lift out 2 cups of the pan juices and heat the fruit in the juices. When the bird is tender and well glazed, open the vent and let all juices run into pan. Discard the cavity stuffing. Transfer the bird to a platter and spoon some of the mixed fruit and pan juices over it. Serve the rest in a sauceboat. The remaining pan juices can be defatted, thickened if you like, and served as additional gravy. An 8-pound goose should be well roasted in 3 hours and 20 minutes, but test the drumstick to be sure. It is impossible with frozen birds to gauge their age or tenderness before cooking. Makes 8 to 10 servings.

Golden baked chicken

Prepare this when you wish to serve a crispy brown chicken cut into serving pieces. Baking chicken in this manner combines the roasting and poaching methods, because it is cooked covered and a higher heat is required. This is delicious served cold for a picnic.

1 egg
2 tablespoons water
2 teaspoons salt
½ teaspoon pepper
½ teaspoon crumbled dried basil
1 frying chicken (3 pounds), cut into pieces
½ cup wheat germ or fine bread crumbs
2 tablespoons butter
Chopped parsley (optional)

Break the egg into a bowl and beat with the water, salt, pepper and basil. Drop the chicken pieces into this and stir around until all the pieces are well coated. Roll each piece in the wheat germ or bread crumbs. Place in a buttered shallow baking pan and dot with remaining butter. Cover with aluminum foil and bake in a 400° F. oven for 1 hour, or until the chicken is tender. Sprinkle with parsley and serve. Makes 4 servings.

BRAISING AND POT-ROASTING POULTRY

While poultry usually becomes tender without the long slow cooking needed for some cuts of meat, these methods can be applied to poultry with success. The birds, or parts of birds, become juicy, tender and flavorful. 🗝 While it is possible to partly cook meats in advance, poultry loses some of its flavor and tenderness if it is not served when it is ready, and reheating tends to dry it out. 0━ If the food does not fit snugly in the pot, cover the food with a sheet of foil to prevent steaming.

Braised Rock Cornish game hens

3 Rock Cornish game hens (about 1¼ pounds each)
6 strips of bacon
1 tablespoon olive oil
1 bay leaf
2 cups canned tomatoes
6 celery ribs, chopped
Salt and pepper
24 small white onions (silverskins)
3 tablespoons butter
1½ tablespoons sugar

If the birds are frozen, let them defrost in the refrigerator overnight. Remove the packages of giblets. Wipe the birds inside and out with a damp paper towel and pat them dry. Leave them whole, or split them.

Cut 3 bacon strips into halves and dice the rest. Put the dice in a heavy pan with the oil and sauté until the bacon is about half cooked. With a slotted spoon transfer the pieces to a heavy casserole just big enough to hold the birds. Brown the birds on all sides in the fat in the pan, then arrange them on top of the diced bacon. Add the bay leaf, tomatoes and celery. Sprinkle with salt and pepper. Put half a piece of bacon on each half bird, or 2 pieces over the breast of each whole bird. Cover the pot and braise the birds in a 325° F. oven for 45 minutes to 1 hour.

Meanwhile, rinse the giblets. If you plan to use them, add the hearts and gizzards to the braising pot, but do not add the livers until half of the cooking time has elapsed (they cook more quickly). Drop the onions into boiling water, leave them for 1 minute, then transfer to cold water and peel. Steam them in a small amount of salted water for about 15 minutes. Drain on paper towels. Discard the fat from the pan used to brown the birds and wipe the pan with paper towels. Add the butter and onions to the pan and stir over heat until the vegetables are hot and well coated with butter. Add the sugar. Stir the onions over low heat until they are browned and slightly caramelized.

Transfer the birds to a hot platter and purée the braising vegetables through a sieve or in a blender. Serve a half bird, some of the purée and some of the onions on a bed of noodles. Makes 6 servings. *Note:* If your birds are partly frozen when you start, you will need to cook them longer. Test for doneness, but do not overcook these tender birds.

Ducks in the apple orchard

Unlike chicken, which is drier, duck and other fatty meats survive better when cooked in advance. In fact with this method you can remove fat from the cooking juices with ease.

2 ducks (5 pounds each)
2 onions, chopped
2 carrots, chopped
3 whole cloves
3 ounces (6 tablespoons) applejack
2 cups apple juice or cider (approximately)
16 cored apple slices, sautéed in butter

With poultry shears cut each bird into four pieces, or into smaller pieces if you prefer. Brown a few pieces at a time in a frying pan. There should be enough fat in the duck so that no extra fat is needed. Put the onions, carrots and cloves in a large braising pan and add the duck pieces. Pour the applejack over them, heat and ignite it. When the flames die down, add 1 cup of the apple juice or cider. Cover the pan and braise the duck in a 325° F. oven for 1 hour.

Test the duck; if it is not tender, cook it a little longer. Add more apple juice if the vegetables or the birds seem to be drying or browning too quickly. When the duck is done, cool, then refrigerate for 1 hour, or overnight if necessary. Remove all the fat—this is easy when the dish is cold—and strain the juices. Return duck and pan juices to the pan. Add more apple juice if necessary; there should be about 2 cups liquid. Return to the oven and heat until the liquid simmers and the duck is very hot. Spoon about 3 tablespoons of the pan juices over each piece and garnish with the apple rings. Serve with green peas, green beans or braised celery. Makes 8 servings.

Braised turkey roll

The boneless turkey roll of part white and part dark meat, or of white meat only, makes an excellent roast for a party occasion because it is so easy to carve and serve. This turkey is more succulent when it has been braised, because like all frozen poultry it tends to be somewhat dry.

1 boneless turkey roll (about 5 pounds)
2 tablespoons peanut oil
2 tablespoons butter
1½ cups canned mushroom pieces and liquid
3 leeks, cleaned and sliced
1 teaspoon dried savory
4 juniper berries, bruised in a mortar
Salt and pepper
3 cups dry red wine
Cornstarch or potato starch

Defrost the turkey roll in the refrigerator for at least 30 hours. Pat dry, then brown in the oil and butter till golden on all sides. Drain off the mushroom liquid and set aside to use later. Put the mushroom pieces, sliced leeks, savory and juniper berries in the braising pan. Add the browned turkey roll. Sprinkle with salt and pepper. Pour ½ cup of wine over the turkey, cover the pan and put in a 350° F. oven. After 20 minutes add another ½ cup of wine. Add the remaining wine, ½ cup at a time, at 20-minute intervals. Add the reserved mushroom liquid last. The turkey should be cooked in about 2 hours. If it seems to be getting dry, reduce the oven heat to 325° F.

Strain or purée the pan juices and thicken them with cornstarch or potato starch; use 1 tablespoon for each cup of liquid. To make it easier to slice the roll, cut a piece off the bottom so it will lie flat on the platter. Makes 10 to 12 servings.

Chicken Catalan

This marriage of pot-roasted chicken with fresh lemon makes a delicious casserole. The Catalans serve it with broiled tomatoes, heavily sprinkled with minced chives, and hot French bread.

1 chicken (3 to 4 pounds)
4 tablespoons butter
Salt and pepper
2 or 3 garlic cloves
3 lemons, unpeeled
¼ teaspoon crumbled dried thyme
1 bay leaf
1 cup chicken stock
1 tablespoon cornstarch
¼ cup cold heavy cream

Cut chicken into pieces. Heat butter in a casserole and brown the chicken in it. Sprinkle with salt and pepper. Crush garlic cloves and add them to the chicken; stir until the garlic is brown. Cut unpeeled lemons into very thin slices. Add to the chicken with thyme and bay leaf. Add stock and bring to a boil. Cover. Cook over medium heat until chicken is tender, 40 to 60 minutes.

Place the chicken on a deep hot serving platter. Arrange the lemon slices over the chicken, but discard the bay leaf. Stir cornstarch with cold heavy cream. Add to the liquid in the casserole and stir over medium heat until the sauce is creamy and transparent. Strain the sauce over the chicken. Makes 4 to 6 servings.

Pheasant with cabbage

French cooks have developed many superb recipes for game birds, using fresh cabbage or sauerkraut, white wine and juniper berries. If you have wild birds that are young and tender, treat them like any domestic bird. This recipe can be used for pheasant or partridge. It is an especially good dish if you have an older, tougher bird.

- 1 pheasant (4 to 5 pounds)
- 1 large green cabbage (about 2 pounds)
- 2 carrots
- 2 onions
- 2 apples, unpeeled
- ½ pound kielbasa (Polish sausage)
- Salt and pepper
- 2 cups red wine
- 2 cups beef stock

Wipe the bird with damp paper towels and cut it into serving portions. If it is a wild bird, be sure to remove any pieces of shot or bone splinters. Remove the core from the cabbage and separate the leaves. Blanch the leaves for 8 minutes, then plunge in cold water to refresh. (This will help keep them greener in the casserole.) Cut carrots, onions, apples and kielbasa into small cubes. Sauté until lightly browned. There should be enough fat in the kielbasa, but if not, add a tablespoon of peanut oil.

Assemble the ingredients in a large casserole—enameled cast iron is good. Scatter a few of the sautéed vegetables and sausage pieces in the bottom. Add a layer of cabbage leaves, then a few more of the cubes. Then put the legs of the bird in. Cover with more cabbage leaves, add a few more dice, then the backs and wings. Continue layering until all the pieces are used except the breasts; set them aside to add later because they cook more quickly than the other pieces.

Sprinkle the layers with a little salt and pepper and cover the top with the last of the cabbage leaves. Add the wine and stock. Cook over very low heat on top of the stove, or in a 325° F. oven, for about 1 hour. Then open the casserole, lift off the top cabbage layer, add the breast pieces and return cabbage. Cover again and return to the heat for at least 1 hour longer (if the bird is not tender, cook it for an additional hour or less). Add more wine and stock if the liquid evaporates too fast.

If you like, you can omit the pepper and use 4 to 6 crushed peppercorns instead; or use 4 juniper berries or whole cloves. The juices can be thickened. Serve a piece of breast and a piece of the leg for each serving. The bonier pieces and any pan juices and cabbage remaining can be used to make a thick soup for another meal. Makes 4 servings.

Chicken and rice casserole

This is an adaptation of a classic Spanish casserole. Use chicken wings, a small broiler quartered, chicken legs or breasts, or any other parts you prefer.

- 1/4 cup flour
- 1 teaspoon paprika
- 1/4 teaspoon ground thyme
- 1 teaspoon salt
- 1 teaspoon curry powder *or* 1/8 teaspoon ground saffron *or* 1 teaspoon ground turmeric
- 3 to 4 pounds chicken pieces
- 3 tablespoons butter
- 3 tablespoons olive oil
- 1 1/2 cups uncooked long-grain rice
- 3 cups water or chicken stock

Combine flour, paprika, thyme, salt, curry powder (or saffron, to make this dish the Spanish way; or ground turmeric, to make it the French way). Stir all together so that spices and seasonings are well mixed with the flour. Roll chicken pieces, a few at a time, in this mixture. Brown a few pieces at a time in butter and olive oil over medium heat. Transfer the browned pieces to a large casserole. Add the rice to the fat remaining in the pan. Stir until lightly browned, then pour over the chicken. Pour in the water or chicken stock. Cover and bake in a 350° F. oven for 45 minutes. Makes 6 servings.

BROILING AND BARBECUING POULTRY

Except for the fatty ducks and geese, poultry is much drier than meat and therefore needs more care in broiling. Split squabs, Rock Cornish game hens, broilers, quartered broilers or fryers, cut-up fryers, ducks, geese and turkeys can be used. Small turkeys (baby turkeys) can be split and broiled. Thicker pieces are broiled farther from the source of heat, while thin pieces should be quickly cooked closer to the heat source so they do not dry out. Marinades are good to use with poultry (Chapter 6).

0━ For more even cooking, cut the tendons of poultry so that each piece will lie as flat as possible. Heat shrinks the tendons and can keep parts of the bird from lying flat. The wing tips or drumsticks, for instance, will be charred, and the parts at the base of the joint may remain uncooked.

Brush the pieces with butter or oil or one of the basting sauces (Chapter 6), or use part of a marinade if you are using one.

Broiled chicken

1 broiler (2½ to 3 pounds)
Salt and pepper
3 tablespoons salad oil
1 teaspoon paprika
½ teaspoon crumbled dried tarragon, basil or savory
or ¼ teaspoon ground thyme or sage

Separate the chicken into halves with poultry shears or good kitchen scissors by cutting down the back first, then turn and cut through the breastbone. Remove the backbone and neck and use these for chicken stock. Twist the wing joints in their sockets so the pieces will lie flat. Place the bird skin side down directly on the broiler pan, not on a rack. Season the top with salt and pepper, pour the salad oil on top and sprinkle with paprika. If you like, sprinkle on the herb of your choice.

Place the broiler pan in the lowest part of the preheated broiler, as far as possible from the source of heat. Broil on one side for 30 minutes, then turn and baste the top with the juices in the pan. Broil on the other side for another 30 minutes, or until skin is crisped and golden brown. After 15 minutes, decrease the heat if the skin is browning too rapidly. Serve with a large bowl of crisp cool green salad and a bottle of chutney. Makes 4 servings.

This dish is delicious served cold, but it is even better when it has not been refrigerated.

Scandinavian broiled chicken

The Scandinavians are masters in the art of using sugar with their food. This chicken is an excellent example. The combination of sugar and lemon juice gives a special tang and a crisp crust.

1 lemon
2 plump 2½-pound broilers, split *or* one 3- to 3½-pound broiler, quartered
3 teaspoons salt
½ teaspoon freshly ground pepper
1 teaspoon paprika
½ cup melted butter *or* ¼ cup melted butter and ¼ cup chicken fat
2 tablespoons sugar

Grate the rind of the lemon, then cut lemon into halves.

Place the small broilers or the quarters in the bottom of the broiling pan. Rub and squeeze the lemon halves over the chicken. Blend the salt, pepper and paprika and sprinkle on top of the chicken. Use a brush to coat both sides of the pieces with the melted butter, or mixed butter and chicken fat. Arrange the pieces skin side down and sprinkle with half of the sugar.

Broil as for Broiled Chicken (preceding recipe). When the chicken is turned, baste with the remaining butter and sprinkle with the rest of the sugar. Serve with broiled tomatoes and parsleyed rice. Makes 4 servings.

Chinese deviled chicken

The Chinese part of this recipe is the blanching trick that is performed before broiling. This is good for chicken breasts or a large cut-up broiler.

2 pounds chicken breasts *or* 1 chicken (3½ to 4 pounds), quartered
4 tablespoons butter or peanut oil
1 tablespoon cider or wine vinegar
½ teaspoon crumbled dried tarragon
1 teaspoon dry mustard
1 teaspoon sugar
Salt and pepper

Fill a bowl with boiling water and drop the pieces of chicken into it, letting them stand for about 5 minutes with no additional heat. Drain, then pat dry with absorbent paper or a clean towel.

Heat the butter or peanut oil and add the vinegar, tarragon and mustard. Brush the chicken pieces on both sides with this mixture. Sprinkle with the sugar. Place skin side down on the broiler rack. Broil as for Broiled Chicken (p. 350), but remember the total broiling time may be 15 minutes less because of the hot dip at the beginning. When ready, place on a hot dish. Sprinkle salt and pepper on each piece and serve. Makes 4 servings.

Barbecued split broilers

Split 2 broiler chickens and cut leg and wing tendons so the halves will lie flat. Cook slowly about 4 inches above the coals, turning every 10 minutes, or use a basket on a motorized spit. A split 2-pound broiler takes from 45 to 60 minutes. If you put the bird closer to the coals—3 inches away—it will cook in 20 to 30 minutes. It should be turned every 5 minutes and be basted as it turns. Allow half of a 2-pound broiler for each serving.

BASTING SAUCE

½ cup salad oil
½ cup butter
½ cup sherry, white wine, lemon juice or chicken stock
1 teaspoon salt
¼ teaspoon pepper
1 teaspoon crumbled dried tarragon or rosemary
1 garlic clove, crushed (optional)

Mix all together and bring to a boil. Keep the sauce hot while basting with a brush. Makes 1½ cups sauce.

Broiled baby turkey

1 baby turkey (about 6 pounds) *or* 4 pounds turkey breasts
Honey Basting Sauce (p. 205)

Split the baby bird, cut tendons and flatten slightly; or halve each turkey breast and flatten. Put the pieces skin side down directly in the broiler pan and brush with some of the sauce. Place the pan as far as possible from the source of heat and broil for 30 to 40 minutes. Baste twice during this time. Then turn over and broil for another 40 minutes, or longer if necessary. Baste twice during this time. The breast pieces, without bones or skin, will dry more and need to be watched carefully. Serve with Spiced Apricots (p. 735) or Mustard-Pickled Green Tomatoes (p. 461) and garnish with parsley bouquets. Makes 6 to 8 servings.

Golden glazed broilers

The handsome golden glaze on these birds comes from undiluted frozen orange juice. Cook these on a covered barbecue.

2 broilers (2½ pounds each)
½ teaspoon crumbled dried rosemary or basil
Salad oil
1 can (6 ounces) condensed frozen orange juice, undiluted
1 tablespoon soy sauce
½ teaspoon ground ginger
½ teaspoon salt
2 or more oranges, cut into thin slices
Sprigs of fresh mint

Place ¼ teaspoon of the rosemary or basil in each of the chicken cavities. Tie each chicken together firmly. Rub the outsides with salad oil. Combine the orange juice, soy sauce, ginger and salt.

Prepare the fire for indirect cooking. Place the chicken on the grill and cover the barbecue. Cook for 1 hour and 20 to 30 minutes. Baste the birds with the orange mixture every 5 minutes during the last 20 to 30 minutes.

Place the cooked chickens on a hot platter over a layer of thin slices of oranges. Pour any drippings left in the foil pan over the chickens. Push a bouquet of fresh mint in the opening of the cavities, and serve. Makes 4 to 6 servings.

SAUTÉING AND PANFRYING POULTRY

Chicken, squab and Rock Cornish game hens can be sautéed. With other kinds of poultry this method usually will not cook the pieces sufficiently. Turkey pieces can be panfried. Of course, any kind of poultry may sometimes be sautéed as a part of the cooking, to brown the outside (as with the braised game hens) or to release some of the fat (as with the braised ducks). Chicken breasts are often sautéed, then sauced in the same pan. The breast of the bird, which is the most tender, cooks in 5 to 8 minutes and should still be juicy when done. Overcooking ruins it. Poultry can be sautéed just as it is, or with a coating of seasoned flour, or egg and crumbs, or a batter.

O━ Remember, as with meat, sauté or panfry only as much poultry as will fit comfortably in your pan. Do not crowd the pieces or they will steam rather than fry.

In the next two recipes the chicken pieces are first sautéed, then poached. This is a good method for flavorful casseroles, because the browning both accentuates the flavor and improves the appearance.

Chicken Torcello

A specialty of Torcello, an island near Venice; surely an elegant way to serve spaghetti.

- 1 broiler (2 to 3 pounds)
- 2 tablespoons flour
- ½ teaspoon salt
- 1 teaspoon paprika
- 1 teaspoon crumbled dried basil
- ½ teaspoon garlic powder
- 2 tablespoons olive oil
- 1 tablespoon butter
- 1 cup chicken stock
- 4 large ripe tomatoes, peeled and seeded
- ½ cup minced parsley
- 1 medium-size green pepper, diced
- 8 ounces thin spaghetti
- ½ cup grated Parmesan cheese

Cut the broiler into serving pieces, then cut each piece into halves. Mix the flour, salt, paprika, basil and garlic powder on a plate. Roll each piece of chicken in the seasoned flour until well coated. Heat the olive oil and butter together in a large frying pan. Add the chicken and cook over medium heat until brown. Pour in the chicken stock. Cut the tomatoes into coarse pieces and add to the chicken. Bring to a boil, then cover and simmer over low heat for 25 to 30 minutes, until chicken is tender.

Uncover the pan and boil fast until the liquid is reduced to the consistency of light cream. Add the parsley and green pepper. Cover and remove from heat, but let stand in a warm place.

In the meantime, boil the spaghetti according to directions on the package. Drain and place in a warm bowl; pour chicken and sauce on top. Sprinkle the cheese over all and serve. Makes 4 servings.

Chicken Antonia

- 1 broiler (2½ to 3 pounds)
- 3 tablespoons olive oil
- 2 carrots, thinly sliced
- 2 onions, finely chopped
- 4 celery ribs, diced
- 3 slices of ham, diced
- 1 green or red pepper, cut into slivers
- ½ pound fresh mushrooms, left whole
- 2 teaspoons cornstarch
- ½ teaspoon curry powder
- 1 teaspoon paprika
- Salt and pepper
- 1 cup chicken stock
- 3 tablespoons dry port wine (optional)

Cut the broiler into serving pieces. Heat the oil in a large pan. Add the carrots, onions, celery, ham and chicken pieces. Stir and brown lightly over medium heat. Add the green or red pepper slivers and the mushrooms. Stir to mix. Sprinkle with the cornstarch, curry powder and paprika. Salt lightly and add a dash of pepper. Add the chicken stock. Stir until the liquid starts to boil. Cover and cook over very low heat until the chicken is tender, 30 to 45 minutes. Stir the port into the sauce, cook for 1 minute and serve. Makes 4 servings.

Chicken breasts with orange and onion

- 3 whole chicken breasts (6 pieces), from fryers
- 2 tablespoons peanut oil
- 2 tablespoons butter
- 12 orange slices
- 6 thick slices of red onion (about 1 large onion)
- ½ cup chicken stock
- Pepper
- Watercress

Wipe the chicken breasts. You can bone them if you prefer, but for this simple recipe it is not necessary. Heat the oil and butter in a heavy frying pan and sauté about half the chicken at a time. Put the pieces in skin side down first, then turn over and cook until golden brown and tender, about 12 minutes with the bones, about 8 minutes without the bones. Transfer chicken to a plate and keep hot.

Sauté the orange slices until lightly browned, about 2 minutes. Then sauté the onion slices for about 4 minutes. Arrange each chicken piece on 2 orange slices and crown with an onion slice. Pour the stock into the frying pan and cook over high heat just long enough to scrape up all the browned bits and reduce the liquid to 6 tablespoons. Spoon 1 tablespoon over each serving, sprinkle with pepper and garnish with watercress. Makes 6 servings.

Chicken with cream

1 broiler (2½ pounds)
Salt and pepper
1 tablespoon butter
2 tablespoons oil
2 tablespoons minced onion
1 cup heavy cream
¼ cup white wine
1 teaspoon dried tarragon

Cut chicken into pieces and sprinkle with salt and pepper. Sauté in butter and oil until brown. Cover. Cook slowly about 20 to 25 minutes. Remove chicken from pan. Pour off from pan all but a tablespoon of fat, and add onions. Cook for 1 minute. Pour in cream and wine. Boil down rapidly until mixture thickens. Stir in tarragon. Pour over chicken. Makes 4 servings.

DEEP-FRYING POULTRY

Fried chicken, once a great Southern dish and now a favorite all over the country, is the best known form of deep-fried poultry. Other poultry can be prepared this way, but it is better to use only drier kinds such as chicken or turkey. Be sure to read the general information on deep-frying (p. 303).

Fried chicken

You can use complete cut-up chickens for this recipe, but some parts—backs and wings—do not have much meat on them. You may wish to cook only halved breasts, legs and thighs and reserve the other portions for stock.

4 pounds chicken pieces
Beer Batter (recipe follows)
Peanut oil or vegetable shortening for deep-frying
Salt

Wipe the chicken pieces with damp paper towels, then pat dry. Dip into the batter and then place them, a few at a time, in a frying basket. Heat the oil or shortening to 375° F. on a frying thermometer, and fry the chicken for about 15 minutes. Test with a fork; if the juices are absolutely clear, the chicken is done. Transfer cooked pieces to baking sheets lined with paper towels and keep the chicken warm in a low oven until all the pieces are cooked. Sprinkle with salt just before serving. For traditional serving, put the pieces in a large basket and serve with other finger food. Be sure there are saltshakers handy, because most people like more salt. Makes 6 to 8 servings.

For a thicker coating, dip the pieces first into beaten egg, then into flour, then into batter. 0┳ For greater success in keeping the batter on the chicken, chill the pieces for 1 hour after they have been coated. Place them in a single layer on a plate, not overlapping or touching each other.

BEER BATTER

2 cups flour
1 teaspoon salt
1 teaspoon paprika
2 whole eggs
4 tablespoons peanut oil or corn oil
2 cups flat beer
2 extra egg whites *or* ½ cup carbonated water

In a bowl sift together flour, salt and paprika. In another bowl beat whole eggs, oil and beer together. Then blend the two mixtures until smooth. Refrigerate for 2 hours. Then stir again and mix in the egg whites, beaten until almost stiff, or the carbonated water.

This batter can be flavored with curry powder, poultry seasoning, ground dill or cuminseeds. Makes enough for about 6 pounds of chicken.

Turkey croquettes

4 cups turkey pieces
¼ cup peanut oil
½ cup flour
1 cup milk
1 cup turkey stock or gravy
1 teaspoon salt
¼ teaspoon white pepper
½ teaspoon onion juice
¼ teaspoon ground nutmeg
1 teaspoon Italian seasoning (without onion) (p. 128) *or* ½ teaspoon barbecue spice
¼ cup diced fresh dill
¼ cup minced parsley
Flour
Peanut oil for deep-frying

This is a good recipe for the leftover holiday bird. Remove all meat remaining on the bones until you have 4 cupfuls. Then grind or chop the measured amount. Make a thick sauce with the peanut oil, flour, milk and stock or gravy. Season with the salt, white pepper, onion juice and Italian seasoning or barbecue spice. Mix the turkey, dill and parsley into the sauce until well blended. Chill the mixture until stiff enough to shape, then mold into 6 or 8 chop-shaped flat portions, or form into turkey legs if you prefer. Chill for at least 1 hour.

Flour the chops or legs and fry a few at a time in a frying basket in oil heated to 385° F. Since the turkey is already cooked, you will need only a few minutes to brown the pieces. Lift them out of the basket carefully because they will be fragile. Drain on paper towels. Sprinkle with salt and serve accompanied with Mustard-Pickled Green Tomatoes (p. 461). Makes about 6 servings.

POACHING OR STEWING POULTRY

Poaching is the ideal way to prepare poultry to be served cold. The meat will be juicy and very flavorful. Read the general directions on these cooking methods (p. 307). Especially with poultry, remember to reduce the cooking time and let the bird cool in the cooking liquid if you are planning to serve it cold.

Poached birds served hot are also good. Many Frenchwomen built a reputation and a restaurant around a poached chicken. The flavorful cooking liquid can be used to make delicious sauces for the bird and accompanying vegetables.

Duck and goose can be poached, and the meat will be much less fatty than if they have been roasted. You will have duck or goose broth to use, and all the fat can be used, if you wish, for other cooking. It will not be burned or browned as it sometimes is in roasting. If you like the appearance of browned skin, the bird can be finished in the oven or broiler.

The bird will be done when the flesh of the leg feels soft and the meat has just begun to shrink from the tip of the drumstick.

Poached chicken

This is the classic poached chicken known as *bonne femme*. Apart from the potatoes, many other fresh vegetables can be added. With a little imagination, this recipe can undergo many transformations. You can adapt it for any other kind of bird.

1 chicken (3 to 4 pounds)
2 tablespoons flour
1 teaspoon salt
¼ teaspoon pepper
¼ teaspoon ground thyme or curry powder
⅓ cup butter, chicken fat or salad oil
2 garlic cloves, minced, *or* 1 onion, minced
8 to 10 small potatoes, peeled
2 cups chicken stock or water

Cut the chicken into serving pieces. Place the flour, salt, pepper and thyme or curry powder in a paper bag. Put the chicken in the bag with this mixture and shake until each piece is lightly coated. Do each piece separately.

Heat the fat in a large saucepan with a cover; add the garlic or onion and the chicken pieces. Add only a few pieces at a time if the saucepan is not large enough to hold them all in one layer. Brown the chicken on all sides, then drain on paper towels and return all the chicken pieces to the pan. Scatter the potatoes around them. Pour the chicken stock or water on top. Cover tightly and poach over low heat until the chicken is tender, 40 to 50 minutes.

Remove the chicken and potatoes and place on a hot platter. Boil the liquid, uncovered, over high heat until slightly reduced; then pour it over the chicken. Makes 4 servings.

Poached capon à la ficelle

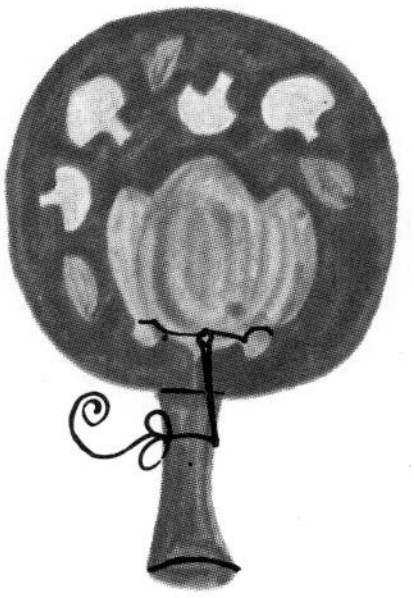

Ficelle means string, and you will see how this name applies. This recipe gives you a perfectly poached chicken and a delicate and tasty soup. It also makes chicken-flavored fat that you can use to cook with another time.

1 capon (4 to 6 pounds) *or* 1 large stewing chicken
¼ pound salt pork, diced
2 tablespoons butter
1 tablespoon olive oil or salad oil
6 to 8 green onions, chopped
½ pound fresh mushrooms, diced
¼ cup chopped fresh parsley
½ teaspoon dried thyme
1 bay leaf
1 tablespoon salt
½ teaspoon pepper
1 garlic clove, crushed
5 cups boiling water

Choose a heavy metal saucepan with a good cover. The saucepan should be sufficiently deep to hold the chicken vertically. Tie the chicken legs together with a string long enough to tie to the handle of the saucepan.

Melt the salt pork with the butter and oil over medium heat until the diced pork is golden. Brown the chicken lightly all over in the fat, then add both the green and white parts of the onions. Stir to coat them with fat. Remove the saucepan from the heat.

Tie the chicken to the handle of the saucepan in such a way that the bird will hang, neck opening down, against the side of the saucepan. Add the mushrooms, parsley, thyme, bay leaf, salt, pepper and garlic. Pour the boiling water over all. Cover the pan tightly. Since only about a quarter of the chicken is actually in the water, this might be called steaming rather than poaching. Cook the chicken for about 2 hours until it is tender.

When the bird is done, untie it and place it breast side down in the bouillon in the pan. Cover and leave until cold. Then if you wish to serve it hot, warm it.

When the bird is cool, remove it. To make soup, add 3 to 4 cups hot water to the bouillon remaining in the pan. Taste for seasoning and add more if necessary. Bring to a boil and add ½ cup very fine noodles. Simmer for 20 minutes.

Serve thin slices of the chicken with Sauce Velouté (p. 189) and parsleyed rice. Makes about 8 servings.

Chicken in creamy sauce

This is an example of oven-poaching. For a satisfying country-style meal, serve this with hot biscuits and cabbage and apple salad.

- 2 cloves
- 1 small onion
- 1 chicken (3 to 4 pounds)
- 1 bay leaf
- 3 cups milk
- 1 celery rib with leaves, diced
- ¼ cup chopped parsley
- ¼ teaspoon grated mace
- 2 teaspoons salt
- Pepper
- 3 tablespoons soft butter
- 3 tablespoons all-purpose flour

Stick cloves in the onion and place in the cavity of the chicken. Tie the legs loosely. Place the bird in a deep casserole and put the bay leaf on top. Add milk, celery, parsley, mace, salt and a little pepper. Cover. Bake in a 275° F. oven for 2 to 3 hours, depending on the size of the chicken. When the chicken is tender, remove from the baking dish and cut into pieces.

Mix soft butter with flour. Add to the hot milk and stir well until thickened and creamy. Taste and add more seasoning if necessary. Strain the sauce over the chicken. Makes 6 servings.

Poached chicken for salad

The best bird for this recipe is a large fowl. The moist, slow cooking will make it very tender and flavorful. However, you can use two fryers. Of course, the cooking time for the smaller and younger birds will be much less.

1 fowl (about 5 pounds)
2 leeks, washed and split
2 celery ribs with leaves
1 bay leaf
1 tablespoon salt
3 tablespoons parsley stems

Truss the fowl; it will be much easier to handle later. Cover it with cold water, bring to a boil and cook for about 2 minutes. Discard the water and wash the pot if a lot of scum has been deposited around the sides. If you are using fryers or cut-up chicken, omit this first blanching step. Cover the bird again with water and add all the flavoring ingredients. Bring to a boil, then reduce to a simmer and poach for about 2 hours. Let the bird cool in the broth.

Remove all the meat from the bones and refrigerate it. If you wish to make stock, return the bones to the cooking pot and cook the broth for another hour. Discard the flavoring vegetables and strain the stock.

Poach fryers for 30 minutes and cut-up chicken for about 20 minutes, or less if it is to be cooked further in some other preparation.

Chicken salad

3 cups diced poached chicken
1 orange
1 slice of Bermuda onion, minced
¼ cup sliced pitted black olives
½ cup mayonnaise
½ cup French dressing made with lemon juice (p. 208)
Salt and pepper
3 Belgian endives

🗝 Cut the chicken into large dice; this is one of the secrets of a good poultry salad. If the pieces are too small, the chicken will not be as tasty.

Peel the orange; you can use the rind as a garnish if you like. Section the fruit and cut each into 3 pieces. Add the pieces and any juice to the chicken along with the onion and olives. Toss to mix. Then add both dressings and season with salt and pepper. Add more dressing if you like. Serve on endive leaves arranged spoke fashion. Makes 6 servings.

Nuns' chicken pie

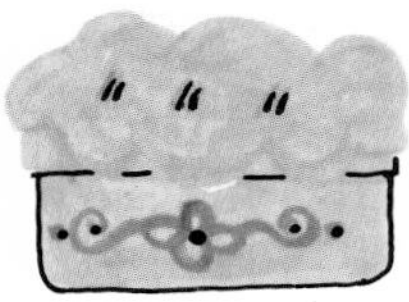

This tasty chicken dish is time-consuming, but the chicken and broth are prepared the day before and refrigerated overnight.

- 1 fowl (5 to 6 pounds)
- 1 tablespoon salt
- ½ teaspoon pepper
- 1 cup celery leaves
- 1 large onion, quartered
- ½ teaspoon crumbled dried savory or thyme
- 1 bay leaf
- 6 cups boiling water
- 3 cups sliced carrots
- 2 cups diced celery
- 12 to 24 small white onions
- ¾ cup butter
- ¾ cup all-purpose flour
- 2 cups milk
- 1 cup heavy cream
- 1 tablespoon lemon juice
- ½ cup minced parsley
- Pie pastry for a large 2-crust pie

Place the chicken in a large saucepan with the next seven ingredients. Bring to a boil. Cover, then simmer over low heat until the chicken is tender, from 1½ to 2 hours. When done, leave the bird in the broth until cool enough to handle.

Remove the chicken skin, pull the meat off the bones and place the meat in a large bowl. Pass the skin through a meat grinder and mix it with the chicken. Put the bones back in the pot and boil the broth, uncovered, until reduced to two thirds of the original quantity. Strain the broth over the chicken. Cover and refrigerate overnight.

The next day place the carrots and diced celery in a bowl and cover completely with boiling water. Let it stand for 1 hour. Peel the small onions and boil for 15 minutes.

Heat the chicken just enough so the broth can be strained off. Measure 3 cups of the broth; if there is more than this, save it for another recipe. Melt the butter, add the flour and stir until well blended. Add the milk, cream and 3 cups broth, and cook until the sauce is creamy. Add the well-drained onions, carrots and celery to the sauce. Then add the chicken pieces, lemon juice and parsley. Season to taste.

Line a pudding dish or deep pie dish with pastry and pour in the chicken mixture. Top with more pastry. Crimp or flute the edges and make a few holes for steam to escape. Bake in a preheated 400° F. oven for 40 to 50 minutes, or until golden brown. This chicken pie freezes very well and reheats beautifully. Makes 8 to 10 servings.

Chicken stew with okra

This is a simple and mild version of a Creole gumbo, not authentic but delicious and simple to prepare. To give it more of the flavor of Louisiana-style cooking, add hot-pepper sauce to taste.

- 1 fowl (about 5 pounds)
- 1/4 cup peanut oil or corn oil
- 2 large onions, chopped
- 2 green peppers, trimmed and sliced
- 1 tablespoon sugar
- 2 teaspoons salt
- 4 cups stewed tomatoes (fresh or canned)
- 1 pound small okra, washed
- Chicken stock or water

Cut the chicken into small pieces, not sections. (For example, make at least three pieces of each thigh and about six pieces of each section of the breast.) This will reduce the cooking time and help to make all the pieces tender at the same time. Leave the bones in for better flavor. Brown the pieces, a few at a time, in the oil and set them aside. Then sauté the onions and peppers in the oil until lightly browned. Pour off as much fat as possible. Sprinkle the vegetables with the sugar. Return the chicken to the pot and sprinkle with salt. Add the tomatoes. Cover the pot and simmer the stew for about 40 minutes, or until the chicken is cooked. The okra can be added whole or sliced. If it is sliced, it helps to thicken the stew. Cook for 10 minutes after the okra is added. If the tomatoes cook away too fast, add a little chicken stock or water. The stew should be quite juicy when done. Serve over rice in deep plates. Makes about 8 servings.

Chicken fricassee

This recipe is similar to the recipe for Fricassee of Veal (p. 316), but the chicken cooks in less time than the veal.

- 1 chicken (3 1/4 to 4 pounds)
- 4 tablespoons butter
- Salt and pepper
- Pinch or two of grated nutmeg
- 1 small onion, finely chopped
- 1 cup milk
- 1 celery rib
- 1 carrot, sliced
- 1 bay leaf
- 1 teaspoon salt
- 3 cups water
- 1 teaspoon diced chicken fat
- 4 tablespoons flour
- 2 to 3 tablespoons heavy cream

With a sharp pointed knife remove all the meat from the chicken. Save the carcass. Cut the boned meat into 1- or 2-inch pieces.

Melt 2 tablespoons of the butter in a saucepan. When the butter is golden brown, add the pieces of chicken and brown them on all sides over medium heat. Sprinkle with salt and pepper and add the nutmeg and onion. Pour the milk on top. Bring to a simmer, cover tightly and simmer over very low heat, or cook in a 250° F. oven, for 1 hour.

While the meat of the chicken cooks, place the carcass in a saucepan with the celery, carrot, bay leaf, salt and water. Bring to a boil, cover and simmer over low heat for 1 hour. Pass through a fine strainer. Measure. If there is more than 2 cups stock, return the whole to the rinsed saucepan and boil fast, uncovered, until reduced to 2 cups.

Make a *sauce velouté* by melting the remaining 2 tablespoons of butter and the chicken fat. When the fat is melted, add the flour; then stir and blend together for 3 minutes, over low heat. The flour and butter must not be brown. The cooking and stirring is important; this partly cooks the flour and prevents a starchy flavor in the finished sauce. Strain the milk from the chicken into the cooked butter-flour mixture. Beat with a whisk to blend. Add the 2 cups of stock. Beat and stir over medium heat until smooth.

Pour the sauce over the chicken. Simmer together for a minute while stirring gently. Taste for seasoning. O━ At this point the secret of the French chef is to add the cream, whipped stiff. This is stirred into the sauce just when the chicken is ready to serve. Do not cook after adding the cream. Makes 4 to 6 servings.

Poached duck

- 1 duckling (about 5 pounds)
- 1 apple
- 2 leeks, washed
- 2 carrots
- 4 celery ribs
- 4 peppercorns, crushed
- 1 bay leaf

If the duckling is frozen, defrost in the refrigerator for about 24 hours. Remove the bag of giblets. Make a *court bouillon* with the apple, leeks, carrots and celery, all chopped or sliced, the peppercorns, bay leaf and about 2 quarts of water. Bring it to a boil and simmer for 30 minutes. Let it cool.

Truss the duck and put it in the prepared liquid. Bring it to a boil again and simmer for 1 hour, or until almost tender. Let it cool in the liquid, then remove it to a refrigerator dish and chill. If you wish to save the liquid, strain it and discard the flavoring vegetables. Transfer the liquid to refrigerator jars and chill until the fat can be lifted off. The liquid can be used to cook noodles or rice or in any of the ways stock is used.

Carve the duck from the bones. Try to make long, even pieces. To serve hot, reheat gently in Sauce Madère (p. 192) or Sauce Diable (p. 193). To serve cold, glaze with Madeira-flavored aspic; or use in salads with orange or grapefruit sections. Giblets can be poached with the duck. Makes about 6 servings.

Poultry livers

Although most birds come with their giblets in a package, we seldom do anything very imaginative with the hearts or gizzards. Usually they are cooked along with the bird or reserved for making stock. Livers, on the other hand, make delicious dishes by themselves or mixed with other ingredients. For recipes for chicken livers, consult the index. Duck, goose or turkey livers can be prepared in the same ways, but they take a few minutes longer to cook because they are larger. Any of them can be poached whole, sliced and sautéed, or braised. They are all good in omelets or ground to make pâtés or sandwich spreads. Many people who dislike calf or beef liver will like poultry livers.

«11»

Fish and Shellfish

Cleaning fresh fish • Baking fish •
Timetables for baking, broiling fish •
Braising fish • Broiling steaks, whole
and split fish, fresh and frozen fillets •
Sautéing and panfrying fish •
Deep-frying, steaming and poaching fish •
Cooking oysters, clams, mussels,
scallops, shrimp, crabs and lobster •
How to eat lobster

People who live near the sea are especially blessed; they can often enjoy fish caught, cooked and eaten in less than 24 hours. People who live inland, on the other hand, may never know the special flavor of a fish which has flipped out of the water and into a pan. Many young people today know only the taste of frozen fish. Although some sportsmen must travel great distances to fish because their nearby streams and lakes have become polluted, freshwater fishing has increased in popularity with the general public. Our continent is still rich in fish and shellfish, and these foods can add variety and nutrition to our meals.

Some nutritionists and doctors recommend that fish be eaten as often as four times a week. The reasons are many. Fish is very low in cholesterol. It is an easily digested high-protein food, and whether it is large, small, strong, weak, salt- or freshwater, it is always tender. Fish can be cooked, with some slight variations, in much the same way as very tender cuts of meat. There is a distinct difference, however: fish is cooked to develop flavor, while meat is cooked to make it tender.

When you purchase fresh fish, refrigerate it as quickly as possible. Fresh fish has no unpleasant smell, but if it has been out of the water or the refrigerator too long it will develop an objectionable odor. You can keep fish refrigerated for two or three days at the most. After that, its flavor will be greatly affected.

Some types of frozen fish on the market today need defrosting before cooking and some do not. Always read the label on the package. The best way to defrost fish is to transfer it to the refrigerator from the freezer. Thaw until pliable enough to handle easily; do not allow it to get too soft. Defrost small pieces or fillets until the pieces can be separated easily. To defrost a pound of frozen fillets in the refrigerator usually takes from eight to ten hours. Place the fish on a plate while it defrosts to keep it from leaking on other foods.

CLEANING FRESH FISH

If you buy your fish at a fish market, the dealer will clean and trim it to order, or he will clean it in the usual fashion, which includes removing the head. 0→ Fish retains its juices and has more flavor if it is cooked with the head intact. Remember, you must tell your fish dealer that you want the head. Even if you do not want to cook the head with the fish, ask to have it included and use it for making stock. (If the sight of the head disturbs you, you can always cut it off before you serve the fish.)

If you have some freshly caught fish, you must scale and clean them yourself as soon as possible after they are caught. Wet the fish (seawater is best, but fresh cold water will do). Hold the fish firmly by the tail and scrape away from you toward the head with a scaler, the scaling edge of a kitchen scissors or a knife. Be sure to remove all the scales, but do not cut into the fish. Rinse the fish until all the loose scales are washed away. (If you are doing this in your kitchen sink, do not let the scales go down the drain.)

Next slit the belly of the fish forward from the vent and pull out the intestines. Some fish contain roe or milt (the eggs or sperm of female or male fish). These can be cooked with the fish or used to make sauces.

Most fish have several sets of fins. Simply cutting them off is not enough; the bones attached to them will remain in the fish. Cut into the fish along each side of the fin and pull out the entire clump of bones and fin together. If you poach a whole fish, remove the fins after cooking. Of course, if you cut the fish into pieces, it is easy to remove the bones as you cut. Remember that all the bony parts and any attached flesh can be used for making stock.

The dressed fish can be split lengthwise, cut crosswise into steaks or filleted. A fillet is one whole side of the fish with the skin and bones removed. Fish can be boned and stuffed with various stuffings or soufflé mixtures.

To bone a long fish and keep it in one piece, cut into the fish from the top or back along both sides of the backbone. When the backbone is loosened, cut it off with scissors at the head and tail ends and pull it out with the smaller bones attached to it. The fish is now ready to be stuffed and baked.

To bone a flat fish such as sole or flounder, cut along the backbone on the underneath side from head to tail. Then cut between the fillet and the bones on each side. Use a sharp knife. Press the knife against the bone as you cut. This tears the flesh as little as possible. Cut the backbone at the head and tail. Fold back the fillets. Use scissors to cut the bony framework at the sides. Pull it out, cutting it free from the fillets beneath with your filleting knife. The fish is now ready to be stuffed and baked.

The first time you fillet or bone a fish you will find it a slow process, but after a little practice it will go quickly. If you have a fisherman in the family, you may at times have more fish than you can use. While small fish can be frozen whole, it is wise to fillet larger fish, or cut them into steaks. Even a few large whole fish take up far too much space for the average home freezer.

Some fish, such as shad, are difficult to bone raw, and because of this the dealer may charge a high price for boning. Most people find it easier to cook the shad first and remove the bones at the table.

To bone a whole cooked fish for serving, cut away the little ridges of bones you will find along the near and far edges of the fish, then lift off the top fillet and transfer it to a plate. You may find it easier to cut the fillet into halves along the center division, and move each half separately. Remove the backbone; most of the other bones will come out with it, but if any remain, remove them. Then replace the top fillets and reshape the fish.

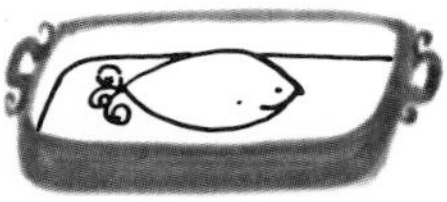

BAKING FISH

Any kind of fish can be baked: whole, stuffed or unstuffed, steaks or fillets. To gauge the required cooking time, know the approximate weight of the fish when it is ready for the oven. This is another occasion when a kitchen scale is a handy thing to have.

Whenever possible bake fish with the head intact, except for salmon. Wash the fish in very cold well-salted water. Use 1/4 cup coarse salt for 2 to 3 quarts water. Never allow a fish to soak. Wash it quickly, and dry it thoroughly with paper towels.

Oil a shallow pan, line it with heavy-duty foil, then oil the foil. Arrange the fish on the foil. If the fish is to be stuffed, insert the stuffing and sew up the opening or fasten it with poultry pins made fast with string, just as in stuffing a chicken. Shape the foil around the sides of the fish, but do not cover the top. The foil will hold the juices of the fish and will make it easier to remove from the pan without breaking.

O-т Never rub the pan or foil with butter or margarine, because these will cause the fish to stick. Use salad oil, olive oil or bacon fat.

Whole fish, steaks or fillets can be sprinkled with any of a variety of toppings before baking. Here are two favorites.

Bread-crumb topping

Brush the fish with beaten egg, and sprinkle generously with fine bread crumbs flavored with herbs or spices or seasoned with salt and pepper. This topping is excellent on fish with edible skin, such as trout, whitefish and small haddock. It is not suitable for salmon. This kind of topping helps to keep the fish juicy.

Flour topping

Sprinkle the top and sides of the fish lightly with flour. Spread it generously with soft butter or lay bacon strips over the fish.

The fish is now ready to bake. You may prepare the fish for the oven a few hours ahead of time if you have room in your refrigerator for the baking pan. If not, prepare the fish just before baking; it cannot be kept waiting on the kitchen counter.

O-т When baking any type of fish, stuffed or unstuffed, it is very important to put the fish in a preheated oven. The temperature should be a constant 400° F. It will take about 15 minutes for the oven to reach that temperature. When the fish is put in at precisely this temperature it will be baked properly. If you take the fish cold from the refrigerator and place it in a cold oven, or in an oven that has not yet reached 400°, the fish will not bake but steam as its temperature and the oven temperature slowly rise.

Basting fish

Baked fish will be tasty and moist if basted every 5 to 10 minutes. Many types of hot or cold liquid can be used. Each of the following liquids will impart a different flavor and texture to the fish, but any one will give excellent results.

½ water and ½ butter, hot
½ water and ½ white wine, hot
½ cup water and juice of ½ lemon, cold
Apple or tomato juice, hot
Dry white wine, cold
Sour cream or heavy cream, cold
French dressing, cold

Baking time for fish

Professional chefs use the thickness and weight of a fish to gauge the cooking time. For quick figuring, allow 10 to 12 minutes of baking time for each 1 inch of thickness. Measure the thickness before baking by holding two fingers (1 inch) across the thickest part of the fish. If you are in doubt, check with a ruler. The following table is a more professional guide and will give surer results. This can be used for whole fish, steaks or fillets.

Timetable for baking fish

Type of fish	Thickness in inches	Baking time in minutes
Flounder or sole	1	2 per ounce
Haddock	3¼	10 per pound
Mackerel	2½	2 per pound
Pike	2¼	1¼ per ounce
Salmon (head off)	2¼	11 per pound
Sea bass	1½	1½ per ounce
Striped bass	2½	12 per pound
Whitefish	1½	15 per pound

If you are baking a fish not listed on the chart, follow the rule for the type that is most similar.

0┳ Never turn a baking fish, not even a small one; baked fish breaks easily because of its delicate texture.

Cornell Method for baking fish fillets or steaks

Brush fillets or steaks with butter, oil or soft bacon fat; then roll in very fine crumbs.

Place in a shallow glass or ceramic baking dish or a jelly-roll pan. Preheat oven to 550° F.; this will take 15 to 20 minutes. Put the pan in the oven on the second rack from the bottom. Bake for exactly 8 minutes. The fish will have a nice brown color and will be properly cooked.

Fish baked *en papillote*

The French chef calls this method of cooking *en papillote*, but we might call it "poaching in the oven" to distinguish it from poaching in liquid. No extra liquid is added but the fish's own liquid is retained. A fish cooked *en papillote* is delicious. You will find that it is most adaptable for the diet conscious, since fat can be cut down almost completely. Usually each individual serving is put in a separate package.

Use cooking parchment if possible. It can be found in department stores, usually with kitchen or freezer paper. Wet the parchment and then squeeze out the water to make the paper soft and pliable. You may also use a piece of heavy-duty foil, large enough to wrap the fish completely. Brush one side of the foil or parchment generously with salad oil. Place the fish on the oiled side of the paper or foil and sprinkle with salt and pepper. You may want to add a sprinkling of curry powder. Brush the fish with more oil. Sprinkle with lemon juice to taste. Add an herb of your choice, such as sage, dill, oregano or basil. Fold the parchment or foil and seal tightly by pinching or crimping the edges. It is important that the covering follow the shape of the fish. Place wrapped fish in a shallow baking dish and bake in a preheated 400° F. oven for 12 minutes per pound.

Unwrap the package carefully and slide the fish onto a hot plate; or serve with the top folded back to show the fish. If you remove the fish from the package, be sure to pour all the accumulated juice over the fish. This is a perfect method for small fish such as brook trout and a good way to cook pompano.

Baked stuffed salmon

This is the king of all salmon dishes. Use a large salmon. Serve it with new potatoes and fresh green peas.

- 1 tablespoon salt
- 3 tablespoons lemon juice
- 1 whole fresh salmon (8 to 12 pounds)
- 1 cup chopped celery
- 1 cup minced celery leaves
- 2 medium-size onions, sliced thin
- ¼ cup butter or salad oil
- 4 cups diced whole-wheat or rye bread
- 2 eggs, lightly beaten
- ¼ teaspoon ground thyme or sage
- Salt and pepper

Mix the salt and lemon juice together. Rub the cleaned fish inside and out with this mixture.

For the stuffing: Over medium-low heat sauté the celery, celery leaves and onions in the butter or salad oil until the onions are soft, transparent and lightly browned. Put the diced bread in a bowl, add the sautéed vegetables and butter or oil and blend well. Then add the beaten eggs, herb, and salt and pepper to taste. Stir until well mixed. Stuff the fish. Sew up the opening with coarse thread or close it with poultry pins. Weigh the stuffed fish.

Place the fish on a well-oiled baking sheet or one that has been rubbed with a thick coating of bacon fat. Bake in an oven preheated to 400° F. for 10 minutes per pound of weight after stuffing, or follow the timetable for baked fish (p. 372).

Serve with a hollandaise sauce, a rich white sauce flavored with dill, or a tomato sauce, or simply with a bowl containing equal parts of melted butter and lemon juice mixed. Makes 10 to 16 servings.

Any large whole fish can be baked this way. Adjust seasoning and stuffing ingredients to suit the particular fish and the menu.

Mackerel with herbs

- 3 mackerel (1½ pounds each)
- 1 tablespoon corn oil
- ⅔ cup fresh bread crumbs
- 1 teaspoon salt
- ½ teaspoon black pepper
- 1 teaspoon crumbled dried marjoram, *or* 6 tiny sprigs of fresh marjoram
- 1 teaspoon crumbled dried savory, *or* 6 tiny sprigs of fresh savory
- 6 tablespoons lemon juice
- 3 egg yolks

Mackerel do not have scales; just wash them. Remove the fins and split the fish lengthwise. Remove the bones if you like; it makes the fish easier to serve. Discard the trimmings; mackerel is too fatty for stock making.

Use a shallow baking dish large enough to hold all the pieces of fish in a single layer; a lasagne dish is excellent. Rub the dish with oil and sprinkle with half the crumbs. Lay the mackerel skin side down, and sprinkle with salt, pepper and herbs. If you are using fresh herbs, lay a sprig of each herb on each piece of fish. Beat lemon juice and egg yolks together and spoon over the fish. Sprinkle the remainder of the crumbs over the top. Bake, uncovered, in a preheated 400° F. oven for about 20 minutes. Makes 6 servings.

Baked bluefish

- 1 bluefish (4 to 5 pounds)
- 2 strips of bacon
- 2 slices of white bread
- 1 small onion
- 8 pitted green olives
- 1 bay leaf
- 1 cup very dry white wine

Scale and dress the bluefish. Sauté the bacon until crisp, then drain and crumble. Use about 1 tablespoon of the bacon fat to grease the baking dish. Cut the bread into cubes, leaving the crusts on if you wish. Mince onion and olives. Combine bacon, bread, onion and olives, and stuff the fish with the mixture. Put a bay leaf into the middle of the stuffing. Skewer the fish closed with poultry pins. Place fish in the oiled baking dish and add the wine. Bake, uncovered, in a preheated 400° F. oven for about 1 hour. Baste with the wine in the dish every 10 minutes. Makes 6 servings.

Trout in foil cases

- 6 fresh trout (about 1 pound each)
- Salt and pepper
- Oil
- 18 to 24 shallots
- 6 tablespoons minced parsley
- ¾ cup sherry (not too sweet)

Clean the trout; for easier wrapping cut off the heads. Sprinkle fish with salt and pepper inside and out. Oil 6 pieces of foil each large enough to wrap around a fish. Place a trout in the center of each piece. Peel the shallots and chop into pieces about the size of peas. Divide shallots and parsley evenly among the packages. Fold up the foil and pour 2 tablespoons sherry into each package. Close the foil and crimp the edges. Slide the packages onto a baking sheet, and bake in a preheated 400° F. oven for about 15 minutes. Test one package for doneness. If the fish is not done, cook for a few minutes longer. The shallots will be crunchy. Makes 6 servings.

Baked fish casseroles

In addition to baking fish by itself or with an accompanying sauce, you can use fish of many kinds in casserole mixtures and puddings. Because fish can be cooked quickly, these preparations are often handier than slow-cooking meat dishes. The additional ingredients can make a tasty dish out of bland frozen fish.

Pink cod garnished

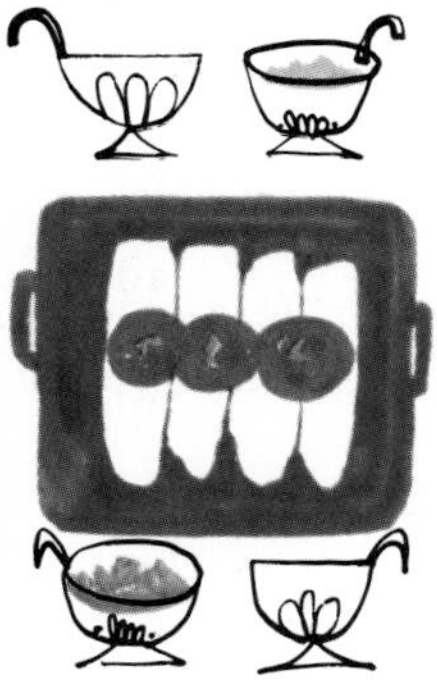

1 pound frozen cod fillets
1 teaspoon salt
1/4 teaspoon pepper
3 tomatoes
1 teaspoon sugar
3 tablespoons chopped fresh dill or parsley
2 tablespoons butter
1/2 cup light cream
3 hard-cooked eggs
1/2 cup chopped parsley
1/4 cup prepared horseradish

Partially thaw the cod fillets, then with a sharp knife cut the block into 1/2-inch slices. Arrange slices side by side in a buttered dish, or overlap them slightly. Sprinkle with salt and pepper.

Peel and slice the tomatoes, and place them over the fish. Sprinkle with sugar and dill or parsley. Dot with butter, and pour cream over all. Cover with a lid or foil and bake at 375° F. for 25 to 30 minutes. Allow to cool in the dish, still covered, then refrigerate until ready to serve.

Remove the egg whites from yolks. Chop or grate the whites and yolks and place in separate small bowls. Put the chopped parsley and the horseradish in separate bowls. Serve as garnishes. Makes 4 servings.

Serve this cod dish in the winter, too. For the fresh tomatoes you may substitute 2 cups canned tomatoes. Drain off most of the liquid (which can be used in soups or sauces) and slice or chop the tomatoes.

BRAISING FISH

Whole fish, fillets and steaks can be braised. Lay the prepared fish on a bed of flavoring vegetables. If the fish is lean, add diced salt pork to the vegetables, or sprinkle it on top. Or arrange strips of bacon over the fish. Add a little white or red wine or some tomato purée, according to the kind of sauce you plan to make. 🗝 Cover with parchment paper or foil placed directly on top of the fish. Do this even if the baking dish or cooking pan has its own cover; otherwise, the fish will be steamed rather than braised. Make a few tiny holes in the foil or parchment with a fork to let any steam escape. In this way the juices from the braised vegetables and the fish will remain flavorful and undiluted.

Braised haddock with savory balls

7 slices of bacon
1½ to 2 pounds fillets of haddock
Grated rind of 1 lemon
½ teaspoon salt
¼ teaspoon freshly ground pepper
Savory Balls (below)

Line a baking dish with 4 slices of bacon. Top with the haddock. Spread the remaining bacon on top of the fish. Mix the grated lemon rind with the salt and pepper. Sprinkle over fish and bacon. Place the Savory Balls around the fish. Cover the fish with foil and the cover of the dish. Bake in a preheated oven for 25 minutes at 425° F. Uncover and bake 5 minutes longer. Makes 6 servings.

SAVORY BALLS

⅔ cup well-packed fresh bread crumbs
1 tablespoon dried parsley
¼ teaspoon dried sage or savory
1 small onion, minced
2 slices of bacon, diced
½ teaspoon salt
¼ teaspoon pepper
2 eggs

Place all the ingredients in a bowl. Mash and blend them by hand until they are well mixed. Shape into small balls. Use with any fish as described above, or bake separately and use them to garnish plain vegetables such as stewed tomatoes, spinach or kale.

November fish and oysters

Everything in this dish is plentiful in November in the Northeast. People who claim to dislike fish usually like this.

1½ to 2 pounds fresh fillet of haddock
8 ounces shelled fresh oysters
2 large leeks, trimmed and washed
3 tablespoons corn oil
3 tablespoons butter
4 tablespoons flour
¾ cup milk or light cream
¾ cup chicken stock
1 small onion, minced
1 ripe sweet red pepper, chopped
⅓ cup fresh parsley, chopped
Salt

Rinse the haddock fillet and cut it into serving pieces. Drain the oysters in a sieve. Slice the leeks and cook them in 2 tablespoons of oil and 2 tablespoons of butter over very low heat. The leeks should be soft and tender but not browned. Stir in the flour to make a leek-flavored béchamel. When the flour is completely blended with the leeks and fat, add the milk or cream and stock and cook slowly until the sauce is thick and hot. Set the sauce aside but keep it warm.

Put the remaining butter and oil in a saucepan; heat, and add onion and red pepper. (Be sure to discard all the pepper seeds.) Cook over low heat, stirring occasionally, until the vegetables are tender. Add the parsley and stir until it is coated with oil. Spread the vegetable mixture over bottom of a shallow baking pan. Arrange the fish pieces in the pan and top with the drained oysters. Sprinkle with salt, and pour the warm, leek-flavored sauce over all. Cover with foil. Pierce a few holes in the foil before placing the pan in a preheated 400° F. oven for 45 minutes. The parsley and the pepper will retain their vivid colors. Makes 4 servings.

Sea bass Marseille style

- 1 sea bass (about 3 pounds)
- Fennel sprigs
- 2 bay leaves
- 1 garlic clove, split
- ½ cup olive oil
- ½ cup dry white wine
- ½ pound mushrooms, cleaned and chopped
- 2 medium-size onions, chopped
- ⅔ cup black olives, pitted
- Salt and pepper
- 12 cherry tomatoes
- 12 tiny parsley sprigs

Dress the fish, but do not remove the head. Place the fish in a baking dish. Put the fennel sprigs, bay leaves and pieces of garlic inside the fish. Pour oil and wine over the fish, and arrange the mushrooms, onions and olives around it. Sprinkle all with salt and pepper and cover with foil. Bake in a preheated 400° F. oven for about 1 hour.

To serve, remove the foil and garnish with stemmed cherry tomatoes. Place a parsley sprig on each tomato. Serve with Mayonnaise Niçoise (see p. 200) if you like. Makes 4 to 6 servings.

BROILING FISH

This is a favorite method of cooking fish steaks and fillets because it is quick and easy and always successful. You can also broil small whole fish without stuffing as well as split fish under 4 pounds.

The heat used is 550° F. The distance from the source of the heat varies with the type of fish. Consult the timetable. At this high temperature so close to the heat source the fish cooks quickly, becomes golden brown, retains all its flavor and has no fishy odor.

Fish steaks

Sprinkle the steaks lightly with flour and paprika. Dot them with soft butter, or dribble salad oil over them. Preheat the broiler for 10 minutes. Place the fish on a generously oiled broiler pan, or on an oiled foil-lined pan. Broil 2 inches from the heat source. Do not season before broiling. Baste once on each side with any of the combinations given for baked fish (p. 372). Broil according to the following timetable.

Timetable for broiling fish steaks

Type of fish	Thickness in inches	First side, minutes	Second side, minutes
Salmon	1	3	5 (Baste only once when turned.)
Halibut	1	4	5
Bass	1	4	5

Whole fish

Prepare as for fish steaks. Broil according to following timetable, but baste three times during the cooking time.

Timetable for broiling whole fish

Type of fish	Distance from heat in inches	First side, minutes	Second side, minutes
Carp, 2½ to 3 pounds	6	12	14
Flounder or sole	3	10 in all; do not turn	
Pike	6	5	8
Small bass	3	4	5

Split fish

Any fish from 2 to 4 pounds can be split and broiled. If you have a choice, leave the backbone in. The fish will be juicier and more flavorful. Never turn split fish. Place them skin side down in the bottom of a broiler pan, not on a rack. Proceed as for fish steaks. Baste often.

Timetable for broiling split fish

Type of fish	Distance from heat in inches	Thickness in inches	Broiling time, minutes
Bass	3	¾	8
Mackerel	2	¾ to 1	8 to 10
Pike	3	¼ to 1¼	8 to 10
Sea bass	3	½ to 1	6 to 8
Whitefish	3	½ to 1½	10 to 12

Fresh and frozen fillets

O┳ To dry fresh or properly thawed fillets, wrap them in absorbent paper or cloth and leave them wrapped for 20 minutes.

Roll each fillet lightly in fine bread or cracker crumbs, or in cornmeal. Set on a broiler pan 2 to 3 inches from the heat source, just as for fish steaks. Do not turn fish fillets during the broiling period. The entire broiling time should take from 5 to 10 minutes for ¼- to 1-inch-thick fillets. Do not overcook; even thick fillets are thinner than steaks and may dry out quickly. When done, season and sprinkle with fresh lemon juice to taste.

SAUTÉING AND PANFRYING FISH

This is almost instant cooking and is the technique used most often for cooking fish. Small dressed fish, steaks ½ to ¾ inch thick and fillets can be sautéed. They can also be panfried. The difference between the two techniques is explained on p. 298.

To sauté fish, use an equal amount of butter and salad oil, bacon fat, shortening, margarine, or half margarine and half any other fat mentioned above. Melt just enough to cover the bottom of the pan. For panfried fish, fill the pan about ¼ inch deep.

For either method use a large frying pan of heavy metal, cast iron, enameled cast iron or heavy stainless steel. Never attempt to sauté or to panfry in too small a pan where fish would be crowded. Always use a heavy pan because the heat will be more evenly distributed for gentle cooking.

When preparing a fish for sautéing, roll the fillets or steaks lightly in seasoned flour. Use paprika as part of the seasoning; it helps to brown the fish quickly.

For panfrying, roll the fish in seasoned flour, or coat with egg and crumbs, or with cornmeal.

Whichever method you use, remember to turn the fish only once. Cook until the fish flakes. To test for flakiness, insert a fork in the thickest part of the piece of fish. Probe gently to see if the fish separates and falls easily into its own natural divisions, and at the same time shows a faint line of creamy, milky-white substance. The fish should be opaque but still moist. If the fish breaks, or shrinks, or looks dry, or has a fishy smell, it is overcooked.

There is a tendency to overcook when sautéing or panfrying fish. Remember that the composition of fish is much like that of eggs: albumin and fat. Fish will cook in almost the same time it takes to panfry an egg. The real danger is overcooking.

Mountain trout with cucumber sauce

½ cup all-purpose flour
½ teaspoon salt
¼ teaspoon freshly ground pepper
⅛ teaspoon baking powder
6 to 9 small mountain trout
2 thin slices of salt pork
4 tablespoons butter
Cucumber Sauce (recipe follows)

Mix flour with salt, pepper and baking powder. Clean the trout. Roll them in the flour mixture until well coated. Sauté the salt pork. Discard the crisp pieces and leave the fat in the pan. Add 1 tablespoon butter. Brown the trout in the fat for about 3 minutes per side. Transfer trout to a baking dish. Dot them with remaining butter and bake at 450° F. for 5 minutes. Serve with Cucumber Sauce. Makes 6 servings.

CUCUMBER SAUCE

1 small cucumber
½ cup heavy cream
¼ teaspoon salt
Few drops of hot-pepper sauce
Juice of ½ lemon

If the cucumber is coated with wax, wash thoroughly. Shred unpeeled cucumber and press to remove excess water. Whip cream until stiff. Add the cucumber, salt, hot-pepper sauce and lemon juice. Stir to mix well. Serve with trout or other fish. Makes about 1½ cups.

Sole with green herbs

6 fillets of sole or flounder
Salt and pepper
½ cup flour
8 tablespoons butter
6 tablespoons corn oil
2 cups chopped washed raw spinach
½ cup chopped chives
¼ cup chopped parsley
2 tablespoons minced fresh tarragon
1 tablespoon minced fresh mint

Rinse the fillets; roll in paper to dry thoroughly. Season on both sides with salt and pepper and roll in flour. Heat 6 tablespoons of the butter and all the oil (or use part of both and add more as needed). Sauté the fish until each piece is golden brown on both sides; a few minutes should do it. Add the remaining 2 tablespoons butter and as soon as it is melted pour all the minced greens into the pan. Partly cover the pan and cook 3 to 5 minutes longer. The herbs should be bright green. Makes 6 servings.

Any kind of lean fish can be sautéed or panfried. Fatty fish, such as salmon, swordfish or mackerel, are best cooked by other methods.

DEEP-FRYING FISH

Small fish such as smelts, moderately small fish such as lake perch, fish fillets of many kinds and croquettes and fish balls are excellent deep-fried.

Clean fish when necessary in salted ice-cold water, or rub with cider vinegar. Dip into milk or a mixture of 1 egg beaten with 2 tablespoons cold water. Then roll in fine bread or cracker crumbs or in cornmeal.

Use a frying basket, and be careful not to overcrowd the pieces. Heat shortening or peanut oil 3 to 4 inches deep to 365° to 375° F. Use a frying thermometer, or a thermostatically controlled electric fryer. If you have neither, use the bread-cube test (p. 304).

For a fish to retain its moistness and yet turn a beautiful golden brown, 3 to 5 minutes of cooking time should be enough, the time of course depending upon the size of the fish. When the fish is done, remove it from the pan, drain it on paper towels and season with salt and pepper to taste while it is still hot.

Fish croquettes

- ¼ cup butter
- ½ cup flour
- 2 cups milk
- 1½ teaspoons salt
- ½ teaspoon white pepper
- ½ teaspoon curry powder
- Pinch of cayenne
- 3½ cups minced or flaked cooked fish
- 2 tablespoons minced parsley
- 1 tablespoon lemon juice
- 1 tablespoon minced onion or shallot
- 1 egg
- 1½ cups cornmeal
- Peanut oil for deep-frying

Make a thick white sauce with the butter, flour and milk. Season well with salt, white pepper, curry powder and cayenne. Add the fish, parsley, lemon juice and onion or shallot. Mix thoroughly. Spread in a flat pan and refrigerate for 1 hour or longer.

Form the mixture into croquettes with a cookie cutter, or shape it into round balls or cone-shaped pieces. Do not make the individual pieces too thick. Beat the egg with 2 tablespoons water. Spread the cornmeal on a sheet of wax paper. Dip each croquette into the egg mixture and then roll in cornmeal. Refrigerate again to set the coating.

Heat the oil to 375° to 385° F. Drop the croquettes, a few at a time, into a frying basket and fry until brown on all sides. This will only take a few minutes (remember, the fish is already cooked). Drain the croquettes and transfer them to a plate lined with paper towels. Keep warm until all are cooked. Serve with Tartar Sauce (p. 200) or Tomato Sauce I (p. 203). Makes 12 croquettes, 4 to 6 servings.

You can make croquettes with raw fish, too. Heat the fat to 365° to 375° F., and cook the croquettes for about 5 minutes. Test one to be sure it is done and adjust the time for the rest accordingly.

Batter-fried fish

Fish and chips is probably the best-known batter-fried fish specialty. (Of course only the fish is batter-fried; the chips—potatoes—are French fried in the usual way.) Small fish, such as smelts, can be cooked whole.

Larger fish, such as cod, haddock or sole, can be cut into sticks or filleted.

1 cup all-purpose flour	1 lemon, halved
½ teaspoon salt	Salt and pepper
Pinch of ground thyme	Flour
1 tablespoon salad oil	Peanut oil for deep-frying
1 egg, beaten	
¾ cup milk	
18 small whole smelts, cleaned, *or* 12 small fillets, *or* 2 pounds fish sticks	

Prepare the batter ahead of time. Mix flour, salt and thyme. Stir in the salad oil, egg and milk. Beat until thoroughly blended. Refrigerate for at least 1 hour before using.

About 1 hour before coating with batter, rub the fish with lemon, season with salt and pepper and set the pieces side by side on a plate. Do not overlap and do not cover. Refrigerate the fish to dry it and make the batter cling better.

When both the batter and the fish have chilled for at least 1 hour, dip the fish into flour and then into the batter, until it is completely coated. Allow excess batter to drip off.

Heat the peanut oil to 360° F. on a frying thermometer and drop the fish in gently. Cook for 5 to 6 minutes, or until fish is brown and crisp. Drain on absorbent paper. Serve immediately, with any flavorful sauce. Makes 6 servings.

Fish roe fritters

Use the frying batter described in the preceding recipe. Flavor it with another herb if you wish, or with cumin seeds or curry powder. Chill it at least 1 hour. Cut large roe into sections (shad roe for instance) or use small whole roe. Season the roe with salt and pepper and chill them. Dip the roe into flour, and then into batter, and cook in hot oil for 4 or 5 minutes. Drain, sprinkle with salt, and garnish. Serve with browned butter and lemon juice.

To make a dish like Italian *fritto misto,* serve the roe with batter-fried vegetables such as mushrooms, pieces of green or red sweet peppers, cubed eggplant, flowerets from cauliflower, green beans and fennel chunks. Cook the vegetables first; the roe fritters take less time. When you serve a mixed fry like this, be sure to make Tartar Sauce (p. 200), Mayonnaise Niçoise (p. 200) or Curry Mayonnaise (p. 200) as accompaniment.

STEAMING FISH

This is an old Chinese method. It is one of the most appreciated ways of cooking fish because of the purity of flavor which it develops. It is also recommended for those on low-fat or reducing diets.

Any fish can be steamed, and steamed fish can be served hot or cold, plain or with sauce.

Place 1½ to 2 inches of water in a deep large saucepan with a good cover that fits securely. Place the cleaned fish, steaks or fillets, on a heatproof platter small enough to fit inside the saucepan. Dot fish with butter and sprinkle with grated lemon or lime rind or fresh lemon or lime juice, and very little salt and pepper. O━ Lime juice and a bit of grated fresh gingerroot on fresh salmon is superb. Place the platter on a rack or an inverted low can, or arrange it in any way so that the platter is above the level of the liquid. Cover the saucepan tightly, place over medium-high heat, and steam. If you have a regular steamer, put the fish in the upper part by itself or on a plate.

For small fish, fillets or steaks less than 2 inches thick in the thickest part, steam for 1 minute per ounce. Fish fillets or steaks thicker than 2 inches should be steamed for 10 minutes per pound. The water should boil for the entire cooking time. A steamed fish is best simply sprinkled with a little fresh lemon or lime juice. Do not add salt or pepper, but eat it just as is.

Finnan savory pudding

Finnan (or Findon) haddocks were named after a small fishing port near Aberdeen, Scotland. It was there that haddocks were smoked, dried over seaweed, and sprinkled with saltwater during the smoking process. Finnan haddie can be grilled, steamed, poached or made into a loaf. They have an affinity for butter, milk and potatoes. They are economical too. In this recipe, the fish is steamed first.

1 pound finnan haddie
2 slices of bacon
4 tablespoons butter
2 cups mashed potatoes
Juice of ½ lemon
1 small onion, minced
½ teaspoon celery salt
3 tablespoons minced parsley
¼ teaspoon dried savory
Salt and pepper
3 eggs

Place the fish in a shallow pan. Top with the bacon and enough water to cover the bottom of the pan. Cover and steam over medium heat for 10 minutes. Remove the fish to a plate. Rub the fish with 1 tablespoon of the butter. Cool.

Flake the cooked fish and stir it into the mashed potatoes. Add lemon juice, onion, celery salt, parsley, savory, and salt and pepper to taste. Beat well. Melt the remaining 3 tablespoons of butter and stir into the fish and potato mixture. Separate the eggs. Beat yolks until light and add them. Beat whites until stiff, then fold gently into the fish and potato mixture.

Pour the mixture into a buttered casserole or soufflé dish. Bake at 350° F. for 30 to 40 minutes, or until golden and puffed up. Makes 6 servings.

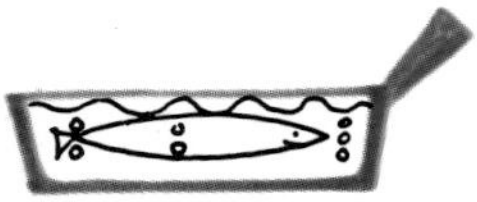

POACHING FISH

0━ Whether fish is to be poached in a *court bouillon* or in plenty of salted water, and whether it is whole fish or simply a piece, it should be tied in a cheesecloth, leaving long ends free so that the fish can be lifted easily from the hot liquid without breaking.

0━ The liquid must never boil, but should always be kept at a simmer for perfect poaching.

A *court bouillon* is made with water, onion, carrot, herbs, wine or vinegar or lemon juice, and seasoning to taste. There must be enough liquid to completely cover the fish. Use 2 tablespoons wine, vinegar or lemon juice to ½ cup water unless a recipe calls for other proportions. Lemon juice or vinegar are preferred with salmon; vinegar is used more often with shellfish.

Place all the flavoring ingredients in the saucepan, add the liquids and boil uncovered for 20 to 30 minutes before adding the fish.

If plain salted water is used for poaching, bring it to a full rolling boil.

When you are ready to put in the fish, remove the *court bouillon* or water from the heat. Once the fish has been added, bring the liquid to a simmer and continue to cook, covered, over low heat. Figure 6 to 8 minutes per pound of fish, or allow 10 minutes for each inch of thickness.

When the fish is done, remove it from the cooking liquid. To serve the fish cold, cool fish and liquid separately until both are tepid, then pour enough of the liquid over the unwrapped fish to cover completely. Another method is to reduce the cooking time and let the fish complete its cooking as the *court bouillon* cools. Refrigerate until cold. Unwrap and serve.

Poaching can also be done in the oven. Assemble the ingredients for the *court bouillon;* boil as above; strain. Then pour the liquid over the cheesecloth-wrapped fish in a baking pan. Cover the pan and place in a preheated 375° F. oven. Poach for about 10 minutes per pound, or until the fish flakes easily when tested with a fork.

White-wine court bouillon

2 carrots, sliced
2 medium-size onions, sliced
6 shallots, chopped
4 tablespoons chopped parsley stems
1 teaspoon minced fresh thyme, *or* ½ teaspoon dried thyme
2 bay leaves
12 peppercorns, crushed in a mortar
1 tablespoon salt
4 cups white wine
4 cups water

Other herbs or seasoning can be used. Also, the boiled *court bouillon* (p. 386) can be strained for top-of-the-stove poaching as well as for oven poaching.

Red-wine court bouillon

Follow the directions for White-Wine Court Bouillon, substituting red wine for white. This is unusual for American tastes, but it is good to use with fatty fish, such as eels and mackerel (but not with salmon) and in making stews with freshwater fish.

Vinegar court bouillon

Use 4 cups water and 1 cup vinegar. Reduce flavoring ingredients by about half. This is good for poaching salmon and shellfish.

Fish stock and clam juice can also be used in poaching, when you want to intensify the flavor of the sauce, or to make fish chowder or similar preparations. Plain tap water or seawater can also be used. Use milk to poach salted or smoked fish. It reduces the saltiness to some extent.

Poached salmon

3 quarts water
Juice of 1 lemon
2 carrots, sliced
2 onions, sliced
12 peppercorns
2 tablespoons salt
6 to 10 parsley sprigs
1 bay leaf
1 whole fresh salmon (5 to 10 pounds)

Place the water and all other ingredients except the salmon into a pot or saucepan large enough to hold the fish. A roasting pan covered with foil can be used for a large fish. Boil the mixture for 30 minutes.

Following the rule for poached fish, wrap the cleaned salmon in a piece of cheesecloth. Remove the pan from the heat, and place the fish in the water. Cover and cook over medium heat for 6 to 8 minutes per pound.

Remove fish from the pan by inserting two large forks, one at each end of the fish, through the cheesecloth. Place on a hot platter. Slowly pull away the cloth from under the fish, or remove by turning the fish over with the cloth (more difficult to manage).

To serve the salmon hot: remove the skin; garnish with parsley; sprinkle the top with a little curry powder, and spread a little Egg Sauce (p. 188) all along the back. Serve the remainder of the sauce separately.

To serve the fish cold, place it on a platter. Soak a cheesecloth in the fish broth and completely cover the fish with it. Pour a few spoonfuls of broth over the top. This will keep the fish moist. Refrigerate until ready to serve. Remove the cloth carefully; then remove the skin. Spread the fish with mayonnaise and decorate with capers. Serve with a large bowl of sauce; Sour-Cream Cucumber Sauce is especially good (p. 207). Makes 8 to 15 servings.

Poached salmon, French style

The French use salmon steak for this colorful and tasty dish. Following this method it is as easy to cook for 10 as for 2.

1 tablespoon salad oil
4 to 6 salmon steaks
Juice of 1 lemon
Grated rind of ½ lemon
6 peppercorns, crushed
1 tablespoon salt
1 small onion, quartered
Sauce Verte (p. 199)
3 to 6 parsley sprigs

Spread the oil in the bottom of a nonstick frying pan or a shallow baking dish. Place the salmon steaks in the pan next to each other but not overlapping. Add lemon juice and rind, crushed peppercorns, salt, quartered onion and just enough hot water to cover the fish. Cover the pan. In a frying pan, poach the salmon steaks on top of the stove over low heat for 10 to 20 minutes. In a baking dish, cover and poach the steaks in a 325° F. oven for the same length of time, or until the salmon flakes.

Cool the fish in the liquid. Lift the fish carefully from the pan. Drain well and remove the skin. Arrange on a serving platter, completely cover the fish with Sauce Verte (p. 199) and garnish with several parsley sprigs. Serve with a cucumber salad. Makes 4 to 6 servings.

Oven-poached trout with clam dressing

Some women are fortunate enough to have fresh trout brought home to them by the family fishermen. This is a good way to prepare the extras, because they will keep in the refrigerator for 3 to 5 days. Frozen fillets of sole, sliced into ½-inch blocks, can be used instead of trout.

2 tablespoons salad oil
1 to 2 pounds fresh trout, whole or filleted
1 teaspoon salt
Chopped parsley or dill
Juice of 1 lemon
1 can (5 ounces) baby clams
¼ teaspoon dried marjoram or thyme
12 to 15 stuffed olives, sliced

Spread the salad oil over the bottom of a baking dish. Without overlapping the pieces, place the trout (whole or filleted) on it. Sprinkle the trout with salt, chopped parsley or dill, and lemon juice. Drain and reserve the clams; pour the clam juice over the fish. Sprinkle with marjoram or thyme. Cover the dish with a lid or foil. Poach the trout in a 375° F. oven for about 25 minutes.

Cool. Then carefully drain off the liquid without

disturbing the fish. Refrigerate fish, broth and clams separately.

When ready to serve, mix together the reserved clams and the sliced olives. Add the broth, stir, and taste for seasoning. Pour the dressing over the fish. Serve with a bowl of radishes and a plate of tomato slices. Makes 4 or 5 servings.

Monsieur Manière fish soup

Fish soups and chowders are also made by poaching. For this you can use any white-fleshed fresh or frozen fish.

3 tablespoons olive oil
1 garlic clove, minced
1 onion, chopped
½ teaspoon dried thyme
Pinch of ground saffron
1½ pounds fish fillets
½ teaspoon salt
¼ teaspoon pepper
1 cup dry white wine
3 cups water
⅓ cup tomato paste
½ teaspoon crushed fennel seeds
3 tablespoons brandy
2 cups heavy cream

Heat olive oil. Add garlic and onion. Brown lightly, then add thyme and a pinch of saffron. Stir until blended. Add fish fillets, salt and pepper. Stir lightly over medium heat, to heat and break up the fish while mixing with the onion. Add wine, water, tomato paste and fennel seeds. Bring to a boil, cover, then simmer over low heat for 15 minutes. Add brandy and heavy cream. Stir until hot. Serve with hot toast. Makes 6 to 8 servings.

Leftover poached fish can be used in countless ways —for salads, sandwich spreads, soufflés and to fill omelets. The following are a few examples.

Swedish salmon and vegetable salad

1½ cups cooked salmon
2 peeled tomatoes, chopped
1 peeled cucumber, diced
1 cup cooked or canned peas
2 tablespoons lemon juice
1 teaspoon sugar
1 teaspoon salt
½ teaspoon pepper
½ cup mayonnaise
Fresh parsley, chopped

Flake the salmon and mix lightly with the tomatoes, cucumber and peas. Beat together lemon juice, sugar, salt, pepper and mayonnaise. Add to the fish mixture and blend lightly. Form a neat mound in a serving dish or bowl, and cover thickly with parsley. Cover and refrigerate until needed. Makes 4 to 6 servings.

Finnan savory

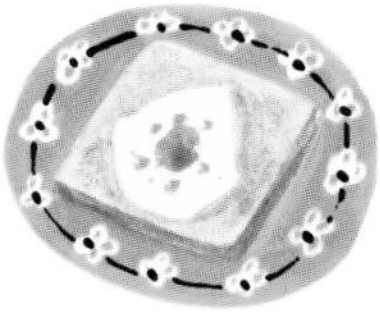

Leftover finnan haddie makes a creamy breakfast dish, or serve it on toast for lunch. Use chutney or curry powder to flavor the breakfast dish, and cayenne for the luncheon treat served on hot buttered toast.

1 tablespoon butter
Cayenne
or ½ teaspoon curry powder
1 to 1½ cups cooked and flaked finnan haddie
2 tablespoons heavy cream
1 tablespoon capers
Salt
Fresh parsley, chopped

Melt the butter and add cayenne or curry powder to taste. Stir until the butter is light brown. Add flaked fish, cream and capers. Simmer over low heat until the fish has absorbed most of the cream. Add salt to taste and sprinkle with parsley. Makes 4 servings.

SHELLFISH

Shellfish include oysters, clams, mussels, scallops, shrimp, crabs and lobster. In various sections of the country other species are found, such as conch in Florida waters, crayfish in the Gulf states, abalone in California. They are not available fresh outside these special areas because they are perishable.

If it seems too expensive to serve shellfish, you may be surprised to find that pound for pound most shellfish costs no more than good-quality meat, and in some cases even less. If necessary you can use a little less of the shellfish and serve a substantial first course; or add other ingredients to the shellfish to make a main dish. For example, a pint of shucked oysters contains no waste; nutritionally it is equivalent to 1¼ pounds of good-quality meat, and it costs about the same. If you find this is too much for your budget, buy half a pint and combine the oysters with other ingredients in a main dish, such as scalloped oysters.

Oysters

The oyster is a bivalve mollusk found in tidal waters along most coasts of the world. Different species live in different areas. Fresh oysters are available from

September to April in the shell or shucked. Oysters in the shell are sold by the dozen or half dozen, and shucked oysters are sold by the pint or half pint or in 8-ounce tins. They are graded according to size. Canned oysters, packed in water or oyster liquor, and frozen oysters are available in most markets.

Raw oysters on the half shell, the bottom half, are a popular and elegant appetizer. They are also served hot on the half shell, crowned with a spoon of seasoned vegetables, bread crumbs or bits of bacon and baked or broiled until sizzling.

Oysters are delicious cooked in many different ways—oyster stew, scalloped oysters, chicken and oyster pie, oyster omelet, and creamed mushrooms and oysters.

O━ Since oysters are so full of liquid, they need to be drained for some dishes. The liquor may be used as part of the liquid in the recipe. Another common preparatory step is to poach them gently in their own liquor until the edges curl. This is especially useful if the oysters are to be added to sauce mixtures; otherwise they would dilute the sauce.

Fried oysters

Thick batter should never be used for oysters. It will make them heavy and tasteless.

½ pint shucked oysters
1 egg white
¼ cup cold water
½ cup flour
1 teaspoon salt
¼ teaspoon pepper
½ teaspoon paprika
1 cup fine dry bread crumbs
Peanut oil or lard

Rinse the oysters under cold running water. Drain and spread on absorbent towels to dry as much as possible. Beat the egg white slightly with the water. Mix the flour, salt, pepper and paprika and place on a flat plate. Put the bread crumbs on another flat plate. Roll each oyster in the seasoned flour, then in the egg-white mixture, and then in the fine bread crumbs. Then place the coated oysters side by side on a large platter.

Put enough peanut oil or melted lard into a heavy pan to reach a depth of 2 inches. Heat to 375° F. on a frying thermometer, or until a 1-inch cube of bread browns in 40 seconds. Fry the oysters, a few at a time. As soon as each batch is browned, drain on absorbent paper. Serve with a dip or sauce of your choice. Makes 4 servings.

Louisiana little loaves

Serve for lunch, with a salad of endives or mixed greens, or as an after-theater supper.

- 8 crusty French rolls
- 5 tablespoons butter
- ½ pint shucked oysters
- Grated rind of ½ lemon
- Pinch of grated nutmeg
- Salt and pepper
- 1 tablespoon flour
- ½ cup milk
- ¼ teaspoon MSG
- 2 teaspoons mayonnaise
- 1 teaspoon fresh lemon juice
- Minced parsley or chives

Slice the tops from the rolls and hollow out the interiors, saving the crumbs. Brush insides and outsides with 2 tablespoons of the butter, melted. Place the rolls in a 350° F. oven to brown. Melt 2 more tablespoons butter in a frying pan. Add the crumbs removed from the rolls and sauté over low heat until golden brown. Toss the crumbs and butter with a fork to brown evenly. Place the oysters in their own liquor in another saucepan with the lemon rind, nutmeg, ¼ teaspoon salt and ⅛ teaspoon pepper. Simmer over low heat until the edges ruffle.

Make a white sauce with the remaining 1 tablespoon butter, the flour and milk. When creamy, add the MSG, salt and pepper to taste, then the mayonnaise and fresh lemon juice. Stir until blended. Add to the oysters. Stir gently until well mixed; then stir in half of the sautéed crumbs. Spoon mixture into hot rolls. Sprinkle tops with remaining crumbs and minced parsley or chives. Makes 8 small servings.

Baked oysters with mushrooms

- 3 dozen oysters in shells
- 36 small mushrooms, or 12 large ones
- 6 ounces prosciutto
- 2 pimientos
- 3 tablespoons butter
- 3 tablespoons flour
- ½ teaspoon dry mustard
- 1 to 1¼ cups light cream
- Salt
- White pepper
- Cayenne
- 1 cup small, fresh white-bread crumbs

Shuck the oysters, keeping all of the liquor, and poach them in their liquor in a large saucepan until oysters curl up at the edges. Remove oysters and let them dry on paper towels. Reduce the oyster liquor to about ½ cup and strain it through a double layer of cheesecloth to remove any bits of shell. Trim the mushrooms. If you use large ones, cut into 3 slices each. Chop prosciutto into small pieces and sauté until brown and crisp but not hard or dried out. There should be enough fat in the meat, but if not, use about 1 tablespoon peanut oil. Chop the pimientos and add to prosciutto. Arrange 6 oysters each in 6 individual shallow baking dishes. Place a mushroom or mushroom slice on each oyster, and scatter prosciutto and pimientos over all.

Melt butter; stir in flour and mustard. Mix the strained oyster liquor with enough cream to make 1½ cups. Cook the roux until golden, stir in the liquid and cook until thick. Season to taste. Spoon about ¼ cup sauce over each baking dish, and sprinkle with about 2½ tablespoons crumbs. Bake in a preheated 400° F. oven for about 10 minutes. The sauce should be bubbling. If you like, you can flavor the béchamel sauce with some grated Romano or Parmesan cheese. Makes 6 servings.

Clams

The clam is another mollusk. Soft-shell clams live in the area between high- and low-tide limits and burrow into the sand. They are dug out with clam rakes. Hard-shell clams are found beyond the low-tide limit, where they are dug out with rakes or dredges. The shells are creamy white and ridged. Soft-shells are thinner and flatter and the shell itself is thinner and can be broken by finger pressure. Hard-shells are often referred to as "quahogs," especially around Cape Cod. Their shells are rock hard and they are rounder and fatter than soft-shells. Cherrystone and Littleneck clams, which are small quahogs, are usually served raw on the half shell like oysters. Larger clams are chopped and used for chowder. Clams can be bought in the shell like oysters, and they are available canned whole, large or baby type, as well as minced.

Whole or chopped clams make delicious sauces for spaghetti or linguine. They are delicious fried in the same way as oysters. Clams are often added to other seafood to make dishes such as *cioppino* or *paella*.

Steamed clams

Scrub soft-shell clams carefully. Put them in a deep heavy pot and add about ½ cup water. Do not add salt because clams are very salty. Cover the pot and steam clams for 10 to 12 minutes, until the shells open. Turn them over after 3 or 4 minutes to ensure even steaming. Lift them out with a slotted spoon and serve in bowls.

Serve them with a dipping sauce. The best is 1 cup of the strained broth heated with ¼ cup butter, the juice of 1 lemon and 1 teaspoon Worcestershire sauce. Allow about 4 dozen clams for 4 servings.

Linguine with fresh clam sauce

1 pound linguine or spaghettini
½ cup olive oil
Salt
2 garlic cloves
1 cup chopped parsley
6 very ripe fresh tomatoes, *or* 3 cups canned tomatoes
3 dozen small hard-shell clams
Black pepper

Make this on a day when you have dug the clams yourself, or buy very fresh clams. Someone in your house must be able to open these with a clam knife. This very simple dish will be memorable if you follow the directions exactly.

Cook the linguine in water with 1 tablespoon of the oil and enough salt to suit your taste, usually 2 tablespoons to 6 quarts water. Cook until firm (in Italian, *al dente*), about 12 minutes. Drain the pasta, and return it to the pot; add 1 tablespoon oil to keep the strands from sticking. Stir with a fork. Keep warm.

Pour the remainder of the oil into a saucepan. Mash the garlic and chop to a purée. (If garlic is objectionable to anyone in your house, pierce the cloves with toothpicks and retrieve them after cooking in oil; the flavor is needed in the sauce.) Cook the garlic in the oil until lightly browned. Add the parsley, which will sputter. Stir with a wooden spoon until the parsley is well coated with oil. If you do this first, the parsley will stay green even when the tomatoes are added. Peel and chop the fresh tomatoes, or chop the canned ones, and add to the saucepan. Cook until the tomatoes are soft and the mixture is well blended. Then shuck the clams and drop them whole with all the juices into the sauce. Simmer for barely 5 minutes and serve over the pasta.

If you cannot shuck the clams, you will have to steam them open (see Steamed Clams). This will affect the taste. Do not chop the clams for this sauce, but enjoy them whole. Makes 6 generous servings.

Mussels

Mussels, a most delicious shellfish, are bivalve mollusks resembling clams, with rather thin, bluish-black shells. There are saltwater and freshwater varieties. You can collect them yourself if you live where they are to be found. You also can buy them at your fish store. Mussels are sold in the shell by the pound. You will have to steam them open yourself. Buy 1 pound of mussels for 2 or 3 main-course servings.

Mussels require thorough cleaning, which is a little tedious. First, scrub each shell with a rough brush under running water. Then remove the beard; this resembles old dried grass and is usually tightly caught between the two shells. Cut off the part that shows with scissors. The mussel holds onto rocks, poles, wharves, by means of the beard. Cover the cleaned mussels with very cold water and allow to soak for 2 hours. During this soaking period they will throw off any sand that remains inside the shells. Lift them out of the water to drain. The sand will remain in the water. Discard any that are open or broken. The rest are ready to be steamed.

Steamed mussels

The liquid used to steam mussels can be plain salted water or half white wine, half water. Put only 1 inch of liquid in the bottom of a large heavy pan. Add the cleaned mussels. Cover the pan and steam the mussels for 5 minutes, or until the shells open. If you are cooking a large quantity of mussels, turn them with a large spoon or skimmer after 2 minutes to help them steam evenly. Lift them out of the pan and discard any that have not opened; they may be filled with mud. Serve the mussels, in their shells, on large plates. To eat, pick a mussel out of its shell with a fork, and dip it into plain or lemon butter or the cooking broth. To use the broth, strain through a fine sieve lined with a double layer of moistened cheesecloth.

Moules marinière

This famous French preparation is one of the best ways to serve mussels.

In a saucepan combine ½ cup dry white wine, 1 chopped green onion and ¼ cup butter. Heat until the butter is melted. Add 2 to 3 pounds of cleaned mussels. Cover and simmer over medium heat until the mussels open, about 5 minutes. Lift out the mussels and divide them among large deep plates. Discard any mussels that have not opened. Pour the broth through a fine sieve lined with a double layer of moistened cheesecloth into a hot bowl. Thicken the broth with *beurre manié* (1 tablespoon butter mixed with 1 tablespoon flour) and add 1 tablespoon minced parsley. If you prefer, stir in ¼ cup heavy cream, or a mixture of the cream and 1 egg yolk. Spoon some of the thickened sauce into individual bowls. Makes about 6 appetizer servings.

Scallops

This is another mollusk, but only a part of the creature is used—the muscle that opens and closes the shell. In Europe the whole scallop comes to market, and the roe or coral, looking like a small orange tongue, can be used as well. We never see this on our side of the Atlantic, but European recipes that call for the coral can be made without it. Because there is no waste, scallops can be an economical buy in season—from November to May for deep-sea scallops.

Bay scallops are available in the East during the early fall. They are usually more expensive, but they are very delicate in flavor and very tender.

Place the scallops in a sieve and spray with cold water. Never soak them in water. Then empty the scallops onto an absorbent towel or a clean cloth and pat as dry as possible. Roll up in the cloth and refrigerate until ready to cook.

When using frozen scallops, always defrost before cooking and roll in a cloth just as with the fresh variety.

Sautéed scallops

Roll scallops in seasoned flour. Melt some butter or margarine, or heat some olive oil, in a heavy frying pan. When very hot, add as many scallops as the pan will accommodate. Sauté quickly over medium heat, turning only once, for 2 minutes. Do not overcook scallops or they will lose flavor and tenderness. Scallops are all white, and they look better when garnished with parsley, chives or sautéed cherry tomatoes. For 4 to 6 servings allow 1 pound of scallops. If they are very large, cut them into smaller pieces.

Scallop bisque

- 3 tablespoons butter
- 2 celery ribs with leaves, chopped
- 1 onion, chopped
- 1 leek, chopped
- 1/4 teaspoon dried marjoram
- 2 cups white wine
- 1 pound fresh scallops, chopped
- 6 cups chicken stock
- *Beurre manié*, if needed
- Salt
- White pepper
- 2 cups light cream
- 4 tablespoons dry Madeira

Melt the butter and add celery, onion, leek and marjoram. Cook over low heat until the vegetables are tender but not browned. Add white wine and bring to a simmer. Add the chopped scallops and continue to simmer until the scallops are cooked; 5 to 8 minutes will be ample. Overcooking makes scallops tough. Cool the mixture a few minutes and then purée in a blender half at a time, adding some chicken stock if necessary to help the process. Mix purée and stock in a saucepan and heat, but do not boil. The soup should have the texture of thick cream. If it is not thick enough, stir in a little *beurre manié* (2 tablespoons butter mixed with 2 tablespoons flour). Season with salt and white pepper. Add cream and Madeira just before serving, and heat the soup to serving temperature. Do not boil. Garnish each serving with 3 watercress leaves, a tiny cream puff or a sprinkling of paprika. Makes 8 servings.

Shrimp

Shrimp are crustaceans with ten legs, but generally the legs have been removed along with the heads before they are brought to market.

Uncooked shrimp are often referred to as green shrimp, though they are not truly green in color. However, the familiar shrimp-pink color appears only after the shrimp have been cooked, and it is the shells that have the most color.

There are many different kinds of shrimp, from large to small, and the color of the uncooked shells varies considerably. Related species are langoustines, prawns and scampi, all of which are larger, although there is much disagreement about which name belongs to which. Any of them can be cooked by the methods used for shrimp.

Frozen shrimp: Shrimp frozen in their shells should be thawed and washed under cold running water. Place them in a pan with just the water that clings to them, cover tightly, and cook them in their own steam over medium heat for about 5 minutes, or until the shells turn pink. Drain off the water that accumulates during cooking. Peel and devein the shrimp, and they are ready to use.

When the shrimp are frozen without shells, thaw and devein, then drop into enough boiling water to cover. Add 1 teaspoon salt per pound of shrimp and 2 slices of unpeeled lemon. Bring the water to a rolling boil, cover, reduce the heat and simmer the shrimp for 3 minutes.

When adding frozen shrimp to a sauce, peel if necessary, devein, and add directly to the sauce without thawing.

Whether fresh or frozen, one pound of shrimp can be the basis of a main dish or salad to serve 3 or 4 persons.

Poached shrimp

Place 1 pound uncooked shrimp in a saucepan. Add 3 slices of unpeeled lemon, ¼ teaspoon dried thyme, 1 bay leaf, 1 tablespoon chopped celery leaves, 2 teaspoons salt and enough cold water to cover. Bring to a boil, uncovered, over medium heat. As soon as the water boils, lower the heat and simmer gently for 3 to 5 minutes, or until shrimp turn pink. Drain immediately and cool. Peel off the shells and remove the black veins down the backs with the point of a knife. The shrimp are now ready to eat just as they are, or in other preparations. If they are not to be used immediately, refrigerate them, covered, until needed.

Shrimp can also be cooked in water seasoned with *crab boil*, a seasoning mixture used in the South. For 1 pound shrimp, boil 1 tablespoon of the spice mixture in 2 quarts water for 15 minutes. Add 2 teaspoons salt. Add shelled, cleaned shrimp and simmer for 5 minutes. Put the *crab boil* in a cheesecloth bag if you do not want the bits sticking to the shrimp.

Fried shrimp

This recipe can also be used for clams or mussels. The batter is so light and crisp it will not overpower the delicate flavor of the shellfish.

½ cup flour
¼ teaspoon salt
½ teaspoon paprika
¼ teaspoon curry powder
1 egg
1½ teaspoons lemon juice
⅓ cup milk
24 cleaned fresh shrimp, uncooked or cooked
Peanut oil or lard for deep-frying

Mix together the flour, salt, paprika and curry powder. Beat the egg, add the lemon juice and milk, and beat the liquids into the flour until the mixture is smooth. If the batter is too heavy, add a little milk, 1 teaspoon at a time.

Use a deep pan if you do not have a deep fryer. Put oil or lard in the pan to a depth of 2 inches. Heat the fat to 350° F. on a frying thermometer. One by one dip the shrimp into the batter and then drop gently into the hot fat. Fry for about 3 minutes, until brown on both sides, turning once. If you are using cooked shrimp, be particularly careful not to overcook them. Drain on absorbent paper and serve. Makes 4 servings.

Barbecued shrimp

A 7-pound box of frozen uncooked shrimp (purchased from a wholesale fish dealer) makes an exciting barbecue for 10 persons. Adjust other ingredients accordingly.

2 to 3 pounds uncooked shrimp
⅓ cup olive oil
⅓ cup plus 1 teaspoon lemon juice
1½ teaspoons curry powder
1 teaspoon crushed garlic, *or* ½ teaspoon garlic powder
1 teaspoon salt
1 cup chutney
2 tablespoons brandy

Rinse shrimp in cold water. If they are frozen, soak them for 30 minutes and they will be easy to separate. Then shell and devein. Stir together olive oil, ⅓ cup lemon juice, curry powder, garlic or garlic powder, and salt. Add the shelled shrimp to the mixture and stir until well blended. Cover and refrigerate for 3 to 6 hours, stirring once or twice if possible. Then lift shrimp from marinade, strain and reserve the liquid.

Adjust barbecue grill 3 inches from prepared hot coals. Place shrimp on the grill and cook for 5 minutes without turning. Baste several times with the marinade. Mix chutney with remaining 1 teaspoon lemon juice and the brandy. Use this mixture as a dip. Makes 4 to 6 servings.

Shrimp or lobster Sakana

1 cup soy sauce
¼ cup brown sugar
1 teaspoon grated unpeeled green gingerroot
2 pounds large shrimp, shelled, *or* 2 live lobsters (1½ pounds each), split

Mix the marinade and pour it over the shrimp, or spoon it onto the cut sides of the lobsters. Let them stand for about 1 hour. Then grill the shrimp for 3 minutes on each side. Grill the lobsters shell sides down for about 20 minutes. Set the grill about 3 inches from the coals for shrimp, 5 inches for lobsters. The shrimp will make 6 to 8 servings; lobsters, 4 servings.

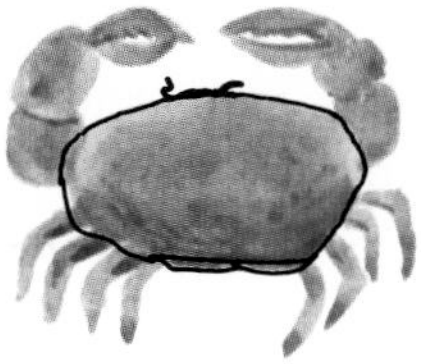

Crabs

Like the shrimp, a crab is a decapod crustacean. There are many different species of crabs and they are found all over the world.

Fresh crabs in the shell are expensive. One must learn how to open the shells and extract the meat. It is a lot of work to collect enough for a meal.

It is more economical and much less work to buy fresh or frozen crab meat by the pound. Also there is no basic cooking needed because the crab is already cooked. Canned crab is also available.

Soft-shell crabs are hard-shell crabs that have sloughed off their tight old shells and whose new, larger shells have not yet had time to harden. It takes about 48 hours for the new shell to harden, so there is only this short time to capture the defenseless soft-shell. This is what makes this delicate seafood hard to get and usually expensive.

Fried soft-shell crabs

Clean the soft-shell crabs by removing the spongy substance under the pointed flap and the feathery gills on either side. Then cut across the front to remove the eyes and sandbag; or have your fish dealer do this for you.

Sprinkle cleaned crabs all over with a mixture of equal amounts of salt and MSG. Dip them into flour. Heat enough butter in a heavy cast-iron frying pan to fill it ½ inch deep. Fry the crab on both sides over medium heat for about 3 minutes on each side, turning only once, until golden in color. Serve with melted butter and lime juice or with tartar sauce.

Seafood ramekins

A ramekin is a round or oval individual ovenware dish. This quick and easy recipe will give you a light seafood mixture with a crunchy topping. It is delicious made with any type of cooked seafood, but it is best with crab and lobster.

6 tablespoons butter
¼ cup dry sherry
1 to 1½ cups flaked crab meat or lobster
2 tablespoons flour
¾ cup light cream
2 egg yolks
Salt and pepper
¼ cup cracker meal
¼ teaspoon paprika
Grated rind of ½ lemon
1 tablespoon crushed potato chips
2 teaspoons grated Parmesan cheese

Melt 2 tablespoons of the butter and add the sherry. Heat together, then simmer for 1 minute. Add the crab meat or lobster. Stir to blend. Cover and let stand away from heat.

Melt another 2 tablespoons of the butter, add the flour and stir together for 1 minute. Remove from the heat, and stir in the cream and the hot liquid drained from the sherried crab meat or lobster. Return the sauce to the heat and cook, stirring constantly, until smooth and creamy.

Beat the egg yolks and stir them into the hot sauce while beating. Add the shellfish. Taste for seasoning and add salt or pepper if needed. Divide into 4 to 6 buttered ramekins (or use large custard cups or other individual baking dishes).

Combine the cracker meal, paprika, lemon rind, crushed potato chips and grated cheese. Melt the remaining 2 tablespoons butter and stir into the crumb mixture. Sprinkle evenly over the ramekins. Bake in a 300° F. oven for 10 minutes, or until the tops are delicately browned. Makes 4 to 6 servings.

Crab and oysters Vancouver

1 pound fresh crab meat
½ pound fresh mushrooms, finely chopped
½ pint fresh oysters
Juice of 1 lemon
Milk or light cream as required
3 tablespoons butter
3 tablespoons flour
Salt and pepper
3 cups hot cooked rice
Toasted chopped almonds

Place the crab meat on top of a steamer or in a sieve. Set over hot water. Cover and steam until hot through.

Place the mushrooms in a frying pan over medium-high heat and stir constantly until mushrooms start to brown.

Pour the oysters into a saucepan and add the lemon juice. Cover and simmer over low heat until oysters curl at the edges. Drain the liquid from the oysters and add enough milk or light cream to make 2 cups, and reserve.

Make a white sauce with the butter, flour and the reserved oyster liquid. When the sauce is smooth and creamy, add salt and pepper to taste. Stir in the mushrooms and the oysters. Season and butter the hot cooked rice. Place a good helping of hot crab meat on a plate. Top with a round scoop of rice and sprinkle the rice with toasted chopped almonds. Spoon the oyster sauce over all. Makes 6 servings.

Lobster

Fresh lobster tops the list for elegant eating. It is the most expensive of all seafood because there is a great deal of waste. Nevertheless, you have been deprived of the full romance of the sea if you have never cooked a live lobster. When cooked with care, a lobster can be spectacular in taste and appearance. Perhaps many people avoid lobster, not because of the price, but because it seems so difficult to cook and shell.

The shells of live lobsters are dark green, almost black, to blend in with their natural surroundings of rock and kelp. They become buff red and fragrant when cooked. Both the male and female lobsters contain tomalley, the green liver, considered by many the most delicate part of the meal, but the coral or red-colored roe, which is also delicious, is found only in the female.

Lobster is often referred to as the "treasure from the bottom of the sea." You may think it is indeed if you plan to serve it whole in the shell, either boiled or broiled, for you will need a whole lobster per person. Each lobster should weigh about 1½ pounds. The same lobster can serve 2 persons if the meat is removed from the shell and prepared in a sauce.

Another kind of lobster—the rock lobster or spiny lobster or crawfish—is a related species but has no large front claws. The tail meat of the rock lobster is the chief edible part, and these lobster tails are frozen and shipped all over the world, chiefly from South Africa. While the flavor is similar, these are not as tender as our northern lobster. Frozen lobster tails were once moderate in price, but now they too are very costly; however there is less waste and they can be used in any recipe calling for lobster meat.

Boiled live lobster

Many cookbooks will tell you to "plunge live lobsters head first into boiling water to cover." A better way is to choose a large saucepan or soup kettle. Place the lobster on its back on a large piece of clean cotton or cheesecloth and tie the corners together at each end. (This is not absolutely necessary, but it makes it easy to remove the lobster from the cooking liquid later—simply lift the cloth bag with long forks slipped into the knotted ends.)

Cover the lobster completely with cold water and add 1 tablespoon coarse salt. If you are lucky enough to be near the sea, use seawater and omit the salt. Bring the water to a boil over high heat, and let it boil for 3 to 4 minutes. Then lower the heat and simmer for another 12 to 18 minutes, depending on the size of the lobster. An overcooked lobster will have stringy or mushy meat.

As soon as the lobster is cooked, remove it from the water and plunge it briefly into a bowl of cold water. This will stop the cooking without cooling the meat.

How to eat cooked lobsters

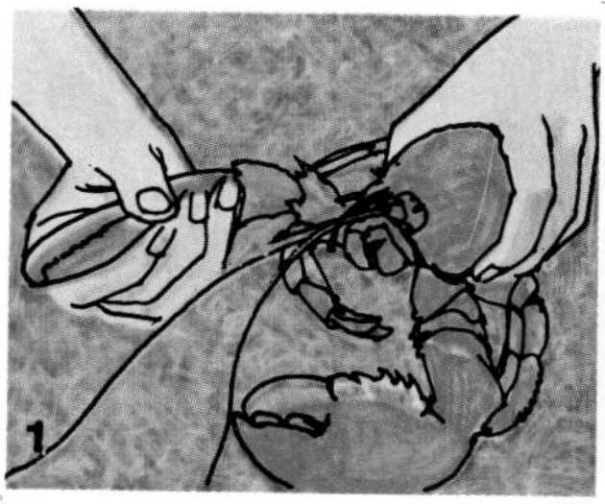

Twist off the claws.

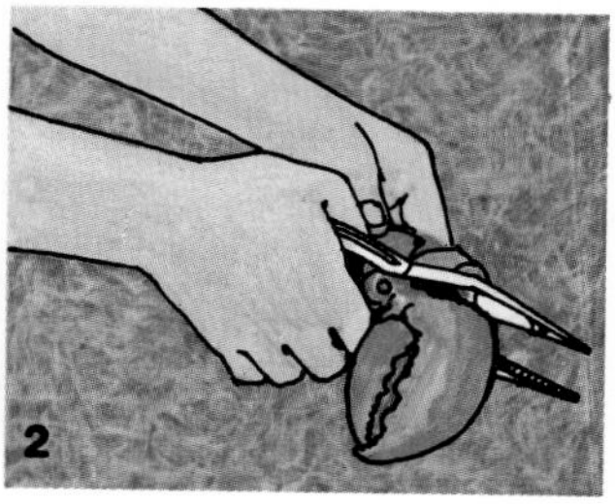

Crack each claw with a nutcracker, hammer or rock.

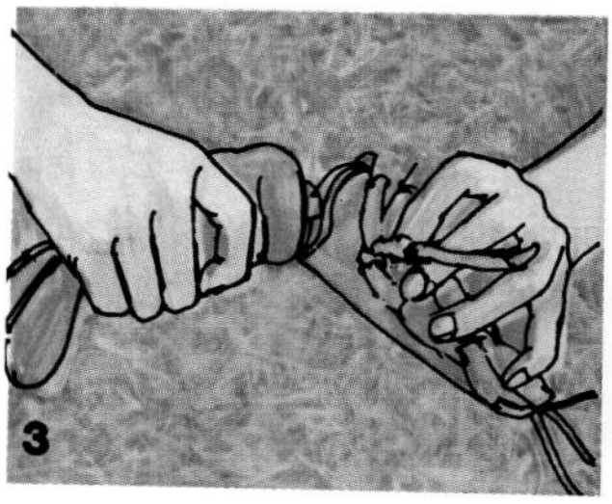

Separate tail from the body by arching the back until it cracks.

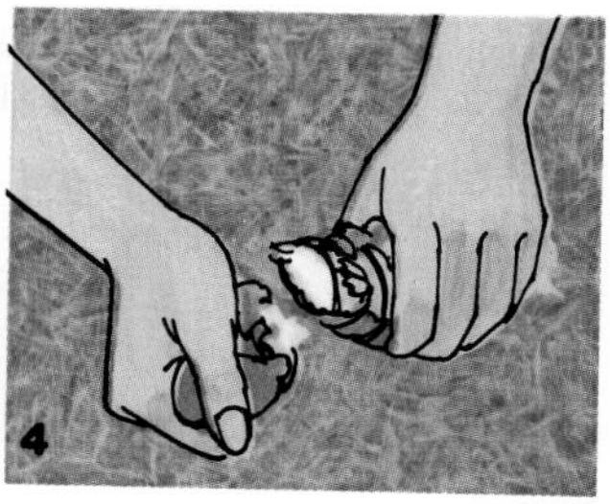

Bend back and break off the flippers from the tailpiece.

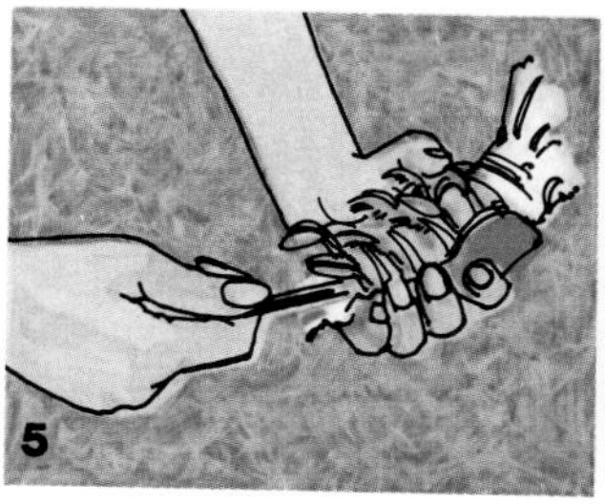

Insert a narrow fork where the flippers broke off and push out meat.

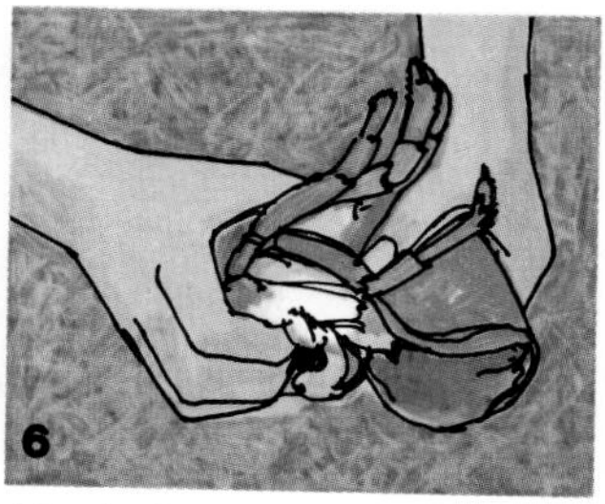

The body contains the delicious green tomalley or liver, and, if female, the coral or red roe.

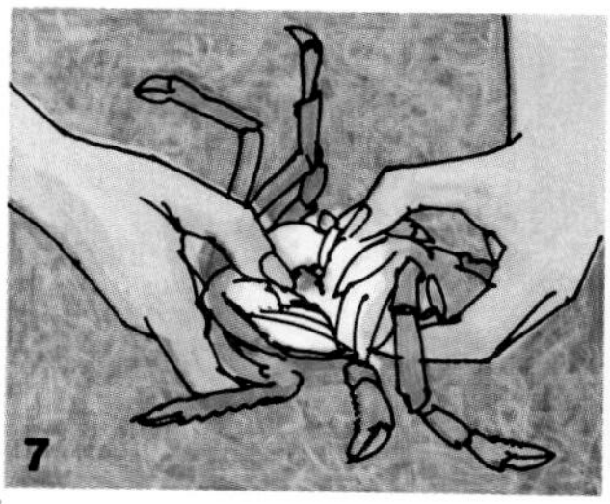

Crack the remaining section of the body apart sideways.

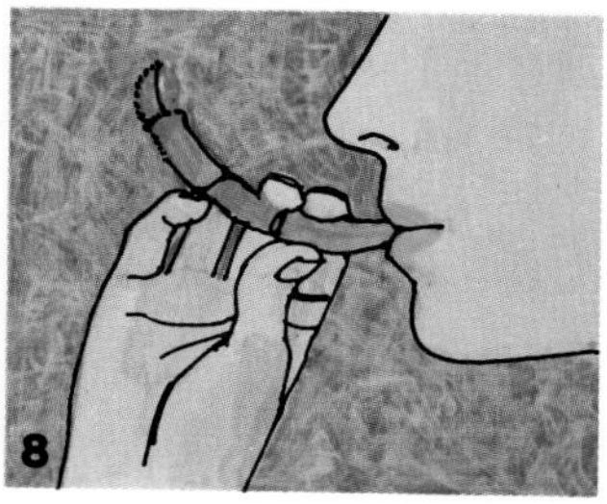

Suck out the juicy, sweet meat in the small side claws.

Lobster salad

1 to $1\frac{1}{4}$ cups cooked lobster, cut into slices
$\frac{1}{4}$ cup French dressing
$\frac{3}{4}$ cup chopped celery
$\frac{1}{2}$ cup mayonnaise
2 teaspoons minced onion
$\frac{1}{4}$ teaspoon salt
Dash of pepper

In a bowl combine lobster, French dressing and celery. Chill one hour. Add remaining ingredients and toss lightly. Refrigerate. At serving time arrange lobster salad on greens. Makes 3 to 4 servings.

Steamed lobster

Only baby lobsters, Eighths ($1\frac{1}{8}$ pounds), Quarters ($1\frac{1}{4}$ pounds), and Selects ($1\frac{1}{2}$ pounds) should be steamed.

Place lobsters on a rack in a large saucepan containing 2 to 4 cups of boiling water under the rack. Cover tightly. This is very important. If the cover does not adjust properly, place a sheet of foil or a large cloth between saucepan and cover and fasten tightly to the pot. Steam for 6 to 8 minutes, at most, after the water has come to a boil. Keep heat high during the entire cooking period.

If the lobster is to be used cold, as for a salad, let it get cold before removing the meat.

Broiled lobster

Do not attempt to broil or bake a lobster that has been cooked. It will be hard, dry and stringy. Ask your fish dealer to split a live lobster and to remove the stomach sac and sand vein for you.

Rub each half with melted butter and add a sprinkle of grated lemon rind or a pinch of tarragon to taste. Place on a rack 4 inches from the source of heat and broil, with the door of the oven partly open, for 10 to 15 minutes. Serve directly from the oven when ready.

Plain split lobsters can also be barbecued. Baste them frequently with Lemon Basting Sauce (p. 205) and grill for about 20 minutes, shell sides down.

Baked lobster

Split and clean as for broiled lobster. Place in a shallow roasting pan with shell side down. Brush with this herb butter: 2 tablespoons melted butter, pinch of dried tarragon or rosemary, $\frac{1}{4}$ teaspoon dry mustard, $\frac{1}{4}$ teaspoon salt and some freshly ground pepper. Bake in a preheated 450° F. oven for 15 to 18 minutes.

Transfer to a warm platter and pour remaining herb butter over the top.

Lobster Newburg

A true Newburg is more than canned lobster stirred into a white sauce colored with paprika. It is said that the recipe was originated at Delmonico's, a New York restaurant famous in the 19th century. The sauce was made with Madeira in those days, and spiced with cayenne.

- 4 egg yolks, slightly beaten
- 1½ cups heavy cream
- ⅓ cup milk
- 2 tablespoons flour
- ⅓ cup soft butter
- Pinch of grated mace
- 2 to 2½ cups cooked fresh lobster meat
- Salt
- 2 tablespoons dry sherry

Place egg yolks, cream and milk in the top part of a double boiler and heat to scalding, stirring often.

Make a paste of the flour, butter and mace. Add this to the egg-yolk mixture and cook until creamy and smooth, stirring often. Thin sauce to the consistency you prefer with a little milk. Add lobster meat and salt to taste. Simmer for 10 to 12 minutes and add sherry. Serve on buttered toast points. Makes 4 to 6 servings.

Spring sauce for lobster

Serve this classic French sauce with broiled or baked lobster.

- 2 shallots or spring onions, minced
- ½ cup dry white wine
- 4 tablespoons butter
- 3 tablespoons flour
- 1¼ cups milk or light cream
- Salt and pepper
- 1 tablespoon lemon juice

Slowly simmer the shallots in the white wine until reduced to 2 tablespoons. This will take about 30 minutes; no stirring or attention is necessary.

Make a cream sauce using 3 tablespoons of the butter, the flour, and the milk or light cream. Season with salt and pepper to taste. Add the reduced wine and shallots; blend well. Add the remaining 1 tablespoon butter and the lemon juice. Stir just enough to melt the butter, and serve. Makes about 1½ cups sauce.

«12»

Be Kind to Vegetables

Preserving nutritive value and flavor • Basic cooking methods: blanching and refreshing, steaming, pan-cooking, Chinese stir-frying, steam-baking, baking with dry heat, French-frying or deep-frying • Cooking root vegetables, onions and their relatives, the cabbage family, fresh and dried legumes, greens, edible thistles, crunchy stalks, seasonal vegetables, cereal grains

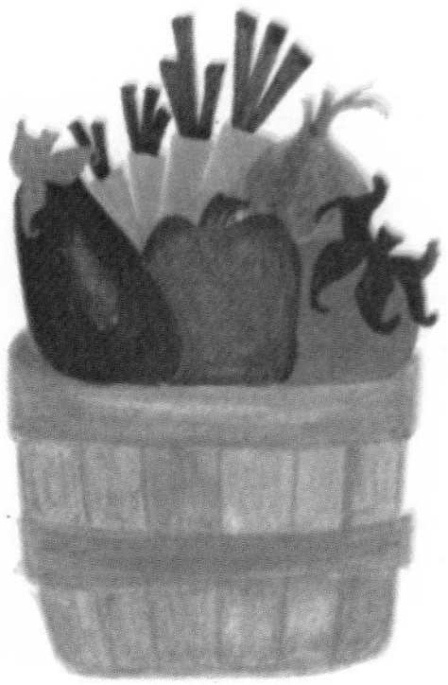

Although we often wish that we could pick our vegetables dewy fresh from the garden and cook and eat them immediately afterward, this is only possible for country dwellers. In urban and suburban areas, the cook must rely on her skill in selecting the best and freshest vegetables from the stalls of supermarkets and specialty shops. You can develop this skill by learning as much as possible about the qualities of vegetables and about their seasons.

O━ Here is one steadfast rule: always buy the best you can afford. It is far better to get a higher-priced firm cabbage, for instance, all of which can be used, than a cheaper one of the same size which is damp and soggy and only three quarters usable. In reality, this is a case of the cheaper being the more expensive.

It is fairly easy to judge the freshness of a vegetable by the texture, color and appearance. Look for crisp, plump, well-colored produce. Do not settle for dry, soft, bruised or faded vegetables.

PRESERVING NUTRITIVE VALUE AND FLAVOR

Of all foods, vegetables—fresh, frozen or canned—are the most abused by poor cooking. Follow these keys and your vegetables will be cooked properly:

O━ Never let vegetables stand in cold water before cooking. The one apparent exception is that members of the cabbage family should be soaked in cold salted water to dislodge any insects, but even this soaking should last for only a few minutes.

O━ Prepare vegetables just before cooking; this includes the peeling, slicing or dicing. When exposed to air or soaked in water, vegetables lose much of their vitamin content and flavor.

O━ Never add baking soda when cooking green vegetables. It will keep them green but destroys their vitamin content. A far better method both for appearance and nutrition is to cook the vegetables by blanching (pp. 411 and 412).

O━ Do not add salt to vegetables (except potatoes) while cooking. O━ Add ½ teaspoon sugar instead of salt to all vegetables while cooking. This will improve the flavor and in some cases even improve the color. It will not make vegetables taste sweet; it simply restores their natural sweetness. Add salt only when ready to serve the vegetable.

0┳ Cook vegetables whole or in large pieces whenever you can. For example, nutritive elements are present next to the skin of potatoes. When they are cut into pieces and peeled, their surfaces become exposed to air—the greatest enemy of vitamins.

0┳ Use herbs frequently with vegetables while cooking and after cooking; they can spark a vegetable without destroying its natural flavor. For example: savory with green beans; mint with peas; sage with lima beans; thyme with carrots. In the chapter on herbs and spices you will find many other suggestions.

Covering vegetables while cooking is a subject about which experts disagree. Some think all vegetables should be covered. Others say never to cover green vegetables. Obviously baked or braised vegetables are covered, and spinach steamed in the water that clings to the leaves must be covered. In the descriptions of cooking methods that follow, you will see that each method has its own rules.

Cook the vegetables only until barely fork-tender; they must retain a bit of their original crispness.

0┳ To give your vegetables a meaty flavor when served with a roast or chops, add ½ chicken or beef bouillon cube to the cooking water. It usually salts them sufficiently.

BASIC COOKING METHODS FOR VEGETABLES

Some vegetables need special attention, but these constitute a minority. Most are cooked according to a few basic methods. It is important to learn about basic cooking methods for all foods, but perhaps even more so when cooking vegetables. As to the flavoring and seasoning, let your own taste buds be your guide.

Blanching and refreshing, professional method

To serve a deep-green vegetable, even greener than when fresh, follow the chef's trick—blanch the vegetable before cooking it further. This will not require another saucepan or a lot of complications, and it does have the added advantage of enabling you to cook vegetables hours ahead of time. When ready to serve, dip them in hot water for a few minutes to reheat, or sauté briefly in butter or oil, or heat in an appropriate sauce. They will lose none of their flavor, quality or color. If convenient, you can serve them immediately after blanching and draining.

Fill a large saucepan with water and bring it to a rolling boil. Gradually add the cleaned vegetable. If you have lots of water, it will quickly return to the boil. This is important because the more quickly the water returns to the boiling point, the greener the vegetable will be.

The cooking period varies with the different vegetables, their degree of freshness and the way they are cut. As an average, count 8 to 12 minutes for a whole vegetable and only 3 to 4 minutes for a sliced or diced vegetable. To test, take a piece out of the water and taste it. You will be surprised how quickly most vegetables cook. Once you have experimented, make notes as a reminder, stating exactly how long you prefer to cook that particular vegetable.

If the vegetables are to be served without delay, then drain, butter and serve. If they are to be eaten cold, or later in the day, then they must be refreshed; this is another trick used by the professional chef. To refresh blanched vegetables, drain the water, or lift the vegetables out with a wire skimmer or a perforated spoon, and toss them into a bowl of ice-cold water. This cold bath stops the cooking immediately, sets the color and preserves both the texture and the flavor. Place an absorbent cloth in a dish. Skim the vegetables out of the cold water and place them in the cloth-lined dish. Refrigerate until ready to serve. To reheat, place the vegetables in a saucepan and pour enough boiling water over them to cover. Boil for ½ minute, drain and serve.

Steaming

Vegetables—whole, or pared and cut into serving pieces, or sliced or diced—can be cooked by steaming. However, green vegetables cooked by this method do not retain the beautiful green color, which they keep if blanched.

First, use a thick stainless-steel or enameled cast-iron saucepan. Add just enough liquid to cover the bottom of the pan. The liquid can be water, bouillon or consommé, homemade stock, milk or vegetable water. Do not salt and pepper before cooking, but you may add herbs and spices to the water. Bring the liquid to a rolling boil. Add the prepared vegetables and return to a rolling boil. Cover and cook over medium-low heat until tender. The degree of heat is important because the steam developed by the water should cook the vegetables. If the water boils too fast, it will not cook by steam; also it may boil away. The average time needed to cook the vegetable ranges from 5 to 25 minutes; make notes of your preferences. Uncover the pan as infrequently as possible. Experience will soon teach you the correct timing.

As soon as the vegetable is cooked to the desired tenderness, pour it into a sieve to drain. Place in a hot vegetable dish, add salt, pepper and butter (or any other seasoning you like) and serve. Do not put the vegetable back into the hot saucepan to wait, because it will continue to cook by the heat retained in the pan. It will then wilt and lose flavor and color.

A vegetable can be steamed ahead of time and refreshed, as described for blanching, then reheated in water or in a sauce at serving time.

Pan-cooking

This method was created by Ida Bailey Allen in the 1930s. She may have been inspired by the ancient Chinese method of stir-frying vegetables.

Melt 2 tablespoons of any fat you prefer in a heavy wide frying pan. Add boiling water to a depth of 1 inch and bring again to a fast rolling boil. Add the vegetables and cover the pan. Reduce the heat to a slow simmer and cook until the vegetable is tender. Holding the cover, shake the pan from time to time to distribute the vegetables and ensure even cooking.

At first this may seem to be the same as steaming vegetables, but there is more liquid in pan-cooking and the fat makes a difference. When you have actually used both methods you will discover the difference in the final result. This is an excellent method for sliced or diced winter root vegetables, shredded cabbage, sliced onions and slivered carrots.

Chinese stir-frying

The Chinese prepare vegetables with as much care as fish or meat. A cooked vegetable should be crisp, excellent in flavor and bright in color. For these reasons vegetables cooked by this method are never soft, with the color and flavor boiled out of them, but neither are they raw. To many vegetable lovers, the Oriental way of cooking, serving and eating vegetables is the height of perfection. Once you have learned this technique, you can apply it to any vegetable. The time is almost the same for all; if there is a difference, it is only a matter of a minute or two.

Cut the vegetable on the bias into slivers. For each pound, or approximately 3½ to 4 cups prepared vegetables, measure ½ cup water or bouillon and add ½ teaspoon sugar. As a variation, add 1 tablespoon soy sauce, fresh lemon juice or cider vinegar. Set this aside.

For each pound of vegetable heat 2 tablespoons salad oil in a large frying pan or wok. Add ½ teaspoon salt; stir for a few seconds. As a variation at this point you can add three thin slices of fresh gingerroot. Put the prepared vegetable into the hot salted oil and stir over high heat until well coated with the oil; just a few seconds. This seals the pores so that the vegetable retains color and flavor.

Add the prepared liquid. Stir quickly for a few seconds over high heat. Cover, lower heat and simmer until the vegetable is tender, from 3 to 5 minutes.

To cook whole vegetables or vegetables cut into large pieces, they must be blanched first for 3 to 5 minutes and refreshed, as previously explained. When drained and patted dry, they are stirred into the hot oil and cooked just as the slivers are cooked.

When a stir-fry vegetable cannot be served immediately, do not cover. The heat retained by covering the vegetables will create a moist steam that will soften the crisp texture, fade the color and make the pieces limp and gray.

When several vegetables are cooked together, those needing a longer cooking period, such as onions, celery, green peppers and carrots, go into the pan with the hot oil first; they are stirred for a few seconds longer than usual. Then the more tender vegetables, such as tomatoes, spinach and green onions, are added.

You can vary the liquid and flavoring in many ways and you may decide this method is the easiest and most creative way of cooking vegetables. If you are familiar with Chinese cooking, you will recognize this way as typical of cooking in a wok, and the wok is a perfect pan to use.

Steam-baking

We seldom consider that any vegetable other than the potato can be baked, yet many vegetables, especially the winter roots, gain by being baked. Some are steam-baked while others are baked with dry heat.

To steam-bake, scrub the vegetable—carrots, beets, parsnips—and remove any imperfections. Then rub all over with salad oil, bacon fat or soft margarine. An easy way to do this is to place a small piece of fat in your hand, or pour a little oil into your palm, then roll the vegetable around. Then place the oiled vegetables in a casserole without crowding. Add just enough boiling water to cover the bottom of the casserole. Cover tightly. Steam-bake in a preheated oven, 350° to 375° F., for 40 to 50 minutes, or until the vegetable is tender. Time varies according to the size of the vegetable and the oven heat. The possible variation in the oven heat enables you to steam-bake your vegetable when the oven is used for other baking.

When the vegetable is half done, turn the pieces over in the casserole, then finish. Uncover if you prefer to have the liquid completely evaporated and the vegetable slightly browned on top.

Baking with dry heat

Beets, onions, potatoes, pumpkin and squash can be baked. If you have never tasted a baked onion, you are in for a pleasant surprise. There is a world of difference between onions that have been boiled and those that have been baked.

To bake potatoes or any other vegetables, scrub but do not peel. Remove the imperfections, just as for steam-baked vegetables. Rub with oil or fat, then roll in coarse salt until a few grains stick to the vegetable.

Place a sheet of foil on the oven rack to protect the stove from drippings and put the oiled vegetables on the foil. Bake in a preheated oven at 375° to 400° F.

until the vegetable is tender. The average time is about 1 hour.

Pumpkins and squashes are cut into halves. The seeds and strings are scooped out. Put a small pat of butter in the bottom and sprinkle with a tiny bit of salt, or add a few spoonfuls of honey or maple syrup. This improves the bland flavor of squash without making it too sweet.

French frying or deep-frying

French frying can be used for preparing vegetables other than potatoes: cauliflowers; finger-length sticks of eggplant; blanched and refreshed carrots and parsnips; pieces of pumpkin or winter squash; rings of onions or green peppers.

Wash and prepare the vegetables but do not soak them in cold water, except potatoes. Put enough vegetable oil, shortening or lard in a deep heavy saucepan or French fryer to fill it to one third of the depth. Heat to 350° F. on a frying thermometer, or until the oil will brown a 1-inch cube of bread in 1 minute. Carefully slide the vegetable into the hot oil, a few pieces at a time, and fry until golden brown. Remove the vegetable with a perforated spoon. Drain on crumpled paper towels. Dust with salt when you are ready to serve the vegetable.

For French fried potatoes, cut 12 to 16 finger-length pieces from a good-size potato. Soak in ice-cold water for 1 hour, drain and dry.

For French fried eggplant, cut it into finger-length strips. Dust with flour and a little MSG (monosodium glutamate). Dip into 1 egg slightly beaten with ¼ cup water. Coat at once with fine dry crumbs.

For French fried carrots, parsnips, pumpkin or winter squash, half-cook them, then cut into finger-length strips and dip into egg and crumbs as for eggplant.

For French fried cauliflower, wash and separate into its natural flowerets. Do not precook. Dip into egg and crumbs as for eggplant.

For French fried onion rings, use the large Spanish onions. Peel and cut into ½-inch-thick crosswise slices. Separate into rings. For these and green pepper rings, dip into eggs and crumbs, then fry as directed for eggplant.

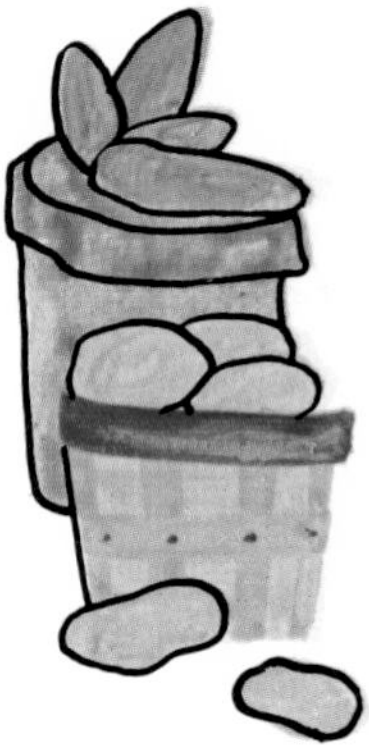

ROOT VEGETABLES

Potatoes

It took 200 years for the potato to reach its present popularity, and today nobody could imagine how it could lose its place.

TO PREPARE: Valuable nutrients lie close to the skin of the potato, so it is wasteful to peel them when not absolutely necessary, or to peel them and let them stand in cold water for hours. The *quantity* of the vegetable remains, but part of the essential *quality* is destroyed.

When possible, leave the skin on old potatoes, but scrub with a stiff brush. Keeping the skin retains flavor and the mineral salts, and much waste in material and time is avoided. On the other hand, new potatoes lose much of their skin when scrubbed because it is still thin and delicate. Simply wash them and cook in their skins.

TO COOK: There are hundreds of ways to cook potatoes, but the method used most is plain boiling. 🗝 Old or winter potatoes should be started in cold water and allowed to come to the boiling point, then simmered until tender. 🗝 New potatoes should be added to rapidly boiling water. 🗝 Try to choose potatoes of the same size for boiling, or cut the larger ones to match the size of the smaller ones so that all will be cooked at the same time and none overcooked. To test boiled potatoes for doneness, use a skewer or a cake tester. Do not use a fork. Too many holes will make the potatoes watery.

When the potatoes are cooked, drain the water immediately and put the saucepan, uncovered, back over medium heat, shaking the pan gently for a minute or two to dry them out quickly; wet and soggy boiled potatoes are unappetizing.

🗝 When boiled potatoes cannot be served immediately, remove the pan from the heat. Place a folded cloth or a double thickness of absorbent paper toweling on top of the potatoes. Set the cover loosely on the cloth. Keep on the back of the stove. The hot steam from the potatoes will be absorbed by the cloth or paper; the potatoes will stay dry instead of becoming soft and mushy. Potatoes can wait in this manner for 15 to 20 minutes.

Scalloped potatoes

Peel 6 large potatoes. Slice thin and place in layers in a buttered 2-quart baking dish. Sprinkle each layer with a little flour. Dot each layer with butter and season with salt and pepper. Fill the dish with hot milk up to the top layer of potatoes. Bake in a 350° F. oven for about 1¼ hours, or until tender. Cover for the first 20 minutes, then cook uncovered for the remaining period. Makes 6 servings.

Mashed potatoes

Use winter potatoes. Peel them and cut into equal-size pieces. Boil and drain. Dry over low heat for a few minutes. Mash with a potato masher, or put through a potato ricer, but do this very quickly so the potatoes remain hot. Add 1 tablespoon butter (or more or less if you like) for each 2 potatoes, and salt to your taste. Add a little mace if you wish. Beat until the butter is melted. 🗝 Only then add milk or light cream that has been heated but not brought to the boil. (If you add cold liquid, the potatoes will be cold and gummy.) With a wooden spatula or a potato masher, beat the liquid into the potatoes to make a smooth fluffy mixture. Add only enough liquid to make the mixture smooth, about 1 tablespoon for each potato. All this should be done as quickly as possible so the potatoes never have a chance to get cold—that is the secret of delicious mashed potatoes!

🗝 Here is another secret if you like your potatoes absolutely snow white. Add salt and white pepper to taste to the mashed or riced potatoes. Then add ½ to 1 cup commercial sour cream and 1 tablespoon lemon juice for 6 to 10 potatoes. Beat until creamy. If you like, flavor the potatoes with minced parsley, chives or savory. Add any of the herbs with the salt and pepper.

Potato puffs

Fry 4 slices of bacon until crisp. Crumble into small pieces. Combine with 4 cups leftover or fresh-mashed potatoes and 2 beaten eggs. Sift 1 cup flour, 2 teaspoons baking powder and 1 teaspoon salt into the potato mixture. Blend well.

Heat fat in a deep pan to 385° F. on a frying thermometer; the fat should be about 2 inches deep. Drop the potato mixture by tablespoons into the hot fat. Fry for 3 to 5 minutes, or until brown. Excellent with roast beef. Makes about 8 servings.

Note: You can substitute 4 cups instant mashed potatoes, prepared as directed on the package, for the fresh or leftover potatoes.

Duchess potatoes

This is a very useful recipe when you wish to prepare potatoes in advance. Keep refrigerated, and put in the oven when needed.

Combine 2 cups mashed potatoes and 2 tablespoons melted butter. Beat until creamy. Add 2 well-beaten eggs, ½ cup milk, and salt and pepper to taste. Place in a greased 1½-quart baking dish or casserole. At this point the casserole can be refrigerated. About 30 minutes before serving, put in a 375° F. oven and bake until browned on the top. If you bake it just after assembling it, 20 minutes will be enough to heat through.

Duchess potatoes can be piped around meat or fish to be finished in the broiler. Or small mounds of these potatoes can be baked on a baking sheet to be used as a garnish. Makes 4 servings.

Fisherman's potato cakes

Boil and mash 8 large potatoes. Cut 1 pound salt-pork fatback into large pieces and fry until the fat is rendered and pork is golden. Add the pieces to the mashed potatoes. Then mix in 2½ cups sifted flour and 3 teaspoons baking powder. Form into cakes. Bake at 350° F. for 30 minutes. Serve with poached fish. Makes 8 or more servings.

Sweet potatoes

The sweet potato, a native of America, is a plant of a different family from the white potato; it is a relative of the morning glory and has no poisonous associations. There is a drier yellow potato and an orangey, moister and sweeter potato popularly but incorrectly called a yam. (A true yam is a vegetable of coarser texture which is also edible.)

Whipped sweet potatoes

Peel 6 to 8 sweet potatoes. Cut into quarters. Boil in salted water for about 15 minutes, or until fork tender. Drain. Add a big lump of butter; a pinch each of ground cinnamon, ground cloves and crushed cardamom; and 2 tablespoons heavy cream, orange juice or brandy. Beat to a fluff. Serve. Makes 6 to 8 servings.

Sweet potatoes California

6 large sweet potatoes
3 oranges
¼ pound butter
1 cup light brown sugar
½ teaspoon salt
⅛ teaspoon ground cinnamon
1 cup unsweetened pineapple or apple juice
¼ cup brandy (optional)

Peel potatoes and slice thin. Grate the rind of one of the oranges and set it aside. Pare the oranges and cut into slices. Arrange potato and orange slices in layers in a buttered 1½-quart baking dish, dotting each layer with butter and sprinkling with a mixture of sugar, salt, cinnamon and the grated orange rind. Pour pineapple or apple juice over the potatoes. Cover and bake in a 375° F. oven for 1 hour. Thick syrup should have formed by this time. If you wish, pour brandy on top of the potatoes before serving. Makes 6 to 8 servings.

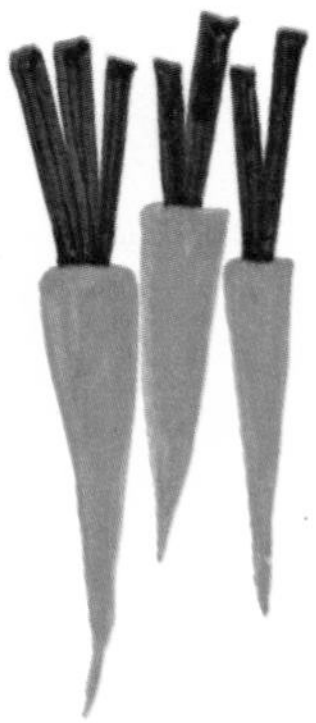

Carrots

The carrot seems almost indispensable all year round, but by no means is it beneath the notice of an epicure when it is cooked with care.

TO PREPARE: Here are two important points most people ignore. Most of the vitamins in carrots are near the skin, so it is advisable to remove as little of the skin as possible. Use a potato peeler to take off a very thin layer only. When the carrots are very young and small, scrub them instead of peeling them. Trim the root and stalk ends.

The second important point is to remove the stalk ends before storing them. If they are left on, the stems and leaves absorb too much of the natural moisture in the roots, causing them to shrivel, and the carrots do not keep fresh as long.

TO COOK: All the methods used to cook vegetables can be applied to carrots, depending on their age, size or the way they are cut. The carrot is another vegetable that loses its flavor when overcooked. Always serve them on the crunchy side.

Carrots Véronique

Véronique, in the classic French repertoire of food terms, means a food garnished with seedless green grapes, cooked to an opaque texture. This recipe is a variation on this classic.

2 to 3 cups diced carrots
⅔ cup seedless green grapes
3 tablespoons heavy cream
Pinch of grated nutmeg
¼ teaspoon ground basil
Salt and pepper

Blanch the carrots for 3 minutes. Freshen. (This can be done ahead of time.) Drain and refrigerate.

Place all the ingredients in a saucepan. Simmer, uncovered, for 15 to 20 minutes, until the sauce is slightly thickened or reduced. Makes about 6 servings.

Note: If you use canned green grapes, add them after the carrots and cream have cooked for about 7 minutes, or they will become mushy.

Carrot vegetarian casserole

A luncheon or light dinner meal can be made of this. It can be served cold for a picnic, with thin slices of ham and a good mustard.

3 cups thin-sliced carrots
2 eggs, beaten
4 to 6 tablespoons melted butter
¼ cup light cream or milk
1 cup grated sharp cheese
½ teaspoon minced fresh sage *or* ¼ teaspoon dried thyme
1½ cups tiny bread croutons
Salt and pepper
Paprika

Blanch the carrots for 3 minutes, freshen, and drain. Beat together the eggs, butter, cream or milk, cheese and fresh sage or dried thyme. The croutons can be left as is, or dry-browned in the oven, or browned in butter. They are at their best when oven dried to a crisp brown. Add the croutons and carrots to the cheese mixture. Season to taste with salt and pepper. Grease a baking dish. Pour in the mixture and sprinkle the top with paprika. Bake in a preheated 400° F. oven for 20 minutes, or until browned on top. Makes 4 servings.

Chef's glazed carrots

1 bunch of carrots (about 1 pound)
1 tablespoon salad oil
2 tablespoons butter
⅓ cup boiling water
½ teaspoon salt
½ teaspoon sugar

Cut the carrots slantwise into long ovals. Heat the oil and butter in a heavy frying pan with a good cover.

Add the carrots and stir-fry over high heat for 2 minutes, until the carrots are shiny and have a deep, rich color. Stir constantly. Add boiling water, salt and sugar. Stir and then cover tightly. Keep over low heat for 7 to 10 minutes. By that time most of the water should be evaporated and the carrots will be beautifully glazed. If too much liquid is left when the carrots are tender, simply uncover and cook over high heat, stirring gently. In a minute or so you will have only the buttery carrots left. Makes 6 to 8 servings.

Variation: Use 4 to 6 carrots and 4 celery ribs, all cut slantwise, and 2 to 4 sliced green onions. Proceed in the same manner with the three vegetables. Flavor with a pinch of thyme. Makes 4 to 6 servings.

Parsnips

The parsnip does not deserve to be ignored. It has good nutritive value and is delicious when properly cooked. Parsnips are available in the late fall and winter when many other fresh vegetables are scarce. In choosing parsnips look for smooth, firm, well-shaped roots. Never buy those that are soft, shriveled or too large.

Parsnips can be sautéed, stir-fried, deep-fried, steam-baked, added to soups and stews or served in a sauce. They are delicious mashed, either by themselves or with an equal quantity of potatoes, mixed with butter, cream, parsley, salt and pepper. Fat is needed to bring out the best flavor in this vegetable, and butter is the best to use.

Do not peel parsnips ahead of time; this will not only discolor them but cause loss of vitamins. As you peel and cut them just before cooking, drop them into acidulated cold water to prevent discoloration (1 tablespoon vinegar or lemon juice for each 3 to 4 cups of water). Cut into dice or sticks, or leave whole. Always remove tough or woody cores.

All recipes for carrots can be applied to parsnips.

Turnips

This name is used for two root vegetables. One is actually the *rutabaga,* a vegetable of Swedish or Lapp origin that is none other than our own large yellow turnip. It contains 92 percent water, no starch or sugar, but has a pungent essential oil. It is crisp, solid and nutritious and does not have an odor if it is properly cooked. The *true turnip* is the small white tuber, topped with a crown of purple, which is used almost exclusively in Europe but also is sold here. There is also a white rutabaga, as large as the yellow but more delicate in flavor. Turnip and rutabaga can be cooked by the same methods.

Turnips have leafy green tops that can be used as a green vegetable. For directions for cooking turnip greens, see the section on Greens (pp. 440 to 445).

TO PREPARE: The turnip has a thicker peel than is usually found on other vegetables. There is a thin, well-marked colored line between the peel and the inside of the turnip. This marks the point to which the peel must be removed, because this is where the bitterness is. Peel the vegetable only when you are ready to cook it.

TO COOK: Slice or cut into pieces. Add just enough boiling water to cover, plus a pinch of sugar and a pinch of pepper. Cook, uncovered, for 20 to 35 minutes. Do not overcook; prolonged cooking changes the color of the turnip and makes it hard to digest. When peeled and grated, a turnip cooks in 5 minutes.

Turnips are very good sliced thin and stir-fried served with lots of minced fresh parsley.

Mashed turnips

1 turnip (rutabaga), about 1 pound
½ teaspoon sugar
1 tablespoon commercial sour cream
2 tablespoons butter
⅛ teaspoon pepper
Minced parsley

Peel the turnip and cut into thin strips. Cover with boiling water and add the sugar. Boil for 8 to 9 minutes over high heat. Drain in a sieve. Return the turnip to the saucepan and add the sour cream, butter and pepper. Mash. Stir well and serve, garnished with minced parsley. Makes 4 to 6 servings.

Turnips gratiné

2 cups mashed turnips
1 egg
5 tablespoons butter
Pinch of ground savory
Salt and pepper
3 tablespoons flour
1 cup milk
½ cup grated cheese

Blend together the mashed turnips, egg, 2 tablespoons of the butter, savory, and salt and pepper to taste. Stir well. Place this mixture in a small, buttered baking dish.

Make a thick white sauce with the remaining 3 tablespoons of butter, the flour and the milk. Spoon the sauce over the turnips and sprinkle with the grated cheese. Bake in a 400° F. oven for 25 minutes, or until the cheese has melted. Makes 4 servings.

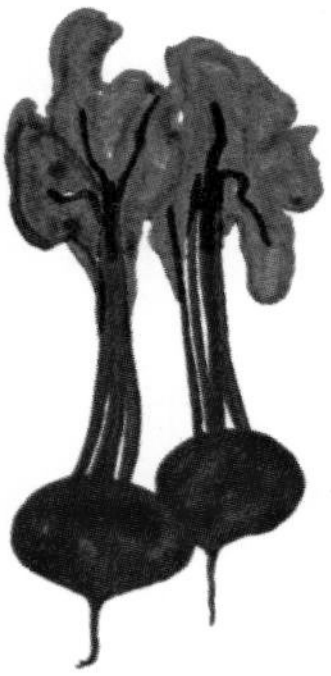

Beets

Did you know that beets are first cousins to spinach? And did you know that beet tops are good sources of vitamins A and C, iron and riboflavin? Since you get them free, look for young beets with fresh green tops when you buy them. For information on preparing and cooking beet greens, see the section on Greens (pp. 440 to 445).

TO PREPARE: Cut off the leafy tops but leave 2 to 3 inches of the stems on the beets themselves, otherwise the beets will lose their deep red color while cooking. Scrub the beets, but do not peel or remove the root end.

TO COOK: Bring enough water to a boil to cover the beets halfway. Add the juice of 1 lemon or 2 tablespoons vinegar and the beets. Cover and boil over medium-low heat from 30 minutes to 1½ hours, depending on the age, size and type of beets you happen to be cooking. You can tell they are cooked when the skin slips off easily.

After cooking, drain them and plunge them into cold water. Slip off the skins by rolling the beets, one at a time, between your fingers.

TO SERVE: Slice, dice or leave whole. Season with butter, salt and pepper to taste, or with a few tablespoons of fat gravy when they are being served with a roast.

Boiled new beets are delicious simply stirred with commercial sour cream and chopped green onion to suit your taste.

Make cooked beets into a salad by shredding them into matchsticks and mixing with diced apples, lemon juice and sour cream to taste. Then season with salt and pepper and a bit of brown sugar.

Beet salad

- 6 to 8 beets, cooked or canned
- 2 garlic cloves, crushed
- 6 tablespoons salad oil
- 3 tablespoons cider or red-wine vinegar
- Salt and pepper
- 1 pound uncooked fresh spinach, washed and chopped
- Juice of ½ lemon
- Chives or parsley, minced

Drain the beets well and slice. Blend them with the crushed garlic, 4 tablespoons of the salad oil, vinegar, and salt and pepper to taste. Marinate in the refrigerator until ready to serve.

Heat the remaining 2 tablespoons salad oil in a large frying pan. Add the chopped spinach and stir over medium heat for 2 or 3 minutes, until the spinach is limp. Pour into a bowl and add the lemon juice and salt and pepper to taste. Chop with two knives until well mixed and chopped very fine. Then place spinach in a mound in the middle of a round plate.

To serve, make a ring of the marinated beets around the spinach and place a few beets on top. Sprinkle the beets with minced chives or parsley to taste. Serve with cold cuts. Makes 6 servings.

Variation: Instead of garlic, flavor the salad with grated orange or lemon rind.

Radishes

These are seldom served any way but raw, as a garnish, appetizer or salad ingredient. They are perishable. Wash and trim them as soon as they arrive from the market, then cover with cold water in a container and store in the refrigerator to crisp them. They will keep 4 to 5 days, but change the water daily. Cooked, their flavor is similar to turnips.

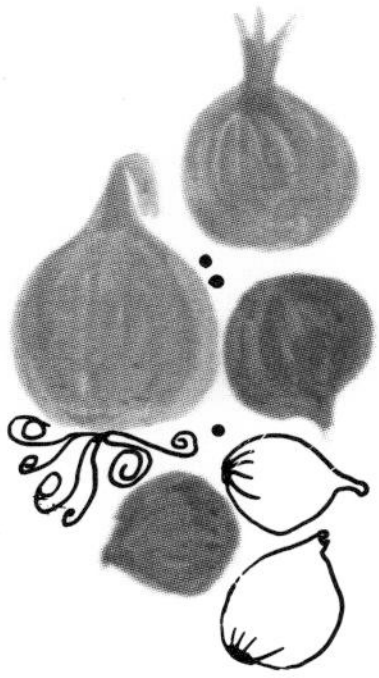

ONIONS AND THEIR RELATIVES

While the most used domestic onions are usually available all year long, some of the others, such as Bermuda and Spanish onions, appear only seasonally. Most onions are sold dried or "cured," but green onions, leeks and chives are sold fresh.

TO PREPARE: Peel under running cold water. Another method is to follow the chef's way, especially if you have many onions. 🗝 Drop the unpeeled onions into a saucepan of rapidly boiling water and leave for 1 minute. Drain, put them into a bowl of ice water and simply slip off the skins.

TO COOK: Overcooked onions lose their true flavor and give off a strong smell. Onions can be cooked by any of the various basic methods, depending upon how they are cut and how you plan to serve them.

Leeks

Leeks belong to the same family as the onion. They are delicate in flavor. Sometimes difficult to find, they are nearly always expensive. In France, where they are easily available, they are known as "the poor man's asparagus." In Wales, leeks are the national emblem.

Leeks have long, flat, green leaves, closely folded together. The bottom, or bulb, is white and only a little fatter than the leaves, in contrast to the more familiar onion which develops a much larger-size bulb.

TO PREPARE: First cut off the root ends and about 2 inches of the green tops. Then peel off the first leaves, from top to bottom. Soak the trimmed leeks in cold water to loosen the soil. Leeks are very gritty, so they must be cleaned carefully and thoroughly. After a brief soaking, run water into the tops and down through the leaves, opening the leaves to let the water go down as deep as possible. If the leeks are to be sliced, make two lengthwise cuts in the green part so you can open the tightly folded leaves and wash them.

TO COOK: Leeks can be cooked and served in much the same way as celery and asparagus. They can be blanched whole for 20 minutes, then freshened, cooled and served with a French dressing for a salad. They are the base of the well-known soup vichyssoise.

Welsh leek pie

This is a good buffet dish. Serve it hot with sliced cold chicken or turkey.

6 leeks
½ cup chicken stock
Juice and grated rind of ½ lemon
2 tablespoons butter
2 cups fine cottage cheese *or* 8 ounces cream cheese
¼ cup heavy cream
4 eggs
Salt and pepper
3 tablespoons fine dry bread crumbs
Pie pastry for 1-crust 8-inch pie

Clean the leeks and cut both the white and the green parts into 1-inch pieces. Bring the chicken stock to a boil along with the lemon juice, rind and butter. Add the leeks and cook, uncovered, over medium heat for 12 to 15 minutes.

Beat together the cheese, cream and eggs until well blended and creamy. Add ½ cup of the cooking stock while stirring. Add this mixture to the cooked leeks and remaining stock. Simmer for a few moments, stirring, until the mixture thickens to the consistency of a light cream sauce. Add salt and pepper to taste.

Grease a pie plate and dust it with fine bread crumbs. Line with the pastry and flute the edge. Pour in the leek mixture. Bake in a preheated 375° F. oven for about 40 minutes, or until the top is golden brown and the custard is set. Makes 4 to 6 servings.

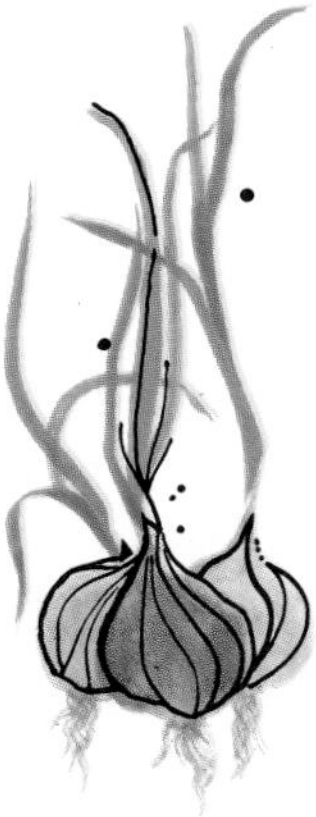

Shallots

Shallots are the aristocrat of the onion family. A favorite of French chefs, shallots combine the best flavor characteristics of onions, garlic and scallions. The flavor is pungent yet delicate, savory yet freshly sweet. Shallots are small and shaped like a head of garlic. They have a brown outer skin and an onionlike interior, shading from light green to violet. Several shallots grow together in a cluster, each one as a clove of the larger bulb; each little clove has its own purple-brown skin. Shallots are sold cured, like dry onions, but are not easy to find.

When purchasing shallots, select those that are firm, with glistening brown skin. They will keep for up to four months if stored in a cool dry place.

TO PREPARE: Peel off the outer brown skin, then slice, chop or mince according to recipe directions. When a recipe calls for one shallot, this means one clove of a shallot.

TO COOK: Shallots can be used in a variety of ways. Whip together softened butter and minced shallots and serve as a topper for broiled steaks. Add chopped fresh shallots to scrambled eggs and omelets. Substitute shallots for onions in creamy sauces for meats and vegetables. Use chopped shallots in salad dressings and thin slices in salads. Use them minced in a marinade for meats and seafood. They are delicious with shrimp cooked in butter and sherry. Stir a small amount of chopped shallots into your favorite rice, macaroni or noodle casserole. Try them in place of onion or garlic whenever you wish a mild, intriguing flavor.

Garlic

Some cooks are afraid of this small but powerful member of the onion family, but it can work wonders in flavoring certain foods. When used well it is a friend, not an enemy. You will find more about garlic in Chapter 5 on herbs and spices.

Chives

Chives, another member of the onion family, are used as a flavoring herb. They look like miniature green onions. You will find more about them in Chapter 5 on herbs and spices.

THE CABBAGE FAMILY

The cabbage family includes red and green cabbages with large, heavy heads somewhat flattened on the top; Savoy cabbage with a smaller, looser head and very crinkly leaves; Chinese or celery cabbage with a long head or stalk like an overgrown stalk of celery; broccoli; Brussels sprouts; cauliflower; kale; kohlrabi. The cabbage itself is a native British plant. The others have been developed through long culture that started in the 16th and 17th centuries.

The mortal sin committed against cabbage—apart from reducing it to coleslaw—is to overcook it. People complain about its obnoxious smell, but this is only present if the vegetable is overcooked. O━ The moment any member of the cabbage family loses its original color you can be sure it has been overcooked. It is at this point that it develops a strong smell. Also the vitamin C, plentiful in cabbage, is lost through overcooking.

Cabbage

All true cabbages can be cooked following the same methods.

TO PREPARE: Remove coarse or discolored outside leaves. Halve the head. Cut out the thick white stem. This can either be used or discarded. O━ To use the stem, pass it over a shredder and cook it with the cabbage; it will cook quickly this way.

The leaves can be cut into fine or coarse shreds with a sharp knife, into pieces about 2 inches square, or into quarters.

Cover any kind of cabbage with cold water and soak for a few minutes. Add a teaspoon of coarse salt to dislodge any slugs or other unwelcome guests. If you plan to shred the cabbage, cut it into halves or quarters and soak it *before* shredding.

TO COOK: The best method to cook quartered cabbage is the professional method—blanching and refreshing.

Shredded cabbage is best cooked by pan-cooking or stir-frying.

If cabbage is cut into big squares, then steam or steam-bake it.

The average cooking time will be from 7 to 15 minutes for shredded and cut squares and 20 minutes for larger pieces, quarters or halves. Add a few more minutes for Savoy cabbage.

Red cabbage bruxelloise

Belgium excels in the cooking of red cabbage, and this recipe is one of their classics. In the autumn, when small wild birds or small ducks are available, they brown them in butter, stuff them with chestnuts, bury them in cabbage and simmer together slowly.

- 1 medium-size red cabbage
- 3 apples, washed and cored
- 4 tablespoons plus 1 teaspoon butter
- 1 bay leaf
- 3 tablespoons brown sugar
- 4 juniper berries (optional)
- 3 whole cloves
- ¼ cup red wine or apple juice or orange juice
- 1 teaspoon salt
- ¼ teaspoon pepper

Clean and shred the cabbage. Cut the unpeeled apples into thin slices. Melt 4 tablespoons of butter in a large saucepan, add the apples and stir for a few minutes. Add the cabbage and stir to mix with the apples. Add the rest of the ingredients. Mix well and simmer, covered, for 1 hour. Most of the liquid should evaporate. If too much is left, uncover the pan and boil fast for a few minutes. Stir in 1 teaspoon of butter just before serving. Makes 4 to 6 servings.

Algerian stuffed cabbage leaves

Stuffed cabbage leaves are made in almost every country in the world. This Algerian method is unbeatable for lightness and flavor. The original hot spices have been replaced with allspice.

1 cup uncooked rice
4 cups water
3 or 4 lamb bones, any type
1 cinnamon stick
1 head of white or Savoy cabbage
½ to 1 pound ground lamb
¼ cup melted or soft pan drippings or oil
½ teaspoon ground allspice
Salt and pepper
Juice and grated rind of 1 lemon
2 tablespoons olive oil (optional)

Cover the rice with cold water and let it soak for 1 hour.

Pour the 4 cups of water over the lamb bones, add the cinnamon stick and simmer, covered, for 2 hours.

Remove the core from the cabbage with a pointed knife. Separate the leaves. Blanch the leaves for 5 minutes and freshen in the professional way. When cool, wrap in an absorbent towel to remove excess moisture. Cut the large leaves into halves.

Prepare the filling by mixing together the ground lamb, well-drained soaked rice, melted pan drippings or oil, allspice, and salt and pepper to taste. Put about a tablespoon on each cabbage leaf. Close like an envelope, tucking down the ends.

Remove the lamb bones from the broth and place them in a wide-bottomed saucepan. Set the stuffed rolled leaves across the bones, making successive layers if needed. Add enough of the broth to cover the rolls. Sprinkle with a little salt. Set a plate or a cover on top of the rolls to hold them in place. Cover the pan tightly and simmer over low heat for 1 hour.

Place the rolls on a hot platter. Measure 1 cup of the broth and add the lemon juice and rind. Add the olive oil to the broth and lemon if you wish. Pour this mixture over the rolls. Serve hot. Makes 8 or more servings depending on the size of the cabbage and the amount of lamb you use.

Broccoli

TO PREPARE: Soak the broccoli in cold salted water for 10 minutes; drain. Cut off the ends of stems and large leaves around the flower head. Peel the stems.

TO COOK: Broccoli can be cooked whole, chopped or cut into small serving pieces; or the stems can be slivered and the heads cut into flowerets.

To cook the whole broccoli, use the professional method—blanching in lots of water for 20 minutes. Freshen quickly.

To cook in small pieces, use the pan-cooking method.

The stir-fry method is best for the slivered stems and flowerets.

Broccoli divan with tuna

A true broccoli divan is wine-poached chicken breast that is set on a bed of cooked broccoli heads, topped with hollandaise sauce and a layer of grated Swiss cheese, and baked. This version can be made quickly when you are in a hurry.

1 bunch of broccoli *or* 2 packages (10 ounces each) frozen broccoli
2 cans (7 ounces each) albacore tuna
3 green onions, finely chopped
1 can (10½ ounces) cream of mushroom soup, undiluted
1 teaspoon curry powder
½ cup commercial sour cream
⅓ cup grated cheese
2 tablespoons butter
Paprika

Prepare the fresh broccoli and cut into slivers or leave whole, according to your taste. Butter a baking dish. Cook the slivered broccoli by the stir-fry method; cook the whole heads by the professional method. Drain. Place in the bottom of the baking dish. If you choose the frozen broccoli, cook as directed on the package and leave whole.

Break the tuna into large pieces and make a layer over the broccoli. Sprinkle the green onions on the tuna. Blend together the undiluted soup, curry powder and sour cream. Pour over the tuna. Top with the grated cheese, dot with the butter and sprinkle paprika on top. Bake at 375° F. for 20 to 25 minutes, or until browned on top. Makes 6 to 8 servings.

Brussels sprouts

TO PREPARE: Trim away any jutting stalks and discolored outer leaves, and be very particular about soaking in salted cold water to dislodge any insects.

TO COOK: In the cabbage family, Brussels sprouts represent quality versus quantity. They are dainty and delicious, but easily ruined when badly cooked. The smaller ones are the best. When possible, select all the same size. To help cook them evenly, cut a cross in the stem end of each one.

Use the professional method of blanching for 5 to 8 minutes, then quickly refresh them in cold water. Cook the sprouts early in the day and refrigerate until ready to serve, when only a tossing in melted butter over low heat will warm them up in 5 minutes.

TO SERVE: Browned butter, toasted sesame seeds or toasted almonds are good companions to Brussels sprouts. The very best accompaniment is chestnuts.

Brussels sprouts and chestnuts

Use canned unsweetened water-packed chestnuts, imported from France, or buy fresh chestnuts. Use 1 pound fresh chestnuts or one 8-ounce can of water-packed chestnuts for each 2 quarts of Brussels sprouts.

To prepare fresh chestnuts, make a crisscross on the flat top of each nut with a sharp-pointed knife. Cover with cold water, bring to a boil and cook for 20 minutes. Then remove the hard shell and the brown skin covering the chestnut. Cook the peeled chestnuts in salted water, or in chicken or beef stock if you prefer, for 10 to 20 minutes, or until tender. Drain.

If using canned chestnuts, just drain them.

Cook the Brussels sprouts. Melt 2 to 4 tablespoons butter in a saucepan. Fry a few finely chopped green onions in this melted butter. Add the drained cooked Brussels sprouts and the chestnuts and toss together until hot. Add salt and pepper to taste, and serve. Makes about 8 servings.

Cauliflower

TO PREPARE: Cut off the hard stem and any big leaves. The small leaves near the flowerets may remain. Soak in salted water, head down, for 10 minutes. Be certain that no insect is hiding among the thick stems.

TO COOK: When cooking cauliflower whole, it is important to cut crisscross slashes into the thick stalks to ensure even cooking. Use the professional method: blanch, head up, for 15 to 18 minutes, or until tender to taste. Avoid overcooking. 0┳ If the head is rubbed with half a cut lemon before cooking, it will keep its beautiful creamy-white color.

Broken into flowerets, cauliflower can be stir-fried or pan-cooked.

TO SERVE: Grated cheese, butter and lemon, hollandaise sauce or buttered brown croutons are the best garnishes to use with cauliflower. Or serve in cream sauce, topped with grated cheese and browned under the broiler or in the oven.

Golden cauliflower

Ruth Conrad Bateman is an American food expert who has written many culinary books and has a wonderful flair with food. This golden cauliflower is her idea.

1 cauliflower
½ cup grated Swiss cheese
¼ cup mayonnaise
1 egg white
1 teaspoon lemon juice
2 tablespoons grated Parmesan cheese

Separate the cauliflower into flowerets. Cook by the professional method, blanching for 10 minutes.

Drain the flowerets and place them in a shallow baking dish that can go under the broiler.

Combine the Swiss cheese and the mayonnaise. Beat the egg white and fold into the cheese and mayonnaise mixture. Add the lemon juice. Spread this mixture over the cauliflower and sprinkle with Parmesan cheese. Broil 6 inches from the source of heat for about 5 minutes, until the sauce puffs up and is golden. Makes about 6 servings.

FRESH LEGUMES

These plants have seeds that grow within pods, which open along the sides when the seeds are ripe. We eat pod and all of some legumes, such as green or yellow snap beans and snow peas, before the seeds are developed. Other legumes such as peas and lima beans we eat after the seeds are developed but are still green. Chick-peas, lentils and, surprisingly, the peanut are also legumes.

Fresh snap beans

Green beans, yellow or wax beans, and the hard-to-find mottled green and purple beans are the best-known and most-used beans of those that are eaten in the pods. Of course there are many other kinds. Every country has its own tasty and different way of cooking and serving them.

TO PREPARE: Wash beans in cold water. Snip off the top and bottom ends. It may happen that some have threads or strings that should be pulled away when the ends are snipped off. If you trim the beans ahead of time, place them in a plastic bag and refrigerate until you are ready to cook them.

TO COOK: The beans can be left whole, cut into 1-inch pieces or into halves, cut on the diagonal into three pieces, or cut into long thin shreds with a sharp knife or a special cutter. Beans cut into shreds are referred to as "French-style."

The usual method of cooking snap beans is to blanch them, but they can be stir-fried. Wax beans can also be steam-baked.

Fresh beans will cook in 5 to 12 minutes. Avoid overcooking them; they are more tasty and far more digestible when a bit on the crunchy side.

TO SERVE: The classic way to serve green beans is with butter plus lemon juice or lemon rind.

The Germans add a pinch of dried savory to the water while cooking the beans; then only butter is used to dress them.

The Greeks fry an onion in salad oil, then add chopped parsley, mint and a tablespoon of tomato paste. When these ingredients are well mixed, a little water is added and whole green beans are put into the boiling liquid. The beans are cooked quickly and served in their own juice with a bowl of rice.

Amandine garnish

This garnish is often used on French-style beans. For 1 pound green beans, sliver ¼ cup blanched almonds into thin shreds. Brown 2 tablespoons butter, add the almonds and cook until almonds and butter have a deep brown color. Add 1 tablespoon of fresh lemon juice. Pour over the beans as soon as they are cooked.

This garnish has become so popular that it is almost routine. For a difference, use chopped hazelnuts, pearl onions or minced tomato—browned in the same way as the almonds.

Mennonite green beans

2 tablespoons butter
1/3 cup water
1/4 to 1/2 teaspoon dried savory
Salt and pepper
1 pound green beans, cut into halves
1 tablespoon cornstarch
1 tablespoon tomato paste
1/2 cup light cream
1/3 cup grated sharp Cheddar cheese

Melt the butter in a saucepan. Add the water, savory, and salt and pepper to taste. Bring to a boil. Add the beans, cover tightly and steam for 15 minutes. Drain the beans into a hot serving dish, reserving the cooking liquid.

Put the reserved liquid back in the pan. Mix the cornstarch with the tomato paste and the cream. Add to the bean liquid. Cook, stirring, until the mixture turns into a slightly thickened sauce. Add the cheese and stir until it melts, then pour over the beans. Makes 4 servings.

Snap bean salad

This is an excellent salad to serve with barbecued steak.

1 pound green or yellow snap beans
1 teaspoon sugar
1 white onion
2 tablespoons salad oil
Juice of 1/2 lemon
1 or 2 pinches of dried oregano
Salt and pepper

Trim and wash the beans and place them in a saucepan with the sugar. Cover with boiling water and boil for 6 to 8 minutes. Drain and rinse in cold water. Drain again on absorbent paper. Cool and refrigerate.

Slice the onion as thin as possible. Break the slices into rings and place in a bowl. Cover with ice cubes and let stand until ice has melted. This will take the bite out of the onion and make the slices crisp.

When ready to serve, mix the beans with the salad oil, lemon juice, oregano, and salt and pepper to taste. Toss until all the beans are well coated, then place in a salad bowl. Drain the onion rings and sprinkle over the salad. Makes 4 to 6 servings.

Lima beans

Unlike the other fresh beans just described, the pods of lima beans are not eaten because they are too tough. Instead they are allowed to ripen until the beans inside reach an edible size.

TO PREPARE: If possible, do not shell the beans until you are ready to cook them. Sometimes shelled limas appear in markets. While this does save work at home, these beans are always a little tougher and less flavorful. Limas are difficult to shell. Use a sharp knife to cut a lengthwise slice down the pod, then pry apart the sides of the pod. The pods are so tight that the beans will not need to be washed before cooking.

TO COOK: Lima beans can be blanched and refreshed, or steamed. These take longer to cook than other fresh beans, 15 to 25 minutes. Taste a bean to avoid overcooking.

TO SERVE: Add salt, pepper and a bit of butter; try lemon juice for an interesting change. The pale green beans look especially appetizing with minced fresh parsley or grated orange rind.

If you have a blender, place the cooked lima beans with ½ cup of their cooking water in the blender container. Cover and blend into a purée. Add butter plus salt and pepper to taste.

Cook lima beans in chicken stock instead of water, and thicken the liquid to a cream sauce. Serve with a few slices of bacon, cooked and diced, and chopped fresh parsley.

To make succotash, mix equal parts of cooked fresh beans and cooked fresh or canned corn kernels. Add butter and salt to taste. Minced red and green peppers are good with this.

Peas

Green peas are a favorite vegetable all around the world. Canned peas are surely the most popular. Garden-fresh peas are only truly perfect when picked young from the garden and cooked immediately.

A variety of peas with edible pods is frequently used in Oriental cooking. Called snow or sugar peas, they are eaten pod and all. The pod is flat and much paler green than the regular variety; the peas inside the pod are tiny. They can always be found in season at Oriental groceries. Although expensive, there is no loss since the whole vegetable is eaten. These are also available frozen.

TO PREPARE: Shell green peas only when ready to cook. If you do it sooner the peas will dry out. One pound in the pods equals about 1 cup shelled peas.

Snow peas are not shelled. Trim the ends and pull off any strings; wash.

TO COOK: Peas and snow peas are usually cooked by the professional method: blanch them for 10 to 15 minutes. Stir-fry, pan-cook or steam. If your peas are not very young, add a little sugar to the cooking liquid.

TO SERVE: Butter, fresh mint, minced shallots, cooked small white onions or parsley are all good additions to cooked green peas.

DRIED LEGUMES

Dried legumes are excellent winter fare because they are both nourishing and warming, as well as extremely economical. They double in bulk when cooked; 1 cup of a dried legume can make 4 servings. They can be served as a main dish, a soup or a vegetable. You can cook more than is needed for a single meal because they can be stored in your refrigerator for as long as eight to ten days without spoiling. They also freeze very well. It is true they take fairly long to cook, but they require little supervision and can be reheated without problems.

O━ If you are searching for a way to economize on meat, serve a dried legume dish instead of meat once a week. There are many, such as dried lima and kidney beans and chick-peas. The most interesting for casseroles and soups are lentils and split peas.

Lentils

Lentils are like miniature peas except they are flat. They have an outer membrane with the seed inside. The seeds of lentils are split like the seeds of peas. Whole lentils are sold as brown lentils and have a greenish-brown color; the inside is a golden orange. The split or so-called Egyptian lentils are easier to find than the whole brown lentils. The split ones will cook in 20 to 30 minutes; the whole ones take 1 to 1½ hours. Neither requires a soaking period. Brown lentils have more flavor than the split lentils.

Creamed lentils

Serve as a vegetable, or as a main dish by adding diced leftover meat at the same time as the sour cream.

1 pound brown lentils
10 cups cold water
1 teaspoon celery salt
Salt and pepper
1 cup commercial sour cream
2 tablespoons butter

Place the lentils in a colander and rinse under running cold water. Place the beans and the cold water in a saucepan. Set over low heat, cover and *slowly* bring to a boil. 🗝 This is important, because the slow cooking will give a preliminary softening to the lentils. This usually takes 40 to 45 minutes. When the water boils, cook a little faster, as the water must be evaporated when the lentils are cooked. This should take another 45 minutes.

Toward the end of the cooking, add the celery salt plus salt and pepper to taste. When the lentils are soft and the water has all been absorbed, add the sour cream and the butter. Taste for seasoning and add more salt and pepper if necessary. Stir gently until the sour cream and butter are well blended in with the beans. Makes about 6 servings.

As a variation, sprinkle with minced parsley or fried onions.

Lentil soup

This delicious soup makes a perfect winter lunch accompanied by a thick wedge of warm apple pie with cheese and a big cup of hot tea. This soup freezes very well.

2 cups brown lentils
4 cups cold water
2 tablespoons salt
¼ teaspoon pepper
½ cup butter
1 large can (1 pound, 13 ounces) tomatoes
1 large onion, diced
2 tablespoons minced fresh dill *or* 1 tablespoon dill seeds
2 garlic cloves, crushed
2 bay leaves

Place all the ingredients in a saucepan. Slowly bring to a boil. Cover and simmer over low heat for 2 to 2½ hours. Makes about 6 servings.

Split peas

Green split peas are usually hulled from peas called Small Blues or Imperial. The process used for hulling gives a larger, more tasty split pea, and also accounts for the difference in size between these and other split peas. The peas are washed lightly, soaked and dried. This process loosens the skin, which is then easily removed, and the peas fall apart. They cook quickly.

Scotch pease pudding

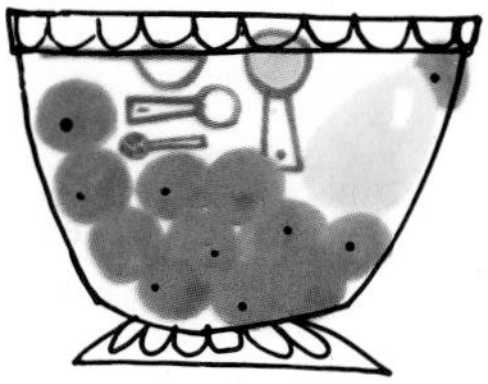

This old-fashioned dish is similar in texture to "Scotch brose," a pudding made with oatmeal. Boiled bacon or lamb, homemade rhubarb chutney and pease pudding is a true Scottish country meal, wonderful after a day of hunting or just roaming in the woods.

3 cups green split peas
4 tablespoons butter
1 teaspoon salt
¼ teaspoon pepper
1 teaspoon brown sugar
1 egg, lightly beaten
Melted butter

Soak the peas in cold water overnight. Drain, then tie them loosely in cheesecloth, leaving room for them to swell. Place in a large saucepan. Add enough boiling water to cover by about 2 inches. Cover and simmer over low heat for 3 hours, until soft. Remove from the water and drain thoroughly. Lightly flour the cheesecloth.

Place the peas in a bowl and add the 4 tablespoons butter, salt, pepper, brown sugar and egg. Beat together with a wire whisk or a rotary beater. The mixture will be soft but thick. Return to the floured cheesecloth. Tie up the cheesecloth tightly in the shape of a pudding. Put it in a pan of boiling water and boil for 30 to 40 minutes. Unwrap and place on a hot dish. Pour melted butter to taste on top. Slice and serve. Makes about 8 servings.

If you happen to have any leftover pudding, slice it when cold, then brown the slices slowly in butter or bacon fat.

Dried beans

All kinds of dried beans can be cooked by the same methods, but of course smaller varieties cook more quickly than the larger beans. Also, beans that have been stored longer and are therefore drier and harder will need more time to cook. It may be hard for you to determine this, so taste a bean near the end of the cooking time to avoid overcooking, unless you want them to be very soft for puréeing.

Rinse the dried beans. Pick over them only if you bought them in bulk (sometimes small stones get into the bags). Cover the beans with a lot of water and let them stand overnight. Drain. They are ready to simmer or bake.

If you do not have time to let them stand overnight, put the beans in a large pot and add enough water to cover by at least 1 inch. Bring to a boil and cook for 5 minutes. Let them stand until the water is almost absorbed and almost cool. Then proceed with the recipe.

Beans are enhanced when cooked with a ham bone, a bay leaf, an onion stuck with cloves, a carrot and a celery rib. Any kind of dried beans can be used for soup, baked beans, salads and casseroles. Black beans are especially good for soup or with rice. Pea beans and marrow beans are enhanced by tomatoes. White cannellini beans with vinaigrette sauce and minced red onions make a delicious salad or hors d'oeuvre.

One particular bean, the flageolet, which is a small, green, oval-shaped bean, is available fresh in France, but we can buy these only canned or dried. They are expensive, but when you taste a Breton-style lamb dish garnished with these delicious little beans, you will think them worth the cost (p. 286).

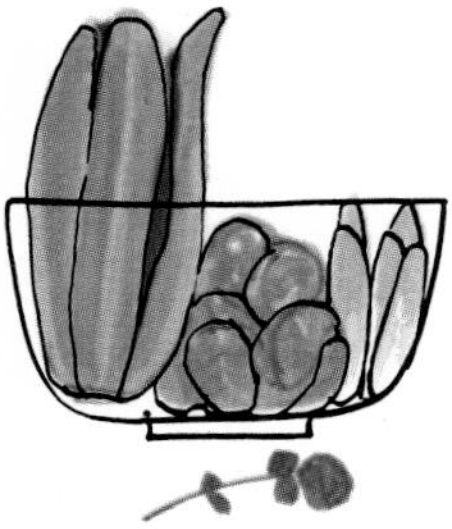

GREENS

Under this general heading we usually include all the plants we cultivate chiefly for their leaves. First, the whole family of salad greens: chicory, dandelion greens, endive, escarole, watercress, as well as Boston, Bibb, iceberg, romaine and garden leaf lettuces. There is also kale (a member of the cabbage family), Swiss chard, mustard greens and sorrel; also turnip tops and beet greens plus other leaves of plants we usually grow for the roots. The most famous green is spinach. Another green is fiddleheads, a specialty in Maine and Eastern Canada.

TO PREPARE: All salad greens except iceberg lettuce and Belgian endive should be washed under running cold water. After thoroughly shaking out the water, place the vegetable on absorbent cloth in the bottom of a plastic bag. Fill the bag loosely with the cleaned greens and refrigerate in the vegetable crisper. O┳ The cloth placed in the bottom absorbs any moisture remaining in the greens and prevents rusting. It also keeps the leaves crisped and fresh for a day or two or even longer.

If you trim salad greens before storing them, do not use a knife. Break off the parts you wish to discard. Using a knife on greens causes rust spots on the leaves.

Greens to be cooked should be cleaned carefully; they are likely to have grit and soil attached to them. Wash repeatedly by immersing them in a large bowl of tepid water. Change the water and repeat. Separate the leaves—especially important for kale—and run under cold water.

TO COOK: Do not drain the greens after the final cleaning; the water clinging to the leaves is usually sufficient liquid in which to cook them. All recipes for celery and spinach can be used for cooking greens.

Endives

The endive is often served cooked in Europe, but usually we think of it only as a salad green. This vegetable is expensive, but there is scarcely any waste.

Braised endives

Allow two heads per person. Trim off roots without cutting leaves. Remove any discolored leaves.

Generously rub the bottom of a casserole with butter and add the endives, whole or halved lengthwise, the juice of ½ lemon, and enough chicken stock (your own or canned) to half cover the endives. Bring to a boil on top of the stove. Place a round of buttered wax paper directly on top of the endives. Cover the casserole and place it in a preheated 325° F. oven. Cook for 1 hour, or until the endives are tender when pierced with the point of a small sharp knife; they should be lightly browned.

To serve, lift the endives out onto a hot serving dish. Boil down the liquids in the pan over high heat, uncovered, until you have about 1 tablespoon per person. Pour this over the endives. Sprinkle with minced fresh parsley.

Variation: Instead of all chicken stock, use half dry white wine or sherry. Sprinkle the finished endives with minced sautéed hazelnuts.

Watercress

Watercress has dark green, smooth, peppery leaves, and is especially popular in salads. It grows in running shallow water, usually where the water is quite cool. While watercress does grow wild in the United States, the little bunches sold in markets are picked from cultivated beds. Watercress must be used without delay, for the leaves start to turn yellow about two days after the sprigs are cut.

Watercress soup

- 2 bunches of watercress
- 3 tablespoons butter
- 1 medium-size onion, chopped
- 1 teaspoon curry powder
- 4 large potatoes, peeled and chopped
- 4 cups chicken stock
- 1 cup mushroom broth (p. 177)
- Salt
- White pepper
- 1 cup light cream

Cut off the bottom half inch of the watercress stems; discard. Wash the rest of the watercress carefully; sometimes tiny freshwater snails are lurking in the leaves. Cut off the leafy tips of the sprigs and put them on absorbent towels until later. Cut the stems into short lengths. Heat the butter. Cook the onion in it until golden, then add the curry powder and cook until the curry is lightly browned. Add the watercress stems and cook for 5 minutes longer. Add the potatoes and stir well. Pour in the chicken stock and mushroom broth. Simmer over low heat until the potatoes are completely soft.

Whirl the mixture, a part at a time, in an electric blender, then strain through a coarse sieve to remove the pieces of watercress stems. Return to the heat and add the reserved leaves. Simmer for 1 minute, then whirl in the blender once more. Taste the soup and add salt and white pepper. If the soup is to be served hot, stir in the cream and heat until just ready to serve; do not let soup boil after the cream is added. If it is to be served cold, let the purée cool, and stir in the cream just before serving. Makes 8 servings or more.

Watercress sandwiches

Cut off the heel of a loaf of firm white bread. Spread the cut slice with sweet butter and cut off as thin a slice as possible. Continue to butter the cut end of the loaf and cut off slices until you have enough. Trim off the crusts and put all the slices, buttered sides up, on a damp towel.

Wash and dry 2 sprigs of watercress for each sandwich. Mix together equal parts of mayonnaise and lemon-based French dressing. Dip the sprigs in this mixture, then place two on each buttered slice, near one corner, with the stem ends toward the center and the leafy tips toward the outside. Roll up diagonally; the leaves should just show at the end. Fasten with toothpicks. When all the sandwiches are rolled, cover with wax paper and refrigerate until time to serve. Remove the toothpicks before serving.

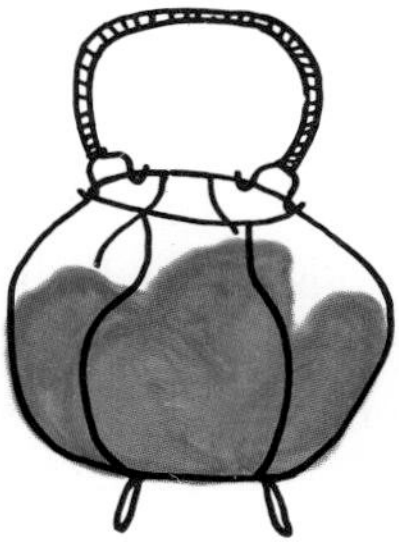

Spinach

Supposedly spinach came originally from Asia through Spain. Our familiar spinach is available fresh all year long. The whole of a small plant is pulled up and the root end and stems are often very sandy. Thorough washing is necessary. This chore makes the frozen vegetable increasingly popular, but fresh spinach is far more delicious. These glossy green leaves are the basis of many an epicurean dish, such as sole florentine and spinach soufflé.

Another green is New Zealand spinach, a plant of a different species but also an excellent vegetable. Since this is gathered leaf by leaf from plants that continue to bear, it is much easier to clean.

TO PREPARE: To clean spinach, first cut off the root ends and discard any wilted leaves. Then fill a large pan with cold water; change the water several times while washing the leaves. Lift the spinach from the water, or use the directions given for cleaning greens. Even the packaged precleaned spinach should be washed to freshen it. Remove any tough stems.

TO COOK: In nine cases out of ten spinach is spoiled by using too much water, which not only washes away its mineral salts but deprives it of its fine flavor. Spinach should be cooked quickly in its own juices, which will develop in cooking, and in the moisture adhering to its leaves after washing.

Pack tightly in a stainless-steel saucepan. Cover and set over high heat. After 2 minutes, lift the cover and turn the spinach over from top to bottom. The bottom is then almost cooked. Cover again and cook for another 2 or 3 minutes. Put it into a colander and press out the water. The water will be dark green; reserve this for soup or gravy. Chop the spinach as fine or as coarse as you wish; use a sharp knife and a fork and chop directly in the colander. The spinach is then ready to be used in any recipe.

A good quick way is to cream it. When 1 pound fresh spinach has been drained and chopped, return it to the saucepan. Sprinkle the top with 1 tablespoon flour. Add a piece of butter, 2 tablespoons of light cream or milk, salt and pepper to taste and a dash of grated nutmeg. Stir together over medium heat until creamy and well blended, about 1 minute. Serve.

To prepare spinach as a base for a soufflé, cook it by the professional method: blanch for 1 minute, refresh in cold water and drain thoroughly in a sieve.

Spinach is often found in dishes called "Florentine," and apparently was and is a favorite green for Italian cooks. For an example of a dish using spinach in the Italian fashion, see Mushrooms Verona (p. 464).

Spinach and cucumber salad

With slight variations, this recipe belongs to Greek, Turkish and Armenian cuisines. It is especially good served with roast lamb and chutney.

1 pound fresh spinach
2 cucumbers
1 cup slivered celery
½ cup minced fresh parsley
½ cup green olives, chopped
½ cup black olives, chopped
¼ cup pine nuts or almonds
¼ cup salad oil
⅛ cup red-wine or cider vinegar
½ teaspoon salt
¼ teaspoon freshly ground pepper
Pinch of dried oregano or marjoram

Wash the spinach and dry thoroughly. Cut off the stems and chop the leaves into coarse pieces. There should be about 4 cups. Peel and dice the cucumbers; discard seeds if they are large. Place the dice in a large bowl and add the celery, parsley, green and black olives, pine nuts or almonds, and the chopped spinach.

Mix together the salad oil, vinegar, salt, pepper and oregano or marjoram; pour over the vegetable mixture. Toss the salad together until it is well mixed. Makes 4 servings.

Mustard greens, turnip greens, beet greens, kale

All these greens are treated similarly. Wash like any green, but be sure to cut off the coarse stems. Beet stems are red and tend to color the dish, so remove them even if they are tender. Kale has tough ribs from which the leaves should be pulled. Beet greens will cook in 5 minutes. Mustard and turnip greens are much tougher and will need 30 to 40 minutes. Both are enhanced with vinegar, and in the South they are cooked with diced salt pork or served with crumbled bacon. Kale should be cooked about 15 minutes, and is better steamed than blanched. It too is enhanced with bacon or vinegar, but it is a delicious green served plain—provided it has not been overcooked. All can be chopped after cooking, drained well, sauced with butter or sprinkled with chopped hard-cooked eggs and flavored bread crumbs.

Swiss chard

This is one of the most successful plants for the home garden. It will continue to produce all summer and can even be picked late in the fall after the first frosts. It is actually a member of the beet family, and there is a variety with red stems. Individual leaves can be picked so the plants continue to grow. The whole leaves can be cooked, or the green edges can be cooked separately from the white ribs. Treat this like spinach, but the ribs alone can be cooked like asparagus, and they are good with cheese sauce.

EDIBLE THISTLES

Artichokes

The French or globe artichoke is one of the oldest cultivated vegetables in the world. It takes its name from the Arabic word *alkhurshuf*. It is a kind of huge thistle, of which only the fleshy base of each leaf and the heart can be eaten.

TO PREPARE: Dip each vegetable, tips down, into a bowl of cold water. Do it many times, shaking out the water each time, until the artichoke is free of all dust and any foreign particles. Cut off the stems, leaving no more than about an inch of stem remaining; stems are usually tough and stringy. Pull off any dried or discolored leaves on the outside. Cut off the sharp spiny leaf tips with scissors. To avoid discoloration, rub a cut piece of lemon on all cut parts.

TO COOK: Blanch and freshen by the professional method; blanch for 20 to 30 minutes, or until a leaf can be pulled away easily. The age and size of the artichoke can vary the cooking time by 10 to 12 minutes. Drain thoroughly.

TO SERVE: Place each artichoke on a large plate, or provide an extra plate for the discarded leaves. Whole artichokes are appropriate only for informal meals, because they are finger food. Each leaf is pulled off, dipped into the sauce if you are serving one, then the fleshy portion at the base is eaten by pulling it through the teeth. When you reach the choke, a center of prickly little leaves, this must be removed with a spoon or small knife. Underneath the choke is the *heart* or *bottom,* which is the most delicious part. This is cut into pieces and dipped into the sauce. The usual sauces are melted butter, butter and fresh lemon juice heated together, hollandaise or mayonnaise. And many people enjoy artichokes served without sauce. The artichokes can be served hot, cold or at room temperature.

Artichokes with fennel

4 artichokes
½ lemon
2 garlic cloves, peeled and halved
3 peppercorns, crushed
2 teaspoons salt
2 teaspoons fennel seeds

Wash the artichokes and trim. Rub all portions with the lemon half. Have ready a stainless-steel or heat-proof glass pot filled with enough water to cover the artichokes. Drop them into the pot, squeeze any remaining lemon juice over them and drop the lemon rind into the pot also. Add halved garlic cloves, peppercorns crushed in a mortar, salt and fennel seeds bruised in the mortar. The artichokes will not be submerged at the start, but will sink as they cook. Cover the pot and cook for 20 minutes. Then pull off a leaf and taste it. Cook longer if they are not done.

Artichokes cooked with this seasoning are delicious plain. The fennel seeds will be wedged in the leaves and will add a crunchy, spicy taste. Makes 4 servings.

Artichoke hearts

This is the fleshy base with the tender little center leaves around it and the choke removed. It is possible, but tedious, to trim large artichokes to the size of little hearts; but it is much easier to buy them canned or frozen. These hearts are prepared from a smaller kind of artichoke.

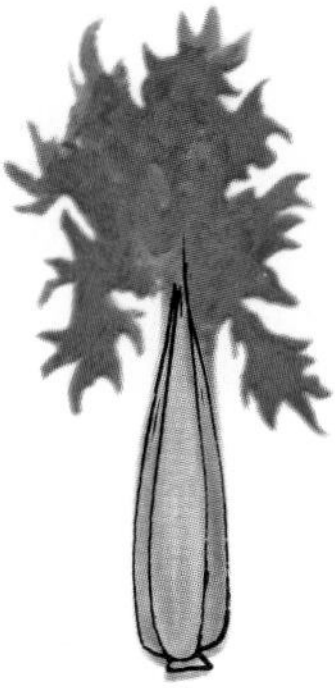

CRUNCHY STALKS

Celery

Celery is as well known and widely used as carrots. It has a watery, crunchy texture, a strong aromatic odor and a freshness that gives it an attractive appetizing flavor. It is a good food for dieters because it is very low in caloric value. Two varieties are familiar in the United States: a blanched celery with white ribs and Pascal, a taller green plant.

TO PREPARE: Purchase heads of celery with as many fresh leaves on them as possible. Rinse the whole head, leafy end up, under running water. Shake out as much water as possible. Cut off the leaves with as much of the ribs as you wish. Place the leaves in a plastic bag and keep them to chop and add to salads, soups, sauces, stews, meat loaves, poultry and fish. The leaves can also be dried, to be used for flavoring when fresh celery is not available.

Trim the root end and then rub with a cut lemon or a little vinegar to prevent discoloration. The ribs can be left together on the root; or separated, then washed or brushed under running water. When separated, keep them in a plastic bag in the vegetable crisper of your refrigerator.

TO COOK: Although celery is mostly eaten as a raw vegetable, it can be cooked whole, halved, diced, sliced or chopped. The most successful methods to follow when cooking are blanching, stir-frying, pan-cooking, steaming and steam-baking. Whatever the method, however, remember that celery, being mostly water, should be cooked in a very small amount of water or consommé, usually ¼ cup to each 2 cups of vegetable. The cooking time varies from 7 to 10 minutes.

Celery amandine in casserole

This is a delicious casserole, nice served with cold meat or poultry and curry-flavored rice.

1 head of celery
2 eggs, well beaten
1 cup chicken stock
1 cup light cream
½ cup slivered blanched almonds
1 tablespoon butter
Salt and pepper
½ cup buttered crumbs

Clean the head of the celery by first cutting off the leafy part, then trim the root end. Do not separate the ribs; wash under running water, opening the ribs to let the water run through. Shake out as much of the water as possible. Then, holding the head of celery together with one hand, start cutting from the top into thin slices, making crescent-shaped pieces. Blanch for 3 minutes; freshen. Drain thoroughly.

Beat together the eggs, stock and cream. Brown the slivered almonds in the butter over medium heat. Add these to the egg mixture. Add salt and pepper to taste. Place the drained celery in a buttered casserole, 3- to 4-cup size, and pour the almond mixture on top. Sprinkle with the buttered crumbs. Bake at 350° F. for 30 minutes. Makes 4 servings.

SEASONAL TREASURES

Today produce of all kinds is shipped from all over the United States and other parts of the world, so most vegetables can be found in markets all year long. Of course, they will be more plentiful and cheaper during the natural season for that crop. However, there is nothing that can replace the flavor of a fresh vegetable in its own proper season. Some of these even when available at other times of the year—frozen asparagus or hot-house tomatoes, for instance—are not like the seasonal vegetables in their appearance or taste or texture.

Asparagus

A plant of the lily of the valley family, asparagus comes with the first breath of spring, and is considered a luxury. In France, asparagus is often served as an hors d'oeuvre. When cooked, asparagus is drained and presented on a folded white napkin, with an individual bowl of hollandaise sauce into which it is dipped. On other occasions, asparagus is usually served as a separate course, to be savored without distraction, either hot on toast, with butter sauce or at room temperature with vinaigrette sauce.

TO PREPARE: Snap off the tough lower portion of the stalk by holding the vegetable with both hands and bending gently to find the place where the tough portion ends. Even if you wish them all to be the same length for the sake of appearance, snap them first, then place the tips evenly together and cut the ends level with each other.

Do not discard the tough ends. Wash them and simmer in a small amount of water, covered, for 1 hour. Then strain the liquid and use it for sauces and soups.

Thoroughly rinse the trimmed asparagus under running cold water; sand often accumulates in the small scales. Do not let asparagus soak in water, however. When cleaned ahead of time, wrap the washed stalks in absorbent paper or cloth and refrigerate in the vegetable crisper until ready to use.

TO COOK: Asparagus can be tied together in convenient bunches, or the stalks can be cooked loose. They can be cooked standing upright in a deep pan with a few inches of water in the bottom. This is a difficult way to cook them, and most of the time part of the stem becomes discolored.

The easiest way is pan-cooking. They will cook in 8 to 12 minutes, depending on their size and how tender you wish them to be.

When they are cut into 1- or 2-inch lengths, cook them by the stir-fry method. It takes scarcely longer than 5 minutes. It is a good idea to cut them this way when 1 pound of asparagus must serve four as a vegetable dish.

When they are to be served cold or as part of a salad, cook by the professional method of blanching and refreshing.

TO SERVE: Melted butter and lemon juice or a hollandaise or maltaise sauce are especially good for hot asparagus. Asparagus is also nice topped with small croutons fried in butter and mixed with a grated hard-cooked egg, a kind of polonaise sauce.

To serve as an entrée or a luncheon dish, cook, then cool to room temperature. Pour French dressing (vinaigrette sauce) on top and sprinkle with grated hard-cooked eggs, capers and a dash of grated nutmeg.

Corn

The summer sweet corn on the cob must be garden fresh to be tender and moist; once picked, corn quickly loses its sweetness and moisture. Corn is at its very best when you can go into your garden, gather it fresh and cook and eat it immediately.

TO PREPARE: Remove husks and all shreds of silk; or remove outside leaves of the husks, separate the remaining leaves from the top, remove all shreds of silk and then close the leaves again.

TO COOK: Even if you cook corn the moment it is picked, as it should be cooked, you can very easily ruin it by overcooking. Use a large saucepan. Put enough water to cover the bottom, about 1 inch, in a pot large enough to hold all the corn. Add 1 cup of milk and 1 tablespoon sugar. Above all, *no salt*. When the water is boiling, place the completely or partially cleaned corn in the pot. Cover tightly and steam for 8 to 10 minutes over medium heat. 🔑 Cooking corn with some of the husk left on increases the flavor.

Leftover corn on the cob does not reheat well, but you can cut it from the cobs and reheat the kernels with a little milk and a piece of butter.

The corn kernels can be cut from the cob before cooking. Do this with a sharp knife. Sauté the kernels in a small amount of butter for a few minutes and serve. You can also heat the kernels for 20 minutes in the top part of a double boiler with a few spoonfuls of milk or cream. Either method is good when you wish to serve fresh kernels instead of corn on the cob.

Squaw corn

This recipe comes from a Canadian Indian trapper. It is a great dish for hungry people, fine for brunch.

- 1 pound sausages or bacon
- 1 large onion, chopped
- 6 eggs
- 12 ears of corn and ½ cup light cream *or* 1 can (about 1 pound) cream-style corn

Place the sausages or bacon in a cold frying pan without any fat. Brown over medium-low heat until done to your taste, but do not overcook the sausages. Remove some of the fat as it accumulates. When the sausages or bacon is cooked, set aside in a warm place. Keep about ⅓ cup of the fat, or less, in the pan and pour off the rest. Add the onion and fry until golden brown, stirring often.

Lightly beat the eggs. If you use fresh corn cut from the cobs, cook in the cream for 8 minutes, then add to the eggs. If you are using canned corn, simply add it to the eggs without cooking.

Add the corn and eggs to the fried onion. Cut each sausage into 4 pieces, or crumble the bacon, and add to the eggs and corn. Then scramble the whole mixture together and season. Makes about 6 servings.

Roast corn

This is the best corn you have ever tasted, a perfect accompaniment to any barbecue.

To cook on a covered barbecue, loosen husks of freshly gathered corn only enough to remove the silks. Dip the ears into a deep pail of water; shake well. Rewrap husks around the ears. Plunge into the water again and let them stand a few minutes until the husks are thoroughly soaked. Place them on the grill of a covered barbecue. Cook by direct heat, covered, for 45 minutes to 1 hour, depending on size of corn.

To make buttered roasted corn on an open barbecue, remove husks and silks. Cream ¼ cup butter with ½ teaspoon sugar and ¼ teaspoon each of salt and paprika. Spread on the ears. This is enough butter for 6 to 10 ears. Wrap each ear loosely in heavy-duty aluminum foil, sealing carefully. Place 3 inches from glowing coals. Roast for 20 to 25 minutes, turning frequently. Serve in the foil wrappings.

Cucumbers

TO PREPARE: Any recipe used to cook squash, gourds and zucchini can be used for cucumbers. They can be salted, drained and cooked; or simply cut into thick slices, blanched for 5 minutes, and freshened; or stir-fried, which is the best way.

Cucumbers can also be used uncooked for flavor and texture in the same way as celery.

They are a summer treat when sliced and fried in butter, especially when served with steak.

Spanish cucumbers

3 medium-size cucumbers
3 tablespoons olive oil
1 large onion, chopped
3 tomatoes, diced,
or 1 tablespoon tomato paste
½ cup chopped olives
2 tablespoons minced fresh dill
or 1 teaspoon dill seeds
¼ cup chicken stock
Garlic powder
Salt and pepper

Pare and quarter the cucumbers. Remove the seeds and cut each quarter into 3 or 4 sticks.

Heat the oil in a frying pan and add the onion; sauté until light brown. Add the tomatoes or tomato paste, the olives, dill, stock and cucumbers. Stir gently until the mixture boils. Add garlic powder and salt and pepper to taste. Boil gently, uncovered, for about 10 minutes, or until the mixture forms a sauce around the cucumbers.

Note: The same recipe can be used for zucchini.

Cucumber and yoghurt salad

Yoghurt and cucumber have a natural affinity. When cucumbers are to be served with fish, Greek cooks use sour cream instead of yoghurt. Both are good.

4 medium-size, slender cucumbers
1 teaspoon salt
1 cup yoghurt
1½ teaspoons cider vinegar
1 garlic clove, crushed
¼ teaspoon dill seeds
2 tablespoons minced fresh mint

Peel the cucumbers. Cut lengthwise into quarters and slice very thin. Sprinkle with the salt, toss together and set aside.

Blend together the yoghurt, vinegar, garlic and dill seeds. Stir into the drained cucumbers when ready to serve. Adjust seasoning to taste. To serve, place in a glass salad bowl and top with the minced mint. Makes about 6 servings.

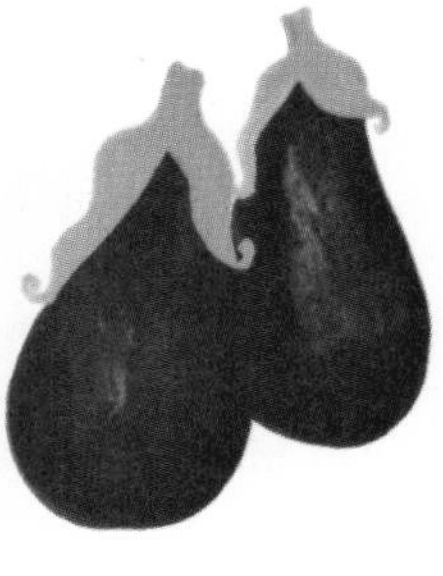

Eggplant

Eggplant belongs to the potato family. It is a colorful, beautiful vegetable. Eggplant varies from the size and length of cucumbers to the size of pineapples. There are also small eggplants no larger than pears. Besides a purple-skinned variety, there is an equally good white-skinned kind. Choose an eggplant that is heavy for its size, with fresh, shining skin. Eggplant is available all year, but you will discover that it is at its best during the late summer and early fall.

TO PREPARE: Eggplant can be cooked whole, peeled and sliced or cubed before cooking. Remove the leaves and stem end. The old tradition required that eggplant slices be salted and allowed to macerate in the salt for some time before cooking. If you have freshly picked eggplant, this is not necessary. If the vegetable is older and has developed seeds, salting may help eliminate some bitterness.

TO COOK: To bake, wash and dry the eggplant. Do not peel. Cut lengthwise into halves. Cut the flesh side with crisscross gashes about 1 inch deep over the entire surface, then pour melted butter over the top. Set the pieces on a pan and bake in a 350° F. oven for 30 minutes.

Another method of baking is to place the whole eggplant on a baking sheet and bake in a 400° F. oven for 1 hour, or until the eggplant has a collapsed appearance. Then remove the skin. Mash the flesh with butter, lots of chopped fresh parsley and the juice of a lemon. Add salt and pepper to taste.

To broil eggplant, wash but do not peel. Cut into ½-inch-thick round slices. Spread with soft butter on both sides. Broil 4 inches from the source of heat for 5 minutes on each side. It is only necessary to turn the slices once.

Slices of eggplant can also be baked. Place unpeeled slices on a generously buttered baking sheet. Spread soft butter on top of the slices and sprinkle with salt and pepper to taste. Bake in a preheated 400° F. oven for 15 to 20 minutes. Do not turn.

For the quickest cooking method, cut the vegetable into large chunks and steam them over salted water. The eggplant will be cooked in 5 minutes, and will be delicious.

Ratatouille niçoise

This vegetable mixture comes from the French Riviera. It is delicious as an accompaniment to a roast. This dish also makes a fine meal with hot crusty bread and a bottle of red wine. *Ratatouille* will keep 8 to 15 days, if covered and refrigerated. It can be served hot, cold or at room temperature.

4 medium-size tomatoes, peeled and sliced
3 zucchini, unpeeled and sliced
1 medium-size eggplant, peeled and diced
2 green peppers, trimmed and sliced
2 onions, sliced
2 garlic cloves, chopped fine
½ teaspoon sugar
¾ cup olive oil
Salt and pepper
¼ teaspoon dried thyme
Juice of 1 lemon

First prepare all the vegetables and the garlic. Place them separately on a large platter. Sprinkle the sugar on the tomatoes.

Heat ½ cup of the oil in a heavy metal saucepan over high heat. Then proceed in the following order: add the onions and brown lightly; add the eggplant and cook, stirring, for about 3 minutes, or until slightly softened; add the tomatoes and crush into the mixture with a wooden spoon, stirring and blending for another 3 minutes; add the zucchini, the garlic and the green peppers; stir until well mixed.

Cook over high heat for a few minutes, stirring frequently. Season with salt and pepper to taste. Add the thyme. Then cook, uncovered, over low heat for about 1 hour, stirring occasionally. By that time the mixture should have the texture of a thick tomato sauce. Pour into a covered dish and refrigerate for 10 to 12 hours.

Before serving, stir in the remaining ¼ cup oil and the lemon juice. Makes 6 to 8 servings.

Okra

Okra is an essential ingredient in the stews and gumbos of the Gulf States. This vegetable will grow in the North too, and it is an attractive plant with yellow and red blossoms like mallows. The flowers are rapidly followed by the little pods. Buy pods that are about 3 inches long. When larger than this, the outside becomes stringy and the seeds become hard. If you grow your own, pick them every two days or they will grow too large before you notice it.

TO PREPARE: Scrub the pods. Leave whole, including the little stem and cap. Blanch for about 5 minutes, drain, then refresh. Cut off the stem and cap. Do not cut into the pods until they are blanched because the juices will escape.

TO COOK: Add the whole pods, or sliced pods, to stews or gumbos toward the end of the cooking time. To cook separately, sauté in butter with a squeeze of lemon juice. Or cook with onion, green pepper and tomato for a Creole-style dish. Or cook in a little chicken or beef stock and thicken with *beurre manié* or toasted plain or cheese croutons. Or dip into batter and pan-fry or deep-fry.

Peppers

The pepper family is a big one that includes many varieties of large and small pods of varying pepperishness and different shapes and colors. The strong peppers—cayenne, tabasco and chili—are used in hot sauces and in dishes that should have bite. They are very different from the sweet, gentle pimiento, the kind used to stuff olives. Peppers, a good source of vitamin C, also contain some vitamin A and many minerals.

The only pepper used often as a vegetable by itself is the big, bell-shaped, sweet green pepper. It makes a handsome container for other foods and so is stuffed often. As a salad vegetable it is highly esteemed, and rings of green pepper make a nice crispy garnish by themselves. Fried green peppers are delicious as an accompaniment to meat.

TO PREPARE: Slice off the stem ends of peppers; remove the seeds and white ribs. Rinse to eliminate any remaining seeds. The trimmed vegetables can be left whole, or cut into any shape you wish.

TO COOK: The professional method is the best for a plain cooked pepper: blanch 20 minutes. Freshen.

Stuffed green peppers

This is a basic recipe. It makes a good luncheon dish. If you have no cooked meat, use minced raw meat. Brown the raw meat in butter before adding it to the other ingredients.

4 nicely shaped, squatty green peppers
Salt and pepper
Savory or thyme or curry powder
1 cup cooked rice
1 teaspoon minced onion
1 cup ground cooked lamb, ham, beef or other meat
Tomato sauce or mushroom soup or gravy to moisten
Grated cheese

Cut off a slice from the top of each pepper. Remove ribs and seeds. Place the peppers in a saucepan with ½ inch of boiling water. Cover tightly and steam for 5 minutes. Dust inside with salt and pepper and a little ground savory or thyme or curry powder. Combine rice, onion and meat with enough sauce, soup or gravy to moisten the mixture. Use this to fill the peppers. Top with cheese. Place in a pan with ½ inch of water on the bottom. Bake at 350° F. for 40 minutes. Serve with more of the sauce or gravy used to moisten the filling. Makes 4 servings.

Green-pepper appetizer

This delicious salad is nice in the summer, served cold on a thick bed of sliced tomatoes. Use also as a dip with fingers of toasted French bread. Serve very cold with meat curry.

3 red or green peppers
Salt
3 tablespoons olive oil
½ cup yoghurt
½ teaspoon curry powder
2 tablespoons minced celery leaves

Roast the peppers over direct heat until the skins are blackened all over. Do this quickly because the peppers themselves should not be really cooked. Turn them to roast evenly all over. Then wash off the skins under running cold water. Cut off the tops and remove ribs and seeds. Slice peppers into shreds; sprinkle with salt; pour oil over them. Marinate for 1 hour.

Put the peppers through a food chopper, or purée in a blender. Stir the purée into the yoghurt along with the curry powder and finely minced celery leaves. Makes about 1½ cups of salad or dip.

Pimientos

The pimiento is a bright red thick-walled pepper. It is sold packed in cans or jars. The outer skin has been removed by roasting, in the way described for the Green-Pepper Appetizer. Pimientos have good nutritional value, like other peppers, and have only 7 calories. This is a good vegetable to become familiar with because it can be used in place of fresh red peppers, which are seasonal, and in place of tomatoes when you want a red garnish for winter foods. They come whole, sliced and sometimes chopped.

An open jar of pimientos will keep refrigerated, with a bit of oil on top, for seven to ten days. Pimientos, frozen in their own juice, will keep for six to eight months. They thaw out very fast when needed, or can be added to a hot liquid without being thawed.

Squash

This plant family includes various summer squash, yellow crooknecks and straightnecks and zucchini. Small finger-length specimens start coming into market early in the summer; later, larger squash are available. In the late summer, white pattypans, or cymlings, appear, plus other long green squashes. In the Southwest the chayote, a pear-shaped vegetable similar to the squash, is a great favorite. It is not a true squash, but it can be prepared in the same way. Winter squash include the small green-skinned acorns, yellow butternuts, large green Hubbards, orange turbans and the familiar pumpkins. Winter squash keep very well in a cool dry place and provide a good source of vitamins A and C at a time when other fresh vegetables are poor in quality. All squash have a net of seeds in the center, forming a hollow in the ripe specimens; in the butternut the net is very small, in the pumpkin it is very large.

TO PREPARE: If the squash is very young and tender, scrub but do not peel. Cut off blossom and stem ends. For older specimens, peel with a swivel peeler, taking off the thinnest possible layer of skin. For the tougher winter squash, cut into pieces small enough to handle, then pare with a sharp knife. Discard the seeds of any that have developed mature seeds. If you like, these can be dried and salted like pumpkin seeds, or they make good snacks for birds.

TO COOK: Yellow summer squash and zucchini can be blanched whole or in pieces or can be steamed, or pan-cooked or stir-fried, sliced or diced. Pattypans can be steamed, but their shape suggests the more usual cooking, which is to stuff them and bake them.

Acorn squashes and chayotes can be baked after being halved. To keep them tender and speed the cooking process, put them cut side down in a pan with about ½ inch of water. Bake for 15 minutes; the water will be nearly cooked away. Then turn them over, season the cavity, add butter or other flavoring and bake until done.

The larger squash need to be cut into pieces for cooking. They can be steamed, but baking is a very good method. For either, the skin can be left on, and it will be easy to remove after cooking; for baked pieces, the skin can be left on for serving.

Hubbards, pumpkins and butternuts make delicious purée; blanch, steam or bake the pieces, then mash or put through a food mill. Season simply, or add herbs or spices. Pumpkin purée is the first stage for pumpkin pie, an American harvest specialty, but equally good pies can be made with any of the winter squash.

All smaller squash can be stuffed. Finger-length strips can be dipped into egg and crumbs or into batter and deep-fried. Summer squash can be grated and creamed or used raw in salads.

Edith-for-lunch squash

Make this in August or September when all the vegetables are plentiful.

- 3 pounds yellow summer squash
- 3 large yellow onions
- 3 large green peppers
- 4 large tomatoes, fully ripe or still green
- ½ cup peanut or corn oil
- Salt and pepper
- ½ cup chopped parsley
- 1 cup soft white bread crumbs

Peel the squash if the skin is tough. Cut into ½-inch-thick slices. Peel and slice the onions. Trim the peppers, remove ribs and seeds and cut into rings. Wash the tomatoes. You can peel them if you wish, but they tend to fall apart if you do. Cut into thick slices. Heat a little of the oil and start to sauté the vegetables. Do some of each kind and transfer them to a 2-quart casserole as they are browned. Add more of the oil as you need it. Arrange the vegetables in layers, and sprinkle each layer with salt, pepper and parsley. When all are sautéed and layered, sprinkle the bread crumbs on top. Bake the casserole in a 400° F. oven for about 45 minutes, or in a 350° F. oven for 1 hour, or in an even cooler oven for longer. This casserole is very adaptable to your other oven needs. If you like, dot the top with butter or sprinkle with grated Swiss cheese. Makes about 8 servings.

Tomatoes

Since tomatoes belong to the same family as nightshade, it is only in recent years that we have made them one of our most popular vegetables. Cooking with tomatoes, or just eating a fully ripe tomato, is something very special when this vegetable is in its peak season. At that time, tomatoes are so plentiful we are almost staggered by their abundance, and we come across them everywhere. In past years, that meant endless canning, gallons of hot water, infinite processing and an all-pervading, overpowering smell of steaming tomatoes throughout the house. Today we can buy commercially canned tomatoes at a reasonable price, so process them only if you do something special with them, such as making a tomato sauce for pasta or a favorite preserve like tomato marmalade.

TO PREPARE: To peel tomatoes, place them in a bowl and pour boiling water over them. Let stand for 2 minutes, then drain off the water and place the tomatoes in a bowl of cold water. The skin then comes off easily. Start peeling from the blossom end.

To peel only 1 or 2 tomatoes, spear on the tip of a fork and hold over direct heat until the skin blisters here and there. Then peel.

To remove some of the acidity from tomatoes, press out the seeds by pressing the tomato gently in your hand, holding the cut side down. 🔑 When cooking tomatoes, always add 1 teaspoon sugar for each 4 tomatoes. It does not make them sweet, but brings out their flavor and color. 🔑 Always keep ripe tomatoes refrigerated, but bring to room temperature when serving them raw. They have more flavor warm than cold.

Aunt Amelia's tomato soup

24 medium-size sweet red tomatoes
1 tablespoon sugar
2 tablespoons butter
1 onion, quartered
2 bay leaves
2 celery ribs with leaves
1 teaspoon minced fresh basil or crumbled dried basil
1 teaspoon salt
1/4 teaspoon freshly ground pepper
3 tablespoons minced parsley
Juice of 1/2 lemon
1/2 cup whipped cream

Cut the unpeeled tomatoes into quarters. Place in a heavy metal saucepan with the sugar, butter, onion, bay leaves, celery and basil. Cover and simmer over *low* heat for 30 minutes. Do not add water at any time. Pass through a food mill or a sieve. Put back in the saucepan and add the salt, pepper, parsley and lemon juice. Simmer for a few minutes. Taste for seasoning. Serve hot in cups, topped with a spoonful of whipped cream, slightly salted. Makes 8 or more servings.

Parmesan broiled tomatoes

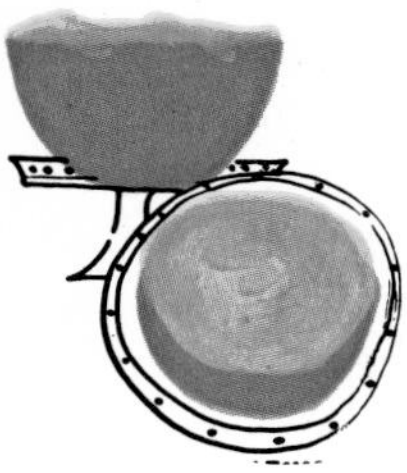

Serve this as an accompaniment to steak, hamburger or veal chops.

6 firm, ripe tomatoes
Salt and pepper
Sugar
2 tablespoons grated Parmesan cheese
2 tablespoons butter

Halve tomatoes crosswise and sprinkle with salt and pepper and a generous pinch of sugar. Top each with about ½ teaspoon Parmesan cheese and dot with ½ teaspoon butter. Broil about 6 inches from the source of heat for 4 to 5 minutes. Makes 6 servings.

Variation: Cut tomatoes into 4 thick slices each. Sprinkle each slice with a little sugar and brush the tops with melted butter. Season with salt and a sprinkle of dried or ground basil. Put the slices under the broiler 4 inches from the source of heat and broil for 3 minutes. You can use this version with either lamb or pork.

Tomato and cucumber salad

This is a good salad to serve with an outdoor meal, and it takes only a few minutes to prepare.

4 tomatoes, sliced
¼ cup salad oil
¼ cup red-wine or cider vinegar
1 tablespoon chopped parsley
Fresh dill, minced, or dried dill
3 green onions, finely chopped
1 small head of lettuce
2 cucumbers, peeled and sliced
Salt and pepper

Place the tomatoes in a bowl with the oil, vinegar, parsley, dill and green onions. Refrigerate for 1 to 2 hours. When ready to serve, shred the lettuce just as you would a cabbage. Add the lettuce and cucumbers to the tomatoes. Season with salt and pepper to taste. Toss lightly until well blended and serve. Makes 4 to 6 servings.

Mustard-pickled green tomatoes

- 2 quarts green tomatoes
- 1 quart white onions (silverskins)
- 1 large head of green cabbage
- 1 large stalk of celery, green or white
- 6 sweet red peppers
- 1 tablespoon celery seeds
- 1 cup salt
- 4 quarts water
- 1 cup flour
- 4 tablespoons dry mustard
- 2 cups sugar
- 2 teaspoons ground turmeric
- 2 quarts vinegar

Chop the tomatoes, onions, cabbage, celery and peppers into ½-inch pieces, or larger if you prefer. Mix all together and stir in the celery seeds. Dissolve the salt in the water, and pour the solution over the chopped vegetables in an enamelware kettle. Use more than one pot if necessary, but do not use aluminum pots. Let the vegetables rest in the pickling solution overnight.

The next day, bring the vegetables to a boil, then drain them in a large colander. Mix the flour, mustard, sugar and turmeric. Put the vinegar in the pickling kettle and bring it to a boil. Stir in the flour and mustard mixture and keep stirring until the mixture thickens. Add the drained vegetables and boil all together for 5 minutes. Cool, then bottle in sterilized jars. Makes enough to fill ten 1-cup jars.

OTHER "VEGETABLES"

There are some foods we treat as vegetables although they are not true vegetables. Among these are mushrooms (fungi) and water chestnuts (fruit of a water plant).

Mushrooms

The mushroom is a flavorful food with great versatility. A mushroom has no apparent leaves, blossoms or fruits. Indeed, it is not a true plant but a fungus. The mushroom itself is the fruit of the fungus and contains the spores or seeds. Mushrooms come in all shapes and colors—some delicious, some deadly. Today, cultivated nonpoisonous mushrooms are to be found in most supermarkets. If you would like a bit of woodsy flavor with your cultivated fresh mushrooms, get an ounce or two of dried wild mushrooms and add one or two, crushed, to the dish. These dried mushrooms come from all over the world; they too are safe to eat. Dried mushrooms retain the unmistakable scent of their original habitat, a smell of the woods, the mountains or the fields.

Mushrooms are good for dieters because they are very low in calories.

Use mushrooms as soon as possible after buying them. Do not leave them exposed to sun or air. Refrigerate them, tightly closed in their container, as soon as you bring them home.

TO PREPARE: Cultivated fresh mushrooms need not be peeled. Cut off ¼ inch of the stem if it has turned brown. If it is white and clean, it does not have to be removed. Peeling the skin from the cap causes some loss of the finest flavor of the mushroom.

Do not peel mushrooms that are to be broiled or pan-cooked, those that are to be cooked after slicing or those that are to be stuffed. Removing the skin weakens the structure of the mushroom. However, mushrooms can be peeled when they are to be used raw in a salad. But even then, if they are white and fresh and are to be marinated first, it is not necessary to peel them.

Do not throw away the mushroom stems or peelings. The stems can be used chopped in sauces, stuffings and soups. The peelings can be used to flavor sauces or soups that are strained before serving.

To wash the mushrooms, place them in a colander and hold under warm—not hot—running water, tossing them about for 3 or 4 seconds. Then rinse again under cold running water for about 2 seconds. Turn mushrooms onto absorbent paper and gently dry them. Too much washing will cause the mushrooms to turn dark brown when cooking, just as energetic handling will cause quick bruising. They are a delicate food and should be handled gently. Under no condition should they stand for any time after they are washed; wash them just before cooking, unless they are to be sau-

JOKER

JOKER

téed. For sautéing, wash them ahead and let them dry thoroughly.

Recently some delicious brown mushrooms have appeared in our markets. Do not peel them, but scrub carefully with a sponge or cloth. They are especially good stuffed.

Sautéed mushrooms

A perfect sautéed mushroom is delicious in flavor and texture. This makes a good luncheon dish.

½ pound mushrooms
3 tablespoons butter
Salt
Freshly ground pepper
2 slices of buttered toast
Parsley or chives, minced

Cut the cleaned mushrooms into thin slices. Melt the butter in a heavy metal pan until it has a nutty brown color. Add the mushrooms and cook over high heat, stirring constantly, for 2 or 3 minutes. Remove from the heat, add salt and pepper to taste and place on the toast. Sprinkle with parsley or chives. A sprinkling of tarragon or basil, dried or fresh, can be used instead of the parsley or chives. Makes 2 servings.

Creamed mushrooms

This is another classic way to cook and serve mushrooms. A cup or two of diced cooked chicken, turkey, ham, salmon, lobster or shrimp can be added to the sauce, and this dish can be served with rice or noodles for a whole meal.

1 pound mushrooms
4 tablespoons butter
1 garlic clove, minced
Salt and pepper
½ cup flour
1 cup light cream
1 cup commercial sour cream
¼ teaspoon dried tarragon
¼ cup sherry (optional)
Parsley

Wash the mushrooms and remove the stems from the caps. Leave the caps whole but mince the stems. Melt 3 tablespoons of the butter. Add the garlic. Brown the caps with the garlic over high heat, stirring constantly. Add the minced stems. Brown quickly and remove from the heat. Add salt and pepper to taste.

Melt the remaining 1 tablespoon of butter in a saucepan. Add the flour and cream. Blend together thoroughly and cook over low heat, stirring, until the sauce is creamy. Add the sour cream and the tarragon. Heat but do not boil.

Finally add the browned mushrooms and the sherry. Simmer for a few minutes, but do not boil. Taste for seasoning. Serve with parsley sprigs, or sprinkle with minced parsley. Makes 4 servings.

Marinated mushrooms

½ pound mushrooms
4 tablespoons olive oil
2 tablespoons cider vinegar or wine
½ teaspoon salt
⅛ teaspoon pepper
2 green onions, minced

Chop the stems and caps of the mushrooms very fine. Add the remaining ingredients. Mix together and let stand for 1 hour before using.

Here are some of the many ways these can be used:

- Sprinkle them on salad greens instead of dressing; taste for seasoning; toss and serve.
- Place on unbuttered rounds of French bread or toast; serve as appetizers.
- Use as dressing for cold chicken, lobster or shrimp.
- Add to the mixture 2 chopped hard-cooked eggs, 1 tablespoon capers, 1 minced pimiento; serve as a salad on lettuce leaves, or garnish with watercress.
- Use as a filling for small sandwiches for afternoon tea.

Mushrooms Verona

Serve as a vegetarian main dish or as an accompaniment for veal or lamb chops.

2 pounds fresh spinach
2 tablespoons butter
2 medium-size onions, minced
1 pound mushrooms, sliced thin
2 tablespoons flour
¾ cup milk or chicken stock
⅛ teaspoon ground basil
Pinch of grated nutmeg
Salt and pepper
1 cup small bread cubes
1 tablespoon butter, melted

Place the washed spinach in a saucepan without any water. Cover and cook over medium-high heat for 3 to 4 minutes. Drain in a sieve, pressing out as much water as possible. Place in a buttered shallow casserole.

Melt the 2 tablespoons butter in a frying pan. Add the onions and mushrooms and cook over high heat, stirring constantly, for 3 to 4 minutes. Add the flour. Stir until well mixed, then add the milk or stock and cook, stirring, until smooth and creamy. Add the basil, nutmeg, and salt and pepper to taste. Pour over the spinach. Mix together the bread cubes and the melted butter and arrange them over the casserole. Bake in a 350° F. oven for 20 to 25 minutes. Serve hot. Makes 4 servings as a main dish.

Water chestnuts

You will find peeled whole water chestnuts at Oriental grocers, or canned at your supermarket. Fresh water chestnuts have a tough brown skin that should be peeled off before using. To store, cover them—and also cover canned ones that have been opened—with water, and refrigerate. Use fresh and canned water chestnuts interchangeably in recipes because neither requires cooking.

Try water chestnuts first in Chinese or Japanese preparations. Chop them along with pork, chicken or seafood, and with mushrooms and green onions, to make minced fillings for *won tons* and egg rolls. Drop water chestnuts into soups and broths; slice or sliver them into meat, poultry and seafood specialties; add them to crisp-cooked vegetables.

Rumaki

Make this famous hors d'oeuvre in your hibachi, barbecue or oven broiler.

- ½ pound chicken livers
- ¼ cup soy sauce
- 1 garlic clove, minced
- 1 can (5 ounces) water chestnuts, drained
- 15 slices of bacon

Cut each chicken liver into 3 pieces. Marinate the pieces in the soy sauce and garlic at room temperature for 3 hours, or in the refrigerator overnight.

Cut each water chestnut into 3 pieces. Halve the bacon slices. Wrap a piece of water chestnut and a piece of chicken liver with half a slice of bacon. Secure with a toothpick. Place on a wire rack set over a shallow pan and bake in a hot oven, 425° F., or on a grill over charcoal. Cook, turning occasionally, until the bacon is crisp, about 25 minutes. Makes about 30.

CEREAL GRAINS

These ancient foods do not play as large a role in our diet as they did for early man, but they are still good sources of essential minerals and vitamins. Since cereal grains are relatively bland, they are excellent accompaniments to other more flavorful or spicy foods. Because their starches absorb liquids even after cooking, they are good to serve with stews and sauced foods. Aside from their use as breakfast cereal, they can be used in stews and salads, as accompaniments with main dishes, for breakfast or supper dishes and for desserts.

Rice

The neutral flavor of rice makes it possible to combine it with almost every type of food. Rice can be served with a main course, as a salad and as a dessert, and it is also useful as a hot or cold cereal. Brown rice, white rice and converted rice can all be cooked by the same general method but for different lengths of time.

At the turn of the century we were told to wash rice in many waters before cooking it in quarts of water. Today this is unnecessary since packaged rice is as clean as any other packaged cereal. Why boil the rice in quarts of water that will be poured into the sink, carrying away the nutrients? To cook your rice, follow the directions given on the package, or use one of the methods below.

We also have by-products of white rice. Instant rice (precooked white rice) cooks very fast. Freeze-dried instant rice cooks still faster. In addition there is a long list of rice convenience foods, such as canned rice pudding, ready-seasoned rice, a mixture of white and wild rice, frozen rice and canned and frozen fried rice. Regular rice is the best buy, since 1 cup of raw rice will yield 3 full cups cooked; but this is not the case with all the new types of processed rice.

Rice is actually a true convenience product since it can be stored on the cupboard shelf for years. In India, older rice is much valued. Cooked rice keeps very well after cooking. Cover it tightly and refrigerate, and it will keep for as long as seven days. To reheat it, put a few tablespoons of water in a saucepan, add the rice, cover and warm over low heat for 5 or 6 minutes, stirring once with a fork. Or put the water and rice in a baking dish, cover it and heat in a 350° F. oven for 10 minutes. Cooked rice can be frozen, but defrosting takes as long as cooking it, so it is not an economical use of your freezer.

With 1 cup of uncooked rice—3 cups cooked—you can usually make four generous servings as an accompaniment to a main dish.

Slow-cooking white rice

Pour 1 cup rice into a 2-quart saucepan. Add 3 cups cold water, 1 teaspoon salt, 1 teaspoon fresh lemon juice and ½ teaspoon salad oil. Cover with a tight-fitting lid. Bring to a brisk boil; this should take 3 to 5 minutes. Then reduce the heat to the lowest possible and cook for 18 to 22 minutes, or until all the water is absorbed. This makes a rice with firm grains. If you are not sure the rice is done, test by chewing a single grain. You can tell that the water is nearly absorbed when a series of little holes or "eyes" appear at the top of the rice. If you like softer rice, use 2 or 3 tablespoons extra water and cook 23 to 27 minutes. In either case, when the rice is done, remove the cover, put a folded kitchen paper towel over the pot and replace the cover. Let the rice steam dry, away from the source of heat. This will give you separate grains.

Slow-cooking brown rice

Follow the same method as for white rice. For 1 cup brown rice use 1 teaspoon salt and 3 cups cold water. Cook the rice for 35 minutes. Let the cooked rice dry for 10 minutes.

Baked rice

This is a useful method to follow when the oven is already in use.

Place 1 cup rice in a baking dish with a cover. Bring to a boil 2 cups water with 1 teaspoon salt. Pour it over the rice and stir; cover the pan. Bake in a 350° F. oven for 25 minutes.

For brown and converted rice, bake for 45 to 50 minutes.

Italian buttered rice

Melt 3 tablespoons butter in a heavy metal saucepan. Add 1 cup rice. Stir constantly over medium heat until the rice is golden in color. Add 2¼ cups hot chicken or beef stock or consommé, or broth made from bouillon cubes. Stir well, taste for salt and pour into a 2-quart casserole. Cover and bake in a 350° F. oven for 35 to 40 minutes. Serve with a bowl of grated Parmesan cheese.

Wild rice

This native American grain grows wild in Minnesota and Wisconsin and on the Canadian side of the border in Ontario and Manitoba. Since it can only be harvested by boat, and the crop is utterly dependent on the vagaries of nature, it is always expensive and in some years very scarce.

To get the most from that costly package, follow this method: wash the grains, lift out of the washing water and put in a large, deep saucepan. Cover with boiling water, cover the pot and leave until the water is cool. Drain off the water and cover with boiling water once again. Let cool; drain. Do this two more times. (If you want to serve it for Thursday, start this on Wednesday.) In the last soaking, add 1½ teaspoons salt for 12 ounces of rice. Drain the cooled rice and store in the refrigerator. The rice will be swollen to four times its original size, and it will be delicious and fluffy.

Before serving, sauté as much as you need in butter and/or oil, or once more pour boiling water over it and this time let it simmer for about 5 minutes. Drain and serve.

The soaked rice can be stored for at least a week and used as you need it. You can make 6 to 10 servings from 12 ounces of rice prepared this way.

Cracked wheat (*Bulgur*)

This grain, made from crushed dried kernels of wheat, is a food staple in the Middle East and has become increasingly popular in the United States. It can be cooked by any of the recipes used for rice.

Bulgur pilaf with mushrooms

- 4 tablespoons olive oil
- 1 garlic clove, peeled
- 1 medium-size onion, chopped
- ½ pound small mushrooms
- 1 cup cracked wheat
- 4 cups chicken stock
- 1 teaspoon salt
- ¼ teaspoon cuminseeds, crushed
- 2 tablespoons chopped fresh parsley

Heat the oil in a heavy pan with a cover. Put a toothpick through the garlic and add it to the oil along with the chopped onion. While the onion wilts over low heat, wipe the mushrooms and remove the stems. Peel the stems and chop them; set the caps aside. When the onions are about half cooked, remove the garlic (you can retrieve it more easily with the toothpick in it). Add the chopped stems and continue to sauté until the onions are beginning to brown. Add the cracked wheat and stir until all grains are covered with oil. Continue to cook until the wheat starts to brown, then add the chicken stock, salt and cuminseeds. Stir well, cover the pan and cook over very low heat for 20 minutes. Then stir in the reserved whole mushroom caps and cook for 10 minutes longer. Add more stock if necessary. Just before serving, stir in the parsley. Makes 6 servings.

This can be baked in a moderate oven if you prefer.

Bulgur salad

- 1 cup cracked wheat
- 1 chicken bouillon cube
- ¼ teaspoon ground sage
- ½ teaspoon salt
- 2 cups boiling water
- ¼ cup chopped fresh mint
- ¼ cup chopped fresh parsley
- 2 tablespoons snipped chives
- 1 lemon
- 3 tablespoons olive oil
- 2 ripe tomatoes
- 12 oil-cured black olives

Put the cracked wheat in a large heatproof bowl. Break up the bouillon cube and sprinkle it, the sage and the salt over the wheat. Pour the boiling water over all and stir until well mixed. Let it stand until the water is all absorbed and the wheat cool, about 30 minutes. Then stir in the mint, parsley and chives. (You can add more parsley and chives if you like.)

Squeeze the lemon. Mix the juice with the oil for a dressing, and stir into the wheat. (You can add more dressing if you like.) Arrange the salad in a serving bowl. Peel the tomatoes and cut each one into 6 wedges. Arrange them around the bowl and put an olive in each piece. Serve the salad on shredded lettuce to accompany cold meat, poultry or fish. Makes about 8 servings.

«13»

Working with Flour

Kinds of flour • Techniques of bread-making • Mixing dough • Kneading • Rising • Shaping and second rising • Baking • Glazing • Yeast and quick breads • Cakes • Cookies • Pastry ingredients • Mixing and rolling piecrusts • Fluting and crimping • Lattice top • How to prevent a soggy bottom crust • How to solve some other pastry-making problems • Rolling and fitting dough • A few favorite pies

The cultivation of grains for food began at least as long ago as the New Stone Age. Barley and emmer wheats grew wild in the Near East, rice in the valleys of Asiatic rivers, maize in the Americas; wheat as we know it probably originated in Persia. The seeds of these plants were collected, mashed with water to a paste, then baked—man's first kind of bread. Primitive ears of grain were meager compared to those we know; the development of today's superior plant is the result of many generations of plant husbandry. Nevertheless, those primitive grains—all members of the huge botanical family of grasses—enabled man to make the transition from nomadic to settled life, because for the first time they supplied a food that could be stored.

In America, a kind of bread was made from acorns and other nuts. Pumpkins, potatoes, legumes and many roots have been used in times of famine, but man's concern to find substitutes for cereal grains indicates how important bread was to him. It was truly the "staff of life" in past centuries.

That familiar expression may sound odd to the modern man who eats only an occasional piece of toast at breakfast and perhaps another slice or two in a sandwich. Today we eat such a varied diet that bread has a relatively minor place. But since grains are such a rich source of nutrients, bread can still be an important element in our diet.

FLOUR

Flour is the essential ingredient for making yeast breads and quick breads as well as cakes and pastries. Flour is made by grinding cereal grains to a fine powder. The term "meal" means that the grain has been less finely ground. Wheat is the preferred grain for flour. It contains the proteins gliadin and glutenin which when combined with liquid form gluten, an elastic part of the dough that lets the dough expand as yeast or other leaven releases gasses. When the dough is baked, the gluten coagulates and gives structure to the finished bread. For home baking we can get many other kinds of flour, including those made from potatoes, chestnuts and soybeans, as well as buckwheat, rye, corn, rice and millet.

All-purpose flour is a blend of hard and soft wheats. It can be used for all general cooking and it makes good bread.

Unbleached flour is similar to all-purpose but it has not been bleached. It is a little more nutritious than bleached flour, since bleaching removes part of the nutrients. You can sometimes find this flour with added wheat germ, which makes it especially healthful. It is somewhat heavier than all-purpose flour.

Pastry flour is not available everywhere, but if you can find it, it does make a good pastry. This is unbleached flour usually made from soft wheat.

Bread flour is usually available only to professional bakers, but it makes excellent bread. This is a mixture of both spring and winter hard wheats.

Cake flour is made from soft wheat and is very finely ground and always bleached. Do not use this for bread because it will not develop enough gluten for proper rising.

Self-rising flour is a mixture of flour, baking soda and baking powder; it can be used for cake making, but special recipes are needed.

Whole-wheat flour is the whole grain, with nothing removed and no bleaching. Often this is ground between stones in the old-fashioned way, which makes it especially nutritious.

Rye flour is darker than wheat. The gluten properties are similar, but in different proportions so the gluten lacks stability. Rye flour is often used, therefore, in combination with wheat flour. An all-rye bread will have a very dense texture because the dough will not rise as much.

Oats, corn and *barley* do not form gluten. Although they are used in breads, they cannot make good breads when used alone. This sad discovery about corn by early American colonists, who were unable to grow wheat, led to experiments that have given us almost endless versions of corn bread.

A recent development is the so-called *instantized flour*. This has been ground much finer than all-purpose, and is so soft and silky it needs no sifting. While it is possible to use it for bread, it is more successful in such cooking procedures as sauce making, where it dissolves smoothly without lumping. Do not use this very soft flour for cookies that are shaped in a cookie press or for foods that must hold their shape without a mold or pan.

All flours can become unfit for use if not stored properly. Keep them in a cool, dry place free of insects. Whole-grain flours, which contain the fatty germ, can become rancid if stored too long, or at too high temperatures. It is best to buy them only in small amounts and store them in airtight containers in your refrigerator. Buy only from dealers whose stocks are fresh and properly stored.

YEAST

The air around us is thronging with microscopic organisms—some are the beneficial plants called yeasts. These, probably with a mixture of other organisms, started the first natural fermentations. The ancients recognized and could control fermentations to produce beverages similar to our wines and beers, and to make leavened bread.

Recently, pure, dependable strains of yeasts have been developed that are easily available to the home baker and make bread-making techniques simple and quick. Fresh yeast is compressed and packed in small blocks (.6 of an ounce), or in 2-ounce packages. Dried yeast, which is granular, is sold in ¼-ounce packets. The recipes in this chapter all specify dried yeast, but a small block of fresh yeast can be substituted in every case. Each will raise about 6 cups of flour.

Since yeast is a living organism, it needs to be treated with care. Fresh yeast must be kept refrigerated, but do not try to keep it too long. In good condition it breaks somewhat crisply; you can cut off a smooth slice. Dry yeast keeps much longer. The packets you buy are dated, and if stored in foil wrappers in a cool, dry place, well protected from air, the yeast will be good for use at least as long as the date indicates. Stored at too high temperatures, it will lose some of its effectiveness, and the dough it is used in will rise more slowly and not as much.

To soften the yeast and start the fermentation, dissolve either kind in water or in part of the liquid required in the recipe. For one package use at least ¼ cup liquid. Fresh yeast needs lukewarm water (80° to

90° F.). For dried yeast use warmer water (110° to 115° F.). The dissolved yeast is mixed with other ingredients according to the recipe directions. For the Rapidmix© method, mix dried yeast with some or all of the dried ingredients; the liquids added must be at a still higher temperature, 120° to 130° F.

OTHER INGREDIENTS

Milk is one of many liquids that can be used in bread baking, but it plays an important role because of its nutritional value. Many old cookbooks and even some new ones direct the baker to scald fresh milk, because it was observed that unscalded milk caused slack (soft) dough and interfered with rising. Pasteurization seems to alter milk chemistry enough to prevent that effect, so for the home baker it is safe to skip scalding and cooling. However, it is usually convenient to warm milk or any other liquid enough to melt butter or to liquify honey or molasses or sugar; use the temperature best for the kind of yeast you use.

Fats make doughs more rich and tender, but they can slow the rising. A baked loaf with some fat will not become hard and stale as soon as a simpler loaf.

Salt brings out the flavor of the other ingredients. It also controls the yeast development enough so that the rising is not too rapid. Too much salt would slow the action of the yeast. Salt also hardens the gluten developed in the flour.

Sugar (or honey or molasses) adds flavor and color to the loaf and helps to make a brown crust. Sweet doughs, like fat doughs, are slower to rise.

THE TECHNIQUES OF BREAD-MAKING

Mixing dough

Since flours vary not only from kind to kind but from bag to bag, most recipes direct you to add only "enough flour to make a dough." This is because the ability of any flour to absorb liquid is unpredictable. When too much flour is used, the bread will be tough.

You can add the flour to the liquid, as many recipes direct, or try another way. Put all the flour on a mixing board (any large, flat, smooth surface—board or countertop) or in a bowl. Make a well in the center of the flour and put in the liquid needed to dissolve the yeast. Sprinkle the yeast over the liquid. When the yeast is dissolved, gradually mix all together, adding as much more liquid as the flour needs to form a dough that is easy to handle. Either of these mixing methods is called the "direct method."

Another way is the "starter method." In this method a portion of the liquid and a portion of the flour are mixed with the yeast. The ball of dough is dropped into a bowl of water heated to 105° to 110° F. As the yeast expands, the ball becomes lighter and rises to the top of the water. It is then ready to mix with the balance of the ingredients. You can use this method with most recipes if you prefer.

All ingredients should be at room temperature before you start to mix them, and the liquids should be at the proper warm temperatures.

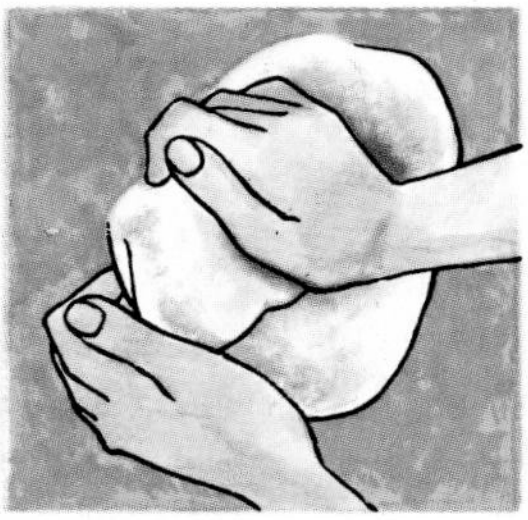

Kneading

Very soft doughs, like those for batter breads, are "kneaded" by beating hard with a wooden spoon or with the dough hook of an electric mixer, usually for about 5 minutes.

Firmer doughs are kneaded by hand, and there is nothing in cookery more satisfying. Most American recipes tell you to fold the dough in half, push the ball of dough with the heels of your hands and keep folding, turning and pushing until the dough is no longer sticky and is smooth and satiny. Most French cookbooks tell you to use one hand only. Use whichever method is comfortable for you.

Here is how to proceed with one hand: with your right hand (or left if you are left-handed) grasp a portion of the dough from the end farthest from you, while lightly holding the end nearest you. With the dough between palm and fingers, push it away from you along the mixing board. Then grasp another handful and push that away. Do this quickly—in a moment the whole ball of dough will be moved. Turn the dough over and turn it sideways; repeat the process of pushing the dough, handful by handful. What you are doing is stretching the dough, and you will feel it becoming more smooth and elastic as you continue to knead.

"Knead until smooth and elastic" is the expression

you will find in most books, including this one, and once the dough has reached that stage you will recognize just what the words mean. Usually 10 minutes is long enough to knead. If you knead too little, not enough gluten will develop.

Another kind of dough is "crashed" on the counter rather than kneaded. This is the procedure for very rich and buttery doughs like Danish pastry.

Rising

Pat the dough into a smooth ball and put it in a clean bowl that has been rubbed with butter or oil. Turn the dough over and move it around so that it becomes covered with butter or oil. This helps prevent drying and toughening of the top surface. Cover the bowl with a towel and let the dough rise until it has doubled in bulk. A very rich dough like *Stollen* will not double but will increase only by half.

The best temperature for the dough to rise is 75° to 85° F., and the dough should be in a place free from drafts. At cooler temperatures, rising will be slowed; at higher temperatures it will be speeded up. High humidity can also speed up the rising. Guard against too high a temperature, as that could kill the living yeast cells.

You can test whether the dough has risen enough by poking the edge of the dough with your finger. If the dent fills up, the dough must rise more; if it remains a dent, the dough is ready for the next step.

Shaping and second rising

With your fist, punch the ball of dough; it will collapse. Fold the edges toward the middle and turn the dough over in the bowl. Then either leave it in the bowl or turn it out on a board. Let the dough rest for 10 minutes. Then cut it into portions and shape according to the recipe.

For loaves that will be baked on a flat sheet, it is best to put the dough for each loaf on a floured board and roll it out into a rectangle, then roll up tightly. Seal the long edge and the ends, or taper the ends by pulling and rolling between the palms of your hands to form the typical tapered shape of French bread. Shape small loaves and rolls according to directions given in individual recipes. Dough with good gluten development will hold its shape even when baked on a flat surface.

Most breads are baked in a standard bread pan, 9 × 5 × 3 inches. Small pans, 5 × 3 × 2 inches, make neat little loaves. These are the two sizes most often indicated in the recipes that follow. However, breads can be baked in all sorts of pans. You can use casseroles, round pans, baking sheets or whatever suits the recipe. Rub pans with butter or oil. Shape the dough to fit neatly into the pan, about half filling the depth.

After shaping, let the dough rise again until doubled. Test with a finger (p. 477) if you are not sure it is ready.

Shaped risen loaves can be frozen before baking. Let them defrost in the refrigerator overnight and then bring them to room temperature before baking.

CoolRise© is a recently developed method in which the dough rises in the refrigerator. Special recipes are needed, but a busy housewife will find them worth looking for. In this method the dough is mixed, kneaded, and then allowed to rest for 20 minutes. It is then shaped and stored in the refrigerator for 2 to 24 hours. When you are ready to bake the bread or rolls, remove from refrigerator, let stand at room temperature for 10 minutes, then bake.

Baking

Be certain the oven has reached the correct temperature before you put the loaves in. If you have doubts about the accuracy of your thermostat, use a separate oven thermometer and adjust the heat accordingly.

Place the risen loaves in the center of the oven, on a middle shelf, with room for air circulation all around. An average-size oven can hold four standard loaves.

A loaf is done when it sounds hollow when tapped on the bottom or sides. It should look well risen and nicely browned. For another test, pierce the loaf with a metal tester and immediately touch the end of the tester to your wrist. It should be almost hot enough to burn you (but it won't). Of course there should be no uncooked dough or moisture on the tester.

Fully baked bread, when cooled, can be frozen in moistureproof wrappings and stored for 3 to 6 months. To defrost it, reheat at the baking temperature.

Glazes

Breads can be baked with only their own browned crusts, or they can be glazed. The risen loaves can be brushed with water. Milk or melted butter give a soft crust. For shiny crusts use an egg beaten with a tablespoon of water. For brown and shiny crusts, use an egg yolk beaten with a tablespoon of water; lightly beaten egg white can be used to make a crisper crust.

YEAST BREADS

Flat bread

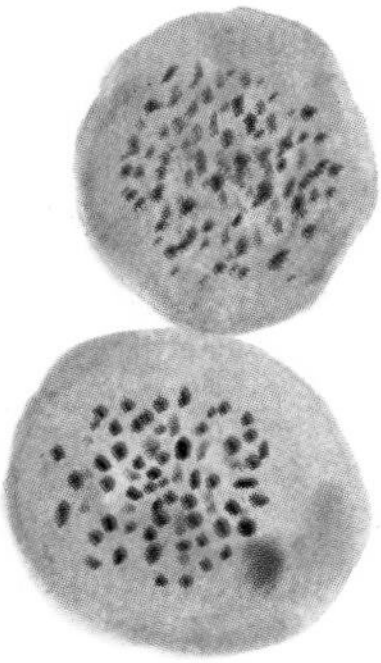

If you have never baked bread, try this simple recipe first. It is made of only flour, yeast and water, but with two different seasonings. One loaf will taste like Middle Eastern bread, the other like Italian bread.

- 1 package dry yeast
- 1½ cups warm water
- 6 cups all-purpose flour
- 1 teaspoon olive oil
- 1 tablespoon sesame seeds
- 1 tablespoon Italian seasoning (p. 128)

Dissolve the yeast in the warm water. Stir in 5 cups of the flour, then stir in the rest little by little, adding only enough to make a dough. Turn out on a floured board and knead until the dough is smooth and elastic and does not stick to your hands. Pat it into a ball. Pour ½ teaspoon of the oil into the palm of your hand and roll the dough ball around until it is coated with oil. Put it in a bowl, cover with a towel and let rise until doubled, 30 to 40 minutes.

Punch down and divide into two portions. With your hands or a rolling pin, flatten out each portion to a plate-size round. Use the rest of the oil to brush the tops of the rounds. Sprinkle one with sesame seeds and the other with Italian seasoning. Put on baking sheets, cover with bowls and let rise until doubled, about 30 minutes. Bake in a preheated 400° F. oven for 20 to 30 minutes, until golden on top.

French bread

French bread is so delicious that all home bakers hope to be able to make it, but the loaf baked in the home kitchen can never reproduce the genuine article. In

France, bread is baked by professional bakers, with generations of baking skill behind them, using perfectly heated professional ovens as well as French flour and water. To come close to the French, use unbleached flour and bake the loaves on a baking sheet sprinkled with cornmeal.

1 package dry yeast
1½ cups warm water
½ tablespoon salt
1 tablespoon sugar
4 to 5 cups unbleached flour
Cornmeal

Dissolve the yeast in the water. Mix salt, sugar and 2 cups unbleached flour; stir into the yeast. Add 2 more cups of flour and as much more of the last cup as you need to make a dough. Turn out on a floured board and knead for 8 to 10 minutes, until the dough is smooth and elastic and does not stick to your hands. Transfer the ball of dough to a buttered bowl and roll the dough around to butter the whole surface. Cover the bowl with a towel and let the dough rise until at least doubled, about 1 hour.

Punch down the dough and knead it for about 1 minute. Cut the dough into two portions. Roll out each portion into a large rectangle about the length of your baking sheet. Roll up each rectangle tightly lengthwise and taper the ends. Cut a few diagonal slashes in the top of each loaf. Put them on a greased baking sheet sprinkled with cornmeal, and let rise again until doubled, about 1 hour.

Brush the loaves with cold water or with egg white. Bake in a preheated 400° F. oven for about 30 minutes, until golden brown and crisp on top.

White bread

This recipe, which uses unconventional flour, skim rather than whole milk and honey rather than sugar, is an illustration of the Rapidmix© Method. It makes a loaf with a very fine crumb, which can be cut into extremely thin slices for tea sandwiches or Melba toast without breaking apart.

1 package dry yeast
6 cups instantized flour
1 tablespoon salt
2 tablespoons margarine
2¼ cups milk made from nonfat dried skim milk
2 tablespoons honey

JOKER

In a large bowl mix dry yeast, 2 cups of the flour, and the salt. Put margarine, milk and honey in a saucepan and heat together to 120° to 130° F. Add to the dry mixture and mix thoroughly. Then add the rest of the flour. Use a little more flour if necessary to make a dough. Turn out on a board and knead quickly until smooth and elastic. Turn the ball of dough into a greased bowl, cover and let rise until doubled, about 1 hour.

Punch down the dough, knead for 1 minute, then cut the ball into halves. Pat into loaf shape and place in greased standard bread pans. Cover the pans and let the dough rise again until it fills the pans and is rounded on top. Bake in a preheated 400° F. oven for about 40 minutes, until the loaves test done. Makes 2 loaves, each weighing about 1¼ pounds.

Cracked wheat bread

- 1 cup cracked wheat
- 1 cup boiling water
- 1 cup milk
- 4 tablespoons butter
- 1½ teaspoons salt
- 3 tablespoons brown sugar
- 1 package dry yeast
- ¼ cup warm water
- 5 cups unbleached flour

Measure the cracked wheat into a saucepan. Pour boiling water over it and let stand until cooled. (You can let the wheat cook for a few minutes if you prefer a softer bread.) Heat the milk to 110° F. and stir in the butter, salt and sugar. Dissolve the yeast in the warm water in a large bowl. Stir milk mixture into the cracked wheat, then stir that and the flour into the dissolved yeast. Mix well, then turn out and knead until smooth and elastic. Turn into a greased bowl, cover and let rise until doubled, about 1½ hours.

Punch down, cut into portions, shape into loaves and put in greased pans. Let rise again until the dough fills the pans and is rounded on top. Bake in a 400° F. oven for about 1 hour, or until the loaves test done. Makes 2 standard loaves or 4 small ones.

Pumpkin ginger bread

This is an illustration of the method of mixing directly on a board, which you may come to prefer to using a bowl. Instead of adding more flour as needed, you start out with all the flour the recipe needs and add more liquid if necessary.

½ cup orange juice
1 cup pumpkin purée
3 tablespoons butter or margarine
½ tablespoon salt
1 tablespoon ground cardamom
¼ cup ginger preserve with the liquid that clings to the pieces
5 cups unbleached flour
1 cup whole-wheat flour
2 packages dry yeast
½ cup warm water
2 eggs

In a large saucepan heat orange juice to 110° F. Add puréed pumpkin, butter or margarine, salt and cardamom. Mince the ginger preserve. Put both flours on a mixing board and mix them together. Then make a well in the center and sprinkle yeast into the well. Gently add the water. In a few minutes the yeast will start to bubble at the edges. Let it dissolve for 10 minutes, then start mixing flour into the dissolved yeast around the edges until the yeast mixture is all blended in.

Add the rest of the liquids, a little at a time, mixing around the edges of the well. Break the eggs into the well and mix in. Finally add the ginger. If more liquid is needed, add a little more orange juice or water. When everything is mixed into a dough, knead for 10 minutes until smooth and elastic. Turn into a greased bowl, cover and let rise until doubled in bulk, about 1 hour.

Punch down the dough, then knead again for a few minutes. Cut into 3 or 6 portions and pat into loaves. Put in greased loaf pans and let rise again until the dough has filled the pans and is rounded on top. Bake in a preheated 400° F. oven for about 10 minutes, then reduce heat to 350° F. and bake for another 20 minutes for small loaves, another 30 minutes for standard loaves. Makes 3 standard or 6 small loaves.

For an interesting variation, add golden raisins or chopped dried apricots to the dough. These loaves are golden colored and not overly sweet in spite of the ginger and orange juice. Delicious for tea, spread with cream cheese.

Light rye bread

This is an illustration of a bread that rises in the refrigerator after shaping, similar to the method called CoolRise©. (The usual method of rising in a warm temperature can be used instead.) This bread, also, is mixed on a board rather than in a bowl.

1½ cups sour milk
¼ cup molasses
2 tablespoons margarine
1 teaspoon salt
3 cups rye flour
3 cups unbleached flour
1 package dry yeast
¼ cup warm water
Caraway seeds (2 tablespoons or more)
Peanut oil

Heat sour milk, molasses, margarine and salt to 110° F. Put 2½ cups rye flour and 2½ cups unbleached flour on a board and mix thoroughly. Make a well in the center and sprinkle in the yeast. Add the warm water and let yeast dissolve for 10 minutes. Then start mixing in the flour at the edges. Gradually add the milk and molasses mixture and stir all together. Add the rest of the flour, or as much of it as you need to make a dough.

Knead the dough for 10 minutes, until smooth and elastic. Put the ball of dough in a greased bowl and turn it around to be sure the top is well greased. Cover the bowl and let the dough rise until doubled, about 2 hours.

Punch down the dough and cut into 2 pieces. Roll out each piece into a rectangle and sprinkle with half of the caraway seeds. Roll up the rectangles and fit into pans. Brush tops of loaves with peanut oil. Cover the pans loosely with wax paper or plastic and refrigerate overnight, or for at least 2 hours.

Remove loaves from refrigerator and uncover them carefully. Let them stand at room temperature for 10 minutes. Then bake in a preheated 375° F. oven for 45 minutes. Makes 2 standard loaves or 4 small ones.

Whole-wheat potato bread

2 medium-size potatoes
1 teaspoon plus ½ cup granulated sugar
½ cup lukewarm water
1 package dry yeast
2 eggs
½ cup shortening or margarine
2 teaspoons salt
6 cups (approximately) whole-wheat flour, or half all-purpose and half whole-wheat

Scrub the potatoes and boil, unpeeled, until very tender; they must be softer than usual. Measure ¾ cup of the water in which the potatoes were cooked. If too much water has evaporated in cooking, make up the difference with warm water. If you have more of the potato water left, set it aside in case you need extra liquid. Pour the measured water into a large bowl and let it cool until lukewarm. Meanwhile, dissolve the teaspoon of sugar in the lukewarm water. Sprinkle the yeast on top of the sugared water. Let stand for 10 minutes, then stir well. Break the eggs into a small bowl and beat.

Peel the potatoes and mash them in the reserved lukewarm potato water. (Or purée potatoes with the water in a blender.) Stir in ½ cup sugar, the shortening or margarine, and the salt. Blend well. Add the dissolved yeast, then the eggs. Blend thoroughly. Beat in the flour, a little at a time, with a wooden spoon. If you need more liquid, add some of the still-warm potato water or a little warmed milk; add a tablespoon at a time. The dough should be stiff enough to be handled easily, and it should come away from the sides of the bowl. Turn out the dough on a lightly floured board and knead until smooth and elastic, about 10 minutes. Cover and let rise for 1½ hours, or until doubled in bulk. Meanwhile, grease 3 standard loaf pans or 6 small ones.

Punch down the risen dough and knead again for about 5 minutes. Divide dough into 3 or 6 portions and shape into loaves. Place in well-greased loaf pans and let rise again until doubled, usually about 1 hour.

Preheat the oven to 400° F. Bake loaves at this temperature for 20 minutes, then reduce heat to 350° F. and bake for an additional 20 minutes. This bread freezes very well. Makes 3 standard or 6 small loaves.

Cheese bread

- ½ cup sour cream
- 1 cup milk made with nonfat dried skim milk
- ½ tablespoon salt
- ½ tablespoon sugar
- 1 package dry yeast
- ¼ cup warm water
- 4 to 6 cups all-purpose or unbleached flour
- ⅓ pound sharp Cheddar cheese, grated
- 1 egg white, lightly beaten

Stir sour cream into milk and add salt and sugar. Heat milk to about 110° F. Dissolve yeast in warm water. Mix milk and yeast, and stir in 4 cups flour, a cup at a time. Add the cheese. Add as much additional flour as you need to make a dough. Turn out the dough and knead until smooth and elastic. Put in a greased bowl, cover and let rise until doubled, about 1½ hours.

Punch down, knead for a minute, then cut into 3 pieces. Put each piece in a round pan about 5 inches across; 1-pound coffee cans are ideal. Cover the dough and let rise again until the dough fills the pans and is rounded on top. Brush the tops with the lightly beaten egg white. Bake in a preheated 400° F. oven for 35 to 40 minutes, until golden brown and shiny on top. Makes 3 loaves, about 1 pound each.

This makes delicious toast; the cheese flavor is much more pronounced when the bread is toasted. If you make your toast in an electric toaster, you may prefer to bake this in 2 conventional bread pans.

Oatmeal bread

- 1½ cups rolled oats
- 2 cups boiling water
- 2 teaspoons salt
- 2 tablespoons butter
- 1 package dry yeast
- ¼ cup warm water
- 6 to 8 cups all-purpose flour
- 6 tablespoons light brown sugar
- 1 teaspoon grated orange rind
- ½ teaspoon ground cinnamon

Put the oats in a saucepan and pour the boiling water over them. Stir in the salt and butter. Let cool. Dissolve the yeast in warm water. Add 3 cups flour to the yeast, then the brown sugar, orange rind and cinnamon. Stir in the oats and mix well. Add more flour, 1 cup at a time, until the mixture forms a dough. Turn out and knead until smooth and elastic, about 10 minutes. Turn the ball of dough into a greased bowl, cover and let rise until doubled in bulk, about 1 hour.

Punch down, knead again for a minute, then cut the dough into halves. Put each portion into a greased loaf pan, cover and let rise again until the dough fills the pans and is rounded on top. Bake in a preheated 400° F. oven for about 40 minutes, or until the loaves test done.

Buttermilk bread

6 cups unbleached flour
1½ cups buttermilk
3 tablespoons butter
4 tablespoons honey
1 teaspoon salt
1 package dry yeast
¼ cup warm water

Measure flour into a bowl or onto a board. Heat buttermilk, butter, honey and salt to 110° F. In a separate bowl or in a well in the mound of the flour, dissolve the yeast in the warm water. Mix yeast, liquids and flour together. Add a little more flour or warm buttermilk if necessary to form a dough. Turn out the dough and knead for 10 minutes, until smooth and elastic. Put the ball of dough in a buttered bowl and turn over to butter the top. Cover. Let rise until doubled, about 1 hour.

Turn out the dough, punch down and cut into 2 or 3 pieces. Fit into greased bread pans; or roll out each piece into a rectangle, roll up into a long loaf shape and arrange on greased baking sheets. Let the loaves rise until doubled. Bake in a preheated 400° F. oven for 30 to 40 minutes. Brush the tops with melted butter and let the loaves cool. This bread is very nutritious and tastes delicious. In spite of the slightly sweet taste, it makes a good sandwich bread. Because of the honey, it keeps soft for 8 to 10 days. Makes 2½ pounds of bread.

Braided egg bread

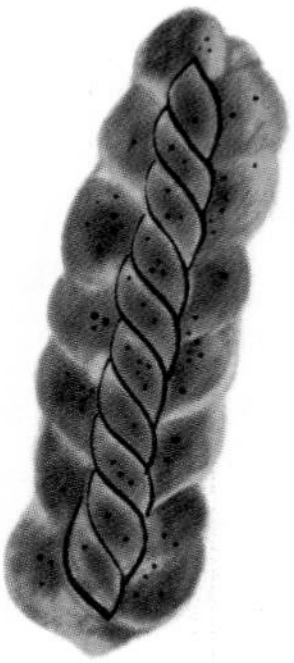

This recipe is an adaptation of *challah* or *hallah,* the braided white bread baked for the Friday night Sabbath meal. Leavened bread was common among the ancient Israelites perhaps as far back as 3000 B.C. The *hallah* was originally the priest's share, 1/24 of the dough of a private household, and the dough was made of certain specified grains. One of these golden braids is a beautiful addition to any meal.

The recipe illustrates the "starter method." A "sponge" is made with the yeast and water and a portion of the flour.

1 package dry yeast
½ cup warm water
4½ cups all-purpose flour
4 teaspoons sugar
3 eggs
3 tablespoons vegetable oil
1 teaspoon salt
1 tablespoon poppy seeds

Sprinkle the yeast over the water in a bowl and let it dissolve. Stir well, then add 1½ cups of the flour and all the sugar. Mix together to make a small ball of soft dough. Make a cross in the top of the ball. Drop it into a deep bowl filled with water at 105° F. As the dough expands, it will rise to the top; this is called the sponge.

Separate 1 egg and put the yolk aside in a small bowl. Add the egg white to the 2 other eggs and beat together with the oil. Sift 2 cups of the flour with the salt into a bowl. Add the sponge, then the eggs and oil. Mix together, adding a little more of the remaining cup of flour if you need it to make a dough. Turn out the dough and knead until smooth and elastic, about 10 minutes. Put the dough into an oiled bowl, turn to oil the top, and cover. Let rise until doubled, 1¼ to 1½ hours.

Punch down the dough. For one large, impressive loaf, divide dough into 5 pieces, 2 of them slightly smaller than the others. For two smaller braided loaves, divide the dough into 6 equal parts. Round each portion into a ball and let rest for 10 minutes.

Pull each ball into a long rope. For the single large loaf, make 3 ropes about 20 inches long, and 2 ropes about 15 inches long. Braid the longer pieces; press the ends tightly together. Twist the shorter pieces into a single rope and put on top of the braid, pressing securely into place. To be sure the parts do not separate during baking, insert wooden toothpicks through them in about five places.

If you are making 2 loaves, pull each half of dough to make ropes about 15 inches long and braid together 3 of the ropes for each loaf. Fasten the ends firmly together to seal. Put the bread on an oiled baking sheet, cover with a damp towel and let rise until doubled in bulk, about 45 minutes.

Add 1 tablespoon water to the reserved egg yolk and stir with a fork until well mixed. With a pastry brush, paint the egg-yolk glaze all over the top, then sprinkle with the poppy seeds. Bake in a preheated 375° F. oven for about 1 hour, until the bread sounds hollow and is brown and shiny on top. Cool on a rack. Makes one 18-inch loaf, about 1½ pounds, or 2 loaves about 12 inches long.

Sandwich rolls

This dough is just like that for French bread except for the addition of butter, but when baked into small rolls it tastes quite different.

1 package dry yeast
1 ½ cups warm water
½ tablespoon salt
1 tablespoon sugar
4 to 5 cups unbleached flour
2 tablespoons butter or margarine, melted and cooled
1 egg yolk
Sesame seeds or poppy seeds or caraway seeds with coarse salt

Dissolve the yeast in the water. Mix salt, sugar, 4 cups flour and the butter and mix with dissolved yeast. Add as much more of the remaining flour as you need to make a dough. Turn out on a floured board and knead until smooth and elastic. Put the dough into a buttered bowl, turn to butter the top of the dough, and cover the bowl with a towel. Let the dough rise until doubled, about 1 hour.

Punch down the dough and cut it into 4 pieces. Roll each piece into a narrow rectangle about 12 inches wide, and cut into 3 pieces. Roll up each 4-inch piece like a miniature bread. Press the edges to seal. Place the rolls on a greased baking sheet, cover and let rise until doubled, about 1 hour. Brush the tops of the rolls with the egg yolk beaten with 1 tablespoon of water. Sprinkle with sesame seeds, poppy seeds, or caraway seeds and a little coarse salt. Bake in a preheated 375° F. oven for 15 to 20 minutes, or until done and well browned on top. Makes 12 rolls.

You can shape these into round rolls if you prefer. Divide the dough into 8 to 10 pieces and shape each into a ball, then flatten the balls into 4-inch circles. When risen, brush with glaze and sprinkle with seeds (and salt if caraway seeds are used). Bake like the oval rolls.

Onion rolls

1 teaspoon plus 2 tablespoons sugar
½ cup lukewarm water
1 package dry yeast
5 tablespoons butter
1 teaspoon salt
1 egg, well beaten
4 cups sifted all-purpose flour
Onion Filling (recipe follows)

Dissolve the teaspoon of sugar in the lukewarm

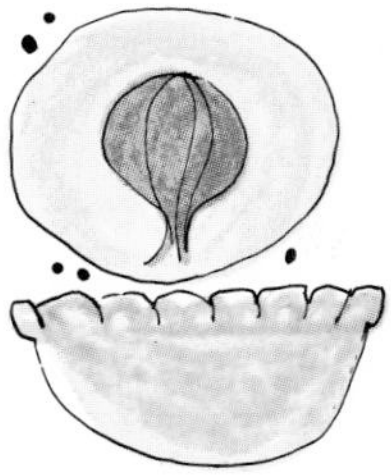

water. Sprinkle the yeast on top of the water. Let it stand for 10 minutes, then stir well.

Cream the butter thoroughly. Gradually add the 2 tablespoons sugar and the salt and continue beating until creamy. Add the egg and beat until smooth. Add the yeast mixture and mix thoroughly. Stir in the flour. When dough is stiff enough to be handled easily, turn onto a floured board and knead for about 5 minutes. Place in a greased bowl, cover with a towel and let rise for 1½ hours, or until doubled.

Punch down the dough and pull the sides into the center. Turn onto a floured board and knead again for about 3 minutes. Roll out the dough on a floured board to ¼-inch thickness. Using a 3-inch cookie cutter, cut the dough into circles. Place 1 teaspoon of onion filling in the center of each circle. Dampen the edge of half of each circle with water. Fold the other half over and press edges together firmly. Place on greased baking sheets. Cover with a towel and let rise again for about 30 minutes, or until doubled in bulk. Meanwhile preheat oven to 400° F. When rolls have doubled, bake for 15 minutes. Makes about 24 rolls.

ONION FILLING

- ½ cup butter
- 2 cups minced green onions
- ¼ teaspoon salt
- ⅛ teaspoon pepper
- ⅛ teaspoon ground sage
- Pinch of caraway seeds

Melt the butter. Add the minced onions and sauté them until soft but not browned, about 5 minutes. Blend in the remaining ingredients. Let this mixture cool before using in the rolls.

English muffins

- 1 package dry yeast
- ¼ cup warm water
- 1 cup milk
- 3 tablespoons butter or margarine
- 2 tablespoons sugar
- 1 teaspoon salt
- 4 to 5 cups all-purpose or unbleached flour
- 1 egg
- White cornmeal

Dissolve the yeast in the water. Heat milk with butter, sugar and salt to 110° F. Measure 2 cups of the flour into a large bowl and add the warm milk, the egg and the yeast. Stir well. Add 2 more cups of flour;

if necessary, add a little more flour to make a dough. Turn out the dough and knead for about 5 minutes, until smooth and elastic. It may be a little sticky, but do not add any more flour; the dough should not be stiff. Put the dough in a buttered bowl, cover and let rise for about 1 hour, until doubled in bulk.

Punch down the dough and divide into 2 or 3 portions. Sprinkle a large board with cornmeal and roll out one portion of dough into a sheet about ¼ inch thick. With a muffin cutter (about 3 inches across) or a doughnut cutter with the centerpiece removed, cut out as many circles as possible. Sprinkle another board or a tray with more cornmeal and turn the rounds upside down on the second board. Roll out the rest of the dough and cut it into rounds. Gather up the rest of the dough (the part between the rounds), pat together and roll out again. Cut rounds until all the dough is used. Put a towel over the muffins and let them rise on the boards or trays until doubled in size, 30 to 45 minutes.

Heat a heavy griddle but do not grease it. Place the muffins on the griddle and "bake" them for 5 minutes on each side. Start with a hot griddle, but lower the heat so the cornmeal does not burn. (The muffins will rise higher as they "bake" but shrink sideways. If you want muffins that are larger around, you must cut larger rounds to begin with.) Brush the griddle clean and sprinkle fresh cornmeal on before cooking each batch of muffins. Makes about 24 large muffins.

To toast, pull the muffins apart, or separate with a fork; do not cut them.

You can make smaller muffins if you prefer, even very tiny ones for hors d'oeuvres. These can be frozen after baking; let them defrost before toasting. English muffins get very hard unless they are well wrapped.

Sweet Yeast Breads

Every country that has a baking tradition has some breads for special occasions. The German Christmas bread, *Stollen,* is one example; the Polish *babka* and the Russian *kulich* are Easter cakes; the Italian coffeecake *panettone* is also a holiday specialty. These are all sweet breads, some of them more like cakes. Here are American versions of two of these holiday breads;

Thanksgiving Morning Bread is an adaptation of *panettone.*

Thanksgiving morning bread

- 2 packages dry yeast
- 1 cup warm water
- 1/4 pound butter
- 1/2 cup granulated sugar
- 3 whole eggs
- 2 extra egg yolks
- 1 teaspoon salt
- 1 teaspoon grated lemon rind
- 6 to 7 cups all-purpose flour
- 1 cup fresh cranberries
- 3/4 cup hazelnuts
- 3/4 cup yellow raisins
- 1/4 cup light brown sugar
- Melted butter

Dissolve the yeast in the warm water. Cream the butter in a very large bowl and beat in the granulated sugar until it is no longer grainy. Add whole eggs and egg yolks, one at a time, beating well after each addition. Sprinkle in the salt and lemon rind and add 4 cups of the flour. Mix together, then stir in the dissolved yeast. Mix in 2 more cups of the flour and as much of the last cup as you need to make a dough.

Turn out on a floured board and knead for 7 to 8 minutes, until smooth and elastic. Add a little more flour if the dough seems sticky. Put the dough in a buttered bowl, butter the top, and cover. Let the dough rise until doubled, about 1 1/2 hours.

Punch down the dough and pat into a flattened round. Mix cranberries, hazelnuts, raisins and brown sugar. Scatter mixture on the dough and knead into the dough until the fruits and nuts are evenly distributed. Cut dough into 3 pieces and shape each piece into a round. Put rounds in well-buttered 1-pound coffee cans or shortening cans (*panettone* is always round). Cover. Let the dough rise again until it reaches the top of the cans and is rounded at the top.

Bake in a preheated 350° F. oven for 45 minutes to 1 hour, or until the loaves test done. Remove them from the cans and put them on a rack. Brush the tops with melted butter. These are sometimes iced or glazed. Each loaf will make at least 8 large pieces.

These loaves can rise in the refrigerator overnight, but be sure they are at room temperature before baking so the moistened dough around the cranberries will be fully baked.

Stollen

This delicious bread takes considerable effort in preparation, so it is worthwhile to make a large amount at one time. But be sure you have room in your oven for all the loaves if you plan to bake them all at the same time; otherwise, place the remaining dough in a bowl, cover with foil and store in the refrigerator until the first batch has finished baking. The average oven will hold only four standard loaves, because heat must circulate around the pans.

- 8 ounces blanched almonds
- 8 ounces raisins
- 8 ounces dried currants
- 4 ounces candied orange peel
- 4 ounces candied lemon peel
- ½ cup applejack
- 3 cups milk
- 1 pound butter
- 2 packages dry yeast
- ½ cup warm water
- ¾ cup granulated sugar
- ¾ cup honey
- 9 to 12 cups all-purpose flour
- 1 teaspoon salt
- ½ teaspoon ground cardamom (6 pods)
- 1 teaspoon lemon extract
- Confectioners' sugar

Blanch the almonds according to the directions on p. 639, or buy them already blanched. Split them into halves.

Put all the fruits into a bowl with a cover that can be sealed. Pour the applejack over them. Cover tightly, then shake to moisten all the fruits. This much can be done a day before baking.

Put the milk into a large saucepan. Cut the butter into pieces and heat it with the milk until melted. Soften the yeast in the water in your largest bowl. Stir sugar and honey into the milk and butter. Let the milk cool to 100° F. Sift together 9 cups of flour plus the salt and cardamom. Add liquids and flour alternately to the dissolved yeast, stirring well to mix. Add lemon extract to fruits. Then mix fruits and soaking liquid and the split almonds into the dough. Add more of the flour if necessary to make a dough that leaves the sides of the bowl.

Turn out the dough on a large board or counter top—you need a lot of space. Knead until the dough is smooth and elastic, adding more flour if the dough is sticky. This is hard work because the dough is rich with butter and sugar. Finally, return the dough to the buttered bowl, butter the top and cover. Let it rise until increased by half, about 2 hours.

Turn out the dough and cut it into 6 pieces. Roll out each piece to a large oval 14 to 16 inches long. Then fold lengthwise to make a flap (like a giant-size Parker House roll). This is the traditional shape for *Stollen*. Put the loaves on buttered baking sheets, cover and let rise again for about 1 hour.

Place loaves in a 375° F. oven, but do not put them too close together. The loaves rise quite high, so make sure the oven shelves are far enough apart. Bake for about 1 hour, until the loaves test done. Put them on racks to cool and then sprinkle with sifted confectioners' sugar. Makes 6 large loaves, weighing about 1½ pounds each.

QUICK BREADS

This kind of bread usually uses baking powder instead of yeast as leavening, or baking soda in combination with an acid ingredient such as buttermilk or molasses. In some recipes the liquid and the air beaten in with the ingredients are the sources of leavening. During baking the air expands and liquids are changed to steam, which cause the rising action.

Many quick breads are baked in loaves and may look like yeast breads, but also counted as breads are biscuits and muffins, which are baked in individual portions, soft breads such as spoon breads and other corn breads, which are baked in casseroles or flat pans, and even pancakes. Pancakes were probably the earliest form of bread, but the present-day breakfast cake and the delicate dessert crêpe, both very tender and usually made with eggs, have little resemblance to the coarse cakes our primitive ancestors made of roughly ground or crushed grains and baked on a hot stone, with probably a few ashes from the fire as garnish.

The kind of grain you use will make a difference in the quick bread, just as it does when working with yeast. The major difference is that with quick breads there is no waiting time for the dough to rise. In fact, you must be sure your oven is preheated to the required temperature by the time the dough or batter is mixed. If quick bread doughs have to wait, there could be loss of the air that was mixed in and the bread will fail to rise enough. Doughs for quick breads cannot stand the sort of handling that yeast doughs require for proper development. 🗝 When working with baking powder or baking soda, do not beat the batter; stir only enough to mix it. Overmixing tends to make large holes in the bread and sometimes toughens it.

Nut bread

- 2 cups all-purpose flour
- 4 tablespoons sugar
- 6 teaspoons baking powder
- 1 teaspoon salt
- 1 teaspoon baking soda
- ¼ teaspoon ground marjoram
- 1 cup whole-wheat flour
- 4 tablespoons honey
- 2 cups milk
- ½ cup chopped walnuts
- ¼ cup chopped pecans

Sift together three times the all-purpose flour, sugar, baking powder, salt, baking soda and marjoram (marjoram enhances the nutty flavor). Stir in the whole-wheat flour and mix as thoroughly as possible. Mix honey into the milk; pour all at once over the flour mixture. Add walnuts and pecans; mix just enough to blend. Spoon into a greased loaf pan (9 × 5 × 3 inches). Bake in a preheated 375° F. oven for 50 minutes; it is done when a straw comes out clean. This bread is delicious spread with unsalted butter.

Peanut bread

- 3 cups unbleached flour
- 6 teaspoons baking powder
- 2 teaspoons salt
- 6 tablespoons sugar
- ⅔ cup nonfat dried skim-milk powder
- ½ cup peanut butter
- ¾ cup peeled, roasted, unsalted peanuts, chopped
- 1½ cups water

Sift flour, baking powder, salt and sugar into a large bowl. Stir in the skim-milk powder, then the peanut butter and peanuts. Add water and stir only until the dough is mixed. Spoon into a well-greased loaf pan (9 × 5 × 3 inches) and smooth the top. Bake in a preheated 350° F. oven for about 1 hour, until the bread tests done. Cool before slicing. This bread is tasty and very nutritious. It makes good sandwiches for children's lunches and snacks.

Pumpkin loaf

¼ cup butter
¾ cup light brown sugar
2 eggs
¾ cup pumpkin purée
1⅔ cups all-purpose flour
½ teaspoon salt
3 teaspoons baking powder
½ teaspoon ground allspice
½ cup mixed candied fruits, chopped

Cream the butter and the sugar until the sugar is dissolved. Add the eggs, one at a time, and beat well after each addition. Stir in the pumpkin and mix until well blended. Sift flour, salt, baking powder and allspice. Stir into the pumpkin mixture just enough to make everything smooth. Stir in the candied fruits. Spoon into a well-greased loaf pan (9 × 5 × 3 inches) or into 2 small pans (5 × 3 × 2 inches), and smooth the top. Bake in a preheated 350° F. oven—40 to 50 minutes for the large loaf, about 35 minutes for the small loaves.

Irish soda bread

This bread, which is like a very large biscuit, evolved in a country where farmhouse cooking was extremely simple. The true Irish bread has no butter, but it tastes better with this addition.

3 cups unbleached flour
1 teaspoon salt
1 teaspoon baking soda
2 tablespoons butter
1 cup buttermilk

Mix flour, salt and baking soda. Cut in the butter until the mixture looks like cornmeal. Add the buttermilk and stir until the dry ingredients are moistened. Turn out the ball of dough. Knead for 1 minute, then pat into a round, rather flat cake about the size of a 9-inch pie pan. Put the dough on a buttered cookie sheet and cut a large cross in the top. Bake in a preheated 425° F. oven for about 40 minutes. If the loaf is done, it will sound hollow when you tap it.

Variations

To make whole-wheat soda bread, use 2 cups whole-wheat flour and 1 cup unbleached flour. To make oaten soda bread, use 1 cup quick-cooking Irish oats and 2 cups unbleached flour, and roll the shaped loaf in oats before baking.

For a sweeter loaf for a party or with tea, add ⅓ cup

raisins, ⅓ cup dried currants, 2 more tablespoons butter, 2 tablespoons honey or molasses and 2 tablespoons sugar. You can double the ingredients and bake this in a shallow pan 13 × 9 inches. It is then easy to cut into squares for serving.

Cinnamon coffee cake

This fragrant, fluffy coffee cake can be served hot or cold. It will keep fresh for 48 hours.

½ cup butter
¾ cup sugar
2 eggs
1 teaspoon baking soda
1 cup commercial sour cream
1½ cups all-purpose flour
1½ teaspoons baking powder
Pinch of salt
1 teaspoon vanilla extract
1 tablespoon ground cinnamon
2 tablespoons chopped walnuts

Cream the butter with ½ cup sugar. Add the eggs, one at a time, beating well after each addition. Mix the baking soda with the sour cream and gradually beat into the butter mixture. When the mixture is light and fluffy, add the flour sifted with the baking powder and salt. Add the vanilla.

Prepare cinnamon-walnut topping by mixing ¼ cup sugar, 1 tablespoon ground cinnamon and 2 tablespoons chopped walnuts.

Pour half of the batter into a 9-inch-square pan. Sprinkle half of the topping over it, then pour in the rest of the batter and sprinkle the remainder of the topping mixture over it. Bake in a preheated 350° F. oven for 40 minutes. Makes 9 large servings, or more if you cut smaller pieces.

Spoon bread

This bread, too soft to be sliced, is served with a spoon to accompany the main course of a meal.

2 cups cornmeal
1 teaspoon salt
2 cups cold water
2 cups boiling water
4 tablespoons butter
2 tablespoons brown sugar
½ teaspoon ground mace
3 eggs, separated
1½ cups light cream

Mix cornmeal and salt with cold water in the top part of a double boiler. Bring the water in the bottom to a boil, then reduce to a simmer. Pour 2 cups boiling water into the cornmeal and stir to mix well. Cook over the simmering water until the meal is thickened. Remove from the lower pan. Stir in the butter, sugar and mace. Let the mixture cool.

Beat egg yolks and cream together and stir into the cooled meal. Beat egg whites until thick and fluffy, then fold them into the cornmeal mixture. Pour the batter into a well-buttered 2-quart casserole. Bake in a preheated 350° F. oven for about 45 minutes, until puffed and lightly browned. Makes 6 to 8 servings.

In the South, white cornmeal is preferred for spoon bread, but it is good made with yellow meal too. You can make it more buttery or sweeter if you like. A nice variation is to add 1 cup fresh corn kernels cut from cobs, with ½ cup light cream in addition to the amount already used. Serve with roast chicken or baked ham.

Aniseed sweet bread

- 2 eggs
- ½ cup granulated sugar
- Juice and grated rind of 1 lemon
- ¼ teaspoon vanilla extract
- 2 to 2½ cups all-purpose flour
- 1½ teaspoons baking powder
- ½ cup minced almonds
- ¼ cup creamed butter
- Aniseeds
- Confectioners' sugar

Beat the eggs until light. Then add the granulated sugar and continue beating. Add the lemon juice and rind, the vanilla and 1 cup of the flour mixed with the baking powder. Mix well. Add the almonds. Blend in the creamed butter and another cup of flour. The dough will be sticky but it should be stiff enough to hold its shape; if not, add up to ½ cup more flour.

Dust some additional flour on a sheet of wax paper and turn out half of the dough on it. Use the wax paper to help you shape the dough into a long loaf about 2 inches thick. Roll the dough onto another sheet of wax paper sprinkled thickly with aniseeds. Then transfer the dough to a buttered baking sheet. Pat again into shape if necessary. Repeat the procedure with remaining dough. Bake in a 350° F. oven for 20 minutes.

Remove from the oven, cool for 20 minutes and cut while still warm into slices 1 inch thick. Turn each slice flat on the pan. Put back into the oven for about 20 minutes, or until golden brown. Cool and sprinkle with confectioners' sugar. The shaping of the loaves is difficult because the dough is soft, but the little slices, twice baked, are delicious.

Apple muffins

- ½ cup plus 1 tablespoon sugar
- 4 tablespoons butter
- 1 egg, lightly beaten
- 2½ cups all-purpose flour
- 3½ teaspoons baking powder
- ½ teaspoon salt
- ¼ teaspoon grated nutmeg
- 1 cup milk
- Grated rind of 1 lemon
- 1½ cups grated apple
- 1 tablespoon brown sugar
- ½ teaspoon ground cinnamon

Cream ½ cup sugar with butter. Add the lightly beaten egg and beat until smooth. Sift together flour, baking powder, salt and nutmeg. Add to the first mixture alternately with the milk. Add the grated lemon rind. Beat until well blended. Fold in the grated apple.

Prepare topping by mixing remaining tablespoon of granulated sugar with the brown sugar and the cinnamon.

Spoon batter into small greased muffin tins, filling them only half full. Sprinkle the top of each muffin with some of the topping mixture. Bake in a preheated 425° F. oven for 15 to 20 minutes. Makes about 24 small (1¾-inch) muffins.

These freeze beautifully. To serve, reheat without thawing first.

Bran and prune muffins

- 1 cup lightly packed dried prunes
- 1 cup unbleached flour
- 1 teaspoon salt
- 1 teaspoon baking soda
- 2 cups bran flakes
- 2 eggs
- 1 cup buttermilk
- 3 tablespoons butter or margarine
- ½ cup plus 1 tablespoon molasses

Put the prunes into a saucepan and cover with boiling water. When the water is cool, drain the prunes and cut them into pieces with kitchen scissors.

Mix together flour, salt and baking soda. Stir in

bran flakes. Beat together eggs and buttermilk. Melt butter or margarine and stir in the molasses until it is warmed and flows easily. Stir the two liquid mixtures together and then pour into the dry ingredients; mix. Add the prunes and stir only enough to mix; do not beat. Spoon into well-greased muffin tins, or tins with paper liners, and bake in a preheated 375° F. oven for 35 minutes. Makes 24 small (1¾-inch) muffins, or about 16 larger (2½-inch) muffins.

Old-fashioned biscuits

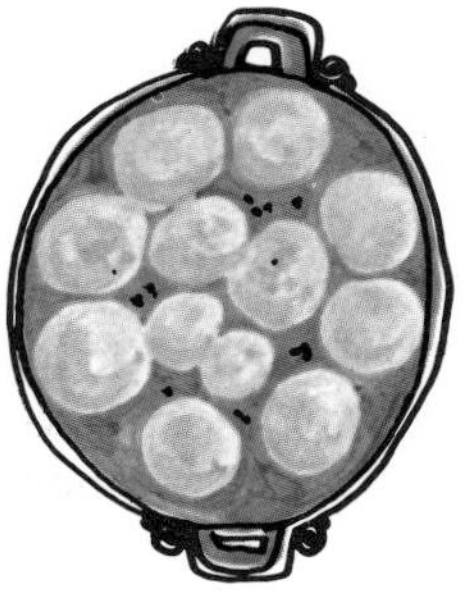

3 cups all-purpose flour
1 teaspoon salt
1½ teaspoons baking soda
1 tablespoon cream of tartar
1 teaspoon baking powder
½ cup butter or margarine
1⅓ cups milk

Sift flour, salt, baking soda, cream of tartar and baking powder. Cut in the butter with two knives until the mixture resembles coarse crumbs. Add the milk and stir with a fork until the dough is mixed and pulls away from the sides of the bowl.

For drop biscuits, drop tablespoons of the dough onto buttered baking sheets.

For rolled biscuits, turn the dough onto a floured board and roll it into a sheet about 1 inch thick. Use a round cutter to cut out the biscuits. Do not handle the dough too much, for this will make the biscuits less tender.

For square biscuits, roll out the dough and cut into squares, or pat the dough into a buttered 9-inch-square pan or a rectangular pan 8 × 10 inches. Cut into squares when done.

Bake in a preheated 400° F. oven for 20 to 30 minutes, or until they are golden brown. Makes 16 to 24 biscuits.

Spicy biscuits

2 cups unbleached flour
½ cup wheat germ
1 tablespoon baking powder
½ teaspoon baking soda
½ teaspoon medium Hungarian paprika
½ teaspoon salt
½ teaspoon crumbled dried oregano
½ teaspoon ground cuminseed
2 tablespoons butter
1¼ cups buttermilk

Mix all the dry ingredients in a bowl. Cut in the

butter with two knives (p. 515). Stir in the buttermilk. Mix until well blended, then turn out and knead for about 1 minute. On a floured board, roll out to a thickness of about 1 inch. With a 4-inch cutter (a coffeepot lid is good) cut out large biscuits. Place them on baking sheets covered with single sheets of wax paper. Bake in a preheated 400° F. oven for about 20 minutes. When the biscuits are cooled, store in an airtight tin. Split them to make sandwiches. Makes 8 large biscuits.

Popovers

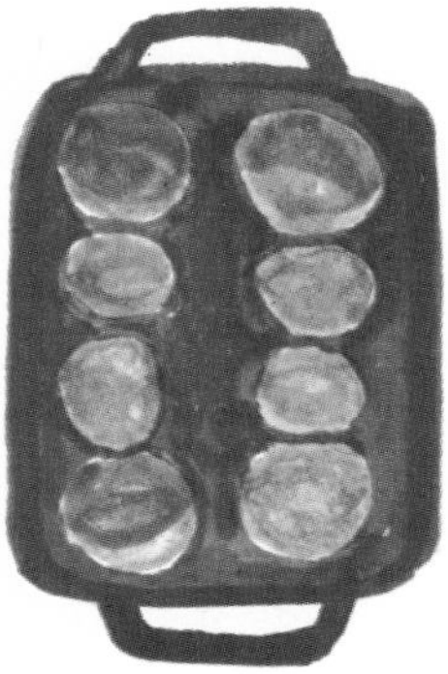

Prepare the batter for the Yorkshire Pudding (p. 272), and add 1 tablespoon melted butter or oil. Grease an iron popover pan that has 8 depressions. Pour in the batter to fill them about two thirds full. (You can use muffin pans or custard cups, but the iron pan is best.) Put them in a cold oven, then heat oven to 425° F. and bake for 40 to 50 minutes. The liquid in the milk and eggs turns to steam and expands the dough. Do not open the oven door until 40 minutes have elapsed. The popovers should be puffed up very high and beautifully browned, and the centers should be hollow. Makes 8 large popovers.

Pancakes

These "skillet breads" are good for occasions other than breakfast; the little crêpes that make such delicious desserts can also be used for other dishes. Omit sugar from the crêpes and you can serve them filled with creamed chicken or seafood or mushrooms or cheese, with delicious sauces spooned over them, for luncheon main dishes or for first courses at dinners. Tiny pancakes made with the buttermilk recipe are good with caviar and sour cream. You will notice that buttermilk pancakes are actually a yeast bread.

If you have never made pancakes or crêpes, start with a good packaged mix to practice how to cook them just right. 🗝 Be sure your griddle is hot, but not too hot. To test, toss a few drops of water on the pan; the water should sizzle. 🗝 Use only enough butter or oil or shortening to make a very thin film on the pan; brush it on with a pastry brush. Some batters with enough butter or oil in them may not need any in the pan, and nonstick pans will not require any. Pour out just enough batter for one pancake or crêpe all at once, and turn each cake only once.

Buttermilk pancakes

- ½ package active dry yeast
- 2 tablespoons warm water
- 2 cups sifted all-purpose flour
- 1 tablespoon baking powder
- 1 tablespoon baking soda
- 1 tablespoon sugar
- ½ teaspoon salt
- 2 cups buttermilk
- 2 tablespoons melted butter or shortening
- 3 eggs
- ½ cup heavy cream
- Shortening for griddle

Sprinkle the yeast over the warm water; let stand for 10 minutes, then stir. Sift into a bowl the flour, baking powder, baking soda, sugar and salt. Pour in the buttermilk and beat into a smooth batter. Then mix in the well-stirred yeast and the melted butter. Beat the eggs slightly with the cream and add to the batter.

Heat a large griddle and grease the surface with shortening. Pour out just enough batter for each pancake in one quick pouring. Cook until the pancake looks slightly dry on top and tiny bubbles appear. Flip onto the other side and brown. Never turn more than once. Continue until the batter is all cooked. Makes 4 to 6 servings.

Apple pancake

Instead of making many small pancakes, try this for a different delicious dessert—one large pancake baked in the oven. It needs no extra sauce.

- 3 eggs
- ½ cup all-purpose flour
- ½ teaspoon salt
- ½ cup milk
- 1 large or 2 medium-size apples
- 2 tablespoons soft butter
- 1 tablespoon melted butter
- ½ cup confectioners' sugar
- 1 teaspoon ground cinnamon
- Juice of 1 lemon

Beat the eggs until very light, using a whisk or rotary beater. Add the flour and salt; mix. Add the milk, then beat again with the whisk until the batter is very smooth. Core and peel the apples and cut them into thin slices.

Spread the bottom and sides of a large 9- or 11-inch iron frying pan with the soft butter. Pour the batter into the buttered pan. Cover with the thin apple slices. Bake in a 400° F. oven for 20 minutes. Reduce heat to 325° F. and cook until the pancake is well puffed all around the sides and golden brown all over.

Slip the pancake onto a hot round platter. Pour the melted butter on top, then sprinkle with the confectioners' sugar and cinnamon mixed together. Squeeze the lemon juice over all. Serve hot. Makes 4 servings.

Lemon crêpes

This Australian specialty is served at luncheon or dinner as a dessert.

¼ cup soft unsalted butter	½ cup milk
¼ cup sugar	½ cup all-purpose flour
2 eggs, separated	Butter
Grated rind of ½ lemon	Sugar
	2 lemons, cut into wedges

Cream together the butter and sugar. Beat the egg yolks lightly, then add them to the creamed mixture. Mix well, then stir in the lemon rind and milk. With a whisk, beat in the flour until the batter is smooth. Beat the egg whites until stiff, then fold them into the batter.

Drop the batter by generous tablespoons onto a well-buttered heated heavy frying pan or crêpe pan. Brown the crêpes on both sides. As they are finished, fold them into quarters and set on a warm platter. Sprinkle lightly with sugar. Serve with the lemon wedges. Each person may add lemon and more sugar to his own taste. Makes about 18 small crêpes.

Simone's crêpes

1 tablespoon brandy	2 tablespoons sugar
1 cup apricot or strawberry jam	1 cup milk
1 cup all-purpose flour	2 eggs
⅛ teaspoon salt	Melted butter
	Vanilla sugar

Stir the brandy into the jam. Set aside.

In a bowl stir together the flour, salt and sugar. Gradually add milk and eggs. Stir or beat with a wire whisk until you have a smooth batter with the texture of heavy cream.

Heat a 7- or 8-inch frying pan and coat it with melted butter. Pour in just enough batter to cover the bottom with a thin layer. Tilt the pan to spread the batter evenly. Cook over medium heat until top is firm. Turn and brown the second side lightly. Place on a warm platter and go on cooking more crêpes until the batter is all used. In the meantime, as each crêpe is cooked, spread the surface with a thin coating of prepared jam. Roll crêpes neatly and set one next to the other in an ovenproof dish. When all are done, sprinkle with vanilla sugar. Warm in a 250° F. oven for a few minutes. Makes about 20 crêpes.

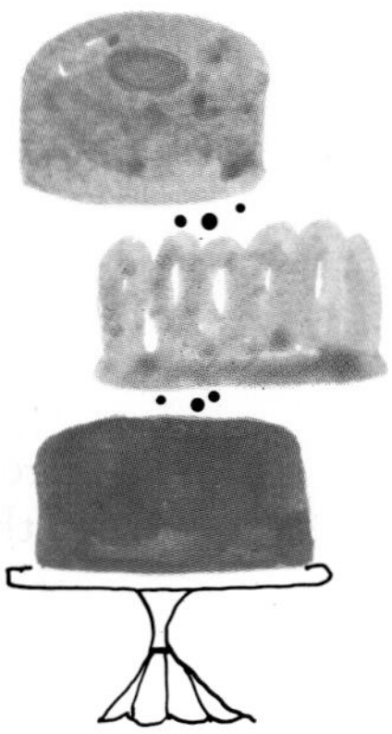

CAKES

Homemade cakes are the glory of flour bakery. Some are baked in loaf pans, like breads, others in ring molds or springform pans, and some in shallow pans to make thin layers that are later sandwiched together with delicious filling or frosting.

Sponge cake is made with whole eggs but without fat. Angel food cake is made with only the whites of eggs but also without fat. Pound cakes were originally made with one pound each of sugar, butter, eggs and flour, but the recipes in this book have been scaled down to modern needs.

There are eggless cakes, too, and among the recipes that follow you will find a cake that is raised by yeast. With the help of electric appliances like the mixer, cake making has become much simpler. The electric mixer speeds up the process of blending the ingredients and it beats a lot of air into them. A new kind of cake was developed—a one-bowl cake. The batter is prepared in one bowl with the electric mixer, and usually shortening rather than butter is used: with these cakes all the ingredients must be at room temperature to mix well.

Ingredients for cakes

Like quick breads, cakes may be leavened with baking powder or baking soda, or with air beaten into the batter. Eggs, too, provide leavening action.

Cakes can be made with all-purpose flour, but cake flour makes a lighter cake. If you use self-rising flour, be sure to omit any other baking powder or baking soda. Do not overbeat cake batter after adding the flour or too much gluten will develop and toughen the cake.

Granulated or confectioners' sugar are the usual sugars for cakes. Confectioners' sugar makes a fine-grained cake, but it will dry out sooner than one made with granulated sugar. When using confectioners' sugar, be sure to sift it, because the cornstarch in it may have absorbed moisture and caused lumps.

Butter used as the shortening gives delicious flavor, and sweet butter is especially good. You may also use vegetable shortenings, alone or in combination with butter.

Eggs for cakes are beaten vigorously to get as much air as possible into them. Follow the directions for each cake for mixing and beating, because different recipes need different handling. Read the section on meringues (p. 246) for information on beating egg whites. Also read about folding egg whites into a soufflé mixture (p. 238); this is similar to the procedure for folding them into a cake batter. The freshest eggs give the most volume, and this is especially important for sponge cakes, angel food and pound cakes.

Chocolate is one of the favorite flavorings for cakes. Unsweetened chocolate is used most often; it comes in square or rectangular blocks, and also in premelted 1-ounce packets. Semisweet and sweet chocolate are used in some recipes. Solid chocolate is melted before adding it to cake mixtures. O━ Be sure to cool melted chocolate before adding it to eggs, because the eggs should not start cooking until the pans go in the oven. O━ Melt chocolate over very low heat, or in the top of a double boiler over hot water. Butter melted with the chocolate helps to prevent burning the chocolate and also makes it easier to clean the pan afterward.

Before you start mixing a cake, set your oven at the correct temperature, to be certain it will be hot enough when your batter is ready, and prepare your pans. Grease pans well, or line them with wax paper, or leave them ungreased, as the recipe directs. Sometimes a cake pan is greased, then dusted with flour or sprinkled with sugar or fine crumbs. If a recipe specifies any of these, knock the pan gently to shake out excess particles before you put the batter into the pan.

Lemon pound cake

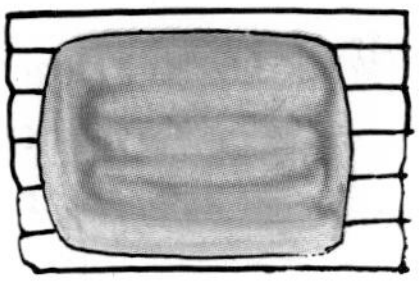

Soft butter
2 cups sifted pastry or cake flour
½ teaspoon salt
¼ teaspoon baking powder
⅔ cup butter, softened
1 cup superfine sugar
4 eggs
1 teaspoon grated lemon rind
1½ tablespoons lemon juice

Brush the bottom and sides of a loaf pan (8½ × 4½ × 2½ inches) with soft butter. Line the bottom with a single thickness of wax paper, then brush the paper with butter.

Sift together the flour, salt and baking powder. Cream the ⅔ cup soft butter and gradually beat in the sugar. Continue to beat until light and fluffy. Add the eggs one at a time, beating well after each addition. Beat in the lemon rind and juice.

Add the sifted dry ingredients, a little at a time, to the creamed mixture and mix lightly after each addition. Spread the batter evenly in the prepared pan. Bake in a preheated 350° F. oven for 1 to 1½ hours, or until a cake tester or toothpick inserted in the center comes out clean. Cool in the pan on a rack for about 10 minutes. Loosen around the edges with a knife and remove from the pan. Peel off the paper and cool completely on a rack.

Rose-geranium pound cake

Rosewater can be purchased in drugstores. If you cannot find a rose geranium plant, bake the cake without the leaves; it will still be good.

1 cup unsalted butter, softened
1 cup sugar
¼ cup clear honey
5 eggs
2 cups cake flour, sifted
Grated rind of ½ lemon
1 teaspoon rosewater
2 teaspoons lemon juice
5 fresh leaves of rose geranium

Cream the butter and sugar until very light and fluffy. Add the honey and mix well. Add the eggs, one at a time, beating well after each addition. Gradually add the cake flour, blending thoroughly after each addition. (If using an electric mixer, do this at moderate speed.) Add the lemon rind, rosewater and lemon juice; stir well.

Grease a loaf pan (9 × 5 × 3 inches) and line the bottom with the rose-geranium leaves. If these are unavailable, line the pan with wax paper and grease the paper. Pour in the batter. Bake in a 350° F. oven for about 1¼ hours.

When the cake is baked, place on a rack and let it stand for 15 minutes before unmolding. Cool completely, then wrap in a double layer of foil. This cake will keep fresh without refrigeration for 2 to 3 weeks and requires no icing. If desired, icing sugar can be sprinkled on top just before serving.

Double-rich chocolate cake

- 2 cups sifted pastry or cake flour
- 1 teaspoon baking soda
- ¼ teaspoon salt
- ½ cup butter
- 1¼ cups superfine sugar
- 2 eggs
- 3 ounces (3 squares) unsweetened chocolate
- 1 cup milk
- 1 teaspoon almond extract
- Chocolate Frosting (recipe follows)

Sift flour and measure out 2 cups. Sift again with the baking soda and the salt. Cream the butter and gradually add the sugar. Beat together until light and fluffy. Add the eggs, one at a time, and beat well after each addition. Melt the chocolate and cool it. Add it to the butter mixture and mix thoroughly. Add the sifted flour mixture gradually, alternating with the milk to which the almond extract has been added. Divide the batter between two buttered 8-inch layer-cake pans. Bake in a preheated 350° F. oven for 25 to 30 minutes. Unmold and cool. Fill and frost.

DOUBLE-RICH CHOCOLATE FROSTING

- 2 eggs
- 2 cups sifted confectioners' sugar
- Pinch of salt
- 1 teaspoon vanilla extract
- ¼ teaspoon almond extract
- ¼ cup milk
- 5 ounces (5 squares) unsweetened chocolate
- 2 tablespoons butter

Break the eggs into a bowl and add the confectioners' sugar and salt. Add the vanilla and almond extracts and the milk. Beat until smooth and creamy. Set this bowl in a larger bowl filled with ice cubes.

Melt the chocolate with the butter. Add this gradually to the sugar and egg mixture. Continue beating with a hand beater until very thick, 8 to 10 minutes. Use to fill and frost the cake.

An 8-inch round cake will make 8 to 12 servings, depending on how big you make the pieces.

Buttermilk spice cake

Keep this handy in your freezer for an emergency. For a picnic, bring it along in its baking pan, wrapped and frozen. There are no eggs in this cake.

- 2 1/4 cups all-purpose flour
- 1 1/2 cups sugar
- 1 1/2 teaspoons baking soda
- 1 teaspoon baking powder
- 1/4 teaspoon salt
- 1 teaspoon ground cinnamon
- 1/2 teaspoon ground cloves
- 1/2 cup melted butter or margarine
- 1 1/2 cups buttermilk, at room temperature
- Sugar

Sift together into a mixing bowl the flour, sugar, baking soda, baking powder, salt, cinnamon and cloves. Cool the melted butter or margarine and stir into the flour mixture along with the buttermilk. Mix vigorously until the batter is very smooth.

Grease a 10-inch tube cake pan and dust lightly with granulated sugar. Pour in the batter. Bake in a preheated 325° to 350° F. oven for about 1 hour, or until a cake tester comes out clean. Cool on a cake rack for 15 minutes, then unmold.

To freeze, cool for at least 3 hours before wrapping. To serve, slice thin.

Rose sponge cake

- 6 eggs
- 1/2 teaspoon salt
- 1 1/2 cups superfine sugar
- 1 tablespoon rosewater
- 1 tablespoon grated orange rind
- 3 tablespoons orange juice
- 3 tablespoons lemon juice
- 1 3/4 cups all-purpose flour
- Confectioners' sugar

Take the eggs out of the refrigerator at least an hour before making the cake, but separate the eggs while they are still cold.

When they have reached room temperature, beat the whites in the large bowl of an electric mixer at medium speed until foamy. Add the salt. Add 1/2 cup of the superfine sugar, beating in 2 tablespoons at a time. Continue beating until soft peaks form when beater is slowly raised. Set aside.

In another bowl, beat the yolks until thick and lemon-colored. Then gradually add the remaining cup of superfine sugar to the yolks, beating until very thick. Then add the orange rind, rosewater and fruit juices. When well mixed, gradually add the flour. Do not stir more than 1 minute. Fold in the beaten egg whites very carefully until well blended. Pour the batter into an ungreased 10-inch tube pan. Bake in a 350° F. oven for 40 minutes, or until done. Invert the pan on a bottle or funnel if the tube has a hole, or turn it over on a wire rack. Let cool completely before unmolding. Then turn out onto a large round plate.

To decorate, sprinkle the cake with pink sugar, then with sifted confectioners' sugar. Make pink sugar by adding a few drops of red vegetable coloring to granulated sugar and rubbing with the back of a spoon until the sugar is evenly colored. Decorate with fresh roses. Makes 10 to 12 servings.

Orange baba

This cake can be prepared a day or so ahead. It is delicious by itself, or with ice cream, or with thawed frozen strawberries.

- 2 cups all-purpose flour
- 1 teaspoon baking powder
- ½ teaspoon baking soda
- ¼ teaspoon salt
- ½ cup butter or margarine
- Grated rind of 1 orange
- 1 cup granulated sugar
- 2 eggs, separated
- 1 cup commercial sour cream
- ½ cup chopped walnuts
- ½ cup candied cherries, cut into halves
- Juice of 2 oranges
- ½ cup confectioners' sugar

Sift together twice the flour, baking powder, baking soda and salt. Cream the butter or margarine until soft and fluffy, then gradually add the grated orange rind and the granulated sugar. Continue creaming until light. Beat the egg yolks and add to the creamed mixture. Beat vigorously. Add the sifted dry ingredients alternately with the sour cream, mixing well. Add the walnuts and the halved cherries. Beat the egg whites until stiff and fold them into the creamed mixture. Pour the batter into a greased and floured loaf pan (8 × 4 × 3 inches), filling the pan only three quarters full. Bake in a 350° F. oven for about 50 minutes, until golden brown.

Stir the orange juice and confectioners' sugar together. Pour over the cake while it is still warm. Cool on a cake rack and unmold when cold. Makes 8 or more servings.

Grapefruit cake

¼ pound butter
1 cup sugar
6 egg yolks
1 teaspoon vanilla extract
½ teaspoon grated grapefruit rind (optional)
2 cups all-purpose flour
1 cup cornstarch
3 teaspoons baking powder
½ teaspoon salt
½ teaspoon grated nutmeg
⅓ cup honey
1 cup grapefruit juice

Cream the butter. Add sugar and cream it until it is dissolved in the butter. Add egg yolks separately, beating after each addition, plus vanilla and grated rind. (Grapefruit rind is more bitter than other citrus rinds; do not use any more than this, or leave it out if you prefer.) Sift flour, cornstarch, baking powder, salt and nutmeg. Mix honey with grapefruit juice. Add dry ingredients and liquids to the butter mixture. Mix only until the batter is smooth, then put it in a buttered 8-inch ring mold. The mold should be two thirds full. Bake the cake in a preheated 375° F. oven for 45 minutes to 1 hour. Let the cake cool for a few minutes, then invert it on a rack and let it cool completely. If you like, ice it with confectioners' sugar icing (recipe follows) made with grapefruit juice. Makes about 12 pieces.

CONFECTIONERS' SUGAR ICING

½ cup butter
5 cups sifted confectioners' sugar
¼ to ½ cup liquid (citrus juice, milk, coffee, liqueur, etc.)
½ teaspoon salt (if using sweet butter)

Cream butter; add sugar and beat well until the mixture is smooth. Add the liquid (with the salt, if you are using sweet butter), a few tablespoons at a time, until the icing has a good consistency for spreading. Makes about 2 cups.

Cinnamon orange savarin

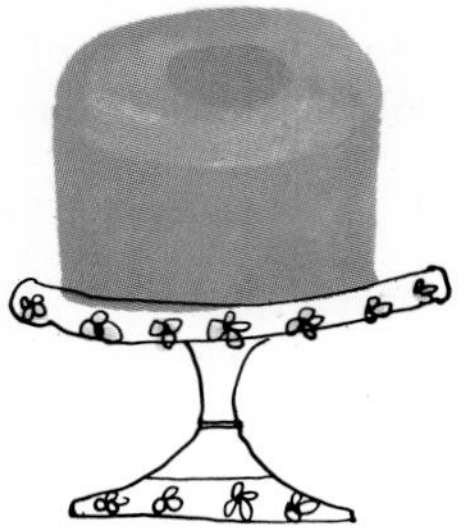

This famous French cake is raised with yeast, like bread. Although some recipes give directions for kneading, the dough is so soft it is better to treat it like a batter bread and encourage the gluten development by beating.

1 package dry yeast
1/4 cup warm water
3 cups cake flour
1 teaspoon salt
3 tablespoons confectioners' sugar
1 tablespoon ground cinnamon
4 eggs
1/4 cup orange juice
10 tablespoons sweet butter

In a large bowl, dissolve the yeast in the water. Sift together the flour, salt, sugar and cinnamon. Beat the eggs until fluffy. Heat the orange juice to 110° F. and, beating all the while, add it to the eggs. Then add dry ingredients and liquids to the yeast. Mix well. Beat with a wooden spoon for 10 minutes. Cover the bowl and let the dough rise until doubled, 45 minutes to 1 hour.

Cream the butter until soft and fluffy and very light in color. Punch down the risen dough and beat the butter into it. Spoon the dough—it will be soft—into a buttered 10-inch tube pan with removable sides; the dough should half fill the pan. (There are special pans for savarins with much larger center holes. If you can find one of these, use it instead.) Smooth the top of the dough with a spatula. Cover the pan and let the dough rise again until it nearly fills the pan, about 20 minutes.

Preheat oven to 375° F. Bake the savarin for 30 minutes, until it tests done. Meanwhile, make the syrup which is an essential part of this classic cake.

CINNAMON ORANGE SYRUP

1 1/2 cups orange juice
1 cup sugar
2 cinnamon sticks
1/4 cup 151-proof rum

In a large pan (at least 2-quart size) over low heat, heat orange juice and sugar until sugar is all dissolved. Add cinnamon sticks and bring the syrup to a boil; let it boil gently for 10 minutes. Occasionally stir the syrup. *Turn off the heat.* While standing away from the pot, add the rum. It will instantly boil up in a furious foam; you can understand why you need a large pot.

By this time the cake should be baked. Let it rest for a few minutes, then run a thin-bladed knife around the outside edge of the cake and lift the center portion out of the sides. Let the cake rest for a few more minutes, then loosen the spindle and the bottom of the cake. As soon as the cake is just cool enough to hold, lift it off the pan onto a large round plate with a rather deep center. Pierce the cake all over the top with a metal skewer or with a 2-tined kitchen fork. Ladle some of the hot syrup over the cake. When that is absorbed, pour more over. Make more holes in the top now and then. If too much syrup gathers in the bottom of the plate, gently pour it back into the syrup pan. Keep pouring syrup over the cake until it is all absorbed. This process takes quite a long time; it is easier if the cake is warm and the syrup hot.

With a dampened paper towel, clean off the edges of the plate. Savarins are often glazed, or decorated with candied fruits or filled with fruits soaked in liqueurs. However, even without them the cake is very rich and looks attractive because of the syrup. Makes 20 to 30 servings.

COOKIES

The first two cookie doughs below must be rolled out and cut into rounds. The oat and raisin cookies are cut into bars after baking. In the fourth recipe the dough is dropped from a spoon onto a cookie sheet.

Lampi's ginger cookies

½ cup sugar
1½ cups molasses
1 cup butter or shortening
4 cups all-purpose flour
1 tablespoon baking soda
½ tablespoon ground cinnamon
½ tablespoon ground ginger
1 teaspoon ground cardamom
½ teaspoon salt
1 cup buttermilk
2 egg whites
Sugar

Place the sugar and molasses in a saucepan. Stir over low heat until the sugar is melted. Add the butter or shortening and continue to stir over low heat until the butter is melted. Then remove from heat and cool.

Sift 3 cups of flour with the baking soda, cinnamon, ginger, cardamom and salt. Measure the fourth cup of flour and set aside. Add the dry ingredients to the molasses mixture alternately with the buttermilk, then mix thoroughly until you have a soft dough. If needed, use some of the reserved flour. Turn out the dough on a floured table and knead for 5 minutes. Wrap and refrigerate for 5 to 8 hours.

Roll out the dough into a sheet ¼ inch thick. Cut into 2-inch rounds. Brush each round with slightly beaten egg white. If you wish, sprinkle each one with a pinch of sugar. Place the cookies 1 inch apart on buttered baking sheets. Bake in a 350° F. oven for 15 to 20 minutes. Makes about 4 dozen cookies.

Vanilla cookies

- ½ cup salted butter
- 1 cup sifted confectioners' sugar
- 2 small eggs, well beaten
- 1½ tablespoons vanilla extract
- 3 to 4 cups sifted all-purpose flour
- Vanilla sugar (made with granulated sugar)

Cream the butter until very fluffy, then beat in the confectioners' sugar. Add eggs and vanilla and mix well. Then add as much of the flour as needed to make a dough you can roll out. Put about a third of the dough at a time on a pastry cloth or floured board (use as little flour as possible on the board). Roll out the dough as thin as you can, and cut with a small cookie cutter. Put the rounds on baking sheets covered with wax paper. Sprinkle the tops with vanilla sugar. Bake in a preheated 350° F. oven for about 12 minutes, until cookies are just lightly browned on the edges. Do not let them get too brown. Makes about 50 cookies.

For variations, use cinnamon or anisette sugar for the tops; or sandwich 2 cookies together with lemon or chocolate icing. The plain cookies are good with fruits such as strawberries, or with ice cream and sherbet.

Oat and raisin bars

- ⅓ cup shortening
- ⅔ cup brown sugar
- 2 tablespoons molasses
- 1 egg
- ½ cup sifted all-purpose flour
- ¼ teaspoon baking soda
- ¼ teaspoon salt
- ¾ cup quick-cooking rolled oats
- 1 cup seedless raisins, rinsed and drained

Melt the shortening and pour it into a bowl. Stir in the sugar and molasses. Add the egg and beat well. Sift the flour, baking soda and salt into the shortening mixture. Then blend in the rolled oats and the raisins. Turn into a greased 8-inch-square pan. Bake in a 350° F. oven for 25 to 30 minutes. Cool. Cut into bars. Makes 32 small bars.

Oatmeal fruit cookies

This is the kind of cookie called a "drop cookie" because the dough is dropped by the spoonful onto a baking sheet without further shaping. Often this type of cookie spreads out during baking, so you must leave space between the mounds of batter.

- 1½ cups all-purpose flour
- 1¾ cups sugar
- 1 teaspoon baking powder
- ½ teaspoon baking soda
- 1 teaspoon salt
- 1 teaspoon ground cinnamon
- 3 cups rolled oats
- 1 cup chopped candied cherries
- ½ cup chopped walnuts
- 1 cup melted butter or margarine
- 2 eggs
- ½ cup milk

Sift together the flour, sugar, baking powder, baking soda, salt and cinnamon. Add the oats, candied cherries and walnuts. Stir together. Make a well in the middle and add the melted butter or margarine. Then add the eggs and finally the milk. Mix until thoroughly blended. Drop by spoonfuls onto an ungreased baking sheet, leaving about 1½ inches between the spoonfuls of batter. Bake in a preheated 400° F. oven for 10 to 12 minutes. Cool on a wire rack. Store in an airtight box. Makes about 72 cookies.

PASTRY

Pastry ingredients

The principal ingredients of all pastry crusts are flour, fat and liquid. Their proportions and the methods of combining them account for the differences in the various types of piecrusts.

Pastry flours

The best flour for pastry, in general, is *all-purpose flour,* sifted once before measuring. Cake flour is not satisfactory, and instantized flour works well only with specially adapted recipes. *Pastry flour* can be used too, but it is not easy to work with and the baked pastry is often brittle. Use it only for recipes that specify it. You will find some in the material that follows.

Shortenings

Lard, butter, margarine or vegetable shortenings are the fats used in pastry making. These are what make the pastry "short"—that is, tender, flaky, crumbly. The fat in the mixture coats the particles of flour so water cannot reach them. This keeps the gluten strands shorter; only the particles not coated with shortening develop gluten. (Gluten, so essential for yeast breads, makes pastry tough.)

LARD is the shortest of all and makes excellent pastry.

BUTTER is the best when flavor and flakiness are the prime requirements, as in puff pastry, but it is difficult to make such pastry without lots of practice, and butter pastry does not keep well. For other types of pastry, do not use butter alone, because it does not have the proper shortening power and it provides too much moisture.

VEGETABLE SHORTENING is used most often in pastry. While the word "shortening" is sometimes applied to any fat, including butter and margarine and even oil, in baking it usually means the vegetable shortenings that are solid at room temperature and have no characteristic taste or odor of their own. There are several of these generally available, and they do make short pastry, but not the flakiest ones.

Whatever the fat, it should be well chilled before it is used.

Liquids

The most-used liquid in piecrusts is water, but milk, cream, lemon juice or eggs are used in various recipes. Cold liquid, not necessarily iced, gives the best results. Lukewarm liquid softens the fat and produces pastry that is too hard or brittle. The exception to this is hot-water pastry, which is made with very hot water according to a different set of rules.

Mixing piecrust

The first step is to measure the once-sifted flour with whatever other dry ingredients are called for in the recipe. Put these dry ingredients into a bowl large enough to blend everything with ease.

The next step is to cut in the cold shortening. By "cutting in" is meant literally cutting the fat into tiny particles as you mix it in the flour. A pastry blender is designed especially for this purpose, but you can use two round-ended knives. Hold a knife in each hand and cut through the fat and flour, moving the knives in opposite directions but parallel to each other. In a few minutes you will have a mixture that looks like rough cornmeal—not smooth but a little lumpy. The finer the fat is cut into the flour, the more tender and crumbly the crust will be. Larger pieces of fat make the piecrust more flaky.

Since it is important that pastry be both tender and flaky, a modern method is to divide the fat required for the recipe into two lots. Cut the first lot into the flour as fine as possible, then cut in the other lot to make particles the size of large peas. A good rule is: a little cutting rather than too much with the second half of the fat.

Do not be tempted to mix the fat into the flour with your hands. The warmth of your hands would soften the fat, preventing formation of the separate particles of fat and their even distribution throughout

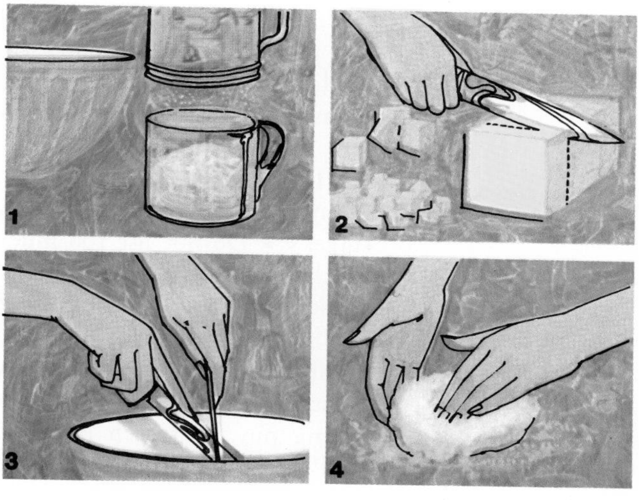

1. Measure the sifted flour and any other dry ingredients.

2. Cut the cold shortening into small pieces and add to the dry ingredients.

3. Cut the shortening into the flour mixture with a pastry blender or 2 knives.

4. When the liquid is added, work the dough into a round mass with the tips of the fingers.

the flour. Do not use a fork either, as it will tend to mash the fat as though creaming it, and the fat will become too soft.

Then comes the addition of the liquid. This is the most critical step in mixing piecrust. The difficulty is caused by the variations in the flours we use. Some absorb much more liquid than others, and there is nothing on the bag of flour to tell you about it. Therefore it is impossible to give exact measurements for the amount of liquid required. To understand the desired texture, learn how to feel it.

Add cold measured liquid one tablespoon at a time, sprinkling it over the dry mixture and mixing lightly, preferably with a fork. Little clumps will form; push them to one side of the bowl and sprinkle in more liquid until all the mixture is lightly moistened. It should be stirred only enough to make a shapeless mass. Do not try to make a ball of dough in the bowl—that would require the addition of too much liquid. The dough should be soft, semidry, not sticky, but moist enough to hold together when you start working it together with your fingertips.

At this point, do not worry about handling the dough too much. Turn the dough out onto a floured board and form it into a round ball with your fingers. If any of it falls away from the mass, moisten it with a few drops of water until it will cling to the rest in the ball.

Some types of pastry dough, usually those made with lard or vegetable shortening, can be rolled out at this point. But pastry made with butter benefits from chilling for 4 to 12 hours in the refrigerator, which firms the butter and produces flakier crusts.

Rolling piecrust

Many a good pastry recipe has been spoiled at this stage. 🗝 Do not use too much flour on the table or on the rolling pin, as it hardens the best of doughs. A stockinette covering the rolling pin helps greatly but is not essential.

First, cut off a piece of dough big enough for a crust, then pat it into a semiflat round. Now use the rolling pin to stretch it out to a flat, round sheet. Roll the pastry from the center out, all around.

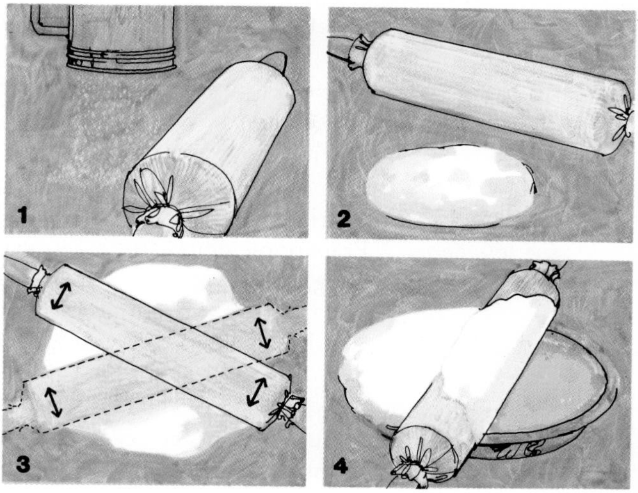

1. Sprinkle the table with flour and use a rolling pin with a stockinette covering.

2. Shape a piece of dough into a semiflat round.

3. Roll the pastry from the center out, all around.

4. Roll the finished dough onto the rolling pin and transfer to the pie plate.

Lift the pastry if necessary to add more flour on the table, but try not to turn it over. If some corners break, simply stick them together with your fingers. When the rolling is finished, the easiest way to transfer the dough to the pie pan is this: place the rolling pin gently on the dough at one side and roll the dough up onto the pin. Then position the rolling pin over one side of the pan and unroll the dough over it.

The next step is to fit the pastry very loosely into the pan. 🔑 Do not attempt to smooth it perfectly, for this will cause shrinkage during baking.

Fluting and crimping

To flute is to pinch the edges of pastry together along the rim of the pie plate, making little folds or pleats at regular intervals. You can do this with your fingertips or with a knife handle, and you can make the fluting as simple or as fancy as you please. Another way is to crimp the edges of the dough with the tines

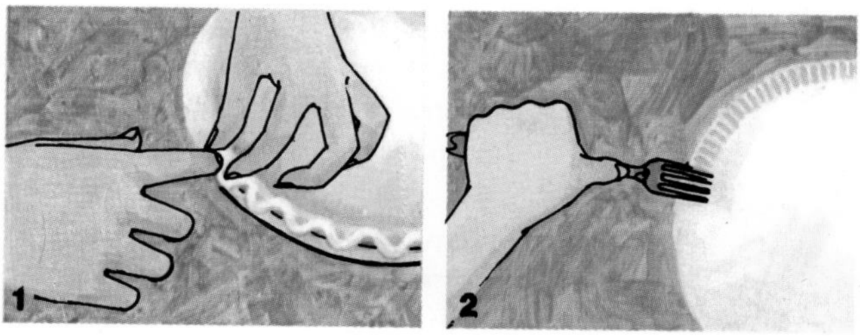

1. Use your fingertips to make a folded or pleated edge.

2. Make an edge around the pie by pressing with the tines of a fork.

of a fork. These finishes at the rim of the pie pans not only make the pies look neat but seal together the upper and lower crusts so that the filling will not ooze out, or give more stiffness to the edge of a 1-crust pie and prevent its shrinking away from the rim.

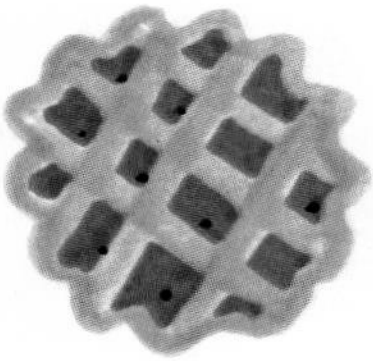

Lattice top

Prepare pie dough for a 2-crust 9-inch pie. Divide the dough. Roll out half and fit it into the pie pan. Roll out the rest and cut it into strips ½ inch wide. Fill the dough-lined pan and lay half of the pastry strips over the filling about 1 inch apart. Fold alternate strips back a little more than halfway. Place a strip of dough across the center of the filling at right angles to the first strips. Unfold strips that were turned back. Now fold back the strips in the first row that were not turned back at first. Lay the next strip at right angles again, and lay the folded strips back. Continue this process to the edge. Then work from the center to the opposite edge in the same manner. This will give a basket-weave lattice. Cut the ends of the strips even with the edge of the pie pan. Fold lower crust over these ends and press together tightly. Flute or crimp to form a sealed edge. Bake as for any 2-crust pie.

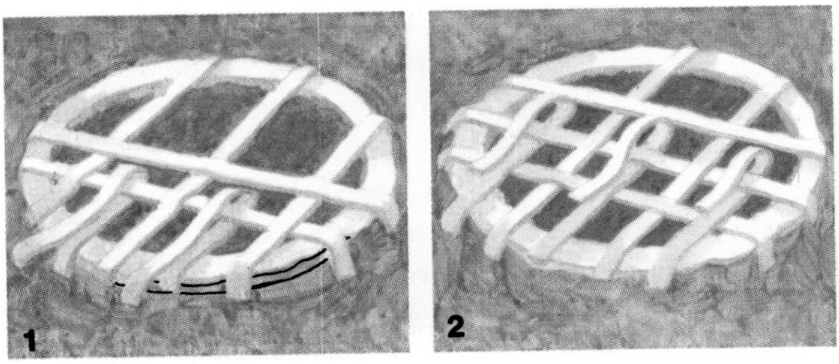

1. Placing the second strip across; alternate strips are folded back.

2. Placing the third strip across; when the original strips are returned to place, the over-under lattice will be complete.

Professional finish of top crust

When ready to bake, brush the top crust or lattice top with either 1 egg white lightly beaten or 1 egg yolk beaten with 2 teaspoons cold water and ½ teaspoon sugar, or simply with cream or milk. This will add crispness, glaze and rich color to the top crust.

How to prevent a soggy bottom crust

O━ If you are filling the unbaked crust with a wet filling such as custard, first set the crust: prick the crust all over. Brush the inside with 1 egg white lightly beaten with 1 teaspoon of cold water. Chill for 30 minutes, then put into a preheated 450° F. oven for 5 minutes. Let the crust cool to room temperature, pour the filling in and then bake according to the recipe requirements.

🗝 When you have a single crust to be baked before filling, prick the crust, brush with the same mixture of egg white and water and chill for 1 hour. Then bake and cool before adding the filling.

🗝 Never pour a hot filling into a hot or cold pie shell; both must be cooled.

🗝 For a pie to be filled with fruits, it helps to coat the bottom crust first with a mixture of 1 teaspoon each of flour and sugar. After the pie is filled, bake it in a preheated 425° F. oven for 15 to 20 minutes, then lower the heat to recipe specifications to finish the cooking.

In general, sear all wet pies in a preheated 425° F. oven for 15 minutes. Then lower the heat to 350° F. and watch to avoid overcooking.

🗝 Bake an unfilled pie shell quickly in the middle of an upper shelf of the oven, but bake a double-crust pie on a lower shelf where the bottom crust will set faster.

How to solve some other pastry-making problems

Here are answers to some of the questions you may have when your pies are not quite right.

Why is the crust hard? Too little shortening, or too much water, or handling the dough too long when adding the water, or excess flour on table and rolling pin could cause this trouble.

Why does lemon pie filling turn runny when cold? Not only lemon pie does this; chocolate cream pie or butterscotch pie made with brown sugar may also turn runny. All these pie fillings include ingredients that act upon the starch used in thickening and prevent its full effectiveness.

In a lemon pie, your recipe may be right one time and runny the next; an extra-sour lemon may cause the trouble. 🗝 To be sure with lemon pie, add 1 teaspoon more of the starch thickener than your recipe specifies.

In cream fillings thickened partly with starch and partly with eggs, incomplete cooking is usually the cause of trouble. Be sure the mixture is thoroughly cooked before adding the eggs. The best way to make sure is to taste a bit of the mixture. You will feel the grittiness of the flour or cornstarch on your tongue if they are not thoroughly cooked. When the maximum thickening is obtained, add the eggs called for in the recipe and cook for 3 minutes longer.

Another cause of a runny filling may be that too much sugar was used. Sugar liquifies during cooking and tends to thin the mixture.

Why does the crust shrink in the plate? Too much fat in the pastry may be the cause, or pastry may not have been fitted loosely enough in the plate. It is better to let a few creases or wrinkles remain in the crust rather than to stretch the pastry while smoothing it.

Why does a single crust puff and get bumpy? Puffiness and bumpiness are caused by air trapped under the crust. Tap the crust with the tips of your fingers after it is fitted into the pan, then prick it all over with the tines of a fork before it goes into the oven. And be sure your oven is preheated.

How do you stop juices in fruit pies from running over the stove? The best method is to use what our grandmothers used with their fruit pies—a ceramic bird, head up, mouth open. These were called "pie birds" and are still fairly easy to find in the stores. If you do not have one, insert four to five pieces of uncooked macaroni in openings in the upper crust. The excess juice boils up into these and not out at the edges of the pie. Another way is to make a funnel or tube of stiff paper. Whatever you use, remove it before serving the pie.

How do you prevent "weepy" meringue? Be sure the meringue is spread over *cooled* filling and completely touches the edges of the crust all around. After baking, cool it away from drafts, and never in the refrigerator. Other important suggestions for successful meringues are found on pages 246 to 247.

Basic pastry

The following all-purpose shortening pastry is a basic crust, light and flaky, and a good one for beginners to practice on. The basic ingredients are nothing more than pastry flour and vegetable shortening.

Size of pie–inches	Pastry flour sifted once–cups	Salt–teaspoons	Shortening–cups	Cold water–tablespoons
1 crust–7 or 8	1	½	⅓	1 to 2
2 crusts–7 or 8	1½	1	½	2 to 3
1 crust–9	1½	1	½	2 to 3
2 crusts–9	2	1¼	⅔	3 to 4

1. Sift some flour. Measure what you need and sift it with the salt into a bowl.

2. Cut in the shortening with a pastry blender or two knives, until the mixture has the general consistency of cornmeal with some of the lumps the size of small peas.

3. Sprinkle cold water, 1 tablespoon at a time, over different parts of the flour mixture. Toss together lightly with a fork. Use just enough water to moisten the dough.

4. Turn dough out on wax paper. Knead three to six times with the tips of your fingers. Press gently with the wax paper to form into a ball. Let stand for 15 to 20 minutes.

5. Lightly flour a pastry cloth or board and a rolling pin (or the pin can be covered with a stockinette to make rolling out easier).

Rolling and fitting dough

These rules for rolling and fitting dough apply to most crusts.

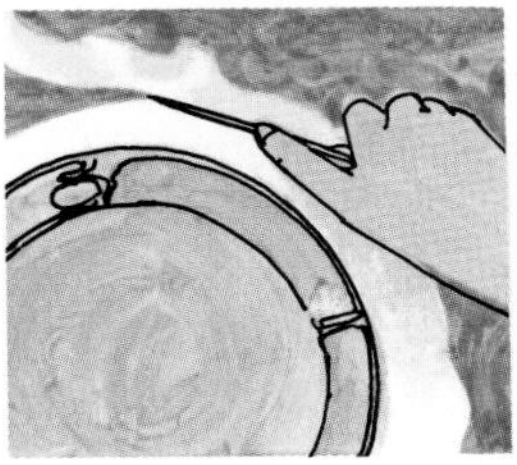

For 1-crust pie

1. Roll the dough into a sheet ⅛ inch thick. To measure, invert the pie pan on the dough and mark a circle 1½ inches larger than the pan.

2. Fold the dough over the rolling pin and lift onto the pan. Fit the pastry loosely; do not stretch it. Trim edges of pastry and fold under to fit the rim of the pie pan. Flute the edges.

3. For a baked pastry shell, prick pastry evenly with a fork. Bake in a preheated 450° F. oven for 10 to 12 minutes. For unbaked pastry, sear in a preheated

450° F. oven for 5 minutes, then cool. Add filling and bake according to directions for the filling.

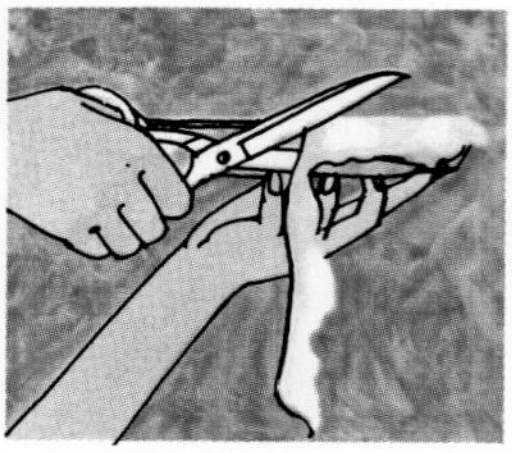

For 2-crust pie

1. Divide dough into halves.
2. Roll out the dough for the bottom crust as for the 1-crust pie, but trim the pastry at the rim of the pie pan.
3. Roll out and cut a strip of dough 1-inch wide, long enough to go around the edge of the pan. (It can be in two or three pieces.) Use water on your fingertips or pastry brush to moisten the edge of the dough on the pan. Then press the strip of dough to the edge all around, making it even with the outside edge of the pan.
4. Roll out the rest of the dough into a circle ⅛ inch thick and large enough to extend ½ inch beyond the edge of the pie pan.
5. Pour the filling into the pastry.
6. Place top crust over the filling. Cut a few slits in it, to allow steam to escape. Fold the edge of the top pastry under the edge of the bottom pastry and seal by pressing the two crusts together. Flute the edge of the crust. Bake the pie according to the directions for the filling.

Electric-mixer pastry

This pastry takes only 45 seconds to mix.

Size of pie–inches	Shortening (soft)–cups	Pastry flour–cups	Salt–teaspoons	Water–tablespoons
1 crust–8 or 9	¼	¾	½	2
2 crusts–8	½	1½	1	4
2 crusts–9	⅔	1¾	1	4

1. Place shortening, pastry flour and salt in the bowl of an electric mixer. Blend at low speed for about 30 seconds, or until the mixture has the consistency of coarse cornmeal.
2. Add the cold water all at once and mix the ingredients at low speed for about 15 seconds, or until dough clings together.
3. Shape dough into a ball with floured hands. The dough should feel wet.
4. Turn onto a floured board and roll according to directions for the Basic Pastry (p. 521).

Vegetable-oil pastry

For 2-crust 8- or 9-inch pie

1. Sift pastry flour and measure 2 cups, or measure 2 cups all-purpose flour. Stir in 1 teaspoon salt and 1 teaspoon sugar.

2. Combine ½ cup vegetable oil and ¼ cup plus 1 tablespoon ice water in a small bowl and beat with a fork until creamy.

3. Pour the oil and water mixture all at once over the flour and salt. Toss with a fork to blend. The dough will be moist. Flour your hands and shape the dough into a ball. Divide into halves.

4. Shape each half into a flat round and place between two 12-inch squares of wax paper. Pass a damp cloth over the counter under the wax paper before rolling, to keep the paper from slipping. This wax-paper method prevents having to use extra flour and makes the rolling easy; the wet-textured dough does not stick to the wax paper. Roll out the dough between the sheets of paper to make a circle.

5. Remove the top sheet of paper and invert the pastry over the pie pan. Peel off the other sheet and fit the pastry loosely into the pan. Trim edges. Fill pie. Roll the second half of the dough in the same manner as the bottom crust and set it over the filling. Fold edges, seal, flute. Bake the pie according to the directions for the filling you are using.

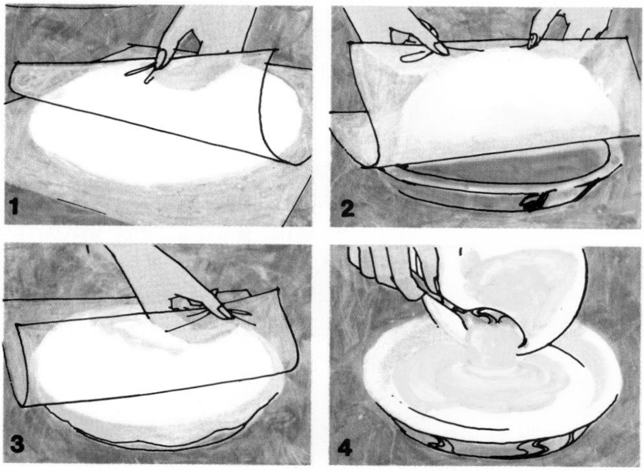

1. Roll out the dough between two 12-inch squares of wax paper; then peel off the top sheet.

2. Lift the round of dough onto the pie plate with the bottom sheet of wax paper on top.

3. Peel off the remaining sheet of paper.

4. Pour the filling into the dough-lined pie plate.

For two 1-crust pie shells

Divide dough into halves, roll, then fit into two pie

pans. Prick all over with a fork. Bake in a 425° F. oven for 14 minutes.

Baking-powder pastry

Many cooks find the following method failureproof.

1. Mix and sift once 2¼ cups all-purpose flour (do not use pastry flour for this crust), 1 teaspoon baking powder and ¾ teaspoon salt.
2. Measure ¼ cup cold water into a bowl. Add ⅓ cup of the sifted flour mixture. Blend them together into a smooth paste.
3. Cut ¾ cup cold shortening into the remaining flour mixture until the particles are the size of peas.
4. Drop the moist flour paste here and there over the dry flour and shortening mixture. Mix lightly with a fork until the pastry will just hold together. Do not overmix.
5. Gather into a ball and wrap in wax paper. Chill for 30 minutes. This makes enough for two pie shells or one 2-crust pie.

No-roll pastry

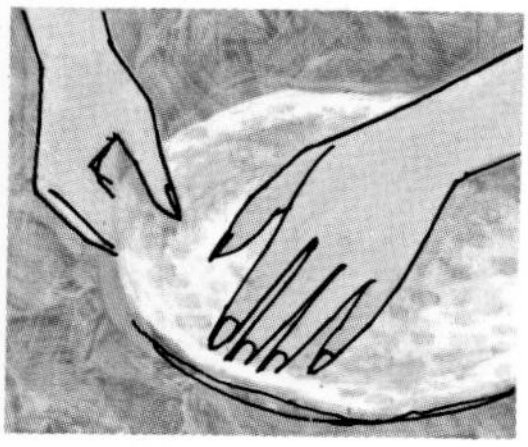

This recipe has merit when you are in a rush or when you want a pie with a special texture. The bottom crust is not rolled, but pressed into the pan; the top crust is made by crumbling bits of the dough mix over the filling.

For 2-crust 8- or 9-inch pie

1. Sift together directly into a pie plate 2 cups all-purpose flour, 2 teaspoons sugar and 1 teaspoon salt.
2. Combine ⅔ cup salad oil and 4 tablespoons cold milk in a measuring cup. Beat with a fork until creamy. Pour all at once into the center of the flour mixture.
3. Mix with a fork until the flour is evenly dampened. Set aside one third of the mixture for the top.
4. Push and press the remaining mixture with your fingers to line the bottom and sides of the pie plate with a layer of uniform thickness. Shape and press to even the edges, and pinch lightly to flute the crust.
5. Fill with the desired filling. Crumble the reserved mixture into small bits with your fingers. Sprinkle over the filling.
6. Bake this type of pie in a preheated 400° F. oven for 15 minutes, then reduce heat to 350° F. and bake

for 30 to 40 minutes longer, or until the filling is done.

For 1-crust 8- or 9-inch pie

Use 1 ½ cups all-purpose flour, 1 ½ teaspoons sugar, ¾ teaspoon salt, ½ cup vegetable oil, 3 tablespoons cold milk. Proceed just as for the 2-crust pie, but use the entire amount without reserving any for the topping. Prick the entire surface of the dough with a fork. Bake in a preheated 425° F. oven for 12 to 15 minutes.

IMPORTANT: Prepare this type of pastry just before baking, and never store or refrigerate it unbaked.

Lard pastry

This is the very best pastry to use for fruit or meat pies, as well as for deep-dish pies. It can be rolled as soon as it is mixed. Also, it keeps excellently for 10 to 12 days if refrigerated. Lard is the old-fashioned type of fat used for piecrust and is still the best.

For two 2-crust pies or four 1-crust pies

1. Sift 3 cups all-purpose flour (do not use pastry flour) with ½ teaspoon salt, ¾ tablespoon sugar and ⅛ teaspoon baking soda.
2. Cut in 1 cup pure lard until the mixture has the consistency of small peas.
3. Beat together 1 egg, 2 tablespoons lemon juice and 4 tablespoons ice water. Add this, a little at a time, to the flour mixture, until the pastry holds together. Turn out on a table and knead into a ball. Use immediately, or wrap and refrigerate until ready to use.

Lemon-juice pastry

This is a perfect pastry for tarts, rich fillings and fancy pies.

For two 2-crust pies or four 1-crust pies

1. Sift some pastry flour, then measure 3 cups and sift again with 1 teaspoon salt.
2. Cut in 1 cup shortening or lard until the mixture has the consistency of cornmeal and small peas.
3. Beat together 1 egg, 3 tablespoons fresh lemon juice and 4 tablespoons ice-cold water.
4. Add the liquid mixture, a little at a time, to the flour mixture; use only what you need to hold the pastry together. Then knead. Roll or store the same as lard pastry.

Viennese cream-cheese pastry

1. Cream 1 cup unsalted butter until very light. Add 8 ounces soft cream cheese and beat until very creamy. This is quickly and easily done with an electric mixer.

2. Add 2 cups all-purpose flour. Stir gradually into the creamy mixture with a large fork until no visible crumbs are left.

3. Turn the mixture onto a sheet of wax paper. Bring the paper up around the mixture and work the dough until it is in a ball. Refrigerate for 6 to 12 hours.

4. To roll, remove from the refrigerator 30 to 60 minutes ahead of time. Roll out on a lightly floured board.

5. When making an unfilled shell, fit the dough into the pie plate and refrigerate for 1 hour before baking. Prick the dough all over. Bake in a preheated 450° F. oven until the pastry begins to take on a light color, 5 to 8 minutes, then lower the heat to 400° F. to finish the baking for 10 to 15 minutes, or until golden brown.

6. 🗝 When baking this pastry with a juicy fruit filling, line the pie plate with the pastry, then sprinkle crushed ladyfingers or fine bread crumbs over the bottom before putting in the fruits; 1/8 inch of crumbs is sufficient. The crumbs will absorb the berry juice and keep the crust from becoming soggy.

Chocolate piecrust

1. Sift together 1 cup of once-sifted pastry flour, 1/4 teaspoon salt, 4 teaspoons powdered cocoa and 4 teaspoons sugar.

2. Cut in 1/3 cup shortening with a pastry blender or two knives until the mixture has the consistency of cornmeal and small peas.

3. Stir together 1 teaspoon vanilla extract and 4 tablespoons cold water. Gradually sprinkle enough of this over the flour mixture to dampen it. Blend with a fork. Place the dough on wax paper; lift the paper all around the dough and knead while holding the paper until the dough shapes into a ball. Then let it stand for 15 minutes.

4. Roll out the dough and fit it loosely into a pie pan. Do not stretch it. Flute the edge. Fill to taste. Or bake as a pie shell in a preheated 425° F. oven for 8 to 10 minutes. Cool.

Cornflake crust

Measure 4 cups cornflakes, crush and measure again; there should be 1 cup. Add ⅓ cup melted butter, ¼ cup sugar and a pinch of grated nutmeg or ground cinnamon. Press firmly into a 9-inch pie plate. Chill for 1 hour.

Graham-cracker crust

Measure 1½ cups crushed graham crackers (about 18 crackers). Add ⅓ cup melted butter and 2 tablespoons superfine sugar. Press firmly into a 9-inch pie plate, making a layer on bottom and sides. Chill for 30 minutes. Fill and bake.

For a firmer crust, chill the graham-cracker crust for several hours, then bake in a preheated 350° F. oven for 8 minutes. Cool and fill.

European flan pastry

This pastry is used for small tarts to be filled with cream and fruits. A flan pastry is somewhat a cross between pastry and rich biscuit.

1. Place in a bowl ½ cup plus 1½ teaspoons soft unsalted butter. Add 3 tablespoons superfine sugar and stir until creamy and light. Add 1 egg and stir until creamy, soft and fluffy. An electric beater works very well for this.
2. Sift and measure 1¼ cups all-purpose flour. Mix with the creamed mixture until well blended.
3. Remove the dough from the bowl, wrap in foil and refrigerate for 1 hour.

For baked pastry rounds

Divide the dough into two or three pieces. Roll each piece into a 7- or 8-inch round. Place the rounds on a baking sheet and bake in a preheated 400° F. oven for 20 to 25 minutes, or until golden brown. Cool.

Use them this way: sandwich the cooled baked rounds together with fruit purée and whipped cream, custard or chiffon-pie mixture, or with other appropriate filling. Decorate the top with whipped cream. Or use only one circle and top it with fresh berries, cover with melted apricot jam or jelly, then decorate with whipped cream.

For baked pastry shells for small or large tarts

Many a French dessert is prepared from these little pastry shells. The shells are always removed from the baking pan for serving.

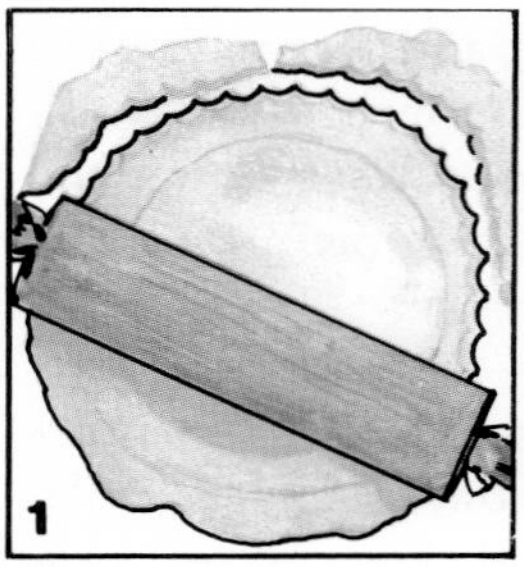

Fit the pastry into the flan ring or tart pan and cut off the dough even with the top edge with the rolling pin or with a knife.

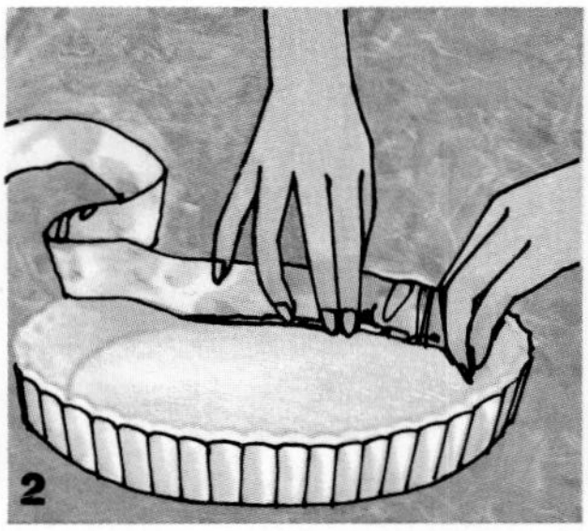

Put a strip of lightly greased foil along the inside edges to keep dough from sliding down. When the pastry is set, remove foil and finish baking.

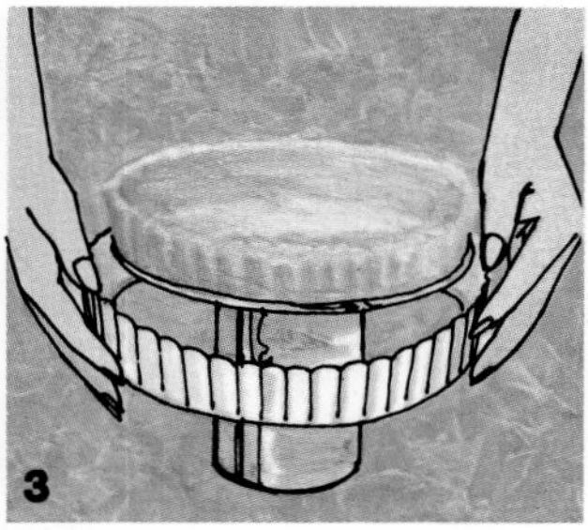

When using a springform pan with a bottom, set it on a can or jar until cool. Remove the ring. With a spatula gently slide the shell onto a serving plate.

Roll out the flan pastry and use it to line shallow individual tart pans; or use an 8- to 9-inch flan ring or springform pan. Flan rings are metal loops of various heights and diameter, which are placed on baking sheets. Flan pastry is loosely fitted into the ring and on the baking sheet. After baking and cooling, the flan ring is then removed and the pastry shell is placed on a serving plate.

Pat the dough onto the pan or into the ring so it takes the shape of it. Put a strip of lightly greased foil along the edges, as a support, so that the dough does not slide down during baking. Bake in a preheated 400° F. oven. Cool. Unmold before filling.

Scandinavian flan crust

This is a rich biscuit dough, quite different in texture from European flan pastry. Handle it like the No-Roll Pastry (p. 524). It is perfect for all fruit tarts or rich fillings.

1. Cream ¼ pound (½ cup) soft unsalted butter with 1 tablespoon sugar until very fluffy.
2. Sift and measure 1 cup pastry flour. Add to the butter mixture, working it in your hands, until the dough can be shaped into a ball.
3. Pat the dough into a 9-inch pie plate with your hands and flute the edge. Refrigerate for 1 hour.
4. Bake in a preheated 450° F. oven for 5 minutes. Reduce heat to 400° F. and bake for 10 to 15 minutes more. Check often so it will not brown too much. Cool thoroughly before unmolding.

Puff pastry

Puff pastry is made of many thin layers—or leaves—of dough, and that is how it gets its name, *pâte feuilletée*, from the French words for pastry and leaf. To make the layers, the pastry is folded, rolled, then chilled, over and over again. Each folding and rolling is called a "turn." This is one pastry that is always baked before being filled, because filling would prevent perfect rising. You can use puff pastry for pies or tarts, but it is more often used for fancy French pastry, patty shells, miniature patty shells for hors d'oeuvres, and for large patty shells which, when filled with some delicious mixture of your own choice, can serve as an entrée.

Puff pastry is difficult to work out successfully without practice, but what a joy when you have acquired the feel and you see the high-rise puff, as light as air, full of the perfume of sweet butter.

Puff pastry, like all other pastry, consists of flour, fat and water. It is the way it is worked—the mixing, rolling, folding and chilling—that makes the difference, and the fat *must* be butter. It is not made in a jiffy, but it is nice to know how to make it when you want something very special.

Trimmings from puff pastry can be used for appetizers or for teatime snacks just as bits and pieces of pie dough are used.

3 cups *pastry* flour
1 tablespoon *soft* unsalted butter
¾ cup *ice-cold* water
Juice of 1 lemon
½ to ¾ pound unsalted *cold* butter

1. Place the flour, sifted once before measuring, into a large bowl. Work in the *soft* butter with a pastry blender.

2. Make a well in the center and pour in the ice-cold water and lemon juice. Contrary to mixing methods for other pastries, work this one together with the tips of your fingers, gradually adding the flour to the cold water. Keep blending with your fingers until you have a smooth dough. Then flour your hands and knead the dough for a few minutes. Cover the mixture and refrigerate for 15 to 20 minutes.

3. Roll out the cold dough on a lightly floured table into a square ½ inch thick.

1. Make a smooth dough with the first 4 ingredients; blend with the fingers.

2. Flour your hands and knead for a few minutes.

3. Cut the cold butter into thin even slices.

4. Place the butter slices on half of the rolled-out square of dough and fold over the other half.

5. Roll the dough into a rectangle by rolling in the direction of the fold; do not let the butter ooze out.

6. Fold the stretched dough into thirds, like an envelope, and refrigerate.

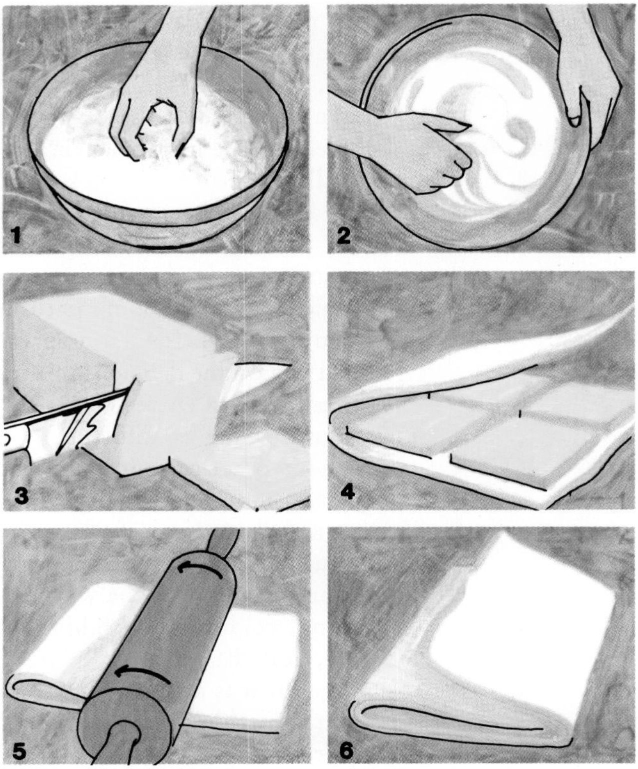

4. Cut the *cold* butter into thin, neat, even slices. Place the butter squares on the dough, one next to the other, in such a way that only half of the dough is covered. Fold the other half of the dough over the butter.

5. Make sure the edges are even with each other. Then lightly press together the two layers of dough and the butter. Form the dough into a rectangle by rolling toward the folded edge. Make sure that you roll with light, even strokes to keep the butter from oozing out.

6. When the dough is stretched, fold it into thirds, like an envelope. Place on a sheet of foil and refrigerate for 1 hour.

7. Then place the dough with the open edge farthest away from you and roll again into a rectangle the same as before. Again fold into thirds and refrigerate, this time for 20 minutes.

8. Repeat the rolling and cooling in the refrigerator

for 20 minutes each time, twice, or even three times, if you have the patience. After the final rolling, wrap in foil and refrigerate overnight.

9. The next day, roll half or all of the cold dough into a sheet ¼ inch thick and cut into rounds or ovals or squares according to needs.

10. Puff pastry is baked in a preheated 475° F. oven for 25 minutes, or according to the special directions for a particular recipe.

For patty shells

1. Roll the pastry into a sheet ¼ inch thick. Cut out rounds with a buttered 3- or 4-inch cookie cutter. Use another cutter, slightly smaller, or an inverted glass, to make holes in half of the rounds. *Do not* remove the small rounds of dough.

2. Moisten the edges of the solid rounds with cold water. Place the rounds with the holes on top of the solid rounds and gently press together the edges of the two. Brush the tops lightly with cold water.

3. Bake in a preheated 475° F. oven for 25 minutes, or until well puffed and golden brown. Remove from the oven and cool on a cake rack.

4. When cool, carefully remove the precut piece of dough in the center of the top. Use a sharp knife. Scrape out any soft dough inside the patty to make a hollow. Fill the hollow with the prepared filling. Put back the little lid.

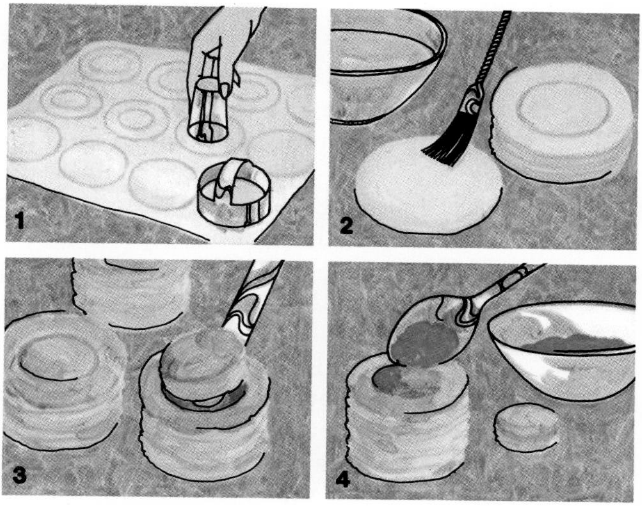

1. Cut out rounds with a cookie cutter and then make holes in half of the rounds with a smaller cutter. Do not lift out the small rounds.

2. Brush the edges of the solid rounds with water and top with the rounds marked with holes.

3. When the patty shells are baked, lift out the small rounds with a sharp knife and scrape out any soft dough to make a little hollow.

4. Fill the shell with the prepared filling and top with the little lid.

These will keep fresh and crisp in a cool place for 2 to 3 days, but do not refrigerate them. If you want to serve them hot, warm in a 300° F. oven for 10 minutes.

To freeze, place patty shells between layers of wax paper in a metal or plastic box. They will keep in the freezer for 3 to 4 months. Thaw in a 300° F. oven before using.

Make-your-own pastry mix

	SMALL RECIPE YIELD: about 9 cups	LARGE RECIPE YIELD: about 18 cups
Pastry flour	6½ cups, sifted	13 cups, sifted
Salt	1 tablespoon	2 tablespoons
Shortening	2 cups	4 cups

Sift flour with salt into a bowl. Cut in the shortening, using a pastry blender or two knives, until the mixture has the consistency of cornmeal and small peas. Store in a covered container in the refrigerator. Use as needed to make pie dough.

SIZE OF PIE	PASTRY MIX	WATER
1 crust—7 or 8 inches	1¼ cups	1 to 2 tblsp.
2 crusts—7 or 8 inches	2 cups	2 to 3 tblsp.
1 crust—9 inches	1½ cups	2 to 3 tblsp.
2 crusts—9 inches	2½ cups	3 to 4 tblsp.
8 tart shells—3½ inches	4½ cups	5 to 7 tblsp.

Place pastry mix in a bowl. Sprinkle cold water, a little at a time, over different parts of the mix. Toss together lightly with a fork. Use as little water as possible—just enough to moisten the dough. Place the dough on wax paper and knead three times. Press gently with the paper into a ball. Let stand at room temperature for 15 to 20 minutes. Shape dough for 1- and 2-crust pies according to the basic directions.

A FEW FAVORITE PIES

What is America's favorite dessert? Most people would probably put pie at the top of the list. Here are four fresh fruit pies, two lemon pies, a special chiffon pie and a raisin cheese pie.

Scandinavian apple pie

- 1 cup brown sugar
- ½ teaspoon ground coriander
- 1 teaspoon ground cardamom
- ⅛ teaspoon salt
- ¼ cup all-purpose flour
- Pie pastry for one-crust 9-inch pie
- 1 cup commercial sour cream
- 6 cups thin-sliced peeled apples

Mix sugar, coriander, cardamom, salt and flour. Line a 9-inch pie pan with a pastry of your choice and flute the edge. Sprinkle ¼ cup of the sugar and flour mixture over the bottom of the crust.

Add the remaining mixture to the sour cream. Mix well and fold in the apples. Turn into the pastry-lined pan. Bake in a preheated 450° F. oven for 10 minutes. Reduce the heat to 350° F. and continue baking for 40 minutes longer. Cool before serving. Makes 6 to 8 servings.

Balcom upside-down apple pie

- 4 to 6 apples
- 1½ cups sugar
- 1 teaspoon ground cinnamon
- 1 tablespoon water
- ½ cup butter
- 2 eggs, separated
- 1½ cups all-purpose flour
- 2 teaspoons baking powder
- ¼ teaspoon salt
- 1 teaspoon vanilla extract
- 1 cup milk
- Grated nutmeg

Peel, core and slice enough of the apples to cover the bottom of a deep 9-inch pie dish with a thick layer. Put a pie bird or a piece of stiff paper rolled into a tube or funnel into the middle of the apples. Mix ¼ cup of the sugar with the cinnamon. Sprinkle this over the apples, along with the tablespoon of water. Cover the pie dish with its own cover or a piece of foil, and bake in a preheated 350° F. oven for 15 minutes.

Cream the butter in a large bowl and gradually add 1 cup of the sugar, creaming both together. The sugar granules must be dissolved in the butter, and the mixture should be light and fluffy, not gritty. This can be done with an electric mixer; 5 to 10 minutes is usually required.

When well mixed, add the egg yolks (save the whites) and beat by hand until smooth and light.

Sift together flour, baking powder and salt. Add vanilla to the milk. Add the dry mixture alternately with the milk to the creamed mixture, beating well after each addition. Spread this cake mixture over the apples, leaving the top of the pie bird or funnel uncovered.

Bake in a preheated 350° F. oven for 35 to 40 minutes, or until the top is golden brown. Remove the pie bird or funnel. Cool on a cake rack.

Invert the pie on a deep heatproof serving plate. Beat the reserved 2 egg whites until stiff. Gradually add remaining ¼ cup sugar, and continue to beat until stiff. Spread this meringue on top of the inverted pie. Sprinkle with a dash of grated nutmeg. Brown the meringue in a preheated 400° F. oven. Serve cold. Makes 8 servings.

Country apple pie

The success of an apple pie depends partly on the kind of apples you use. Juicy summer apples, such as green apples or Duchess apples, make tasty, soft-textured pies. In the winter, a good pie apple is Rome Beauty.

- Pastry for two-crust 9-inch pie
- 1 tablespoon plus ½ teaspoon granulated sugar
- 1¼ teaspoons grated nutmeg
- 6 cups sliced peeled apples
- 1 cup light brown sugar
- 2 tablespoons all-purpose flour
- 2 tablespoons butter
- ¼ to ½ cup grated Cheddar cheese

Line a deep 9-inch pie plate with half of the pastry; set aside the rest for the top. Sprinkle the bottom pastry with 1 tablespoon of the sugar, mixed with ¼ teaspoon of the grated nutmeg.

In a bowl mix the apples, brown sugar, flour and 1 teaspoon of the nutmeg. Toss together until apples are well covered with the flour mixture. Fill the piecrust with the apple mixture. Dot with butter.

Roll the second part of the pastry into a round and sprinkle it with the grated cheese. Fold in thirds and roll again to fit the top of the pie. Press the edges of the pastry together and flute them. Sprinkle remaining ½ teaspoon granulated sugar on top of the crust. Bake in a preheated 425° F. oven for 40 to 45 minutes, or until the apples are tender. Serve hot or cold. Makes 8 servings.

Glazed strawberry pie

4 cups fresh strawberries
½ cup sifted confectioners' sugar
1 cup water
1½ tablespoons cornstarch
½ cup granulated sugar
8-inch piecrust, baked

Wash the strawberries and remove the hulls. Add confectioners' sugar to 3 cups of the berries. Let stand for 1 hour. Crush the remaining cup of berries. Cook these with 1 cup water for 2 minutes. Mix cornstarch and granulated sugar and stir into the cooked berries. Cook gently, stirring constantly, for about 20 minutes, or until clear.

Fill the baked piecrust with the whole berries. Cover with the hot sauce. Cool. The sauce will become a beautiful clear glaze when it is cold. Makes 6 servings.

Variations

Other fresh berries can be used instead of the strawberries in this recipe. Raspberries, blackberries and blueberries are excellent. Berries heavy with seeds should be sieved before being thickened. This pie can also be made with fresh peaches.

Classic lemon meringue pie

Pastry for 1-crust 8-inch pie
3 teaspoons grated lemon rind
¼ cup cornstarch
1½ cups milk
¾ cup granulated sugar
¾ teaspoon salt
2 eggs, separated
1 tablespoon butter
5 tablespoons lemon juice (about 2 lemons)
4 tablespoons superfine sugar

Prepare the pastry, adding 1 teaspoon of the grated lemon rind to the flour and fat mixture. Bake before filling.

Dissolve the cornstarch in a little of the milk. Add remaining milk, the granulated sugar and ½ teaspoon salt. Cook over low heat until thick, stirring constantly. Gradually stir a little of the hot mixture into the well-beaten egg yolks (save the egg whites). Add the egg mixture to the rest of the hot mixture, stirring as you do. Cook for 2 minutes longer, stirring constantly. Add butter, 1 teaspoon grated lemon rind and the lemon juice. Cool the filling while making the meringue. When cooled, pour into the baked 8-inch piecrust.

To make the meringue, sprinkle remaining 1/4 teaspoon salt over the reserved egg whites. Beat the whites until soft peaks form when the beater is lifted. Sprinkle superfine sugar, a little at a time, over the whites. Continue to beat until the meringue forms definite peaks. Fold in remaining lemon rind. Spoon the meringue over the pie, making sure the meringue touches the crust all the way around. Bake in a very slow oven, 300° F., for 15 to 20 minutes. Makes 6 servings.

Luscious lemon pie

1 1/2 cups granulated sugar
1/4 cup cornstarch
1/4 cup all-purpose flour
2 cups boiling water
4 eggs, separated
Grated rind of 2 lemons
1/4 teaspoon salt
2 tablespoons butter
1/2 cup fresh lemon juice
Pastry for 1-crust 9-inch pie, baked
1/2 cup superfine sugar

Thoroughly mix the granulated sugar, cornstarch and flour. Gradually add the boiling water, stirring constantly. (If you have a wire whisk, use it for this operation.) Cook over medium heat, stirring all the time, until the mixture is creamy and somewhat transparent. Leave over very low heat while preparing the next step.

Beat the egg yolks slightly (save the egg whites). Stir in a few tablespoons of the hot mixture and beat hard. Add the grated lemon rind, salt and butter to the egg yolks. Pour this mixture into the hot sugar mixture. Place over low heat and cook and stir until clear yellow and thick. Remove from the heat and add the lemon juice. Stir until well blended. Then set the mixture aside to cool.

Bake the pie shell; cool. Fill with the cooled mixture. Make the meringue by beating the reserved egg whites until stiff and then gradually adding the superfine sugar, 1 tablespoon at a time. Spoon the meringue over the pie, spreading it to the edge all around. Brown the meringue in a preheated 400° F. oven for 3 to 5 minutes. Makes 6 to 8 servings.

Citrus chiffon pie

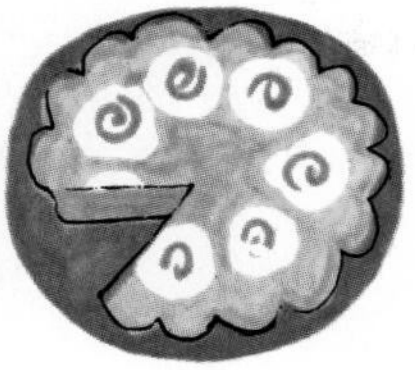

There is something special about a chiffon pie, especially when it is made with Viennese Cream-Cheese Pastry (p. 526) or Scandinavian Flan Crust (p. 528). The lime juice and rind of the following recipe can be replaced by lemon or orange juice and rind.

Pastry for 1-crust 9- or 10-inch pie
1 envelope unflavored gelatin
¼ cup cold water
½ cup granulated sugar
½ teaspoon salt
4 eggs, separated
⅓ cup fresh lime juice
Grated rind of 1 lime
Food coloring
½ cup superfine sugar

Make the pastry and bake a 9- or 10-inch shell.

Soften gelatin in cold water. In the top part of a double boiler beat granulated sugar, salt and egg yolks (save the egg whites). Stir in lime juice. Cook over boiling water, stirring often, until mixture is the consistency of custard. Add softened gelatin and grated lime rind. Stir until the gelatin is melted. Add a few drops of green coloring. (Use yellow coloring for lemon, and yellow with a little red for orange.) Chill the gelatin mixture in the refrigerator until it is slightly thickened, like white of egg.

Beat the reserved egg whites stiff and gradually add the superfine sugar. Beat the thickened gelatin mixture with a wire whisk or a hand beater. Fold in the beaten whites until thoroughly incorporated. Pour this chiffon mixture into the cooled pie shell. Chill in the refrigerator until firm. Garnish with whipped cream, or with fresh berries. Makes 8 servings.

Raisin cheese pie

Pastry for 1-crust 9-inch pie
¼ cup soft butter
⅓ cup superfine sugar
½ cup seedless raisins
1 egg yolk
Grated rind of 1 lemon
1½ cups cottage cheese
Additional superfine sugar

Line an 8- or 9-inch pie plate with pastry. Bake and cool.

Mix together butter, ⅓ cup sugar, raisins, egg yolk, lemon rind and cottage cheese. Pour into the baked and cooled pastry shell. Bake in a 375° F. oven for 15 minutes. Cool, then sprinkle the top with more sugar. Cool completely and serve. Makes 6 to 8 servings.

«14»

Cold Cookery

Kinds of aspic • What molds to use • How to unmold aspic • How to chill aspic • Basic vegetable, meat, fish and dessert aspics • Lining a mold with aspic • Making mousses • Equipment for making your own ice cream • Why salt is important • Packing the freezer • Ingredients in ice cream • Variations with vanilla ice cream • Making refrigerator ice cream • Kinds of sherbet

With all the marvelous chilling and freezing equipment at our disposal today, it is hard to imagine how the cooks of an earlier age, with their limited facilities, ever produced such frozen desserts as ice cream. Nevertheless, they did; ice cream was served at Mount Vernon, and centuries earlier the Persians and Arabs knew how to make sherbets or frappés. The Romans are said to have brought ice down from the Alps to chill shellfish, so it is likely that they too knew how to make ices and other chilled preparations.

All the dishes described in this chapter depend on cold for the development of their final appearance, shape and texture—even though some of them start with cooking. With the aid of your refrigerator, they are simple to complete, and have one tremendous advantage over other kinds of dishes: they can be prepared far in advance of the moment you plan to serve them.

ASPICS

An aspic is a jelly. It can be flavored and served by itself, or may contain pieces of meat, poultry, game, fish, vegetables, fruits, or a mixture of several foods. An aspic can be a main course, an entrée, a salad course, a garnish or a dessert. Either freshly cooked food or leftovers can be added to the gelatin. An aspic has form, shape and sparkle. Sweet aspics or sweet gelatins are for desserts.

A snow is a gelatin mixture that has egg whites, beaten until light and fluffy, added to it when the gelatin is partly set. This is put into a mold and refrigerated until set.

A chiffon is a gelatin mixture made with egg yolks, cooked and cooled, then mixed with beaten egg whites.

When a white sauce is added to a partly set gelatin mixture, it becomes a white *chaud-froid,* a jellied sauce to be spread on cold roast chicken, turkey or ham, for a buffet dish. There is also a brown *chaud-froid* sauce.

Few people can spare the many hours of tedious work required to produce a tasty jelly out of calf's feet, calf's head, veal bones, fish bones or other gelatin-bearing foods. However, if you do have the time to do so, see the chapter on stocks. Many books on classic

French cuisine suggest using chicken feet or calf's feet for aspic stocks. In United States markets, chickens rarely appear with their feet attached, so we must discard this idea. Calf's feet are available in many markets, and you can add one to the stockpot if you plan to prepare your own aspic. Calf's feet can be used with any kind of stock, not just with veal.

Actually, if you have small work space and limited time, you can achieve perfect success with the high-quality unflavored gelatin that can be kept in the kitchen cupboard all year round. Well-seasoned canned consommés may also be used instead of the stocks. Many liquids can be used and many can be combined. For example, gelatin mixed with white wine and clam juice makes a delectable jelly for such foods as salmon, shrimp and sole. Red wine and tomato juice are ideal with pink slices of roast beef or lamb. Consommé and orange juice may be served with duck or game. And these are but a few of the many types of aspics you can make. Blended apple juice can be used instead of wine, and lime or lemon juice will give the necessary zip.

What molds to use

Many utensils can serve as molds for gelatin dishes: custard cups, teacups, demitasses, muffin tins, large or individual ring molds, ice-cube trays, coffee cans, mixing bowls, baking pans, even paper cups. It is easiest to unmold from metal, however.

If a recipe calls for a 6-cup ring mold and you do not have one, you can use a 6-cup bowl or loaf pan. Or use an 8-inch-square pan. Once the mixture in the square pan is set, cut the jelly into squares rather than unmolding it.

O┳ Rub the mold with some colorless, tasteless, sweet almond oil, which can be purchased at a drugstore. This enables you to unmold the aspic easily, and it also adds a shiny film to the top of the aspic.

To unmold

Loosen the set aspic from the mold by circling the edge with the tip of a paring knife. For small molds this may be enough to loosen the jelly, which can be gently shaken out onto individual plates.

When working with a large mold, run cold water over the dish you plan to use for serving the aspic. Place the dish on top of the mold and turn both upside down, holding them together tightly. Shake gently to loosen the aspic, holding the dish firmly against the mold. When the aspic settles on the dish, carefully lift off the mold.

O━ If the aspic is not centered on the serving dish, it is easy to slide it into place because of the cold water on the dish. If you must touch the unmolded aspic, do so with wet hands.

If the aspic does not shake loose, wrap the outside of the mold with a towel wrung out in hot water. Or the mold can be dipped into hot water for a few seconds, although this must be done with great care; too long a dip will cause the jelly to melt. Then proceed to unmold as described.

Aspic mathematics

One envelope of unflavored gelatin equals 1/4 ounce or about 1 tablespoon, and it will set 1 3/4 to 2 cups of liquid.

Soften 1 envelope of gelatin by sprinkling it on 1/2 cup of whatever cold liquid is called for in the recipe. Let stand for 5 minutes.

If a recipe calls for 1 tablespoon or more of sugar, it is not necessary for you to soften the gelatin in liquid. Just mix the gelatin with the sugar and then add the liquid.

When the gelatin has been softened in the liquid, place over very low heat and stir until dissolved. Remove from the heat and add the remaining liquid called for in the recipe. Stir until well mixed, then pour into the mold.

An aspic gelatin will take 3 to 5 hours to set in the refrigerator.

O━ Acid is important for gelatin dishes. Use fresh lemon or lime juice, or wine or cider vinegar. It helps to tenderize the gelatin. Use 2 tablespoons of acid for 1 cup of liquid; too much may prevent setting.

O━ To all commercial flavored gelatins, add juice of 1 orange, lemon or lime, counting it as part of the liquid required. It will give the aspic a most interesting flavor.

Chilling aspic mixtures

When other ingredients are to be added to an aspic—such as meat and vegetables—the basic jelly mixture must be chilled first. (And, of course, the ingredients you add must also be cold.) Different degrees of chilling are used, depending on the type of gelatin mixture being prepared.

For simple aspic to be garnished, or for a chiffon mixture: Chill until the mixture pours from a spoon in an unbroken stream, or until chilled to the consistency of unbeaten egg white.

For whips and snows: Chill until the mixture dribbles unevenly from a spoon, or to a consistency thicker than unbeaten egg white.

For chaud-froid and whipped-cream mousse: Chill until the mixture is thick enough to mound slightly when dropped from a spoon.

To quick-chill a gelatin base: Set the container with the gelatin mixture in a bowl filled with ice cubes or crushed ice. Stir until the gelatin mixture thickens to the desired consistency. A second method is to place the container in a freezer compartment for about 10 minutes. Stir occasionally so that it will chill evenly. The first method is preferred because the mixture chills more evenly and has a better texture.

If the mixture becomes too solid you must remelt it over boiling water and chill again to the required consistency.

Practice with the following recipes, which illustrate various types of aspics. Then experiment with different liquids, ingredients and flavorings to suit your taste.

Basic aspic

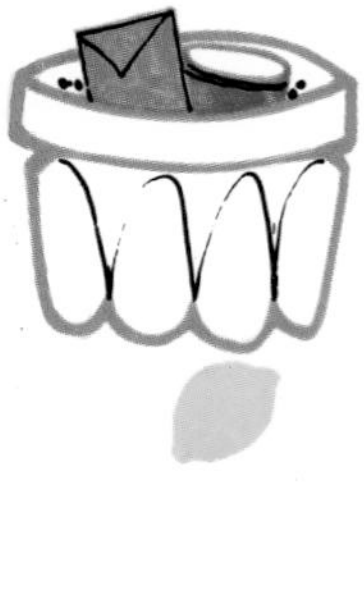

This simple type of aspic is most professional looking when well done. Vary the liquid and the garnish, mold individually, or make into one fancy mold. Use as entrée, main dish or canapés.

- 1 envelope unflavored gelatin
- 1 can (10½ ounces) condensed beef or chicken broth, undiluted
- 8 to 10 drops of hot-pepper sauce
- ½ cup Madeira, sherry, or red wine; *or* ¼ cup each of lemon juice and water
- Sweet almond oil

In a saucepan, sprinkle the gelatin over 1 cup of the beef or chicken broth. Let stand for 5 minutes to soften. Place over low heat and stir until gelatin is dissolved. Remove from heat and stir in pepper sauce and remaining broth plus the wine. Stir until well blended. Pour into a mold oiled with sweet almond oil. Garnish to your taste. Makes about 4 servings.

Jellied canapés

Make basic aspic. Rub an 8-inch-square pan with sweet almond oil and pour half of the mixture into it. Refrigerate until almost firm (this should take 20 to 30 minutes). Chill the rest of the mixture until it is somewhat thickened but not set.

Slice or halve 6 hard-cooked eggs. Arrange 1 inch apart on top of the set jelly. Spoon on the remaining soft jelly, keeping eggs in place and covering well with aspic jelly. Chill until firm.

To serve, prepare 12 rounds of toasted bread. Spread with a savory paste, such as liver or lobster. Cut the aspic with a round cookie cutter, to have a neat circle of set aspic around each egg; cut straight through to the bottom of the pan. Place the aspic rounds on the prepared toast.

Chop the aspic remaining in the pan into small pieces with a knife, and use these shining bits to garnish the serving platter of canapés. Makes 12.

Tomato vegetable aspic

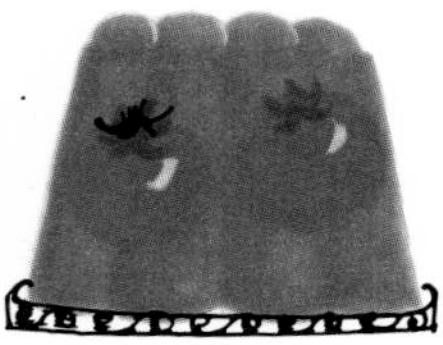

This recipe can serve as a pattern for any preparation that adds vegetable, fish or meat to a gelatin base. Again, liquid and garnish can be varied in many ways.

- 1 envelope unflavored gelatin
- 1¾ cups tomato juice
- ¼ teaspoon salt
- ½ teaspoon sugar
- ½ teaspoon crumbled dried basil or curry powder
- Juice of 1 lemon
- 1 teaspoon Worcestershire sauce
- Few drops of hot-pepper sauce
- 1 cup fine-shredded cabbage
- ½ cup diced celery
- ¼ cup diced green pepper
- 3 green onions, chopped fine

Sprinkle the gelatin on top of ½ cup tomato juice. Let stand for 5 minutes. Place over very low heat and stir until gelatin is dissolved. Remove from heat and stir in remaining tomato juice, salt, sugar, basil or curry powder, lemon juice, Worcestershire sauce and pepper sauce. Stir until well blended. Refrigerate until the mixture is the consistency of unbeaten egg white.

Then fold in the cabbage, celery, green pepper and green onions. The vegetables will stay suspended in the jelly because it is partly set. Turn the mixture into a well-oiled 3-cup mold. Chill until firm. Unmold and garnish to taste. Makes 4 servings.

Meat or fish aspic

Proceed in the same manner, replacing some or all of the vegetables with diced cooked meat or fish.

Salmon mold

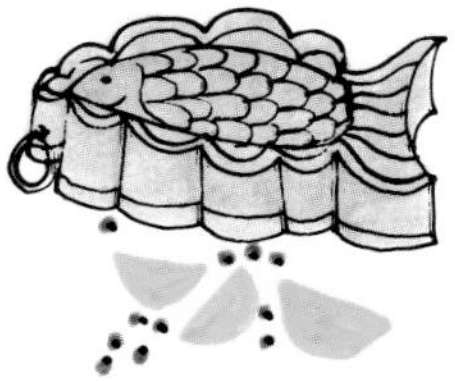

Here is an attractive way to use leftover pieces of a good poached or baked salmon. Or you can start with a thick slice of poached salmon.

2 to 3 cups cooked salmon
1 envelope unflavored gelatin
¼ cup cold water
1 cup mayonnaise
1 teaspoon curry powder
2 teaspoons prepared mustard
Capers
Lemon wedges
Shredded lettuce

Remove the skin and bones from the salmon. Pack the pieces into an oiled mold. Cover and refrigerate for a few hours.

Sprinkle the gelatin over the cold water and let soften for 5 minutes. Set over a pan of hot water to melt. Mix together the mayonnaise, curry powder and prepared mustard. Add the gelatin slowly while beating constantly. Refrigerate for 10 minutes, or until partly set.

Unmold the fish on a serving platter. Spread generously with the jellied mayonnaise. If any is left, spread it around the unmolded fish. Decorate the top with dots of capers. Stand lemon wedges against the fish. Surround with a thick layer of shredded lettuce. Refrigerate until ready to serve. Makes 6 servings.

Another way to do this is to combine the mayonnaise and gelatin mixture with the salmon and pack the whole mixture in a mold. To make a perfect presentation for a buffet, glaze the finished mold with clear aspic, or first line the mold with clear aspic, let it set until firm, then fill the mold with the mixture.

To line a mold with aspic

This is really a simple trick, but it looks very impressive. Make a clear aspic, with unflavored gelatin for entrée or hors-d'oeuvre aspics, or with a flavored aspic for a dessert. Let it chill until syrupy, and at the same time chill the mold. Spoon a little of the syrupy mixture into the mold and swirl it around until the inside is coated. If the mold is really cold and the gelatin on the point of setting, it should set as soon as you spoon it. Don't try to make a thick layer; instead, make several thin layers. You can add decorations to this aspic lining, such as pieces of pimiento, herb leaves or slivers of fruit—whatever is appropriate to the filling. This will produce a professional-looking finish when the mold is turned out.

Pork in jelly

This is an example of an aspic in which the gelatin comes from the meats rather than from added gelatin. The pigs' knuckles are a rich source of gelatin, just as veal knuckles are.

2 cups white or cider vinegar
1 cup sliced onions
1 teaspoon pickling spices
2 garlic cloves
1 teaspoon sugar
4 pounds shoulder of pork
2 pounds pigs' knuckles
1 tablespoon salt
2 hard-cooked eggs, sliced
1 cup green peas
Pickled beets

Mix the first 5 ingredients in a bowl. Add the shoulder of pork and pigs' knuckles. Stir until the meats are well coated with the vinegar mixture. Cover and refrigerate for 48 hours.

Drain the meat and place in a saucepan. Pour on just enough boiling water to cover meat. Add salt. Bring to a boil, cover and simmer until the meat falls off the bones. Let cool slightly. Remove the bones and shred the meat coarsely. Reduce the bouillon to 3 cups by boiling.

Cover the bottom of a mold with egg slices and fill the gaps with green peas. Place the meat on top. Strain the bouillon and pour over all. Cover and place in the refrigerator until set. Garnish with pickled beets before serving. Makes 6 servings or more.

Striped bass in aspic

Start this preparation at least one day ahead. While no single step is difficult, there are many different processes.

- 1 striped bass, 5 to 6 pounds
- 2 quarts white-wine *court bouillon* (p. 387)
- ½ cup tomato purée
- 1 envelope unflavored gelatin
- 2 carrots
- 1 small onion
- ½ pound mushrooms
- 2 tablespoons corn oil
- 2 tablespoons butter
- ½ teaspoon ground dill or dill seasoning
- Salt
- 1 pimiento-stuffed green olive, halved crosswise
- 1 pimiento
- Dill or fennel sprigs

Be sure your fish man leaves the head and tail on the bass. Let him remove fins and clean and scale the fish. Wash the fish in salted water. Make the *court bouillon,* simmer it for 30 minutes, then let it cool to room temperature. Wrap the whole fish in cheesecloth with enough of the cloth at each end of the package to use as a handle. Lower the package into fish poacher or place it diagonally in a large roasting pan. Cover with the cooled *court bouillon* (add water if necessary to cover the fish) and bring to a boil. Simmer for about 50 minutes, or 10 minutes per pound. *Do not overcook.* Let the fish cool in the liquid.

Transfer the fish to a large platter (retain liquid). Carefully remove the top layer of skin. With the help of the cheesecloth, turn the fish over and remove the skin from the other side. Remove the eye of the fish, but leave the head in place. Gently turn the fish onto the serving platter you plan to use, with the better looking side of the fish uppermost. Let it chill until cold. You will need a lot of space in your refrigerator.

Meanwhile, combine the retained cooking liquid with the tomato purée and simmer until it has reduced to half. Strain it, clarify it and test for jelling (p. 179). You will probably need to add some unflavored gelatin. Let the aspic cool.

Scrape the carrots and put them through a vegetable cutter to make slivers about an inch long. Mince the onion. Wash and trim the mushrooms (do *not* peel them), and slice. Cook all three in the oil and butter until tender but not browned. Season with dill and add salt to taste. Since this will be used inside the fish, it can be well seasoned. Lift the vegetables out of the oil and drain as much of the oil as possible. Then cool.

Remove the well-chilled fish from the refrigerator. Carefully lift off the top half of the fish. Sever the backbone just below the head and remove it. All the interior bones should come out in one piece; if they do not, take care to hunt for any that are left. Remove the bones and fill the cavity with the vegetable mixture; replace the top half of the fish. Place an olive half in the eye cavity. Cut the pimiento into shapes of fins and a tail. Carefully spoon some cold aspic over the fish, then pin the pimiento fins in place with a toothpick or tiny skewer. Let the fish chill until that layer is set.

Add a second layer of aspic and let it set. Then remove the toothpicks; by now the fins should be glued by the aspic. Add a third layer of aspic. When the fish is well glazed, arrange the dill or fennel sprigs around the fish and spoon the rest of the aspic over them and on the platter. Let chill until serving time. This is a beautiful buffet dish. Makes 8 to 10 servings.

This same preparation can be made with salmon or any other large whole fish that is not fatty. Or you can use the same idea for several small whole fish, or for fish steaks. To make this dish even more attractive, arrange tiny shrimp or vegetable flowers in the aspic surrounding the fish.

Fish in fish molds

If you do not have room in your refrigerator for a large platter, you can still make an impressive fish aspic with a fish-shaped mold. Line the mold with clear aspic and place the pimiento fins (see preceding recipe) in the mold. Gently flake the fish, mix it with aspic and pack it into the mold. Just be sure the decorations are well fixed and everything is cold. 🔑 If you need a large platter for your mold, and your refrigerator is too small for it, you can chill it with ice cubes.

Cold meats in aspic

Arrange overlapping slices on a serving platter and cover with liquid aspic that is appropriately flavored. When the aspic has set, garnish with mustard pickles or a spiced fruit.

Chicken Madeleine

6 single chicken breasts
1 pound mushrooms
2 tablespoons butter
4 cups chicken stock
1 envelope unflavored gelatin
1 egg, hard cooked
6 chives

Bone the chicken breasts (save the bones) and flatten slightly with the side of a heavy knife. Cut a pocket in each chicken breast. Wash, trim and mince the mushrooms. Cook mushrooms in the butter, with just enough water to keep them from sticking, until they are reduced to a dry purée. Put some of the mushrooms in each chicken piece and close the opening with a metal skewer or wooden toothpick. Poach the chicken in the stock for about 10 minutes, just until tender (if you overcook them they will be tough). Let them cool in the stock. Then transfer them to a plate, cover and refrigerate until they are cold.

Meanwhile, add all the bones from the chicken to the stock and cook it until reduced by one quarter. Strain it, clarify and test for jelling (p. 179). You may need to add some unflavored gelatin. Cool the aspic until syrupy, then spoon a little over each piece of chicken. Decorate each breast with a flower made of egg-white petals with a grated egg-yolk center and a chive stem. Continue to coat the chicken until well glazed.

Many variations of this idea can be developed, and you will think of many garnishes. Makes 6 servings.

Crab meat chiffon aspic

In this recipe, heavy or light cream can be used instead of the milk when a richer texture is desired.

1 envelope unflavored gelatin
1¾ cups milk
2 eggs, separated
1 teaspoon salt
Pinch of white pepper
1 teaspoon prepared Dijon-style mustard
2 teaspoons prepared horseradish
1 cup fresh, frozen or canned crab meat
Juice of 1 lemon
½ cup diced celery (optional)
2 to 4 tablespoons minced pimiento

Sprinkle the gelatin into ½ cup milk. Let stand for 5 minutes. Beat the egg yolks and add the remaining milk, the salt and the pepper. Place over low heat.

When hot, add the softened gelatin and stir constantly over low heat until the gelatin is dissolved (about 5 minutes). Do not let the mixture boil. Chill to the consistency of unbeaten egg white.

In the meantime, combine in a bowl the remaining ingredients except egg whites. Beat the egg whites until stiff but not dry. Thoroughly fold the crabmeat mixture and the egg whites into the chilled jelly. Turn into a well-oiled 3-cup ring mold or individual molds. Chill until firm. Unmold. Makes 4 servings.

Sweet dessert aspic

The method used for this kind of aspic is the same as that used for Tomato Vegetable Aspic (p. 544).

Remember, when sugar is used with gelatin, you can omit softening the gelatin in cold liquid. Simply combine the unflavored gelatin with the sugar. However, there is one problem when using sugar with gelatin: more than 3 tablespoons of sugar to 1 cup of liquid will keep the gelatin from setting, so when you are experimenting and inventing your own combination of ingredients, be sure to keep the proper proportion of sugar to liquid.

The liquid used can be varied infinitely: strong coffee, tea, fresh fruit juice, sweet wine, and so on. The liquid can be tinted by adding vegetable coloring.

As for the fruit, you can use what you like, with this one precaution: if fresh or frozen pineapple is used, boil it in syrup for 2 minutes before adding it to the gelatin mixture. Fresh pineapple contains an enzyme that prevents the gelatin from setting.

Wine and cherry aspic

- 1 envelope unflavored gelatin
- 2 to 4 tablespoons sugar
- Pinch of salt
- 1 3/4 cups white or red wine, sherry or port, fruit juice, or a mixture of any of these
- Juice of 1/2 lime *or* 1 tablespoon lemon juice
- 2 cups pitted black cherries, fresh or canned

Thoroughly mix the gelatin, sugar (to taste) and salt. Add 1/2 cup of the chosen liquid and stir over low heat until the gelatin is dissolved. Add the remaining liquid, including the lime or lemon juice, and refrigerate until the mixture has the consistency of unbeaten egg white. Then fold in the cherries. Turn into a well-oiled fancy 3-cup mold, or 6 individual molds, and refrigerate until the aspic is firm. Makes 6 servings.

Concord grape whip

Whips can be made with many fruits such as prunes, apricots, peaches, strawberries and oranges. This one has good flavor and texture.

- 1 envelope unflavored gelatin
- 1¾ cups grape juice
- ½ cup sugar
- 2 tablespoons lemon juice
- ¾ cup evaporated milk or heavy cream, chilled
- ½ cup nonfat dry milk

Soak the gelatin in ½ cup grape juice for 5 minutes. Dissolve over low heat. Add the sugar, lemon juice and remaining 1¼ cups grape juice. Chill until the gelatin is half set.

Beat the chilled evaporated milk or heavy cream until stiff. Add the powdered milk to the whipped milk or cream and beat lightly. Beat the half-set jelly until foamy. Fold in the beaten cream. Pour into a 4-cup ring mold and refrigerate until set. Makes about 6 servings.

Orange and lemon snow

Snows are sweet, light, fluffy aspics. They are used mostly for desserts, but they are nice to serve as a garnish to fruit salads as well.

- 1 envelope unflavored gelatin
- ½ cup sugar
- ⅛ teaspoon salt
- 1½ cups orange juice
- ¼ cup lemon juice
- 2 egg whites, unbeaten
- Grated rinds of 1 orange and 1 lemon

Thoroughly mix the gelatin with the sugar and salt in a small saucepan. Add ½ cup orange juice. Place over low heat and stir constantly until gelatin is dissolved. Remove from heat and stir in the remaining orange juice and the lemon juice. Chill until slightly thicker than unbeaten egg white.

Add the unbeaten egg whites and the grated lemon and orange rinds. Beat the mixture with an electric beater until it foams up and begins to hold its shape.

Spoon into a glass dessert dish or small molds and chill until firm. Top with thawed berries of your choice, or a custard sauce made with the remaining egg yolks. Makes 8 servings.

Pink snow

1 bunch of winter rhubarb *or* 5 or 6 stalks of young fresh spring rhubarb, diced into 1-inch pieces
1 envelope unflavored gelatin
3 tablespoons water
¼ cup maple syrup
3 to 4 tablespoons nonfat dry milk

Clean the rhubarb before dicing. Place in a steamer or sieve set over boiling water. Cover the pan and steam for 10 to 15 minutes, or until the rhubarb is soft. Pour the cooked rhubarb into a pan.

Soak the gelatin in the water for 10 minutes. Stir into the hot rhubarb until gelatin is dissolved. Add maple syrup. Cool.

When the rhubarb is tepid, sprinkle with dry milk. Beat with a wire whisk or rotary beater until the mixture is frothy, pale pink and slightly thickened. Pour into a dish and refrigerate until set. Unmold on a serving platter and serve cold with hot maple syrup. Makes 4 servings.

Swedish cream

This beautifully smooth cream can be made 3 to 5 days ahead of time.

2 envelopes unflavored gelatin
¼ cup cold water
2 cups heavy cream
1 cup sugar
2 cups commercial sour cream
1 teaspoon vanilla extract
1 teaspoon rosewater (optional)

Sprinkle gelatin over water and let stand for 5 minutes. Heat heavy cream but do not boil. Add the gelatin and sugar and stir until completely dissolved. Cool to room temperature.

Fold sour cream, vanilla extract and rosewater into the gelatin mixture. Pour into a dish and chill until the mixture is set. Serve the cream plain, or top with sugared fresh fruits, frozen fruits or jam. Makes 4 to 6 servings. This dessert can be varied in many ways. When the mixture begins to set, you may add fresh grated or canned coconut, chopped fresh or canned fruit such as cherries or strawberries, or canned crushed pineapple.

Victorian blancmange

While this old-fashioned dish is not based on gelatin, it depends on cold to give it a firm shape.

3 cups cold milk
¼ cup cornstarch
2 tablespoons granulated sugar
¼ teaspoon salt
1 egg
2 tablespoons superfine sugar
1 teaspoon vanilla extract
¼ teaspoon almond extract
1 cup heavy cream
2 tablespoons confectioners' sugar
2 ounces (4 tablespoons) rum
Pinch of grated nutmeg

Scald 2¼ cups milk. Stir together the remaining ¾ cup cold milk, cornstarch, granulated sugar and salt. Stir into the scalded milk. Cook in the top part of a double boiler over hot water, stirring often, until the mixture thickens and no taste of starch remains. Beat the egg with the superfine sugar. Add to the thickened milk and whisk quickly until well mixed. Add the vanilla and almond extracts. Stir over the hot water for another 5 minutes. Pour into one large mold or small individual molds. Refrigerate, covered, until ready to serve, preferably overnight.

When you are ready to serve the blancmange, mix the cream, confectioners' sugar, rum and grated nutmeg for a sauce. Serve this cold in a pitcher. Makes 4 to 6 servings.

MOUSSES

A mousse is a fluffy mixture given shape by whipped cream, whole eggs or egg whites. Gelatin is often used to give the mixture greater firmness, but many mousses are made without it. A mousse might be considered a close relative of a whip or snow, since it is never clear like an aspic. O┳ If you intend to add whipped cream or beaten egg white to a mixture that has been cooked, be sure the cooked mixture is thoroughly cooled before adding the whipped ingredient. O┳ Also, do not overbeat the cream you are adding; it should be softer than for cake fillings or dessert sauces.

Cheese mousse

- 2 envelopes unflavored gelatin
- ½ cup consommé
- ¼ cup butter
- ½ cup flour
- 1¼ cups milk
- 4 eggs, separated
- ⅔ cup grated Cheddar or Swiss cheese
- 1 shallot, chopped
- 1 teaspoon dry mustard
- Salt and pepper
- ¼ cup heavy cream
- Butter
- Chives or shallots, minced
- Watercress

Soak gelatin in consommé for 5 minutes. Make a white sauce by melting the butter and stirring in the flour. Add milk all at once, whisking until smooth and thickened. Add the softened gelatin and stir until melted. Beat the egg yolks with grated cheese, chopped shallot and dry mustard. Add to the white sauce, stirring until well mixed. Add salt and pepper to taste. Cool for about 25 minutes.

Beat the egg whites. Whip heavy cream. Fold both into the cheese sauce. Lightly butter individual molds or one large mold. Sprinkle the inside with minced chives or shallots, then gently pour in the cheese mixture. Refrigerate overnight. Unmold on a nest of watercress and serve with thin-sliced rye bread. Makes 4 servings.

Chicken mousse

Any cooked meat or seafood can be used instead of the chicken in this recipe. An *haute cuisine* recipe can be prepared with white Bordeaux, Rhine or Moselle wine, fresh-cooked lobster and diced raw mushrooms. Garnish the top with a few spoonfuls of caviar.

- 1 envelope unflavored gelatin
- 1½ cups chicken consommé, *or* 1 cup dry white wine and ½ cup chicken consommé
- 1 small white onion, grated
- ¼ teaspoon crumbled dried tarragon
- 1 cup heavy cream
- 1½ cups diced cooked chicken
- 2 tablespoons chopped celery
- 1 tablespoon minced green or black olives

Sprinkle the gelatin on ½ cup of the consommé. Let stand for 5 minutes. Place over low heat and stir until gelatin is dissolved. Remove from heat and stir in the remaining consommé, or wine and consommé, the grated onion and the tarragon. Refrigerate until the mixture has the consistency of unbeaten egg white.

Whip the cream and fold it into the gelatin mixture along with the chicken, celery and olives. Blend thoroughly. Refrigerate until firm in a well-oiled 4-cup mold. Unmold and garnish to taste. Makes 6 servings.

Ham mousse

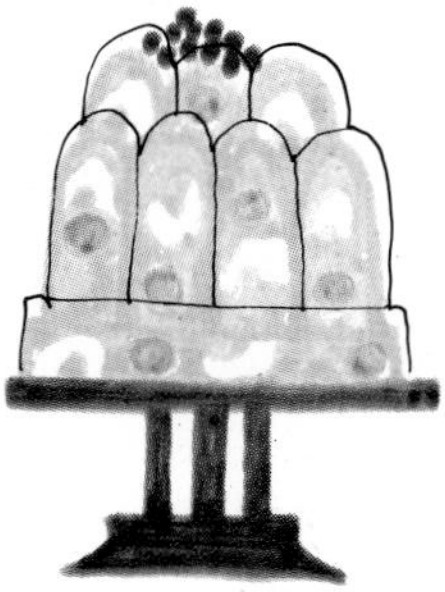

1 pound cooked ham (about 2 cups diced)
1 envelope unflavored gelatin
1 cup chicken stock (unsalted)
1 cup rosé wine
3 eggs, separated
4 drops of onion juice
1 teaspoon prepared Dijon-style mustard
10 green olives
¼ cup chopped pecans
1 cup heavy cream
Endive
Watercress
Spiced apricots

Trim the ham of all fat and connective tissue. Chop ham into small pieces and put through a food grinder twice to make a smooth mixture. Soften the gelatin in ½ cup chicken stock. Mix remaining stock, wine and slightly beaten egg yolks. Cook over low heat until the custard is thickened. Add the onion juice, the mustard and the gelatin. Continue to cook until the gelatin is dissolved and the custard very thick. Keep the heat very low; the mixture should never be allowed to boil. Stir often. (You can do this in a double boiler over simmering water if you prefer.) Stir the ground ham into the mixture and let cool.

Meanwhile, blanch the olives in boiling water, remove pits, and chop olives into small pieces. When the mixture is cold, beat the egg whites until stiff. Fold olives, pecans and egg whites into the mixture. Then beat the cream and fold it in. Refrigerate the mousse until firm in a well-oiled 6-cup mold, which will be filled to the brim. Unmold and decorate with endive and watercress. Serve with spiced apricots. Makes about 8 servings.

If you prefer, this mousse or the Chicken Mousse can be put into larger molds lined with clear aspic and decorated. For instance, this one could have the olives as a decoration on the outside of the mousse rather than mixed in. Because ham and olives are salty, you will probably not need any seasoning, but taste the mousse before chilling it to be sure. You will be surprised at the difference the pecans make.

Applesauce mousse

2 medium-size apples
1 cup sugar
1 cup water
2 lemons
1 envelope unflavored gelatin
2 egg whites

Peel and core the apples and cut them into thin slices. Heat the sugar and water together in a saucepan until the sugar is dissolved. Toss in the apple slices and continue cooking until the fruit is transparent and the syrup slightly thickened.

While the apples cook, grate the rinds from both lemons, then extract the juice. Add enough water to the lemon juice to make 1 cup. Sprinkle the gelatin over ¼ cup of this liquid. Remove the apples from the heat and stir in the lemon rind, softened gelatin and remaining lemon and water mixture. Let it cool, then refrigerate until it becomes as thick as unbeaten egg white.

Whip the egg whites until stiff enough to hold a point. Beat the apple mixture until the slices are broken down into little chunks. Gently mix in the stiff egg whites. Refrigerate the mixture for 2½ to 3 hours, or until the dessert is reasonably firm; it will never become really solid. Serve plain, with sweetened whipped cream or custard sauce. Makes 4 servings.

Lemon mousse

4 eggs, separated
½ teaspoon salt
1 cup sugar
Grated rind of 1 lemon
½ cup fresh lemon juice
1 envelope unflavored gelatin
¼ cup cold water
1 cup heavy cream

Add the egg yolks, salt and ½ cup sugar to the lemon rind and juice in the top part of a double boiler. Stir over boiling water until the mixture thickens. Soak the gelatin in the cold water for 5 minutes, then add to the cooked egg-yolk mixture. Stir until the gelatin has dissolved. Refrigerate until cool.

In a large bowl beat the egg whites until stiff.

Gradually add the remaining ½ cup sugar, beating until the whites hold a peak. Whip the cream and pour it over the egg whites. Fold in the cooled lemon mixture, then fold all together with a wire whisk or rubber spatula. Pour into a cut-glass bowl. Refrigerate. Makes 6 servings.

Honey mousse

¾ cup fine honey
Juice and grated rind of 1 lemon
4 eggs
2 cups heavy cream

Heat the honey, lemon juice and rind in the top part of a double boiler. Beat the eggs while slowly pouring in the hot honey. Put back into the double boiler and stir over boiling water until the mixture thickens. Pour into a bowl and refrigerate until cold.

Whip the cream and fold it into the cold mixture. Turn into the dish you plan to serve it in and freeze for at least 3 hours. It will never become really firm because of the large amount of honey.

For a really exotic taste, use some special kind of honey; Lindisfarne honey with Lindisfarne liqueur is especially good. If your honey is bland in flavor, you may want to add 1 teaspoon flavoring extract or liqueur. Serve the mousse from the dish. It is so smooth and delicious it needs no sauce. Makes about 1½ quarts, 6 to 8 servings.

Chocolate mousse

Mousse au chocolat is one of the most delightful classic desserts of the French chef's repertoire. Make it one day ahead. It keeps well for several days when refrigerated.

2 packages (8 ounces each) chocolate chips
¼ cup brandy or water
5 egg yolks, beaten
1 cup egg whites (6 to 8 whites)
¼ teaspoon salt

Melt the chocolate chips in the top part of a double boiler over hot, not boiling, water. Stir occasionally until the chocolate is softened. Then add the brandy or water and mix thoroughly with the chocolate. Add the egg yolks. Stir well and cook for another 2 minutes. Remove from the heat and allow to cool while the egg whites are being beaten.

Add salt to the egg whites and beat until they form stiff peaks. Add one fourth to the cooled chocolate mixture, beating very hard. Then fold in the balance with a rubber spatula. Turn into a large soufflé dish or crystal bowl. Chill for 6 to 24 hours before serving. Makes about 8 servings.

Belgian rice mold

- 2 cups milk
- 4 tablespoons uncooked long-grain rice
- 2 egg yolks
- ½ cup plus 1 tablespoon sugar
- ⅓ cup raisins, soaked in 2 tablespoons rum for 10 to 15 minutes
- 1 envelope unflavored gelatin
- Dash of vanilla extract
- Grated rind of 1 lemon
- Grated rind of 1 orange
- 1 cup heavy cream

Heat the milk in the top part of a double boiler, uncovered, over boiling water until a film shines on top. Add the rice and stir until the grains are well separated. Cook, covered, stirring occasionally, for 45 minutes, or until rice is soft.

Beat the egg yolks. Stir in 6 tablespoons of sugar, raisins, gelatin, vanilla, and lemon and orange rinds. Gradually combine with the rice, beating vigorously. Cook for 10 minutes over boiling water, stirring constantly with a wooden spatula. Remove from heat and refrigerate until cool, stirring the mixture occasionally until it is thick.

Combine the cream and remaining 3 tablespoons sugar and whip until very thick. Fold into the cooled rice mixture. Chill in a 4-cup mold. Serve with Apricot Jam Sauce (recipe follows). Makes about 6 servings.

APRICOT JAM SAUCE

- 8 ounces apricot jam
- 6 tablespoons sugar
- ½ cup water
- 1 tablespoon Cognac or Grand Marnier

Combine jam, sugar and water in a saucepan. Cook over moderate heat for 5 minutes, stirring constantly. Strain through a fine sieve. Stir in Cognac or Grand Marnier. Serve hot with the cold rice mold (preceding recipe). Makes about 1½ cups.

Macaroon gâteau glacé

Serve this rich, buttery mousse after a light meal.

1 pound unsalted butter
1 pound confectioners' sugar
4 eggs, separated
½ cup orange juice
¼ cup lemon juice
Grated rind of ½ orange
Grated rind of ½ lemon
2 dozen thin ladyfingers
2 dozen almond macaroons, crumbled
1 cup heavy cream, whipped

Whip the butter. Beat the sugar into the butter. Add the beaten egg yolks and mix well. Blend in juices and rinds thoroughly. Beat egg whites until stiff and fold them in.

Line a 10-inch springform pan with the ladyfingers. Spread one third of the butter mixture in the pan, then a layer of macaroon crumbs. Continue in this manner, making 3 layers each of butter mixture and of crumbs. Wrap in transparent plastic and refrigerate for at least 24 hours. Before serving, garnish with the whipped cream. Makes 20 servings.

Soufflé glacé

A cold soufflé is really a kind of mousse, and the reason it is called by this name is that it is molded in a soufflé dish and made to look like the baked preparation. A true soufflé is baked, and the air trapped in the mixture rises as it is heated and pushes the batter straight up out of the mold. To make a mousse look like a soufflé, tie a collar of wax paper around the outside, extending a few inches above the dish, and fill it. When the mixture is frozen, peel the collar off and you will have an icy cold preparation that looks like the baked soufflé. This will work only with mixtures that become firm; Honey Mousse, for instance, will not make a cold soufflé but Lemon Mousse can be prepared that way.

ICE CREAM AND SHERBET

Ice cream is one of the most universally popular desserts ever created. The first printed recipe for ice cream that we know of appeared in a British book in 1769. In the United States, Philip Lenzi advertised in a New York paper in 1774 that his shop was open for the sale of ice cream by special order. Nancy Johnson in 1846 invented the portable hand-cranked freezer, replacing the old pot freezer, which had to be shaken up and down in a container of ice and salt to freeze the ingredients.

Not until 1851, however, did ice cream make a sweeping advance. Jacob Fussell, a Baltimore milk dealer, established the first ice cream factory. By 1864 he had opened plants in Washington, D.C., Boston, and New York. Ten years later the ice cream soda was invented at the Franklin Institute in Philadelphia. Ice cream cones were introduced at the St. Louis Fair in 1904, and the chocolate-covered ice cream bar in 1921.

Ice cream is not difficult to make. Here are a few basic ideas.

Equipment for making ice cream

First, buy a 4-quart ice-cream freezer. The hand type, needless to say, is considerably cheaper than an electric model. You can get either at most hardware or department stores, and usually stores that sell them carry a good variety. Carefully read the instructions that come with the machine before you use it.

Second, get a 4-pronged ice shaver, available at hardware stores or hotel-supply outlets. This is not indispensable, but it does make the work much easier.

Third, unless you make your own ice, find a place where you can buy a cake of ice. Or try this trick: fill 3 plastic bowls with water and place them in the freezer overnight. The next day it takes only a few minutes to break the ice with the ice shaver.

Why salt is important

The ice, which is packed with salt around the ice-cream can, does not actually chill the mixture, but it is vitally important. The salt reduces the ice to water without raising its temperature. It does not melt the ice in the sense we usually associate with the process of melting—a process that requires energy, which in turn is heat.

The outside of an ice-cream freezer is made of wood or some other insulating material that prevents melting of the ice by external heat. The salt acting on the ice reduces the temperature inside sufficiently to freeze water, so that the creamy mixture soon freezes.

Only ice-cream salt, rock salt or coarse kosher salt

will work. Rock salt is the best and it is not difficult to find, but the others will also work effectively.

Packing the freezer

Fill the can with the ice-cream mixture. (Recipes for various mixtures follow.) Set it in the wooden ice bucket and then affix the dasher and the cover. When this is tightly set, prepare the ice.

Shave the ice into small pieces with the 4-pronged ice shaver. Place enough chopped ice in the freezer to fill about 4 inches of the space around the can. Add a layer of rock salt one third as thick. Then put in more ice, then more salt, until the freezer is full of layers of ice and salt, ending with a layer of salt on the top. With the handle of a fork or any type of stick, push the ice down around the container. Fill the bucket to the top. Now you are ready to start turning.

Keep turning until the handle becomes difficult to move; or, if you are using an electric freezer, until the motor starts to labor. Stop churning and open the can. Clean the top of the can, making sure that no ice or salt spills into the ice cream itself. Taste the ice cream to test whether it is sufficiently frozen; if it is, remove the dasher.

When the dasher is out, put the cover back on the metal can and use either a cork or paper plug to close the hole into which the dasher fitted. *At this point only,* pour out most of the salty water in the bucket and add more chipped ice. Just a little more salt is needed at this stage. Pack tightly with layers of newspaper. The ice cream will then ripen and keep perfectly for 3 to 4 hours.

Ice-cream mixtures

Homemade ice cream takes about 20 minutes to freeze. Very rich mixtures may take 10 to 15 minutes longer. Fruits such as peaches, strawberries, bananas and raspberries seem to make the ice cream freeze more quickly.

When fruits are used, it is better to crush them thoroughly and very quickly, in an electric blender or a food mill (which does not take much longer). Pushing them through a sieve is the most time-consuming method but can be done without difficulty with any of the fruits mentioned. Soft fruits such as strawberries can be crushed with a fork in a bowl, or directly in the freezer can itself. Whichever way you choose to crush the fruit is fine, just as long as they *are* crushed. When fruits are quite acid, sweeten them before adding them to the cream.

Cream, both light and heavy, is usually the base of homemade ice cream. However, with a quart of milk, a can of evaporated milk, about a cup of sugar and 2 tablespoons of vanilla extract you can make ice cream better than almost any you can buy. The ice cream will not be rich but it will be tasty. 0━ The more cream you can afford to put into the mixture, the smoother the ice cream will be. This is because there is more water in milk than in cream, so milk naturally freezes with more tiny granules of ice in it. This is why evaporated milk is added when ice cream is being made with milk; the evaporated milk is not as rich in butterfat as cream is, but a good deal of water has been removed and it freezes more smoothly. However, do not add evaporated milk when you are using all light or heavy cream, or mostly cream, in the mixture. If you do not like the taste of evaporated milk, you can still use it in your ice-cream mixture; frozen, the taste is completely lost.

Eggs used in ice cream act as a binder, leavener, thickener and stabilizer. They also give texture and flavor.

Sugar sweetens the ice cream and also prevents crystallization. However, too sweet a mixture delays the freezing.

Gelatin also acts as a stabilizer and holds the ice crystals apart.

When milk is used, it should always be scalded or brought to a boil to reduce its water content and concentrate its protein. Evaporated milk, however, need not be scalded; its proteins have already been concentrated during the manufacturing process.

Flavoring has no effect on the freezing process. It is added only to give the ice cream flavor.

Always make a full can of ice cream. After serving, pack what is left into plastic containers, leaving 1-inch headspace in each container. Fill this space with crumpled wax paper. Cover and keep in the freezer.

In any of these recipes, it would be senseless to state how many servings you will get, since no one can judge a person's appetite for these delicious desserts.

American vanilla ice cream

This is a basic ice cream that can be made with many variations. It requires preliminary cooking, as in the French method, but differs slightly in texture.

1 tablespoon flour
1 cup sugar
¼ teaspoon salt
2 egg yolks, slightly beaten
2 cups milk, scalded
2 teaspoons vanilla extract
4 cups light cream or undiluted evaporated milk

In a saucepan combine the flour, sugar, salt and beaten egg yolks. Stir briskly and constantly while pouring the scalded milk into the mixture. Cook over very low heat, stirring constantly, for 6 to 8 minutes, until the custard coats the spoon. Strain and cool. Add the vanilla and the light cream or evaporated milk. Pack in 3 parts ice, 1 part rock salt, and freeze until solid. Makes about 2 quarts.

Philadelphia vanilla ice cream

Philadelphia ice cream, in contrast to American and French ice creams, requires no preliminary cooking and is richer than either of the other two.

3 cups light cream
1 cup heavy cream
1½ cups superfine sugar
¼ teaspoon salt
2 teaspoons vanilla extract

Combine all ingredients in the freezer can. Stir until the sugar is dissolved. Pack in 3 parts ice, 1 part rock salt. Freeze. Makes about 1½ quarts.

French vanilla ice cream

The difference between American and French ice cream is slight. In one, flour is used; in the other, more egg yolks are used, and heavy cream instead of light cream. Both are cooked before freezing.

½ cup sugar
¼ teaspoon salt
4 egg yolks, slightly beaten
2 cups homogenized milk, scalded
1 cup heavy cream
2 teaspoons vanilla extract

In a saucepan combine the sugar, salt and beaten

egg yolks. Pour in scalded milk and cook over a low heat, slowly stirring all the time, until mixture coats the spoon. Strain through a sieve. Chill. Add heavy cream (do not whip). Add vanilla. Pack in 3 parts ice, 1 part rock salt. Freeze. Makes about 1½ quarts.

Strawberry ice cream

This recipe can be used all year round because it is made with frozen strawberries.

- 2 packages (10½ ounces each) frozen, sliced, sweetened strawberries
- 2⅔ cups milk, scalded and chilled
- 2 cups light cream
- 1½ cups undiluted evaporated milk
- 1 cup sugar
- 2 teaspoons vanilla extract *or* 1 teaspoon rosewater

Thaw the strawberries and crush to a liquid purée either in a blender or through a food mill or sieve. Add the milk, light cream, evaporated milk and sugar. Stir. Taste for sweetness, adding more sugar if desired. 🗝 All ice cream should taste a little sweeter than what you think you will like, because it is slightly less sweet when frozen.

Add the vanilla or rosewater. Pack in 3 parts ice, 1 part rock salt. Freeze. Makes about 3 quarts.

Strawberry ice cream with fresh berries

- 4 egg yolks
- 1 cup fine granulated sugar
- 2 cups heavy cream
- 1 tablespoon rosewater
- 1 quart fresh strawberries
- Orange-flavored liqueur

Beat the egg yolks and sugar with an electric beater until they are almost white. Beat in the cream just enough to blend. Pour into the top part of a double boiler. Set over hot water and cook, stirring frequently, until the mixture is velvety smooth and resembles a thick cream, *but on no account allow it to boil.* Add the rosewater. Turn mixture into a bowl and refrigerate until cool.

Wash and hull the berries and whirl in a blender or pass through a sieve to purée. You should have 1 full cup of purée. Add to the cooled cream mixture. Pack in 3 parts ice, 1 part rock salt. Freeze. Serve with a teaspoon of orange-flavored liqueur poured on top of each serving. Makes 4 to 6 servings.

Banana ice cream

Be sure to use only very ripe bananas. You may use the recipe on page 563 for either the French or American vanilla ice cream.

- 1½ to 2 quarts vanilla ice cream
- 4 bananas, peeled and mashed
- Juice of ½ lemon
- ¼ teaspoon salt
- 1 teaspoon vanilla extract (optional)
- 3 tablespoons rum *or* 1 teaspoon rum extract (optional)

Prepare the ice cream. Before putting the mixture in the freezer can, mash the bananas with the lemon juice and salt. Add to the ice cream. If you wish, you can add vanilla and rum or rum extract. Pack in 3 parts ice, 1 part rock salt. Freeze. Makes about 2 quarts.

Chocolate ice cream

- 1¼ cups granulated sugar
- ¼ teaspoon salt
- 4 to 6 tablespoons powdered cocoa *or* 2 ounces (2 squares) unsweetened chocolate
- 2 cups milk, scalded
- 2 whole eggs, beaten
- 2 cups heavy cream
- 1 tablespoon vanilla extract

Sift together the sugar, salt and cocoa (omit cocoa if chocolate is used). Add the unsweetened chocolate (if that is your choice) to the scalded milk. Remove the mixture from the heat until chocolate is melted. Add the beaten eggs and mix well. Then slowly pour the scalded milk into the sugar mixture, stirring all the time. Cook over low heat, stirring constantly, until the mixture coats the spoon. Chill. Add heavy cream and vanilla. Pack in 3 parts ice, 1 part rock salt. Freeze. Makes about 2 quarts.

Coffee ice cream

A superb Austrian ice cream made with coffee beans. A large quantity of beans is used because they are not ground.

- 1 cup coffee beans
- 4 cups light cream
- ½ to 1 cup sugar
- ¼ teaspoon salt
- 1 teaspoon vanilla extract

Place the coffee beans in a cake pan. Set in a 300° F. oven for 15 to 20 minutes, or until hot. Scald the cream and add the coffee beans. Simmer together over low heat for 5 minutes. Remove from heat and add the sugar. Stir until sugar is melted. Cover the saucepan and chill the mixture. Strain through a fine sieve. Add the salt and vanilla. Pack in 3 parts ice, 1 part rock salt. Freeze. Makes about 1½ quarts.

For a quick coffee ice cream, add 2 tablespoons instant coffee powder to either the French or American ice-cream recipe before freezing.

Maple walnut ice cream

This is an old Vermont classic. Only pure maple syrup should be used; imitation maple syrup can give an off-taste to the finished ice cream.

1½ cups maple syrup
2 eggs, slightly beaten
2 cups heavy cream
⅛ teaspoon salt
½ teaspoon vanilla extract
½ cup chopped walnuts

Heat syrup, but do not boil. Slowly add the beaten eggs, while beating hard (a wire whisk is perfect for this). Remove from the heat and continue to beat until the mixture is tepid.

Whip the cream until it has reached the consistency of custard and add to the cool syrup with the salt, vanilla and walnuts. Pack in 3 parts ice, 1 part rock salt. Freeze. Makes about 1½ quarts.

Variations with vanilla ice cream

If your family loves ice cream, keep vanilla and chocolate in the freezer for everyday use. A few emergency ice creams that have something special about them are good for party occasions.

To prepare, make vanilla ice cream, using whichever recipe you prefer, or use commercial ice cream. Proceed as follows:

Dutch chocolate ice cream

1 quart vanilla ice cream
3 tablespoons Dutch-process cocoa
3 tablespoons strong prepared coffee
1 teaspoon vanilla extract
2 ounces sweet chocolate
½ cup finely chopped pecans

Soften vanilla ice cream. In a small saucepan heat together cocoa, prepared coffee, vanilla and sweet chocolate. Stir until the chocolate is melted and the whole is blended. Cool. Add to softened ice cream. Mix in pecans. Package and freeze.

Chocolate-butterscotch ice cream

Slightly soften 1 quart vanilla ice cream. Place a layer of ice cream in the bottom of a container. Drizzle 4 tablespoons chocolate sauce on top. Cover with another layer of ice cream and drizzle 4 tablespoons butterscotch sauce on top, and so on until all the ice cream is used. With a long-handled knife, gently stir the ice cream back and forth three or four times. This will make uneven stripes of the sauce. Package and freeze.

Make your own sauces, and cool before using. Or make this with good commercial sauces. Or use sieved fruit purées in the same way, or layers of sherbets.

Double-coffee ice cream

Place 1 quart vanilla ice cream in a bowl and let it soften slightly. Add ½ cup instant coffee powder. Grind 3 tablespoons black coffee beans in your grinder until powdery fine. Add to the ice cream and beat in until thoroughly blended (you can do this in an electric mixer). Put back in container, cover and freeze.

Double-raspberry ice cream

- 1 quart vanilla ice cream
- 1 package (10 ounces) frozen raspberries, thawed
- 1 cup raspberry jelly or jam
- 3 tablespoons brandy *or* grated rind of 1 orange

Soften ice cream. Pass thawed raspberries through a fine sieve. Mix with jelly or jam, and brandy or the grated rind of 1 orange. Blend. Package and freeze.

Refrigerator ice cream

Invest in one or two ice-cube trays and keep them just for making refrigerator ice cream; use plastic containers for storing ice cream.

If you are not making your ice cream in an ice-cream freezer, it is better to freeze it in the ice-cube trays in a freezer or refrigerator-freezer combination rather than in a conventional refrigerator.

Rich chocolate ice cream

This is a rich, tasty ice cream, almost a parfait. The buttered toasted diced almonds can be omitted, but think of them at party time.

1 tablespoon maple syrup
¼ cup corn syrup
2 tablespoons cold water
3 ounces (3 squares) semisweet chocolate
2 teaspoons vanilla extract
½ teaspoon almond extract
2 cups heavy cream
1 tablespoon butter
¼ to ½ cup almonds, diced

Place the maple and corn syrup, water and chocolate in a small saucepan. Stir over low heat until chocolate is melted. Remove from heat. Add vanilla and almond extracts. Cool.

Place the cooled mixture and the cream in the large bowl of an electric mixer. Refrigerate 30 to 40 minutes. Then beat with electric mixer at high speed until mixture is thick and soft peaks form when beaters are lifted. Spoon the mixture into an ice-cube tray, cover with foil and freeze until firm.

Melt the butter. Add almonds and stir over low heat until light brown. Spread on absorbent paper. Sprinkle on ice cream when serving. Makes about 1½ quarts.

Refrigerator vanilla ice cream

Use a vanilla bean to make this ice cream; the flavor it imparts is hard to substitute.

1 piece (4 inches) vanilla bean
½ cup light cream
½ cup milk
2 egg yolks
Pinch of salt
½ cup superfine sugar
1 cup heavy cream

Place the vanilla bean, light cream and milk in the top part of a double boiler. Simmer over direct low heat until the milk is scalded.

Meanwhile, beat the egg yolks with the salt and sugar until creamy and thickened. Slowly add this to the milk mixture, beating all the time. Cook over hot water, stirring constantly, until the custard coats the spoon, about 12 to 15 minutes. Cool, then refrigerate about 1 hour. Remove and save the vanilla bean for another use.

Whip the cream until it has the consistency of custard. Fold into the chilled mixture and pour into an ice-cube tray. Freeze until almost firm, about 1 hour. Turn into the large bowl of your electric mixer and beat at high speed until smooth. Return to the tray and freeze until firm, at least 4 or 5 hours. Cover with foil. Makes about 1 quart.

Note: Two teaspoons of vanilla extract can be used instead of the vanilla bean. Just add the extract to the chilled custard.

Refrigerator strawberry ice cream

The marshmallows in this are used as a stabilizer.

- 1 pint fresh strawberries
- 12 marshmallows
- ¾ cup sugar
- 1 teaspoon fresh lemon juice
- 2 cups heavy cream
- 1 tablespoon vanilla extract *or* 1 teaspoon rosewater

Wash and hull the strawberries. Place in a saucepan with the marshmallows, sugar and lemon juice. Cook over low heat for 10 to 15 minutes, stirring occasionally, until it has formed a thick syrup.

Remove from the heat and pass through a sieve or food mill. Cool in the refrigerator. Whip the cream until stiff. Blend in the cooled strawberry mixture and the vanilla or rosewater. Pour into an ice-cube tray and freeze until mushy.

Beat thoroughly with a hand beater. Then freeze again until firm. Cover the tray with foil. Makes about 1½ quarts.

Toffee ice cream

- 1 package (4 ounces) butterscotch pudding mix
- 1 to 2 tablespoons instant coffee powder
- ¼ cup firmly packed brown sugar
- 2 cups milk
- 1 cup heavy cream
- ½ teaspoon vanilla or caramel extract
- ½ cup chopped pecans or walnuts
- 1 tablespoon butter

Combine the pudding mix, instant coffee powder, sugar and milk. Cook over medium heat, stirring constantly, until the mixture comes to a full rolling boil. Pour into a freezing tray and freeze for 30 minutes.

Whip the cream. Beat the cold pudding mixture with a hand beater. Fold in the whipped cream and add the vanilla or caramel extract. Pour into a freezing tray and freeze for about 1 hour, or until partially firm.

Sauté the pecans or walnuts in the butter until golden; set aside.

Spoon the partially frozen mixture into a bowl and beat with a hand beater until smooth. Fold in the nuts and pour back into the freezing tray. Freeze for 3 to 4 hours, until firm. Cover the tray with foil if you are not serving the ice cream immediately. Makes about 1 quart.

Frozen parfait

A parfait is easy to make and looks much more glamorous than plain ice cream. Well covered, it will keep in the freezer for 4 to 6 days. It is easily varied to suit the menu.

1 cup sugar
¼ cup water
2 egg whites
Pinch of salt
2 teaspoons vanilla extract
2 cups heavy cream

Boil sugar and water together without stirring until the syrup forms a thread when lifted on a spoon or fork, about 233° F. on a candy thermometer. Beat the egg whites with the salt until stiff. Slowly pour the hot syrup into the egg whites, beating constantly until thick. This is very easy to do with an electric mixer.

Cool, then add the vanilla. Whip the cream until thick. Fold it into the mixture. Pour into individual parfait glasses. Freeze without stirring. Serve as is, or topped with fruits or toasted almonds and whipped cream. You can also layer the parfait with fruits or toasted almonds: alternate when pouring into glasses. Makes 8 servings.

Brandy or rum parfait
Use 3 tablespoons brandy or rum instead of vanilla extract. Serve with a light chocolate sauce.

Coffee parfait
Add 1 tablespoon instant coffee powder to the syrup. When cool, add 1 tablespoon dark rum.

Strawberry parfait
Add 1½ cups crushed strawberries and the grated rind of ½ orange to the syrup.

Macaroon parfait
Use 1 tablespoon brandy or kirsch instead of vanilla extract. After adding the whipped cream, fold in 1 cup crumbled almond macaroons.

SHERBET

Many people often bypass ice cream because of its rich cream content. Instead, they develop a partiality to sherbet, which has fewer calories.

SHERBET can be a water ice, a frozen punch, a milk ice or a frappé.

WATER ICE consists of fruit juices, water and sugar.

FROZEN PUNCH is a water ice that is highly flavored, sometimes with spices. It is often made with a mixture of fruit juices.

MILK ICE is similar to a water ice, but with milk replacing all or part of the water.

FRAPPÉ is a fruit water ice frozen to a coarse mush.

Ice-cube trays with the partitions removed can be used to freeze sherbet, and with the proper beating a very good sherbet or ice can be made this way. Ice-cube trays come in different sizes, of course, so the number of trays needed for these recipes will depend on the size of tray you use. Of course a sherbet can be frozen in an ice-cream freezer.

The size of the crystals, which give sherbet its texture, can be regulated by the amount of air beaten in before freezing the ice, by the texture of the mixture itself, and by the speed of the freezing process. It is important to use recipes especially designed for freezing in the refrigerator. Well made, the following ices and sherbets should have a flaky, crystalline texture, which you will find very pleasant.

Because all of these preparations contain a large proportion of liquid and fruit juice, special treatment is required for keeping the texture solid and smooth. Beaten egg whites, marshmallows and gelatin are often used as stabilizers.

When made in the refrigerator, sherbets are stirred once or twice while freezing. This is done before they get too hard: after they are about half frozen, or still mushy. To do this properly, scrape the sherbet from the sides and bottom of the tray or mold with a large spoon, stir, then return to the freezer compartment to continue freezing until half frozen. Then take out the mixture again, turn it into a bowl and beat hard.

0‒ This stirring and beating done at the right time is most important: if the sherbet is stirred too soon, it will invariably return to its original liquid state. If it freezes too hard, it becomes difficult to stir into a smooth mush without beating so hard that the air which was incorporated with the stabilizer is lost. These operations are not required, of course, when the sherbet is made in an ice-cream freezer, either a hand-operated or electric one. In this case, the same rule of packing the freezer with 3 parts ice to 1 part salt applies as for ice cream.

It is important to chill the sherbet mixture before freezing it. Never fill the mold, the freezer tray or the freezer can more than three quarters full, because the mixture increases in bulk when stirred.

Pack any sherbet that is left over in plastic containers, as described in the section for ice cream, and store them in the freezer.

Lemon ice

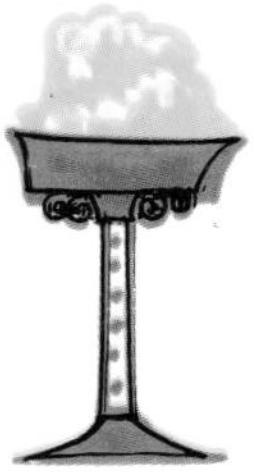

This simple ice is made with water and fruit juice. For a variation, use orange or lime juice instead of the lemon.

3 cups cold water
1 cup sugar
¾ cup corn syrup
Grated rind of 1 lemon
⅔ cup fresh lemon juice

Place the water, sugar, corn syrup and lemon rind in a saucepan. Stir over medium heat until the sugar is dissolved. As soon as the mixture boils, stop stirring, but boil for an extra 5 minutes. Remove from the heat and cool for 15 minutes. Add the lemon juice, then cool thoroughly. Pour the mixture into ice-cube trays and freeze until firm.

Remove from the trays, break into chunks and place in the bowl of an electric mixer (or use an electric hand beater). Beat the ice until it has a mushy consistency. This is important, because the beating will incorporate air into the ice. Put back into the ice-cube trays and cover with foil. Freeze until the ice is the right consistency. Since the ice melts quickly, it should be taken from the freezer only when ready to serve. Makes about 1 quart.

Cranberry sherbet

If you have uncooked cranberries in your freezer, this is a dessert you can make all year round. It is particularly delightful served with fruit salad in the summer.

- 2 cups fresh cranberries
- 1 1/4 cups cold water or apple juice
- 1 cup sugar
- 1 teaspoon unflavored gelatin
- 1/4 cup cold water
- Juice of 1 lemon

Cook the cranberries in 1 1/4 cups water or apple juice until the skins pop, about 3 or 4 minutes. Pass them through a sieve or food mill to make a purée. Put back into the saucepan and add the sugar. Stir over medium heat until the sugar is dissolved. Simmer for 5 minutes. Soak the gelatin in 1/4 cup water for 1 minute, or until the gelatin is dissolved. Add the lemon juice. Stir the dissolved gelatin and the lemon juice into the sweetened cranberry purée and cool the mixture. Freeze, beat, then freeze again, in the same way as for Lemon Ice (p. 572). Makes about 1 quart.

Strawberry sherbet

- 1 package (10 ounces) frozen strawberries
- 3/4 cup sugar
- 1 1/2 teaspoons unflavored gelatin
- 1/2 cup water or white wine
- Juice of 1 lemon
- 2 egg whites, beaten

Simmer strawberries and sugar together in a saucepan for 5 or 6 minutes. Stir frequently until blended. Soak gelatin in water or wine for 5 minutes. Add to the hot strawberries and stir until the gelatin is melted. Add the lemon juice. Pour into a mold and freeze until half set, then transfer to a bowl and beat until light. Fold in the beaten egg whites. Pour back into the mold and freeze until firm. Makes 4 servings.

Rhubarb sherbet

- 4 cups sliced rhubarb
- 1/2 cup water
- Grated rind and juice of 1 lemon
- 1/2 cup orange juice
- 1/2 cup maple syrup
- 1/2 teaspoon salt
- 2 whole eggs
- 1 cup sugar

Wash the rhubarb and cut it into small slices, then measure 4 cups. Place in a saucepan with 1/2 cup water. Cover and boil over high heat for 5 to 8 minutes, stirring once or twice to break up the pieces.

Add the lemon rind and juice, the orange juice, maple syrup and salt to the rhubarb. Stir over low heat until well mixed, then cool as rapidly as possible by placing the bowl in the refrigerator or freezer. 0‒ Quick cooling will preserve the deep red color in the rhubarb. The mixture cools in about 15 minutes.

Beat the eggs until light and pale yellow, then gradually add the sugar. Beat until very fluffy and pale, about 5 to 8 minutes with an electric mixer.

Remove the rhubarb mixture from the refrigerator and beat in the egg mixture. Pour into ice-cube trays and cover with foil. Freeze, beat and freeze again, just as for the Lemon Ice (p. 572). Makes about 1½ quarts.

Lime milk sherbet

This excellent milk sherbet lends itself to variations. Strawberry, cherry or any other flavor gelatin can be used instead of lime.

- 1 package (3 ounces) lime-flavored gelatin
- 1 cup boiling water *or* ½ cup boiling water and ½ cup fresh lime juice
- ½ cup sugar
- 2 cups milk
- 1 cup light cream or top milk
- ¼ cup lemon juice
- 1 teaspoon grated lemon rind

Place the gelatin in a bowl. Pour in the boiling water or the boiling water and lime juice. Stir until the gelatin is dissolved. Add the remaining ingredients and mix thoroughly. Freeze. Beat, then freeze again, as in the Lemon Ice recipe. Makes about 1½ quarts.

Strawberry milk sherbet

This sherbet should be made with fresh strawberries.

- 1 envelope unflavored gelatin
- ¼ cup cold water
- 2 eggs, separated
- 1 cup sugar
- ¼ teaspoon salt
- 1½ teaspoons vanilla extract or rosewater
- 2 cups milk or light cream
- 2 cups crushed fresh strawberries

Soak the gelatin in the water for 5 minutes. Dissolve over hot water, or set the bowl in a pan of hot water. Beat the egg yolks well, then beat with ¾ cup of the sugar, the salt, vanilla or rosewater, milk or cream, and crushed strawberries (measure the berries after they are crushed). When well mixed, beat in the dissolved gelatin. Mix thoroughly, then freeze in ice-cube trays.

When frozen, break into chunks in a chilled bowl. Beat with an electric or hand beater until smooth and fluffy. Beat the egg whites until stiff. Gradually add remaining ¼ cup sugar, then beat until thick. Fold this meringue into the beaten strawberry mixture. Return quickly to trays and freeze until firm. Makes about 2 quarts.

Peach milk sherbet

This interesting summer sherbet is made with whipped dry milk. In winter, replace the fresh peaches with a package of thawed frozen peaches. You must have an electric mixer to make this particular sherbet.

- 2 egg whites
- 2 tablespoons lemon juice
- 1½ cups sugar
- 2 cups ripe peaches, peeled and sliced
- ½ cup nonfat dry milk
- ½ cup ice water

Place the egg whites and 1 tablespoon lemon juice in a mixing bowl and beat until well mixed. Beat in the sugar, a spoonful at a time. (If you are using 1 package of frozen peaches, add 1 cup sugar instead of 1½ cups.) Add the peaches, ½ cup at a time, until thoroughly mixed, then beat at high speed for 12 to 15 minutes. The mixture will be doubled in bulk.

In another bowl, sprinkle the dry milk over the ice water. Add the remaining tablespoon of lemon juice and beat until stiff. Fold the milk mixture into the peaches with a rubber spatula. Pour into a 7-inch springform pan or another mold of your choice. You can also use ice-cube trays. Cover with foil and freeze for 12 to 14 hours. This sherbet should not be stirred, even before serving. Makes about 1½ quarts.

Raspberry cream sherbet

Full of color, exciting in flavor, this is a delightful way to end an elegant meal. You can make this 6 to 10 days ahead of time.

- 3 packages (10 ounces each) frozen raspberries
- 1 cup sugar
- 1 teaspoon rosewater or orange-flower water
- 3 cups light cream
- 4 egg whites, beaten stiff
- ¼ teaspoon salt

Thaw the berries. Add the sugar and stir until sugar is dissolved. Then put the berries through a sieve to remove the seeds. Add the rosewater or orange-flower water. Blend together the cream, beaten egg whites and salt. Freeze to a mush; add the strained berries. Blend well. Pour the mixture into a 2-quart mold, cover and freeze until ready to serve. Makes 8 to 10 servings.

Fruit freeze

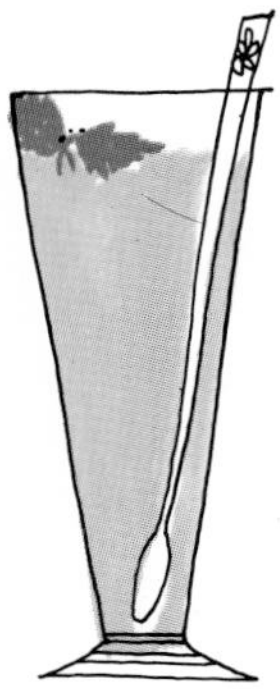

This is an example of a frappé. Serve in tall glasses and garnish with fresh mint. Any soft drink you prefer can be substituted for the ginger ale.

1 envelope unflavored gelatin
¼ cup cold water
¾ cup hot apple juice
1½ cups sugar
¼ cup lemon or orange juice
2 cups unsweetened pineapple juice
1 cup water
2 cups dry ginger ale

Soak the gelatin in ¼ cup water for 5 minutes. Pour into the hot apple juice and stir until dissolved. Add the sugar and stir over low heat until the sugar is dissolved. Cool. Add lemon or orange juice, pineapple juice, water and ginger ale. Pour into freezer trays and freeze to a mush. Remove and beat with a hand or electric beater. Freeze again to a mush. Serve with long spoons. Makes about 2 quarts.

Variations

For something special, place 1 tablespoon crushed pineapple and 1 tablespoon rum or brandy in the bottom of each glass. Pour the frappé on top.

Beat the mixture after the first freezing, then add 2 egg whites beaten with ¼ cup sugar. Freeze again.

When a frappé is made in advance and it is frozen too hard, remove from the freezer, let soften, then beat it quickly for a few seconds with a hand or electric beater just before serving.

Granita di caffè

This Italian specialty is one of the simplest frozen desserts to prepare. It is refreshing on a hot afternoon. Black roasted coffee was used in the original recipe.

Since no egg whites or gelatin are added to a *granita,* and the flavoring and sugar are never boiled, the finished product has a grainy quality different from other ices and sherbet.

4 tablespoons instant coffee powder
2 cups boiling water
¼ to ½ cup sugar
2 teaspoons vanilla extract *or* 1 teaspoon aromatic orange bitters
Whipped cream (optional)

In a saucepan, combine the instant coffee powder, boiling water, and sugar (according to taste). Stir over medium heat, just until the sugar is dissolved. Do not boil. Cool, then add the vanilla or bitters. Pour the mixture into a shallow pan or refrigerator freezing tray and freeze until almost firm. Turn into a bowl and beat well; an electric hand beater is ideal because it will beat more air into the mixture and make it lighter. Freeze until it has the consistency of sherbet.

To serve, spoon into sherbet glasses or punch cups and top with unsweetened whipped cream to taste. Makes about 3 cups.

Florida orange ice

This is similar to a *granita* in the way it is made, but because honey is used for sweetening it will not have the same grainy quality.

For summer, freeze some of this in ice-cube trays to use in place of water ice cubes in lemonade or orange drinks.

4 cups fresh orange juice
1 can (6 ounces) undiluted frozen orange juice
Grated rind of 1 orange
Juice of 1 lemon
¼ cup clear honey
3 tablespoons rum (optional)

Squeeze the oranges only when you are ready to use the juice. Partially thaw the frozen orange juice, then add it along with the remaining ingredients to the fresh juice. Stir until the honey is absorbed into the mixture. Pour into ice-cube trays and freeze. When it has frozen, cover the trays with aluminum foil. Remove the ice from the freezer about 5 to 10 minutes before serving to soften it slightly. Makes about 1½ quarts.

«15»

Freezing Foods

The convenience of a freezer · Arrangement, filling and placement of a freezer · What not to freeze · Planning the season's food supply · Freezing seasonal foods · Packaging and wrapping · How long to store frozen foods · How to freeze fruits · Thawing and serving frozen fruits · How to freeze vegetables, eggs, meat · Cooking frozen meats · How to freeze poultry, fish, breads, cakes, pies, dairy products

THE CONVENIENCE OF A FREEZER

The two main reasons for buying a freezer are convenience and economy. The convenience offered by a good freezer is obvious, but it is not always easy to judge the extent to which this major investment will help you with your food budget. Here are some of the factors to consider when you evaluate the economic usefulness of a freezer:

1. At first glance it would seem that buying wholesale cuts of meat, such as a quarter or a half of beef, can offer you great savings. But it is not that simple. You need a very large freezer to hold a wholesale cut of a big animal, and you must know how to cut up these large sections. What's more, the only way you really save is to use all the fat, bones and other low-cost parts of the cut. This does not mean that it is impossible to economize on the monthly meat bill through use of a freezer. It *is* possible because nearly every store runs weekly or seasonal low-price specials on retail cuts, which do not include the fat, bones and gristle present in the quarter or half of beef. 🗝 When you own a freezer, you can take advantage of these special prices and stock up before the prices go higher. By following specials and noting when they are offered, you will know when to take advantage of the best buys.

2. You can save by dividing your low-cost purchases. For example, a large turkey may be too much for your family at once, but it may be a better buy than a smaller bird. Buy the turkey that costs less per pound and ask the butcher to cut it into halves. Wrap one half and freeze it for later use.

3. The freezer can help you achieve greater variety in meals. It will no longer be necessary to eat some particular prepared food until your family is tired of it. If you freeze part of it, it will be an appetizing new dish for another occasion instead of a boring leftover.

4. There are advantages and savings when you buy four to six frying chickens at a time when they are offered as specials. You can freeze legs or wings or livers; then, when time or money is short, you can turn to the freezer for a good chicken dinner.

🗝 If you have a dozen chicken legs in your freezer, you have uniform pieces for guests; or you can prepare attractive dishes for occasions such as a buffet.

5. You might suppose that one of the main purposes of a freezer is to store commercial frozen fruits and vegetables, but this is economical only when you are able to take advantage of a real bargain. Generally speaking, it is easy to purchase frozen products when you need them; they are always readily available. Buy commercial frozen vegetables and fruits only when they are offered at special prices.

Packaging and freezing a surplus of fresh vegetables in the summer when the price is low is economical. But do not overlook the fact that vegetables and fruits—particularly lettuce, celery, tomatoes, citrus fruits, as well as many others—are available as fresh produce and at fair cost throughout much of the year. Use these fresh foods as often as possible. A family may get tired of an uninterrupted diet of frozen foods, especially commercially frozen foods.

When freezing vegetables and fruits that are in full season and at lowest cost, remember these two important factors: buy the freshest ingredients and freeze them as soon as they reach your kitchen. Fruits and vegetables that sit all night will not give as good a frozen product as those frozen as quickly as possible after purchase. Better still, freeze after gathering fresh from your garden.

6. When you are preparing dishes that require long cooking, such as stews or foods like cakes or pies that call for use of the oven, you can economize on fuel with the help of the freezer. Instead of making only one cake, make several and freeze the extras. Instead of making stew for one occasion, make a larger amount and freeze enough for later meals.

7. If ice cream is a favorite dessert in your family, stock your freezer when prices are low. Also, use the freezer to make certain kinds of ice cream. The freezer makes it possible to have all sorts of special or party ice creams on hand. Suggestions are in Chapter 14 on Cold Cookery.

8. A freezer can be a tremendous help to a family if the housewife must be absent for any length of time. Individual or family-size servings can be kept to feed the family while she's away. Small casseroles and desserts can be frozen in special types of dishes

that can go directly from the freezer into the oven.

9. The housewife with a freezer can cut down the number of her shopping trips, saving time and money.

10. Some foods that are normally stored in packages in a food cupboard will keep fresher and retain taste and color better if stored in the freezer. Nuts and candied or glazed fruits are good examples.

11. Leftovers can be frozen for later use. For instance, leftover vegetables stored in the freezer can be puréed to make nutritious soups, or can be added to stews or salads for variety. Freezing can reduce waste in your kitchen and thereby save on food costs.

12. Usually any serving of meat or poultry will leave you with a few bones. If you freeze these bones each time, at the end of a few weeks you will have enough to make stock, which in turn can be stored in the freezer. Store each kind of bone separately. Beef, veal and chicken bones are the best. Game carcasses can be used also. Fish heads and bones can be stored for a few weeks to make fish stock.

13. The freezer can be the greatest help to the family who entertains. All kinds of foods can be completely prepared and frozen, and need only defrosting to be ready for serving. Other dishes can be partially prepared, to be finished after defrosting. Although this kind of preparation requires a great deal of work, it is far cheaper than catered entertainment—and much more personal.

14. One wonderful aspect of a home freezer is that no matter what the circumstances, the cupboard is never bare. Friends can appear at opportune or inopportune times; the weather may be too unpleasant to go shopping; you may not feel up to shopping or cooking. Whatever the circumstances, you will never find yourself at a disadvantage if you have been wise enough to keep your freezer well stocked.

Arrangement, filling and placement of freezer

Have an orderly arrangement of foods in your freezer. Store frozen fruits in one part, vegetables in another and baked goods in another. Mark dates on the food packages.

Do not try to freeze too much food at one time. Add no more than 2 or 3 pounds for each cubic foot of freezer capacity during any 24-hour period. More than this will raise the temperature inside the box, which may spoil foods already stored there and slow the freezing of the new items. Quick freezing makes a better, more nutritious product, less likely to spoil. Slower freezing causes formation of more ice crystals. With meats, this means loss of more juices in thawing.

The freezer is designed to work best at ordinary room temperature. Even though it is below freezing inside the box, the outside should not be below 40° F. or the motor lubricants will start to congeal. Therefore, place the freezer in the same sort of area as your refrigerator.

WHAT NOT TO FREEZE

There are only a few foods that cannot be frozen successfully. Tomatoes, cucumbers and cabbage cannot be frozen when raw. Pears do not freeze satisfactorily because they turn brown. 🔑 Celery cannot be frozen whole, but it can be if cut into pieces. This is handy because it is used often in cooked dishes. Mince the leaves. Dice the celery ribs. Package, uncooked, in separate bags. Add while still frozen to the dish to be cooked. Frozen celery cannot be used in a salad, or raw in any uncooked preparations, because it will wilt when it is defrosted.

Boiled potatoes become mealy when frozen. If you are planning to freeze a stew or casserole, omit the potatoes.

Boiled frosting turns sticky.

Commercial sour cream separates.

Mayonnaise separates. 🔑 However, if you plan to use it in sandwiches, mix it thoroughly with creamed butter; this prevents separation.

Custard and cream pies should not be frozen. They have a tendency to curdle or separate.

Stuffed poultry of all types should not be frozen, but poultry stuffing can be frozen separately.

Cured meats—bacon, ham, sausages—can be frozen, but the salt used in curing slows down the freezing process and tends to cause the fat in the tissues to become rancid. Therefore, these meats have a comparatively short freezer life. It is better to use the space for foods that are more successful when frozen.

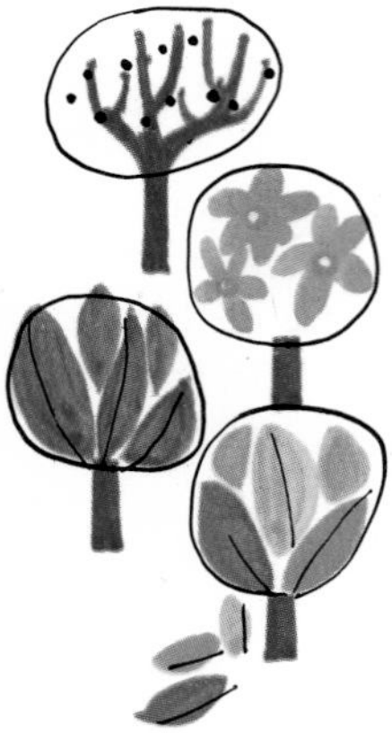

PLANNING THE SEASON'S FOOD SUPPLY

Be methodical when planning the food supply in a freezer for a season or for a full year. 0‒ Keep an annual record of what you wanted to have in the freezer; what you did have; what did not keep well; what was most useful or most economical; the cost or the economy realized on different items; menus of the meals served with the foods in the freezer, ready-cooked and to be cooked. This will help you eliminate items that prove too costly.

A generation ago people believed they had to grow the fruits and vegetables they wanted to freeze. This does not apply today. Technical discoveries have so improved the quality of commercial frozen foods that they are often better than home-frozen foods, and competition has made them cheaper than ever. 0‒ Process fruits and vegetables yourself only when you have an inexpensive supply of first-class produce available; when you can freeze some kind not readily available commercially that your family enjoys; when you do something special to the food such as turning fruits such as peaches and apricots into sauces, or preparing soup base from leeks.

Fruits and vegetables

The tables below give an estimate of the number of 1-pint (or 1-pound) packages a family of four might use in a year. Remove from the lists items you know your family would never eat.

Apples, whole	10 packages
Apples, sliced	5 packages
Applesauce	20 packages
Blueberries	25 packages
Cherries,	20 packages
Grapefruit in syrup	10 packages
Peaches	25 packages
Pineapple	20 packages
Raspberries	15 packages
Rhubarb	15 packages
Strawberries	30 packages
	195 packages

This list represents about one package of fruit or fruit products per day for the part of the year when fresh counterparts are not available locally. Those fruits can be either home-processed or commercial brands. Further on in this chapter you will find details on how to do your own processing, packaging and wrapping.

Asparagus	20 to 25 packages
Beet greens	6 to 8 packages
Broccoli	10 packages
Carrots	20 packages
Cauliflower	10 packages
Corn, cut from cobs	20 packages
Corn, on the cobs, 6 ears per package	8 to 10 packages
Leeks	10 packages
Mushrooms, blanched	12 packages
Mushrooms, buttered	10 packages
Onions	5 packages
Peas, green	25 packages
Peppers, green and red	10 packages
Pumpkin (for pies)	15 packages
Spinach	10 packages
	191 packages

Meats, poultry, fish

While the eating habits of people vary a good deal in consumption of fruits and vegetables, they differ still more with regard to meats. This makes it difficult to estimate the amount of meat a family should store in the freezer. Here is the best way to make an assessment of the number of pounds of meat each person will need for a year:

Assume meat is served an average of once per day. Four ounces per serving would add up to 90 pounds of meat a year for each person. But since your family probably will not eat at home every day, a fair estimate is 75 pounds per person per year, or about 300 pounds per year for a family of four.

This estimate includes beef, lamb, pork, ham, chicken, turkey, duck. Include fish also, and count on at least one meal a week at which fish is served rather than meat or poultry.

Take advantage of the special prices in your supermarket and keep your freezer stocked with the different cuts of meat, poultry and fish which you and your family prefer.

Miscellaneous foods

This is a list of very different foods that might be found in a large family freezer. Many of these items are constantly being used, such as butter, bread, ready-cooked foods and stock. You can add your own personal needs to this list.

Breads	6 loaves
Butter, unsalted and salted	5 pounds
Cake without icing	4 cakes
Candies	2 pounds
Coconut, fresh, grated or sliced	2 to 5 packages
Egg yolks	5 packages
Egg whites	10 packages
Gingerroot, fresh	3 roots
Ice cream	4 quarts
Lemon and orange rinds, grated	10 to 12 packages
Nuts, in the shell	2 pounds
Nuts, shelled, assorted	4 pounds
Pies	6 pies
Poultry stuffing	6 packages
Rolls	3 dozen
Stocks	6 to 8 quarts

FREEZING

Seasoning foods to be frozen

O━ Some of the spices—pepper and cloves, for example—tend to intensify in flavor when they are frozen. Also, certain foods such as garlic, celery and green pepper taste stronger. Curry develops a musty flavor. When you are preparing food for freezing, it is always a good idea to season with a light hand and to adjust the seasoning, as it is needed, when the food is reheated.

O━ Salt tends to lose flavor when frozen. The first time you prepare baked goods such as cakes, pies and cookies for the freezer, use the quantity of salt called for in the recipe. After your family has sampled the first batch, you can increase the amount of salt to their taste the next time you bake the same recipe for freezing. Remember to keep a record of the quantity of salt you have used so that you can refer to it in the future.

Packaging and wrapping

Packages for freezing must give adequate protection against moisture and vapor losses. Moisture loss means that color, flavor and texture will deteriorate. Also, the package material must be odorless and tasteless.

Frozen food containers are usually sold in 16-ounce (1-pint) and 32-ounce (1-quart) sizes. Choose the size that will hold only enough fruit or vegetable or prepared food for one meal for your family. This is particularly important with cooked foods. Uniformity of package size helps in saving freezer space, too. Rigid containers made of heavy aluminum foil, plastic or heavily waxed cardboard are suitable for both dry pack and liquid pack.

When filling containers, keep in mind that liquids expand when frozen. Always allow ½-inch headspace at the top of cartons holding liquids or foods that have been packed in liquids.

When selecting a container or wrapping for foods, keep in mind how the food will be handled when thawed for serving. Foods such as meat loaves, casserole dishes and pies, which require heating in the oven, must be packed in containers of metal, ovenproof glass or pottery. Breads that require reheating should be wrapped in aluminum foil. Cakes and cookies that do not need reheating or must be unwrapped for baking can be stored in boxes, polyethylene bags or transparent plastic wrapping. Never put a plastic-wrapped package in the oven.

Foods that will be removed from the containers to be reheated can be stored in polyethylene containers, waxed containers or coffee cans.

To keep foods at the peak of freshness, they must be completely sealed to keep out all air. When the food surface is exposed to air, evaporation—a form of freezer burn—takes place.

Some containers have covers that fit so tightly further sealing is not necessary. When in doubt, seal the edge of the cover with freezer tape. When using aluminum foil, shape it around the food. When you have ice cream left in the container, smooth off the surface and place a sheet of foil directly over the ice cream to avoid freezer burn.

Pipe-stem cleaners and twist strips (twisters) are good for sealing plastic bags. Force out the air and twist the cleaner or twister around the open end several times. For other freezer wrappings, use the drugstore wrap, a technique described below.

Bags made from cellophane, laminated paper and locker paper are often heat-sealed. However, this operation requires exacting conditions of temperature and technique. To heat-seal, force out the excess air by pressing the sides together. Then place the open edge on a flat surface and seal with a warm iron. If the bag is made of plastic material, a piece of paper should be placed between it and the iron.

Common gummed paper tapes and Scotch tape are not satisfactory for sealing freezer packages. These tapes tend to loosen and peel off at low temperatures. Use locker tape (sometimes called freezer tape) for sealing and labeling.

Drugstore wrap

Place the food in the center of the wrapping material. Pad any sharp or protruding edges with extra wrapping or with a small piece of foil.

Bring the long ends of the wrapping up over the food and fold together, over and over, until the fold rests on the food. Press gently, molding the wrapping to the food as tightly as possible so that air pockets are removed.

Turn the corners toward the center at both ends to form a point, then fold each one over and down against the food. If you use foil, no further sealing will be needed. Other types of wrapping need to be securely closed with freezer tape or tied with good string.

Good labels are important

After food is wrapped and sealed it should be carefully labeled with the contents, the number of servings and the date. The date is important because the length of time foods can be stored is an important economic factor. (See charts later in this chapter.)

The ink in some freezer marking pens is indelible, so it is a good idea to attach a piece of freezer tape in a conspicuous place on reusable containers, and print all information on the tape. Do not forget the labels; as the weeks go by, frozen-food packages begin to look more alike and your memory can trick you.

STORAGE TIME

Food should be stored in the freezer only as long as it retains its full food value and flavor. After too long there will not only be loss of both food value and flavor, but actual deterioration of the food itself, caused by enzymes within it. This brief chart gives some idea of these storage times. For best taste and nutrition, use your frozen foods within the months listed under Best.

	BEST	GOOD	FAIR	POOR
Apples, sliced, partly cooked	6	12		
Peaches	6	24		
Cherries, sour, fresh	12	24		
Strawberries, home frozen	4	6	12	
Most vegetables	6	12	18	
Baked goods	4	8		
Butter	3	6		12
Ice cream, sherbet	1	2	3	
Poultry, whole, dressed	6	9	12	
Poultry, cut up	3	6		
Prepared foods, homemade and leftovers	1	2	3	6

HOW TO FREEZE FRUITS

The condition of fruit before freezing largely determines its quality when served. Select only fresh fruits that are at an ideal state of maturity for good eating. Do not freeze fruit that is green, overripe, bruised or beginning to spoil.

Assemble equipment, ingredients and packages before starting to prepare fruit. Prepare fruit quickly and carefully, working with only enough to fill four containers at one time.

Freeze fruit at 0° F., or lower, as soon as possible

after packaging. Place packages to be frozen in the fastest freezing area, stacking them so that air can circulate freely. If a delay in getting the packages into the freezer is unavoidable, refrigerate them as soon as they are sealed.

Label all packages with the name of the fruit and date frozen, and any other details that will be helpful when the food is thawed.

Packing and sealing

Use any of the following containers for fruits: (1) rectangular freezer cartons with polyethylene inner bags; (2) plastic freezer bags for dry packs; (3) heavily waxed, cylindrical freezer cartons with slip-over or slip-in lids; (4) flexible plastic containers.

When using liquid pack, it is essential to leave a headspace of ¼ to ½ inch in containers.

Pack fruit tightly to cut down on the amount of air in the package. Seal carton according to the type used.

When fruit is packed in bags, press air out of the unfilled part of the bag. Press firmly to prevent air getting back in. Seal immediately, allowing adequate headspace for the particular product.

Ascorbic acid

It is advisable to treat cherries, apricots, peaches and prune plums with ascorbic acid in order to prevent oxidation or browning. Ascorbic acid can be purchased at drugstores in powdered or tablet form. The ascorbic acid is added either to the syrup or, in the case of dry sugar pack, to the fruit before the sugar is added.

If you use a commercial preparation recommended for preserving the natural color of the fruit, follow the manufacturer's directions.

Ascorbic acid for syrup pack: Use ¼ teaspoon powdered ascorbic acid for each 4 cups syrup, or 800 milligrams in tablet form for each 4 cups sugar.

Ascorbic acid for dry sugar pack: Use ⅛ teaspoon powdered ascorbic acid for each 1-pint container of fruit. Dissolve the ascorbic acid in 2 tablespoons cold water. Sprinkle over the fruit in a bowl and mix gently; then mix in dry sugar. Or use 400 milligrams in tablet form for each 1-pint container of fruit. Crush tablets, then dissolve in 2 tablespoons cold water. Sprinkle over fruit in a bowl and mix gently; then mix in dry sugar. The amount of sugar per pint depends on the fruit used.

Syrup

Make syrup just before preparing fruit. Avoid making any that is not immediately required. Ascorbic acid is not stable in solution, so its strength will deteriorate when stored. Allow ⅔ to 1 cup syrup for each 16-fluid-ounce container.

Add the ascorbic acid (powdered or crushed tablets) to the measured amount of water and stir until dissolved. Add the required amount of sugar, and again stir to dissolve. Chill while preparing fruit.

TYPE OF SYRUP	SUGAR	WATER	YIELD
Thin	1 cup	2 cups	about 2½ cups
Moderately thin	1 cup	1½ cups	about 2 cups
Medium	1 cup	1 cup	about 1½ cups
Heavy	1 cup	¾ cup	about 1¼ cups

Packing fruits with sugar or syrup

Dry sugar pack: Place fruit, ascorbic acid and sugar in a bowl and mix gently. Fill containers, seal and freeze.

Syrup pack: Use the strength of syrup that best suits the tartness of the fruit and your personal taste. Slice large fruits directly into containers that have about ⅓ to ½ cup syrup in them. Be sure that the syrup covers the fruit and that you have left headspace for expansion.

To keep fruit such as peaches under the syrup and to help prevent surface discoloration, place a crumpled piece of wax paper on top of fruit.

Uncooked whole apples

Freeze whole apples for baking, or for use in pies and puddings. The tartness of a summer apple seems to give a better apple flavor throughout the winter.

Wash firm apples without blemishes, then place six to ten in a polyethylene freezer bag and freeze.

To prepare the frozen fruit for cooking, run cold water over each frozen apple for 3 to 5 minutes, then peel, core or slice—whatever the recipe requires. Work fast; apples that are allowed to thaw before peeling darken quickly. Peel, then cut. To bake them, peel, prepare according to recipe and bake even if the apple is not completely thawed out.

Baked apples

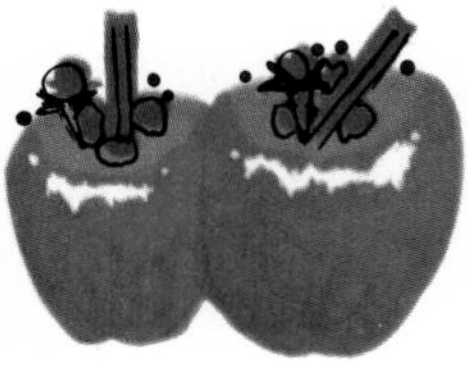

Use a good baking apple, such as a Jonathan, Rome Beauty or Baldwin. Peel and core. Make a syrup with 2 cups sugar, 1 cup water, 3 whole cloves, a 2-inch piece of cinnamon stick and 8 to 10 coriander seeds. Dip each apple into the boiling syrup for 3 minutes, then lift to a baking pan. In each apple cavity, put a few raisins, then 1 teaspoon brown sugar and 1 tablespoon butter. Bake in a 350° F. oven for about 35 minutes, or until the apples are soft but not mushy or broken. Then set under a broiler for a few seconds to brown the tops. Cool. Place the whole uncovered tray in the freezer until the apples are frozen solid. The next day, place the apples in containers, or wrap individually in foil. Label and freeze.

To serve, remove the required number of apples from the container, or unfold the foil from the top of foil-wrapped apples but leave the foil around the base. Let them thaw at room temperature for about 1 hour. If you prefer to serve them hot, place frozen apples in their foil bases on a baking pan and heat in a 425° F. oven for 30 minutes, or until apples are soft.

Sliced apples

First put about 4 quarts of water in a large kettle with a cover. Bring to a vigorous boil. This is for blanching, and the water must be ready when you need it.

Select firm apples and have them at room temperature. Peel, core and cut into twelfths. Work with about five apples at a time, to prevent discoloration. This is enough for one package, which will make one pie.

As the apples are peeled and cut, drop them into a weak salt brine (2 tablespoons salt in 1 gallon water). When one lot is ready, lift apple segments from the brine and place them in a square of cheesecloth or muslin large enough for easy handling.

Lower the muslin square of apples into the vigorously boiling water and cover the kettle. Keep heat high so that water will quickly return to the boil. As soon as water returns to a fast boil, remove the cover. With a large spoon, force the bag of apples down into the water to ensure uniform blanching. Blanch for 60 seconds, counting from the time when the water begins to boil the second time.

Immediately after blanching, plunge apple segments into cold running water, or into ice water, to chill as quickly as possible. Drain. Package dry without sugar or syrup. Place in freezer.

To use, defrost apple segments only enough to separate pieces, then make into pie in the usual way. *Note:* If brown areas appear in the apples after treatment, they were insufficiently blanched.

Pink applesauce

Applesauce is particularly good when made from summer apples. Prepare it in the usual manner, cool quickly and freeze. Even better is this recipe.

In a large saucepan place 2 cups cranberries (fresh or frozen), 2 to 4 cups quartered unpeeled apples and ¾ cup water. Bring to a boil. Cook, uncovered, over low heat until the fruits are tender. Place 1 to 1½ cups sugar in a bowl. Push the hot fruits through a coarse sieve or a food mill into the sugar. Stir until the sugar is dissolved. Add the grated rind of 1 orange. Cool, package, label and freeze.

Apricots

Apricots freeze with only fair success, but if you have a supply available, try these techniques. No fruit is more useful for all kinds of desserts.

The syrup pack is preferred for fruit to be served uncooked. The sugar pack is indicated when the fruit is to be used for pies or other cooked dishes.

Select firm ripe apricots. Wash. Cut apricots into halves or quarters as desired.

Syrup pack: Pack prepared fruit directly into syrup in the containers, using moderately thin syrup. Seal and freeze.

Dry sugar pack: Combine 4 pounds prepared fruit (about 10 cups) with ascorbic acid (p. 590) and 1 pound (2 cups) sugar. Pour into containers, seal and freeze.

Sour cherries

Uncooked sweet cherries freeze only fairly well, but uncooked sour cherries freeze very well.

Syrup pack: Select well-colored fruit with good flavor. Sort, stem, wash and drain. Remove pits if desired; pits tend to give an almondlike flavor to the fruit. Pack cherries into containers with medium syrup. Seal and freeze.

Stewed cherries make a good frozen product with excellent flavor. See recipe for stewed prune plums (p. 595), which is also good for sweet cherries.

Cranberries

There is little work required for freezing cranberries. Buy them during the Christmas season when their price is at its lowest, and freeze them raw. Wrap and label each box. To use, no thawing is necessary, even if only a small quantity is needed, since they do not stick to each other. They will keep in perfect condition for 12 months.

Cranberry relish

The well-known raw-cranberry relish—4 cups raw cranberries and 2 whole oranges (rind and pulp) passed through a food chopper together and stirred with 1½ cups of sugar—will freeze to perfection and keep for 8 to 12 months.

Peaches

Choose firm ripe peaches. Dip them into boiling water for 30 to 45 seconds, then into cold water. Peel. Work with a small quantity of fruit at one time.

Syrup pack: Slice peaches directly into syrup in the containers, using moderately thin syrup.

Dry sugar pack: Combine 4 pounds sliced peaches (about 10 cups) with ascorbic acid and 1 pound sugar (2 cups). Pour into containers, seal and freeze.

Peaches with orange

Ripe peaches, sliced and frozen when they are plentiful, can be used in the winter for breakfast, as a dessert by themselves, or as a sauce over ice cream. The flavor and color of these are splendid.

3 cups fresh orange juice	Juice of 1 lemon
¼ cup sugar	12 to 14 peaches

Remove pits from the orange juice but do not strain it. Mix juice with the sugar and lemon juice. Stir until the sugar is dissolved. Fill ½-pint freezer containers one-third full with the orange-juice mixture.

Pour boiling water over the peaches. Let them stand for 3 minutes, then drain and place in cold water. Peel. Slice directly into the containers. Leave good headspace, then add enough of the orange-juice mixture to cover the fruit. Place a crumpled piece of freezer paper over the peaches; this will keep them submerged in the juice. Adjust the lids and freeze. To use, thaw and serve. Makes 6 to 8 cups.

This can also be made with reconstituted frozen orange juice, and with maple syrup instead of sugar. Use 4 to 6 tablespoons maple syrup.

Grapes and cantaloupe balls

When seedless grapes are sweet and plentiful, mix them with cantaloupe balls in proportions you wish. Pour them into ½-pint boxes (8 ounces) and cover with orange juice or with pink or regular lemonade. (You can use reconstituted frozen juices for these.) Cover, label and freeze. In the winter, serve as is or add to canned fruits for a salad, or serve with a scoop of sherbet on top.

Stewed prune plums

These small blue plums, sometimes called Italian prunes, are dried to make prunes. If you have a tree bearing these plums, you will have a good crop every year. Even if you buy them, they are the least expensive of all plums. Other varieties of plums freeze with only fair quality.

4 pounds prepared plums 1¾ cups sugar
2¼ cups water

Cut washed prune plums into halves. Remove pits and weigh. Bring water to a boil and add prepared fruit. Continue cooking over high heat. Stir in sugar and again bring to a boil. Boil gently, stirring constantly, for 5 to 8 minutes, until fruit is heated through. Remove from heat; cool. Fill containers, seal and freeze.

This same recipe can be used for stewed sweet cherries. To prepare them, wash and remove stems; then weigh and proceed with the recipe.

Uncooked prune plums

While stewed prune plums retain maximum color and flavor, you can also freeze them uncooked. Choose firm ripe fruit. Wash, halve and pit.

Syrup pack: Add fruit to thin syrup in freezer containers. Seal and freeze.

Dry syrup pack: Combine 5 pounds prepared fruit

(about 13 cups) with ascorbic acid and 1 pound sugar. Fill containers, seal and freeze.

Rhubarb

There are two simple ways to deal with rhubarb. First: wash and trim the rhubarb and cut up as if to make sauce. Then simply place in freezer bags, label and freeze.

In the winter, add very little water to a bagful of frozen rhubarb and simmer over low heat until cooked. Remove from heat and add sugar to taste.

The other method is to make the rhubarb into a sauce before freezing. Cool, package and freeze.

Apricot purée

Select fully ripe fruit. Wash, cut into halves, remove pits. Mash fruit a little to start the juice. Add some water to prevent scorching (1 cup water to each 5 pounds fruit). Bring quickly to a boil, stirring occasionally. Boil for 1 minute.

Put fruit through food mill or sieve. Sweeten extracted pulp with 1 pound sugar to each 5 pounds of extracted pulp. Measure ¼ teaspoon ascorbic acid for each 4 cups sweetened pulp. Dissolve ascorbic acid in a small amount of cold water and then add to the mixture. As soon as sugar is dissolved, cool quickly, then fill freezer containers. Seal and freeze.

If preferred, the fruit pulp or purée can be left unsweetened and dissolved ascorbic acid added (¼ teaspoon for each 4 cups). Fill containers, seal and freeze.

Banana purée

Often bananas become too ripe before we have an opportunity to use them. When this happens, peel the bananas and push them through a food mill. Add 1 teaspoon fresh lemon juice, or ¼ teaspoon ascorbic acid, for each 2 cups puréed bananas; then package and freeze.

Use for banana bread or cake by simply thawing the frozen banana purée for 15 to 20 minutes.

Peach purée

Peel and cut fully ripe peaches and crush with a potato masher. Add ½ to 1 cup sugar and ¼ teaspoon ascorbic acid to each 4 cups crushed fruit. Combine well. Fill containers, seal and freeze.

Another method is to use a food mill or sieve; this

makes a smoother purée. Peel and pit peaches and cut into pieces. Mash fruit a little to start juice. Bring quickly to a boil, stirring constantly. Remove from heat and press through a food mill or sieve. Add sugar if desired. Add ascorbic acid (¼ teaspoon to 4 cups fruit pulp). Cool quickly. Fill containers, seal and freeze.

Fruit pie fillings

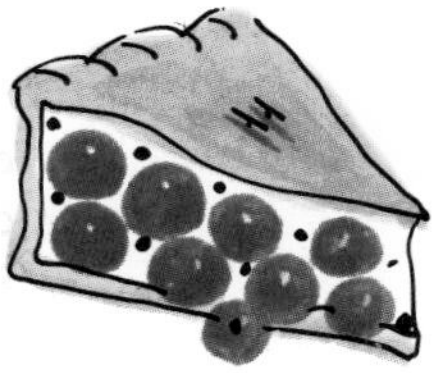

It is not wise to handle too large a batch at one time. Quick cooking is desirable. About 4 pounds of prepared fruit for each batch can be easily handled with the equipment found in most homes.

Choose fruit that is ripe but sound. Wash. Pit cherries. Halve apricots and prunes and remove pits. Scald peaches to remove skins, remove pits and then cut into ½-inch segments.

Use the following table for proportion of fruit, sugar and quick-cooking tapioca.

FRUIT	QUANTITY	SUGAR	QUICK-COOKING TAPIOCA
Apricots	4 lbs.	1 lb.	4 tablespoons
Cherries, sweet	4 lbs.	1 lb.	5 tablespoons
Cherries sour	4 lbs.	1½ lbs.	6 tablespoons
Peaches	4 lbs.	1 lb.	5 tablespoons
Prunes	4 lbs.	1 lb.	4 tablespoons

Place prepared fruit in a heavy saucepan with three quarters of the sugar. Combine well to start the juice flowing. If necessary, add about ⅓ cup water to prevent burning. Place over high heat and bring to a boil. Boil for 1 minute, stirring constantly.

Combine remaining sugar with the quick-cooking tapioca and add this mixture to saucepan. Return the fruit to a full rolling boil. Boil again for 1 minute, stirring constantly.

Remove from heat. Cool as quickly as possible.

This filling can now be made into pies. It can be stored in the refrigerator in jars; it will almost fill two 1-quart jars. The filling can be put into freezer containers, sealed and frozen to be used at a later date for such dishes as pies and tarts.

You can also freeze your fruit pie filling in the following manner: Line an 8- or 9-inch pie plate with heavy foil or with a double thickness of light foil, making sure the foil extends at least 6 inches above the rim. Prepare your pie filling as usual. Pour into the plate and bring foil over the top to cover loosely. Freeze until firm. Then remove filling from pie plate, label and return to freezer until ready to use.

To use, unwrap, place frozen mixture on a pastry-lined pie plate of the same size you used to freeze in, dot with butter and cover as your recipe directs. Place in a preheated 425° F. oven for 45 to 50 minutes, or until crust is golden brown. Keeps for 6 to 8 months.

Fruit sauces

Fruit sauces can be made of apricots, peaches or prune plums. Use the sauces as toppings for desserts and ice cream, or in baking. Fruit sauce is also delicious to serve by itself.

Do not attempt to handle too large a batch at one time. Quick preparation and quick cooking are necessary to give a product that will have good color and flavor. A batch no bigger than 4 pounds of prepared fruit is recommended.

Choose fruit that is ripe but sound. Wash. Pit apricots and prunes. Scald peaches to remove skins and then remove pits.

Weigh 4 pounds of prepared fruit. Put fruit through a food chopper, using the coarse blade; work quickly.

Use the following table for proportion of fruit, sugar and quick-cooking tapioca.

FRUIT	QUANTITY	SUGAR	QUICK-COOKING TAPIOCA
Apricots	4 lbs.	3/4 lb.	2 tablespoons
Peaches	4 lbs.	3/4 lb.	2 1/2 tablespoons
Prunes	4 lbs.	3/4 lb.	2 tablespoons

Mix the tapioca with ½ cup of the sugar. Add remaining sugar to the ground fruit. Place in a heavy saucepan over high heat. Bring to a boil, stirring constantly. Stir in sugar-tapioca mixture. Boil hard, stirring constantly, for 1½ minutes.

Remove from heat. Cool quickly. Fill freezer containers, leaving headspace. Seal and freeze.

Storage of frozen fruits

In general, frozen fruits can be stored for up to one year, but there are some exceptions. See the chart on page 589 and information with specific recipes. Avoid longer storage; fruits will not remain at top quality indefinitely.

Thawing and serving frozen fruits

Thaw fruit just before serving. Defrost in the original sealed package, turning the container over several times to distribute syrup evenly. Thaw only as much as you can use at one time. Cook any leftover thawed fruit.

For thawing a pint container of fruit, allow 6 to 8 hours in the refrigerator, about 3 hours at room temperature, about 1½ hours if the air current of a fan is directed on the container, about 1 hour if the container is placed in a pan under cold running water.

Serve the fruit while it is still cold. Do not let it stand at room temperature after thawing, for the flavor, appearance and texture will deteriorate.

It is not necessary to completely thaw fruits that are to be used for pies, baked puddings or stewed fruit. For pies or puddings, thaw fruit sufficiently to separate the pieces, and then proceed as with fresh fruit. Fruits such as sour cherries, used for pies and tarts, are softened by the freezing process, so they cook in much less time than fresh sour cherries.

To serve unsweetened purées, defrost and use like fresh-fruit purées in various desserts.

To serve sweetened puréed apricots or prune plums as a fruit juice, defrost, measure, then add to an equal amount of water. Stir well. Serve.

HOW TO FREEZE VEGETABLES

Here are a few examples of vegetable specialties that your family might enjoy.

Whole-kernel corn

Corn is one of America's favorite vegetables, and since Colonial days it has been preserved for winter use by drying. However, neither drying nor canning gives as fresh-tasting a vegetable as freezing. This method is the best, but it does require some effort, so freeze corn only if your family really enjoys it.

Use the freshest corn possible. Husk, remove the silk and place the ears in a saucepan. Sprinkle with 1 teaspoon sugar for each 12 ears of corn. Pour on rapidly boiling water to cover completely. Boil fast for 4 minutes. Remove the ears with tongs and place them, one by one, in a large bowl of ice water. Leave them in the ice water for 4 minutes. Then take an ear from the water, wipe it and cut the kernels from the cob. Do this with all the ears, then package the kernels, label and freeze. One-quart plastic freezer bags will usually hold the kernels from three ears of corn.

Broccoli

Broccoli freezes well. Choose compact, dark-green heads. Trim coarse leaves. Wash thoroughly. Peel and cut stalks lengthwise so that heads are about 1½ inches wide. For each pound of broccoli, boil 1 gallon of water. Add broccoli and heat for 3 minutes. Chill in cold water, drain and pack in freezer containers.

Golden glazed carrots

When you thin out the first baby carrots in your garden, glaze some to serve at New Year's dinner. Of course, any fresh carrots can be used.

1½ pounds baby carrots *or* 1½ pounds standard carrots cut into strips
2 tablespoons all-purpose flour
¼ cup light brown sugar or maple sugar
½ teaspoon salt
¼ teaspoon ground thyme
1 tablespoon cider vinegar
1 tablespoon fresh lemon juice
½ cup orange juice
Grated rind of 1 orange
2 tablespoons butter

Place the carrots in a saucepan. Pour boiling water over them and boil for 5 minutes. Drain thoroughly.

Blend the flour, sugar, salt and thyme. Add vinegar, juices and orange rind. Bring to a boil, while stirring, and continue stirring until creamy. Add the butter and cook over very low heat for 5 minutes. Line a casserole with foil, leaving enough around the edge to cover. Put in the blanched carrots and pour the sauce over. Freeze uncovered.

When frozen, cover completely with the foil. Remove the foil-wrapped carrots from the casserole and put them back in the freezer. To serve, unwrap the frozen block of carrots and put back in the same casserole. Bake, covered, in a 350° F. oven for about 40 minutes. Uncover for the last 15 minutes. Makes 6 servings.

Mushrooms

Rinse perfect fresh button mushrooms in a quart of ice-cold water to which you have added 1 tablespoon lemon juice. Then roll the mushrooms in absorbent paper and immediately package in small plastic bags. Label and put into the freezer.

No thawing is needed before cooking them. Brown some butter; then, keeping the pan over high heat, add the frozen mushrooms and stir constantly for 2 to 3 minutes. Remove from heat, season to taste and serve.

When using mushrooms in a sauce, simply add the frozen mushrooms as they come from the bag, or slice them while frozen.

Fresh mushrooms can also be frozen after cooking. Cook quickly in butter, for no more than 3 or 4 minutes. They can be whole or sliced. Cool, package, label and freeze.

Leeks

Leeks are never cheap or plentiful in metropolitan areas, but if you are near a country market where they are available, you will discover that they are among the most successful vegetables to freeze. Clean and slice them and package in 1- or 2-cup portions to use for soups, casseroles and many other dishes. They thaw very quickly.

Leek base for vichyssoise

Make this when leeks are plentiful and you will be able to prepare a gourmet soup in 20 minutes, all year round.

Remove outer coarse leaves from 12 medium-size leeks. Make a long split from the white part to the end of the green part. Wash carefully under cold running water, then shake off surplus water. Cut into thin slices, starting at the white base.

Peel 4 large, mild onions and slice as thin as possible. Melt 1½ cups of butter in a saucepan. Add the leeks and onions and stir well for a few seconds. Cover and cook over very low heat for 25 minutes, stirring a few times. The mixture must soften completely but must not brown. It will reduce as it cooks. Divide by cupfuls into containers and freeze. Makes 6 cups.

Vichyssoise

3 to 4 cups chicken stock
1 cup frozen leek base
1 cup instant mashed potatoes or riced boiled potatoes
½ cup cold milk
1 cup light or heavy cream
Salt and pepper
Chives

Bring stock to a boil and add the leek base. Simmer for 20 minutes. Stir the instant or riced potatoes with the milk and beat into the stock. Simmer together for a few minutes. Add the cream. When the soup is smooth and hot, add seasoning to taste and serve. You may strain or purée the soup if you prefer.

To serve cold, refrigerate until chilled. Sprinkle each serving with snipped chives. Makes 6 servings.

Cucumber purée

Cucumbers, like tomatoes, have a way of flooding the market or the garden all at once. They are not good frozen except as a purée that can be added to a French dressing or to a cream of potato soup, or used as a cold meat sauce with the addition of a little lemon juice, ground cloves or dill. The purée also makes a beautiful aspic.

Peel 12 cucumbers, taking off the thinnest possible layer. Cut lengthwise, remove the seeds and slice thin. Sprinkle with 2 teaspoons salt. Place in a heavy metal saucepan and add ½ cup boiling water. Bring to a boil, then cook, uncovered, for 10 minutes. Pass through a food mill or a sieve. Package in ½-pint (8-ounce) containers and freeze. Enough for 4 containers.

Onions

When small white (silverskin) onions or large sweet red onions are plentiful and cheap on the market, it is time to make the winter provision. Onions can be kept in dry storage, and if you live where these onions are available all year you will not need to freeze them; but in some sections of the country white and red onions are seasonal. Of course, all dry-stored onions tend to sprout, but your frozen vegetables will be in perfect condition whenever you want them.

Simply peel the onions and place them whole in good plastic containers, then freeze. When you need them, open the container and take out what is required; they do not stick together. 🗝 It is much easier to slice or chop onions when they are still partly frozen. If you plan to boil the onions, you do not need to thaw before cooking.

Parsley and other fresh herbs

If you grow your own herbs, gather some when they are at their prime. The best time is after a soft rainfall, when they will be clean. Place small portions, whole or minced as you prefer, in plastic bags. Label and freeze. To use them whole, cut with kitchen shears while crisply frozen. They will taste like fresh herbs and retain their full green color. If you do not grow other herbs, you could freeze fresh green summer parsley and fresh basil.

Green peppers

When these are plentiful, chop, slice or halve. Wrap the pieces and freeze them. They will keep for 3 to 4 months. Like celery, peppers will become limp on defrosting, but they are wonderful to use in cooked preparations. Simply add them still frozen to the recipe. You can freeze just part of a pepper, too, for recipes that call for less than a whole one. You can freeze chopped onions in the same way. When you are ready to use them, just separate as much pepper or onion as you need and return the rest to the freezer.

French fried potatoes

If your family loves French fried potatoes, you can save a lot of time by making many and freezing them in packages large enough for one meal.

Cut the potatoes into long strips about ½ inch thick, or into much smaller strips for matchstick (*allumette*) potatoes, or into thin round slices. Place the pieces in a bowl and cover with cold water. Let stand for 1 hour. Drain and dry thoroughly in a towel. Heat enough peanut oil to measure 3 inches in the saucepan. When the oil is hot (360° to 370° F. on a frying thermometer), fry a few slices at a time for 5 to 7 minutes, or until a light beige. The thinner slices will need only 5 minutes; the thicker slices will take longer. Drain on absorbent paper and repeat with remaining potatoes. Do not salt them before freezing.

Cool to room temperature. Package in convenient portions, seal, label, date and freeze. They will keep for 1 month.

To serve, place frozen potatoes on a greased baking sheet. Preheat oven to 450° F. Put in potatoes and brown for 10 to 15 minutes, turning once. Sprinkle with salt at this point.

Cooking frozen vegetables

These notes apply to both home-frozen and commercial products.

Cook all vegetables, except corn on the cob, without thawing. When they are frozen in a solid block, as is the case with spinach, thaw for 20 to 25 minutes at the most, or enough to separate the block into a few pieces.

Place the frozen vegetables in a saucepan and sprinkle with a pinch of sugar. Pour boiling water on top and bring back to a fast rolling boil. Cover and lower heat to medium. Cook for 4 to 15 minutes. The time depends on the vegetable, the variety, maturity and size of pieces. The most important point to remember about frozen vegetables is not to overcook them. They are already partly cooked. Freezing breaks down fibers and makes the vegetables softer. But in most cases they have also undergone another breaking-down process, actually a cooking process—blanching—which generally reduces the necessary cooking time by 25 to 75 percent. Some vegetables are frozen after being completely cooked; only reheating is necessary for these. Taste a small piece of the vegetable after 4 or 5 minutes; then decide how much longer it needs to cook to your taste.

Use the minimum amount of water in cooking frozen vegetables. Usually ½ cup water is adequate for 1 pint of vegetables.

Add salt to your taste toward the end of the short cooking period. Start with ½ teaspoon for 1 pint of vegetables. It is easy to add more if you like, but impossible to take it out if you have used too much.

A cooked frozen vegetable loses much of its color and flavor if you do not serve it as soon as cooked. This is easy enough because there is no advance preparation.

Corn on the cob, because of its heavy starch and sugar content, is an exception to the rule of cooking without thawing. Place the partially thawed corn in a saucepan and pour boiling water on top. Cover and cook for only 3 to 6 minutes. A longer time will make the corn mealy and hard. Serve as soon as it is ready.

Frozen spinach, pumpkin or squash is usually more flavorful if cooked unthawed, without water, in the top part of a double boiler. Add a piece of butter when the vegetable is partly thawed. Keep the water in the bottom part boiling rapidly, and break up and stir the vegetable often. It takes a little longer, but the final result will be far superior.

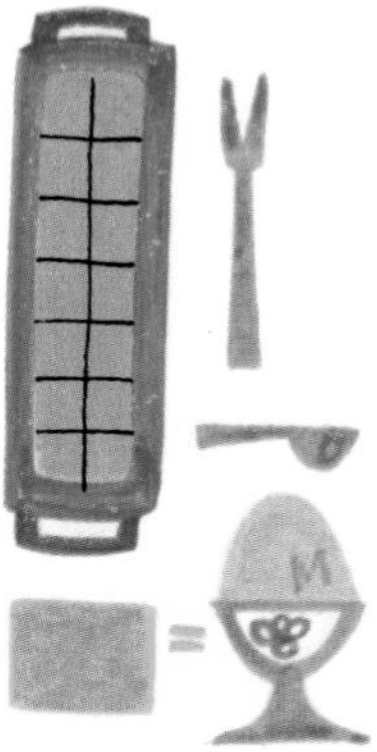

HOW TO FREEZE EGGS

Eggs are more plentiful and as a result cheaper at certain times of the year. You can store them frozen in several ways, but do not expect to make poached or fried eggs with them afterward, because they are not frozen in their shells. Neither whole eggs nor yolks can be frozen without an additional ingredient. While this is unimportant when using them for such foods as cakes, it does affect the taste when using them for egg dishes. Frozen eggs can be kept in storage for 4 months.

Uncooked eggs

WHOLE EGGS: Beat the eggs with a fork just enough to break the yolks and blend them into the whites. Add 1 teaspoon salt for each 2 cups of beaten eggs, or 1 teaspoon sugar, honey or corn syrup. Freeze in an ice-cube tray with the divider in place. When frozen, remove the cubes from the tray and store them in a plastic bag. In 1 large frozen cube you will have about 3 tablespoons, or slightly less than 1 medium-size egg. Use water to measure your own ice cube so that you will know how many tablespoons it contains.

With whole eggs you may wish to package the number required for a specific recipe you make often. For example: a cake may call for 8 whole eggs. Beat the eggs, season with salt and freeze. Package after freezing and label "8 whole eggs for cake."

Some recipes, such as soufflés, require whites or yolks alone. Instead of mixing the parts together, separate the eggs carefully, then measure and freeze.

EGG YOLKS: Beat the egg yolks lightly with a fork. Stir in 1 teaspoon salt or 1 tablespoon sugar, honey or corn syrup to each 1 cup yolks. Freeze in an ice-cube tray with the dividers in place. When frozen, remove the cubes from the tray and store them in a plastic bag. Label as to quantity of yolks and salt or sugar. About 14 egg yolks of medium-size eggs equal 1 cup. A large frozen cube usually equals 3 tablespoons egg yolk, or 2 or 3 egg yolks.

EGG WHITES: Egg whites can be packaged without the addition of either salt or sugar; they need no mixing. Freeze in an ice-cube tray with the divider in place. Store the frozen cubes in bags. Label and freeze just as for egg yolks. About 8 egg whites of medium-size eggs equal 1 cup. A large cube usually equals 3 tablespoons egg white, or 1½ egg whites. Thaw at room temperature or in the refrigerator before beating.

You may never wish to buy eggs for the purpose of freezing them, but in everyday cooking one often has egg whites left after preparing a recipe. Egg yolks are left over less often, but if you bake soufflés you will have extra yolks. Freeze either whites or yolks to use another time. You may want to freeze 1 egg white alone in a small cube to use for glazing breads or pastries. See Chapter 13 on working with flour for more about this.

When thawing uncooked eggs, here is a good rule to follow: 6 eggs will thaw in an unopened container in the refrigerator in 2 to 3 hours, or at room temperature in 30 to 45 minutes. Waterproof containers can be placed unopened in a bowl of cold water for even faster thawing.

Cooked eggs

Hard-cooked eggs will freeze nicely when grated fine. Thaw to use in salads, sandwich fillings, soup garnishes, and to garnish vegetables such as spinach.

HOW TO FREEZE MEAT

First let us consider buying meat in wholesale portions. Although there are disadvantages to this (p. 580), you might find it could result in savings because of the size of your family or its preferences. For instance, if beef is your favorite, you have a 15- to 20-cubic-foot freezer, and your family consists of four or more persons, it can be a long-run economy to buy a half of beef. A half usually runs from 215 to 250 pounds, untrimmed, so you will have a supply of beef for several months. Of course, you will have considerable variety in the cuts, and you will get approximately 30 pounds that can be ground or cut for stew as you prefer. Ask the butcher to leave any ground meat unfrozen so that you can shape it and wrap it yourself.

If your family is smaller, a half of beef is too much. If you are fond of steaks and not interested in such cuts as pot roasts and soups, then a hindquarter might be a good buy, although it will cost more per pound than the half. The roasts in this cut will be rump and sirloin tips. The hindquarter runs slightly smaller than the forequarter.

When the pieces have been cut by the butcher, he may freeze them for you. Be sure the meat is cut into pieces of an appropriate size to cook or it will be difficult for you to manage. Then wrap and store for future use.

If the meat is not frozen for you, follow this general procedure. Chill the meat thoroughly. Pad all projecting bones with freezer paper or foil so they will not pierce the wrapping. Then wrap in a suitable wrapping such as freezer paper or foil. Press the wrapping close to the meat to exclude air. If you are packing steaks or chops, separate individual pieces with sheets of wax paper or freezer paper. Hearts, kidneys and livers can be frozen uncooked, but brains, sweetbreads and tripe should be cooked before freezing. Put the wrapped packages close to the freezer walls for the most rapid freezing.

It is particularly important to label each meat package with date and contents, as different cuts can be stored for different lengths of time. See the chart on page 609 for meat storage times.

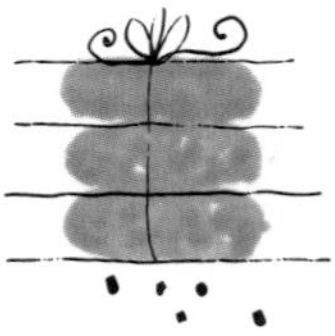

Ground meat

Ground meat is very difficult to manage if it is frozen in a large lump. Not only is it necessary to thaw it out almost completely before it can be used, but after thawing it will not stick together to form a compact patty. It is better to make the patties before freezing, seasoning as you usually do, except for salt, which should be added only when the meat is cooking. This is important because salt in meat that is frozen causes oxidation by preventing quick freezing of the water in the meat.

Shape the ground meat into patties to fit the size bread or bun you usually use. Place squares of wax paper between the patties. Then wrap six to eight per package in moistureproof freezer paper. Place in the freezer.

When you are ready to serve, separate the number you need and rewrap the rest and return them to the freezer. Thaw the patties you are using just enough to remove the paper. Then season each with salt, and other seasonings if you have not already done this before freezing. Cook quickly in butter or oil in a black iron frying pan over medium-high heat. When browned on one side, turn and brown the other side. The whole process should take from 8 to 10 minutes.

Herbed hamburgers

To 1 pound of ground beef add 1 teaspoon MSG, 1/4 teaspoon dried thyme, 1 teaspoon minced fresh parsley, 1/8 teaspoon pepper or 1 tablespoon Worcestershire sauce, no salt, and 1/4 cup undiluted condensed consommé. Blend the whole thoroughly with your hands, shape patties and wrap them. They will keep in the freezer for 4 to 6 weeks.

If you want to have the same seasoning for patties already frozen, separate the patties and sprinkle them with salt and MSG. In a bowl blend the thyme, parsley, Worcestershire sauce and consommé. Soak each patty in the liquid for 5 minutes. Fry them in melted beef suet or oil, or broil them 3 inches from the source of heat for 4 to 6 minutes on each side.

Meat storage time

Although some frozen meats will store satisfactorily for several months if properly wrapped, it is not practical to fill up limited storage space with them for long periods of time. Large or thick cuts can be held considerably longer in storage than small pieces because the small bits tend to dry out and develop off-flavors. It is necessary to label all packages of frozen food, but it is especially important with meats to mark on each package the kind of meat, name of cut, weight and date, and to keep a record so that none will be kept longer than the recommended storage time.

MAXIMUM STORAGE TIMES AT 0° F. FOR MEATS

Bacon, unsliced	1 to 3 months
Beef, roasts, steaks	8 to 12 months
Cooked meats, stews, loaves, etc.	1 to 2 months
Cooked roasts	2 to 3 months
Gravy, unthickened	3 to 4 months
Lamb chops	4 to 5 months
Lamb roasts	8 to 12 months
Minced or ground meat, raw	3 to 4 months
Pork chops, fresh	3 to 4 months
Pork, cured, smoked	1 to 2 months
Pork roasts, fresh	4 to 8 months
Sausages, wieners	1 to 3 months
Variety meats, liver, heart, kidneys, etc.	3 to 4 months
Veal chops	4 to 5 months
Veal roasts	9 to 12 months

Cooking frozen meats

Frozen meats can be cooked from the completely frozen state or after thawing. To thaw meats, place them, while still wrapped, in the bottom of the refrigerator for 6 to 8 hours. Often they do not completely thaw out, but the thawing process is started. You may leave meats at room temperature for 2 to 3 hours. Thawing times vary, of course, with the weight of the piece of meat, its shape and thickness. To thaw meat completely in the refrigerator you must allow from 10 to 12 hours per pound. At room temperature, meat will thaw in 2 to 3 hours per pound. Be sure to keep it wrapped while thawing to prevent evaporation.

Thawing meat in a bowl of cold water, even when still wrapped, is not recommended.

Leftovers and sliced cooked meat are at their best when thawed, still wrapped, over boiling water, or by steaming. This prevents any dryness in the reheated products. Never thaw frozen food by placing it in a slow oven; this will dry it out.

Cooking meat in its frozen state does not in any way change its quality, but of course it must be properly cooked. There is only one disadvantage: it takes longer and consequently uses a larger amount of fuel.

🔑 A very important secret for success in cooking frozen meat is to use a meat thermometer. Timing is absolutely unreliable when dealing with frozen, partially frozen or even totally defrosted meats; their texture varies too much. In general, completely frozen roasts take from half again to twice as long to cook as completely thawed-out roasts. The safest way to determine "doneness" is by the internal temperature; the meat thermometer should read the same as for unfrozen meats. Of course, a thermometer cannot be inserted into a solidly frozen roast or steak. Wait until the meat has cooked for a time and has started to soften before inserting a metal skewer. If the skewer will go in, you can insert the thermometer. As to the cooking and seasoning, you can follow any of the recipes and methods given in the section that describes ways to cook meat.

Here are a few examples of how to cook solidly frozen meat. When you have an emergency and a roast or steak must be started while still frozen, first preheat oven to 450° F.; allow 20 minutes for this temperature to be reached. Set the unwrapped and prepared roast in it and sear for 25 minutes. Lower the heat to 350° F., then cook as you would an ordinary meat roast.

For a steak, use a heavy metal frying pan. Heat the pan and sear the steak on both sides in a minimum amount of fat over high heat. Then finish cooking the steak as usual.

HOW TO FREEZE POULTRY

In general, the rules that apply to meat are useful for poultry. It can be frozen whole, in halves or in pieces. All birds should be eviscerated, cleaned of feathers or hairs and carefully washed and well dried. If you buy it eviscerated, be sure to examine the inside of the carcass and remove any forgotten bits. Remove all extra fat, because this can become rancid. If the bird is to be frozen whole, truss it to give it a more compact form. Do not stuff it; this can encourage the growth of bacteria. Chill the poultry thoroughly. Then wrap it, remembering to be sure to cover any projecting bones just as you should do for meat. Separate pieces if you are freezing cut-up poultry.

Poultry will thaw in about 5 hours in the refrigerator, about 1½ hours at room temperature. It should be thawed in its wrapping. Just as with meat, defrosting poultry by placing it in a bowl of cold water is not recommended.

Cook frozen raw poultry as soon as thawed, and use frozen cooked poultry as soon as thawed.

Leftover cooked poultry can be frozen most successfully when cut from the bones, and of course this saves space. However, even when well wrapped, such poultry tends to dry and lose flavor in the freezer. It is better to pack it with poultry gravy or other appropriate sauce.

Cook frozen poultry by any of the methods described for fresh poultry, but remember that the freezing process affects the food just as partial cooking does, by helping to break down the tissues of the food and make them softer. The ice crystals formed in the muscle fibers help to break them apart and make the meat easier to cut and chew, even though the flavor is unaffected. Therefore the cooking time for completely thawed poultry may be less than for fresh poultry. It is better to thaw or partially thaw frozen poultry before cooking it.

HOW TO FREEZE FISH

Fish can be frozen with considerable success, but the frozen product is very different from freshly caught fish. There is a loss of juice and flavor, particularly with fillets or slices. Whole fish, such as small trout, taste freshest after freezing. Clean the fish as quickly as possible, and keep it cold until you place it in the freezer. Remove any streaks of fat on fish to be frozen because the fat may become rancid; this applies especially to salmon and mackerel.

There are three methods for freezing fish:

Glazing method: Clean the fish and place it on a tray in the freezer until frozen solid. Then dip it into very cold water for 2 minutes and freeze it again. Repeat this dipping a second time, freeze again, then wrap carefully and store.

Brine method: Clean the fish. Make a brine with 1 cup of coarse salt and 4 quarts of cold water. Soak the fish in this for 10 minutes. Drain, wrap carefully and freeze.

Ice-block method: Brook trout, lake trout or any

other fisherman's catch can be frozen this way. Clean the whole fish and place it in a long pan, such as a loaf pan, appropriate to the size of the fish. Cover the fish with ice-cold water. To get water of the right temperature, place ice cubes in a bowl of water for 10 to 15 minutes ahead of time. Finnish housewives sometimes add a few sprigs of fresh dill to the water. Place the fish in the freezer. When frozen solid, unmold from the pan. This will be easy if you let hot water run on the underside of the pan for 2 or 3 seconds. Wrap the block of ice containing the fish in heavy-duty foil. Then return to the freezer.

To thaw a whole fish frozen in this fashion, break up whatever ice you can without touching the fish. Then place the fish in a large bowl in the refrigerator. It may take 4 to 8 hours to thaw, depending on its size.

You can also freeze fish steaks and fillets. Separate individual pieces with two pieces of freezer paper, wrap and freeze. Cut-up chunks of fish can be frozen also; for these the brine method is best.

Shelled clams, oysters, scallops and shrimp can be frozen raw. Pack in cartons and fill spaces with the shellfish's own liquid or with a light brine—1 tablespoon salt to 4 cups water. Crab meat and lobster meat should be cooked before freezing, then cooled and packed in airtight containers.

Frozen fish cakes

All cooked and canned fish except cod can be mixed, formed into cakes and balls, wrapped and frozen.

3 cups cooked fish
3 cups unseasoned mashed potatoes
2 eggs, well beaten
2 tablespoons melted margarine
½ teaspoon salt
¼ teaspoon pepper
½ teaspoon celery seeds or curry powder
½ teaspoon dry mustard
1 teaspoon grated onion
Grated rind of ½ lemon
2 teaspoons lemon juice

Place the fish and mashed potatoes in a large bowl. Add the eggs, margarine and seasonings. Mix thoroughly with your hands until smooth. Form into cakes, wrap with two pieces of freezer paper between cakes and freeze.

To cook, sauté unthawed cakes in vegetable oil or

bacon fat over medium-high heat until brown on both sides. Makes 16 cakes.

Thawing and cooking frozen fish and shellfish

For best flavor, do not store frozen fish for more than 4 months, although it is probably safe for up to 6 months. Oily or fatty fish should be stored for a shorter time because of the possibility of the fat in the tissues becoming rancid. Fish can be cooked without thawing, but if you have fillets or pieces frozen in a solid block (the way commercially frozen fish usually is packed), defrost enough to separate the pieces.

As to shellfish, frozen shrimp should be used within 6 weeks; clams, oysters and scallops within 3 months. Cooked crab meat and lobster meat can be stored longer. However, after 6 weeks the meat tends to toughen, so it is better to use it within that time. Shellfish should be thawed before cooking, unless it is to be cooked in boiling liquid or added to soups or stews.

HOW TO FREEZE BREADS

Put breads and baked products in plastic bags or wrap in aluminum foil. Be sure to put the date on the package so they are used in proper rotation. Most baked products will keep for 3 to 4 months.

Yeast breads can be frozen after they are shaped, before the second rising. This is a great convenience if you make your own bread, because the one ever-present difficulty in working with yeast is that the process takes time.

Frozen bread will go straight from the freezer to your toaster without defrosting.

Quick breads can also be frozen. These take a relatively short time to defrost. Date and nut loaf, for instance, will be cold but ready to eat in 30 minutes, making a very good emergency food.

If your family is a sandwich-carrying group, you may find it practical to make the lunches for several days, or a week, at a time. Put each sandwich in a sandwich bag, then wrap for freezing. Remember not to include any lettuce, tomato or cucumber. Label the packages. The frozen sandwich in its own bag goes off in the lunch box and by noon is defrosted and tastes like a fresh sandwich, still moist and flavorful.

Bread for poultry dressing can be stored dry if it has been slowly dried in the oven, but if you prefer softer stuffings, cut bread into small cubes, package them and store in the freezer. Add fresh herbs to the bread if you like; they freeze well together. Keeps for 8 to 12 months.

Pancakes and crêpes can be frozen too. Make pancakes and cool them completely in a single layer on a wire rack. Then place a double thickness of wax paper between the pancakes. Make a stack of as many as you like, then wrap in foil and freeze. This is a good trick to use when you are planning to serve pancakes to a lot of people.

For breakfast pancakes, preheat oven to 425° F. Remove wax paper from as many pancakes as you wish to serve and rewrap the rest. Bake on a baking sheet for 15 to 18 minutes.

If you have frozen crêpes that you plan to serve filled and sauced, defrost enough for the cakes to be flexible, then fill and heat. If you plan to serve flaming crêpes, let them reach room temperature before bathing in the liqueur sauce.

HOW TO FREEZE CAKES

It is simple enough to freeze cakes that have no frosting. Just cool the cake, wrap and freeze. In addition, some cakes with frostings can be frozen. Frostings made with butter or margarine and confectioners' sugar store best. Boiled or fudge-type frostings also freeze well. Never try to freeze a frosting made with egg whites, such as seven-minute frosting; it becomes very spongy.

The best fillings are fudge and nut-fruit types. Cream and custard fillings are not satisfactory for freezing.

When the cake is frosted, first freeze it uncovered. As soon as it is frozen, wrap and then return it to the freezer immediately.

Wrap fruitcakes in a cloth soaked in orange or lemon juice or brandy and then in heavy-duty foil. You can keep part of the cake sliced with pieces of wax paper between the slices. This makes for quick defrosting when only a few slices are needed. Keeps for 12 months.

Cookies can be frozen successfully. To serve, simply defrost completely.

Doughnuts without filling can be frozen. To serve, reheat in a 300° F. oven.

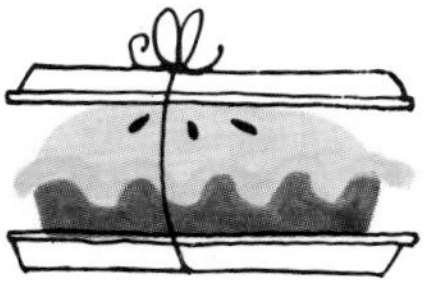

HOW TO FREEZE PIES

Fruit pies and mince pies are better when they are frozen before baking. Sprinkle a little ascorbic-acid solution or lemon juice over fresh apples and peaches to prevent the fruit from darkening.

You may find it helpful to add about one third more flour or cornstarch to the fruit than the recipe calls for. This prevents the lower crust from becoming soggy. It is also better not to make the steam vents in the top crust. If the pie has a fancy fluted edge, freeze before wrapping. This helps protect the edge.

Unbaked pies keep well for 3 to 6 months. To bake them, remove wrappings, cut a steam vent in the top crust and place pie in a very hot oven (450° F.) for 15 minutes. Then reduce heat to moderately hot (375° F.) and continue baking for an additional 45 minutes, or until browned evenly all over.

To freeze baked fruit pies, cool the pies. Place a paper pie plate over each; wrap, seal and freeze them. To thaw, place in a moderately hot oven (375° F.) for 25 to 30 minutes, or let them stand at room temperature for about 3 hours.

Chiffon pies also freeze well and can be stored for about 3 months. To thaw them, let stand at room temperature for about 2½ hours.

Crumb topping for fruit pies

O┳ Do not throw away cake crumbs. Freeze them and use later to make a crunchy topping for a fruit pie.

Mix the frozen cake crumbs with brown sugar and a sprinkling of cinnamon, or another spice of your choice.

HOW TO FREEZE DAIRY PRODUCTS

Butter

Salted butter will keep under ordinary refrigeration for a very long time; however, if you buy it in quantity, it is better to store it in the freezer because there is some flavor loss during refrigeration. Unsalted or sweet butter, on the other hand, is definitely perishable. It is best to store it in the freezer and keep out only what you plan to use within a week. Wrap butter in heavy-duty foil. To use, thaw in the refrigerator for 3 hours, or at room temperature for 1 to 2 hours. Keep for up to 6 months.

Light and heavy cream

It is useful to know that you can freeze cream because fresh cream sours easily. Store in the unopened cartons or freeze in small plastic containers.

Use frozen light cream for cooking only in hot sauces; no need to thaw before adding to the sauce.

Use heavy cream for whipping after thawing in the refrigerator.

Grated cheese

Use fresh-grated cheese of one type, or small leftover pieces grated and mixed; both will be satisfactory. Simply package in small plastic bags, label and freeze. No need to thaw to use.

HOW TO FREEZE MISCELLANEOUS ITEMS

Nutmeats and whole nuts

Store these in plastic ice-cream containers or in heavy polyethylene bags. Keep for 12 to 14 months.

Marshmallows

If you store marshmallows in the freezer, they will not dry out. When they need to be cut for a recipe, your shears will not stick to them while they are still frozen. Keep for 8 to 12 months.

Lemon and orange rinds

These freeze well, lose none of their color and flavor and do not have to be thawed before using. Before squeezing lemons or oranges for juice, grate the rinds and put in small jars. Keep for 6 to 9 months.

Fruit peels and glacéed fruits

Stock up on these at Christmas, when they are fresh and plentiful. Store fruits or peels, still in their original containers, in plastic freezer bags. They will retain their moisture and freshness for a year.

Fresh gingerroots
This spice, a delicious addition to Oriental dishes and other preparations as well, appears in our markets infrequently. If you find it in the supermarket, or have a good Chinese shop near you, buy a supply that will serve for several months. Scrub the roots thoroughly and dry them. Then wrap them or place in a container and freeze. When a recipe calls for ginger, simply grate the frozen root. Keep for 18 months to 2 years.

Ready-cooked casseroles
If you are preparing a casserole for eventual freezing, line the baking dish with heavy-duty foil, allowing enough to fold over the top of the dish. Bake the casserole, cool it, then place it in the freezer. When it is frozen solid, lift the foil-wrapped food from the casserole and wrap it again with extra foil. This saves freezer space. Make a label stating which casserole dish was used and reheat in the same dish. Keep for 2 to 3 months.

Leftover gravy
Freeze leftover gravy in small containers or in an ice-cube tray. Remove from the tray, package, label and store. Very useful for hot meat sandwiches and emergency gravy.

ONE LAST WORD
All this information relates to a freezer, where the temperature is a constant 0° F. or lower, not to a small freezer compartment in the refrigerator. It is true that the small freezer space can be used for many of these purposes, but it is not really safe for long-term storage because it is never cold enough. Also, the constant opening and closing of the refrigerator door makes the temperature fluctuate to some extent. Even those refrigerators that have separate doors for the freezing compartment present the same problem, although to a lesser degree, because the compartment is opened often to take out ice cubes. Small freezing areas are best used for making and storing ice cubes and for short-term storage of items in regular use so that they are replaced fairly often.

«16»

Cheese and Nuts

Storage times for cheese • Ways to use cheese • Cheeses of Great Britain, France, Denmark, Sweden, Norway, Italy, Switzerland, Germany, Holland, Greece, Canada, the United States • Cooking with cheese • Kinds of nuts • Storing, shelling, blanching nuts • Cooking with nuts

Cheese is made from milk curds that are always drained, sometimes pressed and often fermented. Every country produces cheeses, and those that are firm or long-lasting are most frequently exported to America.

When you realize that a quart of sour milk is reduced in cheese making to a small lump of scarcely ⅓ cup, you can better appreciate why cheese is so costly.

Milk itself contains organisms and enzymes that help mature the cheese. And some cheeses are made by adding foreign organisms such as Penicillium molds; blue cheeses are an obvious example.

Cheese can be used for any course in a meal. In France, cheese is always served before dessert, but in America it is generally served before the meal, like hors d'oeuvres, or with fruit at the conclusion of the repast.

Storing cheese

The length of time cheese can be kept depends largely on its type. Soft cheeses such as Brie and Camembert become overripe and strong-tasting if kept too long. Cream cheeses may develop molds that are detrimental to their flavor and texture. On the other hand, hard cheeses such as Cheddar may last for weeks without loss of quality. Should a hard cheese develop a mold, simply scrape or cut off the moldy part. Refrigerate all cheese after wrapping it tightly in wax paper, transparent plastic or foil. ⊶ However, always remove cheese from the refrigerator in time to serve it at room temperature. Even cottage cheese is much better when served at room temperature.

Semihard or hard *natural* cheeses can be stored in the freezer, but they will dry out and lose much of their flavor. The flavor will be good if you let cheese come to room temperature before serving and use it right after thawing. Grated cheese can be kept frozen for up to a year without being affected.

A soft creamy cheese will keep in your refrigerator for up to two weeks. A hard cheese will keep for as long as nine weeks without loss of flavor. The in-between cheeses present a problem of judgment. Since they are continuing to mature, like all natural cheeses, they reach a point of optimum flavor and texture. After that they actually deteriorate, although it is still quite possible to eat them. How long to keep them depends on their condition when you buy them. Three weeks is probably a reasonable storage limit for a cheese that is hard at the center when you purchase it. Blue cheeses become stronger in storage, but they will be better tasting for a longer time if wrapped in a damp cloth and stored in a covered cheese dish with room for air circulation. Processed cheeses have been pasteurized so they no longer ripen, and can be kept under refrigeration much longer than natural cheeses.

Using cheese

There is much more you can do with cheese than serve it with crackers at the end of a meal or decorate apple pie with a slice of Cheddar. All kinds of sandwiches can be made with cheese, and many different cheeses can be used for sauces. Grated hard cheese enhances all sorts of dishes—onion soup, minestrone, pasta dishes, salads. Cheese added to yeast doughs or quick doughs makes delicious bread, rolls or biscuits.

Cheese is a good way to enrich your diet with protein, calcium and vitamin A. Low-calorie diets make extensive use of cottage cheese, especially the skim-milk variety. Most cheese is salty; it contains the concentrated salt of a large quantity of milk. Remember this when using cheese in cooking.

O┳ Low temperatures are important in cheese cookery. High heat can make the cheese harden on the bottom of the pot instead of blending with other ingredients. O┳ If you are adding grated cheese to a hot mixture, add it at the very end and remove the saucepan from the heat immediately. The heat retained in the hot mixture will melt the cheese.

It is useful to know that 1 pound of cheese equals about 2 cups; 6 ounces of grated cheese will fill 1 cup.

CHEESE AROUND THE WORLD

The name of a cheese often reveals its country of origin. Watch for certain prefixes or suffixes to give you a clue. For instance, names of cheeses from Norway or Sweden commonly end with *ost,* meaning cheese. Examples are noekkelost, gjetost. In Denmark, names carry the suffix *bo*. Examples: Danbo, Fynbo, Elbo.

A cheese often derives its name from an ingredient. The German Kümmelkäse means cheese studded with caraway (*kümmel*) seeds. The French La Grappe is a mild, semisoft, creamy cheese covered with dried grape seeds.

However, the same name is sometimes given to a type of cheese, regardless of its point of origin. We have "Swiss cheese" made in Finland and in the United States as well as in Switzerland; the cheese we are copying is Emmental.

GREAT BRITAIN

England is the home of Cheddar cheese, and many of the other cheeses produced there bear a certain resemblance to Cheddar in texture as well as in flavor.

Blarney—a yellow cheese with small eyes and a red coating, from Ireland. This is an imitation of Emmental, but the flavor is very mild.

Caerphilly—semisoft, cream-colored, salty and tasting of buttermilk. This fresh, unripened cheese does not keep long. It was originally made in Wales, but now almost all is made in Somerset. The cheese is made in flattened rounds but is usually marketed in slices in the United States.

Caithness—a cheese only recently available in the United States. Flattened small rounds with a yellow coating contain a delicious fresh semisoft cheese somewhat like Caerphilly in taste but creamier in texture; a very good appetizer cheese.

Cheddar—yellow, firm; becomes sharper in flavor when aged. The true English cheese is seasonal and is made only in Somerset, but cheeses similar to Cheddar are made everywhere. The famous American "store cheese" can be considered a descendant.

Cheshire—similar to Cheddar, but more crumbly and quite salty; this is the oldest British cheese.

Derbyshire—firm cheese, mild in flavor, not as long-lasting as Cheddar.

Dunlop—white pressed cheese, more moist than Cheddar and tasting more buttery; from Scotland.

Gloucester and *Double Gloucester*—white, flattened rounds, similar to Cheshire but milder. Gloucester is soft-textured; Double Gloucester is somewhat crumbly. Nowadays Double Gloucester is sometimes colored orange and looks more like a Cheddar.

Stilton—cream-colored with blue-green veins and sharp in flavor. At its best when fully ripe; especially good with port and crackers.

Wensleydale—soft, white, delicate in flavor when young; more like Cheddar when aged. Invented by Yorkshire monks and still made in Yorkshire. Blue Wensleydale resembles Stilton but is more delicate and creamy in texture.

FRANCE

France has a far greater variety of cheeses than any other country because of its wide range of climatic and soil conditions. In addition, it has many breeds of cows, ewes and goats. In France, cheese is much more than a snack or the filling for a sandwich; more often than not it is a meal in itself. There are more than 400 named cheeses made in France, but only a small number of them ever reach our shores.

Cream cheeses

Boursault and *Boursin*—rich, creamy cheeses sometimes mixed with crushed black peppercorns or with herbs. They are sold in different shapes.

La Grappe—a bland cheese similar to a creamy Gruyère. It is pasteurized after it is made and covered with grape seeds, but has no grape flavor.

Neufchâtel—small loaf-shaped French cheese made of skimmed milk, whole milk or milk with cream added. Cheese of this type is mixed with other ingredients such as pimientos to make processed soft cheese spreads. A similar cheese, Neuchâtel, from Switzerland, and American copies are often used for spreads.

Petit Gervais—similar to Petit Suisse but a little more sour. Both are perfect for desserts.

Petit Suisse—a paper-wrapped, cylindrical, unsalted fresh cream cheese. These come six to a box, with each cylinder individually wrapped. Because these cheeses are perishable, they are usually shipped frozen and are not as delicious as they can be in France.

Saint-Marcellin—soft cream cheese made from half goats' milk and half cows' milk, in small and large sizes. Sometimes the small cheeses are sprinkled with herbs.

Soft cheeses

Banon—goats' milk cheese made in Provence. These little cheeses usually come wrapped in chestnut leaves. Sometimes they are wrapped in herbs to ripen and have an herb flavor when ready to eat.

Brie—a round cheese similar to a large flat cake, with a fine, delicate flavor. If you buy a whole cheese, it is on a straw mat. This cheese was known at least as early as 1500. There are three kinds, all made in Seine-et-Marne. When perfectly ripe, this whole-milk cheese is luscious, melting but not runny. Usually a whole Brie is too much for a family to buy. It is sold in large wedges.

Camembert—a world-famous Normandy cheese made from cows' milk; sold in round boxes. French Camembert is definitely seasonal and is at its best from January to April. Like Brie, it should be luscious and melting when perfect.

Carré de l'Est—soft, slightly salted, milder than Camembert, sold in boxes of various shapes. Not easy to find in our markets.

Chèvre—goats' milk cheese. Many types are made in France, but we import very few. Some are far too strong-tasting for the American palate. Look for chèvre in cheese specialty shops.

Coulommiers or *Brie de Coulommiers*—one of the three types of Brie; a soft, creamy cheese, younger and slightly more pungent than Brie de Meaux.

Pont l'Évêque—a rich, soft, strong cheese; sold in square boxes. Many regard it as the best cheese of Normandy, and it is one of France's oldest cheeses. It is pale yellow with many tiny holes. Delicious with red wine or applejack.

Saint-Benoit—a soft, creamy, mild cheese from the Loire Valley.

Semihard cheeses

Beaumont—a large Alpine cheese similar to Reblochon; usually sold by the piece.

Munster—the regional cheese of Alsace, often mistaken for a German cheese. It has a creamy texture and is semimild. Sometimes it is rolled in crushed cuminseeds or caraway seeds. A seasonal cheese, best in winter.

Port Salut—a smooth yellow cheese with delicious flavor and aroma; made by the Trappists since 1850, and now made in other places as well. This slow-ripening cheese keeps well.

Reblochon—a small round cheese, with creamy texture, from the mountains of Savoy. It is made from the milk of the Tarentais cows. Young Reblochon has the best flavor.

Saint-Paulin—another delicious mild cheese with tiny holes, made by the Trappists and other cheese makers.

Blue cheeses

Bleu de Bresse—the oldest French blue cheese, the mildest, the creamiest and the most delicious.

Fourme d'Ambert—a blue cheese stronger than Roquefort and quite salty and crumbly; this keeps well.

Roquefort—the best-known blue cheese, made of ewes' milk. This name is restricted to cheeses made in the Roquefort area. The cheese is pungent in flavor and is rather dry and crumbly compared to Danish or American blues, which are more spreadable. The Roquefort exported to the United States is often quite salty, but a good Roquefort has no equal.

There are many other French blue cheeses. If any appear in your markets, try them. They are also good but not as famous as Roquefort.

France also produces processed semisoft cheese of excellent quality such as La Vache Qui Rit, Bonbel and Baby Bel.

DENMARK

Although cheese for home consumption has been made in Denmark for generations, since the end of World War II the export trade has rapidly expanded. The country's two most important cheeses are the golden and the blue.

The golden carries the suffix *bo,* and comes mostly from the type Samsoe, which is made from whole milk. It is a golden, semihard cheese with small holes, similar in taste to Edam, in appearance to Emmental. It has a delicious nutty flavor and is rich in body and bouquet.

Crema Danica—a creamy, fresh-tasting cheese in a rectangular block. This recent invention ripens like a Brie but the flavor is more like a cream cheese. Wonderful for breakfast, or with fruits for dessert.

Danbo—a square, creamy, mild cheese.

Danish Blue or *Danablu*—a fine blue cheese similar to Roquefort but more buttery in texture and sharper in flavor, although there is variation in the flavor.

Elbo—another brick-shaped cheese, yellow with a few eyes.

Esrom—deliciously fragrant, sweet and rich, with a beautiful pale yellow color, similar to Port Salut.

Fynbo—like Danbo but nuttier in flavor.

Havarti—a mild cheese similar to German Tilsit.

Tybo—shaped like a brick; resembles a Dutch Edam in texture and color.

SWEDEN AND NORWAY

Much cheese from Sweden and Norway is a dark caramel color and has a special flavor and texture that is almost uncheeselike. Many of these cheeses are made from whey only. They are best served in paper-thin slices; special knives are made in Scandinavia for the purpose. Some cheeses are spiced.

Gjetost—sweet brown-colored Norwegian goats'-milk

cheese, somewhat grainy and very hard; usually served in thin slices, and always served for breakfast in Norway. It looks and tastes like no other cheese.

Hablé Crème Chantilly—a Swedish cream cheese like a French double-crème. Very delicate; for desserts.

Herrgard—a bland cheese with holes, with a taste similar to Gouda.

Jarlsberg—a bland buttery cheese with holes.

Noekkelost—a firm dark yellow cheese with caraway seeds, cuminseeds or cloves, or a mixture of all three. For those who like these spices, it is delicious.

Normannaost—a blue cheese similar to Roquefort; less sharp and creamy than Danish blue, but very good.

Sveciaost—similar to Herrgard.

ITALY

The Italians produce a wide variety of cheeses. Many are soft or semisoft, and most are very mild. In addition, there are cheeses that are kept until hard enough to grate. The blue-veined Gorgonzola is preferred to Stilton or Roquefort by many cheese lovers.

Bel Paese—uncooked, soft, sweet and mild; very pleasant as a table cheese. This is a trade name, not a cheese type.

Cacciocavallo—very hard grating cheese, shaped like an eggplant. These are tied with strings and dried in pairs. While they are used fresh for eating in Italy, usually only the matured hard cheeses are exported to the United States.

Fontina—ivory-colored, mild, creamy; often used for fondue and many other cooked cheese dishes. It is not as readily available as most of the others, but it is worth your efforts to find it.

Gorgonzola—a superior blue cheese made from whole milk. It is more creamy than Roquefort and the veins are green rather than blue. There is also a delicious white Gorgonzola, without veins.

Mozzarella—known as the pizza cheese. It is very mild, tender and moist and can be eaten uncooked.

Parmesan—the true cheese, Parmigiano-Reggiano, is produced in a strictly limited area. It is made according to exacting standards and is always aged for at least two years. No copy can equal it in flavor and granular quality. While it is usually aged and grated, younger cheeses are delicious for eating.

Pecorino—this is the general name for all cheese made of ewes' milk, eaten fresh or grated. Various cheeses can be found under many different brand names at Italian specialty stores. Romano is one of them.

Provolone—uncooked cheese made from whole cows' milk. It is a fairly mild cheese and usually comes shaped like a pear with grooves in it. The grooves are caused by the fiber cords with which it is suspended.

Ricotta—a soft, cooked cheese like cottage cheese, but with a quite different flavor because it is made from whey. Often used in desserts.

Romano—similar to Parmesan but with a more pronounced flavor. The Italians of the South prefer Romano to Parmesan.

SWITZERLAND

The Swiss make, eat and export more pounds of cheese per person than people of any other country.

Appenzell—a whole-milk cheese, very pale yellow with a brown wrinkled skin and pea-size holes. The flavor is much more delicate than that of the other "Swiss" cheeses, and comes partly from a bath of wine and spices.

Emmental—the most imitated cheese, but the real Emmental, with its sweetness and hazelnut flavor, remains by far the best. This is the familiar cheese, made from whole milk, with large holes. Imitations tend to be more "rubbery."

Glarus—a new cheese, made of whole milk, somewhat like Tilsit, but softer and sweeter; made in Glarus canton.

Gruyère—similar to Emmental, with smaller eyes, ranging in size between a pea and a hazelnut; also, the eye formation is less extensive than in Emmental.

The famous Neuchâtel fondue is made with half Emmental and half Gruyère. (There is also a similar French Gruyère.)

Processed Swiss—made of Emmental and Gruyère, and available under many brand names, but recognizable by the way it is packed in foil-wrapped triangular portions. It is different from the natural cheese and keeps for a long time.

Sapsago—hard grating cheese shaped like a cone with its point cut off; made in Glarus canton. An aromatic clover is added to the mixture, which makes the cheese green. It is not sage in spite of the name. The flavor is very distinctive because sour milk and whey are used. This is delicious grated into soups.

Spalen or *Sbrinza*—the oldest Swiss cheese, probably known to Julius Caesar. It is hard, with low water content, and good for grating.

GERMANY

The Germans make many different cheeses, and most are sold in cheese specialty shops. French cheeses are made to be eaten with wine; German cheeses, with their more pungent, strong flavors, are usually eaten with beer.

Bierkäse—a white, strong-flavored cheese intended to be eaten with beer.

Handkäse (Hand Cheese)—strong-tasting little round cheeses originally shaped by hand. There is an American version. They become more pungent with age.

Kochkäse—a slightly fermented pressed cottage cheese, medium mild.

Kümmelkäse—a creamy cheese flavored with caraway seeds.

Limburger—soft, cream-colored, with a highly developed flavor and aroma. Originally this cheese was Belgian and was marketed in Limburg. It has a texture similar to Brie.

Liptauer—originally a Hungarian cheese from Liptó. The Austrians called the cheese and the spread made from it by the same name. Today, mixtures of cottage cheese and pungent seasonings are given this name. (See the recipe for Beer Cheese in this chapter.)

Romadur—similar to Limburger, but milder and less salty.

Tilsit—a semihard cheese with many tiny holes. It is mild tasting and especially good in sandwiches.

HOLLAND

Cheese making is an important part of the agricultural economy of the Netherlands. Dutch cheese is mostly semihard, nutty-flavored, usually mild. It keeps its quality well for a long time. In Holland, a piece of cheese is always served with breakfast.

Edam—spherically shaped, with red exterior, often referred to as "Dutch Red Ball." A delicious eating cheese.

Gouda—whole-milk cheese, more firm than creamy, with a distinctive flavor. It is pale yellow with a red exterior, but more flattened in shape than Edam.

Leyden—a spicy cheese flavored with cuminseeds and sometimes a few cloves.

GREECE

Most cheese made in Greece is soft and somewhat salty, and is chiefly from ewes' milk. The best known are Feta, Kasseri and Kefaloteri. Feta, usually sold packed in brine, is crumbly and is often served in salads. Kasseri, made from a mixture of ewes' and goats' milk, is white, mild and soft-textured. Kefaloteri is similar to Parmesan. These are the chief Greek cheeses available in our markets.

CANADA

Cheddar cheese made from cows' milk has been the mainstay of the Canadian cheese industry and has become a standard cheese in North America. It is often referred to as Canadian cheese. In England, it is more specifically called Canadian Cheddar. It comes in white and yellow and is made soft, medium and strong. Some Canadian brands are known the world over, such as

Black Diamond and Cherry Hill. These are matured under special conditions and sold as commercial brands.

There is also a Colby type that ripens quickly and is softer and moister, with a more open texture than the regular Cheddar. It does not keep as well as regular Cheddar.

UNITED STATES

While every kind of cheese from all over the world is imitated in the United States, there are some cheeses that are American inventions.

Beer Cheese—a pale, firm Wisconsin cheese like its German original Bierkäse, with a rather strong taste and aroma. It is delicious with beer.

Brick—the invention of a Wisconsin farmer; originally bricks were used to press the curds. Firm, cream-colored, with small eyes, it has a flavor between Limburger and Tilsit.

Coon—a superior Cheddar type cured by a patented method; crumbly, with a sharp flavor.

Cottage Cheese—a curdy cheese made from skimmed milk. It has fewer calories and more protein and calcium than cream cheese. There are various types, including skim-milk cheese with low salt content.

Cream Cheese—actually made of whole milk rather than cream, but creamy in texture. American cream cheese is not as delicious in flavor as French cream cheeses such as Fontainebleau, but they are seldom exported to our markets. The cheese can be flavored in countless ways and used in cookery as well as eaten plain.

Farmer Cheese—fresh cottage cheese or pot cheese, molded or pressed to make it drier; it can be sliced.

Herkimer—crumbly yellow cheese similar to Cheddar, made from raw milk. It originated in Herkimer County, New York.

Liederkranz—creamy soft cheese with a flavor and aroma similar to Limburger, but still very individual. Like the other soft cheeses, it develops its full flavor only when completely ripened and allowed to reach room temperature. Packaged in small foil-wrapped rectangles.

Monterey Jack—a mild but delicious pale yellow cheese. There is a semisoft type and a harder one used for grating. This originated in California.

Pineapple Cheese—invented in Litchfield, Connecticut, in the 19th century. A hard cheese of the Cheddar type, it is matured in a net that impresses the pineapple design on it. This is usually served whole to be scooped out.

Sage—a bland white cheese originally flavored with sage leaves, which gave it a mottled green appearance and herb taste. Today the flavor comes from sage oil, and the green bits are other chopped leaves. When this is aged and hard it is grated.

Tillamook—an Oregon Cheddar type made of raw milk, with a wide flavor range.

Vermont Cheddar—sharp-tasting and almost white, made from raw milk. This keeps well.

Two American cheeses that were designed as "copies" of European originals have become something different. Processed Limburger is a creamy, delicious spread that scarcely resembles the original natural cheese. American Munster is quite different from the Alsatian cheese; it is very mild, fresh-tasting, good in sandwiches and cooking, and a fine food for breakfast.

COOKING WITH CHEESE

Marinated Swiss cheese

1 pound Swiss Gruyère
Grated rind of ½ lemon
2 tablespoons lemon juice
4 tablespoons salad oil
Salt and pepper
2 tablespoons minced fresh parsley
¼ teaspoon minced fresh marjoram

Dice the cheese and add the other ingredients. Place in an attractive container. Cover and refrigerate for 4 to 6 hours. Serve the cheese with long forks or skewers at informal occasions, accompanied by dry sherry. Makes 4 to 6 servings.

Beer cheese

This is flavored like the famous Liptauer cheese of middle Europe. The true Liptauer was made of a soft Hungarian pot cheese, and herbs and seasonings were used as a garnish rather than mixed into the cheese.

- 4 ounces cream cheese
- 1 cup cottage cheese
- 3 green onions, finely chopped
- Generous pinch of caraway seeds
- ¼ teaspoon anchovy paste (optional)
- 1 teaspoon capers
- 1 teaspoon Hungarian paprika
- 1 teaspoon prepared French mustard
- 1 teaspoon grated Parmesan cheese
- 1 tablespoon flat beer

Place all the ingredients in a bowl. Mash and mix until well blended and smooth. Pack well in a jar or bowl. Cover and ripen in the refrigerator for 2 days before serving.

Serve with thin slices of black or dark rye bread, unsalted butter and glasses of cold beer. Makes 4 generous servings as a snack, 8 or more appetizer servings.

Cheese fondue

This famous cheese dish can be made with various cheeses and wines in an ordinary pot on top of the stove, but also at the table for an informal meal. Do not try to serve more people than will fit comfortably around your table. If you do not have a fondue pot or chafing dish, use an earthenware casserole on an asbestos pad over an electric or butane cooker.

Fondue is a Swiss national dish. Use aged natural Swiss cheeses. The ingredients and method for this classic Neuchâtel fondue come from the Switzerland Cheese Association.

- 1 garlic clove, split
- ½ pound Emmental cheese
- ½ pound Gruyère cheese
- 1½ cups Neuchâtel white wine
- Salt
- White pepper
- Grated nutmeg
- 1 tablespoon cornstarch
- 3 tablespoons kirsch
- 4 to 6 cups white-bread cubes, each with crust on one side

Rub the garlic around the inside of the fondue pot or casserole; discard garlic. Shred the cheeses. Put the wine in the pot and heat it over low heat. Stir in the cheese gradually. The heat must always be low so the mixture will be creamy. Season to taste with salt, white pepper and nutmeg. Mix the cornstarch with Kirsch and stir into the fondue. Cook for ½ minute longer.

To serve, each person spears a cube of bread and stirs it in the fondue. Serve a glass of the same wine you used in the fondue. Other good things to dunk are celery pieces, green-pepper strips, whole mushrooms, slices of fat-free country-cured ham. An excellent dish for supper or after outdoor sports. Makes 4 to 6 servings.

Roman cheese skewers

¾ cup unsalted butter
8 anchovy fillets
8 slices of white bread
12 slices of Mozzarella cheese

Soften the butter. Chop the anchovies and mash them into the butter. Set the sauce aside.

Use standard bread slices. Cut off the crusts and slice diagonally into halves. Make 4 sandwiches, each with 4 half-slices of bread and 3 slices of cheese. Hold them together with a metal skewer. Bake the skewers in a 450° F. oven for about 10 minutes, until the cheese has melted and the bread is browned. Pour some of the sauce over each skewer. When the sauce is hot, serve the skewers as a first course. Makes 4 servings.

Cheese and chili tarts

Lemon-Juice Pastry (p. 525)
2 tablespoons butter
2 tablespoons flour
1 cup chicken stock
Juice of 1 lemon
Salt
½ pound Monterey Jack cheese, diced
2 eggs, separated
1 can (4 ounces) peeled green chilies
2 to 4 tablespoons grated Romano cheese

Make the pastry; you need only half the recipe for these tarts, so store the rest, or double the remaining ingredients. Line 8 individual tart pans with pastry, crimp the edges and line them with foil filled with dried rice or beans. Bake on the top shelf of a 400° F. oven for 8 to 10 minutes. They should be light brown and about two thirds baked. Let them cool.

Make a béchamel with butter, flour, stock and lemon juice. When the sauce is thick, season with salt, but be cautious because the cheese is salty. Then stir in the diced cheese until melted. Remove the saucepan from the heat. Stir a little sauce into the egg yolks, mix well, then return eggs to the sauce. Meanwhile, rinse the chilies, remove any seeds, cut them into small pieces and add to the sauce.

Beat the egg whites until stiff, then fold them into the sauce. Divide the sauce among the lined tart pans. Sprinkle the tops with the grated cheese. Just before serving, bake the tarts in a 400° F. oven for 10 to 15 minutes, until the tarts are puffed and browned on top. Serve as a first course. Makes 8 servings.

You can make this in very tiny tart pans or in barquette molds for cocktail-party hors d'oeuvres. The recipe will make about 24 tiny tarts.

Scalloped tomatoes and Cheddar

1 large can (32 ounces) peeled plum tomatoes
Butter
¾ teaspoon salt
2 teaspoons sugar
¼ teaspoon crumbled dried thyme
1 bay leaf, crumbled
¼ teaspoon minced basil, fresh or dried
1 slice of dried bread, crumbled
½ teaspoon curry powder or crushed cuminseeds
1 cup grated strong Cheddar cheese

Place the tomatoes in a buttered 6-cup casserole. Stir in salt, sugar, thyme, bay leaf and basil. Add the crumbled bread. Add curry powder or crushed cuminseeds to the grated cheese and stir. Sprinkle over the tomatoes. Bake, uncovered, in a 375° F. oven for 1 hour. Makes 6 servings.

You may substitute fresh tomatoes for the canned ones. Use about 10 medium-size, not too ripe tomatoes, peeled and quartered.

Scalloped potatoes with cheese

This dish is a Swiss mountaineer family specialty.

4 large potatoes
2 cups light cream
½ teaspoon grated nutmeg
1 teaspoon salt
¼ teaspoon pepper
1 egg, beaten
Butter
½ pound Emmental cheese, in one piece

Peel potatoes and slice as thin as possible. Place them in a large saucepan with just enough water to cover.

Bring slowly to a boil and simmer for 8 minutes. Meanwhile, beat together cream, nutmeg, salt, pepper and beaten egg. Butter a casserole dish. Drain the potatoes but do not let them cool. Quickly line the casserole with a layer of well-drained potatoes. Pour part of the cream mixture over potatoes. Repeat with the mixture and potatoes until all are used. Slice cheese as thin as possible. Place the whole ½ pound on top of the potatoes. Bake in a 300° F. oven for 1 hour, or until potatoes are tender and the cheese melted and golden. Do not raise the heat. Makes 4 to 6 servings.

Cheese and fruit

Serve pears with wedges of Roquefort cheese and sesame crackers, apples with ripe Camembert or Brie and crisp wheat crackers, tangerines with cream cheese and nut bread, apricots with Petit Suisse or Crema Danica and hazelnuts. Any of these makes a good finish to a simple meal.

There are other cheese dishes throughout this book. Look for them in the index.

NUTS

Most people think of nuts as a snack or as a garnish to add, whole or crushed, to other foods. This attitude does scant justice to their nutritional value. While there is variation between one type and another, in general they are all rich in fat and protein. Nuts are comparable to meat in the amount and kind of protein they contain, but it is not animal protein, so we cannot substitute nuts for meat and have exactly the same nutritional values. Many nuts are an excellent source of Vitamin B_1. Peanuts also contain riboflavin and niacin. Almonds are a good source of calcium. All nuts are a good source of phosphorus and a most economical source of energy. An apple and ¼ cup fresh peanuts will provide a sustaining emergency lunch.

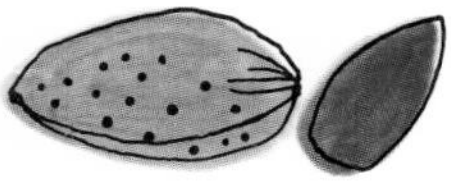

Almonds are available in the shell, as shelled whole nuts, unblanched and blanched, and as sliced, slivered or ground blanched and roasted nuts. There are all kinds of seasoned almonds for snacks. The most economical way to buy them is as shelled and unblanched nuts. Dry-roasted almonds are delicious but expensive.

One pound of almonds in the shell will give you about 1¼ cups shelled nuts. You will lose less than an ounce through blanching.

Brazil Nuts are not true nuts botanically but seeds that grow in a podlike fruit. Each seed is encased in its own hard shell. They are sold in the shell and also shelled whole or sliced in transparent bags.

One pound of Brazil nuts in the shell will give you about 1½ cups shelled nuts.

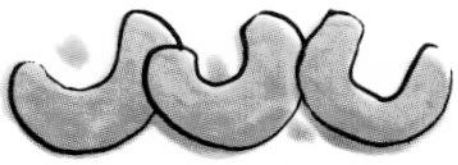

Cashews, also the seeds of a tree, have no shells, but grow dangling from the tree fruits. They are sold plain or salted, in vacuum-packed cans or transparent plastic bags.

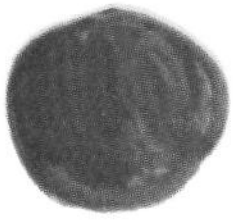

Chestnuts are true nuts, but they are treated like a vegetable and used most often with vegetables or in desserts. You will find directions for shelling and cooking them in the section on vegetables. They are sold in the shell; water-packed canned chestnuts are also available, as well as French *marrons* preserved in syrup.

One pound of chestnuts in the shell will give you about 2½ cups shelled nuts.

Dried chestnuts are available, and they will keep in dry storage for a long time. Fresh chestnuts, on the other hand, will keep for a few months only.

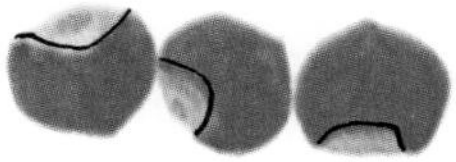

Filberts or *Hazelnuts* are sold in the shell and shelled and come in 3- and 6-ounce transparent plastic bags. You will have to blanch them yourself. They are at their best from November to February.

One pound of hazelnuts in the shell will give you about 1½ cups shelled nuts.

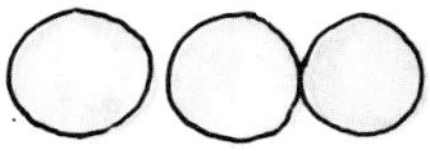

Macadamia Nuts are another example of a tree seed used like a nut. They are almost always husked and shelled before selling and are very expensive.

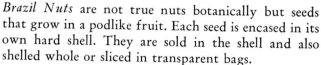

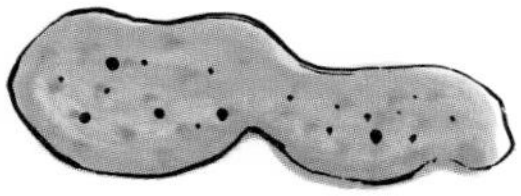

Peanuts are not nuts but the fruits of a vine similar to the green pea vine. The "nuts" are developed underground. They are sold in the shell and also shelled. Shelled peanuts are either salted or unsalted; unsalted are better from a nutritional standpoint. Salted peanuts come in vacuum-packed cans and in transparent plastic bags. Dry-roasted shelled peanuts have been oven-roasted instead of deep-fried; as a result they have fewer calories and are more easily digestible, but the cost is higher.

One pound of peanuts in the shell will give you about 3 cups shelled nuts.

Pecans, native American nuts, were used by Indians for food before Columbus arrived. They are sold in the shell or shelled, either roasted, dry-roasted, salted or plain. In spite of the large crop, they are never cheap. Pecans can be used in every kind of dish.

One pound of pecans in the shell will give you about 2 cups shelled nuts.

Pignolias or *Pine Nuts* are small, elongated, cream-colored nuts, the fruit of several varieties of pines. They are usually sold shelled in small plastic bags.

Pistachios are sold in the shell either in natural color or with the shells artificially colored red. The natural color of the nut inside is pale green. They come boxed or in vacuum-packed cans or in transparent plastic bags. Sometimes you can get them shelled, either salted or unsalted.

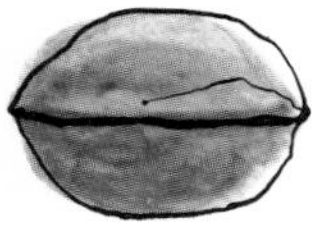

Walnuts are sold in the shell or shelled. Shelled walnuts are sold in 3- and 10-ounce transparent plastic bags. They also come in vacuum-packed cans.

One pound of walnuts in the shell will give you about 2 cups shelled nuts.

Coconuts are the fruit of the coconut palm, which grows wherever the climate reaches the subtropical level. The tree and the fruit are essential and life-supporting in many areas of the world. Coir (the fibers from the husk), copra (dried meat from the nut) and oil pressed from the fresh nuts and from copra are important in world trade.

These are the largest nuts we use, but they seem so different from walnuts or pecans that we do not often think of them as true nuts. Coconuts are large, with very thick shells. A fully ripe nut with no cracks or holes will be heavy and sometimes make a sloshing sound because of the milk inside. To open a coconut, pierce the three indentations at the flatter end and drain off the liquid. Sometimes a slightly less ripe nut will have a thicker jellied liquid and it will not drain. Then bake the nut for about 15 minutes. After that, a few blows with a hammer should crack it. Peel the brown skin from the white meat.

Whole coconuts can be stored for many months, like other nuts in the shell, but after opening use the milk and the meat within a week.

One average coconut in our markets will give about 1 cup milk and about 3 cups chopped meat.

Storing Nuts

Nuts in the shell may be kept at room temperature if you are planning to use them within two months. If you plan to keep them longer, they should be treated like fresh fruits. Since nuts have such a high fat content, they can develop a rancid flavor. Therefore, once a can, jar or bag of shelled nuts has been opened, refrigerate the contents, well covered, or freeze. Unlike most other foods, nuts can be refrozen and do not have to be thawed before you use them in cooking. In fact, they are sometimes easier to slice or cut when still frozen.

Shelling Nuts

Cashews, macadamias and pine nuts are sold without shells. Almonds have such thin shells that they can be shelled with the fingers. Peanuts are also easy to shell. Walnuts and pecans can be shelled by gentle pressure of a nutcracker, and they will usually split neatly. For shelling chestnuts, see page 432. Pistachios need to be pried apart; they are usually already split at one edge. Brazil nuts and the hard-shelled wild nuts are very difficult to shell. To help the process, soak them in hot water or boil them for a few minutes, or freeze them and crack them open while still frozen. A nutpick may be needed with some nuts.

Blanching Nuts

All true nuts have a close skin inside the hard shell. While this skin is edible, it is sometimes sufficiently tough to make peeling advisable. Cashews, pine nuts and macadamias come without skins. Almonds, Brazil nuts and chestnuts are dropped into boiling water; the skins of almonds will be loose enough in 2 minutes to pop off when you squeeze the nut between thumb and forefinger. It will take 5 minutes or longer to loosen the skins of Brazil nuts. Fresh chestnuts take only a few minutes, but as they get older it takes longer soaking. Peanuts, of course, can be peeled easily. Filberts or hazelnuts have an edible skin, but for some preparations you may prefer them peeled. Either blanch them like almonds, or roast them in a 350° F. oven for about 15 minutes and then rub them vigorously in a coarse towel. Walnuts and pecans and the wild American nuts have such tight, thin skins that it is difficult to get them off. Blanching tends to soften the nut, so toasting and rubbing as with hazelnuts may work better, but it will never be easy to get rid of all the skin in the hollows.

COOKING WITH NUTS

Nuts with cheese and a glass of Madeira make a perfect conclusion to a meal. Walnuts with port are an old English tradition. Any nut can be used with cheese, fruit or wine as a delicious dessert.

Deviled almonds and walnuts

- 2 tablespoons unsalted butter
- 2 tablespoons bottled table sauce or chutney sauce
- 1 cup walnut halves
- 1 cup blanched whole almonds
- ½ teaspoon salt
- ½ teaspoon curry powder
- Pinch of cayenne

Melt the butter and stir in the sauce. (The spicier the sauce, the spicier the nuts.) Add the walnuts and almonds. Sprinkle with salt, curry powder and cayenne; stir together. Bake in a 350° F. oven for 15 to 20 minutes, stirring occasionally. Drain on paper towels and serve warm for cocktail parties or tea parties. Enough for 6 to 8 cocktail servings.

Peanut-butter sandwich fillings

With orange—Mix together 1 cup peanut butter, ½ cup orange marmalade, ½ cup honey and the grated rind of 1 orange. Makes enough for 8 sandwiches.

With bacon—Sauté ½ pound bacon until crisp. Drain on paper towels, then crumble. Mix into 1 cup peanut butter with ½ cup pickle relish. Makes enough for 8 sandwiches.

Party squash

4 pounds winter squash
3 tablespoons butter
3 tablespoons sugar
¼ teaspoon ground allspice
¼ teaspoon ground nutmeg
Orange bitters
½ cup pecans

Any winter squash will do for this dish, but it is most delicious when made with butternut squash. Two average ones will weigh about 4 pounds. Cut them into pieces, remove the seeds and cook squash in lightly salted water for 15 minutes, or until tender but not mushy. Peel and turn into a colander.

In the saucepan melt the butter. Add sugar and stir until dissolved, then add spices and several dashes of orange bitters. Add drained squash and stir and mash with a wire whip or potato masher until squash is smooth and well mixed with butter and seasonings. Grind pecans in a nut grinder; if you wish to stir some into the squash, use fine grind, but grind most of them coarsely. Serve squash sprinkled with pecans. The contrast of the smooth squash and the crunchy pecans gives this dish its special character. Makes 8 servings.

Bread Betty with walnuts

4 cups diced buttered toast
1 cup muscat raisins
½ cup fresh orange juice
½ cup walnuts, chopped
Butter
¾ cup brown sugar
4 slices of buttered toast, whole
1 cup milk or light cream
1 egg
1 teaspoon honey
Pinch of grated mace

Use leftover whole-wheat or white bread to make toast. While hot, butter it generously, then cut into small dice. Prepare enough to fill 4 cups. Soak the raisins in the orange juice for 1 hour. Add the raisins and walnuts to the bread cubes. Mix thoroughly.

Generously butter an 8-inch round baking dish. Arrange the bread mixture in layers, sprinkling the brown sugar between the layers. On top place the whole slices of buttered toast, buttered side up, to act as a lid. Mix the milk or cream with the egg, honey and mace. Pour over the bread. Bake in a 300° F. oven for 35 to 40 minutes. Serve hot or warm. Makes 4 or 5 servings.

Charles
NAPA
BURG
Beaujola
POUILLY-F
CHÂTEAU T
SAINT
1967

«17»

A Guide to Wines and Spirits

How wines are classified • Factors in judging wine • How to store wine • Red wines of France, other European countries and the United States • White, rosé and sparkling wines • Fortified and dessert wines • Aperitifs • Kinds of spirits • Temperatures for serving wine • Correct wineglasses • How many drinks to a bottle • How many cocktails to a guest • Cooking with wine and spirits

The wineglass has replaced the silver cup of bygone days, but wine still plays the same role. It promotes friendship and hospitality, and it delights us with its flavor, its aroma or bouquet and its color. The right bottle of wine can make a good dinner superb, because wine has the wonderful faculty of complementing the flavor of food and thus enhancing the enjoyment of eating. It also sparks gay conversation and conviviality.

Basically, wine is the fermented juice of ripe grapes, crushed after harvesting. It may range in color from deep red to light pink to almost colorless "white." The color of the wine depends on the color of the grape skins, which can be red, black or green, and the length of time the skins are allowed to stay in the vat when the wine is made. Although wines can be made of other fruits (and even vegetables), the word "wine" used alone always means an alcoholic drink made from grapes. The magic ingredient that turns the grapes into wine is yeast—the same one-celled fungus discussed in the chapter on flour. Yeast cells are present on the grape skins, and when the fruit is mashed the yeast starts to feed on the sugar in the mash and convert it into alcohol and carbon dioxide. (Grapes normally contain enough sugar to complete this fermentation process, but other fruits and vegetables need added sugar.) When the yeast has ample food, it starts to bud and produces more yeast cells to finish the process. The carbon dioxide bubbles carry the yeast cells through the mash, thus helping to stir and mix it. In dry wines, all the sugar in the grapes is converted to alcohol. When the grapes are sweeter, there is more sugar than the yeast can use and some remains to make a sweeter wine.

The most famous wine-growing areas today are Bordeaux, Burgundy and Champagne, in France. A few other famous regions are the Rhône and Loire valleys and Alsace in France, and the Rhine and Moselle districts in Germany. But wine is made everywhere in the world where grapes can be grown.

CLASSIFYING WINES

In France, wine growers have been well organized for a long time, and French wines must be labeled according to very strict standards. Growers in the Burgundy region have one classification system, those in Bordeaux another, and those in Alsace yet another. No other wine-producing country has anything like the elaborate organization that exists in France.

While we may speak of a Chianti or a Soave with a reasonable certainty as to its general character, to call a wine just a Burgundy or a Bordeaux would reveal much less about it. The difference between the best and the least in these famous French wines is tremendous. Wines marketed under the name of the region alone will be the least impressive; yet they may be quite pleasant, especially if the year has been a good one. Wines designated as being from a small area within the region, such as the Mâconnais or Côte de Beaune in Burgundy, or Médoc or Saint-Emilion in Bordeaux, will have been produced more carefully. Those wines marked with the name of a specific district, town or even vineyard, or in Bordeaux a château, and identified with *Appellation Contrôlée,* have been produced according to very exacting standards. In France, *Appellation Contrôlée* is the mark of authenticity of origin. Of course, all this does not guarantee that the wine is good, or that you will like it. Weather is the ultimate factor in making it good; a grape will yield only what it takes from the soil it grew in, from the sun that warmed it, from the rain that washed it. Your taste determines which wine to buy.

Just to confuse the issue further, there are wines produced in the United States, Chile and South Africa that are labeled "Burgundy" or "Sauternes" or "Champagne." They have no real right to use these regional names, but at least you will recognize that the wine producer intends to sell you a wine of that particular type. These wines are also called generic wines. A more informative system is to name the wine after the principal grape used in making it. Wines so labeled are called varietal wines. Many other wines are named after the places where they are produced.

Factors in judging wine

In all wines there is a delicate balance between acidity and sweetness. This balance depends on the grape and the growing conditions of the year in which it was produced, and in turn determines the wine's ability to improve in the bottle with age. In a truly great wine, this balance is just right. Other aspects of good wines are the bouquet (aroma and fragrance), the breed (character or finesse), the body or the substance of the wine. These characteristics differ not only from type to type, but from vineyard to vineyard. So when you are particularly pleased with a wine, take note of the name of the producer on the label. A Pommard of one vineyard can be quite different from that of another. Half the fun in serving wine is discovering for yourself what you and your friends enjoy, what best enhances the flavor of the food you serve. Every type will give a different taste sensation. Only by tasting wines will you develop preferences.

Vintage

Vintage is the gathering of the grapes, and the particular year when the grapes were gathered and made into wine. It suggests the synthesis of weather and physical conditions of that specific growing season. There are good, poor and in-between years. Vintage is most important in French wines, because Italy, Spain and Portugal are not subject to the same weather variations. The price you pay for a French wine often depends on the quality of its vintage. Modest-priced wines of a good year may be better than expensive wines of a poor year.

In general, wines with no vintage mark on the label are blends of the wines of two or more years. Some wine of a better year is added to a poorer wine to make an acceptable average. Such wines may be pleasant and certainly are adequate for cooking, but they are never distinguished. Unfortunately, in some countries the mark of the vintage need only mean that *most* of the wine was produced in that year—more than half or at least two thirds. These proportions are established by law, but a famous vineyard and a good producer would probably bottle only what his label says.

Wine storage

Wines in bottles with corks should be stored lying on their sides. Those with patent screw caps can stand up. The reason is simple: when the bottle is lying down, the cork is moistened by the wine. This helps the cork

to remain wet and swollen, thus airtight. It does not necessarily mean that you cannot stand corked bottles upright, but if you leave them upright for a long time, air might get in and spoil the wine.

Another important thing to remember is that too much heat or too much cold affects wine adversely. Never allow a bottle to remain in the sun or in an overheated place or to freeze in the freezer. If you have one or two bottles that you plan to serve within a few days, simply keep them cool (under 60° F. if possible) and in a dark place. If you have many bottles that you plan to store for weeks or months, it is important to find a dark spot that is not subject to vibration, is not damp or musty and has a constant temperature of 55° to 60° F. If this is impossible, you will do better to leave the wine with your dealer and gather up the bottles a few at a time as you need them. Remember, wine is still maturing in the bottle. If you chill it for a long time the process stops. If you keep it at too high a temperature, the process is speeded up and the wine may be spoiled.

Wine with food

While some wines are best served alone (very sweet wines or fortified wines), most wine is the perfect companion to food. Choosing the right wine has developed into a status game, but you should ignore all the nonsense and snobbery and just think of the tastes involved. Let us suppose that at one time your main dish is chicken in a cream sauce, and on another occasion you are having a broiled steak. You will sense that the same wine will not do for both meals. The white chicken in its creamy, ivory sauce seems to call for a light wine, such as a Sauternes or Graves, a Vouvray, a Moselle if you feel extravagant, or a simple Orvieto. But a light red would also be acceptable, such as an Italian Valpolicella or a French Beaujolais. On the other hand, the robust flavor of a steak seems to be best accompanied by a full-flavored red such as a Chambertin or a Margaux or an Italian Bardolino. That's all there is to it. Here is a brief outline that may serve as a guide, but do not follow it slavishly.

Serve red wine with beef and lamb roasts, steaks,

stews, game, duck and goose. Veal and cheese are served with red wine also, although white wines and rosés are acceptable with either.

Serve rosé wine or Beaujolais with salmon, fish stews, kidneys, omelets, soufflés, cold cuts.

Serve white wine with fish and shellfish, chicken, turkey and ham.

Serve Champagne with an elaborate meal throughout the whole meal. It should follow other wines only if a toast is being offered at the end of dinner with a specific glass of Champagne.

Serve dessert wines—Marsala, Madeira, sweet sherries, Tokay—with fruits, compotes, rich cakes, tarts and pies, mild or creamy cheeses.

After-dinner wines are served at room temperature. Port is the most usual and is often served with a good Cheddar or Stilton cheese. Cognac or brandy and liqueurs are also served after dinner.

Generally speaking, wines can be classified in four major categories: still table wines, sparkling wines, fortified wines and aperitif wines.

STILL WINES

These include red, white and rosé wines, made in all wine-producing countries.

French red wines

A wine is red when the skins of dark grapes are permitted to remain in the juice during fermentation. The alcohol dissolves the coloring of the skins. A red wine can be pinkish-red, purple-red or even brownish-red in color.

Red wines of great distinction are produced in Burgundy and Bordeaux in France. In these French reds, which are such great American favorites, the grapes are the crucial element. The best Burgundy wine is made from the Pinot grapes (Pinot Noir and Pinot Blanc or white Chardonnay) ; you may see these grape names on labels. However, Gamay grapes are also extensively grown in Burgundy; it is these that produce the Beaujolais. This wine is lighter and less expensive than most red Burgundies. A good quality Beaujolais is excellent whenever you want a lively young red wine. Red Burgundy wines are quite dry, some of them even astringent, and they have a long life. On the other hand, a Beaujolais should be drunk when it is still young.

With an excellent roast beef or a broiled steak, you may want a full-bodied red wine; a Burgundy is perfect for this.

The Bordeaux area of France includes perhaps the most famous vineyard acreage in the world. It is the land of château wines, and there are hundreds of them. A château is the home or center of a wine-producing estate. It may be a true château, an old castle, or it may be simply the office that serves the surrounding vineyards. You may notice on wine bottles that the bottling also has been done at the château (*mise en bouteille au château*). This legend should be stamped on or burned into the cork. (When Burgundies have been estate-bottled, the cork will say *mise en bouteille au domaine.*) Sometimes these wines are very expensive, but occasionally good wines from small châteaux will prove to be quite reasonable.

Some of the great areas producing red Bordeaux wine, or claret as the English call it, are Médoc, Graves, Pomerol, Saint-Emilion. (Graves also produces excellent white wines.) Most Bordeaux grow old gracefully. It is not uncommon for the best of them to be delicious when they are 15 to 20 years old, or even more. However there is no guarantee that the wine you buy will be one of these. Wines of different years have different characteristics and mature at different times.

The Rhône Valley offers several interesting wines, but the best known here is Châteaneuf-du-Pape, soft and delicious, purple-red in color. This wine is a blend of the juice of several grapes, all grown on the slopes near Avignon, where the Romans found wine for their French legions so many centuries ago.

Sometimes you will find in our markets other French reds, blended from wines of several vineyards, made to sell at lower prices. These wines are often quite delicious.

Whenever you travel in wine country, do not miss tasting the *vins ordinaires* or *vins du pays*. These are local or regional wines of the district. Most of them never travel even as far as the next town, for the simple reason that they cannot be shipped from one place to another; it would upset their delicate chemistry. And many wine experts believe that even great wines taste better on their home ground, served with the local food specialties.

Other European red wines

Italy also produces red wines. These do not pretend to compete with the greatest wines of France, but if you are looking for an easy-to-digest wine that seems at home with all types of food, get acquainted with Italian wine. The famous Chianti is not always bottled in a straw-covered flask; good brands are available in conventional bottles. True, well-controlled *classico* Chianti bears the mark of a little black cockerel on the neck of the bottle. Another symbol that indicates excellence is the *putto,* or little angel, which can also be found on the neck of the bottle. Chianti is an oddity in that it is made from a blend of several different grape varieties.

Valpolicella is a light, delicate red wine that seems to go well with many foods. Barolo and Bardolino are robust red wines.

The vintage of Italian wines does not mean very much. This is not because the wine is inferior; in Italy the equitable climate keeps most vintages uniformly good. For this reason the producer is so important for quality, uniformity, continuity: each time you open a bottle of a specific brand, it will be as good as the others you have tried of this brand.

Germany produces only a few red wines and they are seldom exported.

Spain's red wines are exported in small quantities, but now one can occasionally find Rioja wines marked *Reserva,* which have been aged until they are quite good, with a fine color and taste, though fairly tart. There are a few other reds. Portugal also produces some reds, but we do not see them often in our markets.

Hungary sends us a few delicious reds; the best known is Egri Bikavér (bull's blood of Eger), which is different from any other red—robust and delicious. Plavac is the only Yugoslavian red exported to us, and in very small amounts since the Yugoslavs make barely enough to satisfy their own wants.

Greek reds taste of resin, an acquired taste for most of us, but they are palatable and good with Mediterranean food.

Switzerland exports a few reds; Dôle is the most familiar, and it resembles Beaujolais.

Red wines of the United States

The United States now produces millions of gallons of wine annually. California is responsible for the largest amount, and also consumes the largest amount per capita. The generic California wines are all blends, but the varietals must contain at least 51 percent of the juice of the grape named on the label. Here again you must know the producer, because the best will bottle only what the label lists. Among the names you will find are Cabernet Sauvignon, Pinot Noir, Gamay—all true wine grapes similar to the same grapes grown in France. The grape planted most widely in California is the Zinfandel. Less often seen are Barbera, an Italian grape, and Petite Sirah.

The notion that all American wine is cheap is an error. While large amounts of less-expensive wine are bottled in gallons and can indeed be purchased for modest sums, many of these varietals are kept until well matured and are then sold at prices as steep as the price of an imported wine of good quality. Some California wines are very good and show promise of being long-lasting, but the difference between one vineyard and another can be great. The bulk wines are not bad wines, either, and you can start your wine education with these and serve them to your guests without embarrassment.

Smaller amounts of wine come from New York State (about 10 percent of the amount produced in California), Ohio and near Lake Ontario in both the United States and Canada. Most of these eastern wines are made from native American grapes, *Vitis labrusca*, and European wine lovers find them positively distasteful. Most Americans like both, but certainly the *labrusca* wines are entirely different from the *vitis vinifera* wines produced in California and Europe. The word "foxy" has been used to describe *labrusca* wines; they taste of the grapes, with a fruity-earthy quality. Generic wines made of these grapes are totally unlike the true Burgundy or Sauternes. Varietals are made of Delaware and Isabella grapes. Some attempts to produce hybrid grapes and to raise *vinifera* grapes in New York State have been made, and a few good wines have resulted.

The remarkable difference between American and European wines may stem partly from our belief in the efficacy of science and sanitation. Many U.S. wines are produced in stainless-steel continuous systems, and the wine's progress is determined by gauges instead of by the experienced nose and eye of an aged vintner who has spent a lifetime at his trade. Our predilection for blending makes it possible to market a good, palatable, nonvintage wine year after year, but it does take away all the excitement of discovering the marvelous year when all the factors combined to make the perfect wine.

White wines

White wines are made from white grapes, or from dark grapes with the skins removed.

White table wines are generally lighter and less robust in flavor than red wines. In spite of this, many people find them more difficult to digest. Certainly they mix badly with spirits.

White wines are served with fish, seafood, egg dishes and certain types of poultry. Italian chicken dishes with tomato sauce are better with a red wine, but a roasted or broiled chicken is usually served with a light white wine.

There is a large variety of white wines to choose from. The areas in France famous for reds—Burgundy and Bordeaux—also produce great white wines, as do the regions of the Loire and Alsace, the Rhine and Moselle valleys and other areas of Germany, Italy and Switzerland.

White Burgundies are dry, full-flavored, robust. White Montrachet, conceded by connoisseurs to be the greatest white Burgundy, is about the most expensive too. When the name is hyphenated—Chevalier-Montrachet, Bâtard-Montrachet—it is a different wine, lesser in quality and less expensive. Montrachet is a joy to serve on a special occasion. Another fine choice is a good Chablis, a lovely wine with a flinty taste. In the case of Chablis, the shipper's name is important, so be sure to note the full information on the label when you find one you like. Meursault wines are soft and delicate with a wonderful bouquet. Another fine dry white is the ever-popular Pouilly Fuissé. Here, too, the name of the shipper or producer is important.

White Bordeaux wines are many and varied. Among the best known are Sauternes and Graves. Sauternes are generally not dry, but they are perfect for desserts, or for between meals served with wine biscuits. Château d'Yquem, a Sauternes, is the finest of all naturally sweet wines. Of course there are many less expensive than this. The wines of Graves are drier and more versatile.

Vouvray is the best known of the wines of the Loire Valley. It can be sparkling as well as still, and even the still wine is naturally a little *pétillant,* or sparkling. Pouilly Fumé and Sancerre from the upper Loire are also popular. Muscadet from the lower valley is inexpensive, light and delicious, and especially good with fish.

The fragrant wines of Alsace are named after the grapes used—Riesling, Traminer, Gewürztraminer (very perfumed), Sylvaner; they are all somewhat dry and should be drunk when young.

Many connoisseurs consider German white wines the greatest in the world. They often have a flowery quality quite different from French whites.

German wines are attractively bottled in tall thin bottles unlike the French bottles. The Rhine bottles are brown and the label will indicate the area of the river's wine-growing banks—Rheingau, or Rheinhessen, or Rheinpfalz. Moselle wines are marketed in green bottles labeled Mosel-Saar-Ruwer. German wine names were reclassified in 1971 and some of the old names may now refer to a larger vineyard area, while some new designations may be found. Your dealer will help you until these new labels have become more familiar.

German wine terminology is quite different from French. *Spätlese* means "late picked," grapes picked two or three weeks after the normal harvest. *Auslese* indicates wine from even sweeter, very ripe grapes, picked bunch by bunch. *Beerenauslese* is the label on wines made from the ripest and soundest single "berries," picked individually from each bunch. *Trockenbeerenauslese* is wine made from grapes left on the vines so long they have become almost as dry (*trocken*) as raisins. *Cabinet* or *Kabinettwein* is used for the proprietor's own wine, and means something like "private reserve." *Naturwein* is natural wine, without added sugar.

Among Rhine wines some famous names are Johannisberg, Rauenthal and Hochheim (probably the source of the English term "hock"). Bernkastel, Piesport, Brauneberg and Graach are some of the finest Moselle whites. A Moselle is the perfect accompaniment to a freshwater fish such as trout.

Drink German wines when they are young—one, two or three years old—when they are at their best.

Italy produces a large number of good white wines, though only a few are exported. The most familiar exports are Verdicchio dei Castelli di Jesi, Orvieto, Soave, Frascati, Est! Est!! Est!!! and white Chianti. Orvieto (sweet or dry) is inexpensive and delicious. Soave from the right producer is good with many Italian dishes. Frascati, seen in the United States less often, is a delicious golden dry wine. Est! Est!! Est!!! is more distinguished by its odd name than its quality. White Chianti is not as good as the red, but it is satisfactory for an everyday wine and excellent in cooking.

Spain and Portugal export a few white wines. Alicante is pleasant, and there are some whites made in Rioja, where the best Spanish reds come from. Other whites from Portugal and Spain can be found; they are usually inexpensive, but unfortunately they are often "green-tasting" and thin, even acid. The peninsula is distinguished for its fortified wines rather than these.

Hungary has begun to export some excellent white wines from Lake Balaton, made from Riesling and Furmint grapes, and from Somló in western Hungary. Greek whites usually taste of resin like the reds, but there is a delicate white called Pallini.

A few Austrian white wines find their way here. Grinzing, a suburb of Vienna, produces the best known, and a Grinzinger Spätlese of a good year can taste as delicious as good Champagne. Gumpoldskirchener is another delicious, somewhat spicy white. These are different from German wines and absolutely different from French wines. Do not expect to keep them for long; they lose aroma and flavor as they age.

Swiss white wines are more numerous than red. Fendant, Neuchâtel and Dézaley are fairly well known, and there are other wines from Valais canton named according to the grape used. These are particularly good with cheese dishes.

Chile sends us delicious and inexpensive Riesling and Rhine wines, bottled in attractive, squat green bottles. South African wines occasionally find their way into our markets, although more are sold in England. None of them is distinguished.

California white wines can be excellent. They are made from Sauvignon Blanc and Semillon grapes (the same kind of grapes that grow in Bordeaux); Chardonnay (like the Pinot Chardonnay of Burgundy), and Pinot Blanc; Chenin Blanc (like the Loire grape); Riesling, Traminer and Gewürztraminer (like the German and Alsatian grapes). Some hybrid grapes developed in California from white grapes are Emerald Riesling and Flora. Some producers still sell generic wines called Sauterne, Chablis, Rhine and Moselle. Many of these California white wines are delicious and have developed the potential of the grape wonderfully. (Incidentally, you may notice that the California generic wine is spelled "Sauterne," without an *s*.)

New York State white wines are also found under both generic and varietal names; some of the latter are Niagara, Delaware, Catawba, Diana; they taste quite different from California whites.

Rosé wines

Rosé wines are pink or rose colored, easily distinguishable from even the lightest red. They are made by several methods—drawing off the juice from unpressed black grapes; drawing off the juice of grapes before they have fermented very long; adding artificial coloring to, or blending red wines with, various white wines. The *vin gris* of Lorraine (light pink) is made by fermenting red and white grapes together, then lifting the skins when the color is right.

It has become the fashion to say that rosé goes with anything and can take the place of a red or white wine, but that is not strictly true. Generally speaking, rosés are of much less distinction than reds and whites. Nevertheless, they are pleasant and seem particularly suited to some foods. They are good with omelets, brains, simple fish dishes, rabbit.

Among French rosés are Tavel and Lirac from the Rhône Valley, Anjou and Jura rosés; the *vin gris* of Alsace-Lorraine; and several from Provence (one of the best known is Château Ste–Roseline).

Spain produces a few rosés not unlike those of the Rhône, and Portugal has distinguished itself in the production of superior rosés. The best known in the United States are Mateus and Lancers, but there are others. Chilean rosés are excellent.

Rosés produced in the United States are made principally of the Grenache, Gamay and Zinfandel grapes. The color of the wine varies and the taste can be dry or fairly sweet.

SPARKLING WINES

In still table wines, all the carbon dioxide is released before the wine is bottled. In sparkling wines some of the gas is left in the wine, and that is what makes the bubbles. In addition, extra sugar and yeast may be added so that the wine undergoes a second fermentation in the bottle.

There is no reason sparkling wines could not be served to accompany food just as still wines are, but because they seem so special and generally so expensive, we tend to serve them less frequently. An expensive vintage Champagne will not be appreciated properly with a simple or rough meal, and a sweet Champagne will not taste best with a roast. All sparkling wines seem especially designed for festive occasions. Champagne is particularly good for large parties or buffet dinners that offer a variety of foods, for it can be served throughout such a meal. Sparkling rosés, like still rosés, are much simpler and less rich than the heavy sparkling whites or reds, so they can be served with anything you choose. A dry Champagne can make a good aperitif, especially if you are serving a very elegant hors d'oeuvre such as caviar. Sparkling red wines go with any dish suitable for a still red wine.

True Champagne is made only in France, in the small area around the city of Reims on the Marne. No other sparkling wine has the right to use the name, even though some do.

Champagne is costly because making it involves expensive time and labor. Every bottle is first fitted with a temporary cork, then stored cork down in a slanted position for many months. A slight turn is given to each bottle two or three times a week, so that the impurities produced by the fermentation will descend and settle around the cork. Eventually the neck of the bottle is immersed in a brine solution and frozen. The cork is removed with a special kind of pliers, taking the impurities along with it. In the gap left at the top, a small quantity of sugar syrup is added; the amount determines the sweetness or dryness of the finished Champagne. The bottle is then recorked, wired and sealed, and stored for a year or more.

Brut means the driest Champagne; *extra sec* means less dry; *sec,* dry; *demi-sec,* sweet; *doux,* very sweet. Each term indicates a specific percentage of sugar in the Champagne, based on an arrangement special for Champagne. *Demi-sec* and *doux* Champagnes are good with desserts.

Champagne *Blanc de Blancs* means one made entirely from white grapes, whereas most Champagne is made from a mixture of red and white grapes. All Champagnes are blends, but vintage Champagnes are blends of wines of a single year.

Another bubbly wine is sparkling Burgundy, which can be delicious and certainly looks beautiful, although many wine connoisseurs think little of it. It was originally made in order to use inferior wine, but the end result is a rich wine, splendid in the glass.

Italy also produces sparkling red and white wines; these will have *Spumante* on the label. Asti Spumanti is well known, and another variety is Lacrima Christi. A sparkling white wine similar to Champagne, called Sekt, is made in Germany. Spain and Portugal make some excellent sparkling wines. Sparkling rosé wines are made in France and in Portugal. California and New York produce some good as well as some very poor "champagnes."

A few other sparkling French wines are made—Sparkling Vouvray and Saumur of the Loire Valley are two examples.

FORTIFIED WINES, DESSERT WINES

Fortified wines are those to which brandy is added, before or after they have completed their fermentation. Sherry, port and Madeira are the principal examples. Brandy added during fermentation stops the process, and some sugar is left unconverted. This is the method used to make port or muscatel. When the brandy is added after the fermentation is complete, it produces a wine such as sherry.

Sherry comes from the area around Jerez de la Frontera in Andalusia in southern Spain. There are two things specially necessary in the making of sherry: one is *flor,* a yeast or bacteria that grows on the surface of the wine while it is aging in the barrel, and forms a crust shutting out any harmful bacteria. The other is the *solera* system, in which casks are arranged in tiers so that sherry of different ages is slowly blended as it passes from top to bottom. Sherry is always a blend of the wines of several years. Wines labeled Amontillado, Fino or Manzanilla are dry, pale and delicate. Serve these cold as aperitif wines. Amoroso, Oloroso or Brown sherries are rich and sweet. Serve these at room temperature after dinner or on the rocks as an aperitif.

When sherry is used in a sauce, as for meats or game, it should be dry or moderately dry; when used for fruits or desserts, the sweet type is best.

Port comes from Oporto in Portugal. Some of the famous names are not at all Portuguese; rather, they are the names of English shippers who went into the wine business generations ago. Vintage port is not a blend, but other types are blended. Although one can find port labeled "dry," no port is really unsweet. White port, made of white grapes, is the driest and makes a good aperitif. Ruby port is a blend of young wines, fruity, rich in color and sweet. Tawny port, usually made of older wines and matured in wood, is not as sweet as the ruby port.

Madeira is made on the island of Madeira. The long, slow process necessary to mature this wonderful wine means that it is never cheap. It is an exception to the rule for all other wine: it is improved by traveling and was once put in the holds of ships going around the world on the tea trade. We do not drink this delicious wine very much today, but it is good—served cool in small glasses, with a rich soup at the start of a meal or with a strong cheese at the end of a meal or added to sauces for entrées and desserts. For flavoring meats and fruit desserts it is unequaled.

Sercial Madeira is dry and is perfect as an appetizer. Bual is rich, and Malmsey is sweet. Rainwater Madeira is very light in color and texture.

Other good well-known fortified wines are Malaga from Spain and Marsala from Sicily. Malaga is used with game dishes and desserts. Marsala is excellent with cheese dishes and desserts.

Some of the world's most famous wines are the luscious sweet dessert wines. Noted for centuries is the Hungarian wine, Tokay; its grapes grow in volcanic soil between two volcanic cones. The wine is golden and delicious and has a reputation for bringing the dying back to health.

Barsac, a subdivision of the French district of Sauternes, produces a very sweet white wine. Other sweet Sauternes include Château d'Yquem, previously mentioned. These wines are exceptionally sweet because of a mold called "noble rot" (*Botrytis cineria*), which attacks the grapes and sucks out the liquid, leaving them shriveled, like raisins, and much sweeter. This added sweetness and the flavor of the mold itself give a special quality to these wines.

APERITIF WINES

An aperitif wine results from the addition of an infusion of various herbs, roots and barks to the fermented juice of grapes. The combination of the ingredients used is usually a well-guarded secret.

Vermouth, the best known of all aperitif wines, is dry (French type) or sweet (Italian type). There are dozens of other aperitif wines, such as Dubonnet, Saint-Raphaël and Byrrh. Aperitif wines are usually served cold, but follow your own inclination. A slice of lemon or lime is a very pleasant addition to any of them. In recent years, aperitif wines have been served on the rocks as an agreeable, mild substitute for cocktails. In cooking, aperitif wines are often used to flavor desserts, and dry vermouth can be used for meats and sauces just as you would use white wine.

SPIRITS

Spirits (distilled liquors) include brandy, whiskey, rum, gin, liqueurs and cordials, aquavit, and vodka.

Brandy is a spirit distilled from freshly fermented grape wine, or from the juices of other fruits. The most famous of all grape brandies is Cognac, which takes its name from the locality in France where it has been produced for generations. Other brandies are made from apricots, peaches, blackberries, cherries and apples.

Whiskey is a spirit distilled from fermented mashes made from malt alone or from a blend of malt and unmalted cereals.

Rum is a spirit obtained by fermenting and then distilling molasses and sugarcane.

Gin derives its name from the Dutch word *genever,* meaning juniper. It is a spirit distilled from rye or barley and flavored with juniper berries. It is called *schnapps* by the Dutch, although this word is also used in Europe to mean any "hard liquor" taken straight. When Scandinavians say *schnapps,* they mean aquavit. Gin is so extensively made in the Netherlands that it is also called Hollands.

Liqueurs and *cordials* are highly fortified, sweetened spirits flavored with various herbs, aromatic spices, fruits or extracts. They are served in relatively small glasses and sipped slowly. The most famous are Benedictine, Chartreuse, Grand Marnier, Cointreau, Curaçao, crème de menthe, anisette, kirsch and kümmel.

Aquavit is a spirit distilled from a grain mash or potatoes and flavored with caraway.

Vodka is a highly alcoholic spirit distilled from a mash of potatoes or cereals.

SERVING WINES AND SPIRITS

Choosing the right beverage

The choice of what alcoholic beverage to serve with a meal depends on personal taste and the food budget, but of course there are some basic rules.

A single good dry wine may be served throughout the meal. If two or more wines are to be served, here is the sequence to follow: white wine, generally lighter in body and flavor, should be served before red wine, which is more robust and full flavored. But in any case, serve a less good wine or a less robust wine before the better or more full-flavored wine. For instance, drink white wine with the soup or fish and red wine with the meat course. If you have two red or two white wines, the younger one must be served first. For example: a Beaujolais and a Burgundy served at the same meal would be served in that order. When one of the wines is sweeter and the other is drier, let the dry precede the sweet.

However, at a simple family meal, or with close friends at an intimate dinner, it is better to serve only a single wine.

A truly sweet wine is served only with dessert. A more interesting service, however, is to omit the wine with the dessert and serve a liqueur or cordial with the demitasse.

Temperatures for serving wines

White wines and rosé wines should generally be served chilled, at a temperature between 40° and 50° F. Place them in the refrigerator at least two hours before dinner. However, the flowery white wines of the Moselle or Rhine vineyards are better served not quite so cold. Champagne and other sparkling wines should be served extremely cold. Preferably these wines should be chilled in a container filled with crushed ice.

A red wine should be allowed to stand upright, not on its side in a basket, at room temperature for an hour or two before being served. Temperatures between 62° and 70° F. bring out its flavor and bouquet to best advantage. About an hour before dinner, uncork the bottle and let it stand open until you are ready to serve. This permits the wine to breathe and enhances the flavor. Avoid alternate cooling and warming of a wine.

Wineglasses

Wine is its own best ornament and attraction. Thus wineglasses should be stemmed, colorless, clear and thin, so that the color and sparkle of the beverage can be seen to the best advantage. They should be of ample size to allow for the enjoyment of the aroma and bouquet.

The selection of glasses need not be complicated. Choose a 9-ounce bubble-shaped wineglass for reds, an 8-ounce tulip shape for whites. The trend today, however, is toward an all-purpose glass suitable for both red and white wines. A stemmed tulip-shaped wineglass, 10-ounce size, is ideal.

Sherry, Madeira and port are often served in stemmed 4½-ounce glasses.

Champagne is served in flute-shaped glasses, containing between 5 and 7 ounces; a better choice is a tulip-shaped glass containing 8 ounces.

Cordials and liqueurs exhale their fine aroma and display their delicate tints in 1-, 2- or 3-ounce stemmed clear glasses.

Fine brandy, which has its own special body and bouquet, is most enjoyable when sipped from a short-stemmed deep glass of ample width.

A few rules on serving wine

The gracious host sees that his guest's glass is never completely empty, and that it is continually replenished. If the guest declines, however, it is not proper to insist that he have more.

The recipient of a toast, if present, remains seated and does not drink with the other guests. He acknowledges the toast immediately afterward, by rising and expressing appreciation.

Formal dinners should display glassware that is all of the same design. Glasses are set to the right, in the

Correct glasses

ALL-PURPOSE GLASSES

1. 8-ounce for white wines
2. 9-ounce for red wines
3. 10-ounce for red or white wines

CHAMPAGNE GLASSES

4. Tulip
5. Flute

OTHER TYPES OF GLASSES

6. Liqueur
7. Sherry, Madeira, Port
8. Brandy

order in which the wines are served. No more than three glasses, including the water goblet, should be set out at one time. If more than two wines are to be served, the additional glasses are placed on the table immediately before the wine is poured. Glasses may be placed in a straight line in front of the place setting, always beginning with the water goblet on the left; or they may be set at an angle in the same order with the water goblet nearest the center of the table. To save space, they are sometimes arranged in a cluster above the knives.

A wineglass should never be filled to the brim. If you pour enough to fill it almost to the halfway mark, there will be room in the glass for swirling the wine to release its aroma and give you the pleasure of smell as well as taste.

For the first course, the wine is poured after the food has been served. For succeeding courses, the wine is poured as soon as the service for the previous course has been removed.

If there is no server in attendance, the wine is poured from its own bottle by the host. The bottle is never passed around.

Wine should be disturbed as little as possible before serving. It should never be shaken. Avoid serving a fine wine immediately after buying it. Fine old wines should be stored for several weeks or longer before serving to allow any sediment to settle to the bottom of the bottle.

All bottled still wines, with the exception of light white wines, may be recorked after being partly consumed and served again at the table or used for cooking. If you do not use the remaining wine promptly, do as the thrifty French housewife does: keep the wine to make superior vinegar. Champagnes and other sparkling wines must be finished after opening; they lose their effervescence quickly.

How many drinks in a bottle?

If you use a regular jigger measure of 1½ ounces when serving spirits, you can figure on a quart bottle yielding 21 drinks; a fifth (25.6 ounces) yielding 17 drinks; and a pint, 10 drinks. The average bottle of table wine (fifth) will yield 6 glasses, if you pour a

4-ounce serving. For two people a half bottle (4/5 pint) may be sufficient, but for three or four people it is safer to plan on serving a fifth (4/5 quart), or more.

Measuring wines and spirits

Split		6½ oz.
½ bottle	4/5 pint	12.8 oz.
Pint (U.S.)	2 cups	16 oz.
Wine bottle, average size, not otherwise marked		24 oz.
4/5 quart	"Fifth"	25.6 oz.
Quart (U.S.)	4 cups	32 oz.
Magnum (2 bottles in one)		52 oz.
Jeroboam (4 bottles in one)		104 oz.
1 dash		about 1/32 oz.
1 bar spoon	1 tsp.	1/6 oz.
Pony	2 tblsp.	1 oz.
Jigger	3 tblsp.	1½ oz.
1 measuring cup	16 tblsp.	8 oz.
Liqueur glass	usually long stemmed	1 oz.
Port glass	¼ cup	2 oz.
Sherry glass		2½ to 3 oz.
Cocktail glass		3 to 4 oz.
Juice glass	½ cup	4 oz.
Whisky-sour glass		4 to 5 oz.
Punch cup		5 oz.
Wineglass, all-purpose		4 to 7 oz.
Old-fashioned glass	short glass with heavy base	5 to 6 oz.
Champagne glass		5 to 7 oz., or 8 oz.
Brandy inhaler		usually 9 oz.
Highball glass		8 to 10 oz.
Collins glass	same shape as highball	12 oz.

How many drinks to a guest?

Usually, before dinner, a few of your guests will want more than two drinks, although two seems enough for a serious diner; too many cocktails dull enjoyment of good food and good table talk. After dinner, if the evening is to be a long one, figure on two or three drinks each.

COOKING WITH WINE

Cooking with wine is as simple as cooking with water, and a comparatively small quantity will enhance the flavor of the whole dish. The alcohol in the wine evaporates while the food is cooking and only the flavor remains. Not only does wine give a definite taste to food, but its slight acidity also tenderizes. Some examples of using wine for tenderizing can be found in the recipes for marinades.

To use wine in cooking specific foods, follow this general guide: dry red wine with red meat and game; lighter, less dry red wine with kidneys and stews; white wine with fish, shellfish and chicken. Use dry vermouth just as you would use white wine.

But these are not ironclad rules; the famous *coq au vin* is a chicken dish made with red wine, and there are famous French fish stews made with red wine.

O━ Wine should never be added to a dish just before serving. It should simmer with the food or in the sauce while it is being cooked; as the wine cooks, it reduces and becomes an extract which flavors. Wine added too late in the preparation will give a harsh quality to the dish.

Fortified and aperitif wines are an exception to the rule that you should never add wine to a dish at the end of the cooking. These wines are chemically different and they serve as flavoring and seasoning agents. You should add a fortified wine a little at a time, tasting the food as you add, to decide what quantity best suits you.

O━ When both wine and herbs are used in a dish, the final result will be better if an infusion or extract is made of both and then added to the food. To do this, add 1 teaspoon of the chosen herb, or ½ teaspoon of each if you are using two herbs, to 1 cup of red or white wine. Simmer for 10 minutes. Add 1 teaspoon of butter and the grated rind of 1 lemon, and simmer for another 5 minutes. The wine and herb extract is then ready to add to whatever food you wish. Use it all at once, or just a tablespoon at a time. Keep the remainder refrigerated in a tightly closed bottle or jar.

O━ The color of a red-wine sauce is sometimes unattractive. By adding a teaspoon of tomato paste or a small amount of brown sauce or meat gravy you will improve the color and add richness and body to the sauce.

🔑 Remember that even a little wine adds greatly to the flavor of food.

🔑 Leftover wines should never be thrown away. Keep them in a well-corked bottle, refrigerated. It does not matter if a few wines of different types are stored in the same bottle. Use these leftovers to flavor a gravy or stew, or even stewed fruits, or as part of a marinade.

🔑 A tablespoon or two of red wine instead of vinegar added to your French dressing will work wonders on meat or vegetable salads, but don't use wine on lettuce.

🔑 If you run short of wine for a recipe, substitute an equal quantity of apple juice, or ½ cup water with the juice of 1 lemon for each cup of wine required. (This solves the problem of the acid balance, but don't expect it to taste like wine!)

Remember, wine is composed mostly of water. It provides all or part of the liquid you need for the dish you are preparing, plus the subtle flavor that blends so beautifully with meat, fish, fruits or other food. It is used as you would use consommé—to enrich, flavor and moisturize.

It is not true that only a chosen few have the palate or purse to appreciate and to afford cooking with wine. Anyone can enjoy it. All you have to do is buy an occasional bottle and keep it in the refrigerator after opening. Use it only for cooking. Add a bit now and then to your favorite recipes. This is the best and easiest way of learning to cook with wine, and you will be surprised at how far one bottle will go. Remember not to add too much wine, but just enough to enliven the flavor.

If you want a low-priced dry wine for cooking, you can find inexpensive wines that will do very nicely. But if you are planning to prepare a dish with delicate ingredients, or an *haute-cuisine* specialty, you will want a wine with more class to it. It is perfectly true that the better the wine you use, the more delicious your dish will be. Whenever you are in doubt about the kind of wine to use in a dish, an easy rule is to use the same wine you plan to serve with the meal.

There are many recipes in this book that call for wine. In some it is a minor ingredient, but where it plays a significant role, you will find it listed in the index under wine-flavored dishes. Here are a few more recipes to illustrate ways to use wine.

Cheese with port

Fresh cheese is delicious without this treatment, but this is a good way to use up cheese that has dried out or cheese you have frozen.

8 ounces firm yellow cheese (Cheddar type)
4 tablespoons butter
½ cup ruby port
Paprika, minced parsley, minced nuts (optional)

Grind or chop the cheese into small pieces while cool, then let cheese and butter soften at room temperature. Use a mixer to beat them to a light fluffy texture. Add the port, either beating it with a mixer to make the cheese and wine homogeneous, or stirring it with a fork to make a streaky blend. Let it mellow for a few days before using. Serve in a crock, or shape into balls and roll in paprika, parsley or nuts. Makes about 2½ cups.

Anniversary shrimp

1½ pounds fresh shrimp in shells *or* 1 pound flash-frozen shelled shrimp
2 tablespoons butter
1 tablespoon olive oil
3 tablespoons minced shallots
1 cup red wine or dry Madeira
1 cup brown sauce (p. 191)
½ teaspoon minced fresh tarragon *or* ¼ teaspoon dried tarragon
1 teaspoon grated orange rind
2 tablespoons orange juice
Salt
White pepper
2 tablespoons minced chives
2 tablespoons minced parsley

Peel the uncooked fresh shrimp, or drop the frozen shrimp into boiling water for 1 minute, then drain and pat dry. Cut the shrimp lengthwise through the middle. Heat butter and oil in a large sauté pan and drop in the shrimp. Over fairly high heat cook and stir the shrimp until they are pink but not overcooked. Depending on the size of the pan, 5 to 7 minutes should be enough. (You can do this in a wok if you prefer.) Lift out the shrimp with a skimmer and keep them warm. Add the shallots to the sauté pan and cook and stir until the shallots are tender but not mushy. Add the wine (the kind you use determines the final flavor), and simmer shallots and wine until the liquid is reduced to three quarters of the original volume. Then add brown sauce, tarragon, orange rind and orange juice. Simmer for about 12 minutes longer. Season with salt and white pepper to taste. Be sure the sauce is seasoned well because the shrimp are not otherwise salted. Add the shrimp to the sauce and keep over the heat until the shrimp are hot. Just at serving time add chives and parsley. Serve hot as a first course, with lots of French bread to soak up the sauce. Makes 6 servings.

Carco wine consommé

Heat together 3 cans (10½ ounces each) undiluted condensed consommé with 1½ soup cans cold water, or use 6 cups homemade consommé. When boiling, add 1 cup dry red wine. Let the mixture simmer for a few minutes, but do not let it boil again. Garnish each cup with a few long, thin slivers of lemon peel. Makes 6 servings.

Wine-poached salmon steaks in aspic

- 6 salmon steaks, 1 inch thick
- 2 cups plus 2 tablespoons dry white wine or Champagne
- 1 bay leaf
- ½ teaspoon crumbled dried tarragon
- 1 celery rib, chopped
- 1 cup hollandaise sauce (p. 195)
- ¼ cup minced fresh chives
- 1 envelope unflavored gelatin

Tie each steak in a heart shape; pull the long ends inside in a half turn and tie with thread. Place the 2 cups of wine, the bay leaf, tarragon and celery in a shallow pan. Bring this *court bouillon* to a simmer. Place the salmon steaks in it side by side. Cover and simmer for 20 minutes, or until fish flakes readily.

With a perforated ladle remove the steaks from the pan. Strain the *court bouillon* through a cheesecloth. Remove the threads and skin from the salmon. Arrange the steaks on a serving platter. Fill spaces between steaks with hollandaise sauce. Sprinkle the whole with the chives.

Soak the unflavored gelatin in the 2 tablespoons of wine for 5 minutes. Bring the strained *court bouillon* to a simmer, add the soaked gelatin and stir until dissolved. Let the aspic cool.

Spoon a little of the cooled but still liquid aspic over the salmon. Refrigerate until the aspic has set. Then pour more aspic on top in the same manner; refrigerate. Repeat the process until all the jellied *court bouillon* has been used. Refrigerate for 3 to 5 hours before serving. This is a perfect buffet dish. Makes 6 servings.

Boeuf Bourguignon

The meat must be lean beef—top round or meaty short rib—of the very best quality. It must be browned in melted salt pork. Use small whole onions if you cannot get shallots, but shallots are better. To make an authentic dish, do not use celery, carrots or potatoes. Use dry red Burgundy for the liquid; the better the wine, the better the dish. You can prepare this early and reheat it carefully when you are ready to serve it.

3 pounds lean beef (top round or meaty short rib)
½ pound salt pork (more fat than lean)
2 dozen shallots or small white onions
1 teaspoon sugar
2 tablespoons flour (optional)
Freshly ground pepper
2 garlic cloves, crushed
3 inches of orange peel
2 bay leaves
¼ teaspoon dried thyme
½ teaspoon grated mace or nutmeg
4 parsley sprigs
½ teaspoon minced marjoram
½ bottle (or more) dry red Burgundy
2 tablespoons butter
1 cup white button mushrooms
½ cup minced parsley
1 cup croutons, browned in butter

Cut beef into 2-inch cubes. Slice the salt pork into 1-inch cubes and sauté in a heavy enameled cast-iron pan or Dutch oven until crisp and brown. Remove the pieces of pork, leaving the fat; set aside the pork pieces until later. Add the whole shallots or onions to the fat and sprinkle with the sugar; let brown over light heat. Remove shallots or onions from fat and set them aside. Brown the meat on all sides, adding only a few pieces at a time to the pan and removing each batch as it is finished. When all the meat is browned, return it to the pan and sprinkle with the flour; this is optional because some people like a clear sauce while others like a creamy one made with flour. Then sprinkle with freshly ground pepper.

Tie the crushed garlic, orange peel, bay leaves, thyme, mace or nutmeg, parsley sprigs and marjoram in a piece of cheesecloth. Add this to the meat. Do not add salt to this dish. Heat the wine and pour it over the meat. There should be just enough to barely cover the meat, so use more or less as needed. Cover the pan tightly and cook in a 250° F. oven for 2½ to 3 hours. Open only once or twice to check for tenderness. If more liquid is needed during cooking, add a little more hot red wine or beef consommé.

Twenty minutes before the end of the cooking time, add the browned onions and the pieces of browned salt pork. Melt the butter and sauté the mushrooms in it until delicately browned. Stir them into the stew just before serving. Then sprinkle with the minced parsley and the croutons. Makes 6 generous servings; or 4 servings and delicious leftovers, which are even better because the flavors are fully blended.

Leeks in white wine

12 leeks
1 tablespoon diced salt pork
2 tablespoons butter
White pepper
1½ cups dry white wine
Paprika (optional)

Trim the leeks, leaving about 2 inches of the green leaves. Wash them carefully. Cut down to the root end but leave the halves attached at the bottom. Wash again to remove any grit. Tie each leek with soft string to keep them from breaking up in cooking. Melt the diced salt pork and the butter, and sauté the leeks in the fat until they are browned lightly on all sides. Lift out the remaining bits of salt pork and sprinkle leeks with white pepper; no salt is needed. Add the wine, cover the pan and cook over low heat for about 15 minutes. The leeks should not be mushy, and the wine should be reduced to the consistency of syrup. Remove the leeks and untie the strings. If the sauce is not thick enough, reduce a little further. Spoon it over the leeks and dust with a little paprika. Makes 4 or 6 servings.

Note: The well-known English cookbook author Elizabeth David says the French prefer this dish cooked with red wine. Try that for an interesting change.

Oranges Lorenzo

Wash 6 seedless oranges and very carefully peel off but reserve the rinds. Peel the white pith from the oranges, and make certain no pith remains on the rinds. With a sharp knife, cut the rinds into long thin shreds. Cook the rinds in boiling water to cover for 10 minutes. Drain and set aside.

Put 1¼ cups sugar and 2 cups dry red wine into a saucepan large enough to hold all the oranges comfortably. Boil for 5 minutes. Add the oranges and simmer, uncovered, until the syrup is thick and the oranges have taken on a red hue. Place the oranges in a serving dish.

Add the reserved rinds to the syrup in the saucepan and simmer for a few minutes. Pour the syrup and slivers of rind over the oranges. Cover and refrigerate for a few hours before serving. Makes 6 servings.

Madeira cake

1 cup sweet butter
2 cups sifted confectioners' sugar
1 teaspoon grated lemon rind
½ teaspoon lemon extract
1 cup sweet Madeira (Malmsey)
3 cups cake flour
½ teaspoon salt
4 teaspoons baking powder
5 egg whites

Let the butter reach room temperature, then beat it vigorously with a wooden spoon until it is light and fluffy. Add the sugar and beat until it is absorbed in the butter and the mixture is light. Add lemon rind, lemon extract and a tablespoon of the Madeira; mix until smooth.

Sift together the cake flour, salt and baking powder. Add the flour mixture to the butter mixture alternately with the rest of the wine, beating thoroughly after each addition to make a smooth batter. Beat the egg whites until stiff and pour about half of them on top of the batter. Fold in with a spatula until no sign of egg white remains. Turn the remaining egg whites on top of the batter and again fold in, but gently; some egg white may still be apparent in the batter. Use a 9- or 10-inch ring pan with removable sides (an angel-cake pan), and butter the bottom thoroughly, but do not butter the sides. Pour the batter into the pan and smooth the top with a spatula. Bake in a preheated 350° F. oven for 1 to 1¼ hours, until the top of the cake is lightly browned and a few cracks have developed around the top.

Let the cake cool in the pan. Do not turn it upside down like an angel cake. Then remove the pan sides. With a narrow spatula loosen the portion next to the center spindle and the bottom of the cake. When the cake is sufficiently cool to hold, lift it off the pan and onto a cake plate. It is pretty enough to serve without any further embellishment, but if you wish, put a paper doily on top and sift confectioners' sugar through it to make a patterned top. This is a delicate and delicious cake, with a pleasant aroma from the Madeira. It is good served by itself, or accompanied by fresh strawberries or other delicate fruits. A very nice cake for tea. Makes about 20 pieces.

White-wine cup

Put a piece of cucumber peel, a piece of orange peel, a leaf of borage and 2 lumps of sugar in a 12-ounce glass. Pour a liqueur glass (2 tablespoons) of brandy over this and let stand for 20 minutes. Fill the glass half full with white wine (5 or 6 ounces) and add soda water to taste. Add 1 or 2 cubes of ice just before serving. Makes 1 drink.

Spiced hot red wine

2 cups water
1 cup sugar
1 tablespoon whole cloves
3 cinnamon sticks
1 tablespoon whole allspice berries
1 lemon, unpeeled and sliced
2 quarts red wine, French Burgundy or California red

Place the water, sugar and spices in a saucepan. Simmer until the sugar is dissolved. Add the lemon, cover and simmer for 10 minutes. Add the wine and stir to mix. Remove the whole spices. Serve hot with a lemon slice in each glass. Makes 15 punch-size servings.

Summer orange aperitif

Serve cold before lunch or dinner, to those who prefer a lighter aperitif to a martini. Start this 10 days before you plan to use it.

- 4 oranges
- 1 bottle of red Bordeaux wine or Italian Valpolicella
- ¼ cup tiny sugar lumps
- ½ cup vodka

Peel the rinds from the oranges with a sharp knife, or use a zester or peeler to make long shreds or thin peels. Wrap the shreds in wax paper and refrigerate. Remove the white pith from the oranges and dice the pulp. Pour the wine into a larger bottle. Add the diced orange pulp. Cork the bottle. Leave it to macerate in a cool, dark place for 7 days, shaking the bottle every day.

The eighth day, add the reserved orange rinds.

The ninth day, filter the wine; a coffee filter in its holder works beautifully. Add the sugar to the filtered wine and stir until dissolved. Add the vodka. Cork again and refrigerate for 24 hours before serving. Makes 5 to 6 cups.

Sangria maison

In Spain there are many ways to prepare this perfect summer wine punch. The wine, fruits and quantity of each ingredient used change the flavor and texture.

- 1 bottle of red Burgundy or Bordeaux wine or a good red Rioja
- 1 can (6 ounces) condensed frozen pink lemonade
- ¼ cup orange-flavored liqueur
- 2 lemons
- 2 oranges
- 2 fresh peaches
- Sugar
- 1 cinnamon stick

Pour the wine into a glass jug. Add the unthawed pink lemonade and stir until blended. Then add the orange-flavored liqueur. Wash the lemons and oranges. Slice, unpeeled, as thin as possible. Peel the peaches and slice also. Add all these fruits to the wine. Sweeten to your taste and add the cinnamon stick. Cover and refrigerate for 2 to 4 hours before serving. Traditionally, *sangria* should be served from a tall glass jug. If ice is desired, put it in the individual glasses, not in the jug. Makes about 6 cups.

COOKING WITH SPIRITS

Flambéed foods

The French word *flamber* means "to be in flame, to blaze." The *plat flambé* is a dish served in flaming brandy, rum, vodka, whiskey or liqueur. Flaming is sometimes used during the cooking process to give a finer flavor to meats or fish and to remove the harshness of the alcohol. Generally, however, food is flamed just before serving to give it a different taste and to add glamour to the service.

Plats flambés are not difficult to prepare. First, choose a spirit suited to the type of food to be flamed. Brandy, vodka and whiskey are best with meat; light and dark rum and French Cognac with dessert omelets and other desserts; and calvados and applejack with poultry and desserts. Liqueurs are often used for flaming, but because they contain a good deal of sugar it is advisable to use rum or brandy for one quarter to one half of the liqueur required.

Whatever kind of alcohol is used, it must be heated before it is lighted. Never let spirits boil. 🗝 A good trick is to warm the bottle under hot running water.

The food to be served flaming at the table should be arranged first on a warmed, heat-resistant platter, or in a chafing-dish tray or blazer pan and set over heat. Sterno or butane flame are the best types of canned heat to use. They are easily controlled for a high or low flame.

You will need 2 to 4 ounces of hot alcohol to flame a dish yielding six portions. First, pour some of the warm alcohol around the edge of the food, not on top, and light with a long match. Ladle the flaming alcohol on top of the food over and over again.

A word of caution: measure the alcohol or liqueur in a glass or cup. Never pour from the bottle into the pan or around the food. Once a dish is flaming there is danger that the gases in a bottle of spirits will ignite, causing the bottle to explode.

A SHORT GLOSSARY

ALE: A malt brew, containing about 6 percent alcohol.

AMER PICON: French bitters used as aperitif wine when mixed with grenadine or cassis.

ANGOSTURA: Alcohol-based bitters, made in Trinidad, with an infusion of aromatic herbs and plants; used for flavoring cocktails.

ANISETTE: A colorless liqueur flavored with aniseeds; very aromatic.

APPLEJACK: Apple brandy distilled from fermented cider made from fresh tree-ripened apples.

APRICOT BRANDY: A brandy distilled from apricots, used as an after-dinner liqueur; delicious in desserts.

APRICOT LIQUEUR: A sweet liqueur made from apricots and sweetened brandy.

AQUAVIT or AKVAVIT: A colorless or pale yellow liquor distilled from neutral spirits (grain, potatoes) and flavored with caraway; the favorite drink in Scandinavian countries.

ARMAGNAC: A brandy produced in Gers, near Bordeaux; it has a drier, heavier taste than Cognac.

B and B: A liqueur made of brandy and Benedictine, the after-dinner drink *par excellence.*

BEER: A brew fermented from cereals and hops, fermented with yeast; usually 4 percent alcohol.

BENEDICTINE: One of the oldest herb-flavored liqueurs; perfect with after-dinner coffee. A Benedictine monk created the recipe, which is still a secret, about 1510, at the monastery at Fécamp, France. It is now made commercially.

BOTTLED IN BOND: A term meaning that the distiller agrees to store his whiskey in bonded warehouses without paying the excise tax until he withdraws the whiskey from the warehouses. The law provides that such whiskey must be at least four years old and 100 proof; however, "bottled in bond" is not a quality guarantee.

BOURBON: Whiskey distilled from grain mashes, not less than 51 percent of which must be corn. Kentucky is the headquarters of Bourbon production.

BRANDY: Liquor made by distillation of wine or a fermented fruit mash. The term "brandy" used alone refers to liquor made from grape wine.

BYRRH: French aperitif wine flavored with quinine and fortified with brandy.

CALVADOS: French apple brandy, distilled in Normandy; sometimes made like our applejack.

CAMPARI: A bitter red liqueur made in Italy; used as an aperitif, mixed with soda, tonic or dry vermouth, and also used as an ingredient in many cocktails.

CANADIAN WHISKY: A liquor made from superior grains and carefully developed yeasts. It is fermented, distilled and aged under strict controls to produce lightness of body and superior flavor.

CHARTREUSE: Green and yellow liqueurs made with herbs and aromatics on a base of brandy.

CLARET: The English name for a dry red table wine from Bordeaux; from the French word *clairet,* meaning "lighter" than the original rather rough reds made centuries ago.

COGNAC: Brandy distilled from grapes grown in the region around the French city of Cognac, and aged in casks of Limousin oak. This is the best of all French brandies.

COINTREAU: Colorless sweet liqueur with an orange flavor. Popular for after-dinner sipping as well as for flavoring desserts and fruits.

COLD DUCK: A blend of Champagne and sparkling Burgundy; it can be used as an aperitif or late-evening refreshment.

CRÈME DE CACAO: Dark-brown liqueur made of cocoa beans, spices and vanilla with a brandy base. There is also a transparent colorless form, called "white."

CRÈME DE CASSIS: Sweet dark-red liqueur made from black currants.

CRÈME DE MENTHE: Peppermint-flavored liqueur, either white or green.

CURAÇAO: Liqueur made from the skins of oranges grown on Curaçao off the coast of Venezuela.

DUBONNET: A French aperitif wine with a slight quinine taste; white and red varieties are made.

EAU-DE-VIE: The French name for a brandy or spirit distilled from fermented juice of ripe fruits; always colorless; literally, "water of life."

FRAISE: An *eau-de-vie,* a colorless brandy distilled from the juice of strawberries.

FRAMBOISE: An *eau-de-vie*, a colorless brandy distilled from the juice of raspberries.

GIN: A liquor made with a neutral spirit base, flavored with juniper berries and other seeds.

GRAND MARNIER: An orange-flavored liqueur with a brandy base; both red and yellow types are made.

GRENADINE: A sweet red syrup, originally made from pomegranates; now often artificially flavored.

HOCK: The English name for white Rhine wine, probably from Hochheim, one of the famous Rhine wine towns, actually on the river Main.

IRISH MIST: A liqueur made of Irish whiskey, heather honey and herbs.

IRISH WHISKEY: Traditionally a blend of straight pot-still whiskeys, chiefly made of barley; distinctly different from any other kind.

KAHLUA: Mexican coffee liqueur, good alone or in other drinks and useful in cooking.

KIRSCH: A colorless brandy distilled from black cherries and their pits; it is made in France, Germany and Switzerland.

KÜMMEL: A colorless liqueur distilled from grain alcohol and flavored with caraway seeds.

MARASCHINO: A liqueur distilled from sour Marasca cherries; made originally in Dalmatia, now in Italy.

MARC: Spirits distilled from the pressings of crushed grapes after wine making.

MAY WINE: A German favorite, medium sweet and aromatic, made from white wine (Moselle or Rhine) flavored with the herb woodruff.

MESCAL: A colorless Mexican liqueur distilled from fermented roasted leaves of the maguey plant; green tasting and strong.

MIRABELLE: An *eau-de-vie* distilled from the juice of the mirabelle plum, chiefly in Alsace-Lorraine.

ORANGE BITTERS: English bitters flavored with the peel of Seville oranges.

PERNOD: Today's substitute for absinthe, which was banned because of the harmful wormwood used in its manufacture. An aperitif flavored with anise, it becomes cloudy when water is added, like all anise-flavored drinks.

PISCO: Grape brandy made in Peru, similar to French *marc;* used in cocktails.

PROOF: The measurement of alcoholic strength; each degree of proof equals ½ of one percent of alcohol; hence, 100 proof equals 50 percent alcohol.

QUETSCH: An *eau-de-vie* distilled from the juice of purple plums, chiefly in Alsace-Lorraine.

RUM: A liquor made from the distillation of fermented sugarcane. There are three popular types: white, gold, and dark or Jamaica rum.

RYE: Whiskey distilled from grain mashes containing not less than 51 percent rye, and aged in new charred oak barrels.

SACK: The old English name for sherry, derived from *sec*, the French word for "dry." Originally sherry was not sweet.

SAINT-RAPHAËL: A French aperitif wine, red, often served with lemon peel.

SCOTCH WHISKY: A liquor distilled from a mash of barley grain, with yeast, and water. True Scotch whisky cannot be made anywhere else.

SLIVOVITZ: A colorless brandy distilled from purple plums; made in Bulgaria, Czechoslovakia, Hungary and other countries.

SLOE GIN: A cordial made from sloe berries, the fruit of the blackthorn, steeped in gin.

STREGA: A yellow Italian liqueur with licorice flavor.

TEQUILA: A Mexican liquor distilled from the fermented juice of the agave or maguey; also made by redistilling mescal; very dry.

TIA MARIA: Coffee liqueur from Jamaica.

TRIPLE SEC: A colorless liqueur with a slight orange taste, similar to Cointreau.

VERMOUTH: Aromatic herb-flavored aperitif wines. The dry is light in color. The sweet is amber-colored or red, with a bittersweet taste. There is also a colorless very sweet vermouth.

VODKA: The Russian national drink, made from potatoes or grain. Colorless and tasteless, with no aftersmell, it can be used in any drink or recipe calling for gin. It is perfect with caviar.

WHISKY OR WHISKEY: This is the general name for liquors distilled from fermented mash of grain and not less than 80 proof. The spelling "whisky" is used in Scotland and Canada, while "whiskey" is used in Ireland and the United States.

«18»

When You Entertain

How to plan a party • Table-setting checklist • Luncheons • Informal and formal place settings • Informal and formal dinners • Suppers • Buffet place settings • Buffet meals • Outdoor and cocktail parties • Special occasions • Thanksgiving dinner • Christmas Eve party • Christmas dinner • New Year's Eve reception • Easter dinner

The trend in entertaining today is toward buffet-style dining, perhaps because few of us have a trained maid or butler to serve a sit-down dinner. It is never pleasant to give a dinner party where you must hop up and down all through the meal. Your guests may feel guilty to be putting you to so much trouble, and, as a result, they may be uncomfortable. A successful meal depends as much on the atmosphere as the food, and your guests will be relaxed and happy only if you are. It is important to create the illusion that you are managing everything easily, with a minimum of effort, and that you are having as good a time as everybody else. Decide what kind of meal you can serve with your own facilities and then start your planning.

PLANNING

The first step is to decide what you are going to serve; after that comes the shopping plan, then the plan for cooking. The cooking plan should be divided into three categories: advance work, same-day cooking, last-minute work on cooking and setting out the dishes.

The shopping list can be divided in almost the same way as the cooking plan: advance buying and checking on foods that can be used from the emergency shelf; the perishables, to be ordered the day before the party; entertainment-day checking of food that has been prepared in advance.

Make sure that you leave no cooking to do in the late afternoon on the day of the party. That is the time to arrange food on platters and then relax. If you have your working plans on paper and follow them, you will find that everything falls into place.

Let's recapitulate:

Write out your menu.

Make a master grocery list of every item and ingredient you will need.

Check the ingredients already on hand.

Make food-planning and cooking timetable.

List the linen, dishes and cutlery required.

Plan your centerpiece on paper.

Keep a list of your linen, dishes, cutlery and centerpieces. Also list the phone numbers and addresses of stores where you shop and where certain items are available. Menus, with the name and date of the party, are good to keep as a reminder of what you have done other times. If your parties are successful, people may want to eat the same great dishes another time, but it is better to serve something different to the same guests on a later occasion.

Among your plans include the clothes you intend to wear, and make sure they are not in need of dry cleaning or pressing. This is often overlooked until the last minute, and then a hasty switch has to be made which can put you completely off your stride.

Also, include a check on household requirements such as the following:

- cigarettes, matches and ashtrays in the right places
- candles, if you intend to use them
- fresh soap, guest towels and tissues in the bathroom
- cocktail napkins
- coasters
- ice, liquor, mixes, wine, openers, corkscrews
- coat-closet space and hangers

Allow yourself time to dress. Also, a little time to sit and relax before the party begins will work wonders, even though you only have 5 or 10 minutes.

Table-setting checklist

Check all of these items ahead of time so you will be organized before your guests start arriving:

- tablecloth or place mats
- napkins
- plates for each course
- cutlery, on table or on sideboard
- glasses
- coasters for wine bottles
- candles and holders
- salt and pepper shakers
- small dishes for nuts or bonbons, if needed
- serving forks and spoons
- serving dishes
- trivets or hot trays for hot dishes

When choosing your tablecloth or place mats, take into consideration your centerpiece and your candlesticks. The menu and the occasion dictate the type of table setting you should use.

A good menu should offer an appetizing variety of flavors, colors and textures, combining the bland and the sharp, the crisp and the soft, the bright and the pale, all at one meal. Your personal touches make the difference, so change and adjust the menus that follow to make them suit your own needs. And remember that they are just as suitable for a family occasion as they are for entertaining guests.

LUNCHEON

Lunch is a fine meal at which to entertain a few friends. You can serve good food without the formality of a dinner party. Here are two excellent menus.

Lunch for company *(for 6)*

Tomato Soup with Dumplings

Slices of Baked Ham

Creamed Lentils (p. 438)

Belgian Endives with French Dressing (p. 208)

Pulled-Bread Chocolate Pudding

Coffee

Tomato soup with dumplings

3½ cups tomato juice
2 cans (10½ ounces each) undiluted condensed beef consommé
2 teaspoons Angostura bitters
1 teaspoon sugar
2 eggs
2 tablespoons soft butter
5 to 6 tablespoons flour
Salt and pepper
Chives

Heat together the tomato juice and consommé. Add the bitters and sugar and simmer for 5 minutes. In a bowl beat together the eggs, soft butter and flour; this will make a thick sauce. Drop the sauce by coffee spoon into the hot soup. When all the mixture has been used, cover the saucepan, remove from heat and let stand for 15 minutes.

Taste for seasoning; add salt and pepper if needed. Sprinkle chives on top. Makes 6 servings.

Pulled-bread chocolate pudding

- 2 cups milk or light cream
- 4 slices of fresh white bread, or more
- ⅓ cup cocoa, preferably Dutch-process cocoa
- ½ teaspoon salt
- ½ cup brown or white sugar
- 2 eggs, well beaten
- 1 teaspoon vanilla extract
- ¼ cup melted butter
- 1 cup heavy cream

Scald the milk or light cream. Remove crusts from bread and pull the soft center part into enough small pieces to fill 2 cups without packing. Put the bread into a large bowl and pour the scalded milk or cream on top. Let cool.

Mix the cocoa, salt and sugar. Add to the bread and stir until well mixed. Beat the eggs with the vanilla and add to the bread with the melted butter. Mix well. Pour into a generously buttered baking dish or into individual molds. Bake in a 325° F. oven for 1 hour if you are using one baking dish, for 45 minutes if you are using individual molds.

Whip the heavy cream until stiff; sweeten lightly. Serve very cold over the hot pudding. Makes 4 to 6 servings.

Lunch for company *(for 4)*

Onion Soup Mont-Saint-Michel

Vancouver Salmon Salad

French Bread (p. 479)

Apple Pudding

Coffee

Onion soup Mont-Saint-Michel

This soup is special in the French repertoire; instead of sliced onions, the bouillon contains little white onions. Late autumn, when the baby white onions are plentiful on the market, is an especially good season for making this delicious soup.

- 5 tablespoons butter
- 25 to 30 small silverskin onions, peeled
- 1 teaspoon sugar
- ¼ teaspoon ground thyme
- 4 cups beef stock or consommé
- Salt and pepper
- 3 slices of bread, crusts removed
- ¼ cup chopped fresh parsley

Melt 3 tablespoons of the butter in a heavy metal saucepan. Add onions. 0┬ Peel onions under cold water in a bowl to avoid weeping. Toss them in the butter and sprinkle with the sugar. Cook uncovered over medium heat, stirring most of the time, until light brown. Add the thyme, beef stock or consommé, and salt and pepper to taste. Cover and simmer for 20 minutes.

Melt remaining 2 tablespoons of butter in a frying pan. Dice the bread slices and add to the butter. Stir over low heat until golden brown. When ready to serve, taste the soup and add more seasoning if necessary. Pour the hot croutons and the parsley into the soup. Makes 4 servings.

Vancouver salmon salad

1 pound poached fresh salmon
or 1 pound canned salmon
½ cup diced celery
1 can (20 ounces) green peas, drained
2 tablespoons lemon juice
1 teaspoon minced onion
½ teaspoon salt
⅛ teaspoon pepper
¼ teaspoon ground dill
1 cup commercial sour cream
Lettuce
Chopped chives, lemon wedges (optional)

Break up the salmon into bite-size pieces in a medium-size bowl. Add celery and drained peas. (You can use fresh or frozen peas if you prefer.) Combine the next six ingredients to make a dressing. Pour over the salmon and toss lightly with a fork. Chill for several hours. Serve in lettuce cups. Garnish with chopped chives and lemon wedges if desired. Makes 4 generous servings.

Apple pudding

Vermont and French Quebec both claim this recipe as their own. It can be prepared quickly.

3 or 4 apples, peeled and sliced
1 teaspoon ground coriander
1 teaspoon ground cinnamon
6 tablespoons sugar
2 to 4 tablespoons butter
¾ cup all-purpose flour
1 teaspoon baking powder
¼ teaspoon salt
2 eggs
Sour cream

Fill a generously buttered 1-quart baking dish with

a thick layer of sliced apples. Mix the coriander, cinnamon and sugar. Stir into the apples and place generous dabs of butter on top. Sift the flour, baking powder and salt into a bowl. Break the eggs on top of the flour mixture, and mix with a fork. Spread over the apples. Bake in a 350° F. oven until the topping is brown, usually about 35 minutes. Serve with a big bowl of cold sour cream. Makes 4 servings.

INFORMAL DINNER

Today the informal dinner is our favorite way to entertain. It is appropriate for few or many guests, although the number is obviously limited by your space and chairs.

To enjoy yourself and the friends you have invited, there must be very few trips to the kitchen. If you have maid service, you should decide before dinner as to the division of duties. A good trick is to write the maid's duties on paper and tack this up in the kitchen where the maid can refer to it. A small extra table near the hostess for additional plates, cutlery, coffee service and so on makes it possible to pass them without having to get up.

Keep the table setting simple but attractive. If you have flowers, be sure they do not obscure your guests' line of vision. If you have candles, they should not shine directly in the guests' eyes. Have the table ready before your guests arrive.

The soup or first course should be on the table before you sit down; when a maid is available this should be one of her duties. Hot rolls, sauces or any other similar accompaniments can be set on the table ahead of time to simplify the service. If you have a maid, she should clean the ashtrays and collect the cocktail glasses from the living room while you are at the table.

After the soup, either you or the maid serves the main course. If you are serving it yourself, placing the hot course on a hot tray on the sideboard or on a nearby small table before your guests come into the dining room will save much coming and going. If you have help, let the maid clear the soup or first-course plates from the table while you carve; or she can prepare the plates for the main course.

If you are serving the meal yourself, the host should pour and pass the wine while you serve the main course. Later, coffee can be served informally at the table or in the living room.

At such dinners the menu you select is extremely important, especially if you have no maid. Choose dishes that can stand waiting—some hot, some cold—and recipes that can be prepared the day before, or in the early morning on the day of the dinner so that you save yourself last-minute work.

At an informal dinner party where there is no help it is convenient to have trays ready in the living room. When you leave your guests to set the first course on the table, load a tray with ashtrays, empty glasses and the remains of appetizers. Keep clean ashtrays handy to replace the ones you remove; this saves an extra trip back and forth to the kitchen.

When you have no help, a simple three-course meal is the easiest kind to serve. You can even have the first course in the living room. Place the dishes on a tray and pass them around; the guests can continue to enjoy the chatty atmosphere of the preceding cocktail hour. This first course can be an appetizer or soup, but whatever you choose should be simple.

A sit-down dinner for more than 12, even when informal, should never be attempted without the help of at least two well-trained people to serve and another helper in the kitchen. Without this staff, the meal may become a frantic struggle. However, the realities of life today make serving people increasingly difficult to find. If you cannot arrange for help, then plan simpler dinners. Actually, the most successful dinners are those for six or eight people. With more than eight the conversation is seldom general, which makes it more difficult for the hostess. The table is simplest to arrange when you have six. Host and hostess can face each other at opposite ends of the table and the honored lady can sit at the right of the host, with the honored man in the corresponding place at the right of the hostess.

Even with a small group, it is sometimes necessary to have a helping hand. Make arrangements beforehand with a close friend among the guests. If no one in your family can carve, ask the most skillful of your male guests to do this. Be sure to provide him with sharpened tools and an extra plate to receive the pieces as he carves them. No matter how beautiful the garnishes around your roast may be, remove them before carving because they will get in the way.

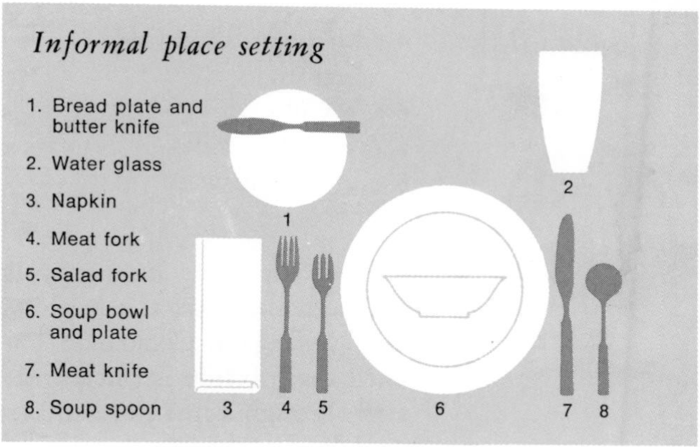

Informal place setting

Dinner for company *(for 4)*

Marinated Swiss Cheese (p. 632)

[*Dry Sherry*]

Boeuf Bourguignon (p. 670)

French Bread (p. 479)

[*Red Burgundy*]

Green Peas à l'Étuvée

Chocolate Flan de Nevers

Coffee

[*Cognac*]

Green peas à l'étuvée

The flavor secrets of this dish are the very low heat used throughout the whole 30 minutes of cooking and the fact that you add no salt. It is especially delicious made with the first fresh peas of the spring.

2 pounds fresh peas
3 tablespoons butter
1 small head of Boston lettuce
½ teaspoon sugar
6 thin green onions, minced
2 tablespoons water

Shell the peas just before cooking. Melt the butter in a saucepan. Chop lettuce into long shreds and add to the butter. Top with the peas. Sprinkle with sugar and minced onions. Add the water. Cover the saucepan and cook over low heat for 30 minutes, stirring 3 or 4 times. Do not add salt. Makes 4 servings.

Chocolate flan de Nevers

- 4 tablespoons superfine sugar
- 6 egg yolks
- 1¼ cups hot milk
- 8 ounces semisweet chocolate
- 1 cup sweet butter
- 30 small ladyfingers or small almond macaroons

Place the sugar and egg yolks in the top part of a double boiler; mix thoroughly. Add the hot milk and mix well again. Cook over hot water, stirring often, until the mixture is thick and creamy. Pour this custard through a fine sieve and let it cool.

Melt the chocolate over hot water. Use the same double boiler in which you made the custard; no need to wash it. Add the butter and stir until well blended. Pour the chocolate into the cooled custard and beat with a rotary beater until smooth.

Line the sides and bottom of a buttered 6-cup mold with ladyfingers or macaroons. Gently pour the chocolate cream into the mold. Cover the top with more ladyfingers or macaroons and a sheet of foil. Refrigerate for 8 to 24 hours. To serve, unmold and garnish with cold Custard Sauce (p. 211) or with chocolate curls. Makes 4 generous servings.

Wild duck dinner for company *(for 6)*

Carco Wine Consommé (p. 669)

Glazed Ducklings

[*Rosé Wine or Dry Red Wine*]

Fruit Garnish

Pungent Brown Rice

Carrots Ninon

Lemon Mousse (p. 556)

Glazed ducklings

These ducklings are not only beautiful and delicious, but they are easy to prepare.

3 wild ducks
  or 2 domestic ducks
Salt and pepper
¾ teaspoon dried rosemary or sage
¼ cup maple syrup
1¼ cups orange juice
1 cup black-currant jelly
1 cup chicken stock or consommé
1 tablespoon grated fresh gingerroot
  or ½ teaspoon ground ginger
1 teaspoon curry powder
¼ teaspoon grated nutmeg

Clean the ducks and place them on a rack in a roasting pan. Sprinkle inside and out with salt and pepper. Rub ¼ teaspoon rosemary or sage inside each duck. For domestic birds, roast in a 400° F. oven for 30 minutes to the pound, or until done. The cooking time for wild birds varies according to type and age; it can take from 30 to 60 minutes altogether. Pierce the skin all over once during the cooking period so that the fat will run out. The ducks are done when the drumsticks move easily in their sockets.

Thirty minutes before the birds are done, stir together the maple syrup and ¼ cup of the orange juice. Pour off the fat from the roasting pan and brush the ducks with the orange-juice mixture. Let the birds continue to cook until tender and beautifully glazed. Remove the ducks from the roasting pan when they are done and keep in a warm place.

Add to the juices in the pan the remaining orange juice, the black-currant jelly, stock or consommé, gingerroot or ginger, curry powder and nutmeg. Boil and stir over direct heat until the sauce has reduced and thickened slightly.

Carve the ducks or cut into individual portions with kitchen shears. Serve covered with the very hot sauce. Makes 6 servings.

Fruit garnish

Roast duck is usually served with applesauce. As a variation, add segments of orange or pitted candied cherries to the applesauce. Fresh pineapple cut into fingers and heated in butter flavored with curry powder makes a very tasty fruit sauce with duck, especially wild duck.

Pungent brown rice

2 cups brown rice
2 tablespoons butter
1 large onion, sliced thin
¼ cup chutney, minced
¼ cup brandy
½ cup commercial sour cream
Salt and pepper

Cook the rice according to the directions on the box, or follow one of the methods in Chapter 12. Melt butter and add the onion; sauté until golden brown. Add chutney, brandy and sour cream. Add this mixture to the cooked rice; stir together. Season to taste with salt and pepper, if necessary. Makes 6 to 8 servings.

Carrots Ninon

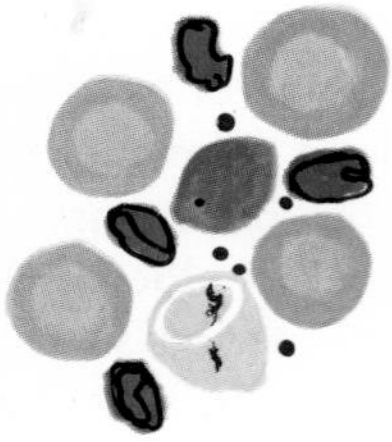

8 to 12 carrots
1 cup seedless golden raisins
Juice of 1 lime or ½ lemon
1 tablespoon butter
Salt and pepper

Peel the carrots and cut into thin diagonal slices. Steam or pan-cook until just tender but still a little on the crisp side; drain well. Add the raisins, lime or lemon juice and butter. Sprinkle with salt and pepper to taste. Stir gently to blend seasonings. Makes 6 servings.

FORMAL DINNER

Because the whole trend of our society is toward informality, a true formal dinner is seldom held in a private home today. But formality is determined more by the elegance of the food than by the presence of a butler behind each chair. We no longer serve a dozen courses with as many wines. Nevertheless, once in a long while such a meal may be appropriate for an honored guest or a very special occasion.

Have the first course already on the table when you and your guests enter the dining room. There should be a service plate at each place. If the first course is hot, a servant places the soup plate or dish for a first course on the service plate. A cold dish or cold soup does not require a service plate because it can be set directly on the table. The exceptions are oysters on the half shell or seafood cocktail served in a deep plate of crushed ice. These should be set on a service plate before the guests enter the room.

Consult the illustrations for the table setting. When

placing extra knives and forks, the rule is simple: those to be used first are laid farthest away from the plate. For example, if the first course is soup, the soup spoon goes to the far right. Melon, grapefruit or other fruit spoons for a first course are placed on the outside right, the same as the soup spoons, and a fork for shellfish goes to the outside right, an exception to the rule of putting forks on the left.

The dessert fork and spoon may be placed on the table when the dessert is served. This keeps the table from being too cluttered with silverware at the beginning of the meal. Whenever possible, set the dessert plates, dessert silver and the dessert itself on a sideboard or service table before dinner.

If cheese is served, a small bread plate and cheese knife should be placed in front of each guest before dessert. You may have these ready on the service table.

Water glasses go slightly to the right of the plate, above the knives. Wineglasses go to the right of the water glasses. If liqueur and coffee are served at the table, bring in the glasses and the bottles on a tray at the same time the coffee is served.

Formal dinner

1. Salt and pepper shakers
2. Water glass
3. Wineglass
4. Napkin
5. Meat fork
6. Plate
7. Meat knife
8. Soup spoon
9. Cocktail fork

In the days when a fish course routinely preceded the roast, it was correct to use fish knives and forks. Hardly anyone owns them today, but if you do serve a fish course before the meat, be sure to have separate utensils for each.

For a formal dinner use linen or lace cloths, table napkins and all your best china, silver and glassware. Arrange an elegant centerpiece, too.

Formal dinner *(for 16)*

This menu has one great advantage—the food can be prepared almost completely the day before the party.

Melon Alcantara

[*Sherry*]

Paupiettes de Sole à l'Écossaise

[*Chablis*]

Jardinière de Légumes

Salade de Cresson

Pêches Dijonnaise

Café Noir

[*Cognac*]

Melon Alcantara

2 cantaloupes
1 Spanish melon
Salt and pepper
Freshly grated nutmeg
¼ pound butter
1 tablespoon grated fresh gingerroot
Juice of 4 limes

Make balls of cantaloupe and Spanish melon, allowing a mixed total of 5 to 7 balls per serving. Put each portion in an individual ovenware dish. Salt and pepper each one. Grate a dash of nutmeg over each. Cut the butter into small dice and divide evenly among the dishes. Mix the grated gingerroot and the lime juice and sprinkle on top of the melon balls. Cover and refrigerate, overnight if convenient.

Shortly before serving, place in a preheated 350° F. oven for 20 minutes. Serve with dry sherry.

Paupiettes de sole à l'Écossaise

This can be made in advance and reheated for dinner.

2 pounds fresh salmon
2 eggs
½ cup minced parsley
1 teaspoon minced tarragon, fresh or dried
Salt and pepper
16 large fillets of sole
Grated rind of 3 lemons
1 bottle dry white wine
5 tablespoons butter
½ cup flour
1 cup heavy cream
½ cup milk
3 tablespoons brandy
½ teaspoon sugar
1 pound fresh mushrooms, sliced thin, *or* 1 large can (14 ounces) imported *chanterelles,* drained
1 green onion, finely chopped

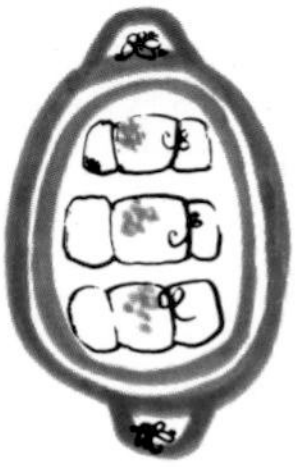

Fillet the uncooked salmon and pass it through a food chopper twice. Add the eggs, parsley, tarragon, 1 teaspoon salt and ½ teaspoon pepper. Beat with a wooden spoon until creamy and well blended. Spread the sole fillets on a table, sprinkle each one lightly with salt and pepper, and sprinkle a pinch of lemon rind on each. Spread each of the fillets with some of the salmon mixture. Roll the fillets and tie each one with a thread.

Warm the white wine in a large frying pan, but do not let it boil. Place half of the rolled fillets in the wine and simmer over low heat for 10 minutes, basting constantly with the wine. Remove the fillets to a deep ovenproof serving platter. Arrange the rolls one next to the other and remove the threads. Do the same with the rest of the rolled fillets. Strain the cooking wine and set it aside.

In the same frying pan, melt 4 tablespoons of the butter and add the flour. Stir until well blended. Pour the strained wine into the roux and add the cream and milk. Cook over medium heat, stirring constantly with a wire whisk, until you have a smooth velvety sauce. Then add the brandy, sugar, and salt and pepper to taste. Stir again for a few minutes. Taste for seasoning. If sauce is too thick, stir in a little milk or cream gradually. Set aside.

Melt remaining 1 tablespoon butter. When butter is light brown add the mushrooms and chopped green onion. Stir over high heat for ½ minute. Arrange the mushroom mixture around the fish. Spoon the sauce evenly over the rolled fillets of fish, leaving some of the mushrooms uncovered.

Shortly before serving, place the platter in a preheated 400° F. oven for 15 to 20 minutes. Makes 16 servings.

Jardinière de légumes

Choose any vegetables you wish. Blanch according to the basic method (p. 411) and roll in creamed butter. Mix and serve.

Salade de cresson

Wash and drain equal amounts of watercress and Bibb lettuce. For 16 servings you will need about 4 bunches of watercress and 6 heads of Bibb lettuce. At serving time toss with Chiffonade Dressing (p. 208).

Pêches Dijonnaise

8 peaches
1 cup fresh orange juice
Grated rind of 2 oranges
1 cup sugar
1 cup water
½ cup black-currant syrup

Wash the peaches but do not peel them. Place the remaining ingredients in a large frying pan with a cover. Bring to a fast rolling boil, stirring constantly. Place the unpeeled peaches in the syrup, cover, lower the heat, and simmer for 25 minutes, turning once. Remove from the heat. Uncover. While the peaches are cooking, prepare the praline mixture.

PRALINE

2 cups sugar
Juice of ½ lemon
1 cup blanched almonds
1 cup unblanched hazelnuts

Place the sugar and lemon juice in a saucepan. Stir constantly over medium heat until the mixture has turned to a light golden syrup. Add the nuts and stir until well mixed. Pour the mixture into a jelly-roll pan with sides, spreading the mixture and nuts as quickly as possible. Set aside until cold, about 1 hour. Then, either crush gradually in a blender at high speed, removing the blended part each time before adding more, or butter a rolling pin and crush a few pieces at a time over a wooden board. Set aside.

Peel the cooled peaches and cut into halves. Place a half, with rounded side up, in an individual heatproof custard cup or soufflé dish. Sprinkle 2 tablespoons of the crushed praline over the top; do this with all the peach halves. Then make the French cream.

FRENCH CREAM

5 whole eggs
4 extra egg yolks
1 cup sugar
4 cups light cream
1 cup milk
1 vanilla bean

Beat together lightly the whole eggs, extra egg yolks and sugar. In the meantime, warm up the cream and milk with the vanilla bean. When hot, remove the vanilla bean. Beat the hot liquid into the egg and sugar mixture. Divide the cream equally in the custard cups, or pour all of it over the peaches in the soufflé dish.

Set the individual dishes in a pan of hot water. Bake in a preheated 350° F. oven until the blade of a knife comes out clean. Cool, then refrigerate overnight or until ready to serve. Serve with Dijon syrup.

DIJON SYRUP

1 cup sugar
1½ cups water
4 tablespoons vanilla extract
4 tablespoons coffee liqueur
1 tablespoon brandy

Place the sugar in a frying pan and stir over medium heat until it turns into a light golden syrup. Remove from heat. Add the cold water, 1 tablespoon at a time. When all is added, put back over the heat and cook, stirring occasionally, until the mixture has formed a light syrup. Remove from heat and cool. Then add the vanilla, coffee liqueur and brandy. Mix well. Place in a jar and refrigerate until ready to pour some over each dessert. This sauce can be kept refrigerated for 2 to 3 weeks. Makes about 3 cups syrup.

Formal dinner *(for 6)*

Stuffed Brown Mushrooms

[*Dry Madeira*]

Anniversary Shrimp (p. 668)

Pat's Golden Birds

[*White Wine*]

Carrots with Coriander

Zucchini with Herbs

French Crêpe Meringue (p. 253)

Coffee

[*Benedictine or Yellow Chartreuse*]

This is a perfect dinner to serve in the early fall when brown mushrooms are in the market and zucchini plentiful, though you can obtain the ingredients at any time of the year.

For this dinner, reduce the quantity of the sauce in the Anniversary Shrimp recipe so that each serving will have only a few tablespoons. Mopping up the sauce may be permitted on informal occasions but it will not do for formal dinners.

Stuffed brown mushrooms

12 large brown mushrooms
8 ounces prosciutto
1 bunch of parsley, flat or curly
1 medium-size onion
1 tablespoon olive oil
2 tablespoons butter
Salt and pepper
4 egg yolks

Wipe the mushrooms with a damp cloth. Cut a thin slice from the bottom of each mushroom stem and then remove the stems, leaving the caps whole. Finely chop the stems, the prosciutto, parsley and onion. Heat oil and butter over low heat and sauté all the chopped ingredients until tender and just beginning to brown. Season well with salt and pepper. Stir in the egg yolks and cook for about 2 minutes longer. Use the mixture to stuff the mushroom caps. Place them on a baking sheet.

Before serving time, bake mushooms in a 400° F. oven for about 20 minutes, until tender and very hot. Serve 2 mushrooms for a serving, either plain or on rounds of fresh toast, with a garnish of a parsley sprig and a lemon slice sprinkled with paprika. Makes 6 servings.

This recipe can be used for a cocktail hors d'oeuvre too. The filling will remain firm enough so that the mushrooms can be cut into quarters or into 6 pieces.

Pat's golden birds

6 Rock Cornish game hens
Livers of the birds
6 dried pear halves
1 cup fresh white bread crumbs
9 tablespoons butter
Salt and pepper
1½ cups quince marmalade or jelly, or apple jelly

If possible, buy birds with the breastbone removed; they are easier to carve. If the birds are frozen, let them defrost completely. Remove the giblets (hearts and gizzards can be used for something else). Rinse the livers, then simmer them in ½ cup water for a few minutes until firm. Save the cooking water. With scissors, cut livers and pears into small bits and mix with bread crumbs. Melt 3 tablespoons of the butter and add to the stuffing mixture. Add enough cooking water to make a slightly moist mixture, and season to taste. Put some stuffing in each bird; they will not be full. Fasten the opening with a poultry pin and tie the legs together.

Put the birds in a large roasting pan; they should not be crowded. Roast them in a preheated 375° F. oven for about 1 hour. Meanwhile, melt together remaining butter and the marmalade. Use this to baste the birds as they cook. Use all the mixture; the birds should be golden and shiny. Serve on a large platter garnished with sprigs of watercress. Makes 6 servings.

Carrots with coriander

- 2 pounds finger-size carrots
- 2 cups salted chicken stock
- 1 teaspoon fennel seeds, crushed in a mortar
- 1/8 teaspoon ground coriander
- 1 teaspoon walnut oil
- 4 teaspoons butter
- 2 tablespoons white wine or apple juice
- Salt

Use only small carrots. Scrub but do not peel. Simmer them in the stock with the fennel seeds until carrots are tender and all the liquid absorbed. If they are still not tender when the liquid is absorbed, add water and continue to cook a little longer. Let them cool, then slip off the thin skins. Peel with a knife if necessary. This much can be done a day ahead.

Before serving, put the carrots in a saucepan and sprinkle with coriander. Add oil, butter, and wine or juice. Simmer until carrots are hot. Add a little salt if necessary. Makes 6 servings.

Zucchini with herbs

- 18 tiny zucchini, whole
- Salt
- 3 tablespoons minced parsley
- 2 tablespoons minced fresh mint
- 1/2 tablespoon minced fresh basil
- 1/2 tablespoon minced fresh marjoram
- 6 tablespoons light cream

With a swivel peeler remove the outer layer of peel from the zucchini, rinse them, and steam in a little salted water until tender. Mix all the herbs into the cream and heat it. Roll the drained zucchini in the cream until hot and well flavored. Makes 6 servings.

SUPPER

If you have had a heavy meal in the middle of the day and do not want another dinner in the evening, you may still entertain guests at a light supper. This is an informal meal with fewer courses, and it is an excellent way to offer refreshment after the theater or a cocktail party. A shared dish, such as a dip or a fondue, is appropriate at supper. The meal can be served in front of the fireplace, on the porch or patio, or even in your kitchen if it has a dining area.

Sunday night supper *(for 6)*

This is an easy meal to prepare because the casserole and its accompanying sauce are the only foods that need to be cooked.

Oysters in Casserole

Hollandaise Sauce (p. 195)

[*Alsatian Riesling*]

Brie Cheese

French Bread

Red and Yellow Apples

Oysters in casserole

1 quart shucked oysters
½ cup melted butter
2 shallots
or 3 green onions, finely chopped
½ teaspoon salt
Pinch of cayenne
1 tablespoon brandy or Scotch whisky
2 eggs, beaten
1 cup fine cracker crumbs
2 tablespoons minced parsley

Drain the oysters. Cut each one into two or three pieces and set the pieces on a sieve as they are cut. Heat ¼ cup of the butter. Add the shallots or green onions and sauté until lightly browned. Add the cut-up oysters and season with the salt, cayenne and brandy. Stir fast over high heat for 1 minute. Remove from the heat. Add the beaten eggs, cracker crumbs, remaining ¼ cup melted butter and the parsley. Mix together and pour into an attractive baking dish. Bake in a 350° F. oven until firm like a custard and light brown on top. Serve with a bowl of hollandaise sauce. Makes 6 servings.

Soup for supper *(for 6)*

Butter Balls Chicken Soup

Cracked-Wheat Bread (p. 481)
with Cherry Jam

Rhubarb Pudding

Butter balls chicken soup

- 1 frying chicken (3 pounds)
- ½ cup chopped celery leaves
- 1 bay leaf
- 10 peppercorns
- 1¼ teaspoons salt
- 5 cups hot water
- 1 cup diced celery
- 2 tablespoons chopped fresh parsley
- 2 tablespoons butter
- 2 eggs
- 5 to 6 tablespoons flour

Cut the chicken into portions. Place the pieces in a saucepan with celery leaves, bay leaf, peppercorns, 1 teaspoon of the salt and the hot water. Bring to a boil, cover and simmer over low heat for about 1 hour, or until chicken is tender. Strain, then return broth to saucepan. Cut chicken into small pieces and add to broth with diced celery and parsley. Bring again to a simmer.

To make the butter balls, cream the butter and add the eggs. Beat. Gradually add the flour and remaining ¼ teaspoon salt. Beat hard until the mixture is like very soft butter. Drop the mixture into the simmering soup in very small balls (¼ or ½ teaspoon each). Cover the pan and let stand over low heat for 5 minutes, until the dumplings are done. Makes 6 servings.

Rhubarb pudding

- 3 cups diced rhubarb
- 5 tablespoons butter
- ⅔ cup plus ½ cup sugar
- 1½ cups all-purpose flour
- ¼ teaspoon salt
- 3 teaspoons baking powder
- 1 egg
- ½ cup milk
- Heavy cream

Pour rapidly boiling water on top of the rhubarb until well covered. Set aside for 10 minutes. Drain through a sieve. Spread 2 tablespoons of the butter in the bottom of a shallow 1½-quart baking dish. Sprinkle with ⅔ cup of the sugar. Place a pie bird or inverted custard cup in the middle to prevent juices from boiling over. Place the rhubarb all around.

Stir together the flour, salt, remaining ½ cup sugar

and the baking powder. Beat egg with milk and remaining 3 tablespoons butter, melted. Add to dry ingredients and stir until blended. It makes a fairly thick dough. Spread over the rhubarb. Bake in a 400° F. oven for 25 to 30 minutes. Serve hot with very cold heavy cream. Makes about 6 servings.

BUFFET MEALS

One reason for the popularity of buffet meals today is that they enable us to entertain a maximum number of people in a minimum amount of space. Generally speaking, too, a buffet is easier to manage without domestic help than a sit-down dinner.

A good arrangement is the buffet service where guests help themselves to the first course and eat at small tables. Dessert and coffee are served to them at their tables by the host or hostess. If you are having a buffet for more than 12 people, try to have at least one person to help set out the dinner, clear away plates, ashtrays and glasses, and clean up superficially.

When planning a buffet meal, do not have too many courses. One good arrangement is to serve one or two hot dishes or one or two cold dishes. Whether you choose the hot or the cold, follow up with a salad or a vegetable dish, a cheese tray, and a spectacular dessert. Be sure to serve lots of each dish.

Remember to have food that can be eaten with a fork only, especially if it has to be balanced on the knees. It is thoughtless to inflict on your guests—particularly male guests—the awkward task of trying to cut up turkey or ham while they are trying to balance wobbling plates. Interesting stews and casseroles are much easier to eat.

Setting the buffet table

The dining table is the natural place to set out the food for your buffet, but you can also use a sideboard or one or two smaller tables placed together. If you have no dining room, use the top of a desk, a shelf set on blocks or a card table. You can cover the top with your finest linen or even with a paper tablecloth. Arrange the table against an imaginative background, or set it away from the wall so that people can walk around it easily when they are serving themselves.

Place the dinner plates, silver and napkins nearest the end where guests will approach the table. If you have room, arrange the silver in a row and the napkins in a row below the silver. If you don't, wrap the silver in the napkins and place the bundles one next to the other. This enables a guest to hold his plate and the silver and napkin bundle in one hand, leaving the other free to serve himself.

When setting out the food, place the main dish first, followed by the vegetables and hot rolls or bread. If you are serving noodles, rice or a similar food, place this just before the main dish for those who like to pour the sauce over the pasta or rice. Place the condiments after the rolls or bread, and after these the salad, cheese and crackers, and then the glasses for beer or wine. (The glasses may be omitted here if you have someone to help with the serving.)

Utensils such as hot trays, electric frying pans or

Buffet setting

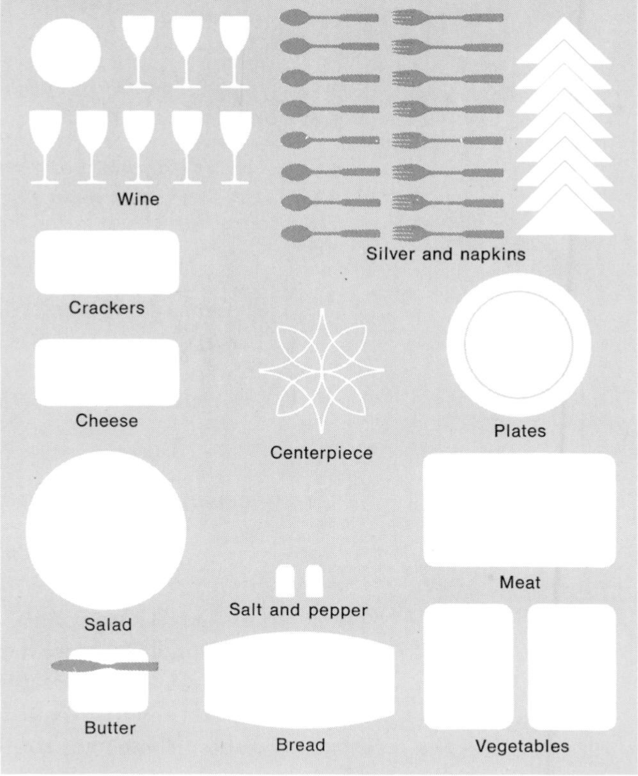

saucepans, or food warmers are almost indispensable at buffet suppers to keep food hot. Set out large serving spoons and forks that will make it easy for the guests to help themselves.

When everything is ready, invite the guests to help themselves, but go to the table yourself to direct the traffic and see that things get moving in the right direction. You can even suggest that guests eat the hot dish first and come back later for the salad and cheese. After everyone has served himself, replace the covers on the hot dishes.

When the main course, cheese and salad are finished, place the dessert where the main dish was originally set, with the necessary plates and silver near it. Liqueurs should be at one end of the table. If you have help, it will be easy to organize the clearing of the table while your guests enjoy themselves and relax before eating dessert.

A casserole buffet *(for 6 or 12)*

This menu offers a choice of main dish; either goes well with all the other dishes. This can be a dinner buffet or a very generous supper, and it will serve for any season of the year.

Chopped Chicken Livers

Hot Crisp Bread

[*Dry Sherry*]

Swiss Chicken Casserole or *Shrimp Curry*

[*Dry white wine*] [*Beer*]

Baked Rice with Herbs

Green-Bean Salad

Fresh Lemon Granité with Strawberry Sauce

Coffee

These recipes are for six servings. If you are entertaining 12 people, make a second bowl of chicken livers, a second casserole or curry dish, and double everything else in the menu. Even if you have very large casserole dishes, it is better to divide the food between two dishes. This makes it easier for you to prepare it, and you can place one dish at each end of the buffet for easier serving. Another possible advantage—if people come at different times in spite of your plans, you can keep one dish hot until it is needed.

Chopped chicken livers

- 2 tablespoons butter
- 2 tablespoons chicken fat (*see note*)
- 2 medium-size white onions, chopped
- 1/4 teaspoon dried tarragon
- 1/2 pound chicken livers
- 2 hard-cooked eggs
- 1/4 cup chopped parsley
- Salt and pepper

THE DAY BEFORE, heat together the butter and chicken fat. Add the chopped onions and sauté until golden. Add the tarragon and the chicken livers and stir over high heat until red juices cease to run. Do not overcook. Place the cooked livers in a chopping bowl and add the eggs. Pour in the fat and onions from the pan. With a sharp knife, chop the whole mixture until fine and well mixed. Add the parsley, then season with salt and pepper to taste. Place in an attractive bowl and refrigerate until serving time. Makes 6 servings.

Note: If you are preparing the chicken casserole, you can easily find enough fat on the bird to make this amount; render it slowly over low heat. If you are making the shrimp curry, use 2 tablespoons olive oil instead.

THE DAY OF THE PARTY, set the bowl in a basket and surround it with hot crisp bread. Put a small spreader on the table next to the basket. Let each guest spread his own bread while you serve the sherry.

Refrigerate the sherry for at least 3 hours before serving if you like an aperitif sherry served cold. The liver paste, sherry and glasses can be set in the living room just before the guests arrive.

Hot crisp bread

THE DAY BEFORE, cut thin slices of rye bread or crusty French bread, about three slices per person. Do not remove the crusts. Butter each slice and sprinkle with celery salt. Place on a baking sheet. Cover with foil and refrigerate until just before serving.

THE DAY OF THE PARTY, place the sheet of bread slices in a preheated 450° F. oven for 10 minutes, or under the direct heat of a broiler for 3 minutes. Watch closely when under the broiler.

Swiss chicken casserole

- 1 large chicken or fowl (5 pounds)
- ½ cup all-purpose flour
- ½ teaspoon salt
- ¼ teaspoon pepper
- 1 teaspoon paprika
- 4 tablespoons butter
- 1 cup water
- ½ cup white wine (*see note*)
- 3 tablespoons minced parsley
- 2 green onions, minced
- 1 garlic clove, minced
- 2 whole cloves
- ½ bay leaf
- ¼ teaspoon dried basil
- ¼ pound Swiss cheese
- 2 tablespoons flour
- ¼ cup light cream

THE DAY BEFORE, cut the chicken into individual portions; save 2 tablespoons of the fat for the chopped chicken livers. On a large plate mix flour, salt, pepper and paprika. Roll the chicken pieces in this. Melt the butter in a large frying pan. Brown the chicken over medium heat. Add water, wine, minced parsley, onions, garlic, cloves, bay leaf and basil. Cover and simmer over low heat until the chicken is tender. Cool and refrigerate.

Grate the cheese; there should be 1 full cup. Wrap and refrigerate.

THE DAY OF THE PARTY, warm the chicken over low heat. Remove 3 tablespoons fat from the surface of the cooking liquid and put it in a small frying pan. Lift the chicken pieces to a plate and strain the cooking liquid. Add the flour to the fat, mix well, and add the strained liquid and the cream. Cook, stirring all the time, until the sauce is smooth and creamy. Season to taste.

Pour half of the sauce in an attractive shallow casserole. Sprinkle half of the cheese over the sauce. Place pieces of chicken on top. Sprinkle with the rest of the cheese and pour on the remaining sauce. Keep at room temperature until ready to bake. Bake the casserole in a preheated 425° F. oven for 30 minutes. Makes 6 to 8 servings.

Note: For six people, plan to have two bottles of the white wine. Use part of one bottle to make the casserole; there will be enough left to give everyone three small glasses (about 3½ ounces each glass).

Shrimp curry

This version of an Indian curry is easily prepared with readily available ingredients. Like all curries, it has the great quality of being even better when reheated. This means that the whole dish can be prepared a day ahead. On the day of the party, just reheat to serve.

- 2 pounds raw shrimp in shells, fresh or frozen
- 2 medium-size onions
- 3 tablespoons butter
- 2 tablespoons curry powder
- 2 garlic cloves, crushed
- 1 lemon *or* 2 limes
- 1 teaspoon ground turmeric
- 1 tablespoon grated fresh gingerroot *or* 1 teaspoon ground ginger
- 1 can (20 ounces) tomatoes
- 1 tablespoon tomato paste
- Salt
- ½ to 1 cup diced celery

THE DAY BEFORE, peel the shrimp. If the shrimp are frozen, soak in cold water for 1 hour, then peel. Clean and set aside. Peel the onions and cut into wafer-thin slices.

Melt the butter in a large saucepan. When golden brown, add the onion slices; they will brown quickly. Remove them with a slotted spoon to a plate. Add curry powder to the butter remaining in the pan and stir until well mixed.

Place crushed garlic in a small bowl with 3 tablespoons water and the juice of the lemon or limes. Add turmeric and ginger; stir well.

Return the browned onions to the curry and butter; heat. Pour in the water and lemon-juice mixture all at once; stir fast. Add tomatoes and tomato paste and stir while bringing to a boil. Then let simmer, uncovered, for 30 to 40 minutes.

At this point add the shrimp and salt to taste and as much celery as you like. Remove immediately from the heat. Pour into a dish, cover and refrigerate.

THE DAY OF THE PARTY, place the curry in a chafing dish, or in an electric frying pan set at 300° F., to reheat at the table; or place in a casserole to reheat uncovered in a 300° F. oven. Whichever way you choose, do not let it boil.

With curry it is customary to serve small dishes of chutney, whole or chopped cashews, small cubes of cantaloupe and toasted coconut. Let your guests help themselves to these accompaniments.

Because of its delicate flavor, wine should not be served with anything as pungent as curry, but beer goes well with it. Chill enough for at least two glasses per person.

Baked rice with herbs

2 tablespoons butter
4 green onions, minced
2 cups uncooked long-grain rice
4 cups chicken consommé (homemade, canned or made from bouillon cubes)
½ teaspoon crumbled dried basil
¼ cup minced fresh parsley

THE DAY BEFORE, melt the butter in a saucepan, add green onions and stir over low heat until onions are limp. Add the uncooked rice and continue to stir over medium heat until the rice is glossy and light golden brown. Place in a casserole with a cover. Pour consommé over the rice. Mix in the basil and parsley. Cover. Refrigerate until 40 minutes before serving.

THE DAY OF THE PARTY, bake the rice in the oven while reheating the chicken casserole or shrimp curry. At a temperature of 375° F. the rice will bake in about 45 minutes. Allow slightly less time at the 425° F. temperature you use for the chicken, or about 1¼ hours at the 300° F. temperature used for the curry.

Green-bean salad

1 pound fresh green snap beans
Pinch of sugar
2 eggs
¼ cup toasted blanched almonds
½ cup salad oil
2 tablespoons cider or tarragon vinegar
½ teaspoon salt
½ teaspoon sugar
½ teaspoon paprika
¼ teaspoon dry mustard
1 teaspoon grated onion
½ teaspoon crumbled dried basil
1 whole garlic clove, peeled
4 tablespoons minced parsley
2 tablespoons minced green onions

THE DAY BEFORE, wash the beans and cut each one into two or three pieces, or split lengthwise. Place in a saucepan with a pinch of sugar, cover with boiling water, and cook over quick heat for 8 minutes. Drain and rinse under cold water. Refrigerate. Hard-cook the eggs and sliver the almonds.

Make an herb French dressing; the dressing can be made a few days ahead if you wish. In a glass jar put the oil, vinegar, salt, sugar, paprika, mustard, onion, basil and garlic clove.

THE DAY OF THE PARTY, add enough dressing to the cooled beans so they are well coated. Place in a salad bowl and garnish the edges with quartered hard-cooked eggs. Sprinkle the middle with a mixture of minced parsley and green onions. Top with slivered almonds.

Fresh lemon granité

- 1 can (6 ounces) evaporated milk *or* 1 cup heavy cream
- 2 eggs, separated
- ¾ cup sugar
- ⅓ cup fresh lemon juice
- Grated rind of 1 lemon

ABOUT TWO DAYS BEFORE THE PARTY, pour the evaporated milk into an ice-cube tray and chill until crystals start to form around the sides. Whip until thick. Or whip the heavy cream.

Mix the egg yolks with ½ cup of the sugar, the lemon juice and rind. Beat until light and foamy. Beat the egg whites stiff, add ¼ cup sugar and beat again until of meringue consistency. Fold into the egg-yolk mixture. Add the whipped evaporated milk or cream. Pour into an ice-cube tray and freeze for 6 to 8 hours. When frozen, cover the *granité* with foil to keep it from drying on the surface.

To serve, cut into 2-inch sections. Let each guest help himself to Strawberry Sauce.

STRAWBERRY SAUCE

- 1 box (10 ounces) frozen strawberries
- ¼ cup port wine
- 2 tablespoons cornstarch
- Grated rind and juice of 1 orange

THE DAY BEFORE, thaw the frozen berries. Place in a saucepan with the wine. Mix the cornstarch with the orange juice and grated rind. Add to the strawberries and stir over medium heat until creamy and transparent. Pour into a dish, cover and refrigerate until ready to serve.

Buffet supper for an evening party
(for 6 or more)

There are occasions when you want to celebrate a family anniversary, a business success or some other special event. Many friends may be invited, some from long distances. Usually the early birds arrive soon after the conventional dinner hour, but others will still be coming as late as nine-thirty or ten. Have drink ingredients arranged in a central place. The host can make a first drink for everyone, and after that guests can make their own. This way no one is trapped as bartender for a whole evening. For snacks with drinks, have one-mouthful tidbits, which guests can eat without any utensils. Good examples are roasted nuts (not too salty), tiny cubes of cheese, small flavorful crackers, pretzel sticks, small squares of firm vegetables—green peppers, celery, carrots. Provide paper napkins.

At 11 P.M., or later if it suits your crowd, after everyone has arrived and before anyone thinks of leaving, serve a simple buffet supper. Have only a single delicious main dish and a beautiful dessert and coffee. All the following recipes are for 6 servings. If you have more guests, double or triple all the ingredients, but remember it is easier to handle two or three ordinary-size casseroles than one huge container.

For a summer buffet on such an occasion, you might serve Chicken Salad or cold Baked Ham (see the Index for these). Have lots of good bread instead of the noodles, and serve the same beautiful dessert made with fresh peaches.

French Beef Daube (p. 312)

Noodles Mitzi

Salad of Mixed Greens with French Dressing (p. 208)

Crème Caramel Renversée aux Pêches (p. 258)

Coffee

Noodles Mitzi

1 pound medium noodles
Salt
6 tablespoons butter
1 cup cottage cheese
Black pepper (½ to 1 teaspoon)

Cook the noodles in salted boiling water until tender but not mushy. Drain in a large colander. Return to the pot and at once stir in the butter until it is melted. Add the cheese and stir until everything is well mixed. Sprinkle with black pepper; this tastes best with a lot of pepper. Makes 6 servings.

July buffet *(for 6)*

This makes a good meal for Independence Day, a reminder of the New England tradition of serving salmon and green peas for the Fourth of July. Everything can be prepared in advance.

Dewey Vodka

Wine-Poached Salmon Steaks in Aspic (p. 669)

Bulgur Salad (p. 469)

Marinated Vegetables

Fresh Cherries

Lemon Pound Cake (p. 505)

Dewey vodka

- 1 small honeydew or Spanish melon
- 1 cup apple juice
- ¼ to ½ cup sugar
- 1 cup vodka
- 6 sprigs of fresh mint
- 2 cups crushed ice

Scoop the flesh from the melon and mash to a pulp. Measure 2 cupfuls. In a saucepan put the mashed melon, apple juice and sugar (for a sweeter drink, use ½ cup sugar). Bring to a boil, then simmer for 5 minutes, stirring frequently. Pour into a dish, cover and refrigerate until ready to serve.

Place the melon syrup in a blender container with the vodka, mint leaves and crushed ice. Cover and blend at high speed for 40 seconds. Serve in tall flute champagne glasses or dainty sherry glasses. The mixture will be like a soft sherbet, very easy to drink or sip through a straw. Makes about 4 cups, 6 to 8 aperitif servings.

Marinated vegetables

- 2 whole celery stalks
- 2 pounds fresh green snap beans
- 1 cauliflower (about 1½ pounds)
- 1 quart cherry tomatoes
- 2 cups water
- 2 cups dry white wine
- ½ cup salad oil
- 2 garlic cloves, whole
- 1 teaspoon salt
- 5 peppercorns, crushed

Trim the celery stalks to 6-inch lengths (save the rest for other uses). Cut each stalk into quarters. Trim ends from the beans and wash them, but leave them whole. Break cauliflower into flowerets, sprinkle with salt and cover with water (to dislodge any tiny insects). Wash tomatoes and remove any stems.

Put water, wine and oil in a large saucepan. Add the garlic cloves (each pierced with a wooden toothpick), salt and peppercorns. Bring to a boil and simmer for about 5 minutes. In the same pan, simmer the celery, beans and drained cauliflower, *cooking only one vegetable at a time,* until each is just tender but not mushy. Allow 10 to 12 minutes for celery, about 10 minutes for beans and about 5 minutes for cauliflower. Let the vegetables and the cooking liquid cool; then refrigerate overnight with the liquid poured over them. Discard the garlic.

To serve, drain the vegetables and arrange them in separate piles on a large serving dish. Place the cherry tomatoes around, and spoon just a little of the marinade over the other vegetables. These taste best at room temperature, a great advantage for buffet service. Makes 8 generous servings.

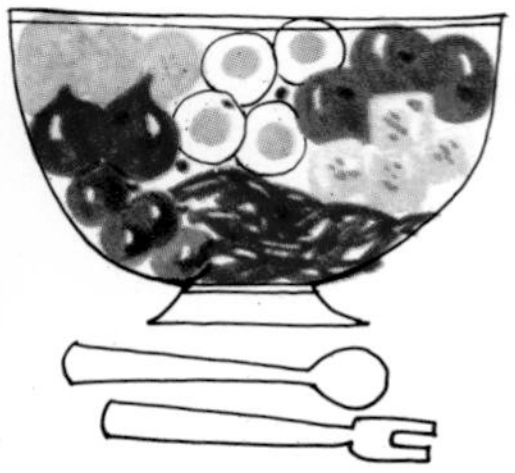

If these particular vegetables are not plentiful in your market, use others. Any vegetable can be prepared this way; just try to select a combination with color and texture contrast. Other herbs can be added to the marinade, such as fennel seeds, bay leaf, thyme and basil.

Another summer buffet

For a more splendid buffet, serve a whole fish, such as striped bass in aspic, or jellied fish molds; see Chapter 14, Cold Cookery, for these. 0━ Remember, aspic will melt when it gets too hot. These dishes will be fine for a normal summer day, but if you are having a heat wave and the temperature goes over 90° F., change the menu. Cold sliced chicken, ham or tongue are good substitutes.

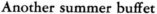

Buffet *(for 6)*

Here is another good summertime menu for a buffet dinner. You can cook the *rumaki* on your outdoor grill if you like.

Summer Orange Aperitif (p. 674)

Rumaki (p. 465)

Leg of Veal Italiano (p. 277)

Spinach and Cucumber Salad (p. 444)

Meringue Pie with Lemon Filling (p. 252)

OUTDOOR PARTIES

Comfort and originality are important factors in the success of an outdoor party. Being in the open always adds to the general spirit of relaxation, but for people to be comfortable everyone should have something to sit on. Make sure you have enough benches and chairs or cushions, and make some arrangement as a substitute for the conventional table. Part of the charm of an outdoor party lies in the setting and visual appeal, so decorations should be natural. Use inexpensive pottery or wooden utensils, and decorate with leaves or flowers. There should be only a few courses at an outdoor meal, because offering too many different dishes makes service and cleanup difficult. As for any other party, try to have most of the food ready to be served and set on platters before the guests arrive.

Here is one way to handle an outdoor meal: have colorful trays, one for each guest, set with plates, cutlery and glasses. When it is time to serve, place the main course on each tray in the kitchen and ask the guests to come in to pick up their trays. Once the food has been eaten, clear away the trays. Then dessert, cheese and coffee can be brought out to a table set with the necessary plates and cutlery.

If you are serving a cold soup as a first course, put the soup in an ice bucket on a tray. This keeps the soup cool to the last drop. Surround the bucket with cups or bowls.

Another easy way is to arrange everything on a picnic table and cover the dishes with net umbrellas or plastic wrap until you are ready to cook or serve. This works well when you are having a barbecue in your own backyard.

Barbecues are good for the dinner hour, but picnics are great fun for lunchtime. All kinds of convenience foods can be used, and many things can be prepared ahead of time and kept well wrapped and ready to go. If you own a freezer you can do a large part of your cooking days or even months ahead. Portable ice chests or insulated containers will hold perishable foods and keep drinks ice cold or piping hot. Plastic plates, tumblers and food boxes are very helpful.

Simple picnic *(for 8)*

Stuffed Eggs (p. 223)

Ham Loaf

Marinated Red Onions

Whole-Wheat Potato Bread (p. 483)

Blueberries à la Canadienne

Pink Lemonade (for children)

Sangria Maison (for adults—p. 674)

Ham loaf

- 1½ pounds lean uncooked ham
- 1½ pounds fresh shoulder of pork
- 2 eggs
- 1 cup milk
- 1 cup fine dry bread crumbs
- ¼ cup minced parsley
- ½ cup light brown sugar
- 2 teaspoons prepared mustard

Ask your butcher to grind the meats together. If you cannot have him do this, put the meats through your food grinder twice. Preheat oven to 325° F.

Add the eggs, milk, bread crumbs and parsley to the meat. Mix together, preferably with your hands, until thoroughly blended. Place in a large meat-loaf pan. Spread half of the brown sugar on top of the meat. Then spread the mustard on the brown sugar and cover with the remaining sugar. Bake for 1¾ hours, basting 3 or 4 times with the pan juices. Makes about 8 servings.

Marinated red onions

- 2 large sweet red onions
- 3 tablespoons cider or wine vinegar
- 3 tablespoons water
- ½ teaspoon salt
- ⅛ teaspoon pepper
- 1 teaspoon sugar

Peel and slice the onions. Place in a jar with a screw

top and add the other ingredients. Keep refrigerated. Shake occasionally. Delicious with ham loaf and bread. These will keep for 3 to 4 weeks.

Blueberries à la canadienne

Clean fresh blueberries the day before the picnic and put them in a plastic bowl. Keep refrigerated until ready to pack the picnic. Bring along maple syrup and rich country cream, or purchase ice cream on the way. For 8 servings, you will need about 2 quarts of berries.

Pink lemonade

2 cups fresh lemon juice
4 teaspoons grated lemon rind
1 cup sugar
½ cup raspberry vinegar or grenadine syrup

Combine all the ingredients in a glass jar or a large vacuum bottle. Cover and shake until the sugar is dissolved. Keep in the refrigerator.

To serve, allow ¼ cup of this syrup for each glass. Add ice cubes and fill with plain water or sparkling water. Makes about 12 drinks.

Summer backyard barbecue *(for 6)*

Tapénade de Nice

[*Champagne or Sparkling Rosé, Chilled*]

Bourbon Steak (p. 293)

Potatoes in Foil, Roasted on the Grill

Beet Salad (p. 425)

Dipped Ice-Cream Cones

Tapénade de Nice

1 slice of dry bread
1 garlic clove, peeled
3 tablespoons red-wine vinegar
¼ pound pine nuts
3 tablespoons capers
4 anchovy fillets
2 hard-cooked egg yolks
12 black olives, pitted
¼ cup minced parsley
1 cup olive oil
Salt and pepper
1 cucumber
1 green pepper
2 carrots
1 can (16 ounces) water-packed artichoke hearts
6 hard-cooked whole eggs

Remove the crust from the bread. Cut the garlic into halves and rub both sides of the bread with the garlic pieces. Break up the bread in a bowl and pour the vinegar on top. Work bread and vinegar with your fingers until mushy.

From this point on, you can use a blender or put the ingredients through a food chopper. In the blender place the bread mixture, pine nuts, capers, anchovy fillets, hard-cooked egg yolks, black olives, parsley and garlic pieces. Add ½ cup of the olive oil. Blend until creamy. Gradually add the balance of the olive oil. When well blended, add salt and pepper to taste. The procedure is the same when using the food chopper; add the oil gradually as the food is chopped.

Pour the mixture into a dish that can be fitted into a bowl filled with ice. The *tapénade* can be prepared 2 or 3 days ahead of time. Keep refrigerated.

Make small sticks of the cucumber, green pepper and carrots. Drain the artichoke hearts and spread on absorbent paper until thoroughly dry. Peel the whole eggs and cut into quarters. Place vegetables and eggs on the ice around the dish of *tapénade* sauce. Makes a dip for 6 or more servings.

Dipped ice-cream cones

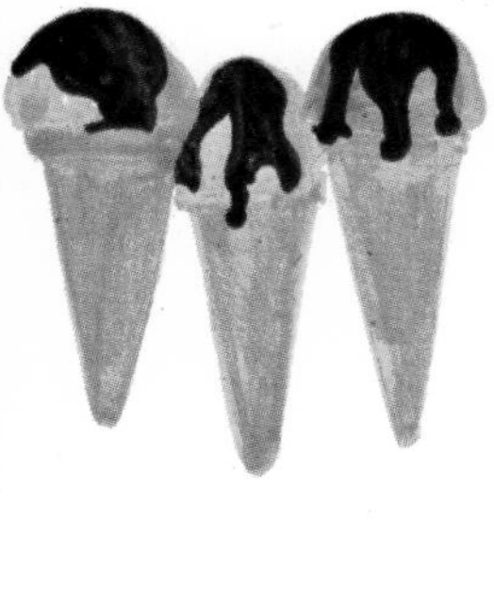

Make scoops of assorted ice-cream flavors and store in the freezer until quite firm. At serving time, arrange the scoops in a cold bowl. Serve cones in a basket. Fill bowls with Chocolate Sauce, Caramel Sauce or Maple Pecan Sauce (pp. 213-215), or use chocolate sprinkles and chopped nuts. Let each guest choose his own ice cream and dip into the sauce of his choice. For 6 servings, you should have 1½ to 2 quarts ice cream; your guests may want to eat more than one of these.

COCKTAIL PARTIES

The cocktail party is a convenient way to entertain a number of people at one time without a great deal of cooking or fussing. Also, it falls at a time between working hours and evening engagements and need not last long. Of course, some cocktail parties for close friends do continue on into the dinner hour; a buffet meal can follow such occasions.

If you plan to have many guests, arrange your furniture to give as much space as possible. Your dining table can be pushed to the wall to serve as a buffet or bar. Do not try to serve every possible kind of drink; a usual arrangement is to have Martinis and Manhattans as well as Scotch and Bourbon, and dry sherry for those who like a milder drink. Some guests may enjoy a glass of Champagne or rosé in place of the usual cocktail. Another good system, especially if you know the tastes of your guests, is to have one mixed drink only—for instance, whiskey sours—and to serve them in a huge brandy snifter or even a punch bowl. While very large parties may seem to call for a professional bartender, it makes a more friendly affair if the host makes the drinks himself. In fact, a party that gets too big can be so crowded and noisy that no one has much fun.

At a small party of eight people or fewer, dips or snacks on toothpicks or skewers can be very good. When more people are invited, it is better to have the kind of food that can be eaten in a single mouthful, that needs no utensil and no unwrapping. Since this is a stand-up party, avoid buttery foods or anything in a sauce.

Small cocktail party *(for 8)*

Beer Cheese (p. 633)

Truffiat Normand

English Muffin Miniatures
with Virginia Peanut
and Salmon or Tuna Spreads

Fresh Pineapple Wedges

With the beer cheese serve small squares of pumpernickel or other dark bread. Cut each standard slice into four squares.

Serve pineapple wedges on plastic toothpicks; they will make a nice contrast to the other foods, all of which are slightly salty.

Truffiat Normand

Pie pastry for 1-crust,
9-inch pie (p. 521)
4 or 5 large, firm potatoes
3 eggs, lightly beaten
4 tablespoons soft butter
1 teaspoon salt
½ teaspoon crumbled
dried savory
Pepper

Line 16 (or more) tiny tart pans or barquette molds with pastry. Refrigerate until ready to use.

Peel the raw potatoes and grate into a bowl of cold water to prevent discoloration. Remove potatoes from the water, drain well and measure; you will need 3 cups of grated potatoes. Add the eggs, butter, salt and savory. Mix well. Sprinkle with pepper to taste. Divide the mixture among the pastry-lined tart pans. Bake in a 350° F. oven for about 25 minutes, or until puffed up and golden brown on top. Serve slightly warm. Makes 16 or more tarts.

This potato pie can be baked in a single 9-inch pan too. In that case, bake for 50 to 60 minutes. A large pie will make 6 to 8 servings.

English muffin miniatures

Make English Muffin dough (p. 489) and cut it into very tiny rounds. Bake on a heated griddle. At this point, you can freeze the muffins.

Let the muffins defrost in the refrigerator overnight. Split them and put them on a baking sheet. Slide under the broiler and let them toast, but watch because they will brown quickly. Then sandwich the halves together with one of the fillings described below. Serve warm or at room temperature.

VIRGINIA PEANUT SANDWICH SPREAD

- 1 cup deviled ham
- 1 cup shelled fresh-roasted peanuts, chopped or ground
- ½ cup chopped apple
- ½ cup mayonnaise
- 1 ounce applejack

Mix ham, peanuts and apple; chop the apple just before using so it does not discolor or dry out. Stir in mayonnaise and at the last minute add the applejack. Makes about 3 cups of spread.

SALMON OR TUNA SANDWICH SPREAD

- 1 pound canned salmon or tuna
- Juice and grated rind of 1 lemon
- ½ cup chutney, minced
- 1 to 1½ teaspoons curry powder
- 3 green onions, minced
- ¼ cup minced parsley

Drain the canned fish and remove skin and bones. Mash the fish and add the other ingredients. Mix thoroughly. Makes about 3 cups of spread.

Large cocktail party *(for 24)*

Dry-Roasted Nuts

Cheese and Chili Tarts (p. 634)

Celery with Brittany Filling

Chicken or Turkey Sandwiches

Watercress Sandwiches (p. 443)

Mushrooms with Smoked Salmon

You will need stamina to prepare for a party like this without help. If you do not have any assistance, ask one or more guests to lend a hand.

The only hot dish is the cheese and chili tarts; make a double recipe of these so each person can have two. Either serve these on trays or have them ready on the table for guests to serve themselves. Serve lots of dry-roasted nuts; they are popular and will keep well—if you do not eat them all.

Celery with Brittany filling

2 celery stalks
2 cans (4 ounces each) skinless, boneless sardines
Juice of 1 lemon
6 hard-cooked eggs, finely chopped
1½ teaspoons curry powder
2 tablespoons soft butter

Separate the celery stalks into ribs, wash them and cut into 1-inch pieces. Drain the sardines thoroughly and mash them. Mix in the chopped eggs, lemon juice, curry powder and butter. Blend to a smooth spread. Shortly before serving time, spread about 1 teaspoon of the filling in each celery piece. Makes about 4 cups of filling.

Chicken or turkey sandwiches

Cut a loaf of white bread and a loaf of whole-wheat bread into thin slices. Use one slice of each for a sandwich. Spread half of the slices with a very thin layer of soft butter, the other half with a very thin layer of mayonnaise. Place thin slices of poached chicken or turkey on one piece of bread. Season with salt and pepper and add the second piece. Cut each sandwich into four tiny squares or finger-length pieces. A standard loaf will give you 40 tiny sandwiches or more.

Mushrooms with smoked salmon

50 small mushrooms (about 1½ pounds)
Salt
½ pound smoked salmon
2 tablespoons minced onion
¼ cup capers plus 2 tablespoons caper vinegar
2 tablespoons mayonnaise
2 tablespoons sour cream

Wipe mushrooms with a damp paper towel; do not peel. Remove all the stems (save to use for something else). Poach the mushrooms in salted water for about 2 minutes; they must still be firm.

Cut salmon into small pieces. Using the other ingredients as liquid, purée the salmon in an electric blender, or put it through a food grinder with onion and capers. Mix everything together. Add a little more mayonnaise or sour cream if necessary to make the texture smooth, or more caper vinegar if needed to make the taste piquant.

Spoon a little of the salmon mixture in each mushroom cap. Place caps in a single layer on a plate and chill until serving time. If you wish, you can double this recipe; these are devoured very quickly.

SPECIAL OCCASIONS

Certain days are so special that we look forward to them for months ahead; other special days are surprises and come upon us without warning. For the hostess, the expected days mean a lot of work, but planning helps to make the work much easier. If you are an old hand at planning, the surprise days will not be too hard either. Here are some suggestions.

Engagement party, teatime *(for 20)*

Stuffed Hot Biscuits

Apple Muffins (p. 498)

Nut Bread, Buttered (p. 494)

Chicken-Salad Puffs

Apricot Delight

Decorate your table prettily for this kind of party. Have a beautiful centerpiece. Put the tea service at one end of the table; if you are serving coffee as well, place the coffee service at the other end. Ask very close friends to pour tea and coffee. Let the guests help themselves to all the other foods. It will make things much easier if you use two sets of serving dishes, one on each side of the table. Make two recipes of the apricot dessert for 20 servings.

If you wish to serve an engagement cake, bring it on with a flourish. It will give the cake and the occasion extra drama. It can be set on a small table or tea wagon in a different room until time to serve it. Be sure to have the bride-to-be cut the cake. It is good practice for her wedding day.

Stuffed hot biscuits

Bake as many 1½-inch tea biscuits as you think you will need, using your favorite recipe or a ready mix. The following filling will be good for 24 biscuits.

Finely chop 1 cup walnuts and ½ cup candied orange peel. Moisten with honey and blend with ½ cup creamed butter. Split the biscuits and fill with a bit of this mixture. Wrap biscuits and place in the freezer 8 to 10 days ahead of time.

To serve, heat the frozen biscuits on a cookie sheet in a preheated 400° F. oven for 8 to 10 minutes.

Nut bread, buttered

Make nut bread in advance and freeze it. Take it from the freezer 24 hours before using. Slice thin and spread with a mixture of half butter and half cream cheese. Set on a silver tray and garnish with watercress.

Chicken-salad puffs

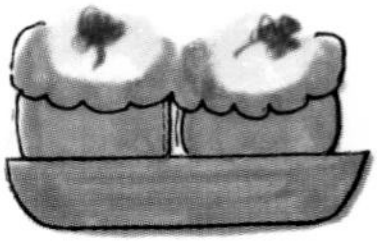

3 cups poached chicken
1 cup finely diced celery
¼ cup capers
4 hard-cooked eggs, finely chopped
1 teaspoon salt
½ teaspoon crumbled dried basil
3 green onions, minced
¼ cup minced fresh parsley
½ cup mayonnaise
3 tablespoons salad oil
Juice of 1 lemon
40 tiny cream-puff shells

Use the recipe for Poached Chicken for Salad (p. 361); it will provide you with plenty for this recipe. Cut the chicken into small pieces. Add celery, capers, eggs, salt, basil, green onions and parsley. Mix in mayonnaise, salad oil and lemon juice. Blend together thoroughly.

Buy the baked cream-puff shells, or make them from a mix. Cut the shells in half and fill with the chicken-salad mixture.

Apricot delight

- 2/3 cup butter
- 2 cups confectioners' sugar
- 4 egg yolks
- 1 1/2 cups mashed, well-drained canned apricots
- 2 cups crushed vanilla wafers
- 1 teaspoon almond extract
- 2 teaspoons vanilla extract
- 1 envelope unflavored gelatin
- 1/4 cup orange juice
- 2 cups heavy cream
- Ladyfingers
- Whipped cream

Cream butter and sugar. When light, add the egg yolks; beat again until creamy. Stir in the apricots, crushed wafers, almond and vanilla extracts. Cook over low heat, stirring until smooth and creamy. Do not boil, for boiling would make it curdle.

Soak the gelatin in the orange juice for 5 minutes. Add to the hot mixture and stir until dissolved. Cool.

Whip the cream and fold into the cooled apricot mixture; be sure it is well mixed. Line a 9-inch spring-form pan with ladyfingers. Make a neat pattern on the bottom of the pan by cutting some ladyfingers into halves. Pour the apricot mixture into the pan. Let stand in the refrigerator for 24 to 48 hours before unmolding. Unmold and serve with a bowl of sweetened whipped cream. Makes about 10 servings.

Baby shower

A baby shower is usually an affair strictly for women. Keep the decorations simple, mostly white and pastel shades. When all the guests have arrived, bring out a tray of your best glasses with a decanter of cooled sherry. Toast the new mother, then present the gifts and serve a simple snack.

Sandwiches in a Circle

Marinated Mushroom Canapés

Bee's Kiss Torte or *Deluxe Charlotte Russe*

Coffee

Sandwiches in a circle

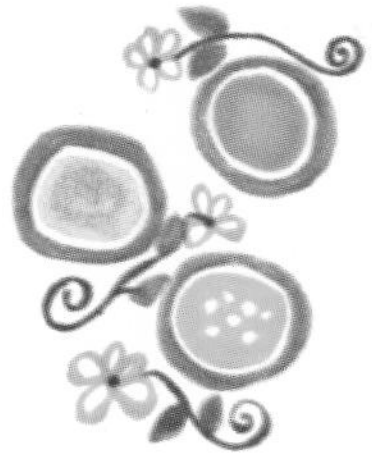

Cut off both ends of crusty rolls. Pull out the insides until you have a hole large enough to fill. Stuff to capacity with your choice of one of the fillings described below. When the rolls are filled, wrap each one in foil or plastic wrap and chill in the refrigerator for 12 hours.

To serve, slice the rolls with a sharp knife into thin round pieces. This way you get crust all around with filling in the center. Each of these recipes will make about 1½ cups of filling. This will be enough to fill 3 large rolls.

Egg filling
Combine 5 chopped or grated hard-cooked eggs, 1 tablespoon minced celery, 2 minced green onions, ¼ cup minced fresh parsley, ¼ teaspoon curry powder, 3 to 4 tablespoons mayonnaise, 1 tablespoon soft butter, and salt and pepper to taste.

Ham filling
Combine ½ pound ground cooked ham and 1 can (2¼ ounces) deviled ham, 1 teaspoon horseradish mustard, 3 tablespoons soft cream cheese or grated mild Cheddar, 1 to 2 tablespoons mayonnaise, and salt to taste.

Cream-cheese filling
Combine 4 ounces soft cream cheese with 2 tablespoons soft butter, 1 tablespoon light cream or top milk, ½ cup minced walnuts or pecans, ¼ cup minced fresh parsley, and salt and pepper to taste.

Lobster or crab filling
Combine 1 cup shredded lobster or crab meat with ¼ cup minced celery, ½ teaspoon minced onion, 1 tablespoon capers, 2 teaspoons fresh lemon juice, enough mayonnaise to hold the mixture together and salt and pepper to taste.

Marinated mushroom canapés

Finely chop ½ pound mushrooms, stems and caps. Add 4 tablespoons olive oil, 2 tablespoons cider vinegar or white wine, ½ teaspoon salt, ⅛ teaspoon pepper and 2 minced green onions. Mix together and let stand for 1 hour before using. Spread on thin rounds of French bread or toast. Makes about 1½ cups of canapé spread.

Bee's kiss torte

1 1/4 cups butter
1/3 cup superfine sugar
1 egg
5 teaspoons vanilla extract
1/2 teaspoon almond extract
2 cups cake flour
2 teaspoons baking powder
1/2 teaspoon salt
5 tablespoons milk
3/4 cup granulated sugar
1/2 cup slivered blanched almonds
1 cup plus 3 tablespoons light cream
3 tablespoons cornstarch

CAKE

Cream together until light 1/4 cup of the butter, the superfine sugar, the egg, 1 teaspoon of the vanilla extract and the almond extract. Sift together flour, baking powder and salt. Blend in the creamed mixture alternately with 3 tablespoons of the milk. This batter has the texture of a hot bread batter.

Generously butter two 6-inch round cake pans. Divide batter between them. Use cake pans with a swivel bar on the bottom that can be turned to loosen the cake. Pat the batter in the pans as evenly as you can.

TOPPING

Melt 1/2 cup of the butter in a saucepan. Add 1/2 cup of the granulated sugar, the almonds, 2 teaspoons of the vanilla extract and remaining 2 tablespoons milk. Stir over low heat until the sugar is dissolved and the mixture is thick and lumpy. Be sure to stir constantly. Divide into two equal portions and spread over the tops of the two uncooked cakes. Bake the cakes in a preheated 400° F. oven for 30 minutes. Unmold and cool on a wire rack.

CREAM FILLING

Bring 1 cup of the cream and remaining 1/4 cup of granulated sugar to a boil. Blend cornstarch and remaining 3 tablespoons of cream. Stir cornstarch mixture into the boiling cream and sugar until the mixture is very thick and transparent. Cover and refrigerate until quite cold.

Beat remaining 1/2 cup softened butter with remaining 2 tablespoons vanilla extract until creamy. Add the cold cornstarch-cream mixture and beat with an electric mixer until light and fluffy. Spread it on one cake. Place the second cake on top and serve. Makes 6 to 8 small servings.

Deluxe charlotte russe

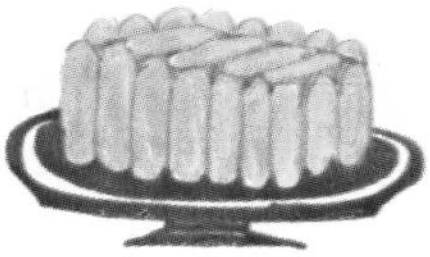

2 tablespoons unflavored gelatin
¼ cup cold water
2 cups milk, scalded
½ cup sugar
4 eggs, separated
½ teaspoon rosewater *or* 1 teaspoon vanilla extract
Salt
2 cups heavy cream
Ladyfingers

Soak the gelatin in the cold water for 5 minutes. Add the hot milk and stir until gelatin is dissolved. Add sugar and stir until dissolved. Beat egg yolks, add a few spoonfuls of the hot milk mixture, stir and pour into the rest of the hot milk. Cook over medium heat, stirring all the time, until the mixture coats the spoon. Add rosewater (obtained from your druggist) or vanilla extract. Remove from heat and cool.

Beat the egg whites with a pinch of salt until stiff. Fold into the cooled custard. Whip the heavy cream until stiff and fold into the custard also. Line 12 individual molds or 1 large mold with ladyfingers. Pour the custard into the molds. Refrigerate for 12 to 14 hours. Makes 12 servings.

Dessert and coffee for an afternoon committee meeting *(for 8 to 10)*

Lemon Snow Eggs

or

Burnt-Sugar Rice Pudding

Coffee

Lemon snow eggs

4 eggs, separated
Grated rind of 1 lemon
2 tablespoons plus ½ cup sugar
2 tablespoons plus 3 cups milk
Piece of lemon peel

Beat the separated egg whites stiff. Add the grated lemon rind and the 2 tablespoons sugar. Whip until the sugar is well blended. Beat the yolks into the 2 tablespoons cold milk; set yolks aside until later. Bring remaining 3 cups milk to a boil and add remaining ½ cup sugar and a small piece of lemon peel. Drop spoonfuls of the beaten egg whites into this hot milk, being careful not to let one dollop touch another. Poach for 1 minute, then turn over carefully and poach for another minute. Do not let the milk boil. As each "snow egg" is done, lift it out with a perforated spoon and set it on an oval platter.

When all the "snow eggs" are cooked, remove the milk from the heat and stir in the beaten egg yolks until the mixture is slightly thickened. If necessary, put this mixture over heat again to thicken the custard, but do not boil. Remove lemon peel and pour custard over the "snow eggs." Refrigerate until ready to serve. The number of "snow eggs" you make depends on the size of the eggs. If you shape them into ovals with two standard tablespoons, you will have about 10 "eggs."

Burnt-sugar rice pudding

- 3 cups milk
- 1 cup seedless raisins
- 1¼ cups cooked white rice
- ¼ teaspoon salt
- ¼ teaspoon grated nutmeg
- 1 teaspoon grated lemon rind
- 1 teaspoon almond extract
- 3 eggs
- 6 tablespoons plus 1 cup brown sugar
- 2 or more tablespoons shredded almonds

Bring the milk, raisins and cooked rice to a boil. As soon as the mixture reaches the boil, take it off the heat. Add salt, nutmeg, lemon rind and almond extract. Beat the eggs lightly with the 6 tablespoons of brown sugar. Add to the rice mixture, stirring constantly. Pour into a buttered 6-cup baking dish; it will be filled to the top. Set the dish in a pan filled with 1 inch of hot water and bake in a preheated 350° F. oven for 1 hour. Cool. Then refrigerate until completely cold.

Sprinkle remaining 1 cup brown sugar and the shredded almonds on top of the chilled pudding. Put it under the broiler to caramelize; it takes only 1 or 2 minutes to brown. Chill again before serving.

This dessert is especially good served with a bowl of rich cream sweetened lightly with maple syrup and flavored with a tablespoon or two of rum. Makes about 12 servings.

HOLIDAYS

Although there are many local traditions for holiday feasts, the usual menus provide turkey for Thanksgiving, roast beef for Christmas and baked ham for Easter. There is no reason for sticking to these customary dishes if other foods are available in your area. Europeans are fond of goose for Christmas, and Mediterranean people think of lamb as the proper dish for Easter. Instead of the famous Thanksgiving bird, a capon or duck or large chicken might be more sensible if you have a small family.

New Year's Day visits used to be an American tradition. If you still like to carry on this custom, the year will come when it is your turn to be "at home." An elaborate buffet or a simple refreshment may be your solution. Either one of these can be a party to remember.

Thanksgiving dinner *(for 10)*

Fresh Fruit Cup with Sherbet

Roasted Turkey with Potato Stuffing (p. 340)

[Sparkling Burgundy]

Cranberry Sauce Special

Turnip Ring with Green Peas

White Onions with Cream and Wine Sauce

Watercress

Pumpkin Pie *Maple-Syrup Pie*

Coffee

Fresh fruit cup with sherbet

- 2 pink grapefruits
- 3 large apples
- 3 large pears
- 1 pound red grapes
- 1 pound seedless green grapes
- 4 ounces light rum
- 1 quart orange sherbet

Section the grapefruits, discarding all the membranes but retaining all the juice. Put juice and fruit in a large bowl. Peel apples and pears and cut into cubes; drop the pieces at once into the grapefruit—the citrus juice will keep them from browning. Wash, stem and halve the red grapes and discard the pits. Wash and stem the green grapes and cut them into halves. Mix all the fruits together. You can do all this the day before.

Before serving, stir in the rum and divide the fruits and some of the juices among the dishes (use short-stemmed glass dessert dishes if possible). Put a scoop of sherbet in each dish. Makes 10 servings, or more.

Cranberry sauce special

1½ pounds fresh cranberries
3 cups bottled cranberry juice
1½ cups red-currant jam or jelly
1½ cups sugar

Wash and pick over cranberries and place in a saucepan. Add remaining ingredients and bring to a boil. Then simmer for about 20 minutes. Turn into a dish, or two dishes, and refrigerate until ready to serve. Or pour into fancy molds brushed with peanut oil. The sauce will turn into a jelly and unmold beautifully when cold. Makes 10 to 12 servings.

Turnip ring with green peas

2 large turnips (1½ to 2 pounds each)
1 teaspoon sugar
½ teaspoon ground sage
4 slices of unpeeled lemon
2 cups applesauce
6 tablespoons butter
Salt
4 pounds green peas *or* 4 packages (10 ounces each) frozen peas, cooked

Peel the turnips and cut into thin slices; do this just before you are ready to cook. Place in a saucepan with the sugar, sage and lemon slices; cover with boiling water and boil for 15 minutes. Drain; remove lemon.

Place the turnip in a bowl and beat with an electric mixer at medium speed until mashed. (Mash by hand if you do not have a mixer.) Add the applesauce and butter, then salt to taste. Form into a ring on a hot vegetable dish. Fill the center with buttered hot green peas. Makes 10 servings.

White onions with cream and wine sauce

3 pounds white onions
Salt
4 tablespoons butter
5 tablespoons flour
1 cup white wine
1 cup light cream
1 teaspoon grated mace
White pepper

Drop the onions into boiling water for 1 minute. Drain, then peel as soon as they are cool enough to handle. Cover them with cold water with 1 teaspoon salt added. Simmer gently until tender. Do not let them boil or they will break apart. You can do all this the day before.

Make a roux with butter and flour. Add the wine and cream. Cook and stir over low heat until the sauce is thick (the juice in the onions will thin it). Season with the mace, white pepper to taste, and more salt if you like. Add the onions and gently heat until ready to serve. It is usually better to serve a sauced vegetable like this in separate dishes. Makes 10 servings or more.

Pumpkin pie

- 2 eggs
- 2 cups mashed cooked pumpkin or winter squash
- ½ cup granulated sugar
- ¼ teaspoon salt
- 1½ cups milk
- ¼ teaspoon ground ginger
- ¼ teaspoon grated nutmeg
- 1½ teaspoons ground cinnamon
- ¼ cup molasses
- 2 tablespoons melted butter
- Pie pastry for 1-crust 9-inch pie (p. 521)

Beat the eggs. Add all remaining ingredients except the pastry and mix thoroughly. Line a 9-inch pie plate with the pastry and crimp or flute the edges. Pour in as much of the pumpkin custard as the pie plate will hold. Do not cover the pie. Bake in a preheated 375° F. oven for 1 hour.

If you have custard left over, pour it into custard cups. Bake for 40 to 50 minutes.

Cool pie and any custards. Serve topped with unsweetened whipped cream or with ice cream. The 9-inch pie will make 6 to 8 servings.

Maple-syrup pie

- Pie pastry for 2-crust 8-inch pie (p. 522)
- 1 cup pure maple syrup
- ½ cup water
- 3 tablespoons cornstarch
- 2 tablespoons cold water
- ¼ cup chopped walnuts
- 1 tablespoon butter

Line an 8-inch pie plate with half of the pastry. Roll out the rest into a round large enough to cover the pie.

Boil the maple syrup and water together for 5 minutes. Thicken with the cornstarch mixed with 2 tablespoons cold water. When creamy and clear, add the chopped nuts and butter. Pour into the pastry-lined pie plate and top with the second round of pastry. Bake in a preheated 450° F. oven for 30 minutes, or until the crust is golden brown. Makes 6 servings.

Trimming the tree, Christmas Eve

Spiced Hot Red Wine (p. 673)

Cheese and Nuts

Celery and Carrot Sticks, Cherry Tomatoes,
Slivers of Green Peppers

Seafood Ramekins (p. 402)

French Bread (p. 479)

Oatmeal Fruit Cookies (p. 513)

Coffee

For an informal Christmas Eve gathering, serve the hot wine rather than stronger drinks because you want everyone alert enough to trim the tree. Cheese and nuts and the vegetable sticks will sustain your guests as they work, and afterward everyone can sit down to enjoy seafood ramekins, French bread, cookies and coffee.

Christmas dinner *(for 8)*

Chicken Consommé (p. 175)

Cheese Straws

[*Dry Sherry*]

Goose with Gooseberries (p. 343)

[*Châteauneuf-du-Pape*]

Wild Rice (p. 468)

Party Squash (p. 640)

Chicory and Cherry Tomatoes with English Dressing
(p. 209)

Currant Sponge Pudding

Black Coffee

Cheese straws

Baking-Powder Pastry (p. 524)
2 cups grated Cheddar cheese
1 cup grated Parmesan cheese
Paprika

Roll out the pastry into an oblong ¼ inch thick. Sprinkle generously with the mixed grated cheeses, then dust with paprika. Press the cheese into the dough. Fold the dough into thirds and press down firmly. Roll again into an oblong. With a pastry wheel or a knife, cut strips measuring 1 by 5 inches; or make shorter pieces if you prefer. Twist each strip gently 2 or 3 times. Place on a baking sheet. Press the ends of the twists down firmly to make them secure. Bake in a preheated 425° F. oven for about 10 minutes. Makes 4 dozen or more.

Currant sponge pudding

6 tablespoons sugar
¾ teaspoon salt
¾ cup all-purpose flour
¾ cup cold milk
3 cups hot milk
6 tablespoons unsalted butter
1½ teaspoons orange-flower water or vanilla extract
6 eggs, separated
1 cup black-currant jelly
Grated rind of 2 oranges
6 tablespoons brandy

Put the sugar, salt and flour in a bowl and blend in the cold milk. Pour and stir into the hot milk. Stir over low heat until creamy and smooth. Add the butter and orange-flower water or vanilla. Beat the egg yolks lightly, then beat them into the pudding mixture with a whisk until well blended. Beat the egg whites until stiff and fold into the mixture. Pour the pudding mixture into a shallow 2-quart baking dish that is attractive enough to bring to the table, and set the dish in a pan filled with 1 inch of hot water. Bake the pudding in a preheated 400° F. oven for 30 to 35 minutes or until the pudding is set.

CURRANT SAUCE: whip the current jelly with a whisk until soft, then add the orange rind and brandy. Mix. Pour a few spoonfuls of currant sauce on top of the pudding just before serving. Serve the rest of the sauce in a bowl; there will be about 1½ cups sauce. Makes about 8 servings.

Another Christmas dinner menu

Recipes for all these dishes can be found in the index.

Watercress Soup
Roast Beef with Yorkshire Pudding
[Red Bordeaux]
Baked Potatoes
Celery Amandine in Casserole
Simone's Crêpes
Coffee
[Brandy]

New Year's Day at home *(for 20)*

Jersey Nog (p. 255)
Deviled Almonds and Walnuts (p. 640)
Cheese with Port (p. 668)
Melba Toast Rounds
Old-Fashioned Pound Cake Ring
French Colonial Fruitcake
Whole Strawberries with Confectioners' Sugar

Make a double recipe of the eggnog if your guests like it; or have sherry, brandy or applejack to serve straight. Make 3 or 4 times the recipe for the deviled nuts. Roll small balls of the cheese in paprika and serve them on a platter surrounded with Melba toast rounds and garnished with watercress. Buy fresh strawberries or use whole berries frozen without sugar. Defrost, pat dry and arrange them in a circle around a mound of sifted confectioners' sugar.

Old-fashioned pound cake ring

3 cups sifted cake flour
2 teaspoons baking powder
Pinch of salt
½ teaspoon ground mace or cinnamon
1 cup soft unsalted butter
1½ cups superfine sugar
3 eggs
½ cup milk
1 teaspoon brandy or vanilla extract
Confectioners' sugar
Red vegetable coloring
Granulated sugar

Sift together 3 times the flour, baking powder, salt, and mace or cinnamon. With the electric mixer set at medium speed, cream together the butter, superfine sugar and eggs until light and fluffy, about 4 minutes. Blend in the sifted flour mixture by hand, alternating with the milk mixed with the brandy or vanilla. Beat after each addition. Pour into a well-greased 2-quart ring mold 11 inches across. Bake in a preheated 350° F. oven for 50 to 60 minutes, or until done. Cool on a wire rack for 10 minutes before unmolding. Loosen with a knife and remove from the pan. Cool.

Dust with confectioners' sugar. Make red sugar by adding a few drops of red vegetable coloring to granulated sugar and rubbing with the back of a spoon until the sugar is colored. Sprinkle the red sugar over the top. Makes about 24 slices.

French colonial fruitcake

- 1 cup butter
- 2½ cups dark brown sugar
- 4 eggs
- 4 cups all-purpose flour
- ½ teaspoon ground ginger
- ½ teaspoon ground allspice
- ½ teaspoon ground cloves
- 1 teaspoon ground cinnamon
- 1 teaspoon grated nutmeg
- 1½ teaspoons salt
- 1 teaspoon baking soda
- 1 cup prune or orange juice
- ⅓ cup brandy
- 1½ cups chopped uncooked dried prunes
- 1½ cups chopped uncooked dried apricots
- 2 cups chopped almonds or walnuts

Make this fruitcake weeks ahead if you wish. Cream the butter and sugar until light and fluffy. Add the eggs and beat until very creamy. Sift together the flour, spices, salt and baking soda. Mix the fruit juice and brandy together. Place the chopped fruits and nuts in a bowl. Sprinkle with ½ cup of the spiced flour. Add the rest of the flour alternately with the liquid to the creamed mixture. Stir well until thoroughly mixed. Add the fruits and nuts and blend in.

CAKE TOPPING

- ¼ cup butter
- 1 cup brown sugar
- 2 tablespoons brandy
- Cooked whole dried prunes and apricots
- Almonds

Melt the butter. Add the sugar and brandy and stir until well mixed. Spread on the bottom of two bread pans or one long loaf pan. Arrange whole prunes and apricots on the sugar mixture and place almonds in between.

Spoon the fruitcake batter on top, taking care not to disturb the arranged fruits. Bake in a 325° F. oven for 2 hours, or until done. Let cool on a wire rack for 20 minutes. Invert and let stand for 10 minutes. Then remove the pan carefully.

This cake will keep well if you keep it wrapped in greased paper or foil and brush it with brandy now and then. Makes 24 slices or more.

New Year reception

For a very elegant reception on New Year's Eve or New Year's Day, when you have help, serve a whole side of smoked salmon or a smoked turkey. You will need someone to carve either as the party goes on. Serve the salmon on plates with a spoonful of minced onion, some capers, a lemon wedge and buttered thin slices of dark rye bread. Serve turkey on plates with a spoonful of preserved mustard fruits and small biscuits. Tiny ham sandwiches are good too.

Easter dinner *(for 8)*

Stuffed Eggs with Caviar

[*Vodka*]

Baked Ham with Honey-Citrus Glaze (p. 282)

[*Rosé Wine*]

Spiced Apricots Escoffier

Whipped Sweet Potatoes (p. 419)

Green Beans with Mushrooms

Cinnamon Orange Savarin (p. 510)

Stuffed eggs with caviar

Obviously one must have Easter eggs for Easter dinner! Hard-cook at least 12 eggs, cool, cut into halves and separate the yolks. Mash yolks with 6 tablespoons mayonnaise and 1 tablespoon prepared mustard. Season with salt and pepper to taste. Stuff the whites, and put a small amount of black or red caviar on each egg half. Serve the eggs in a nest of parsley or watercress sprigs. Vodka is the perfect spirit to drink with caviar.

Spiced apricots Escoffier

2 pounds fresh apricots
½ cup apple juice or water
½ cup brown sugar
⅓ cup cider vinegar
1 cinnamon stick
8 to 10 slices of fresh green gingerroot
¼ teaspoon grated nutmeg
1½ teaspoons whole cloves

Wash apricots and leave whole. Place remaining ingredients except cloves in a saucepan. Boil for 5 to 8 minutes. Add the apricots and simmer over very low heat for 10 minutes. Let the fruit cool in the syrup.

Remove any of the skin that comes off the apricots easily. Stick a clove into each fruit. Cover and chill in the refrigerator.

Serve the apricots in the syrup, strained or not as you prefer, or remove them from the syrup and serve as a garnish. Makes about 4 cups.

Green beans with mushrooms

Trim and wash 2½ pounds fresh green beans. Blanch until tender but still crisp; drain and cool. (You can do this the day before.) Trim and wash 1 pound mushrooms and cut into thick slices. Sauté mushrooms in 2 tablespoons salad oil and 2 tablespoons butter until tender. Add the beans, the juice of 1 lemon, and salt and pepper to taste. Stir gently. Keep over low heat until beans are hot. Makes 8 to 10 servings.

Another Easter dinner

All the recipes for this menu can be found in the index.

Scallop Bisque

Roast Rack of Lamb à la Française

[*Red Bordeaux*]

Bulgur Pilaf with Mushrooms

Broiled Tomatoes with Basil

Spinach and Cucumber Salad

Chocolate Soufflé

Index

A

B

E

F

I

J

K

L

M

R

S

T

U

V

Y

Z

Linear System Theory

The State Space Approach

McGraw-Hill Series in System Science

Editorial Consultants

George Dantzig
William Linvill
Lotfi Zadeh

Zadeh and Desoer Linear System Theory: The State Space Approach

Linear System Theory

The State Space Approach

Lotfi A. Zadeh & Charles A. Desoer

Department of Electrical Engineering
University of California
Berkeley, California

McGraw-Hill Book Company, Inc.

New York / San Francisco / Toronto / London

Linear System Theory: The State Space Approach

 Library of Congress Catalog Card Number 63-14581

72746

To Fay and Claudine

Preface

This book was born out of the authors' conviction that the scientific and technological developments of the last two decades have set the stage for an approach to linear system theory that differs radically from those currently taught in the classroom.

By far the most important of these developments is the advent of large-scale general-purpose digital computers. By providing the means for the analysis and design of highly complex systems, such computers have generated a need for new approaches and concepts bearing on the characterization, identification, and control of systems of various types. Indeed, not long ago an engineer could rely on his intuition, empirical know-how, and a collection of classical analytical and numerical methods for the solution of most of the problems encountered in engineering design and analysis. Today he is frequently called upon to devise a program or an algorithm that in conjunction with a digital computer leads to an optimal configuration for a complex system subjected to a large number of inputs and constraints. It hardly needs arguing that to design a large-scale system in this fashion requires a much greater degree of mathematical sophistication and, more particularly, much more rigorous and extensive training in circuit theory, information theory, control theory, optimization techniques, and computer programming than were necessary in the past.

In addition to its direct impact on system design and analysis, the development of digital computers has stimulated interest in finite-state systems and automata, which in turn has led to many new concepts and techniques centering on the notion of state. Parallel developments in control theory, information processing, and related fields have reawakened interest in the classical phase-space techniques of analysis of systems characterized by first-order vector differential or difference equations. Within the last several years, in particular, the phase-space or, equivalently, state-space approach has come to play a central role in the theories of optimal control of constrained as well as unconstrained systems.

The rapidly growing interest in state-space techniques is reflected in the spirit as well as the choice of subject matter in the book. Instead of following the conventional pattern of starting with the discussion of differential equations and proceeding to the Laplace and Fourier transformations, we introduce the notion of state at the outset and construct a general system-theoretic framework for both linear and nonlinear, nondifferential as well as differential systems. In this way, such notions as object, system, and state equivalence are given precise meaning, and a solid foundation is laid for the state-space approach to linear differential systems which is developed in succeeding chapters.

In order to attain a high level of precision and clarity we have freely used modern mathematical notations and terminology and have stated all significant results and conclusions in the form of theorems, lemmas, or assertions. This should not be construed to imply that the book is addressed to the mathematician. Its mathematical flavor notwithstanding, our exposition is directed primarily at an engineering audience, and it has no pretense at having the level of rigor which prevails in the mathematical literature. Essentially, we assume that the reader is a graduate student or a practicing engineer having the usual background in calculus, complex variable, ordinary differential equations, Laplace and Fourier transformations, and linear circuit theory. Some familiarity with the elements of linear algebra is also taken for granted. For completeness, self-contained expositions of delta functions and distributions, the Fourier and Laplace transformations, and linear vector spaces are included in appendixes.

To aid in the understanding of the subject matter as well as to facilitate the use of the book as a reference, we have numbered and cross-referenced all comments, remarks, assertions, theorems, examples, exercises, etc. The numbering system employed is explained in the Note to the Reader on p. xi.

A fairly good idea of the contents and scope of the book can be obtained by scanning the Contents. However, a few specific comments concerning the subject matter of various chapters may be of help in orienting the reader.

To begin with, the material presented in the first three chapters is essentially an attempt at constructing a conceptual framework for nonlinear as well as linear system theory in which the central notions are those of object, input-ouput relation, input-output-state relation, state, state and system equivalence, state equations, etc. Since much of this material is new, our exposition of it has no claim at definitiveness or completeness. This applies, in particular, to the discussion of such notions as the state space of an interconnection, state and system equivalence in the case of systems whose state space changes with time, input-output-state relations for systems with infinite-dimensional state space, etc.

The material in Chaps. 4 through 11 is concerned in the main with the application of state-space techniques in the analysis of systems characterized by differential equations with time-varying as well as constant coefficients. Since these applications range over a very wide field, we have not attempted to present an exhaustive coverage of them; instead, we have concentrated on a relatively few basic topics which we consider to be of particular relevance to applications of linear system theory. These include the study of modes in time-invariant systems, the association of state vectors and state equations with time-varying systems, the analysis of periodically varying systems, the stability of linear systems, and the notions of controllability and observability.

For convenience of the reader, each chapter includes a list of books under the heading of References and Suggested Reading. These lists are intended to direct the reader to basic sources of information on subjects related to those discussed in the text. To make the book substantially self-contained, compact expositions of the mathematical techniques which are of frequent use in the text are included in the four appendixes which follow Chap. 11.

The reader may want to know how the order of the authors' names was arrived at. The facts are these: one of us (L.A.Z.) wrote the first four chapters and Appendix *B*; the other (C.A.D.) wrote the remaining seven chapters and the other three appendixes. We saw no reason for following the tradition of using the alphabetical order since it puts a perpetual burden on those whose initial happens to be at the end of the alphabet. Therefore, we flipped a fair coin and tails won.

Acknowledgments

The authors thank Glenn Bacon, Jack Wing, and Albert Chang for reading parts of the manuscript and suggesting improvements; and Jocelyn Harleston, LaDelia Gilmore, and Kim Teramoto for typing the manuscript. Finally, the book could not have been written without the generous research support provided by the University of California, the National Science Foundation, and the Department of Defense, in particular the Office of Naval Research, the Office of Scientific Research, and the Army Research Office.

Lotfi A. Zadeh
Charles A. Desoer

Note to the Reader

The following system of numbering and cross-referencing is used in this book: At the top of each page in the outer margin appear chapter and section numbers in boldface italic type; for example, ***3.8*** at the top of a page means that the discussion on that page is part of Chapter *3*, Section *8*. In addition, each item (definition, theorem, example, comment, remark, etc.) is given a number that appears in the left-hand margin; such items are numbered consecutively within each section. Item numbers and all cross references in the text are in italic type. Cross references are of the form "by Definition *5.6.3*"; this means "by the definition which is item *3* of Section *6* in Chapter *5*." Since the four appendixes are labeled *A*, *B*, *C*, and *D*, the reference "*C.17.3*" is to "item *3* in Section *17*, Appendix *C*." When we refer in a section to an item within the same section, only the item number is given; thus "substituting in *7*" means "substituting in Eq. *7* of this section." Also, "*7 et seq.*" means "Eq. *7* and what follows Eq. *7*."

Preceding the index is a glossary of symbols which describes notational conventions and contains brief definitions and references to the principal symbols used in the book. The reader is advised to study this glossary before reading the book. It may be helpful to note a few of the symbols here. The symbol $\triangleq$ stands for "is defined to be" or "represents" or "denotes." For example, F $\triangleq$ force, or F($\triangleq$ force), means "F denotes force." The symbol $\Rightarrow$ stands for "implies." The symbols $\forall$ and $\exists$ mean, respectively, "for all" and "there exists." For example, $\forall t$ means "for all t." The symbol $\triangleleft$ indicates the end of discussion, and the abbreviations R.H.S. and Q.E.D. stand, respectively, for "right-hand side" and "*quod erat demonstrandum.*"

Contents

Chapter 7 Stability of linear differential systems 369

Chapter 8 Impulse response of nondifferential linear systems 393

Chapter 9 Transfer functions and their properties 405

Chapter *10* Discrete-time systems 479

Chapter *11* Controllability and observability 495

Appendix *A* Delta functions and distributions 515

Appendix *B* Laplace transformation and *z* transformation 535

Appendix *C* Vectors and linear transformations 547

Appendix *D* Function of a matrix 593

Language, notation and basic concepts of system theory

1

1 *Introduction*

This is an introductory chapter. As such, it contains few concrete results in the form of theorems, formulae, etc., which abound in the rest of this book. Essentially, the main function of this chapter is to provide a conceptual and notational framework in terms of which the techniques of linear system theory can be presented in a clear and concise fashion.

In the initial stages of our presentation, there will of necessity be some concepts which cannot be defined precisely—indeed, not even explained in completely unequivocal terms. This applies, for example, to the concepts of measurable attribute, physical object, and experimenter. Such concepts, and, in particular, the notion of an "object," constitute the primitive concepts of system theory. In later stages, most of the concepts introduced will be nonprimitive in nature, and they will be defined—though not always in a formal fashion—in terms of the primitive concepts introduced earlier.

In the interest of attaining maximum clarity, we shall not hesitate to depart—whenever it is expedient—from traditional modes of exposition. In particular, we shall frequently interrupt the presentation with comments, notes, remarks, recapitulations, digressions, examples, and exercises. We shall also frequently resort to the pedagogically helpful technique of preceding the formal definition of a term X with an informal explanation whose function is to provide an insight into the significance of X rather than to give X a mathematically precise meaning.

We begin with an informal discussion of the central notion in this book, the notion of a system. A more precise definition of the term "system" will be given in Sec. *10* at the end of this chapter.

2 *System analysis: an example*

According to Webster's dictionary, a system is "a collection of objects united by some form of interaction or interdependence." Since we shall be concerned only with the quantitative aspects of system behavior, the notion of a system will have for us a narrower meaning. Specifically, we shall assume that each object which is part of a system is characterized by a finite number of measurable attributes[1] and that the interaction between such objects as well as the interdependence between the attributes of each object can be expressed in some well-defined mathematical form.

To introduce in an informal way some of the basic concepts of system theory, let us consider a very simple mechanical system such as that shown in Fig. *1.2.1*, which comprises two particles M_1 and M_2, together with a spring S_3 linking them. M_1 and M_2 are constrained to move along the OX axis, and M_1 is subjected to an external force F which varies with time in a manner specified by a given time function f.

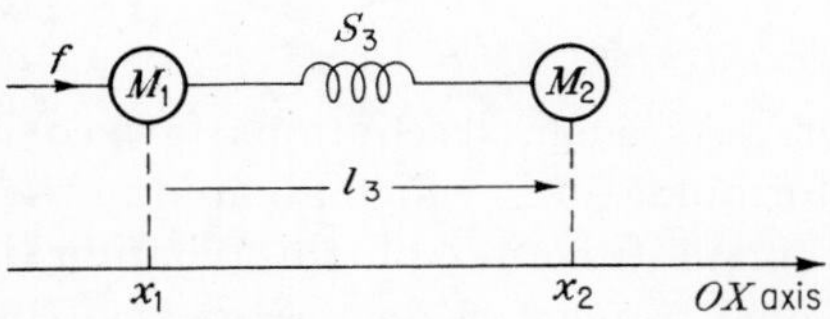

Fig. 1.2.1 Example of a system.

Let us assume for a moment that the analysis of this system, call it $\mathcal{S}$, is presented as a problem to one who is unfamiliar with the laws governing the motion of mechanical systems. What are the questions which will arise in his mind? Among them should be:

What attributes of the objects of which $\mathcal{S}$ is comprised need be considered?

What are the mathematical relations between the relevant attributes of each object in $\mathcal{S}$?

What are the mathematical relations between the attributes of different objects in $\mathcal{S}$; in other words, what are the relations representing the *interactions* of objects in $\mathcal{S}$?

These are essentially the three basic questions which arise in the analysis of most types of system, and learning how to answer them constitutes a large part of the training one receives as an engineer or a

[1] By a *measurable attribute* we mean a characteristic which can be expressed in terms of one or more real or complex numbers. For example, height (a real number), velocity (a real vector), voltage (a real or complex number), impedance (a complex number or a function of frequency), and impedance matrix (a set of complex numbers or complex functions of frequency) are measurable attributes. On the other hand, such attributes as smell, taste, intonation, and beauty are much too subjective and fuzzy to admit of measurement.

physicist. For example, one who is conversant with the analysis of mechanical systems would know that in the case of the system $\mathcal{S}$ the relevant attributes of a particle M are its mass, position, velocity, acceleration, and applied force, while the relevant attributes of a spring are its spring constant, force-free length, and length under tension (or compression). Thus, if the masses are denoted by m (with appropriate subscripts, for example, m_1 is the mass of M_1), the forces by F, the positions by x, the velocities by $\dot{x}$ ($\triangleq dx/dt$), and the spring constant by k, then we have the following three relations:

Relation between the attributes of M_1:

1 $$F_1 = m_1\ddot{x}_1$$

Here F_1 is the total force acting on M_1, with F_1 positive along the positive direction of the OX axis; m_1 is the mass of M_1; and $\ddot{x}_1$ is the second derivative of x_1. Note that *1* relates F_1, m_1, and x_1 through $\ddot{x}_1$ rather than directly.

Relation between the attributes of M_2:

2 $$F_2 = m_2\ddot{x}_2$$

Here F_2 represents the total force acting on M_2, m_2 is the mass of M_2, and $\ddot{x}_2$ is the acceleration of M_2.

Relation between the attributes of S_3:

3 $$F_3 = k(l_3^0 - l_3)$$

Here l_3^0 denotes the length of the spring S_3 when no force is applied to S_3, l_3 is the length of S_3 when an external force F_3 (tending to reduce the length of S_3) is applied, and k is the spring constant ($k > 0$).

4 *Comment* The relation between the applied force and the length of a physical spring is in reality much more complicated than *3*. In effect, *3* may be regarded as a first approximation to the true relation between F_3 and l_3; or alternatively, one may regard S_3 as an idealized spring for which *3* is an exact relation between F_3 and l_3. The results of an analysis in which *3* is used will be approximate or exact depending on whether the first or the second viewpoint is used.

Next, we have the relations representing interactions. These are

5 $$l_3 = x_2 - x_1$$

which means that the length of S_3 is determined by the positions of M_1 and M_2;

6 $$F_1 = f - F_3$$

which means that the total force acting on M_1 is the difference between the externally applied force f and the force exerted on M_1 by the spring S_3; and

7 $$F_2 = F_3$$

which means that the total force acting on M_2 is the force exerted on M_2 by S_3.

In sum, we have six equations involving nine attributes of objects of which $\mathcal{S}$ is comprised, namely, the mass of M_1, the force acting on M_1, the acceleration of M_1, the mass of M_2, the force acting on M_2, the acceleration of M_2, the force acting on S_3, the spring constant, and the length of S_3. These equations can be divided into two groups: Eqs. *1* to *3*, which represent the relations between the attributes of the same object, and Eqs. *5* to *7*, which represent the interactions, i.e., the relations between the attributes of different objects.

A typical problem in connection with the system under consideration might be the determination of the position of M_1 ($\triangleq x_1$) as a function of time, given the external force acting on M_1 ($\triangleq f$) as a function of time. Another way of stating this problem is to say that F is the input to $\mathcal{S}$, that is, F is an attribute of $\mathcal{S}$ which is varied directly by an "experimenter," and that x_1 is the corresponding output, that is, x_1 is an attribute which varies as a result of variation in F and which is observed but not varied directly by the experimenter. To determine x_1 in terms of F, it is necessary to solve Eqs. *1* to *3* and *5* to *7* for x_1 as a function of time, given f as a function of time. This entails the elimination of unwanted attributes $\ddot{x}_1$, x_2, $\ddot{x}_2$, and l_3 from the equations in question. These unwanted variables are what will later be called the *suppressed outputs* of the system (see Sec. *4*).

This brief analysis of the simple mechanical system of Fig. *1.2.1* clearly reveals certain basic problems which appear in one guise or another in the analysis of any system, regardless of its nature, composition, and degree of complexity. These are:

The identification of the relevant attributes of the objects of which the system is comprised

The characterization of the relations between these attributes

The representation of interactions between different objects in terms of interrelations between their attributes

The formation of a system of relations between the attributes of the system as a whole

The determination of relations between the attributes varied by the experimenter (the inputs) and the attributes which are observed but not varied directly (the outputs)

These problems—as well as certain other aspects of system analysis and synthesis which are not placed in evidence by the example just considered—are dealt with in system theory on an abstract rather than a physical level. Thus, what matters in system theory is not the physical identity of the attributes associated with a system but the mathematical relations between the attributes. This is the viewpoint which we shall adopt in this book.

Although the present text is concerned in the main with the theory of linear systems, it will be helpful to begin our exposition on a more general level and define the basic concepts of system theory in a way which makes them applicable to nonlinear as well as linear systems. This is particularly true of such basic concepts as state, input, output, input-output relation, state and system equivalence, and interconnection.

In the sections that follow we shall concern ourselves primarily with terminology and notation. Generally, our exposition will have the pattern of an informal discussion terminating in formal definitions which serve to summarize the preceding discussion. For convenient reference, the definitions, comments, notations, equations, etc., are numbered consecutively within each section.

We begin our discussion with time functions, since in general the measurable attributes of an object are time-dependent quantities.

3 *Time functions*

Notation for time functions

Let v denote a measurable attribute of an object $\mathcal{A}$. Unless stated to the contrary, v will be understood to represent a time function, with the value of v at time t denoted by $v(t)$. Furthermore, it will be understood—unless otherwise indicated—that t ranges over the entire real line $(-\infty, \infty)$, which will be referred to as the *time axis*. (Note that the real line does not include $-\infty$ and ∞.)

If the values which t can assume are restricted to a specified subset T of the time axis, then we write (in the usual mathematical notation) $t \in T$, where $\in$ stands for "belongs to." Typically, T may be a semi-infinite interval $[t_0, \infty)$, where t_0 denotes a particular value of t, or a finite interval $[a,b]$, or a set of equispaced instants of time $(0,h,2h,3h, \ldots)$, where h is the interval between two successive values of t. In the latter case t is a discrete variable, whereas in the former examples t is continuous.

1 *Note* In the sequel we shall frequently be making statements which are subject to the qualification "for all values of t belonging to the set T." To simplify such statements, we shall say "for all t," meaning "for all t in T." When no confusion is likely to arise, we shall use the same convention for variables other than t. For example, "for all x" will mean "for all values of x in the range of x." Furthermore, we shall use the standard symbol $\forall$ (universal quantifier) for "for all" and $\exists$

(existential quantifier) for "there exists." When it is expedient to do so and there is no danger of misinterpretation, we shall place the quantifiers on the right side rather than the left side of an equation.

2 *Example* $f(t) = g(t) \quad \forall t$ has the same meaning as $\forall t[f(t) = g(t)]$, which in turn means "for all values of t in T, $f(t)$ is equal to $g(t)$." $\exists t[f(t) = g(t)]$ means "there exists a value of t in T for which $f(t) = g(t)$." $\forall \alpha \exists t[f(t,\alpha) = g(t,\alpha)]$ means "for all values of α there exists a value of t (*depending on* α) such that $f(t,\alpha) = g(t,\alpha)$." ◁

3 **Remark** In dealing with a time function—or for that matter any function—it is important to distinguish between the time function as such and the value which it assumes at some particular instant of time. More specifically, when we say "a time function v" or, more particularly, "a time function v defined on a set T," we mean the entire curve (graph) of v versus t as t runs through the set T, or, more precisely, the set of pairs $\{(t,v(t))\}$, $t \in T$. On the other hand, when we write $v(t)$, we mean the value which v assumes at the instant t. Unfortunately, it is standard practice to write $v(t)$ when one actually means v, and this gives rise to considerable confusion. [The distinction between v and $v(t)$ is illustrated in Fig. *1.3.1*, where for simplicity it is assumed that $v(t)$ is a real-valued variable for each t in $(-\infty, \infty)$.]

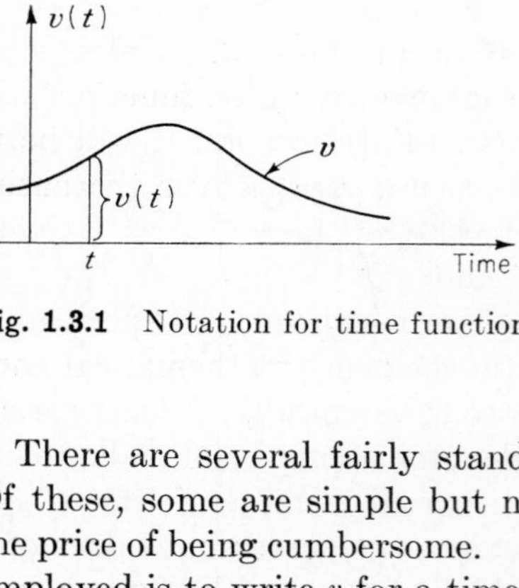

Fig. 1.3.1 Notation for time functions.

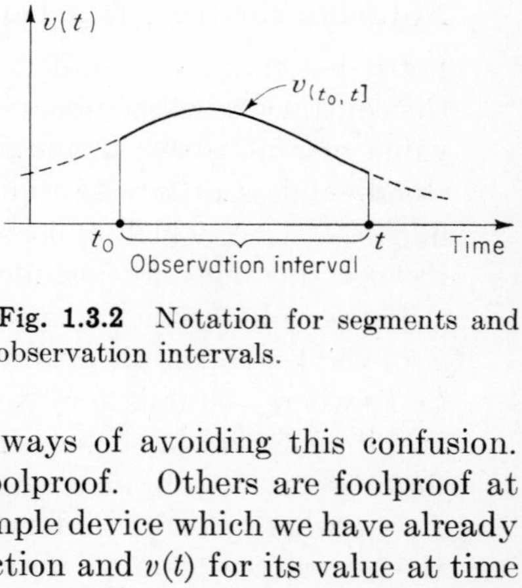

Fig. 1.3.2 Notation for segments and observation intervals.

There are several fairly standard ways of avoiding this confusion. Of these, some are simple but not foolproof. Others are foolproof at the price of being cumbersome. A simple device which we have already employed is to write v for a time function and $v(t)$ for its value at time t. Another is to use a dot in place of t to denote a time function; for example, $v(\cdot)$ is a time function and $v(t)$ is its value at time t. To denote a segment of a time function u over an interval, say, $[t_0,t_1]$, we shall use the symbol $u_{[t_0,t_1]}$, meaning that $u_{[t_0,t_1]}$ is the totality of pairs $\{(t,u(t))\}$, with $t_0 \leq t \leq t_1$. The interval $[t_0,t_1]$ will be referred to as the *observation interval*. Usually, the observation interval will be a semiclosed interval $(t_0,t_1]$ or $[t_0,t_1)$. (See Fig. *1.3.2* for illustration.) Strongly entrenched traditions will force us on occasion to depart from this agreement. For example, following standard practice, a sine function will be written as sin t rather than sin $(\cdot)$ or sin. Similarly, a delta function will be written as $\delta(t)$ rather than δ or $\delta(\cdot)$. Also, the Laplace transform of a time function $f(\cdot)$ will be written as $F(s)$ rather than $F(\cdot)$ or F. Indeed, in sections in which delta functions or Laplace transforms are used extensively, we shall have to rely on the context to indicate whether a symbol such as $v(t)$ should be interpreted as the time function v or as the value of v at time t.

Range of a time function

In general, our concern will be not so much with a single time function v as with a class of time functions $\{v\}$ of which v is an element. (The braces denote a class or a set.) When this is the case, v may be regarded as a variable whose range is the class $\{v\}$. For convenience, the range of v will be denoted by $R[v]$, where R stands for range. Thus, $R[v]$ is a class (space, set) of time functions to which v is constrained to belong.

When v varies over $R[v]$, the values of v at a fixed time t vary over a set which is the *range* of the variable $v(t)$. The range of $v(t)$ will be denoted by $R[v(t)]$.

In general, the range of $v(t)$ may be different from the range of $v(t')$, $t' \neq t$. However, in all of the cases with which we shall be concerned, $R[v(t)]$ is independent of t. Thus, it will be understood, unless stated to the contrary, that the range of $v(t)$ is the same for all values of t in T.

Typically, we shall deal with the following special cases.

$v(t)$ is a real scalar ranging over the real line $(-\infty, \infty)$. (Scalars are identified by lightface type.) In this case, $R[v(t)]$ is the real line; that is, $R[v(t)] = \mathcal{R}^1$ ($\mathcal{R}^1 \triangleq$ space of real numbers).

$v(t)$ is a complex scalar, with the range of $v(t)$ being $\mathcal{C}^1$, the space of complex numbers.

$\mathbf{v}(t)$ is an n-vector (identified by boldface type), with the range of $\mathbf{v}(t)$ being $\mathcal{R}^n$, the space of n-tuples of real numbers. [That is, $\mathcal{R}^n$ is the set of all ordered n-tuples $(\rho_1, \ldots, \rho_n)$, where $\rho_1, \ldots, \rho_n$ are real numbers.]

$\mathbf{v}(t)$ is an n-vector, with the range of $\mathbf{v}(t)$ being $\mathcal{C}^n$, the space of n-tuples of complex numbers. [$\mathcal{C}^n$ is the set of all ordered n-tuples $(x_1, \ldots, x_n)$, where $x_1, \ldots, x_n$ are complex numbers.]

$\mathbf{V}(t)$ is a matrix, with the elements of $\mathbf{V}(t)$ ranging over $\mathcal{R}^1$ or $\mathcal{C}^1$. (Matrices are denoted by boldface uppercase symbols.)

$v(t)$ ranges over a finite set of numbers or letters. For example, $v(t)$ can be any one of the letters of the English alphabet or an integer between, say, -10 and $+10$. In this case, $R[v(t)]$ is a finite set. (When $R[v(t)]$ is a finite set, it is customary to call it an *alphabet* even though its elements may not be letters.)

4 **Remark** In later stages of our discussion, where $\mathbf{v}(t)$ will have a concrete meaning such as input, output, or state, $R[\mathbf{v}(t)]$ will be referred to in a way which will place in evidence the significance of $\mathbf{v}(t)$. Thus, if $\mathbf{v}(t)$ is the input at time t, then $R[\mathbf{v}(t)]$ will be called the *input space*. Similarly, $R[\mathbf{v}(t)]$ will be called the *output space* if $\mathbf{v}(t)$ is the output at time t, and $R[\mathbf{v}(t)]$ will be referred to as the *state space* when $\mathbf{v}(t)$ is the state at time t. $\triangleleft$

It is important to have a clear understanding of the distinction between the range of $\mathbf{v}(t)$, $R[\mathbf{v}(t)]$, and the range of $\mathbf{v}$, $R[\mathbf{v}]$. The former is a set such as $\mathcal{R}^n$, whereas the latter is a set of time functions, i.e., a function space. This distinction is illustrated by the following examples.

5 *Example* Suppose that t ranges over the interval $[0,1]$ and that $\mathbf{v}(t)$ is a 2-vector with components $v_1(t)$ and $v_2(t)$. Assume that the constraints on v_1 and v_2 are (I) $|v_1(t) + v_2(t)| \leq 1$ for all t in $[0,1]$ and (II) $\int_0^1 |v_1(t)|\,dt \leq 2$. In this case, $R[\mathbf{v}(t)]$ is a subset of $\mathcal{R}^2$ (space of pairs of real numbers) defined by (I) and $R[\mathbf{v}]$ is the space of all vector-valued time functions $\mathbf{v}$ defined on $[0,1]$ which satisfy the constraints (I) and (II).

6 *Example* Suppose that T is the set $\{0,1,2, \ldots\}$ and $R[v(t)]$ is the set $\{0,1\}$ (for example, v is a binary sequence). Assume that the successive values of $v(t)$ are constrained by the condition $v(t) + v(t + 1) \leq 1$ for all t. Then $R[v]$ is the set of all binary sequences starting at $t = 0$ in which 1 does not occur twice in a row.

7 **Remark** In most of the problems with which we shall deal in this text, a typical $\mathbf{v}$ will be a vector-valued time function which (I) may contain at most a finite number of delta functions[1] of various orders over any finite interval and (II) is piecewise continuous and has piecewise continuous derivatives of all finite orders on every finite interval over which it has no delta functions. Such a function will be said to be *finitely differentiable in the distribution sense.* Thus, it will be assumed, unless otherwise specified, that $R[\mathbf{v}(t)]$ is $\mathcal{R}^n$ (space of n-tuples of real numbers) and that $R[\mathbf{v}]$ is the space of all vector-valued time functions which are finitely differentiable in the distribution sense.

Usually, a symbol such as $\mathbf{v}$ will be used to denote not the entire time function but a segment of it over an observation interval such as $[t_0,t_1]$. Correspondingly, $R[\mathbf{v}]$ or, more explicitly, $R[\mathbf{v}_{[t_0,t_1]}]$ will denote the set (space) of such segments.

[1] We assume that the reader is familiar with the elementary properties of delta functions, Laplace transforms, and linear vector spaces. Brief treatments of these topics are presented in Appendixes *A*, *B*, and *C*, respectively. The notion of a derivative in the distribution sense is discussed in Appendix *A* and, more sketchily, in Chap. *3*, Sec. *8*.

In most practical problems, neither $R[\mathbf{v}(t)]$ nor $R[\mathbf{v}]$ can be specified in precise terms. For example, suppose that v represents the input to an electronic amplifier. In this case the restrictions on v are rather fuzzy. For instance, $R[v]$ might be specified to be a class of time functions whose amplitude is not much in excess of 10 volts and whose bandwidth is not much in excess of 20,000 cps. This implies that $R[v(t)]$ is a set of numbers which are not much greater than 10 in magnitude. Note that neither $R[v]$ nor $R[v(t)]$ is a well-defined set.

4 *Physical and abstract objects*

Terminal variables and relations

We proceed to introduce in an informal fashion some of the basic notions which are common to systems of all types. The first such notion is that of a *physical object,* by which is usually meant a physical device associated with a number of attributes which are relevant to the purpose for which the device is used. Thus, in the example considered in Sec. *2*, the spring S_3 is an object whose relevant attributes are its spring constant k, its length l_3, its length in the absence of external forces l_3^0, and the external force F_3 applied to S_3. The cost of the spring, its chemical composition, etc., are attributes which are not relevant to the performance of the system $\mathcal{S}$ considered in the example. In the sequel, we shall always assume—unless explicitly stated to the contrary—that we have a priori knowledge of what the relevant attributes of the objects under consideration are and that we have means of measuring them.

As was pointed out in Sec. *1*, what matters in system theory is not the *physical,* but the *mathematical* identity of the attributes of an object and the relations between them. Thus, to a system theorist an object $\mathcal{A}$ is essentially an abstract entity associated with a set of attributes $v_1, v_2, \ldots$ —which in general are numbers or arrays of numbers— which is characterized by the relations between these attributes. Thus, in effect, an *abstract object,* or simply an *object,* is a set of variables together with a set of relations between them.

Before proceeding to enlarge on this informal definition and illustrate its meaning with examples, we shall have to introduce some auxiliary terminology and notations. Specifically, the variables associated with an object $\mathcal{A}$ will be called the *terminal variables* of $\mathcal{A}$ and will be denoted by $v_1, v_2, \ldots$ or other lowercase Latin or Greek letters, with or without subscripts or superscripts, as the need may dictate. The relations between the terminal variables will be referred to as the *terminal variable relations* or simply *terminal relations* for $\mathcal{A}$. An object $\mathcal{A}$ will be said to be *characterized* by its terminal relations, which will be written in the symbolic form

1
$$\begin{aligned} \mathcal{A}^{(1)}(v_1, \ldots, v_n) &= 0 \\ \mathcal{A}^{(2)}(v_1, \ldots, v_n) &= 0 \\ \cdots & \\ \mathcal{A}^{(m)}(v_1, \ldots, v_n) &= 0 \end{aligned}$$

where each $\mathcal{A}^{(j)}$, $j = 1, \ldots, m$, represents a relation between the v_i, $i = 1, \ldots, n$. In the sequel, our attention will be restricted to objects for which both n and m are finite numbers. To denote an object, we shall usually use letters such as $\mathcal{A}$, $\mathcal{B}$, $\mathcal{C}$, often with subscripts and sometimes with superscripts.

The terminal variables are assumed to vary with time, or, for short, to be *time functions*. Thus, unless stated to the contrary,

$$v_i \qquad i = 1, \ldots, n$$

will represent a time function, with the value of v_i at time t denoted by $v_i(t)$. For simplicity, we assume that the $v_i(t)$ are scalar-valued. For convenience, the $v_i(t)$ are identified with the components of an n-vector $\mathbf{v}(t) = (v_1(t), \ldots, v_n(t))$ which will be referred to as the *terminal variable vector* or the *terminal function vector*.

2 *Example* Let $\mathcal{A}$ be an abstract object associated with four terminal variables v_1, v_2, v_3, and v_4, which are related to one another by the differential equations

$$v_3 = a_{11}\frac{dv_1}{dt} + a_{12}\frac{dv_2}{dt}$$

$$v_4 = a_{21}\frac{dv_1}{dt} + a_{22}\frac{dv_2}{dt}$$

where $a_{11}, \ldots, a_{22}$ are constants. These equations constitute the terminal relations which characterize $\mathcal{A}$.

Oriented and nonoriented objects

So far we have not made any mention of inputs and outputs. If an abstract object $\mathcal{A}$ is characterized by relations of the form *1* without any specification as to which variables are the inputs (causes) and which are the outputs (effects), then $\mathcal{A}$ will be said to be *nonoriented.* If, on the other hand, the terminal variables are divided into two categories—input variables and output variables—playing the respective roles of independent and dependent variables, then $\mathcal{A}$ will be said to be *oriented.* Such a division can be made arbitrarily (subject to conditions discussed in Sec. *6*) and carries no implication of physical causality between the inputs and outputs.

The terminal relations *1* can arise from two sources. First, they can be postulated without any reference to physical objects; second, they can be the result of measurements (experiments) performed on a physical object $\mathcal{P}$.

More specifically, consider a physical object $\mathcal{P}$ which is associated with a set of variable attributes $v_1, \ldots, v_n$. Suppose that an experimenter selects a subset of these attributes, say, $v_1, \ldots, v_k$, and proceeds to vary them with time, starting at $t = t_0$ and ending at $t = t_1$ in a manner specified by the time functions $u_1(\cdot), \ldots, u_k(\cdot)$, with $v_i(t) = u_i(t)$, $i = 1, \ldots, k$, $t_0 < t \leq t_1$. Furthermore, suppose that the experimenter observes the resulting variations $y_1(\cdot), \ldots, y_m(\cdot)$ in, say, the attributes $v_{k+1}, \ldots, v_{k+m}$, respectively, and disregards the remaining attributes $v_{k+m+1}, \ldots, v_n$. In such an experiment, the time functions $u_1, \ldots, u_k$ (starting at t_0 and ending at t_1) are the *inputs*, the time functions $y_1, \ldots, y_m$ (starting at t_0 and ending at t_1) are the *outputs* or the *responses*, and the variables $v_{k+m+1}, \ldots, v_n$ are the *suppressed output variables*. For convenience, the k-tuple $(u_1, \ldots, u_k)$ will be referred to as the *input vector* and will be denoted by $\mathbf{u}$. Similarly, the m-tuple $(y_1, \ldots, y_m)$ will be referred to as the *output vector* and will be denoted by $\mathbf{y}$. The $(n\text{-}k\text{-}m)$-tuple $v_{k+m+1}, \ldots, v_n$ will be referred to as the *suppressed output vector* and will be denoted by $\tilde{\mathbf{y}}$. Note that $\mathbf{u}$ and $\mathbf{y}$ are abbreviations for the segments $\mathbf{u}_{(t_0,t_1]}$ and $\mathbf{y}_{(t_0,t_1]}$, respectively. (In later discussions, the observation interval will sometimes be taken to be $[t_0,t_1]$ or $[t_0,t_1)$ (see *1.5.5*).)

3 **Remark** Since $\mathbf{u}$ represents the input to $\mathcal{P}$, the range of $\mathbf{u}(t)$ (see 1.3.4) will be referred to as the *input space* of $\mathcal{P}$ and will be denoted by $R[\mathbf{u}(t)]$. (Unless stated otherwise, it will be assumed that $R[\mathbf{u}(t)]$ is independent of t.) Correspondingly, the range of the time function $\mathbf{u} \triangleq \mathbf{u}_{(t_0,t_1]}$ will be referred to as the *input segment space* of $\mathcal{P}$ and will be denoted by $R[\mathbf{u}]$. Note that $R[\mathbf{u}]$ depends on two parameters, t_0 and t_1, with t_0 and t_1 varying over T. In effect, $\mathcal{P}$ is associated not with a single input segment space $R[\mathbf{u}]$, but with a family $\{R[\mathbf{u}]\}$ which is generated by the parameters t_0 and t_1. The same comment applies to $R[\mathbf{y}]$. Thus, it should be understood that we are using somewhat loose language when we refer to $R[\mathbf{u}]$ as *the* input segment space of $\mathcal{P}$.

It should also be understood that, in cases in which v is a time function defined on, say, $(-\infty, \infty)$, a constraint on v of the form $\int_{-\infty}^{\infty} v^2(t)\, dt \leq 1$ does not induce a corresponding constraint on a segment $v_{[t_0,t_1]}$, whereas a constraint of the form $|v(t)| \leq 1$ for $-\infty < t < \infty$ induces the same constraint on $v_{[t_0,t_1]}$. Thus, in the latter case $R[v_{[t_0,t_1]}]$ is the space of all time functions on $[t_0,t_1]$ satisfying $|v(t)| \leq 1$ for $t_0 \leq t \leq t_1$, whereas in the former case $R[v_{[t_0,t_1]}]$ is merely the space of segments $v_{[t_0,t_1]}$ of time functions v defined on $(-\infty, \infty)$ which satisfy the condition

$$\int_{-\infty}^{\infty} v^2(t)\,dt \leq 1$$

When $R[\mathbf{u}]$ and $R[\mathbf{y}]$ are not specified in explicit terms, it will be understood that they are spaces of vector-valued time functions (defined over a finite or infinite observation interval) which are finitely differentiable in the distribution sense (see *1.3.7*). ◁

By varying the input vector $\mathbf{u}$ over all the values which it is allowed to assume, i.e., over $R[\mathbf{u}]$, and observing the resulting output vector $\mathbf{y}$, the experimenter can derive, at least in principle, a set of relations between the y_j and the u_i which can be expressed in the symbolic form

4
$$\begin{aligned}\mathcal{P}^{(1)}(u_1, \ldots, u_k, y_1, \ldots, y_m) &= 0\\ &\ldots\\ \mathcal{P}^{(m)}(u_1, \ldots, u_k, y_1, \ldots, y_m) &= 0\end{aligned}$$

or more compactly,

5
$$\mathcal{P}(\mathbf{u},\mathbf{y}) = 0$$

where $\mathbf{u}$ and $\mathbf{y}$ range over $R[\mathbf{y}]$ and $R[\mathbf{y}]$, respectively. In the sequel, a relation such as *5* will be referred to as an *input-output relation* for $\mathcal{P}$. Note that the main difference between an *input-output relation* and the *terminal relations* (*1*) of $\mathcal{P}$ is that in the former some of the terminal variables are designated as inputs and others as outputs, whereas in the latter no such designations are made.

6 *Example* Suppose that an experiment of the kind described above is performed on an electrical capacitor $\mathcal{P}$, with the voltage v across the capacitor being the output and the current i through the capacitor being the input. The result of the experiment would be the empirical input-output relation

7
$$C\frac{dv}{dt} = i$$

where C is a constant parameter. In symbolic form, this relation would be written as

8
$$\mathcal{P}(i,v) = 0$$

Observe that *7* does not define v uniquely as a function of i. Rather, v is determined to within an additive constant (constant of integration) which represents the voltage across $\mathcal{P}$ at the beginning of the experiment. Furthermore, *7* remains unchanged when the roles of i and v as input and output are interchanged. Thus *7* may also be regarded as a terminal relation for $\mathcal{P}$, with $\mathcal{P}$ playing the role of a nonoriented object.

Abstract model and physical realization

With reference to *4* and *5*, consider an abstract object $\mathcal{A}$ whose terminal variables are $u_1, \ldots, u_k, y_1, \ldots, y_m$ and which is characterized by an input-output relation

9 $$\mathcal{P}(\mathbf{u},\mathbf{y}) = 0$$

in which $\mathbf{u} \triangleq \mathbf{u}_{(t_0,t_1]}$ and $\mathbf{y} \triangleq {}_{(t_0,t_1]}$, with t_0 and t_1 ranging over T. Such an object $\mathcal{A}$ will be called an *abstract oriented model* of $\mathcal{P}$ and will be denoted by $\mathcal{A}(\mathcal{P})$. Conversely, $\mathcal{P}$ will be called a *physical realization* of $\mathcal{A}$ and will be denoted by $\mathcal{P}(\mathcal{A})$. In effect, an abstract model of $\mathcal{P}$ is merely an abstract object $\mathcal{A}$ whose input-output relation coincides with that of $\mathcal{P}$.

It is obvious that every physical object has an abstract oriented model. However, the converse is not always true, which implies that there exist abstract oriented as well as nonoriented objects which do not have a physical realization. If $\mathcal{A}$ is physically realizable, i.e., if $\mathcal{A}$ has a physical realization, then, in general, it can be realized in a variety of physical forms $\mathcal{P}_1, \mathcal{P}_2, \ldots$. In this case, $\mathcal{A}(\mathcal{P}_1)$, $\mathcal{A}(\mathcal{P}_2)$, ... will all represent the same abstract object $\mathcal{A}$.

We proceed to illustrate these points by simple examples.

10 *Example* Suppose that $\mathcal{A}$ is a nonoriented object with terminal variables v_1 and v_2 connected by the terminal relation

$$v_1(t) = jv_2(t) \qquad \text{for all } t,\ j = \sqrt{-1}$$

It is clear that $\mathcal{A}$ does not admit of physical realization, since either $v_1(t)$ or $v_2(t)$ or both must be complex-valued and hence cannot be identified with the attributes of a physical object. (This implies that we stipulate that the attributes of a physical realization of $\mathcal{A}$ be real-valued.)

11 *Example* Let $\mathcal{P}$ be a particle with mass m. Assume that the variable attributes of $\mathcal{P}$ are the applied force F (along the OX axis), the position of $\mathcal{P}$ ($\triangleq x$) on the OX axis, the velocity of $\mathcal{P}$ ($\triangleq \dot{x}$), and the acceleration of $\mathcal{P}$ ($\triangleq \ddot{x}$). Suppose that the experimenter varies F, observes $\ddot{x}$, and suppresses x and $\dot{x}$. Let $F \triangleq u$, $\ddot{x} \triangleq y$, and $\mathcal{A} \triangleq$ abstract oriented model of $\mathcal{P} \triangleq \mathcal{A}(\mathcal{P})$.

The input-output relation for $\mathcal{P}$ is

12 $$m\ddot{x} = F$$

Correspondingly, the input-output relation for $\mathcal{A}(\mathcal{P})$ is

13 $$my = u$$

Now, if we start with an abstract nonoriented object $\mathcal{A}$ which is characterized by *13*, then $\mathcal{P}$ is a physical realization of $\mathcal{A}$, with $\ddot{x}$ and

F identified with y and u, respectively. Another physical realization is yielded by a resistor in which y is identified with the current through the resistor, u is identified with the voltage across the resistor, and $m = R$ ($\triangleq$ resistance). Still another realization (this time an approximate one) is an amplifier with input voltage y, output voltage u, and amplification factor m. The point of the latter realization is that it shows that a terminal variable of $\mathcal{A}$, say, u, can correspond to an input in one realization (e.g., the force applied to a particle $\mathcal{P}$) and to an output in another realization (e.g., the output voltage of an amplifier). In other words, whether a particular terminal variable v_i of a nonoriented abstract object $\mathcal{A}$ is designated as an input variable or an output variable does not depend on any intrinsic properties of $\mathcal{A}$.

14 *Example* $\mathcal{A}$ (a nonoriented object) is associated with two terminal variables v_1 and v_2 which range over real-valued time functions and which are related by the differential equation

15 $$\frac{dv_2}{dt} = \frac{d^2v_1}{dt^2} + v_1$$

In this case, $\mathcal{A}$ can be realized in a variety of ways. A realization involving an electrical network is shown in Fig. *1.4.1*. Here v_1 plays the role of input voltage and v_2 is the current flowing into the network.

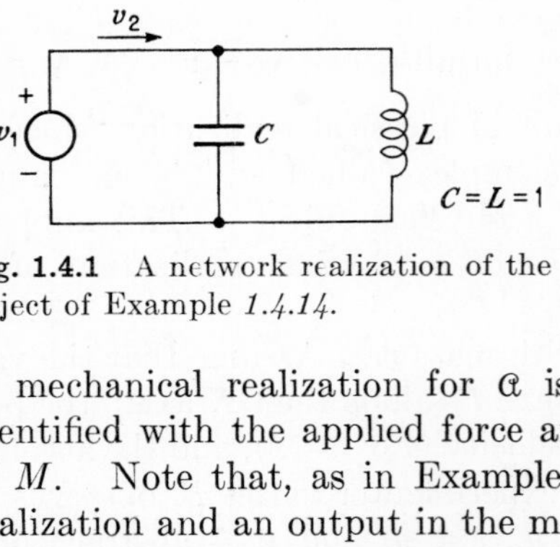

Fig. 1.4.1 A network realization of the object of Example *1.4.14*.

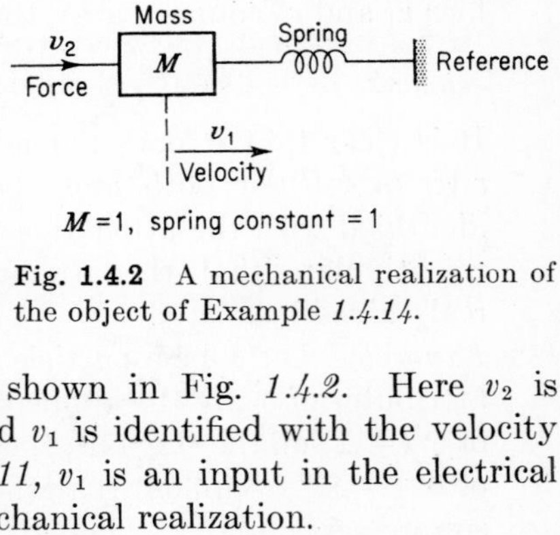

Fig. 1.4.2 A mechanical realization of the object of Example *1.4.14*.

A mechanical realization for $\mathcal{A}$ is shown in Fig. *1.4.2*. Here v_2 is identified with the applied force and v_1 is identified with the velocity of M. Note that, as in Example *11*, v_1 is an input in the electrical realization and an output in the mechanical realization.

16 *Comment* The notion of a nonoriented abstract object helps to clear away some of the confusion surrounding the notion of causality. Specifically, much of this confusion stems from the lack of distinction between a physical object $\mathcal{P}$ and its abstract model $\mathcal{A}(\mathcal{P})$. We saw that, in general, there is no implication of physical causality in the designation of a subset of terminal variables of $\mathcal{A}$ as inputs and the rest as outputs. Furthermore, we have noted that if $\mathcal{A}$ is nonoriented, then a terminal variable of $\mathcal{A}$, say, v_1, may be an input variable in one realization of $\mathcal{A}$ and an output variable in another realization. Also, $\mathcal{A}$ may be physically realizable as a nonoriented object and yet may not

have a physical realization corresponding to a particular orientation. For example, if $\mathcal{A}$ is characterized by the relation $v_2(t) = v_1(t+1)$ for all t, then $\mathcal{A}$ is realizable as a "perfect delay line" with unity delay if v_2 is identified with the input and v_1 with the output of the delay line. On the other hand, if $\mathcal{A}$ is oriented, with v_1 designated as the input and v_2 as the output, then $\mathcal{A}$ has no physical realization, since $\mathcal{P}(\mathcal{A})$ would be a perfect predictor of the future—a physical impossibility.

Formal definition of an abstract object

Up to this point, our discussion of the notion of an abstract object has been informal in nature, its intent being that of preparing the way for the formal definition given in the sequel. Specifically, consider an observation interval such as $[t_0,t_1]$ (or $(t_0,t_1]$ or (t_0,t_1)). Let $(\mathbf{u},\mathbf{y})$, $\mathbf{u} \triangleq \mathbf{u}_{[t_0,t_1]}$, $\mathbf{y} \triangleq \mathbf{y}_{[t_0,t_1]}$, be an ordered pair of time functions defined on this interval and let $R_{[t_0,t_1]} \triangleq \{(\mathbf{u},\mathbf{y})\}$ be a set (space) of such pairs for fixed t_0 and t_1, with $t_0,t_1 \in T$ [$T \triangleq$ range of t (Sec. *3*)]. Furthermore, let $\{R_{[t_0,t_1]}\}$ be a family of such sets generated by varying t_0 and t_1 over T, with $t_1 \geq t_0$. In terms of these symbols, the definition of an oriented abstract object may be formulated as follows:

17 **Definition** An *oriented abstract object* $\mathcal{A}$ is a family $\{R_{[t_0,t_1]}\}$, $t_0,t_1 \in T$, of sets of ordered pairs of time functions, with a generic pair denoted by $(\mathbf{u},\mathbf{y})$, in which the first component, $\mathbf{u} \triangleq \mathbf{u}_{[t_0,t_1]}$, is called an *input segment*, or, simply, an *input*, and the second component, $\mathbf{y} \triangleq \mathbf{y}_{[t_0,t_1]}$, is called an *output segment*, or, simply, an *output*. A pair of time functions $(\mathbf{u},\mathbf{y})$, $\mathbf{u} \triangleq \mathbf{u}_{[t_0,t_1]}$, $\mathbf{y} \triangleq \mathbf{y}_{[t_0,t_1]}$, is an *input-output pair belonging to* $\mathcal{A}$, written as $(\mathbf{u},\mathbf{y}) \in \mathcal{A}$, if $(\mathbf{u},\mathbf{y}) \in R_{[t_0,t_1]}$ for some t_0,t_1 in T. Thus, an oriented abstract object $\mathcal{A}$ can be identified with the totality of input-output pairs which belong to $\mathcal{A}$.

The members of the family $\{R_{[t_0,t_1]}\}$ are required to satisfy the consistency condition: If $(\mathbf{u}_{[t_0,t_1]},\mathbf{y}_{[t_0,t_1]})$ is an input-output pair belonging to $\mathcal{A}$, then so is any section of this pair, i.e., any pair of the form $(\mathbf{u}_{[\tau_0,\tau_1]},\mathbf{y}_{[\tau_0,\tau_1]})$ in which $t_0 \leq \tau_0 \leq t_1$, $\tau_0 \leq \tau_1 \leq t_1$, and $\mathbf{u}_{[\tau_0,\tau_1]} = \mathbf{u}_{[t_0,t_1]}$, $\mathbf{y}_{[\tau_0,\tau_1]} = \mathbf{y}_{[t_0,t_1]}$ over $[\tau_0,\tau_1]$. In plain words, this condition requires that every section of an input-output pair of $\mathcal{A}$ be in itself an input-output pair for $\mathcal{A}$. The purpose of this condition is to ensure that the family $\{R_{[t_0,t_1]}\}$, $t_0,t_1 \in T$, is defined in a consistent fashion.

The set of all segments $\mathbf{u}$ over $[t_0,t_1]$ such that $(\mathbf{u},\mathbf{y}) \in \mathcal{A}$ will be referred to as an *input segment space* of $\mathcal{A}$ and will be denoted by $R[\mathbf{u}]$. Similarly, the set of all segments $\mathbf{y}$ such that $(\mathbf{u},\mathbf{y}) \in \mathcal{A}$ will be referred to as an *output segment space* of $\mathcal{A}$ and will be denoted by $R[\mathbf{y}]$. This implies that $R_{[t_0,t_1]}$, which is the set of all pairs $(\mathbf{u}_{[t_0,t_1]},\mathbf{y}_{[t_0,t_1]})$ belonging to $\mathcal{A}$, is a subset of the product space $R[\mathbf{u}] \times R[\mathbf{y}]$. [By the *product space* of n spaces $X_1, \ldots, X_n$ with generic elements $x_1, \ldots, x_n$ is meant the set of all n-tuples $(x_1, \ldots, x_n)$ with $x_i \in X_i$, $i = 1, \ldots, n$ (see Ref. *2*).] The relationship between $R_{[t_0,t_1]}$ and $R[\mathbf{u}] \times R[\mathbf{y}]$ is depicted in Fig. *1.4.3*, in which $\delta\beta$ and $\gamma\alpha$ represent $R[\mathbf{u}]$ and $R[\mathbf{y}]$,

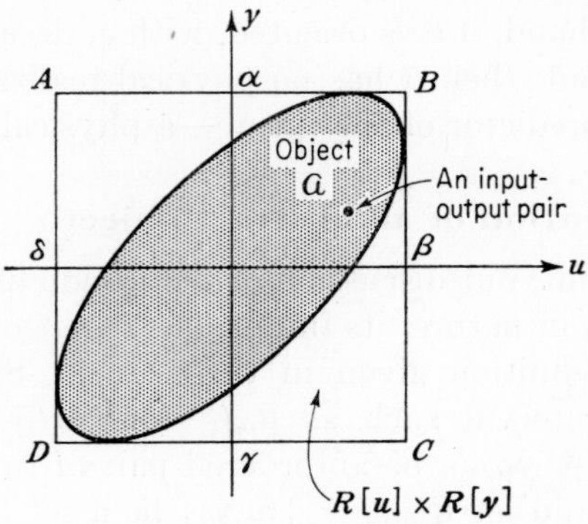

Fig. 1.4.3 Geometrical representation of an abstract object. The segments $\alpha\gamma$ and $\beta\delta$ represent $R[\mathbf{u}]$ and $R[\mathbf{y}]$, respectively; the set bounded by the rectangle $ABCD$ represents the product space $R[\mathbf{u}] \times R[\mathbf{y}]$.

respectively, the rectangle $ABCD$ represents the set $R[\mathbf{u}] \times R[\mathbf{y}]$, and the set labeled $\mathcal{A}$ denotes the set of input-output pairs $\{\mathbf{u},\mathbf{y}\}$.

Finally, a relation—written as $\mathcal{A}(\mathbf{u},\mathbf{y}) = 0$—which defines the set of all input-output pairs belonging to $\mathcal{A}$ will be called an *input-output relation* for $\mathcal{A}$, and $\mathcal{A}$ will be said to be *characterized by* its input-output relation. ◁

18 *Example* Let $\mathcal{A}$ be an object characterized by the input-output relation

19 $$\frac{dy}{dt} = u$$

in which $T = (-\infty, \infty)$ and u ranges over the space of continuous real-valued time functions. In this case, $R_{[t_0,t_1]}$ (which is the space of input-output pairs over a finite interval $[t_0,t_1]$) is the set of all ordered pairs of time functions of the form $\left(u(t), \alpha + \int_{t_0}^{t} u(\xi)\, d\xi\right)$, $t_0 \leq t \leq t_1$, where α is an arbitrary real constant. For example, $(1,t)$, $t_0 \leq t \leq t_1$; $(1,\ 1 + t)$, $t_0 \leq t \leq t_1$; and $\left(t, \frac{t^2}{2} + 1\right)$, $t_0 \leq t \leq t_1$ are input-output pairs for $\mathcal{A}$.

20 *Example* If in the above example the input-output relation is replaced by

21 $$\frac{dy}{dt} + y = u$$

the corresponding expression for an input-output pair belonging to $\mathcal{A}$

can be found by solving *21* for y in terms of u. Thus, in this case, the expression for an input-output pair over $[t_0,t_1]$ reads

22 $$\left(u(t),\, e^{-(t-t_0)}\alpha + \int_{t_0}^{t} e^{-(t-\xi)}u(\xi)\, d\xi\right),\ t_0 \leq t \leq t_1$$

where u ranges over time functions for which $\int_{t_0}^{t} e^{-(t-\xi)}u(\xi)\, d\xi$ is defined for all $t \in [t_0,t_1]$ and α is an arbitrary real number. Note that to each input segment $u_{[t_0,t_1]}$ there corresponds a family of output segments $\{y_{[t_0,t_1]}\}$ given by *22*, with α playing the role of a parameter which generates the family.

Uniform objects

The definition of an oriented object given above is complicated somewhat by the fact that, although every segment of an input-output pair which belongs to $\mathcal{A}$ is likewise an input-output pair belonging to $\mathcal{A}$, the converse is not necessarily true; i.e., in general there can exist input-output pairs which are not segments of other input-output pairs. As a simple example, consider an object $\mathcal{A}$ which, up to time $t = 0$, is characterized by the equation

23 $$y = u$$

and thereafter (for $t \geq 0$) is characterized by

24 $$\frac{dy}{dt} = \frac{du}{dt}$$

In this case, an input-output pair such as (1,2), $t \geq 0$, is not a segment of any input-output pair which is defined on an observation interval which starts at a negative value of t_0. [All such pairs are of the form $(u(t),u(t))$, $t \geq t_0$, $t_0 < 0$.]

It is for this reason that $\mathcal{A}$ must be defined as a family of sets of input-output pairs, rather than a single set of input-output pairs. However, for most applications it is sufficient to restrict one's attention to objects which can be characterized by a single set of input-output pairs defined over T. Such objects will be said to be *uniform*. More formally, they are defined as follows:

25 **Definition** An oriented object $\mathcal{A}$ is *uniform* if every input-output pair $(\mathbf{u}_{[t_0,t_1]},\mathbf{y}_{[t_0,t_1]})$ belonging to $\mathcal{A}$ is a segment of an input-output pair $(\mathbf{u}_T,\mathbf{y}_T)$ defined over the set T. $\triangleleft$

An immediate consequence of this definition is that a uniform oriented object $\mathcal{A}$ can be characterized by a single set of input-output pairs $\{(\mathbf{u}_T,\mathbf{y}_T)\}$. For example, if $T = [0,\infty)$, then $\mathcal{A}$ can be characterized by the set (space) of input-output pairs $\{(\mathbf{u}_{[0,\infty)},\mathbf{y}_{[0,\infty)})\}$ defined over the interval $[0,\infty)$.

Henceforth we shall assume, unless explicitly stated to the contrary, that $\mathcal{A}$ is a uniform oriented object. Since the notion of a uniform oriented object will play a central role in the sequel, it will be helpful to restate its definition in a more complete form as well as to recapitulate the definitions of such related notions as input and output which were given in Definition *17*.

26 **Definition** A *uniform oriented abstract object*, or, simply, an *object*, $\mathcal{A}$, is a set, written as $\mathcal{A} = \{(\mathbf{u}_T,\mathbf{y}_T)\}$, of ordered pairs of time functions $(\mathbf{u}_T,\mathbf{y}_T)$ defined on a set T of the time axis $(-\infty,\infty)$, with the generic values of these time functions at time t denoted by $\mathbf{u}(t)$ and $\mathbf{y}(t)$, respectively. [Thus, $\mathbf{u}_T \triangleq \{(t,\mathbf{u}(t))|t \in T\}$, and similarly for $\mathbf{y}_T$. Unless stated otherwise, it will be understood that $T = (-\infty,\infty)$.]

The set of all $\mathbf{u}_T$ such that $\mathbf{u}_T$ is the first component of a pair belonging to the set $\mathcal{A}$ constitutes the *domain* of $\mathcal{A}$, written as $R[\mathbf{u}_T]$. In symbols

27 $$R[\mathbf{u}_T] = \{\mathbf{u}_T|(\mathbf{u}_T,\mathbf{y}_T) \in \mathcal{A}\} \qquad \text{for some } \mathbf{y}_T$$

Similarly the *range* of $\mathcal{A}$, denoted by $R[\mathbf{y}_T]$, is defined by

28 $$R[\mathbf{y}_T] = \{\mathbf{y}_T|(\mathbf{u}_T,\mathbf{y}_T) \in \mathcal{A}\} \qquad \text{for some } \mathbf{u}_T$$

(In Fig. *1.4.3*, the sets $\delta\beta$ and $\gamma\alpha$ represent $R[\mathbf{u}_T]$ and $R[\mathbf{y}_T]$, respectively.) A segment $\mathbf{u} \triangleq \mathbf{u}_{[t_0,t_1]} \triangleq \{(t,\mathbf{u}(t))|t_0 \le t \le t_1\}$ of $\mathbf{u}_T$ is called an *input segment*, or simply an *input*, over the *observation interval* $[t_0,t_1]$. Similarly, $\mathbf{y} \triangleq \mathbf{y}_{[t_0,t_1]}$ is called an *output segment*, or, simply, an *output*, over $[t_0,t_1]$. A pair $(\mathbf{u},\mathbf{y})$, in which $\mathbf{u}$ and $\mathbf{y}$ are defined over the same observation interval, will be said to be an *input-output pair* belonging to $\mathcal{A}$, or, simply, an *input-output pair*. The set of all $\mathbf{u}$ (over a fixed observation interval) such that, for some $\mathbf{y}$, $(\mathbf{u},\mathbf{y})$ belongs to $\mathcal{A}$ constitutes an *input segment space* of $\mathcal{A}$, written as $R[\mathbf{u}]$. Similarly, $R[\mathbf{y}] = \{\mathbf{y}|(\mathbf{u},\mathbf{y}) \in \mathcal{A}\}$ constitutes an *output segment space* of $\mathcal{A}$. The sets $R[\mathbf{u}(t)] \triangleq \{\mathbf{u}(t)|\mathbf{u}_T \in R[\mathbf{u}_T]\}$ and $R[\mathbf{y}(t)] \triangleq \{\mathbf{y}(t)|\mathbf{y}_T \in R[\mathbf{y}_T]\}$ will be referred to, respectively, as the *input* and *output spaces* of $\mathcal{A}$ and, unless stated to the contrary, will be assumed to be independent of t. ◁

29 *Note* For simplicity, we shall usually refer to both $R[\mathbf{y}_T]$ and $R[\mathbf{y}]$ as the *range* of $\mathcal{A}$, relying on the context for indication of whether it should be interpreted as $R[\mathbf{y}_T]$ or $R[\mathbf{y}]$. The same comment applies to $R[\mathbf{u}_T]$ and $R[\mathbf{u}]$. [Note that $R[\mathbf{u}_T]$ is a set of time functions defined on $(-\infty,\infty)$—assuming that $T = (-\infty,\infty)$—whereas $R[\mathbf{u}]$ is a set of segments of these time functions over a fixed observation interval (see *1.4.3* and *1.4.17*).] On occasion, to differentiate between $R[\mathbf{u}]$ and $R[\mathbf{u}_T]$ the latter will be called the *input-function space* of $\mathcal{A}$.

30 *Comment* It is important to note that, under Definition *26*, to a given input **u** is associated, in general, not a unique output **y**, but a set of distinct **y**'s (see Fig. *1.4.3*) which correspond to different "initial conditions," or, equivalently, "initial states" of $\mathcal{A}$. As we shall see presently, the "state of $\mathcal{A}$" is essentially a label associated with each input-output pair of $\mathcal{A}$ in such a way that **u** ($\triangleq \mathbf{u}_{(t_0,t]}$) and the state of $\mathcal{A}$ at time t_0 uniquely determine $\mathbf{y}_{(t_0,t]}$.

31 *Comment* In mathematical terminology, an abstract object as defined by *26* is a *relation* rather than a function (or an operator). [A relation is a set of ordered pairs (**u**,**y**), whereas a function is a relation in which to every **u** corresponds a unique **y** (see Ref. *11*).] In defining an abstract object as a relation we depart from the conventional and, in our opinion, unsatisfactory definitions found in the literature in which the notion of a system—which has essentially the same meaning as an oriented abstract object—is identified with a function (e.g., a transfer function) or an operator which associates a unique output with each input.

32 *Comment* In the foregoing discussion we have focused our attention on oriented objects, since most of the objects treated in later chapters are of this type and, furthermore, it is a simple matter to extend a definition concerning an oriented object to a nonoriented object. For example, by deleting from *26* the definitions of input, output, and associated concepts, we obtain the definition of a nonoriented object. We shall not formulate this definition, since the reader can easily do it himself.

Parametrization of the space of input-output pairs

As pointed out above in Comment *30*, a central feature of an oriented object $\mathcal{A}$ is the nonuniqueness of the output. More specifically, to each input segment $\mathbf{u} \triangleq \mathbf{u}_{[t_0,t_1]}$ there corresponds, in general, a set of output segments $\mathbf{y} \triangleq \mathbf{y}_{[t_0,t_1]}$ such that **u** and each **y** in the set constitute an input-output pair belonging to $\mathcal{A}$. In a similar fashion, to each output segment **y** there will, in general, correspond a set of input segments **u**.

One way of associating a unique **y** with each **u** consists in attaching to each input-output pair (**u**,**y**) a label (parameter) $\mathbf{s}(t_0)$, ranging over a space Σ (which for simplicity is assumed to be independent of t_0), such that **y** is uniquely determined by **u** and $\mathbf{s}(t_0)$. We shall refer to this process as the *parametrization of the space of input-output pairs*, and we shall call $\mathbf{s}(t_0)$ the *state* of $\mathcal{A}$ at time t_0. As an aid in the visualization of what is involved in this process, assume that $\mathcal{A}$ is represented by a catalog each page of which shows an input **u** and a corresponding output **y**, with (**u**,**y**) constituting an input-output pair belonging to $\mathcal{A}$. The catalog, then, represents the space of input-output pairs, and one natural way of parametrizing this space is to number those pages of the catalog on which the same **u** appears. For example, assuming for simplicity that the number of inputs is finite and that a particular **u**, say $\mathbf{u}^i$, $i = 1, \ldots, k$, appears on pages $1, \ldots, N_i$, then given the page number and $\mathbf{u}^i$ one can uniquely determine the corresponding **y**. In this case, the state space Σ consists of the page numbers $1, \ldots, N$, where $N = \max [N_1, \ldots, N_k]$.

This informal explanation serves merely as a brief introduction to the discussion of the notion of state in Secs. *5* to *7*. As we shall see in the sequel, the notion of state is by no means trivial to define in a satisfactory fashion. We shall also see that the notion of state will play a key role in the development of the theory presented in the following chapters.

5 *An introduction to the notion of state*

1 *Note* In the following discussion the observation interval will usually be denoted by $(t_0,t]$ rather than $[t_0,t_1]$ as in Sec. *4*. ◁

As pointed out above, the state of $\mathcal{A}$ at time t_0 may be regarded as a label $\mathbf{s}(t_0)$ attached to each input-output pair $(\mathbf{u}_{(t_0,t]},\mathbf{y}_{(t_0,t]})$ in such a way that $\mathbf{y}_{(t_0,t]}$ is uniquely determined by $\mathbf{u}_{(t_0,t]}$ and $\mathbf{s}(t_0)$. In this sense, the state of $\mathcal{A}$ at time t_0 serves essentially the purpose of parametrizing the space of input-output pairs $R_{(t_0,t]}$ in such a way that **y** becomes a function of **u** and $\mathbf{s}(t_0)$.

Stated less formally, the state of $\mathcal{A}$ at time t_0 is a collection of numbers, represented by, say, a vector $\boldsymbol{\alpha}$ ranging over a space Σ, such that the knowledge of (I) $\boldsymbol{\alpha}$, (II) input-output relation of $\mathcal{A}$, and (III) input segment $\mathbf{u}_{(t_0,t]}$ is sufficient to determine the output segment $\mathbf{y}_{(t_0,t]}$ uniquely. The vector $\boldsymbol{\alpha}$ plays the role of a value of $\mathbf{s}(t_0)$, the state of $\mathcal{A}$ at time t_0. (In the sequel, in some cases $\boldsymbol{\alpha}$ will stand for a fixed point in Σ; in others, $\boldsymbol{\alpha}$ will be a variable ranging over Σ. The sense in which $\boldsymbol{\alpha}$ is used will be clear in most cases from the context.)

This, however, is not the only property that the state of $\mathcal{A}$ should have. Thus, suppose that we associate a label $\mathbf{s}(t_0)$ with an input-output pair $(\mathbf{u}_{(t_0,\infty)},\mathbf{y}_{(t_0,\infty)})$. Then, if we consider a section of this pair, $(\mathbf{u}_{(t_1,\infty)},\mathbf{y}_{(t_1,\infty)})$, starting at some later time t_1, it is reasonable to stipulate that the label $\mathbf{s}(t_1)$ associated with the input-output pair $(\mathbf{u}_{(t_1,\infty)},\mathbf{y}_{(t_1,\infty)})$ be uniquely determined by $\mathbf{s}(t_0)$ and the input segment $\mathbf{u}_{(t_0,t_1]}$. This property of the state of $\mathcal{A}$ will be discussed in greater detail in Sec. *6*, where it will manifest itself in the form of a consistency condition (*1.6.35*) entering into the definition of the state of $\mathcal{A}$.

2 *Note* We are tacitly assuming here, and will continue to do so in the sequel, that $\mathcal{A}$ contains no random elements. Otherwise we would have to say "the knowledge of (I), (II), and (III) conveys as much information about $\mathbf{y}_{(t_0,t]}$ as does the knowledge of (I), (II), and (III) *plus* the knowledge of all the values of $\mathbf{u}(t)$, $\mathbf{y}(t)$, and $\mathbf{s}(t)$ for $t < t_0$." In any case, the basic property of the state of $\mathcal{A}$ at time t_0 is that it "separates" the future ($t > t_0$) from the past ($t < t_0$) by providing all the information about the past of $\mathcal{A}$ that is relevant to the determination of the response of $\mathcal{A}$ to any input starting at t_0. ◁

Accepting for the moment this informal explanation of the notion of state, let us consider the following basic question. Suppose that we have an oriented object $\mathcal{A}$ which is characterized by a family of sets of input-output pairs or, equivalently, by an input-output relation (see *1.4.17*)

3 $$\mathcal{A}(\mathbf{u},\mathbf{y}) = 0$$

How can we associate a state $\mathbf{s}(t)$ with $\mathcal{A}$? Or, in other words, how can we parametrize the space of input-output pairs of $\mathcal{A}$ in such a way that $\mathbf{y}_{(t_0,t]}$ would be uniquely determined by $\mathbf{s}(t_0)$ and $\mathbf{u}_{(t_0,t]}$ for all $\mathbf{u}_{(t_0,t]}$ in $R[\mathbf{u}]$ and all $\mathbf{s}(t_0)$ in Σ?

A clue to the solution of this problem can be obtained in many cases by raising the question: What do we have to know about the history of $\mathcal{A}$ up to time t_0 in order to be able to determine $\mathbf{y}_{(t_0,t]}$ uniquely when $\mathbf{u}_{(t_0,t]}$ is given? As we shall see in Chap. *4*, in the case of objects characterized by differential equations, the knowledge of a certain finite number of the derivatives of the input and output at time t_0 provides all of the information about the past history of $\mathcal{A}$ that is relevant to the determination of $\mathbf{y}_{(t_0,t]}$. Thus, in the case of such objects, the state of $\mathcal{A}$ at time t_0 is a vector whose components are the derivatives of various orders (or their linear combinations) of the input and output of $\mathcal{A}$ evaluated at time t_0. However, as we have already pointed out, the mere fact that $\mathbf{y}_{(t_0,t]}$ is uniquely determined by $\mathbf{s}(t_0)$ and $\mathbf{u}_{(t_0,t]}$ does not in itself qualify $\mathbf{s}(t_0)$ as the state of $\mathcal{A}$ at time t_0.

4 *Example* In the case of Example *1.4.20* the state of $\mathcal{A}$ at time t_0 is given by $y(t_0)$, which is the value of the output of $\mathcal{A}$ at time t_0. [Here $y(t_0)$ is the zero-order derivative of the output evaluated at t_0.] Note that $y(t)$ (for $t \geq t_0$) is uniquely determined by $y(t_0)$ and the values of u over the interval $[t_0,t]$. Clearly, this is equivalent to saying that $y_{[t_0,t]}$ is uniquely determined by $y(t_0)$ and $u_{[t_0,t]}$.

5 **Remark** Our notation for observation intervals may appear to be somewhat lacking in consistency because in some places we write $\mathbf{u}_{(t_0,t]}$, in others $\mathbf{u}_{[t_0,t]}$, and in still others $\mathbf{u}_{[t_0,t)}$. The explanation for this variability is as follows. In the first place, we generally use semi-closed intervals $(t_0,t]$ or $[t_0,t)$ rather than a closed interval $[t_0,t]$ because of the need to be able to adjoin a segment $\mathbf{u}$ (ending at t) to a segment

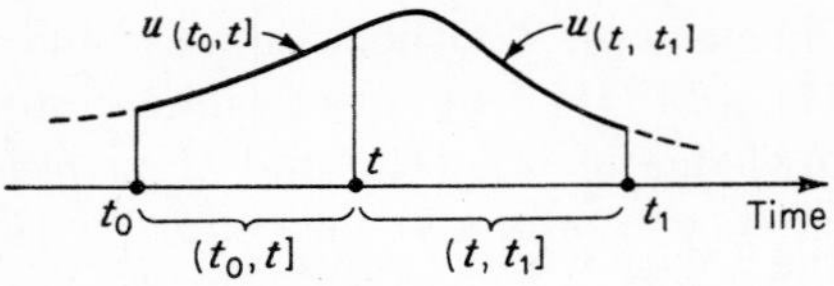

Fig. 1.5.1 Notation for observation intervals and segments.

$\mathbf{v}$ (starting at t) (Fig. *1.5.1*) without creating ambiguity at the common point t when the value of $\mathbf{u}$ at t is different from that of $\mathbf{v}$ at t. So far as this particular consideration is concerned, there is no difference between using $(t_0,t]$ and $[t_0,t)$ so long as we use one or the other consistently.

In the second place, when the state of $\mathcal{A}$ is specified at time t_0, we denote the input segment by $\mathbf{u}_{(t_0,t]}$ in order to indicate that the input $\mathbf{u}$ is applied to $\mathcal{A}$ "slightly" after the state of $\mathcal{A}$ is established. In many cases, however, and particularly in the case of objects characterized by differential equations, it is more convenient to convey the same idea by specifying the state at time t_0- (that is, at time $t_0 - \varepsilon$, where ε is an arbitrarily small positive number) and denoting the input by $\mathbf{u}_{[t_0,t)}$. In this connection, it should be noted that it does not make a difference whether the state is specified at t_0 or t_0- or whether the input is defined over $(t_0,t]$ or $[t_0,t]$ so long as $\mathbf{u}$ is sufficiently "smooth" at $t = t_0$. Thus, in situations in which this is tacitly or explicitly assumed to be true, we may use $\mathbf{s}(t_0)$ and $\mathbf{s}(t_0-)$ interchangeably, as well as $\mathbf{u}_{(t_0,t]}$, $\mathbf{u}_{[t_0,t)}$, and $\mathbf{u}_{[t_0,t]}$, without affecting the results of the analysis. The same comment applies to $\mathbf{y}_{(t_0,t]}$, $\mathbf{y}_{[t_0,t)}$, and $\mathbf{y}_{[t_0,t]}$. $\lhd$

With these remarks and observations in the background, we are in a position to formulate a definition which attaches well-defined meaning to the notion of state. Since the definition in question is rather long and replete with conditions, it will be helpful to explain the idea behind it first.

Let $\mathcal{A}$ be an oriented object which is derived from a nonoriented object $\mathcal{A}'$ by arbitrarily designating a subset of the terminal variables of $\mathcal{A}'$ as the inputs $u_1, \ldots, u_k$ and the remainder as the outputs $y_1, \ldots, y_m$ of $\mathcal{A}$, with the terminal relations of $\mathcal{A}'$ becoming the input-output relation for $\mathcal{A}$.

As we shall see in Chap. *4*, there are many ways in which a state vector $\mathbf{s}(t_0)$ can be associated with $\mathcal{A}$. Thus, if we start with $\mathcal{A}'$, then there is considerable arbitrariness in the way $\mathcal{A}'$ is oriented and, once $\mathcal{A}'$ is oriented, there is further arbitrariness in the way in which a state vector is associated with $\mathcal{A}$. Because of this arbitrariness, the definition given below is essentially a set of qualifying conditions which, if satisfied, enable one to call $\mathbf{s}(t_0)$ a *state vector* or simply *state* of $\mathcal{A}$ at time t_0.

We proceed to formulate the definition in question in the following section.

6 *Definition of state, input, and output*

Let $\mathfrak{A}$ be an oriented abstract object with **u** and **y** denoting, respectively, the input and output of $\mathfrak{A}$ over an observation interval $(t_0,t]$, with the terms "input" and "output" interpreted in the sense of *1.4.17*. Let $R[\mathbf{u}]$ and $R[\mathbf{y}]$ be the corresponding input and output segment spaces of $\mathfrak{A}$ (*1.4.17*), and let $\mathfrak{A}$ be characterized by its input-output relation

1 $$\mathfrak{A}(\mathbf{u},\mathbf{y}) = 0$$

or, equivalently, by the family $\{R_{(t_0,t]}\}$ of spaces of input-output pairs of $\mathfrak{A}$. Furthermore, let $\boldsymbol{\alpha}$ be a variable ranging over a space Σ. (In most of the applications with which we shall be concerned later, Σ will be an n-dimensional linear vector space and $\boldsymbol{\alpha}$ will be an n-vector.)

In these terms, a definition of state, input-output-state relation, etc., can be formulated in the following manner.

2 **Definition** If the spaces of input-output pairs of $\mathfrak{A}$ admit of parametrization in the form of a relation

3 $$\mathbf{y}(t) = \mathbf{A}(\boldsymbol{\alpha};\mathbf{u}_{(t_0,t]}) \qquad \forall t > t_0, \qquad \forall t_0$$

where **A** denotes a function of $\boldsymbol{\alpha}$ and $\mathbf{u}_{(t_0,t]}$, with t_0 and t ranging over T, $\boldsymbol{\alpha}$ ranging over Σ, **u** ranging over $R[\mathbf{u}]$ and **y** ranging over $R[\mathbf{y}]$, which satisfies the four mutual- and self-consistency conditions set forth below, then *3* qualifies to be called an *input-output-state relation* for $\mathfrak{A}$ and Σ qualifies to be called the *state space* of $\mathfrak{A}$, with the elements of Σ being the *states* of $\mathfrak{A}$ and $\boldsymbol{\alpha}$ being the *state of* $\mathfrak{A}$ *at time* t_0. Furthermore, if these conditions are satisfied, we shall say that (I) $\mathfrak{A}$ is *completely characterized* by its input-output-state relation *3*, (II) the segment $\mathbf{y}_{(t_0,t]}$ is the *response segment* of $\mathfrak{A}$ to $\mathbf{u}_{(t_0,t]}$ starting in state $\boldsymbol{\alpha}$, and (III) $\mathbf{u}_{(t_0,t]}$ and $\mathbf{y}_{(t_0,t]}$ constitute an *input-output pair associated with, or with respect to,* $\boldsymbol{\alpha}$. The relation between $\mathbf{y}_{(t_0,t]}$ and $\mathbf{u}_{(t_0,t]}$ will be expressed symbolically as

4 $$\mathbf{y}_{(t_0,t]} = \bar{\mathbf{A}}(\boldsymbol{\alpha};\mathbf{u}_{(t_0,t]})$$

or for short

$$\mathbf{y} = \bar{\mathbf{A}}(\boldsymbol{\alpha};\mathbf{u})$$

where the bar over **A** serves to differentiate between $\mathbf{y}(t)$ and $\mathbf{y}_{(t_0,t]}$. (Note that $\bar{\mathbf{A}}$ is a function on the product space $\Sigma \times R[\mathbf{u}]$ with values in $R[\mathbf{y}]$, whereas **A** is a function on $\Sigma \times R[\mathbf{u}]$ with values in $R[\mathbf{y}(t)]$. In the sequel, both *3* and *4* will be referred to as input-output-state relations for $\mathfrak{A}$, since *3* is derivable from *4* and vice versa.) Finally, a pair $(\mathbf{u}_{(t_0,t]},\mathbf{y}_{(t_0,t]})$ will be said to *satisfy* the input-output-state relation *4* (or, equivalently, *3*) if $\mathbf{u}_{(t_0,t]}$ and $\mathbf{y}_{(t_0,t]}$ constitute an input-output pair with respect to some $\boldsymbol{\alpha}$ in Σ. (Note that in terms of *4* we can write $R[\mathbf{y}] = \{\bar{\mathbf{A}}(\boldsymbol{\alpha};\mathbf{u}) | \boldsymbol{\alpha} \in \Sigma, \mathbf{u} \in R[\mathbf{u}]\}$.) ◁

The consistency conditions in question read as follows:

5 **Mutual-consistency condition** Every input-output pair for $\mathcal{A}$ satisfies the input-output-state relation *4*, and vice versa. More specifically: (I) if $(\mathbf{u}_{(t_0,t]},\mathbf{y}_{(t_0,t]})$ or, more simply, $(\mathbf{u},\mathbf{y})$ is any pair of time functions (with $\mathbf{u} \in R[\mathbf{u}]$ and $\mathbf{y} \in R[\mathbf{y}]$) satisfying *1*, then $(\mathbf{u},\mathbf{y})$ also satisfies *4* in the sense that there exists an $\boldsymbol{\alpha}$ in Σ, say, $\boldsymbol{\alpha}_0$ such that

6 $$\mathbf{y}_{(t_0,t]} = \bar{\mathbf{A}}(\boldsymbol{\alpha}_0;\mathbf{u}_{(t_0,t]})$$

and (II) any pair of time functions $(\mathbf{u},\mathbf{y})$ satisfying *4* for some $\boldsymbol{\alpha} \in \Sigma$ over an observation interval $(t_0,t]$ is an input-output pair for $\mathcal{A}$. (This must hold for all t_0,t in T and all $\mathbf{u}$ in $R[\mathbf{u}]$.) ◁

7 *Example* Suppose that $\mathcal{A}$ is characterized by the input-output relation

8 $$\frac{dy}{dt} = u$$

where u and y are real-valued time functions. Consider the relation

9 $$y(t) = \alpha + \int_{t_0}^{t} u(\xi)\, d\xi$$

where ξ is the variable of integration and α is a real-valued variable ranging over the real line $(-\infty,\infty)$. [That is, $\Sigma = \mathcal{R}^1 \triangleq (-\infty,\infty)$.] Clearly, the mutual-consistency condition is satisfied in this case for the following reasons. (I) Every input-output pair for $\mathcal{A}$ can be represented as

10 $$(u(t),y(t)) = \left(u(t),\, c + \int_{t_0}^{t} u(\xi)\, d\xi\right) \qquad t > t_0$$

where c is a real constant. Hence, *10* satisfies *9* with $\alpha = c$. (II) By direct substitution of *9* into *8* it follows at once that every pair of time functions (u,y) satisfying *9* also satisfies *8*. Note that the mutual-consistency condition would not be satisfied if Σ, the range of α, were restricted to the interval $[0,\infty)$; for in this case there is no α in $[0,\infty)$ with which, for example, the pair $(t, -1 + t^2/2)$—an input-output pair for $\mathcal{A}$—can satisfy *9* over $[0,\infty)$.

Essentially, the purpose of the mutual-consistency condition is to ensure that the input-output relation *1* and the input-output-state relation *3* (or, equivalently, *4*) represent the same object $\mathcal{A}$.

11 **First self-consistency condition** For all t_0, the response $\mathbf{y}(t)$ at any time $t > t_0$ is uniquely determined by $\boldsymbol{\alpha}$ and $\mathbf{u}_{(t_0,t]}$. In other words, in order to qualify as a state space of $\mathcal{A}$, Σ must have the property that, given any point $\boldsymbol{\alpha}$ in Σ (which we call the state of $\mathcal{A}$ at time t_0) and any input $\mathbf{u}_{(t_0,t]}$ in the input segment space of $\mathcal{A}$, the output of $\mathcal{A}$ at time t is uniquely determined by $\boldsymbol{\alpha}$ and $\mathbf{u}_{(t_0,t]}$ and hence is independent of the values of $\mathbf{u}$ and $\mathbf{y}$ prior to t_0. As was stressed in our informal discussion in Sec. *5*, this is the key property of the notion of state. ◁

12 *Example* It is obvious that the input-output-state relation *9* satisfies the first self-consistency condition. Note that this is true regardless of the range of α.

As another example, consider a nonoriented object $\mathcal{A}$ which is characterized by the terminal relation

13 $$v_3 = v_1 + v_2$$

Assume that $\mathcal{A}$ is oriented by designating v_3 as the input variable and v_1 and v_2 as the output variables. That is, $u \triangleq v_3$ and $\mathbf{y} \triangleq (v_1,v_2)$. Furthermore, assume that Σ is identified with $\mathcal{R}^1$ and that

14 $$y_1 = \alpha u \qquad y_1 \triangleq v_1,\ y_2 \triangleq v_2,\ u \triangleq v_3$$
$$y_2 = (1 - \alpha)u$$

in which $\alpha \in \mathcal{R}^1$. Then it is evident that u, y, Σ, and the input-output-state relation *14* satisfy the first self-consistency condition. On the other hand, the mutual-consistency condition is not satisfied, because while it is true that every pair (u,y) which satisfies *14* also satisfies *13*, the converse is clearly untrue. ◁

A simple example of an input-output-state relation which does not satisfy the first self-consistency condition because of nonuniqueness is

$$y^2 = \alpha u \qquad \alpha \in \mathcal{R}^1$$

where u and y are real-valued time functions. Another example is

$$y(t) = \alpha + \int_{t_0}^{t+1} u(\xi)\, d\xi \qquad \alpha \in \mathcal{R}^1,\ t > t_0$$

Here the condition is violated because the output at time t cannot be determined without the knowledge of the values of the input between t and $t + 1$.

15 **Second self-consistency condition** If the input-output-state relation *4* is satisfied by an input-output pair $(\mathbf{u}_{(t_0,t_1]},\mathbf{y}_{(t_0,t_1]})$, then it is also satisfied by all input-output pairs of the form $(\mathbf{u}_{(t,t_1]},\mathbf{y}_{(t,t_1]})$, where $t_0 < t \leq t_1$ and $\mathbf{u}_{(t,t_1]}$ and $\mathbf{y}_{(t,t_1]}$ are sections of $\mathbf{u}_{(t_0,t_1]}$ and $\mathbf{y}_{(t_0,t_1]}$, respectively. This must hold true for all $\boldsymbol{\alpha}$ in Σ and all input-output pairs associated with $\boldsymbol{\alpha}$.

16 **Remark** Before we begin to discuss the significance of this condition it will be helpful to simplify the notation by introducing the following abbreviations.

(I) A segment of the input such as $\mathbf{u}_{(t_0,t]}$ defined over an observation interval $(t_0,t]$ will be denoted simply by $\mathbf{u}$.

(II) A segment of the input defined over $(t,t_1]$ will be denoted by $\mathbf{u}'$.

(III) The segment $\mathbf{u}_{(t_0,t_1]}$, which consists of $\mathbf{u}_{(t_0,t]}$ followed by $\mathbf{u}_{(t,t_1]}$, will be denoted by $\mathbf{uu}'$.

(IV) The response of $\mathcal{A}$ at time t to $\mathbf{u}_{(t_0,t]}$ starting in state $\boldsymbol{\alpha}_0$ will be denoted by

17 $$\mathbf{y}(t) \triangleq \mathbf{A}(\boldsymbol{\alpha}_0;\mathbf{u})$$

and the corresponding response segment $\mathbf{y}_{(t_0,t]}$ will be expressed as

18 $$\mathbf{y}_{(t_0,t]} \triangleq \bar{\mathbf{A}}(\boldsymbol{\alpha}_0;\mathbf{u})$$

with the bar in $\bar{\mathbf{A}}$ signifying that $\bar{\mathbf{A}}(\boldsymbol{\alpha}_0;\mathbf{u})$ is a segment of $\mathbf{y}$ and not just the value of $\mathbf{y}$ at time t.

(V) The symbol $\bar{\mathbf{A}}(\boldsymbol{\alpha}_1;\mathbf{u}')$ will stand for $\mathbf{y}_{(t,t_1]}$, that is, the response segment of $\mathcal{A}$ to $\mathbf{u}'$ ($\triangleq \mathbf{u}_{(t,t_1]}$) with $\mathcal{A}$ starting in state $\boldsymbol{\alpha}_1$ at time t_1. ◁

Using the above notation, let $(\mathbf{uu}',\mathbf{yy}')$ be an input-output pair satisfying the input-output-state relation *4* with $\boldsymbol{\alpha} = \boldsymbol{\alpha}_0$. That is,

19 $$\mathbf{yy}' = \bar{\mathbf{A}}(\boldsymbol{\alpha}_0;\mathbf{uu}')$$

Now, to say that $(\mathbf{u}',\mathbf{y}')$ satisfies *4* is equivalent to saying that there exists a nonempty set Q of values of $\boldsymbol{\alpha}$ in Σ such that

20 $$\mathbf{y}' = \bar{\mathbf{A}}(\boldsymbol{\alpha};\mathbf{u}')$$

is satisfied for all $\boldsymbol{\alpha}$ in Q. In symbols,

21 $$Q \triangleq \{\boldsymbol{\alpha} | \mathbf{y}' = \bar{\mathbf{A}}(\boldsymbol{\alpha};\mathbf{u}')\} \qquad \boldsymbol{\alpha} \in \Sigma$$

that is, Q is the set of all $\boldsymbol{\alpha}$ in Σ which satisfy *20*. Thus, in terms of Q the second self-consistency condition can be expressed as follows.

The set Q is nonempty for all $\mathbf{u}$, $\mathbf{u}'$, *and* $\boldsymbol{\alpha}_0$. This statement is merely an abbreviation of the equivalent statement, *if* $(\mathbf{uu}',\mathbf{yy}')$ *is any input-output pair satisfying the input-output-state relation 4, then* $(\mathbf{u}',\mathbf{y}')$ *also satisfies 4; that is,*

22 $$\mathbf{y}' = \bar{\mathbf{A}}(\boldsymbol{\alpha};\mathbf{u}')$$

for some $\boldsymbol{\alpha}$ *in* Σ (see Fig. *1.6.1*). It is understood that this must hold true for all $\boldsymbol{\alpha} \in \Sigma$, all $\mathbf{uu}'$ in the input segment space of $\mathcal{A}$, and all t_0, t, and t_1.

Essentially, the second self-consistency condition is designed to ensure that the state space Σ is sufficiently "rich" to include all possible initial conditions in $\mathcal{A}$. To illustrate this point, consider the following

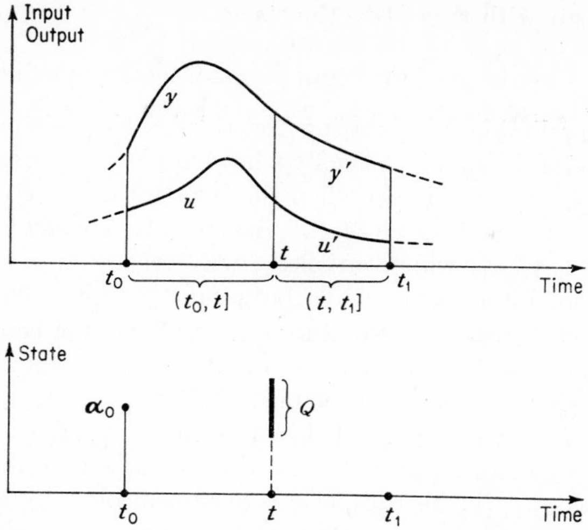

Fig. 1.6.1 Significance of the second self-consistency condition.

23 *Example* Let $\mathcal{A}$ be an object characterized by the input-output-state relation

24
$$y(t) = \alpha^2 + \int_{t_0}^{t} u(\xi)\, d\xi$$

where u and y are real-valued time functions and α ranges over the real line. Suppose that initially (at $t_0 = 0$) α is 1 and $u(t) = -2t$ over the observation interval $[0,3]$. Then $y(t) = 1 - t^2$ over $[0,3]$, so that the input-output pair associated with α_0 ($\alpha_0 = 1$) is $(-2t, 1 - t^2)$ over $[0,3]$.

Let the intermediate time t be 2. Then, it is easy to verify that the only value of α^2 for which *24* can be satisfied by the pair $(-2t, 1 - t^2)$ over $[2,3]$ is given by

25
$$\begin{aligned} \alpha^2 &= 1 + \int_0^2 (-2\xi)\, d\xi \\ &= -3 \end{aligned}$$

Since the equation $\alpha^2 = -3$ does not have a solution in Σ, it follows that Q is empty and hence the second self-consistency condition is not satisfied.

The condition in question would be satisfied if, instead of *24*, we had

26
$$y(t) = \alpha + \int_{t_0}^{t} u(\xi)\, d\xi$$

In this case, for any α_0 in Σ and any τ in the interval $(t_0,t]$ *26* yields

27
$$y(t) = \alpha_0 + \int_{t_0}^{\tau} u(\xi)\, d\xi + \int_{\tau}^{t} u(\xi)\, d\xi \qquad t_0 < \tau \le t$$

which indicates that for every τ in $(t_0,t]$ the pair $(u_{(\tau,t]}, y_{(\tau,t]})$ is an input-output pair with respect to the state

28 $$\alpha_1 = \alpha_0 + \int_{t_0}^{\tau} u(\xi)\, d\xi \quad \triangleleft$$

As a preliminary to stating the third self-consistency condition, it will be helpful to analyze briefly what happens to the set Q in the second self-consistency condition when the segment $\mathbf{u}'$ ($\triangleq \mathbf{u}_{(t,t_1]}$) is varied over the input segment space of $\mathfrak{A}$. Specifically, consider an input-output pair $(\mathbf{u}_{(t_0,t_1]},\mathbf{y}_{(t_0,t_1]})$ which satisfies *4* with respect to a state $\boldsymbol{\alpha}_0$ in Σ, and let t be an intermediate time between t_0 and t_1. Assuming that the second self-consistency condition is satisfied, the set Q of values of $\boldsymbol{\alpha}$ with respect to which $(\mathbf{u}',\mathbf{y}')$ is an input-output pair is nonempty. Since the only variables in the problem are $\boldsymbol{\alpha}_0$, t, $\mathbf{u}_{(t_0,t_1]}$, and $\mathbf{y}_{(t_0,t_1]}$, Q can depend only on these variables. If, in addition, we assume that the first self-consistency condition is satisfied, then $\mathbf{y}_{(t_0,t_1]}$ is uniquely determined by $\boldsymbol{\alpha}_0$ and $\mathbf{u}_{(t_0,t_1]}$. In this case, Q is determined solely by $\boldsymbol{\alpha}_0$, t, and $\mathbf{u}_{(t_0,t_1]}$ or, if t is held fixed, by $\boldsymbol{\alpha}_0$, $\mathbf{u}$, and $\mathbf{u}'$ (since $\mathbf{u}_{(t_0,t_1]} = \mathbf{u}\mathbf{u}'$). To make this more explicit, we shall write Q as $Q(\boldsymbol{\alpha}_0;\mathbf{u},\mathbf{u}')$. Thus

29 $$Q(\boldsymbol{\alpha}_0;\mathbf{u},\mathbf{u}') \triangleq \{\boldsymbol{\alpha}|\mathbf{y}\mathbf{y}' = \bar{\mathbf{A}}(\boldsymbol{\alpha}_0;\mathbf{u}\mathbf{u}') \text{ and } \mathbf{y}' = \bar{\mathbf{A}}(\boldsymbol{\alpha};\mathbf{u}')\}$$

Consider now a series of experiments in which $\boldsymbol{\alpha}_0$ and $\mathbf{u}$ ($\triangleq \mathbf{u}_{(t_0,t]}$) are the same for all experiments but $\mathbf{u}'$ ($\triangleq \mathbf{u}_{(t,t_1]}$) is varied from experiment to experiment. (It is understood that not only the values of $\mathbf{u}'$ over $(t,t_1]$ but also the value of t_1 are varied.) For simplicity, assume that two experiments are performed on $\mathfrak{A}$ and that in one of them the input $\mathbf{u}'$ is equal to, say, $\mathbf{v}$ (that is, $\mathbf{u}_{(t,t_1]} = \mathbf{v}_{(t,t_1]}$) and in the other $\mathbf{u}'$ is equal to $\mathbf{w}$, with $\mathbf{v} \neq \mathbf{w}$. This is illustrated in Fig. *1.6.2*, where $\mathbf{y}_\mathbf{v}$ and $\mathbf{y}_\mathbf{w}$ denote the corresponding response segments of $\mathfrak{A}$.

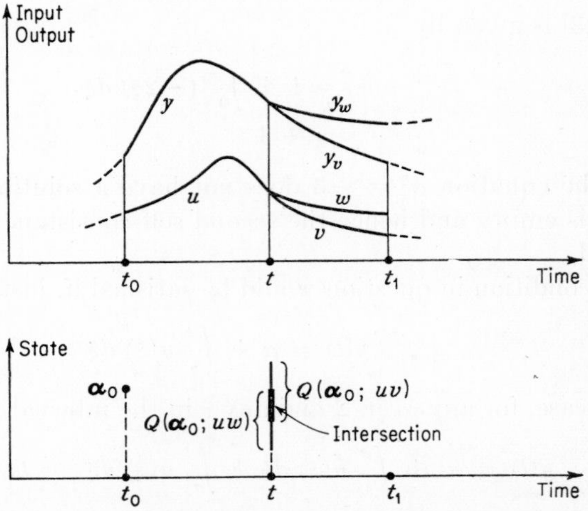

Fig. 1.6.2 Significance of the third self-consistency condition.

Now the set Q for the first experiment is $Q(\boldsymbol{\alpha}_0;\mathbf{u},\mathbf{v})$, and for the second experiment it is $Q(\boldsymbol{\alpha}_0;\mathbf{u},\mathbf{w})$. By definition, $Q(\boldsymbol{\alpha}_0;\mathbf{u},\mathbf{v})$ is the set of all points in Σ with respect to which $(\mathbf{v},\mathbf{y}_\mathbf{v})$ is an input-output pair satisfying

30 $$\mathbf{y}_\mathbf{v} = \bar{\mathbf{A}}(\boldsymbol{\alpha};\mathbf{v})$$

and

31 $$\mathbf{y}\mathbf{y}_\mathbf{v} = \bar{\mathbf{A}}(\boldsymbol{\alpha}_0;\mathbf{u}\mathbf{v})$$

Likewise, $Q(\boldsymbol{\alpha}_0;\mathbf{u},\mathbf{w})$ is the set of all points in Σ with respect to which $(\mathbf{w},\mathbf{y}_\mathbf{w})$ is an input-output pair satisfying

32 $$\mathbf{y}_\mathbf{w} = \bar{\mathbf{A}}(\boldsymbol{\alpha};\mathbf{w})$$

and

33 $$\mathbf{y}\mathbf{y}_\mathbf{w} = \bar{\mathbf{A}}(\boldsymbol{\alpha}_0;\mathbf{u}\mathbf{w})$$

Thus, the set of all points in Σ with respect to which *both* $(\mathbf{v},\mathbf{y}_\mathbf{v})$ and $(\mathbf{w},\mathbf{y}_\mathbf{w})$ are input-output pairs satisfying both *30*, *31* and *32*, *33* is the *intersection* of $Q(\boldsymbol{\alpha}_0;\mathbf{u},\mathbf{v})$ and $Q(\boldsymbol{\alpha}_0;\mathbf{u},\mathbf{w})$, that is, $Q(\boldsymbol{\alpha}_0;\mathbf{u},\mathbf{v}) \cap Q(\boldsymbol{\alpha}_0;\mathbf{u},\mathbf{w})$.

More generally, if we consider the totality of experiments in which $\boldsymbol{\alpha}_0$ and $\mathbf{u}$ are held fixed and $\mathbf{u}'$ is varied over the input segment space of $\mathcal{A}$, and if we form the intersection of all the Q sets corresponding to these experiments, then the intersection (if it is not empty) will constitute the set of all points in Σ with respect to which every pair $(\mathbf{u}',\mathbf{y}')$ satisfying the input-output-state relation

34 $$\mathbf{y}\mathbf{y}' = \bar{\mathbf{A}}(\boldsymbol{\alpha}_0;\mathbf{u}\mathbf{u}')$$

satisfies

$$\mathbf{y}' = \bar{\mathbf{A}}(\boldsymbol{\alpha};\mathbf{u}')$$

for all $\boldsymbol{\alpha}$ in the intersection. Clearly, it would not be meaningful to speak of the "state of $\mathcal{A}$ at time t" if the intersection in question were empty; for to do so would imply that there does not exist a point (state) in Σ which can account for all possible input-output pairs starting at time t.

With these observations as a background, we are prepared to express the third self-consistency condition in a concise fashion.

35 **Third self-consistency condition** Let $(\mathbf{u}\mathbf{u}',\mathbf{y}\mathbf{y}')$ (where $\mathbf{u}\mathbf{u}' \triangleq \mathbf{u}_{(t_0,t_1]}$, $\mathbf{y}\mathbf{y}' \triangleq \mathbf{y}_{(t_0,t_1]}$, $\mathbf{u} \triangleq \mathbf{u}_{(t_0,t]}$, $\mathbf{u}' \triangleq \mathbf{u}_{(t,t_1]}$) be an input-output pair satisfying *4* (or, equivalently, *3*) with respect to some value of $\boldsymbol{\alpha}$, say, $\boldsymbol{\alpha}_0$, in Σ. In symbols,

36 $$\mathbf{y}\mathbf{y}' = \bar{\mathbf{A}}(\boldsymbol{\alpha}_0;\mathbf{u}\mathbf{u}')$$

which is merely a restatement of *34*. Furthermore, let $Q(\boldsymbol{\alpha}_0;\mathbf{u},\mathbf{u}')$ be the set of all $\boldsymbol{\alpha}$ in Σ with respect to which $(\mathbf{u}',\mathbf{y}')$ is an input-output pair satisfying *4*. That is,

37 $$Q(\boldsymbol{\alpha}_0;\mathbf{u},\mathbf{u}') \triangleq \{\boldsymbol{\alpha}|\mathbf{y}' = \bar{\mathbf{A}}(\boldsymbol{\alpha};\mathbf{u}') \text{ and } \mathbf{y}\mathbf{y}' = \bar{\mathbf{A}}(\boldsymbol{\alpha}_0;\mathbf{u}\mathbf{u}')\}$$

which is a restatement of *29*. Then, the third self-consistency condition requires that the intersection

38 $$Q_t \triangleq \bigcap_{\mathbf{u}'} Q(\boldsymbol{\alpha}_0;\mathbf{u},\mathbf{u}')$$

taken over all $\mathbf{u}'(\triangleq \mathbf{u}_{(t,t_1]})$ in the input segment space of $\mathcal{A}$ be nonempty for all t_0, all $\boldsymbol{\alpha}_0 \in \Sigma$, and all segments $\mathbf{u}$ in the input segment space of $\mathcal{A}$. Since Q_t as defined by *38* depends only on $\boldsymbol{\alpha}_0$ and $\mathbf{u}$, we shall denote it by $Q_t(\boldsymbol{\alpha}_0;\mathbf{u})$, where t identifies the right end point of the observation interval on which $\mathbf{u}$ is defined.

39 **Remark** Note that it follows at once from the way in which the third self-consistency condition is formulated that it cannot be satisfied unless all the $Q(\boldsymbol{\alpha}_0;\mathbf{u},\mathbf{u}')$ sets are nonempty, which implies that if the third self-consistency condition is satisfied, then the second self-consistency condition is also satisfied. In this sense, the third self-consistency condition *implies* the second self-consistency condition. The converse, however, is not true. Indeed, it is not difficult to construct examples of relations of the form $\mathbf{y} = \bar{\mathbf{A}}(\boldsymbol{\alpha};\mathbf{u})$ which satisfy the first and second self-consistency conditions but not the third self-consistency condition. (*Exercise:* Construct such an example.)

Essentially, the purpose of the third self-consistency condition is to make it meaningful to speak of "the state of $\mathcal{A}$ at time t." This basic notion will be defined in Sec. *7*. $\lhd$

To illustrate the third self-consistency condition, we shall use a simple

40 *Example* Consider the input-output-state relation

41 $$y(t) = \alpha + \int_{t_0}^{t} u(\xi)\, d\xi$$

where u and y are real-valued time functions and Σ is the real line. For concreteness, let $\alpha_0 = -3$, $t_0 = 0$, $t = 1$, $t_1 > 1$, and $u(\xi) = 2 - 2\xi$ for $0 < \xi \leq t$. The values of $u(\xi)$ for ξ between 1 and t_1 are assumed to vary from experiment to experiment (see Fig. *1.6.2*).

In order to avoid confusion with t (which in our example is fixed at 1), let τ denote the running time in the interval $(1,t_1]$. Then, on dividing the range of integration in *41* into two parts, from 0 to 1 and from 1 to τ, we have for the assumed α_0, t_0, t, and $u_{(0,\tau]}$

42 $$y(\tau) = -3 + \int_0^1 (2 - 2\xi)\, d\xi + \int_1^{\tau} u(\xi)\, d\xi \qquad 1 < \tau \leq t_1$$

or

43 $$y(\tau) = -2 + \int_1^{\tau} u(\xi)\, d\xi \qquad 1 < \tau \leq t_1$$

Clearly, this relation is of the same form as *41*, which implies that $(u_{(1,t_1]}, y_{(1,t_1]})$, where $y_{(1,t_1]}$ is defined by *43*, satisfies the input-output-state relation *41* with $\alpha = -2$. Consequently, the set Q (as defined by *37*) is nonempty, since it contains $\alpha = -2$ as an element. (Note that $u_{(1,t_1]}$ and $y_{(1,t_1]}$ play the roles of $\mathbf{u}'$ and $\mathbf{y}'$, respectively.) Furthermore, no matter what $u_{(1,t_1]}$ is, the pair $(u_{(1,t_1]}, y_{(1,t_1]})$ will satisfy *41* with $\alpha = -2$. Consequently, all the Q sets corresponding to different $u_{(1,t_1]}$ contain the point $\alpha = -2$ and hence so does their intersection Q_1 (defined by *38*). This verifies that Q_1 is nonempty when $t = 1$ and $u(\xi) = 2 - 2\xi$ for $0 < \xi \leq t$. Obviously, the same conclusion holds for arbitrary t between t_0 and t_1 as well as arbitrary $u_{(t_0,t]}$. Consequently, *41* satisfies the third self-consistency condition.

44 **Remark** Suppose that we have established that an input-output-state relation $\mathbf{y} = \mathbf{A}(\boldsymbol{\alpha};\mathbf{u})$, in which $\boldsymbol{\alpha} \in \Sigma$, satisfies the four consistency conditions. Then it is evident that the input-output-state relation $\mathbf{y} = \bar{\mathbf{A}}(\boldsymbol{\alpha}',\mathbf{u})$, where $\boldsymbol{\alpha}'$ is a variable which is in one-one correspondence with $\boldsymbol{\alpha}$, will also satisfy the four consistency conditions. In other words, if $\boldsymbol{\alpha}' = \boldsymbol{\mu}(\boldsymbol{\alpha})$, where $\boldsymbol{\mu}$ denotes a one-one mapping of Σ onto itself, then the values of $\boldsymbol{\alpha}'$ also qualify as states of $\mathcal{A}$. Note that such one-one transformations on the state space amount merely to a relabeling of the elements of Σ and that relabeling does not affect the consistency conditions or the form of the input-output-state relation. However, a relabeling will, in general, change the form of the so-called state equations of $\mathcal{A}$ (see Sec. *8*). For this reason, it may be advantageous in specific cases to use $\boldsymbol{\alpha}'$—where $\boldsymbol{\alpha}'$ is in one-one correspondence with $\boldsymbol{\alpha}$—rather than $\boldsymbol{\alpha}$ itself as a description of a state of $\mathcal{A}$ in order to simplify the form of state equations. In the cases which we shall consider in later chapters, the transformations in question are linear and amount essentially to a change in the coordinate system of Σ. $\lhd$

This concludes our formulation and discussion of Definition *2*. Additional comments and examples clarifying the significance of the various concepts introduced in this definition are presented in the following two sections.

7 *More on the notion of state and oriented objects*

As will be shown in Chap. *2* (*2.2.19*), the set Q_t defined by *1.6.38* comprises values of $\boldsymbol{\alpha}$ which are *equivalent* in the sense that (I) the response of $\mathcal{A}$ to $\mathbf{u}'$ is the same for all starting states in Q_t and (II) this holds true for all $\mathbf{u}'$ in the input segment space of $\mathcal{A}$. In this sense, any $\boldsymbol{\alpha}$ in Q_t can be regarded as a representative of the entire set Q_t.

This fact permits us to define the state of $\mathcal{A}$ at time t as follows.

1 **Definition** Consider an object $\mathcal{A}$ which is characterized by the input-output-state relation (see *1.6.3* and *1.6.4*)

2 $$\mathbf{y}(t) = \mathbf{A}(\boldsymbol{\alpha}_0;\mathbf{u}_{(t_0,t]})$$

or equivalently

$$\mathbf{y}_{(t_0,t]} = \bar{\mathbf{A}}(\boldsymbol{\alpha}_0;\mathbf{u}_{(t_0,t]})$$

where $\boldsymbol{\alpha}_0$ ranges over the state space Σ. Let $\mathbf{u} \triangleq \mathbf{u}_{(t_0,t]}$, $\mathbf{y} \triangleq \mathbf{y}_{(t_0,t]}$, and let $\mathbf{uu}'$ denote the segment $\mathbf{u}$ followed by a segment $\mathbf{u}'$ (see *1.6.16*) and $\mathbf{yy}'$ denote the response of $\mathcal{A}$ to $\mathbf{uu}'$ starting in state $\boldsymbol{\alpha}_0$. Thus

$$\mathbf{yy}' = \bar{\mathbf{A}}(\boldsymbol{\alpha}_0;\mathbf{uu}')$$

As in *1.6.29* and *1.6.38*, define the sets Q and Q_t by

3 $$Q \triangleq Q(\boldsymbol{\alpha}_0;\mathbf{u},\mathbf{u}') \triangleq \{\boldsymbol{\alpha}|\mathbf{yy}' = \bar{\mathbf{A}}(\boldsymbol{\alpha}_0;\mathbf{uu}') \text{ and } \mathbf{y}' = \bar{\mathbf{A}}(\boldsymbol{\alpha};\mathbf{u}')\}$$

4 $$Q_t \triangleq Q_t(\boldsymbol{\alpha}_0;\mathbf{u}) \triangleq \bigcap_{\mathbf{u}'} Q(\boldsymbol{\alpha}_0;\mathbf{u},\mathbf{u}')$$

Then the *state of* $\mathcal{A}$ *at time* t is defined to be any state $\boldsymbol{\alpha}$ in $Q_t(\boldsymbol{\alpha}_0;\mathbf{u})$, with $\boldsymbol{\alpha}_0$ being the state of $\mathcal{A}$ at time t_0, or equivalently, the starting (initial) state of $\mathcal{A}$. [Note that in this definition we could not have said "any state $\boldsymbol{\alpha}$ in Q_t" were it not for the fact that all the elements of Q_t are equivalent to one another (*2.2.19*).] ◁

The state of $\mathcal{A}$ at time t will be denoted by $\mathbf{s}(t)$,[1] with the understanding that $\mathbf{s}(t)$ is merely a label which identifies an element of $Q_t(\boldsymbol{\alpha}_0;\mathbf{u})$, say, $\boldsymbol{\alpha}$, as the state of $\mathcal{A}$ at time t. Consistent with this notation, the initial state of $\mathcal{A}$ at time t_0 will be denoted by $\mathbf{s}(t_0)$. When we wish to place in evidence that $\mathbf{s}(t_0)$ is the initial state of $\mathcal{A}$, the input-output-state relation *2* will be written as

5 $$\mathbf{y}(t) = \mathbf{A}(\mathbf{s}(t_0);\mathbf{u}_{(t_0,t]})$$

Note that $\mathbf{s}(t_0)$ and, more generally, $\mathbf{s}(t)$ range over the state space Σ; that is, for each fixed t, $R[\mathbf{s}(t)] = \Sigma$ (see *1.3.4*). The components of $\mathbf{s}(t)$ will be called the *state variables* of $\mathcal{A}$. ◁

Consider an object $\mathcal{A}$ which is initially in state $\mathbf{s}(t_0)$ and to which an input $\mathbf{u}_{(t_0,t_1]}$ is applied. The state of $\mathcal{A}$ at time t_1, $\mathbf{s}(t_1)$, is called the *terminal state of* $\mathcal{A}$ relative to the input $\mathbf{u}_{(t_0,t_1]}$. Clearly, if the input segment $\mathbf{u}_{(t_0,t_1]}$ is followed by another input segment $\mathbf{u}_{(t_1,t_2]}$, then $\mathbf{s}(t_1)$ plays the dual role of the terminal state for $\mathbf{u}_{(t_0,t_1]}$ and the initial state for $\mathbf{u}_{(t_1,t_2]}$. Note also that the state of $\mathcal{A}$ at time t may be regarded as

[1] In Chap. *3* we shall switch to the symbol $\mathbf{x}(t)$ to denote the state of $\mathcal{A}$ at time t in order to avoid confusion with the complex variable s and to conform more closely to the notation commonly employed in the theory of ordinary differential equations.

the terminal state of $\mathcal{A}$ relative to the input $\mathbf{u}_{(t_0,t]}$. On occasion we shall find it convenient to use the notation $\boldsymbol{\alpha}_0^*$ for the terminal state relative to $\mathbf{u}_{(t_0,t]}$ when the initial state is $\boldsymbol{\alpha}_0$.

6 *Comment* It should be recalled (see *1.3.3*) that the segment $\mathbf{u}_{(t_0,t]}$ is defined as the set of pairs $\{(\tau,\mathbf{u}(\tau))\}$, with $t_0 < \tau \leq t$. Thus, when we write $\mathbf{y}(t) = \mathbf{A}(\mathbf{s}(t_0);\mathbf{u}_{(t_0,t]})$, it is understood that $\mathbf{y}(t)$ depends not only on $\mathbf{s}(t_0)$ and the values of $\mathbf{u}(\tau)$ for $t_0 < \tau \leq t$ but also on the end points t_0 and t. If this is not the case, i.e., if $\mathbf{y}(t)$ depends only on $\mathbf{s}(t_0)$ and $\mathbf{u}(\tau)$, $t_0 < \tau \leq t$, then $\mathcal{A}$ is a *time-invariant* object. The notion of time invariance will be discussed in greater detail in Chap. *3*, Sec. *2*.

7 *Comment* As was pointed out in *1.5.5*, we use $\mathbf{u}_{(t_0,t]}$ rather than $\mathbf{u}_{[t_0,t]}$ in the input-output-state relation for two reasons: (I) to avoid overlap between two adjoining segments such as $\mathbf{u}_{(t_0,t]}$ and $\mathbf{u}_{(t,t_1]}$ and (II) to resolve the ambiguity arising when $\mathbf{u}$ is discontinuous or has a delta function at $t = t_0$. Furthermore, to write the input as $\mathbf{u}_{(t_0,t]}$ is consistent with our intuitive feeling that the input is applied "slightly" after the initial state is established. In later chapters, we shall frequently find it more convenient to resolve the ambiguity in question by identifying the initial state with the state of $\mathcal{A}$ at time t_0-, that is, the instant immediately preceding t_0. In this case, the input will be assumed to start at t_0 rather than at t_0+ (the instant immediately following t_0) as in *5*. (This point will be elaborated upon in later chapters in the course of our discussion of linear systems.) Needless to say, when $\mathbf{u}$ is sufficiently smooth at t_0, it does not matter whether $\mathbf{u}_{(t_0,t]}$ or $\mathbf{u}_{[t_0,t]}$ is used in *5*.

8 *Comment* In dealing with an object $\mathcal{A}$ which is characterized by an input-output relation $\mathcal{A}(\mathbf{u},\mathbf{y}) = 0$ (*1.4.17*), it will be our standard practice to associate a state vector $\mathbf{s}(t)$ with $\mathcal{A}$ by defining $\mathbf{s}(t)$ in terms of $\mathbf{u}_{(t_0,t]}$ and $\mathbf{y}_{(t_0,t]}$ and then proceed to verify that it satisfies the mutual- and self-consistency conditions. As we shall see later in Chap. 4, in cases in which the input-output relation $\mathcal{A}(\mathbf{u},\mathbf{y}) = 0$ is a differential equation, $\mathbf{s}(t)$ can be defined in terms of $\mathbf{u}(t)$, $\mathbf{y}(t)$, and a finite number of their derivatives at t. As was indicated previously (*1.6.44*), a variety of other expressions for $\mathbf{s}(t)$ in terms of $\mathbf{u}_{(t_0,t]}$ and $\mathbf{y}_{(t_0,t]}$ can be obtained by changing the coordinate system in the state space. The important point to bear in mind is that there are many ways in which a state vector $\mathbf{s}(t)$ can be associated with an object characterized by an input-output relation; so that when we speak of $\mathbf{s}(t)$ as *the* state of $\mathcal{A}$ at time t, we do not mean that there is just one way of defining $\mathbf{s}(t)$ in terms of the input and output of $\mathcal{A}$. This point will be elaborated upon in Chap. *4*, Sec. *2*.

9 *Comment* Throughout the foregoing discussion we have tacitly assumed that the time function $\mathbf{s}$ is defined for all t. This assumption is usually satisfied in practice. It is not difficult, however, to envisage situations in which **s** may have discontinuities or, worse, may contain delta functions of various orders. In such cases **s** may be undefined for one or more values of t and, strictly speaking, should be regarded as a distribution (see *A.4.1 et seq.*) rather than a function of time in the classical sense of the term.

We proceed to illustrate the notions introduced above by several informal examples. In the discussion of these examples we shall not attempt to be completely rigorous, since we have not yet developed the necessary techniques for dealing with the types of objects which are used as illustrations. Such techniques will be developed in later chapters.

10 *Example* Consider first a very simple type of object, namely, an electrical capacitor. The abstract model $\mathcal{A}$ of such a capacitor is characterized by the terminal relation

$$i = C\frac{dv}{dt}$$

where $i \triangleq$ current through the capacitor, $v \triangleq$ voltage across the capacitor, and $C \triangleq$ capacitance, which is assumed to be a positive constant.

Let $\mathcal{A}$ be oriented by designating i to be the input and v the output. Now let us ask the question: What does one have to know about $\mathcal{A}$ at time t_0 in order to be able to find the value of the output v at any time $t > t_0$, given the values of the input ($\triangleq i$) between t_0 and t? The answer is clearly $v(t_0)$, for by integrating between t_0 and t, we have

11 $$v(t) = v(t_0) + \frac{1}{C}\int_{t_0}^{t} i(\xi)\, d\xi$$

which in effect is the input-output-state relation for $\mathcal{A}$, with $v(t_0)$ playing the role of $s(t_0)$. Here the state space Σ is the real line $(-\infty, \infty)$, as are the input and output spaces $R[i(t)]$ and $R[v(t)]$.

We have already verified that *11* satisfies the consistency conditions (see *1.6.12* and *1.6.40*), with the state of $\mathcal{A}$ at time t given by $v(t)$. Note that if there is a possibility that i may contain a delta function $\delta(t - t_0)$ at t_0, then *11* should be written as

$$v(t) = v(t_0-) + \frac{1}{C}\int_{t_0}^{t} i(\xi)\, d\xi \qquad t \geq t_0$$

with the understanding that $\delta(t - t_0)$ is included in the range of integration $[t_0,t]$. For example, if $i(t) = \delta(t)$ and $t_0 < 0 < t$, then (see Appendix A)

$$v(t) = v(t_0-) + \frac{1}{C}\int_{t_0}^{t} \delta(\xi)\, d\xi$$

$$= v(t_0-) + \frac{1}{C} \qquad t > 0$$

which shows that there is a jump in v at 0 equal to $1/C$.

It is instructive to consider also the case where $\mathcal{A}$ is oriented by designating v to be the input and i to be the output. In this case, care must be exercised because of the possibility that the input may be discontinuous at t_0. On defining the initial state to be $s(t_0-)$ rather than $s(t_0)$ (see Comment *7*), the input-output-state relation is found to be (see *1.10.18*)

$$i(t) = C\frac{dv}{dt} - Cv(t_0-)\delta(t - t_0)$$

where $\delta(t - t_0)$ is a delta function at $t = t_0$, $v(t_0-)$ represents the state of $\mathcal{A}$ at time t_0-, $v(t)$ is assumed to vanish for $t < t_0$, and dv/dt is the derivative of v in the distribution sense. [For example, if $v(t)$ is the unit step function, $v(t) = 1(t)$, then $dv/dt = \delta(t)$. See Appendix *A* for a fuller discussion.] Note that the state at time t is simply $v(t)$.

12 *Example* Consider the abstract model of a particle $\mathcal{P}$ in one-dimensional space to be an oriented object $\mathcal{A}$ with applied force f as the input and the position of the particle ($\triangleq x$) as the output. In this case, the input-output relation for the object is

13 $$m\ddot{x} = f$$

where $m \triangleq$ mass and $\ddot{x} \triangleq$ acceleration.

We observe that (I) knowing the position and velocity of $\mathcal{A}$ at any time t and (II) knowing $f_{(t_0,t]}$, we can find the position at any time $t > t_0$ by integrating *13* and using the position and velocity at time t_0 as initial conditions. This suggests that the vector

$$\mathbf{s}(t_0) = (x(t_0),\dot{x}(t_0))$$

with components $x(t_0)$ and $\dot{x}(t_0)$, is a likely candidate for the state of $\mathcal{A}$ at time t_0. The corresponding input-output-state relation can readily be found by integrating both sides of *13* twice and substituting $x(t_0)$ and $\dot{x}(t_0)$ for the initial conditions at t_0. The result reads:

14 $$x(t) = x(t_0) + \dot{x}(t_0)(t - t_0) + \frac{1}{m}\int_{t_0}^{t} d\eta \int_{t_0}^{\eta} d\xi\ f(\xi)$$

or in vector form

15 $$x(t) = \langle \mathbf{s}(t_0),\boldsymbol{\tau}(t - t_0)\rangle + \frac{1}{m}\int_{t_0}^{t} d\eta \int_{t_0}^{\eta} d\xi\ f(\xi)$$

where $\langle \mathbf{a},\mathbf{b}\rangle$ denotes the scalar product of two vectors **a** and **b** and $\boldsymbol{\tau}(t - t_0)$ is the vector

$$\boldsymbol{\tau}(t - t_0) = (1,\ t - t_0)$$

If we had assumed that the point in question moves in three-dimensional rather than one-dimensional space, then $\mathbf{x}(t)$ and $\dot{\mathbf{x}}(t)$ would be 3-vectors and the state $\mathbf{s}(t_0)$ would have $\mathbf{x}(t_0)$ and $\dot{\mathbf{x}}(t_0)$ as vector components:

16 $$\mathbf{s}(t_0) = (\mathbf{x}(t_0),\ \dot{\mathbf{x}}(t_0))$$

In this case, the input-output-state relation has exactly the same form as *15* with $x(t)$ and $\dot{x}(t)$ replaced by $\mathbf{x}(t)$ and $\dot{\mathbf{x}}(t)$, respectively. Note that the state space in this case is six-dimensional ($\Sigma = \mathcal{R}^6$), whereas the input and output spaces are three-dimensional ($R[\mathbf{x}(t)] = R[\mathbf{f}(t)] = \mathcal{R}^3$). ($\mathcal{R}^n \triangleq$ space of ordered n-tuples of real numbers.)

It is intuitively obvious and it will be proved in a general way in Chap. *4* that *14* satisfies the four consistency conditions and that the state of $\mathcal{A}$ at time t is given by the vector $\mathbf{s}(t) = (x(t),\dot{x}(t))$. By differentiating *14* with respect to t and forming the vector $(x(t),\dot{x}(t))$, the expression for $\mathbf{s}(t)$ in terms of $\mathbf{s}(t_0)$ and $\mathbf{u}_{(t_0,t]}$ is found to be (in vector form)

17
$$\mathbf{s}(t) = \mathbf{\Phi}(t - t_0)\mathbf{s}(t_0) + \int_{t_0}^{t} \mathbf{h}(t - \xi)f(\xi)\,d\xi \qquad t \geq t_0$$

where

$$\mathbf{\Phi}(t) = \begin{bmatrix} 1 & t \\ 0 & 1 \end{bmatrix} \qquad \mathbf{h}(t) = \begin{bmatrix} t \\ 1 \end{bmatrix} \qquad t \geq 0$$

This is a special instance of a general expression for $\mathbf{s}(t)$ which will be derived in Chap. *3*, Sec. *7*.

Note that the output of $\mathcal{A}$ at time t is expressed in terms of $\mathbf{s}(t)$ by

18
$$x(t) = \langle \mathbf{c},\mathbf{s}(t) \rangle$$

where $\mathbf{c} = (1,0)$. On substituting *17* in *18*, we obtain the input-output-state relation *14*. Thus, the pair of equations *17* and *18* can be deduced from *14*, and *14* in turn is deducible from *17* and *18*. As we shall see at a later point, this is a general property of the so-called *state equations* of $\mathcal{A}$ (see *1.8.2 et seq.*).

19 *Example* Consider a clock with just one hand, the hour hand. Suppose that the position of the hand is represented by a variable x which can take on the values 0, 1, . . . , 11, with the understanding that any time between 0 and 1 and including 1 is regarded as the first hour ($x = 1$), any time between 1 and 2 and including 2 is regarded as the second hour ($x = 2$), etc. Now assume that at the end of each hour an experimenter tosses a die and advances the hour hand manually by the number of hours appearing on the face of the die. For example, if at time $t = 3$ ($t = 0, 1, 2, 3, \ldots$ hr), $x(3)$ is 4 and the number appearing on the face of the die is 6, then the hand is advanced to $x = 4 + 6 = 10$; that is, $x(4) = 10$.

The number appearing on the face of the die at time t is regarded as the input to the clock. As for the output, it is taken to be 0 at time t if $x(t)$ is even and 1 if $x(t)$ is odd. Now as a guide in deciding on how to identify the states of the object in question, let us ask the question: What do we have to know at time t_0 in order to be able to determine the response to any input starting at t_0? The answer is clearly $x(t_0)$. To verify that this is indeed the case, it will suffice to derive the input-output-state relation for the object under consideration and to verify that it satisfies the self-consistency conditions. (Note that the mutual-consistency condition would also have to be verified if the object were initially characterized by an input-output relation. Since this is not the case, only the self-consistency conditions need be satisfied.) To this end, let n mod p denote the least nonnegative residue of an integer n which results when multiples of the integer p are subtracted from or added to n. (For example, 5 mod 3 = 2, 2 mod 3 = 2, 10 mod 5 = 0, 7 mod 2 = 1.) Thus, if the initial position (at $t = t_0$) of the hour hand is denoted by $x(t_0)$ and the successive numbers appearing on the face of the die are denoted by $u(t_0), u(t_0 + 1), \ldots$, we can write

$$x(t) = [x(t_0) + u(t_0) + u(t_0 + 1) + \cdots + u(t - 1)] \bmod 12$$

and since the output is related to $x(t)$ by

20 $$y(t) = x(t) \bmod 2$$

the desired input-output-state relation is

$$y(t) = \{[x(t_0) + u(t_0) + \cdots + u(t - 1)] \bmod 12\} \bmod 2$$

or more simply

21 $$y(t) = [x(t_0) + u(t_0) + u(t_0 + 1) + \cdots + u(t - 1)] \bmod 2$$

since 2 is a divisor of 12.

In this example, the state space is a finite set $\{0,1, \ldots ,11\}$. The input space is likewise a finite set, $R[u(t)] = \{1,2, \ldots ,6\}$. The output space is $R[y(t)] = \{0,1\}$.

To verify that *21* satisfies the consistency conditions, it is expedient to put *21* into the form

22 $$y(t) = [x(t_0) + u(t_0) + \cdots + u(t' - 1) + u(t') + \cdots + u(t - 1)] \bmod 2$$

where t' is an arbitrary time between t_0 and $t - 1$. Then, regarding $u(t'), \ldots ,u(t - 1)$ as an input sequence starting at t', *22* can be written as

23 $$y(t) = [x(t') + u(t') + \cdots + u(t - 1)] \bmod 2 \qquad t' > t$$

where

24 $$x(t') = x(t_0) + u(t_0) + \cdots + u(t' - 1)$$

Since *23* is of the same form as *21*, with $x(t')$ independent of $u(t'), \ldots ,u(t - 1)$, it follows at once that the third self-consistency condition is satisfied and that $x(t')$, as given by *24*, represents the state of

$\mathcal{A}$ at time t'. Note that the arguments used here are similar to those employed in the case of Example *1.6.40*. Note in particular that the first consistency condition is satisfied trivially and that the second self-consistency condition is implied by the third condition (see Remark *1.6.39*).

It is easy to verify that the second self-consistency condition would not be satisfied if the state space were restricted to, say, the set $\{1,3,5,7\}$. In that case, $x(t')$ as determined by *24* would not always be a member of this set, and hence for some u the set $Q_{t'}$ would be empty. Specifically, set $t_0 = 0$, $t' = 4$, $x(t_0) = 7$, $u(t_0 + 1) = u(1) = 1$, $u(t_0 + 2) = u(2) = 4$, $u(t' - 1) = u(3) = 2$. Then $x(t') = (7 + 1 + 4 + 2) \bmod 2 = 0$, and $x(t')$ is not an element of the state space $\{1,3,5,7\}$.

25 *Example* Consider a so-called "perfect delay line" with delay δ ($\delta \triangleq$ constant > 0). The abstract model of such a device is an oriented object $\mathcal{A}$ characterized by the input-output relation

26 $$y(t) = u(t - \delta) \qquad t \geq t_0 + \delta,\ t_0 \in T$$

In other words, the output of $\mathcal{A}$ at time $t \geq t_0 + \delta$ is equal to the value of the input of $\mathcal{A}$ at time $t - \delta$. The state of $\mathcal{A}$ at time t is the input "stored" in the delay line, that is, $u_{[t-\delta,t)}$. The input-output-state relation is expressible as

27 $$\begin{aligned} y(t) &= \text{value of } \mathbf{s}(t_0) \text{ at } 2t_0 - t && \text{for } t_0 \leq t < t_0 + \delta \\ &= u(t - \delta) && \text{for } t \geq t_0 + \delta \end{aligned}$$

where $\mathbf{s}(t_0) \triangleq u_{[t_0-\delta,t_0)}$.

Note that in all of the preceding examples the state space is finite-dimensional. In the present example, it is not. Specifically, the state space is the set of all segments of the form $u_{[t-\delta,t)}$, where u ranges over time functions in the input function space of $\mathcal{A}$.

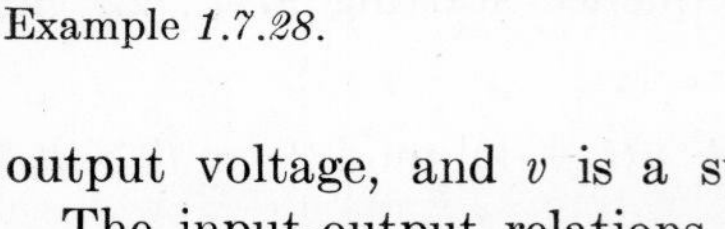

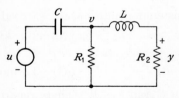

Fig. 1.7.1 System considered in Example *1.7.28*.

28 *Example* Consider the electrical network $\mathcal{A}$ shown in Fig. *1.7.1*. This is an oriented object in which u is the input voltage, y is the output voltage, and v is a suppressed output variable (see Sec. *4*).

The input-output relations for this object (derived by the rules of circuit analysis, see Refs. *3* to *5*) are

29 $$y + \frac{R_2}{R_1} v + R_2 C \dot{v} = R_2 C \dot{u}$$

$$\dot{y} + \frac{R_2}{L} y = \frac{R_2}{L} v$$

As will be shown in a general way in Chap. *4*, Sec. *6*, a vector $\mathbf{s}(t)$ which has as its components the voltages across the capacitors and the currents through the inductors of an *RLC* network $\mathcal{C}$ at time t qualifies as a state vector for $\mathcal{C}$. For the network under consideration this yields

30 $$\mathbf{s}(t) = \left(\frac{y(t)}{R_2}, u(t) - v(t)\right)$$

as the expression for the state vector. The corresponding input-output-state relation can be found from *29* and *30* by using techniques described in Chap. *4*. Employing these techniques and assuming for simplicity that $R_1 = R_2 = C = L = 1$, we obtain

31 $$y(t) = \langle \boldsymbol{\phi}(t - t_0), \mathbf{s}(t_0) \rangle + \int_{t_0}^{t} e^{-(t-\xi)}[\cos (t - \xi) - \sin (t - \xi)]u(\xi)\, d\xi \qquad t \geq t_0$$

where $\langle \mathbf{a},\mathbf{b} \rangle$ denotes the scalar product of $\mathbf{a}$ and $\mathbf{b}$ and the vector $\boldsymbol{\phi}(t)$ is given by

32 $$\boldsymbol{\phi}(t) = (e^{-t} \cos t, \; -e^{-t} \sin t) \qquad t \geq 0$$

Our purpose in considering this example is merely that of illustrating the form of the input-output-state relation in the case of an electrical network such as the one shown in Fig. *1.7.1*, rather than that of justifying the choice of $\mathbf{s}(t)$ as expressed by *30* as the state vector or showing how to derive the input-output-state relation *31* from the circuit equations *29*. This we shall do in a general way in Chap. *4*.

8 *Miscellaneous concepts*

In this and the following two sections, we shall discuss briefly and in quick succession several miscellaneous concepts which will be needed in later chapters. We begin with

State equations

In the course of analyzing Examples *1.7.10*, *1.7.12*, *1.7.19*, and *1.7.28* in the preceding section, we have obtained explicit expressions for the state of $\mathcal{C}$ at time t in terms of the state of $\mathcal{C}$ at time t_0 and the input to $\mathcal{C}$ between t_0 and t. More generally, if the consistency conditions are satisfied, then it can be asserted that $\mathbf{s}(t)$, the state at time t, is uniquely determined by $\mathbf{s}(t_0)$, the state at time t_0, and $\mathbf{u}_{(t_0,t]}$, and that the functional dependence of $\mathbf{s}(t)$ on $\mathbf{s}(t_0)$ and $\mathbf{u}_{(t_0,t]}$ can be derived, at least in principle, from the input-output-state relation

1 $$\mathbf{y}(t) = \mathbf{A}(\mathbf{s}(t_0); \mathbf{u}_{(t_0,t]})$$

This assertion is an immediate consequence of the definition of $\mathbf{s}(t)$ (*1.7.1*). Specifically, we have defined $\mathbf{s}(t)$ to be any element of the set $Q_t(\boldsymbol{\alpha}_0;\mathbf{u}_{(t_0,t]})$, where $\boldsymbol{\alpha}_0 = \mathbf{s}(t_0)$. Clearly, since Q_t depends only on $\boldsymbol{\alpha}_0$ and $\mathbf{u}_{(t_0,t]}$, so must $\mathbf{s}(t)$. Furthermore, from the way in which Q_t is defined (*1.6.38*), it is evident that, given the input-output-state relation *1* and given $\boldsymbol{\alpha}_0$ and $\mathbf{u}_{(t_0,t]}$, one can determine the sets $Q(\boldsymbol{\alpha}_0;\mathbf{u},\mathbf{u}')$, with $\mathbf{u}'$ varying over the input segment space of $\mathcal{A}$, and then determine their intersection, which is Q_t. Thus, in principle at least, Q_t and hence $\mathbf{s}(t)$ can be deduced from $\boldsymbol{\alpha}_0$, $\mathbf{u}_{(t_0,t]}$, and the input-output-state relation *1*. As Examples *1.7.10*, *1.7.12*, and *1.7.19* demonstrate, this can be done quite easily in cases in which it can be shown directly that there exists a state, say, $\boldsymbol{\alpha}$, which belongs to all $Q(\boldsymbol{\alpha}_0;\mathbf{u},\mathbf{u}')$ sets and hence lies in the intersection Q_t.

For convenience in reference, the expression for $\mathbf{s}(t)$ as a function of $\mathbf{s}(t_0)$ and $\mathbf{u}_{(t_0,t]}$ will be called the *state equation* for $\mathcal{A}$ and it will be written in the general form

2 $$\mathbf{s}(t) = \mathbf{s}(\mathbf{s}(t_0);\mathbf{u}_{(t_0,t]})$$

where $\mathbf{s}$ represents a function with values in Σ, defined on the product space (*1.4.17*) of Σ and $R[\mathbf{u}]$. To emphasize that *2* is derivable from *1*, we shall say that the state equation *2* is *induced* by the input-output-state relation *1*. A typical example of a state equation is *1.7.17*.

Now if we let t_0 approach t from the left in both *1* and *2*, then, under suitable regularity assumptions on $\mathbf{s}$ and $\mathbf{u}$, *1* and *2* will tend in the limit to differential equations of the form

3 $$\dot{\mathbf{s}}(t) = \mathbf{f}(\mathbf{s}(t),\mathbf{u}(t), \ldots ,\mathbf{u}^{(k)}(t),t)$$

4 $$\mathbf{y}(t) = \mathbf{g}(\mathbf{s}(t),\mathbf{u}(t), \ldots ,\mathbf{u}^{(l)}(t),t)$$

where $\mathbf{f}$ and $\mathbf{g}$ are ordinary (point) functions of their arguments and $u^{(k)} \triangleq k$th derivative of $\mathbf{u}$. If this holds true for $\mathcal{A}$, then $\mathcal{A}$ will be said to be of *differential type*, or, simply, a *differential object*, and *3* and *4* will be referred to as its *state equations in differential form*. Differential objects and their state equations are of particular interest to us, since most of the systems considered in later chapters will be of differential type.

A somewhat more general type of object is one for which *4* but not necessarily *3* holds true. In this case, the state equations are of the form

5 $$\mathbf{s}(t) = \mathbf{s}(\mathbf{s}(t_0);\mathbf{u}_{(t_0,t]})$$

6 $$\mathbf{y}(t) = \mathbf{g}(\mathbf{s}(t),\mathbf{u}(t), \ldots ,\mathbf{u}^{(k)}(t),t)$$

In most cases, the expression for $\mathbf{y}(t)$ does not involve the derivatives of the input or can be put into such form by a redefinition of $\mathbf{s}(t)$. Thus, the usual form of state equations is

7 $$\mathbf{s}(t) = \mathbf{s}(\mathbf{s}(t_0);\mathbf{u}_{(t_0,t]})$$

8 $$\mathbf{y}(t) = \mathbf{g}(\mathbf{s}(t),\mathbf{u}(t),t)$$

A simple example of an object which admits of the representation *7* and *8* but not *3* and *4* is the "perfect delay line" of Example *1.7.25*. Note that in this case the output at time t depends only on $\mathbf{s}(t)$ and not on $u(t)$.

When there is a need to differentiate between *3* and *5*, we shall say that *5* is a state equation in *explicit form*, whereas *3* is a state equation in differential form. In effect, if $\mathcal{A}$ is characterized by *3* and *4*, then its state equations in explicit form (*5* and *6*) can be obtained, in principle, by solving the vector differential equation *3* for $\mathbf{s}(t)$ and expressing $\mathbf{s}(t)$ as a function of $\mathbf{s}(t_0)$ and $\mathbf{u}_{(t_0,t]}$. On the other hand, if $\mathcal{A}$ is characterized by *5* and *6*, then it may not be possible to put *5* into the differential form *3*.

When we say that $\mathcal{A}$ is *characterized* by *5* and *6*, what we have in mind is that on substituting $\mathbf{s}(t)$ from *5* into *6* one obtains the input-output-state relation for $\mathcal{A}$. Consequently, not only are *5* and *6* deducible (under suitable regularity assumptions on $\mathbf{s}$ and $\mathbf{u}$) from the input-output-state relation *1* but also the input-output-state relation *1* is deducible from the state equations. Consequently, the state equations of $\mathcal{A}$ provide a complete characterization of $\mathcal{A}$ in the sense of Definition *1.6.2*. Note that this is true also of the differential state equations *3* and *4* provided *3* has a unique solution.

In the case of linear differential systems—which are the main concern of this book—the differential state equations assume a particularly simple form, namely,

9 $$\dot{\mathbf{s}}(t) = \mathbf{A}(t)\mathbf{s}(t) + \mathbf{B}(t)\mathbf{u}(t)$$

10 $$\mathbf{y}(t) = \mathbf{C}(t)\mathbf{s}(t) + \mathbf{D}_0(t)\mathbf{u}(t) + \mathbf{D}_1(t)\mathbf{u}^{(1)}(t) + \cdots + \mathbf{D}_k(t)\mathbf{u}^{(k)}(t)$$

where the coefficients are (possibly time-dependent) matrices. Such state equations will be discussed at length in Chaps. *4* through *7*.

Continuous-state, discrete-state, and finite-state objects

The nature of the state space Σ of an object $\mathcal{A}$ is one of its more important characteristics. For most of the objects considered in this book, Σ is a finite-dimensional space or, more specifically, the set of all ordered n-tuples of real or complex numbers. [One simple exception is the state space of a perfect delay line (*1.7.25*), which is infinite-dimensional.] More generally, if Σ is a continuum, we shall say that $\mathcal{A}$ is a *continuous-state object.* If Σ is a countable set, $\mathcal{A}$ will be said to be a *discrete-state object.* And, finally, if Σ is a finite set, we shall say that $\mathcal{A}$ is a *finite-state object.* An example of the latter is the object discussed in *1.7.19*.

Deterministic and probabilistic (stochastic) objects

In defining an abstract object and related concepts we have made the tacit assumption that the behavior of $\mathcal{A}$ does not exhibit any randomness. In effect, we have defined via *1.6.2* an oriented abstract object which is *deterministic* in the sense that $\mathbf{y}(t)$ is uniquely determined by $\mathbf{s}(t_0)$ and $\mathbf{u}_{(t_0,t]}$ for all $t > t_0$. However, it is not difficult to extend the definition in question to *probabilistic* or *stochastic* objects in which, for each t, $\mathbf{y}(t)$ is a random variable. For such objects, the input-output-state relation *1* which characterizes a deterministic object is replaced by an input-output distribution-state relation which expresses the probability measure on the space of response segments $\mathbf{y}_{(t_0,t]}$ as a function of the initial state $\mathbf{s}(t_0)$ and the input segment $\mathbf{u}_{(t_0,t]}$. Correspondingly, the state equation $\mathbf{s}(t) = \mathbf{s}(\mathbf{s}(t_0);\mathbf{u}_{(t_0,t]})$ is replaced by an equation which expresses the conditional probability distribution of $\mathbf{s}(t)$ for each t, given $\mathbf{s}(t_0)$ and $\mathbf{u}_{(t_0,t]}$. We shall not dwell further on the properties of stochastic objects, since we shall have no occasion to treat them in this book.

Single and multiple experiments and measurability of states

Underlying the notions of input and output of an abstract object $\mathcal{A}$ is the informal understanding (see Sec. *4*) that the inputs are those terminal variables of a physical realization $\mathcal{P}(\mathcal{A})$ of $\mathcal{A}$ (if one exists) which are varied directly by an experimenter and that the outputs are the terminal variables which are observed but not varied directly. On the other hand, in our definition of state (*1.7.1*) there was no mention of whether, or to what extent, the initial state $\mathbf{s}(t_0)$ is under the control of the experimenter. The reason for this is that the question can be answered in a number of ways depending on the type of experiment which is performed on $\mathcal{P}(\mathcal{A})$. The following discussion merely touches on some of the aspects of this many-faceted problem.

To begin with, one has to distinguish between a so-called *single experiment*, where it is assumed that the experimenter has at his disposal just one copy of $\mathcal{P}(\mathcal{A})$, and a *multiple experiment*, where the experimenter has access to an unlimited number of identical copies of $\mathcal{P}(\mathcal{A})$, all in the same initial state $\mathbf{s}(t_0)$.[1] In the sequel, the term "experiment" will be used in the sense of "single experiment," unless otherwise noted. It should be noted, however, that any property of $\mathcal{A}$ whose definition involves qualifying conditions such as "for all $\mathbf{u}$" or "for all $\mathbf{s}(t_0)$" cannot be verified, in general, without performing a

[1] The notions of "single experiment" and "multiple experiment" have been introduced by E. F. Moore in his basic work on the theory of sequential machines (see Ref. *6*). Moore uses the term *simple experiment* rather than *single experiment*, as we do here.

multiple experiment on $\mathfrak{A}$. For example, the property of linearity (*3.4.25*) involves such conditions; and thus it is not possible, in general, to determine whether $\mathfrak{A}$ is linear or not by experimenting with a single copy of $\mathfrak{A}$.

In a single or a multiple experiment starting at time t_0, the initial state $\mathbf{s}(t_0)$ is *settable* if, at any initial time t_0, $\mathbf{s}(t_0)$ can be chosen at will within the state space Σ. $\mathbf{s}(t_0)$ is *nonsettable* if the experimenter cannot assign to $\mathbf{s}(t_0)$ an arbitrarily selected value in Σ at the beginning of the experiment.

11 *Example* Consider the clock described in Example *1.7.19*. Here it is conceivable that the experimenter would be permitted to adjust the position of the hour hand at will at the beginning of the experiment. In this case, $\mathbf{s}(t_0)$ would be settable.

On the other hand, consider the network of Fig. *1.7.1* and suppose that it is encapsulated in plastic, with only the input and output terminals accessible to the experimenter. In that case, the initial state of the network would not be settable. A different kind of restriction on the choice of the initial state is discussed in *2.6.24*. ◁

Another notion of importance is that of *measurability*. We shall say that the state of $\mathfrak{A}$ is *measurable* if the experimenter can determine the value of $\mathbf{s}(t)$ for each t either directly or from the knowledge of the input segment $\mathbf{u}_{(t_0,t]}$ and the output segment $\mathbf{y}_{(t_0,t]}$, without knowing the initial state $\mathbf{s}(t_0)$. In this connection it should be noted that, in the case of a deterministic object, the knowledge of $\mathbf{s}(t_0)$ and $\mathbf{u}_{(t_0,t]}$ suffices to determine $\mathbf{s}(t)$, but this is not true of stochastic objects. We shall also say that the state is *intermittently measurable* if the experimenter can determine $\mathbf{s}(t)$ at some but not all instants of time in the course of the experiment. The so-called *interrupted control processes* defined by Bellman and Kalaba (see Ref. *7*) fall into this category.

A basic problem that is encountered in many different contexts is that of the determination of the initial state of $\mathfrak{A}$. In one variant of this problem, the experimenter is given $\mathbf{u}_{(t_0,t]}$ and $\mathbf{y}_{(t_0,t]}$ and is asked to find $\mathbf{s}(t_0)$. In effect, this amounts to solving the input-output-state relation

12
$$\mathbf{y}_{(t_0,t]} = \bar{\mathbf{A}}(\mathbf{s}(t_0);\mathbf{u}_{(t_0,t]})$$

for $\mathbf{s}(t_0)$ in terms of $\mathbf{u}_{(t_0,t]}$ and $\mathbf{y}_{(t_0,t]}$. If this can be done for all $\mathbf{s}(t_0)$ and all $\mathbf{u}$ and $\mathbf{y}$ within $R[\mathbf{u}]$ and $R[\mathbf{y}]$, respectively (see *1.6.2*), and if the solution is unique (to within equivalent states, see *2.2.1*), then $\mathfrak{A}$ will be said to be *initial state determinable in strict sense.*[1] [As will be

[1] A closely related notion in the case of linear systems is that of *observability*, which will be discussed in detail in Chap. *11*, Sec. *4*.

seen later (*3.7.55*), this property is possessed by reduced linear systems.] More generally, $\mathcal{A}$ will be said to be *initial state determinable in wide sense* if no matter what $\mathbf{s}(t_0)$ is, the experimenter can always find an input $\mathbf{u}_{(t_0,t]}$ such that $\mathbf{s}(t_0)$ can be determined uniquely (to within equivalent states) from the knowledge of $\mathbf{u}_{(t_0,t]}$ and $\mathbf{y}_{(t_0,t]}$. Note that the difference between the two definitions is that in the former every $\mathbf{s}(t_0)$ can be determined from *any* $\mathbf{u}_{(t_0,t]}$ and $\mathbf{y}_{(t_0,t]}$ associated with $\mathbf{s}(t_0)$, whereas in the latter *there exists* a $\mathbf{u}_{(t_0,t]}$ [dependent on $\mathbf{s}(t_0)$] such that from this $\mathbf{u}_{(t_0,t]}$ and the response segment $\mathbf{y}_{(t_0,t]}$ the experimenter can determine $\mathbf{s}(t_0)$.

In a similar fashion, one can define *terminal state determinability*, i.e., the determinability of $\mathbf{s}(t)$ from the knowledge of $\mathbf{u}_{(t_0,t]}$ and $\mathbf{y}_{(t_0,t]}$, under the assumption that $\mathbf{s}(t_0)$ is not known. For a discussion of this problem in the context of finite-state systems see Refs. *6* and *8*.

Nonanticipative and anticipative objects

Although we have not stated so explicitly, Definition *1.6.2* defines an object $\mathcal{A}$ that is *nonanticipative*, meaning, roughly, that $\mathcal{A}$ acts only on the present ($t = t_0$) and past ($t < t_0$) values of its input and not on its future ($t > t_0$) values. The tacit assumption that $\mathcal{A}$ is nonanticipative enters into the formulation of the third self-consistency condition (*1.6.35*). To place it in evidence, we make the

13 **Definition** An abstract object $\mathcal{A}$ is *nonanticipative* if and only if for all t_0 in T, all initial states, and all inputs $\mathcal{A}$ has the following property. Using the notation of *1.6.16*, let $\mathbf{uu}'$ be an input segment (consisting of $\mathbf{u}$ followed by $\mathbf{u}'$) and let $\mathbf{yy}'$ be the corresponding output with $\mathcal{A}$ starting in state $\mathbf{s}(t_0)$. Then, if $\mathbf{u}$ is kept fixed and $\mathbf{u}'$ is varied over $R[\mathbf{u}']$, $\mathbf{y}$ remains fixed and $\mathbf{y}'$ varies over $R[\mathbf{y}']$. (In plain words, this means that the input segment $\mathbf{u}'$ has no influence on a prior output segment $\mathbf{y}$.)

An abstract object which is not nonanticipative will be said to be *anticipative.* More particularly, if $\mathcal{A}$ acts only on the present and future values of its input, and not on its past values, it will be said to be *purely anticipative.* In the case of a purely anticipative object, the input-output-state relation has exactly the same form *2* as for a nonanticipative object, with the only difference being that it is valid for $t < t_0$ rather than $t > t_0$. In a sense, a purely anticipative object is a mirror image in time of its nonanticipative counterpart.

14 *Example* An object characterized by the input-output relation

$$y(t) = u(t-1) \qquad t > t_0 + 1,\ t_0 \in T$$

where u and y are real-valued time functions, is nonanticipative. (One physical realization of such an object is a perfect delay line.)

15 *Example* An object characterized by the input-output relation

$$y(t) = u(t+1) \qquad t > t_0,\ t_0 \in T$$

is purely anticipative.

16 *Example* An object characterized by the input-output relation

$$y(t) = u(t-1) + u(t+1) \qquad t > t_0 + 1,\ t < t_0 - 1,\ t_0 \in T$$

is anticipative. *Question:* Why is this relation valid over the intervals indicated? What is the state of this object at time t?

Memoryless and finite-memory objects

17 **Definition** An object $\mathcal{A}$ is *memoryless* if, for each t, $\mathbf{y}(t)$ depends only on $\mathbf{u}(t)$, that is, the input-output relation is of the form

$$\mathbf{y}(t) = \mathbf{g}(\mathbf{u}(t),t)$$

where $\mathbf{g}$ is a function defined on $R[\mathbf{u}(t)] \times T$. For example, a *squarer*, which is an object characterized by the input-output relation

18 $$y(t) = [u(t)]^2$$

is memoryless. On the other hand, a *differentiator*, which is an object characterized by the input-output relation

$$\mathbf{y}(t) = \frac{d\mathbf{u}}{dt}$$

is not memoryless, since $\mathbf{y}(t)$ is determined not only by $\mathbf{u}(t)$ but also by the values of $\mathbf{u}$ in the immediate vicinity of t.

To say that $\mathbf{y}(t)$ depends only on $\mathbf{u}(t)$ and nothing else is equivalent to saying that the state space Σ consists of a single point. In later discussions we shall find it convenient to denote the only state of a memoryless object by a special symbol such as (1).

19 **Definition** An object $\mathcal{A}$ is said to have a *finite memory of length L* if the input-output relation of $\mathcal{A}$ admits of the representation

20 $$\mathbf{y}(t) = \mathbf{g}(\mathbf{u}_{[t-L,t]}) \qquad t > t_0 + L,\ t_0 \in T$$

where $\mathbf{g}$ is a function defined on the space of segments $\{\mathbf{u}_{[t-L,t]}\}$ and L is a finite real number. Essentially, *20* means that for each t the output of $\mathcal{A}$ at time t depends only on the values of the input in the interval $[t - L, t]$. A simple example of a finite memory object is a perfect delay line characterized by the input-output relation

$$y(t) = u(t - L) \qquad t > t_0 + L,\ t_0 \in T$$

Another example is a so-called *moving averager*, which is characterized by the input-output relation

21 $$y(t) = \frac{1}{L}\int_{t-L}^{t} u(\xi)\, d\xi \qquad t > t_0 + L,\ t_0 \in T$$

Sources

Up to this point, we have concerned ourselves with oriented objects which have an input $\mathbf{u}$ ranging over $R[\mathbf{u}]$ and an output $\mathbf{y}$ ranging over $R[\mathbf{y}]$. There is, however, an important class of objects, namely, *sources*, which have an output $\mathbf{y}$ but no input. We have not treated such objects as a separate class because a source $\mathcal{S}$ can be regarded as a degenerate form of an oriented object $\mathcal{A}$ whose input segment space $R[\mathbf{u}]$ comprises a single time function, say, $\mathbf{u}^0$. Based on this viewpoint, a source can be defined as follows.

22 **Definition** A source $\mathcal{S}$ is an object whose output $\mathbf{y}(t)$ admits the representation

23 $$\mathbf{y}(t) = \mathbf{S}(\mathbf{s}(t_0); \mathbf{u}^0_{(t_0, t]}) \qquad \mathbf{s}(t_0) \in \Sigma$$

where $\mathbf{u}^0$ is a fixed time function and *23* is an input-output-state relation. A source is *memoryless* if $\mathcal{S}$ is a memoryless object in the sense of Definition *17*.

24 *Example* A source whose output is expressed by $y(t) = \sin t,\ t \geq t_0$, is a memoryless source. On the other hand, a source whose output is defined by *1.7.25* with, say, $u(t) = \sin t,\ t \geq t_0$, is a source with memory, since the output over the interval $t_0 \leq t \leq t_0 + \delta$ depends on the initial state of $\mathcal{A}$ and is not determined by the values of $u(t)$ for $t \geq t_0$.

9 *Graphical representation and system elements*

So far our discussion has been centered on the notion of a single abstract object $\mathcal{A}$ which is associated with a set of terminal variables and is characterized by the relations between them. Our basic concern, however, is with *systems* of objects rather than single objects, i.e., with the collective behavior of a set of objects which interact with one another. Until we define the term "system" more formally in Sec. *10*, it will be used by us in its usual not well-defined sense.

As a preliminary, we shall dwell briefly on a few topics which involve largely matters of terminology and notation. We begin with a discussion of

Graphical symbols for abstract objects

To denote an oriented abstract object $\mathcal{A}$ in a graphical form, we shall use for the most part the conventional rectangular-block representation illustrated in Fig. *1.9.1*. Here the leads represent the terminal variables and the inputs and outputs are identified by arrowheads which point toward $\mathcal{A}$ in the case of inputs and away from $\mathcal{A}$ in the case of outputs.

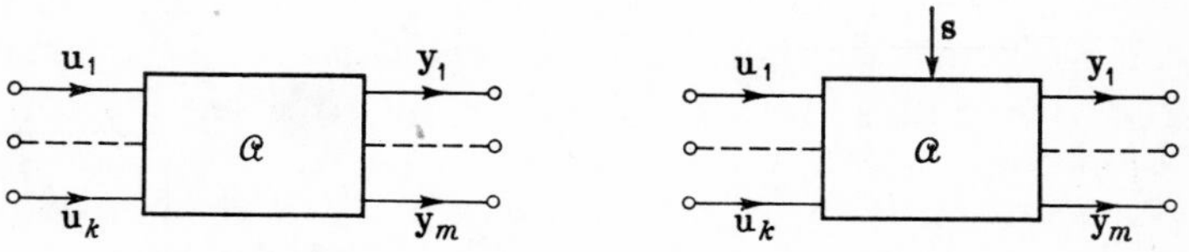

Fig. 1.9.1 Block-diagram representations of an object.

1 **Remark** Note that it is customary, but not really necessary, to associate a scalar rather than a vector variable with each terminal. The only point that matters is that a terminal variable—whatever the nature of its range—must be treated as a single indivisible entity when the object in question is interconnected with other objects. Thus, if an output variable, say, $\mathbf{y}^i$, is a vector with components $y_1^i, \ldots, y_l^i$, then these components cannot be treated as terminal variables in their own right when it comes to connecting $\mathcal{A}$ to other objects in a system (see Sec. *10*). Rather, they must be treated as a single "bundle" which can be connected only to matching input bundles of one or more other objects. ◁

We assume that $\mathcal{A}$ is characterized or is characterizable by an input-output-state relation of the form (*1.6.3*)

2 $$\mathbf{y}(t) = \mathbf{A}(\boldsymbol{\alpha};\mathbf{u})$$

where $\mathbf{u}$ is an input segment $\mathbf{u}_{(t_0,t]}$, $\boldsymbol{\alpha}$ is the state at time t_0, $\mathbf{y}(t)$ is the output at time t, and $\mathbf{A}$ is a function defined on the product of the state space Σ and the input segment space $R[\mathbf{u}]$. Equation *2* implies that each of the components of $\mathbf{y}(t)$ is, like $\mathbf{y}(t)$, a function of $\boldsymbol{\alpha}$ and $\mathbf{u}$. We shall express this by the notation

3 $$y_i(t) = A_i(\boldsymbol{\alpha};\mathbf{u}) \qquad i = 1, \ldots, m$$

where $y_i(t)$ is the ith component of $\mathbf{y}(t)$, $i = 1, \ldots, m$. This implies—as illustrated in Fig. *1.9.2*—that an object $\mathfrak{A}$ having k input variables and m output variables can always be decomposed into m objects $\mathfrak{A}_1, \ldots, \mathfrak{A}_m$ each of which has k input variables and one output variable. Thus, in the case of a system of oriented objects there is no loss in generality in assuming that the system is comprised of oriented

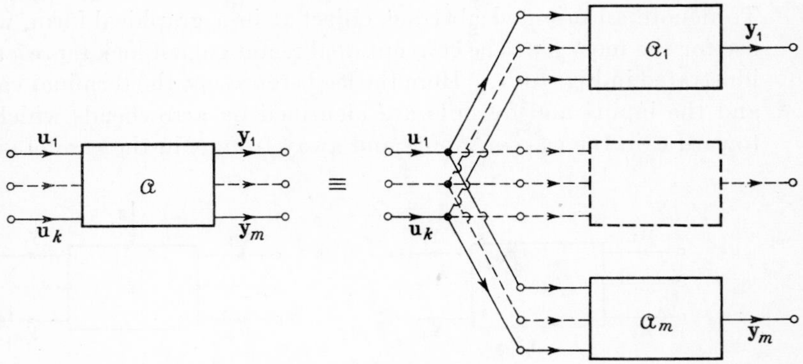

Fig. 1.9.2 Decomposition into objects having a single output terminal.

objects each having just one output variable. To take advantage of this, it is expedient to adopt a simplified notation for oriented objects having k input variables $u_1, \ldots, u_k$ and one output variable y. Two examples of such notation are shown in Fig. *1.9.3*. Here (*a*) depicts the conventional signal-flow-graph type of representation (see Chap. *9*, Sec. *15*) in which the nodes are associated with variables and the

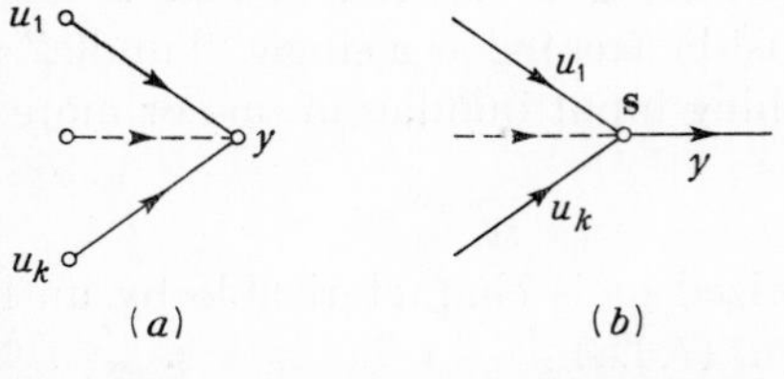

Fig. 1.9.3 (*a*) Signal-flow graph; (*b*) signal-state-graph conventions.

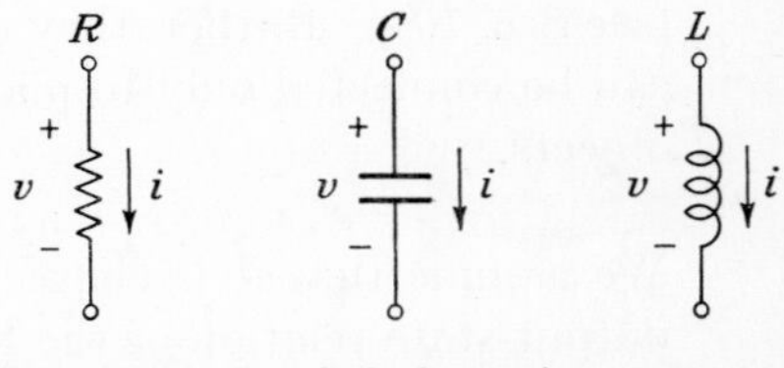

Fig. 1.9.4 Symbols for resistor, capacitor, and inductor.

oriented branches serve to identify the variables that are inputs. For our purposes it will be more convenient to use the *signal-state-graph* representation depicted in (*b*). Here the branches are associated with the input and output variables and the node is associated with state. In this way, it is made clear that the output y depends not only on the inputs $u_1, \ldots, u_k$ but also on the state $\mathbf{s}$.

It should be noted that the diagrammatic representations of $\mathfrak{A}$

depicted in Figs. *1.9.1* to *1.9.3* convey information only concerning the number of terminal variables of $\mathfrak{A}$ and which of these terminal variables are inputs and which are outputs; they do not provide quantitative information on how the input, output, and state variables are related to one another—which is the information contained in the input-output and input-output-state relations of $\mathfrak{A}$. Such information can be supplied, of course, by writing the input-output relation or its equivalent inside or adjacent to the block representing $\mathfrak{A}$. Another obvious way of conveying information concerning the input-output relation of $\mathfrak{A}$ is to use a set of specialized graphical symbols each of which is associated with a particular form of input-output relation. This is what is customarily done in the case of electric circuits, where the symbols shown in Fig. *1.9.4* represent nonoriented objects with terminal variables v and i. These objects, called resistor, capacitor, and inductor, are characterized by the terminal relations $v = Ri$, $i = C\,dv/dt$, and $v = L\,di/dt$, where R, C, and L are constant nonnegative parameters called resistance, capacitance, and inductance, respectively. (The plus sign specifies the positive polarity for v and the arrow indicates the positive sense of current flow for i.)

In the sequel, we shall on occasion use terms that are synonymous with "object" but give it somewhat specialized or different shades of meaning. The terms in question and the reasons for their use are listed below.

Black box To stress that the physical object of which $\mathfrak{A}$ is an abstract model is dealt with through its terminal variables. We shall try to avoid using this term even though it is a very suggestive one, largely because its meaning has become fuzzy through wide and careless usage.

Multipole To indicate that $\mathfrak{A}$ has two or more terminal variables.

n-pole To indicate that $\mathfrak{A}$ has n terminal variables.

2-pole or two-pole To indicate that $\mathfrak{A}$ has one input and one output variable. On occasion we shall find the longer name "single-input single-output system" preferable for our purposes.

System element To stress that $\mathfrak{A}$ is one of a set of objects of which a system is comprised, or to indicate that $\mathfrak{A}$ can be used as a "building block" for other systems.

System To imply that the abstract object in question is a combination of other abstract objects.

There are several types of system element that play a particularly important role in system theory, both because of their frequent occurrence as components of complex systems and because they can be used as building blocks in the synthesis of almost any physically realizable system. A set of such elements is defined in the next subsection.

Adders, multipliers, scalors, delayors, and integrators

The five elements defined below have two significant properties. First, they form an *independent* set, in the sense that none can be constructed out of a finite number of the other four types of element. Second, they form a *complete* set, in the sense that almost any physically realizable system can be synthesized—to an arbitrarily high degree of accuracy—out of a sufficiently large number of such elements. We shall not attempt at this stage to state this assertion in a more precise form. In any case, its proof is outside the scope of our treatment.

The five elements in question are the *adder*, *multiplier*, *scalor*, *delayor*, and *integrator*. We proceed to give brief definitions of these terms.

4 **Definition** An *adder* is a memoryless (*1.8.17*) $(n + 1)$-pole $(n = 2, 3, \ldots)$ having n inputs $u_1, \ldots, u_n$ and one output y. The defining input-output relation for the adder is

5 $$y = u_1 + u_2 + \cdots + u_n$$

An adder is usually represented as a circle with a plus inside (Fig. *1.9.5a*).

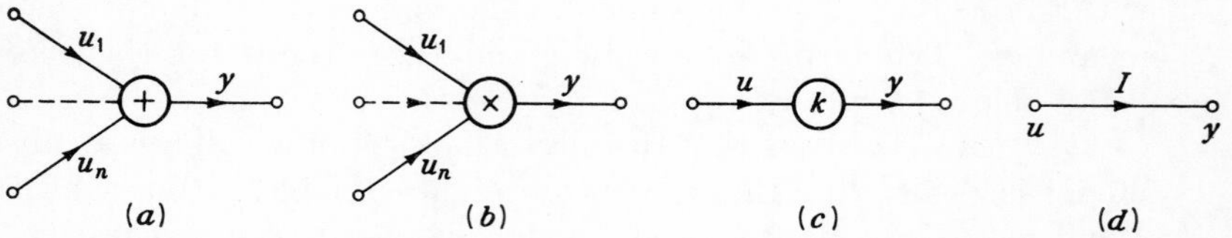

Fig. 1.9.5 Symbols for (*a*) adder, (*b*) multiplier, (*c*) scalor, and (*d*) unitor.

6 *Comment* Equation *5* reads: The output time function is the sum of input time functions. In other words, *5* implies that

$$y(t) = u_1(t) + u_2(t) + \cdots + u_n(t)$$

for all t. The point to note here is that whenever the terms in a relation are time functions (rather than their values at time t, as above), it should be understood that the relation holds for all t. ◁

For each t, the $u_i(t)$ are usually understood to be scalars ranging over the real line $\mathcal{R}^1$. More generally, the range $R[u_i]$ of each u_i can be a function space of the type defined in *1.3.7*. For our purposes, it will suffice to assume that, for each t and each i, $u_i(t)$ is a real or complex scalar. The same comment applies to the multiplier, scalor, and delayor defined below.

7 **Definition** A *multiplier* is an $(n + 1)$-pole $(n = 2, 3, \ldots)$ having n inputs $u_1, \ldots, u_n$ and one output y. The defining input-output

relation for the multiplier is

$$y = u_1 u_2 \ . \ . \ . \ u_n$$

A multiplier is represented as a circle with a cross inside (Fig. *1.9.5b*).

8 **Definition** A *scalor*[1] is a 2-pole characterized by the input-output relation

$$y = ku$$

where k is a constant (not necessarily real or positive). A scalor may be regarded as an "amplifier" having a constant gain k. A scalor is represented as shown in Fig. *1.9.5c*. The constant k will be referred to as the *scale factor* or *gain* of a scalor. A scalor with a unity scale factor will be called a *unitor*, or the *identity operator*, and it will be denoted by 1 or **I** or I. (Fig. *1.9.5d*).

9 **Definition** A *delayor* is a 2-pole characterized by the input-output relation (see *1.7.25*)

$$y(t) = u(t - \delta) \qquad t > t_0 + \delta,\ t_0 \in T$$

where δ (δ = constant > 0) is the amount of delay. In words, the output of the delayor at time t is equal to the value of its input at time $t - \delta$. A delayor is represented as shown in Fig. *1.9.6a*. A delayor

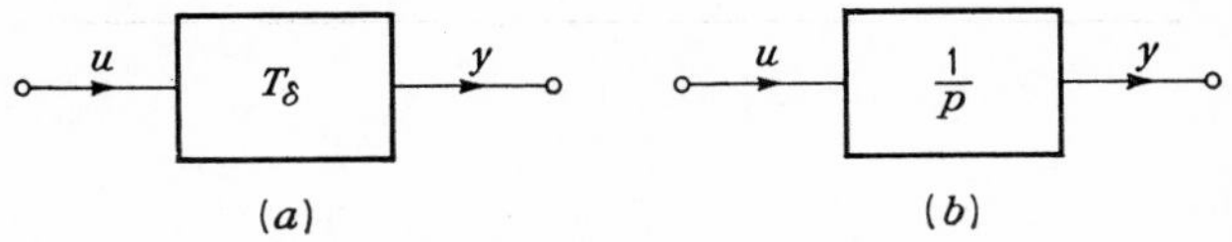

Fig. 1.9.6 Symbols for (*a*) delayor and (*b*) integrator.

with $\delta = 1$ will be called a *unit delayor*, and will be denoted as in Fig. *1.9.6a*, with D replacing T_δ.

10 **Definition** An *integrator* is a 2-pole defined by the input-output-state relation

11 $$y(t) = y(t_0-) + \int_{t_0}^{t} u(\xi)\, d\xi \qquad t \geq t_0,\ t_0 \in T$$

$y(t_0-)$ [$\triangleq s(t_0-)$] is the output of the integrator at time t_0- (see *1.7.10*). An integrator is represented as shown in Fig. *1.9.6b*, where the symbol $1/p$ stands for the operation of integration. (A slightly more general definition of an integrator is given in *4.3.48*. The notion of a *differentiator* is defined in *4.4.37*.) $\triangleleft$

We are now ready to consider the basic question of how two or more objects can be combined with each other to form a *system* of objects, or

[1] The terms "scalor" and "delayor" are due to Prof. W. H. Huggins, Jr., of the Johns Hopkins University, Baltimore, Md.

simply a *system*. In this connection, the notion of an *interconnection* plays a central role. We focus our attention on this and related notions in the following section.

10 *Interconnection of objects*

Roughly speaking, a system is a collection of interacting objects. To concretize the notion of a system, the interactions between the elements $\mathcal{A}_1, \ldots, \mathcal{A}_N$ of a system $\mathcal{S}$ are represented as a set of constraints on terminal variables, of which a typical one reads "μth terminal variable of object $\mathcal{A}_i$ is equal to νth terminal variable of object $\mathcal{A}_j$ for all t in T ($T \triangleq$ range of t)."[1] A collection of objects $\mathcal{A}_1, \ldots, \mathcal{A}_N$ subjected to such constraints is said to be an *interconnection* of $\mathcal{A}_1, \ldots, \mathcal{A}_N$ or simply an *interconnection*. An interconnection is usually represented in the form of a *block diagram* (Fig. *1.10.1*), in which the joining of a

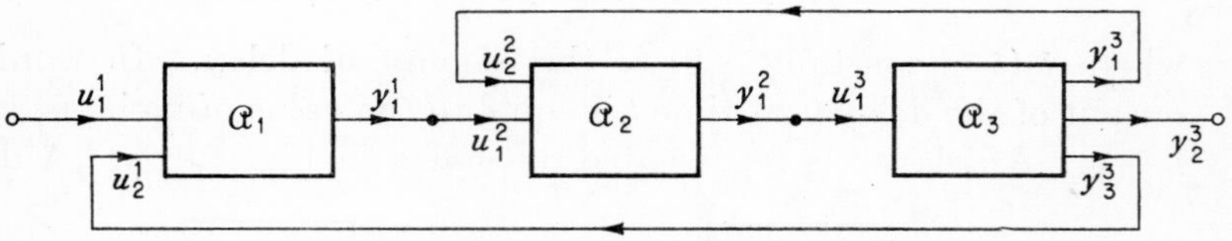

Fig. 1.10.1 An interconnection of $\mathcal{A}_1$, $\mathcal{A}_2$, $\mathcal{A}_3$.

terminal of $\mathcal{A}_i$ to a terminal of $\mathcal{A}_j$ signifies that the corresponding terminal variables are constrained to be equal for all t.

Suppose that $\mathcal{A}_1, \ldots, \mathcal{A}_N$ are characterized by their input-output-state relations and that they are interconnected in a specified manner, forming an object which we call $\mathcal{A}$. There are several questions concerning $\mathcal{A}$ that immediately suggest themselves, namely: What is the input-output-state relation for $\mathcal{A}$? What is the state space of $\mathcal{A}$? What is the output function space of $\mathcal{A}$? To provide a basis for answering these questions, it is convenient to introduce the notion of an *initially free interconnection*, denoted by $\mathcal{A}(t_0)$, in which the connections between the $\mathcal{A}_i$ in $\mathcal{A}$ are broken with switches which remain open till $t = t_0$ (Fig. *1.10.2*). As we shall see in the sequel, the artifice of regarding $\mathcal{A}$ as a limiting form, as $t_0 \to -\infty$, of an initially free interconnection $\mathcal{A}(t_0)$ makes it possible to relate the properties of $\mathcal{A}$ to those of $\mathcal{A}(t_0)$ and, in particular, give a characterization of the state space of

[1] It may appear that this does not apply to electrical networks, in which the constraints on terminal variables have the form of Kirchhoff's current and voltage relations. However, such relations can be put into the form stated in the text by regarding an adder as a network element. See Example *37*.

$\mathcal{C}$—a problem that is much less simple than it may appear to be on the surface.

In general, the questions posed above are by no means easy to answer, for we do not as yet possess a well-developed body of results bearing on the behavior of an interconnection of objects each of which is characterized by an input-output-state relation. Indeed, some of the concepts introduced in this section should be regarded as tentative in nature.

In order to facilitate the understanding of the role played by the notion of an initially free interconnection, we shall introduce it in the

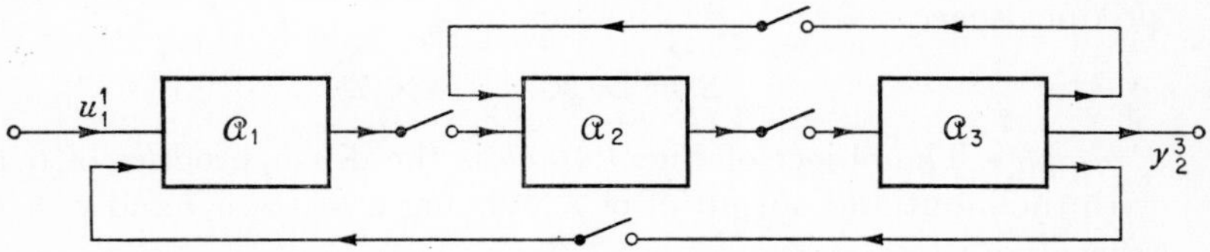

Fig. 1.10.2 Initially free interconnection of $\mathcal{A}_1$, $\mathcal{A}_2$, $\mathcal{A}_3$.

simple context of a tandem combination of two objects. Furthermore, in order to conserve space, most of our definitions will be formulated in terms of oriented objects, since it will usually be quite clear how analogous definitions can be made for nonoriented objects.

We begin our discussion with a degenerate type of interconnection, namely the

Direct product

Consider a collection of objects $\mathcal{A}_1, \ldots, \mathcal{A}_N$ each of which is characterized by an input-output-state relation of the form

1 $$\mathbf{y}^i = \bar{\mathbf{A}}_i(\boldsymbol{\alpha}^i;\mathbf{u}^i) \qquad \boldsymbol{\alpha}^i \in \Sigma_i,\ i = 1, \ldots, N$$

where $\mathbf{u}^i \triangleq \mathbf{u}^i_{(t_0,t]}$ and $\mathbf{y}^i = \mathbf{y}^i_{(t_0,t]}$, with $\mathbf{u}^i$, $\mathbf{y}^i$, and $\boldsymbol{\alpha}^i$ ranging over $R[\mathbf{u}^i]$, $R[\mathbf{y}^i]$, and Σ_i, respectively.

When there is no interaction at all between the $\mathcal{A}_i$, $i = 1, \ldots, N$, the collection $\mathcal{A}_1, \ldots, \mathcal{A}_N$ constitutes the *direct product* of $\mathcal{A}_1, \ldots, \mathcal{A}_N$. More formally, we have the

2 **Definition** The *direct product* of $\mathcal{A}_1, \ldots, \mathcal{A}_N$ is an object $\mathcal{A}$ comprising $\mathcal{A}_1, \ldots, \mathcal{A}_N$ and denoted by $\mathcal{A}_1 \times \cdots \times \mathcal{A}_N$, with the input to and the state of each $\mathcal{A}_i$, $i = 1, \ldots, N$, being independent of the inputs, outputs, and states of other objects in the collection. The input and output of $\mathcal{A}$ are defined to be the composite vectors

3 $$\mathbf{u} = (\mathbf{u}^1, \ldots, \mathbf{u}^N)$$

and

4 $$\mathbf{y} = (\mathbf{y}^1, \ldots, \mathbf{y}^N)$$

respectively. Correspondingly, the input and output segment spaces of $\mathcal{A}$ are the product spaces (*1.4.17*)

5 $$R[\mathbf{u}] = R[\mathbf{u}^1] \times \cdots \times R[\mathbf{u}^N]$$

and

6 $$R[\mathbf{y}] = R[\mathbf{y}^1] \times \cdots \times R[\mathbf{y}^N]$$

Furthermore, as will be shown in *2.6.10*, the composite vector

$$\mathbf{s}(t) = (\mathbf{s}^1(t), \ldots, \mathbf{s}^N(t))$$

qualifies as the state of $\mathcal{A}$ at time t, with the state space of $\mathcal{A}$ being the product space

7 $$\Sigma = \Sigma_1 \times \cdots \times \Sigma_N$$

8 *Example* The object of Fig. *1.10.5b* is the direct product of $\mathcal{A}$ and $\mathcal{B}$, with the input and output of $\mathcal{A} \times \mathcal{B}$ being $\mathbf{u} = (u_1, u_2)$ and $\mathbf{y} = (y_1, y_2)$, respectively. ◁

We turn next to

Initially free tandem combinations and products

Roughly speaking, $\mathcal{A}_1$ and $\mathcal{A}_2$ are connected in *tandem*, with $\mathcal{A}_1$ preceding $\mathcal{A}_2$, if the input to $\mathcal{A}_2$ ($\triangleq \mathbf{u}^2$) is constrained to be equal to the output of $\mathcal{A}_1$ ($\triangleq \mathbf{y}^1$), as illustrated in Fig. *1.10.3*. Here we have to distinguish

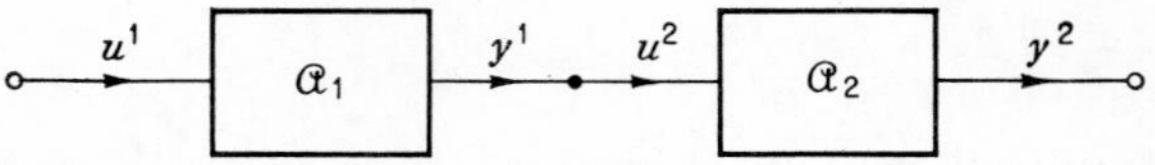

Fig. 1.10.3 Tandem combination of $\mathcal{A}_1$ and $\mathcal{A}_2$, with $\mathcal{A}_1$ preceding $\mathcal{A}_2$.

between two cases: (I) $\mathbf{u}^2 = \mathbf{y}^1$ for $t > t_0$, where t_0 is the instant at which $\mathbf{u}^1$ (input to $\mathcal{A}_1$) starts, and (II) $\mathbf{u}^2 = \mathbf{y}^1$ for all t. In the former case, the tandem combination of $\mathcal{A}_1$ and $\mathcal{A}_2$ will be said to be *initially free* or simply *free*. In the latter case, the tandem combination will be said to be initially *constrained*. Essentially, in case I, the combination of $\mathcal{A}_1$ and $\mathcal{A}_2$ acts like the direct product of $\mathcal{A}_1$ and $\mathcal{A}_2$ for $t < t_0$. This is illustrated in Fig. *1.10.4*, in which the switch K signifies that from time t_0 on (but not before) $\mathbf{u}^2$ is constrained to be equal to $\mathbf{y}^1$.

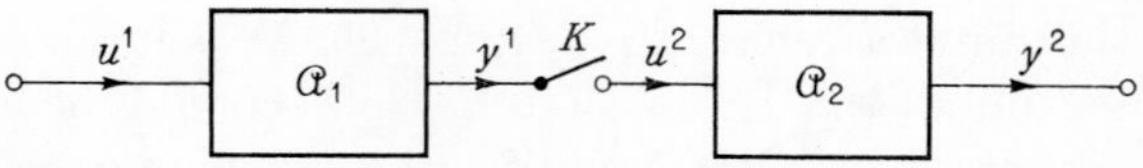

Fig. 1.10.4 Initially free tandem combination of $\mathcal{A}_1$ and $\mathcal{A}_2$.

We assume that $\mathcal{A}_1$ and $\mathcal{A}_2$ are characterized by input-output-state relations of the form *1*, $i = 1, 2$, with the output segment space of $\mathcal{A}_1$

contained in the input segment space of $\mathcal{A}_2$ in order to allow the use of the output of $\mathcal{A}_1$ as input to $\mathcal{A}_2$. Furthermore, we assume that the states of $\mathcal{A}_1$ and $\mathcal{A}_2$ at time t are given by the respective state equations ($i = 1, 2$)

9 $$\mathbf{s}^i(t) = \mathbf{s}^i(\boldsymbol{\alpha}^i;\mathbf{u}^i) \qquad \boldsymbol{\alpha}^i \triangleq \mathbf{s}^i(t_0),\ \mathbf{u}^i \triangleq \mathbf{u}^i_{(t_0,t]}$$

which are induced by the input-output-state relations *1* (see *1.8.2 et seq.*).

We focus our attention first on case I. In this case, the initial states $\boldsymbol{\alpha}^1$ and $\boldsymbol{\alpha}^2$ can be chosen arbitrarily in Σ_1 and Σ_2, respectively, or, equivalently, the pair $(\boldsymbol{\alpha}^1, \boldsymbol{\alpha}^2)$ can be chosen arbitrarily in the product space $\Sigma_1 \times \Sigma_2$. Clearly, given $\boldsymbol{\alpha}^1$, $\boldsymbol{\alpha}^2$, and $\mathbf{u}^1 \triangleq \mathbf{u}^1_{(t_0,t]}$, we can find from *1* and *9* the output $\mathbf{y}^2 \triangleq \mathbf{y}^2_{(t_0,t]}$ and the states $\mathbf{s}^1(t)$ and $\mathbf{s}^2(t)$ for any $t > t_0$. On the basis of this observation, we make the following

10 **Definition** The *free tandem combination* of $\mathcal{A}_1$ and $\mathcal{A}_2$ with $\mathcal{A}_1$ preceding $\mathcal{A}_2$, or, equivalently, the *free product* of $\mathcal{A}_2$ and $\mathcal{A}_1$, is an object $\mathcal{A}(t_0)$ characterized by the input-output-state relation

11 $$\mathbf{y}^2 = \bar{\mathbf{A}}_2[\boldsymbol{\alpha}^2;\bar{\mathbf{A}}_1(\boldsymbol{\alpha}^1;\mathbf{u}^1)]$$

in which the composite state $(\boldsymbol{\alpha}^1,\boldsymbol{\alpha}^2)$ plays the role of the initial state of $\mathcal{A}(t_0)$. Correspondingly, the state of $\mathcal{A}(t_0)$ at time t is given by the pair $(\mathbf{s}^1(t),\mathbf{s}^2(t))$, where $\mathbf{s}^1(t)$ and $\mathbf{s}^2(t)$ are expressed by (see *9*)

12 $$\mathbf{s}^1(t) = \mathbf{s}^1(\boldsymbol{\alpha}^1;\mathbf{u}^1_{(t_0,t]})$$
$$\mathbf{s}^2(t) = \mathbf{s}^2(\boldsymbol{\alpha}^2;\bar{\mathbf{A}}_1(\boldsymbol{\alpha}^1;\mathbf{u}^1_{(t_0,t]}))$$

and the output segment space of $\mathcal{A}(t_0)$ is given by (see *1.6.2*)

13 $$R[\mathbf{y}^2] = \{\mathbf{y}^2 | \mathbf{y}^2 = \bar{\mathbf{A}}_2[\boldsymbol{\alpha}^2;\bar{\mathbf{A}}_1(\boldsymbol{\alpha}^1;\mathbf{u}^1)]\} \qquad \mathbf{u}^1 \in R[\mathbf{u}^1],\ \boldsymbol{\alpha}^1 \in \Sigma_1,\ \boldsymbol{\alpha}^2 \in \Sigma_2$$

14 *Comment* It is evident that *11* satisfies the first self-consistency condition *1.6.11*. This, however, is not sufficient to qualify *11* as an input-output-state relation. The justification for referring to *11* as an input-output-state relation is provided by results which will be established in Chap. *2* (see *2.6.10*).

15 **Remark** It is important to observe that, unlike the initial state $(\boldsymbol{\alpha}^1,\boldsymbol{\alpha}^2)$ which ranges over the product space $\Sigma_1 \times \Sigma_2$, the pair $(\mathbf{s}^1(t),\mathbf{s}^2(t))$, which plays the role of the state of $\mathcal{A}(t_0)$ at time t, ranges over a subset of $\Sigma_1 \times \Sigma_2$ rather than $\Sigma_1 \times \Sigma_2$ itself. The subset in question is defined by

16 $$\Sigma(t_0,t) = \{(\mathbf{s}^1(t),\mathbf{s}^2(t)) | \boldsymbol{\alpha}^1 \in \Sigma_1, \boldsymbol{\alpha}^2 \in \Sigma_2, \mathbf{u}^1 \in R[\mathbf{u}^1]\}$$

where $\mathbf{s}^1(t)$ and $\mathbf{s}^2(t)$ are given by *12*. This subset constitutes the state space of $\mathcal{A}(t_0)$ at time t, and the arguments t_0, t serve to indicate that it depends on both t_0 and t.

17 *Example* Let $\mathcal{A}_1$ be an integrator with input-output-state relation *1.9.11* and let $\mathcal{A}_2$ be a differentiator with input-output-state relation (see *4.4.39*)

18 $$y(t) = -u(t_0-)\delta(t - t_0) + \frac{d}{dt}[1(t - t_0)u(t)]$$

Then the input-output-state relation for the free product of $\mathcal{A}_2$ and $\mathcal{A}_1$ is given by

$$y^2(t) = u^1(t) + (\alpha^1 - \alpha^2)\delta(t - t_0-) \qquad t \geq t_0$$

where $\alpha^1 = y^1(t_0-)$ and $\alpha^2 = u^2(t_0-)$. Since $y^1(t) = u^2(t)$ for $t \geq t_0$, the state space $\Sigma(t,t_0)$ is $\mathcal{R}^2$ for $t = t_0-$ and $\Sigma(t_0,t) = \mathcal{R}^1$ for $t \geq t_0$ (see *22*). Thus, $\Sigma(t_0,t)$ changes from $\mathcal{R}^2$ to $\mathcal{R}^1$ at time t_0 and remains constant thereafter. Later on we shall see that this is characteristic of linear systems (Remark *2.6.8*).

19 **Remark** The definition of the free product of $\mathcal{A}_1$ and $\mathcal{A}_2$ can be extended in an obvious fashion to the free product of $\mathcal{A}_1, \ldots, \mathcal{A}_N$. For example, the input-output-state relation for the free product of $\mathcal{A}_3$, $\mathcal{A}_2$, and $\mathcal{A}_1$ (with $\mathcal{A}_1$, $\mathcal{A}_2$, and $\mathcal{A}_3$ separated by switches which close at t_0) is given by the nested expression

20 $$\mathbf{y}^3 = \bar{\mathbf{A}}_3\{\boldsymbol{\alpha}^3;\bar{\mathbf{A}}_2[\boldsymbol{\alpha}^2;\bar{\mathbf{A}}_1(\boldsymbol{\alpha}^1;\mathbf{u}^1)]\}$$

Note that this expression implies that the free product is associative in the sense that $(\mathcal{A}_3\mathcal{A}_2)\mathcal{A}_1$ and $\mathcal{A}_3(\mathcal{A}_2\mathcal{A}_1)$ are characterized by the same input-output-state relation. This is a special instance of the *associative principle* which is stated in *34*.

Constrained tandem combinations and products

The notion of an initially free tandem combination of $\mathcal{A}_1$ and $\mathcal{A}_2$ provides a convenient way of defining the tandem combination of $\mathcal{A}_1$ and $\mathcal{A}_2$ in which the input to $\mathcal{A}_2$ is constrained to be equal to the output of $\mathcal{A}_1$ for all t rather than $t > t_0$. Such a combination, call it $\mathcal{A}$, is represented diagrammatically as in Fig. *1.10.3*, with the connection of the output of $\mathcal{A}_1$ to the input of $\mathcal{A}_2$ signifying that $\mathbf{y}^1(t) = \mathbf{u}^2(t)$ for all t.

Essentially, we regard a constraint of the form "$\mathbf{y}^1(t) = \mathbf{u}^2(t)$ for all t" as a limiting form (as $t_0 \to -\infty$) of the constraint "$\mathbf{y}^1(t) = \mathbf{u}^2(t)$ for $t > t_0$." This implies that the state space of $\mathcal{A}$ is formally characterized by the limit, if it exists,

21 $$\Sigma(t) = \lim_{t_0 \to -\infty} \Sigma(t_0,t)$$

For general state spaces, the precise meaning which should be attached to *21* and the conditions under which the limit exists are neither simple nor even completely settled questions. For our purposes, it will suffice to take *21* to mean that, for each t, any point in $\Sigma(t)$ can be approached arbitrarily closely (in terms of a metric defined on the product space $\Sigma_1 \times \Sigma_2$) by a point in $\Sigma(t_0,t)$. Actually, the precise meaning of *21* will not play a material role in the following discussion, since our use of *21* on a general level will be largely formal in nature. (See also Remark *2.6.8*.)

22 *Comment* In later chapters we shall be concerned for the most part with differential objects (see *1.8.3 et seq.*) for which the state at time t is defined by a finite number of the derivatives of the input and output at time t. For such systems, $\Sigma(t)$, if it exists, can be determined by a direct process of elimination of identical variables from the expressions for the states of $\mathcal{A}_1$ and $\mathcal{A}_2$ at time t (see *2.6.8*). For example, suppose that $\mathbf{s}^1(t)$ and $\mathbf{s}^2(t)$ are real-valued and are respectively equal to the output of $\mathcal{A}_1$ and input of $\mathcal{A}_2$ at time t, that is, $s^1(t) = y^1(t)$ and $s^2(t) = u^2(t)$. Then the constraint "$y^1(t) = u^2(t)$ for all t" implies "$s^1(t) = s^2(t)$ for all t," and consequently if $y^1(t)$ ranges over $\mathcal{R}^1$ (for all t), so does the pair $(s^1(t),s^2(t))$. Thus, in this case Σ is a subspace $(= \mathcal{R}^1)$ of the product space $\Sigma_1 \times \Sigma_2\ (= \mathcal{R}^2)$. This conclusion is consistent with that of Example *17*.

Note that $\Sigma(t)$ is independent of t by virtue of the assumption that (I) the dependence of $s^1(t)$ and $s^2(t)$ on the input and output does not involve t and (II) the range of $y^1(t)$ is independent of t. Such conditions are satisfied by most of the types of system with which we shall be concerned in later chapters. For this reason, we shall abbreviate $\Sigma(t)$ to Σ, with the tacit understanding that $\Sigma(t)$ exists and is independent of t.

Based on these observations, we make the following

23 **Definition** An object $\mathcal{A}$ is an *initially constrained tandem (series) combination*, or, more simply, *tandem combination* of $\mathcal{A}_1$ and $\mathcal{A}_2$, with $\mathcal{A}_1$ preceding $\mathcal{A}_2$, if the input to $\mathcal{A}_2$ is constrained to be equal to the output of $\mathcal{A}_1$ for all t. The tandem combination of $\mathcal{A}_1$ and $\mathcal{A}_2$ will also be referred to as an *initially constrained product*, or simply *product*, of $\mathcal{A}_2$ and $\mathcal{A}_1$, and it will be denoted by $\mathcal{A}_2\mathcal{A}_1$. $\triangleleft$

We regard $\mathcal{A}$ as a limiting form of the free product $\mathcal{A}(t_0)$ as $t_0 \to -\infty$. Then, the state space of $\mathcal{A}$ is a subset Σ of the product space $\Sigma_1 \times \Sigma_2$, with Σ formally defined by

$$\Sigma = \lim_{t_0 \to -\infty} \{(\mathbf{s}^1(t),\mathbf{s}^2(t)) | \boldsymbol{\alpha}^1 \in \Sigma_1, \boldsymbol{\alpha}^2 \in \Sigma_2, \mathbf{u}^1 \in R[\mathbf{u}^1]\}$$

where $\mathbf{s}^1(t)$ and $\mathbf{s}^2(t)$ are expressed by *12*. Correspondingly, the input-output-state relation of $\mathcal{A}$ is given by *20*, with $(\boldsymbol{\alpha}^1,\boldsymbol{\alpha}^2)$ ranging over Σ.

24 *Comment* As in the case of the free product, the product of $\mathcal{A}_2$ and $\mathcal{A}_1$ has the associative property, and consequently the product of $\mathcal{A}_N$, . . . , $\mathcal{A}_1$ can be written as $\mathcal{A}_N \cdots \mathcal{A}_1$ without the use of parentheses.

25 *Comment* Throughout the foregoing discussion we have assumed that $\mathcal{A}_1$ and $\mathcal{A}_2$ are characterized by their respective input-output-state relations, and our aim was that of obtaining a similar characterization for $\mathcal{A}_2\mathcal{A}_1$. It should be noted, however, that alternatively we could have started with the characterization of $\mathcal{A}_1$ and $\mathcal{A}_2$ in terms of their spaces of input-output pairs (see *1.4.26*) and asked merely for a definition of the space of input-output pairs of $\mathcal{A}_2\mathcal{A}_1$. Specifically, this can be done quite easily as follows. Let $\mathcal{A}_1$ and $\mathcal{A}_2$ be defined symbolically by $\mathcal{A}_1 \triangleq \{(\mathbf{u}^1,\mathbf{y}^1)\}$ and $\mathcal{A}_2 \triangleq \{(\mathbf{u}^2,\mathbf{y}^2)\}$, meaning that $\mathcal{A}_1$ is a specified set of pairs of segmented time functions $\mathbf{u}^1$ and $\mathbf{y}^1$, and likewise for $\mathcal{A}_2$. (Strictly speaking, $\mathcal{A}_1$ and $\mathcal{A}_2$ are families of such sets of pairs, with t_0 and t playing the role of parameters; see *1.4.17*.) Then $\mathcal{A}_2\mathcal{A}_1$ is defined by $\mathcal{A}_2\mathcal{A}_1 = \{(\mathbf{u}^1,\mathbf{y}^2)\}$, where $\mathbf{u}^1$ and $\mathbf{y}^2$ are time functions such that there exists $\mathbf{y}^1$ $(= \mathbf{u}^2)$ with the property $(\mathbf{u}^1,\mathbf{y}^1) \in \mathcal{A}_1$ and $(\mathbf{u}^2,\mathbf{y}^2) \in \mathcal{A}_2$. It is of interest to note that the associative property of the product of $\mathcal{A}_1$ and $\mathcal{A}_2$ is an immediate consequence of this definition. It should also be noted that this way of defining the product of $\mathcal{A}_2$ and $\mathcal{A}_1$ coincides with the conventional way of defining the product of two relations.[1]

Interconnection of N objects

A basic question that arises when we interconnect N objects $\mathcal{A}_1$, . . . , $\mathcal{A}_N$ in an arbitrary fashion—and which does not manifest itself in the case of a tandem combination of $\mathcal{A}_1, \ldots, \mathcal{A}_N$—is whether the interconnection is *determinate*, i.e., whether the input-output-state relation of the interconnection is determined by the input-output-state relations of its constituents.

The notion of determinateness will be discussed in greater detail in Chap. *2*, Sec. *6*. For our present purposes, it will suffice to remark that, essentially, an interconnection $\mathcal{A}$ is determinate if, given the input to $\mathcal{A}$ and the initial states of the components $\mathcal{A}_1, \ldots, \mathcal{A}_N$, one can determine, at least in principle, the outputs of $\mathcal{A}_1, \ldots, \mathcal{A}_N$. As will be shown in Chap. *2* (*2.6.10*), if $\mathcal{A}$ is determinate, then the composite state vector $\mathbf{s}(t) = (\mathbf{s}^1(t), \ldots, \mathbf{s}^N(t))$, where $\mathbf{s}^i(t) \triangleq$ state vector of $\mathcal{A}_i$ at time t, qualifies as the state of $\mathcal{A}$ at time t. In the special case of a tandem combination of $\mathcal{A}_1$ and $\mathcal{A}_2$, this implies that the state of $\mathcal{A}_2\mathcal{A}_1$ is $(\mathbf{s}^1(t),\mathbf{s}^2(t))$—a result which we have already used in our discussion of the tandem combination in the preceding subsection.

As in the case of a tandem combination, a basic problem that arises in the analysis of an interconnection $\mathcal{A}$ is that of the characterization and determination of Σ, the state space of $\mathcal{A}$. We approach this

[1] See, for example, Ref. *11*, p. 41.

problem in a similar way, i.e., by regarding $\mathcal{A}$ as a limiting form of an *initially free* interconnection $\mathcal{A}(t_0)$ which is derived from $\mathcal{A}$ by interposing switches between $\mathcal{A}_1, \ldots, \mathcal{A}_N$ which remain open until t_0, with $t_0 \to -\infty$ (Figs. *1.10.1* and *1.10.2*). It is understood, of course, that the input to $\mathcal{A}$ would be specified for, say, $t \geq t_1$, with the input to $\mathcal{A}(t_0)$ between t_0 and t_1 influencing only the state of $\mathcal{A}(t_0)$ at time t_1.

Again, as in the case of a tandem combination, the state space of $\mathcal{A}$ can be characterized in a formal way by the relation (*1.10.21*)

26 $$\Sigma = \lim_{t_0 \to -\infty} \Sigma(t_0,t)$$

where $\Sigma(t_0,t)$ denotes the state space of $\mathcal{A}(t_0)$ at time t, that is,

$$\Sigma(t_0,t) = \{\mathbf{s}(t) | \mathbf{s}(t_0) \in \Sigma_1 \times \cdots \times \Sigma_N, \mathbf{u} \in R[\mathbf{u}]\}$$

where $\mathbf{u}$ denotes the input to $\mathcal{A}$ and the components of $\mathbf{s}(t)$ are related to those of $\mathbf{s}(t_0)(= \boldsymbol{\alpha})$ by *9*. The determination of Σ from *26* in the general case of an arbitrary interconnection presents many complex and as yet unsolved problems. We shall not concern ourselves with the discussion of these problems, since in the case of systems that are of primary interest to us in this text, namely, linear differential systems, both $\Sigma(t_0,t)$ and Σ can generally be determined in a direct fashion by using a technique sketched in Chap. *2* (*2.6.8*).

Since the relation between a *free interconnection* of $\mathcal{A}_1, \ldots, \mathcal{A}_N$ on the one hand and a *constrained interconnection* on the other is identical with that of a free and constrained tandem combination (*1.10.10* and *1.10.23*), we shall not define these terms in a formal way. Instead, we shall concern ourselves with defining other terms which enter into the description of an interconnection of N objects, with the understanding that by an "interconnection" we mean a "constrained interconnection," which in turn can be regarded as a limiting form of a free interconnection.

27 **Definition** Let $\mathcal{A}$ be a collection $\{\mathcal{A}_i\}$ of N not necessarily oriented objects with respective terminal vectors $\mathbf{v}^i = (v_1^i, \ldots, v_{n_i}^i)$ (*1.4.1 et seq.*). The joining (connecting) of a terminal of $\mathcal{A}_i$ labeled, say, v_μ^i to a terminal of $\mathcal{A}_j$ labeled, say, v_ν^j signifies that $v_\mu^i(t) = v_\nu^j(t)$ for all t in T. The variable v_μ^i (and v_ν^j) is said to be a *shared* or *common* terminal variable. If v_μ^i is an input variable and v_ν^j is an output variable or vice versa, then v_μ^i (and v_ν^j) is said to be an *input-output variable.*

The joining of v_μ^i and v_ν^j is subject to the following compatibility conditions.

(I) v_μ^i and v_ν^j are not both output variables.

(II) If v_μ^i is an output variable and v_ν^j is an input variable, then the range of v_μ^i is contained in that of v_ν^j.

(III) If both v^i_μ and v^j_ν are input variables, then the range of the shared variable is the intersection of the ranges of v^i_μ and v^j_ν.

28 **Definition** The collection $\{\mathcal{A}_i\}$ is said to be an *interconnected set*, or, more simply, an *interconnection*, of the $\mathcal{A}_i$ if every object in the collection shares at least one terminal variable with one or more other objects in this collection. If some or possibly none of the $\mathcal{A}_i$ share terminal variables, the collection is said to be *partially interconnected.* Relations of the form $v^i_\mu = v^j_\nu$ or their equivalents (e.g., Kirchhoff voltage and current law relations in electrical networks) constitute the *interconnection relations* for the $\mathcal{A}_i$.

29 *Examples* In Fig. *1.10.1* is shown an interconnected set of three multipoles $\mathcal{A}_1$, $\mathcal{A}_2$, $\mathcal{A}_3$. Here the interconnection relations are $y^1_1 = u^2_1$, $y^2_1 = u^3_1$, $y^3_3 = u^1_2$, $y^3_1 = u^2_2$. In Fig. *1.10.5a* is shown a partially inter-

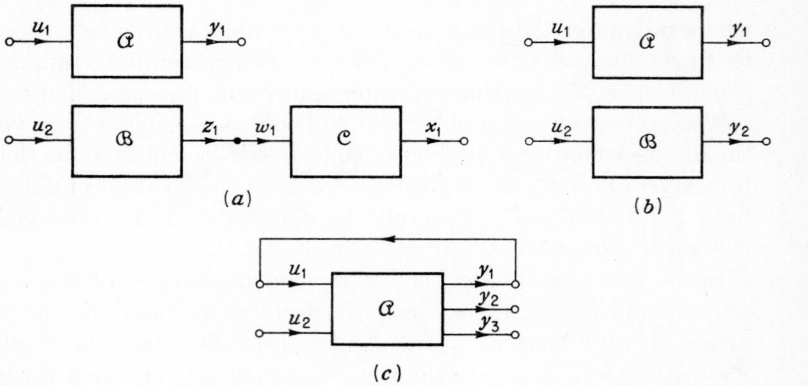

Fig. 1.10.5 (*a*) Partial interconnection; (*b*) direct product; (*c*) self-interconnection.

connected set of three 2-poles $\mathcal{A}$, $\mathcal{B}$, $\mathcal{C}$; in Fig. *1.10.5b* is shown the direct product of two 2-poles; and in Fig. *1.10.5c* is shown a degenerate case of a single interconnected object. To subsume this case under the definition given above, the terminals y_1, u_1 can be regarded as being connected by a fictitious unitor (*1.9.8*). ◁

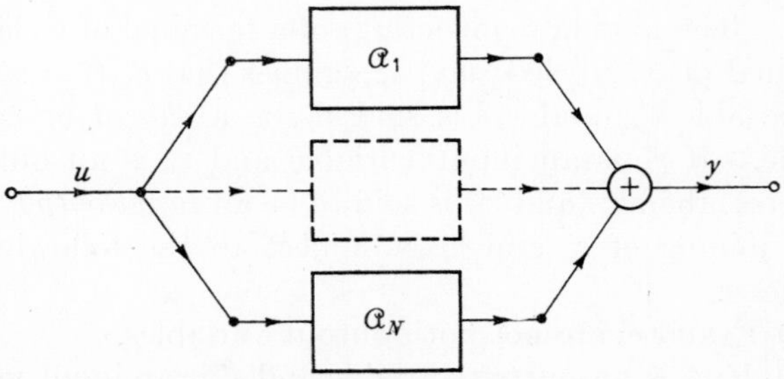

Fig. 1.10.6 Parallel combination.

There are several simple types of interconnection that are encountered quite frequently in system analysis. One is the tandem combination that we have already discussed. Another is the *parallel combination* that is illustrated in Fig. *1.10.6*. The parallel combination of $\mathcal{A}_1, \ldots, \mathcal{A}_N$ is denoted by $\mathcal{A}_1 + \cdots + \mathcal{A}_N$, with the object $\mathcal{A} = \mathcal{A}_1 + \cdots + \mathcal{A}_N$ referred to as the *sum* of $\mathcal{A}_1, \ldots, \mathcal{A}_N$. The input-output-state relation of $\mathcal{A}$ is expressed by

30 $$y = \sum_{i=1}^{N} \bar{\mathbf{A}}_i(\boldsymbol{\alpha}^i; \mathbf{u}^i)$$

with the state space of $\mathcal{A}$ being a subset Σ of the product space $\Sigma_1 \times \cdots \times \Sigma_N$.

31 *Exercise* Give a characterization of Σ as a limiting form of the state space of the free sum of $\mathcal{A}_1, \ldots, \mathcal{A}_N$. $\triangleleft$

By combining series and parallel combinations of 2-poles, one can construct more complex structures of the form shown in Fig. *1.10.7*.

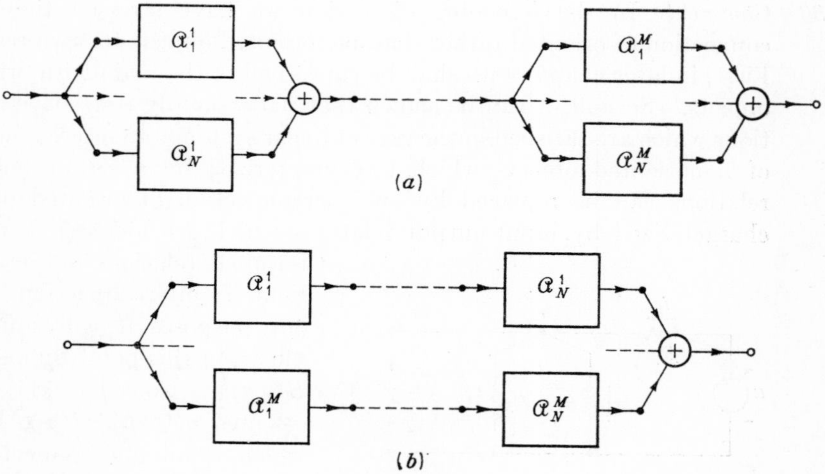

Fig. 1.10.7 (*a*) Series-parallel combination; (*b*) parallel-series combination.

The structure on top is called the *series-parallel* combination, while that below is called the *parallel-series* combination. In symbols, the series-parallel combination is represented by the expression

32 $$(\mathcal{A}_1^M + \cdots + \mathcal{A}_N^M)(\mathcal{A}_1^{M-1} + \cdots + \mathcal{A}_N^{M-1}) \cdots (\mathcal{A}_1^1 + \cdots + \mathcal{A}_N^1)$$

whereas the parallel-series combination is represented by

33 $$\mathcal{A}_N^1 \cdots \mathcal{A}_1^1 + \mathcal{A}_N^2 \cdots \mathcal{A}_1^2 + \cdots + \mathcal{A}_N^M \cdots \mathcal{A}_1^M$$

where the $\mathcal{A}_i^\mu$ ($\mu = 1, \ldots, M, i = 1, \ldots, N$) denote the component 2-poles of these structures. (For an illustration of *33* see *3.8.11*.)

In dealing with interconnections of objects we shall frequently use in a tacit manner the following two basic principles.

34 **Associative principle** If $\mathcal{A}_1, \ldots, \mathcal{A}_N$ are components of an interconnected set $\mathcal{A}$, then any subset of $\mathcal{A}_1, \ldots, \mathcal{A}_N$ may be regarded as a component of $\mathcal{A}$. For example, in Fig. *1.10.1* the combination of $\mathcal{A}_2$ and $\mathcal{A}_3$ may be regarded as a single object with input u_1^2 and outputs y_2^3 and y_3^3.

35 **Substitution principle** If an oriented component $\mathcal{A}_i$ of $\mathcal{A}$ is replaced by an equivalent component (in the sense of Definition *2.5.8*), then the resulting interconnection is equivalent to $\mathcal{A}$. ◁

These statements are *principles* in the sense that they are of general validity and that in specific contexts they can be formulated as provable theorems. We shall not attempt to do this in the present text, except for particular cases involving for the most part linear systems.

36 *Comment* In the foregoing discussion we have stressed the interconnection of oriented rather than nonoriented objects for two reasons. First, in later chapters we shall be concerned in the main with oriented objects. Second, it can be shown that under mildly restrictive conditions which are satisfied in the case of linear systems, an interconnection of nonoriented objects which is characterized by a set of terminal relations can be replaced by an interconnection of oriented objects characterized by input-output relations which are identical with the terminal relations of the nonoriented interconnection.[1] For our purposes it will suffice to illustrate this point by a simple

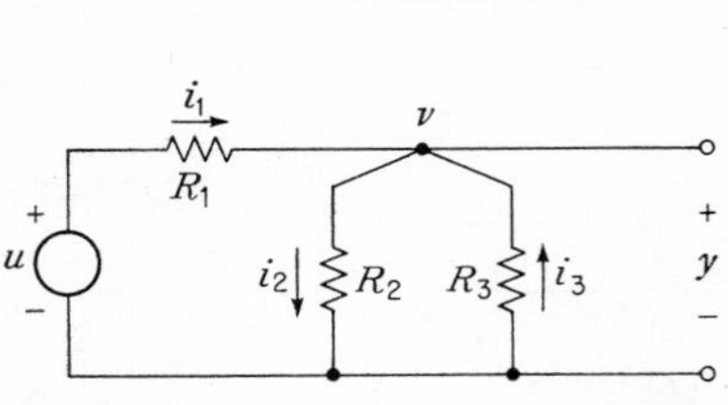

Fig. 1.10.8 Network of Example *1.10.37*.

37 *Example* Consider the nonoriented network of Fig. *1.10.8*, which is an interconnection of nonoriented resistors R_1, R_2, and R_3. Note that in the case of an electrical network a special convention is used to represent the constraints imposed by interconnections. Specifically, the joining of R_1, R_2, and R_3 at a node ν (Fig. *1.10.8*) signifies that

38 $$i_1 - i_2 + i_3 = 0$$

which is a statement of Kirchhoff's current law applied to the currents

[1] This is basic to the signal-flow-graph analysis of electrical networks. See Ref. *9*,

i_1, i_2, and i_3 flowing through R_1, R_2, and R_3, respectively.[1] In effect, this equation constitutes an interconnection relation for this network (see *28*).

The terminal relations for R_1, R_2, and R_3 are

39 R_1: $u - y = R_1 i_1$

R_2: $y = R_2 i_2$

R_3: $y = -R_3 i_3$

Thus, the network as a whole is characterized by the terminal relations *38* and *39*.

Now consider the interconnection of the oriented scalors shown in Fig. *1.10.9*, in which the number inside each block represents its scale

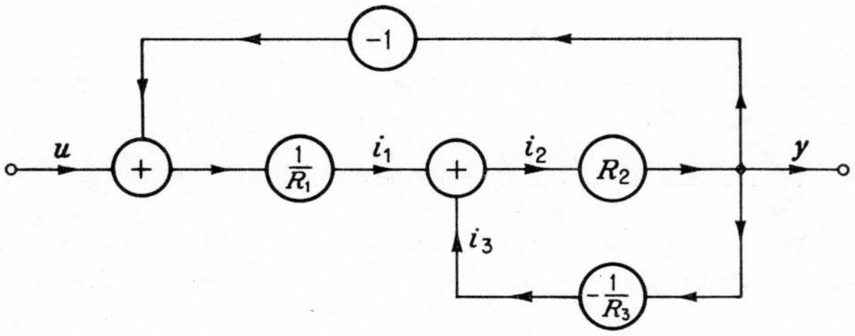

Fig. 1.10.9 Block-diagram representation of the network of Fig. *1.10.8*.

factor (*1.9.8*). Here we have an interconnection of oriented elements, with the input-output and interconnection relations reading

$$i_1 = \frac{1}{R_1}(u - y) \qquad i_3 = -\frac{1}{R_3}y$$

$$y = R_2 i_2 \qquad i_2 = i_1 + i_3$$

Since these equations are identical with the terminal relations of the original network, it follows that the network of Fig. *1.10.8* is equivalent to the interconnection of oriented scalors and adders of Fig. *1.10.9*. This is the point we wanted to illustrate.

Flow graphs and signal-state graphs

A diagrammatic representation of the interconnection of two or more objects, such as shown in Fig. *1.10.1*, is essentially a statement of the orientation of each object in the interconnected set together with an indication of which terminal variables are shared by two or more objects. This information can be conveyed in a number of alternative ways, two of which are discussed very briefly in the sequel.

[1] We assume, of course, that the reader is familiar with elementary electric circuit analysis. A careful discussion of the fundamentals of circuit analysis can be found in Refs. *3*, *4*, and *5*, among others.

First, one can employ the notation and terminology of signal-flow graphs, which will be discussed in greater detail in Chap. *9*, Sec. *15*. In this case, each terminal variable is associated with a node of an oriented graph, and an input-output relation of the form

$$y_1 = f_1(u_1, \ldots, u_n)$$

is represented as a set of oriented branches leading from nodes $u_1, \ldots,$ u_n to node y (Fig. *1.9.3a*).

As an illustration, on applying this convention to the interconnected set of Fig. *1.10.1*, we obtain the signal-flow graph shown in Fig. *1.10.10*.

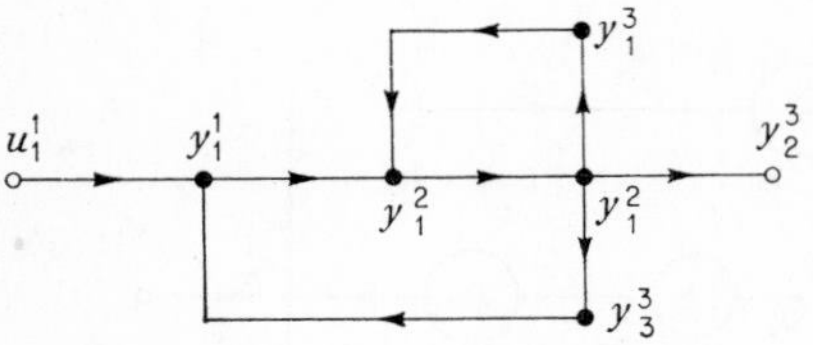

Fig. 1.10.10 Signal-flow graph of the system of Fig. *1.10.1*.

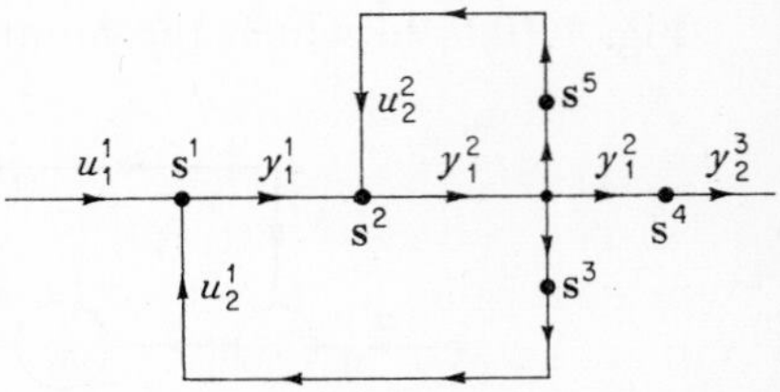

Fig. 1.10.11 Signal-state graph of the system of Fig. *1.10.1*.

Note that it is simpler in appearance than the block diagram of Fig. *1.10.1*. However, this simplicity is attained at a cost of some loss of information, since in order to make the signal-flow-graph representation applicable, it is necessary to decompose each object into component objects each having a single output terminal (see *1.9.3*). As a result, in the signal-flow-graph representation of an interconnected set of objects the individual objects lose their identity. For example, Fig. *1.10.10* does not indicate whether the nodes labeled y_1^3, y_2^3, y_3^3, and y_1^2 represent a single object with one input and three outputs (i.e., the object $\mathcal{A}_3$ in Fig. *1.10.1*) or whether they represent three distinct 2-poles.

Another and, from our viewpoint, more important shortcoming of the conventional signal-flow-graph representation is that it makes no provision for associating a state with an object. As was pointed out previously (see *1.9.3 et seq.*), this can be done by the use of the signal-state-graph representation. Applying this mode of representation to the interconnected set of Fig. *1.10.1*, we obtain the signal-state graph shown in Fig. *1.10.11*. Here $\mathbf{s}^1$ represents the state vector associated with $\mathcal{A}_1$, $\mathbf{s}^2$ is the state vector associated with $\mathcal{A}^2$, and $\mathbf{s}^3$, $\mathbf{s}^4$, and $\mathbf{s}^5$ are the state vectors associated with the 2-poles into which $\mathcal{A}_3$ is decomposed (*1.9.3*). Note that $\mathbf{s}^3$, $\mathbf{s}^4$, and $\mathbf{s}^5$ can be identified with $\mathbf{s}$, the state of $\mathcal{A}_3$. However, if each 2-pole into which $\mathcal{A}_3$ is decomposed is regarded as a separate object, it may be possible that vectors with smaller number of components than **s** may qualify as state vectors for the objects in question. It is for this reason that we use the different symbols $\mathbf{s}^1$, $\mathbf{s}^2$, and $\mathbf{s}^3$ to denote the state vectors of these 2-poles even though **s** qualifies as a state vector for all of them.

We shall not dwell any further on the details of various graphical ways of representing an interconnection of a set of oriented objects. The brief discussion presented above will suffice for our immediate purposes.

System (formal definition)

After this drawn-out introduction, we are finally in a position to define the notion of a system in fairly concrete terms.

40 **Definition** An *abstract system,* or, simply, a *system,* $\mathcal{S}$ is a partially interconnected set (*1.10.28*) of abstract objects $\mathcal{A}_1$, $\mathcal{A}_2$, $\mathcal{A}_3$, . . . , termed the *components* of $\mathcal{S}$. The components of $\mathcal{S}$ may be oriented or nonoriented; they may be finite or infinite in number; and each of them may be associated with a finite or infinite number of terminal variables. ◁

In the sequel we shall assume, unless otherwise noted, that $\mathcal{S}$ has a finite number of components each of which is an oriented object associated with a finite number of terminal variables.

Under the above definition, a system may be regarded as a single object, and conversely any single object may be regarded as a system. If a system comprising the objects $\mathcal{A}_1, \ldots, \mathcal{A}_N$ is regarded as a single object, then the set of terminal variables of $\mathcal{S}$ is the set-theoretic union of the terminal variables of its components. If the components of $\mathcal{S}$ are oriented, then so is $\mathcal{S}$, with the input variables of $\mathcal{S}$ being those input variables of its components which are not input-output variables (*1.10.27*). The aggregate of the shared terminal variables as well as the nonshared output variables of the components of $\mathcal{S}$ constitutes the set of output variables of $\mathcal{S}$. Any subset of the output variables of $\mathcal{S}$ may be disregarded and thus categorized as suppressed output variables of $\mathcal{S}$ (see Sec. *4*).

41 *Example* For the system (interconnected set) shown in Fig. *1.10.1* the terminal variables of $\mathcal{S}$ are u_1^1, u_2^1, y_1^1, u_2^2, y_1^2, y_2^3. (Note that $y_1^1 = u_1^2$, $u_2^2 = y_1^3$, $u_2^1 = y_3^3$.) The variable u_1^1 is the input to $\mathcal{S}$. The output variables are y_1^1, y_1^2, y_1^3, y_2^3, y_3^3 and of these all but y_2^3 are suppressed, leaving y_2^3 as the output of $\mathcal{S}$.

42 *Example* For the system shown in Fig. *1.10.5a* the terminal variables are u_1, y_1, u_2, z_1, x_1. Of these, z_1 is shared. y_1, z_1, and x_1 are the output variables of the system. The variable z_1 is suppressed.

43 *Example* For the nonoriented system shown in Fig. *1.10.8* the terminal variables are u, i_1, i_2, i_3, y. If the system is oriented by designating, say, u as the input and y as the output, then the output variables are i_1, i_2, i_3, and y, and of these i_1, i_2, and i_3 are suppressed. ◁

A question of basic importance in system analysis is the following. Suppose that $\mathcal{S}$ comprises a set of oriented objects $\mathcal{a}_1, \ldots, \mathcal{a}_N$ each of which is completely characterized by an input-output-state relation and all of which are interconnected in a specified way. Is $\mathcal{S}$—regarded as a single object—completely characterized by the aggregate of the input-output-state relations for its components and the interconnection relations? It is easy to construct examples which show that this is not the case in general. However, the answer to this question is in the affirmative for a wide category of systems which subsumes those studied in the book. We shall consider this question in greater detail in Chap. *2* in connection with the discussion of *determinate* systems.

This closes our introduction to the language, notation, and basic concepts of system theory. In the succeeding chapters, we shall examine in greater detail the ramifications and interrelations of the concepts introduced in this chapter, and we shall apply them to the study of a special and yet basic class of systems, namely, the class of linear systems.

REFERENCES AND SUGGESTED READING

1 Apostol, T. M.: "Mathematical Analysis," Addison-Wesley Publishing Company, Inc., Reading, Mass., 1957.
2 Kelley, J. L.: "General Topology," D. Van Nostrand Company, Inc., Princeton, N.J., 1955.
3 Van Valkenburg, M. E.: "Network Analysis," Prentice-Hall, Inc., Englewood Cliffs, N.J., 1955.
4 Seshu, S., and N. Balabanian: "Linear Network Analysis," John Wiley & Sons, Inc., New York, 1959.
5 Friedland, B., O. Wing, and R. Ash: "Principles of Linear Networks," McGraw-Hill Book Company, Inc., New York, 1961.
6 Moore, E. F.: Gedanken Experiments on Sequential Machines, in "Automata Studies," Princeton University Press, Princeton, N.J., 1956.
7 Bellman, R. E., and R. Kalaba: A Note on Interrupted Stochastic Control Processes, *Inf. and Cont.*, vol. 4, pp. 346–349, 1961.
8 Ginsburg, S.: On the Length of the Smallest Uniform Experiment Which Distinguishes the Terminal States of a Machine, *J. Assoc. Comput. Mach.*, vol. 5, pp. 266–280, 1958.
9 Mason, S. J., and H. J. Zimmermann: "Electronic Circuits, Signals and Systems," John Wiley & Sons, Inc., New York, 1960.
10 Bellman, R. E.: "Dynamic Programming," Princeton University Press, Princeton, N.J., 1957.
11 Halmos, P. R.: "Naive Set Theory," D. Van Nostrand Company, Inc., Princeton, N.J., 1960.

Concepts and properties associated with state and state equations

2

1 *Introduction*

In the preceding chapter no attempt was made to interrelate and draw consequences from the various concepts which were introduced there. This we shall begin to do in the present chapter.

Although our main concern in this book is with linear systems, the discussion of input-output-state relations in the following sections is couched in general terms, without any specialization, except through examples, to linear systems. The purpose of this approach is to put the reader in a position from which he can view linear system theory in a broader perspective and thereby acquire a better understanding of the roles played by such general concepts as state equivalence and system equivalence in the special context of linear systems.

Before proceeding to discuss the main topic of this chapter, it will be helpful to recapitulate some of the terminology and notation introduced in Chap. *1*.

Recapitulation of terminology and notation

The symbol $\mathcal{A}$ represents an abstract oriented object with input $\mathbf{u}$, output $\mathbf{y}$, and state $\mathbf{s}$. For each fixed t, the variables $\mathbf{u}(t)$, $\mathbf{y}(t)$, and $\mathbf{s}(t)$ range over the input space $R[\mathbf{u}(t)]$, the output space $R[\mathbf{y}(t)]$, and state space Σ, respectively. These spaces are assumed to be independent of time. In most of the applications we shall be concerned with, $R[\mathbf{u}(t)]$, $R[\mathbf{y}(t)]$, and Σ will be finite-dimensional linear vector spaces. The input segment space of $\mathcal{A}$ is a space $R[\mathbf{u}]$ to which the input segments $\mathbf{u} \triangleq \mathbf{u}_{(t_0,t]}$ are constrained to belong. The same statement applies to the output segment space $R[\mathbf{y}]$ (see Remark *1.4.3* and Definition *1.4.17*).

A generic element of Σ is denoted by $\boldsymbol{\alpha}$ and is called a state of $\mathcal{A}$. When dealing with two or more abstract objects, it may be expedient to use different symbols, say, $\boldsymbol{\alpha}$ to denote a state of $\mathcal{A}$ and $\boldsymbol{\beta}$ to denote a state of $\mathcal{B}$. In some cases $\boldsymbol{\alpha}$ will represent a particular fixed state of $\mathcal{A}$. In other cases $\boldsymbol{\alpha}$ may play the role of a variable ranging over Σ. Whether it is one or the other will usually be clear from the context. If necessary to avoid ambiguity, fixed values of $\boldsymbol{\alpha}$ will be denoted by symbols such as $\boldsymbol{\alpha}_i$ and $\boldsymbol{\alpha}_j$.

The symbols $\mathbf{u}_{[t_0,t_1)}$ and $\mathbf{u}_{(t_0,t_1]}$ represent segments of a time function $\mathbf{u}$ over the semiclosed intervals $[t_0,t_1)$ and $(t_0,t_1]$, respectively. More specifically, $\mathbf{u}_{(t_0,t_1]}$ is the set $\{(t,u(t))|t_0 < t \leq t_1\}$, and likewise for $\mathbf{u}_{[t_0,t_1)}$. The segment $\mathbf{u}_{(t_0,t]}$ will frequently be written in the abbreviated form $\mathbf{u}$ and will be referred to as the input segment or simply input. The same statement applies to $\mathbf{y}$, with $\mathbf{y}_{(t_0,t]}$ representing the output or the response segment of $\mathcal{A}$. The time t_0 represents an arbitrary initial time in T, the range of t. It should be understood that when we say "for all $\mathbf{u}$" or, more specifically, "for all $\mathbf{u}$ in the input segment space of $\mathcal{A}$," we vary not only the values of $\mathbf{u}$ over the observation interval $(t_0,t_1]$ but also the end points of the observation interval. When we say $\mathbf{u}$ is equal to $\mathbf{y}$ (or $\mathbf{u}$ is identical with $\mathbf{y}$) and write $\mathbf{u} = \mathbf{y}$ or

$$\mathbf{u}_{(t_0,t]} = \mathbf{y}_{(t_0,t]}$$

we mean that $\mathbf{u}(\tau) = \mathbf{y}(\tau)$ for all τ in the interval $(t_0,t]$. In order to reduce the cumbersomeness of notation, quantifiers such as $\forall\mathbf{u}$ (for all $\mathbf{u}$), $\forall t$ (for all t), $\forall t_0$ (for all t_0), etc., will frequently be omitted from equations when their presence is clearly implied by the context.

An oriented object $\mathcal{A}$ is characterized by its input-output relation

1 $$\mathcal{A}(\mathbf{u},\mathbf{y}) = 0$$

or equivalently

2 $$\mathbf{y} = \mathcal{A}(\mathbf{u})$$

with the understanding that *2* does not imply that $\mathbf{y}$ is a single-valued function of $\mathbf{u}$. A pair of time functions $(\mathbf{u}_{(t_0,t]},\mathbf{y}_{(t_0,t]})$, or, for short, $(\mathbf{u},\mathbf{y})$, which respectively belong to the input and output segment spaces of $\mathcal{A}$ constitutes an input-output pair for $\mathcal{A}$ if $\mathbf{u}$ and $\mathbf{y}$ satisfy the input-output relation *1* (or *2*). An input-output relation is in effect a means of defining the set of all input-output pairs which belong to $\mathcal{A}$ (see *1.4.17* and *1.4.26*). Essentially, $\mathcal{A}$ is a relation, written as $\mathcal{A} = \{(\mathbf{u},\mathbf{y})\}$, with domain $R[\mathbf{u}]$ and range $R[\mathbf{y}]$ (see *1.4.29*).

An abstract object $\mathcal{A}$ is completely characterized by its input-output-state relation. This relation will be written in two equivalent forms: (I)

3 $$\mathbf{y}(t) = \mathbf{A}(\mathbf{s}(t_0);\mathbf{u}_{(t_0,t]})$$

or, for short,

4 $$\mathbf{y}(t) = \mathbf{A}(\mathbf{s}(t_0);\mathbf{u})$$

and (II)

5 $$\mathbf{y}_{(t_0,t]} = \bar{\mathbf{A}}(\mathbf{s}(t_0);\mathbf{u}_{(t_0,t]})$$

or, for short,

6 $$\mathbf{y} = \bar{\mathbf{A}}(\mathbf{s}(t_0);\mathbf{u})$$

Equation *3* gives the value of the output at time t as a function of $\mathbf{s}(t_0)$, the state of $\mathcal{A}$ at time t_0, and the values of the input between t_0 and t. Equation *5* expresses the relation between the response segment $\mathbf{y}$, the input segment $\mathbf{u}$, and the state of $\mathcal{A}$ at time t_0. The overbar in $\bar{\mathbf{A}}$ serves to emphasize that $\bar{\mathbf{A}}(\mathbf{s}(t_0);\mathbf{u})$ is a segment of a time function rather than its value at a single point. When an equation of the form *3* or *5* is referred to as an input-output-state relation, it is implied that it satisfies the mutual- and self-consistency conditions (see *1.6.2 et seq.*).

An experiment on $\mathcal{A}$ consists in applying to $\mathcal{A}$ an input $\mathbf{u}_{(t_0,t_1]}$ and observing the resulting response segment $\mathbf{y}_{(t_0,t_1]}$. (It should be emphasized that when we write $\mathbf{u}_{(t_0,t_1]}$, we do not imply that the input vanishes outside the interval $(t_0,t_1]$. All we mean is that the input is observed over the interval $(t_0,t_1]$. The same comment applies to $\mathbf{y}$.) The state of $\mathcal{A}$ at time t_0 is the initial or the starting state of $\mathcal{A}$. (Equivalently, the initial state may be taken to be $\mathbf{s}(t_0-)$, in which case the input segment is understood to be $\mathbf{u}_{[t_0,t)}$; see *1.5.5.*) The state of $\mathcal{A}$ at time t_1 is the terminal state of $\mathcal{A}$. When we wish to place in evidence that the initial state of $\mathcal{A}$ is a point $\boldsymbol{\alpha}$ in Σ, the input-output-state relation *6* is written as

7 $$\mathbf{y} = \bar{\mathbf{A}}(\boldsymbol{\alpha};\mathbf{u})$$

The same thing applies to the other forms of the input-output-state relation. If the initial state is $\boldsymbol{\alpha}$ and the terminal state is $\boldsymbol{\alpha}^*$, we shall say that $\boldsymbol{\alpha}$ is taken into $\boldsymbol{\alpha}^*$ by $\mathbf{u}$. We shall also say that $(\mathbf{u},\mathbf{y})$ is an input-output pair associated with or with respect to $\boldsymbol{\alpha}$.

When no confusion can result, the symbol $\mathbf{uu}'$ will be used to denote a segment consisting of a segment $\mathbf{u}$ followed by a segment $\mathbf{u}'$ (see Fig. *1.6.1*). Correspondingly, the response of $\mathcal{A}$ to such a segment will be written as $\mathbf{yy}'$, where

8 $$\mathbf{yy}' = \bar{\mathbf{A}}(\boldsymbol{\alpha};\mathbf{uu}')$$

with $\boldsymbol{\alpha}$ being the state of $\mathcal{A}$ at the beginning of $\mathbf{u}$.

The symbol $\mathbf{s}(t)$ represents the state of $\mathcal{A}$ at time t. The state at time t is related to the state at time t_0 by an equation of the form

9 $$\mathbf{s}(t) = \mathbf{s}(\mathbf{s}(t_0);\mathbf{u}_{(t_0,t]}) \qquad t > t_0$$

where $\mathbf{s}$ is a function defined on the product space $\Sigma \times R[\mathbf{u}]$. This equation is referred to as the state equation of $\mathcal{A}$ (in explicit form). (See *1.8.2 et seq.*) When to this equation is adjoined the limiting equation resulting from letting t_0 approach t from the left in the input-output-state relation *3*, the resulting pair of equations constitutes the state equations of $\mathcal{A}$ (in explicit form). Usually, the state equations in question read

10
$$\mathbf{s}(t) = \mathbf{s}(\mathbf{s}(t_0);\mathbf{u}_{(t_0,t]})$$
$$\mathbf{y}(t) = \mathbf{g}(\mathbf{s}(t),\mathbf{u}(t),t)$$

where $\mathbf{g}$ is a function defined on the product space $\Sigma \times R[\mathbf{u}(t)] \times T$.

In stating assertions, theorems, definitions, etc., we shall frequently be using the standard mathematical symbol $\Rightarrow$ to denote implication. Thus, if $\{a\}$ and $\{b\}$ are two statements, then $\{a\} \Rightarrow \{b\}$, or, simply, $a \Rightarrow b$, should be read "a implies b," in the sense that if a is true, then b is true.[1] Similarly, $a \Leftrightarrow b$ reads "a implies and is implied by b."

11 *Example* Let x be a real number. Then $\{x > 2\} \Rightarrow \{x > 1\}$ means "if (it is true that) $x > 2$, then (it is also true that) $x > 1$."

12 *Example* Let x, y, and z be real numbers. Then $\{x = y \text{ and } y = z\} \Rightarrow \{x = z\}$ means "if x is equal to y and y is equal to z, then x is equal to z." Here, for short, the words enclosed in parentheses in Example *11* are omitted.

13 *Example* Let x and y be time functions. Then

$$\{x \geq y\} \Leftrightarrow \{\forall t(x(t) \geq y(t))\}$$

means that "$x \geq y$" implies and is implied by "$x(t) \geq y(t)$ for all t," or, equivalently, "$x \geq y$ if and only if $x(t) \geq y(t)$ for all t." ◁

We are now ready to take advantage of the compactness afforded by the above notation in defining several basic concepts relating to the notion of state.

By far the most important concept among the concepts in question is that of *equivalent states.* At this point, we shall merely define the notion of state equivalence and make limited use of it in clarifying the concept of the state of a system at time t. A more detailed discussion of the notion of equivalence in the context of linear systems will be presented in Chaps. *3* and *4*.

2 *State equivalence*

Let $\mathcal{A}$ be a system with state space Σ. Suppose that $\boldsymbol{\alpha}_i$ and $\boldsymbol{\alpha}_j$ are two states of $\mathcal{A}$, that is, $\boldsymbol{\alpha}_i \in \Sigma$ and $\boldsymbol{\alpha}_j \in \Sigma$. Consider an experiment on $\mathcal{A}$ under which an input $\mathbf{u}$ ($\triangleq \mathbf{u}_{(t_0,t_1]}$) is applied to $\mathcal{A}$ starting at time t_0 and ending at time t_1, with $\mathcal{A}$ initially in state $\boldsymbol{\alpha}_i$. Denote the segment of

[1] For a more complete discussion of the significance of implication see, for example, Refs. *1* and *2*.

the corresponding output over the observation interval $(t_0,t_1]$ by $\bar{\mathbf{A}}(\boldsymbol{\alpha}_i;\mathbf{u})$.

Consider now the same experiment but with the difference that the initial state is $\boldsymbol{\alpha}_j$ rather than $\boldsymbol{\alpha}_i$. It is conceivable that for the particular input $\mathbf{u}$ applied to $\mathcal{A}$ the segments $\bar{\mathbf{A}}(\boldsymbol{\alpha}_i;\mathbf{u})$ and $\bar{\mathbf{A}}(\boldsymbol{\alpha}_j;\mathbf{u})$ might be identical. It is also conceivable that this may be true not only for the $\mathbf{u}$ in question but for all inputs in the input segment space of $\mathcal{A}$. If this is the case, then $\boldsymbol{\alpha}_i$ and $\boldsymbol{\alpha}_j$ are *equivalent states*,[1] written as $\boldsymbol{\alpha}_i \simeq \boldsymbol{\alpha}_j$, in the sense that $\mathcal{A}$ starting in state $\boldsymbol{\alpha}_i$ exhibits exactly the same behavior as $\mathcal{A}$ starting in state $\boldsymbol{\alpha}_j$. More formally, we can express this idea as a

1 **Definition** $\boldsymbol{\alpha}_i$ is *equivalent* to $\boldsymbol{\alpha}_j$ if and only if for all inputs $\mathbf{u}$ the response segment of $\mathcal{A}$ starting in state $\boldsymbol{\alpha}_i$ is identical with the response segment of $\mathcal{A}$ starting in state $\boldsymbol{\alpha}_j$.

In symbols,

2 $$\{\boldsymbol{\alpha}_i \simeq \boldsymbol{\alpha}_j\} \Leftrightarrow \{\bar{\mathbf{A}}(\boldsymbol{\alpha}_i;\mathbf{u}) = \bar{\mathbf{A}}(\boldsymbol{\alpha}_j;\mathbf{u})\} \qquad \forall \mathbf{u}$$

where the notation $\bar{\mathbf{A}}(\boldsymbol{\alpha}_i;\mathbf{u}) = \bar{\mathbf{A}}(\boldsymbol{\alpha}_j;\mathbf{u})$ signifies that, over the observation interval on which $\mathbf{u}$ is defined, the response segment of $\mathcal{A}$ to $\mathbf{u}$ starting in state $\boldsymbol{\alpha}_i$ is identical with the response segment of $\mathcal{A}$ to $\mathbf{u}$ starting in state $\boldsymbol{\alpha}_j$. The universal quantifier $\forall \mathbf{u}$ signifies that this is true for *all* $\mathbf{u}$ in the input segment space of $\mathcal{A}$, that is, for all $\mathbf{u}$ in $R[\mathbf{u}]$, with t_0 and t_1 varying over T. ◁

An immediate consequence of this definition is the *transitivity of state equivalence*. That is, if $\boldsymbol{\alpha}_i \simeq \boldsymbol{\alpha}_j$ and $\boldsymbol{\alpha}_j \simeq \boldsymbol{\alpha}_k$, then $\boldsymbol{\alpha}_i \simeq \boldsymbol{\alpha}_k$. This follows at once from the transitivity of equality of segments of time functions. Specifically, if $\mathbf{u}_{(t_0,t]} = \mathbf{v}_{(t_0,t]}$ and $\mathbf{v}_{(t_0,t]} = \mathbf{w}_{(t_0,t]}$, then $\mathbf{u}_{(t_0,t]} = \mathbf{w}_{(t_0,t]}$. Thus, if $\bar{\mathbf{A}}(\boldsymbol{\alpha}_i;\mathbf{u}) = \bar{\mathbf{A}}(\boldsymbol{\alpha}_j;\mathbf{u})$ for all $\mathbf{u}$ and $\bar{\mathbf{A}}(\boldsymbol{\alpha}_j;\mathbf{u}) = \bar{\mathbf{A}}(\boldsymbol{\alpha}_k;\mathbf{u})$ for all $\mathbf{u}$, then $\bar{\mathbf{A}}(\boldsymbol{\alpha}_i;\mathbf{u}) = \bar{\mathbf{A}}(\boldsymbol{\alpha}_k;\mathbf{u})$ for all $\mathbf{u}$. Q.E.D.

On negating the definition of equivalent states we obtain the implication: If $\boldsymbol{\alpha}_i$ and $\boldsymbol{\alpha}_j$ are *nonequivalent*, then there exists an input $\mathbf{u}$ such that the response of $\mathcal{A}$ to $\mathbf{u}$ starting in state $\boldsymbol{\alpha}_i$ is not identical with the response of $\mathcal{A}$ to $\mathbf{u}$ starting in state $\boldsymbol{\alpha}_j$. In symbols,

3 $$\{\boldsymbol{\alpha}_i \not\simeq \boldsymbol{\alpha}_j\} \Leftrightarrow \{\exists \mathbf{u}[\bar{\mathbf{A}}(\boldsymbol{\alpha}_i;\mathbf{u}) \neq \bar{\mathbf{A}}(\boldsymbol{\alpha}_j;\mathbf{u})]\}$$

where the expression on the right reads, "there exists a $\mathbf{u}$ such that the response segment $\bar{\mathbf{A}}(\boldsymbol{\alpha}_i;\mathbf{u})$ is not equal to the response segment $\bar{\mathbf{A}}(\boldsymbol{\alpha}_j;\mathbf{u})$." An input $\mathbf{u}$ having this property will be referred to as a *distinguishing input* for $\boldsymbol{\alpha}_i$ and $\boldsymbol{\alpha}_j$, and it will be denoted by the symbol $\mathbf{u}(\boldsymbol{\alpha}_i,\boldsymbol{\alpha}_j)$. Because of its suggestiveness, we shall frequently employ the adjective *distinguishable* to describe two states that are nonequivalent. When $\boldsymbol{\alpha}_i$ and $\boldsymbol{\alpha}_j$ are vectors, $\boldsymbol{\alpha}_i$ and $\boldsymbol{\alpha}_j$ will be said to be *distinct* if $\boldsymbol{\alpha}_i \neq \boldsymbol{\alpha}_j$ in the

[1] The notion of equivalence in the context of finite-state systems was introduced by E. F. Moore, and independently by D. Huffman. See Refs. *3* and *4*.

usual sense of equality of vectors [for example, (2,5) = (2,5) and (2,5) ≠ (4,5)]. Note that distinctness does not imply distinguishability.

4 *Example* Consider the object described in Example *1.7.19*. In this case the state space is the set of numbers $\{0,1,2, \ldots ,11\}$; the input space is the set of numbers $\{1,2, \ldots ,6\}$; the output space is the set of numbers $\{0,1\}$; t ranges over $\{0,1,2, \ldots\}$; and the input-output-state relation is

5 $$y(t) = [s(t_0) + u(t_0) + u(t_0 + 1) + \cdots + u(t-1)] \bmod 2 \qquad t > t_0$$

where $t_0 \triangleq$ initial time, $u(t) \triangleq$ input at time t, $y(t) \triangleq$ output at time t, and $r \bmod 2$ denotes the least nonnegative residue of r which results when multiples of 2 are subtracted from or added to r.

Now, it is clear that for any two integers a and b, we can write

6 $$(a + b) \bmod 2 = (a \bmod 2 + b) \bmod 2$$

Consequently, *5* may be rewritten as

$$y(t) = [s(t_0) \bmod 2 + u(t_0) + \cdots + u(t-1)] \bmod 2 \qquad t > t_0$$

The form of this relation indicates that if α_i and α_j are both even or both odd, for example, $\alpha_i = 2$ and $\alpha_j = 4$, or $\alpha_i = 3$ and $\alpha_j = 7$, then α_i and α_j are equivalent; for $\alpha_i \bmod 2 = \alpha_j \bmod 2$ if α_i and α_j are both even or both odd. Thus, the states 0, 2, 4, 6, 8, and 10 are equivalent to one another and so are the states 1, 3, 5, 7, 9, 11. It should be noted that no even state can be equivalent to an odd state. For example, 3 is nonequivalent to 4 because the input $u(t_0) = 0$ gives the output 1 when $\mathcal{A}$ is initially in state 3 and the output 0 when $\mathcal{A}$ is initially in state 4.

7 *Example* Consider the simple electrical network shown in Fig. *2.2.1a*.

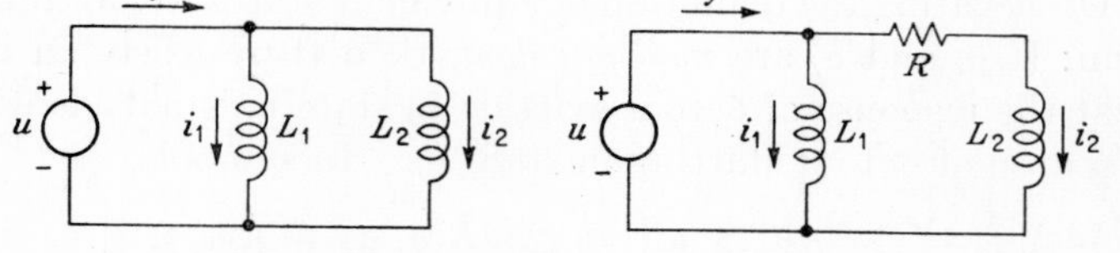

Fig. 2.2.1 (*a*) System with equivalent states; (*b*) system in reduced form.

Here the voltage u is identified with the input, the current y with the output, and the currents $i_1(t)$ and $i_2(t)$ through L_1 and L_2 with the components of the state vector $\mathbf{s}(t)$ (see *1.7.28*). The input-output-state relation—as can be readily verified directly—reads

8 $$y(t) = i_1(t_0) + i_2(t_0) + \left(\frac{1}{L_1} + \frac{1}{L_2}\right) \int_{t_0}^{t} u(\xi)\, d\xi$$

where the first two terms can be represented as the scalar product of the vector (1,1) and the initial state vector $\mathbf{s}(t_0) = (i_1(t_0), i_2(t_0))$.

Now from inspection of *8* it is clear that the only characteristic of $\mathbf{s}(t_0)$ that matters in so far as $y(t)$ is concerned is the sum of the components of $\mathbf{s}(t_0)$. Thus, any two states $\boldsymbol{\alpha}_i$ and $\boldsymbol{\alpha}_j$ such that the sums of their respective components are equal must necessarily be equivalent. For example, $\boldsymbol{\alpha}_i = (5,-2)$ and $\boldsymbol{\alpha}_j = (1,2)$ are equivalent states of the network in question. State equivalences of this type will be discussed in greater detail in Chap. *4*.

9 *Example* It is instructive also to consider a system which has no equivalent states. A simple example of such a system is shown in Fig. *2.2.1b*. This system, call it $\mathcal{A}$, differs from that of Fig. *2.2.1a* only in the addition of a resistor R between L_1 and L_2. As before, the state vector is $\mathbf{s}(t) = (i_1(t), i_2(t))$. For convenience, $R = L_1 = L_2 = 1$.

By using the techniques described in Chap. *4*, the input-output-state relation of $\mathcal{A}$ is readily found to be

10 $$y(t) = i_1(t_0) + i_2(t_0)e^{-(t-t_0)} + \int_{t_0}^{t} (1 + e^{-(t-\xi)})u(\xi)\, d\xi$$

The state space of $\mathcal{A}$ is $\mathcal{R}^2$; that is, Σ is the set of all ordered 2-tuples of real numbers.

Now from inspection of *10* it is clear that in order that a state of $\mathcal{A}$, say (ρ_1,ρ_2), be equivalent to a state (γ_1,γ_2) (where $\rho_1,\gamma_1,\rho_2,\gamma_2$ are real numbers representing the values of i_1 and i_2, respectively), it is necessary and sufficient that

$$\alpha_1 + \alpha_2 e^{-(t-t_0)} = \gamma_1 + \gamma_2 e^{-(t-t_0)}$$

for all t_0 and all $t \geq t_0$. Clearly, this is not possible unless $\alpha_1 = \gamma_1$ and $\alpha_2 = \gamma_2$. Consequently, no two distinct states of $\mathcal{A}$ can be equivalent.

As we shall see later, the system of Example *9* is but a special instance of a *reduced system*. More specifically:

11 **Definition** A system $\mathcal{A}$ is *reduced* or is in *reduced form* if there are no distinct states in its state space which are equivalent to one another. In other words, $\mathcal{A}$ is *reduced* if all of its states are distinguishable.[1] ◁

Consider now the following basic question. Suppose that one is given an input-output-state relation for $\mathcal{A}$ in the form (*2.1.7*)

12 $$\mathbf{y} = \bar{\mathbf{A}}(\boldsymbol{\alpha};\mathbf{u})$$

where $\boldsymbol{\alpha}$ denotes the state of $\mathcal{A}$ at time t_0 (that is, $\mathbf{s}(t_0) = \boldsymbol{\alpha}$), with $\boldsymbol{\alpha}$

[1] In the case of linear systems there is a close connection between the notions of a "reduced" system and a "completely observable" system. The latter notion will be discussed in Chap. *11*.

ranging over the state space Σ. How can one determine from *12* the set of all states in Σ which are equivalent to a particular state $\boldsymbol{\alpha}_0$?

Suppose that an experimenter who does not know that $\mathcal{A}$ is initially in state $\boldsymbol{\alpha}_0$ applies to $\mathcal{A}$ a particular input $\mathbf{u}^1$ and observes the corresponding output $\mathbf{y}^1$. Since he has the input-output-state relation *12*, he can, at least in principle, determine all possible initial states $\boldsymbol{\alpha}$ with respect to which $(\mathbf{u}^1,\mathbf{y}^1)$ is an input-output pair (*2.1.7 et seq.*). Let this set of states be denoted by $Q(\boldsymbol{\alpha}_0;\mathbf{u}^1)$. In symbols,

13 $$Q(\boldsymbol{\alpha}_0;\mathbf{u}^1) = \{\boldsymbol{\alpha}|\bar{\mathbf{A}}(\boldsymbol{\alpha}_0;\mathbf{u}^1) = \bar{\mathbf{A}}(\boldsymbol{\alpha};\mathbf{u}^1)\}$$

Next, the experimenter takes another copy of $\mathcal{A}$ (in the same initial state $\boldsymbol{\alpha}_0$), applies an input $\mathbf{u}^2$, and observes the output $\mathbf{y}^2$. Let the set of states with respect to which $(\mathbf{u}^2,\mathbf{y}^2)$ constitutes an input-output pair be denoted by $Q(\boldsymbol{\alpha}_0;\mathbf{u}^2)$. Then, at the conclusion of the second experiment, the experimenter can assert that $\boldsymbol{\alpha}_0$ must lie in the intersection of $Q(\boldsymbol{\alpha}_0;\mathbf{u}^1)$ and $Q(\boldsymbol{\alpha}_0;\mathbf{u}^2)$.

By repeating this experiment (infinitely many times, if necessary) the experimenter arrives at the conclusion that $\boldsymbol{\alpha}_0$ must lie in the intersection of the family of sets $Q(\boldsymbol{\alpha}_0;\mathbf{u}^1)$, $Q(\boldsymbol{\alpha}_0;\mathbf{u}^2)$, $Q(\boldsymbol{\alpha}_0;\mathbf{u}^3)$, ... [Note that the intersection is nonempty since $\boldsymbol{\alpha}_0 \in Q(\boldsymbol{\alpha}_0;\mathbf{u}^i)$ for all i.] On denoting this intersection by $Q(\boldsymbol{\alpha}_0)$ and dropping the superscript on $\mathbf{u}$, we have in symbols

14 $$Q(\boldsymbol{\alpha}_0) = \bigcap_{\mathbf{u}} Q(\boldsymbol{\alpha}_0;\mathbf{u}) = \bigcap_{\mathbf{u}} \{\boldsymbol{\alpha}|\bar{\mathbf{A}}(\boldsymbol{\alpha}_0;\mathbf{u}) = \bar{\mathbf{A}}(\boldsymbol{\alpha};\mathbf{u})\}$$

where $\bigcap_{\mathbf{u}}$ denotes the intersection taken over all $\mathbf{u}$ in the input segment space of $\mathcal{A}$. Thus, the experimenter's conclusion after performing all these experiments would be that the initial state belongs to $Q(\boldsymbol{\alpha}_0)$, and no further experimentation can give him additional information about the initial state of $\mathcal{A}$.

From the way in which state equivalence is defined, it is evident that the set $Q(\boldsymbol{\alpha}_0)$ defined by *14* is the *set of all states in Σ which are equivalent to* $\boldsymbol{\alpha}_0$. Essentially, this is an immediate consequence of the following relation between the operations $\bigcap_{\mathbf{u}}$ and $\forall\mathbf{u}$. (To place this relation in a clearer perspective, we formulate it in symbols different from those used above.)

15 **Relation between $\bigcap$ and $\forall$** The relation in question may be stated as follows. Let R be a relation, i.e., a set of ordered pairs, $R \triangleq \{(v,w)\}$, with domain D. [The domain of R is the set of all v such that $(v,w) \in R$ for some w.] Define the sets $Q(v)$ and Q by

16 $$Q(v) \triangleq \{w|(v,w) \in R\}$$

and

17 $$Q \triangleq \bigcap_{v \in D} Q(v)$$

Then, Q can be expressed in the form

18 $$Q = \{w|\forall v[(v,w) \in R]\} \qquad v \in D$$

The equivalence between *17* and *18* follows at once from the fact that a point belongs to the intersection $\bigcap_v Q(v)$ if and only if it belongs to every set in the family $\{Q(v)\}$, $v \in D$. ◁

To apply this equivalence to the case under consideration, we identify R with the relation $\bar{\mathbf{A}}(\boldsymbol{\alpha}_0;\mathbf{u}) = \bar{\mathbf{A}}(\boldsymbol{\alpha};\mathbf{u})$. Then, from the definition

$$\text{set of all states equivalent to } \boldsymbol{\alpha}_0 = \{\boldsymbol{\alpha}|\forall \mathbf{u}[\bar{\mathbf{A}}(\boldsymbol{\alpha}_0;\mathbf{u}) = \bar{\mathbf{A}}(\boldsymbol{\alpha};\mathbf{u})]\}$$

we can infer at once the

19 **Assertion** The set of all states in Σ equivalent to $\boldsymbol{\alpha}_0$ is given by

20 $$Q(\boldsymbol{\alpha}_0) = \bigcap_{\mathbf{u}} \{\boldsymbol{\alpha}|\bar{\mathbf{A}}(\boldsymbol{\alpha}_0;\mathbf{u}) = \bar{\mathbf{A}}(\boldsymbol{\alpha};\mathbf{u})\} \qquad ◁$$

One immediate application that we can make of *15* is to prove statement *1.7.1* concerning the equivalence of states in the set Q_t. Specifically, it will be recalled that the set Q_t was defined as the intersection (see *1.6.38*)

21 $$Q_t(\boldsymbol{\alpha}_0;\mathbf{u}) = \bigcap_{\mathbf{u}'} Q(\boldsymbol{\alpha}_0;\mathbf{u},\mathbf{u}')$$

where

22 $$Q(\boldsymbol{\alpha}_0;\mathbf{u},\mathbf{u}') = \{\boldsymbol{\alpha}|\mathbf{y}' = \bar{\mathbf{A}}(\boldsymbol{\alpha};\mathbf{u}')\}$$

and where $\mathbf{y}'$ is defined by the relation

23 $$\mathbf{y}\mathbf{y}' = \bar{\mathbf{A}}(\boldsymbol{\alpha}_0;\mathbf{u}\mathbf{u}')$$

in which $\mathbf{u}\mathbf{u}'$ denotes a segment consisting of a segment $\mathbf{u}$ followed by a segment $\mathbf{u}'$ and $\mathbf{y}\mathbf{y}'$ is the corresponding response segment of $\mathcal{A}$, with $\mathcal{A}$ initially in state $\boldsymbol{\alpha}_0$.

Let $\boldsymbol{\alpha}'$ be any state in $Q_t(\boldsymbol{\alpha}_0;\mathbf{u})$. Then by *21* and *22* we can express $\mathbf{y}'$ as $\mathbf{y}' = \bar{\mathbf{A}}(\boldsymbol{\alpha}';\mathbf{u}')$, and hence *21* can be written as

24 $$Q_t(\boldsymbol{\alpha}_0;\mathbf{u}) = \bigcap_{\mathbf{u}'} \{\boldsymbol{\alpha}|\bar{\mathbf{A}}(\boldsymbol{\alpha}';\mathbf{u}') = \bar{\mathbf{A}}(\boldsymbol{\alpha};\mathbf{u}')\}$$

On applying *15* to *24*, we obtain

$$Q_t(\boldsymbol{\alpha}_0;\mathbf{u}) = \{\boldsymbol{\alpha}|\forall \mathbf{u}'[\bar{\mathbf{A}}(\boldsymbol{\alpha}';\mathbf{u}') = \bar{\mathbf{A}}(\boldsymbol{\alpha};\mathbf{u}')]\}$$

which, in words, states that $Q_t(\boldsymbol{\alpha}_0;\mathbf{u})$ is the set of all states equivalent to $\boldsymbol{\alpha}'$. Consequently, all states in $Q_t(\boldsymbol{\alpha}_0;\mathbf{u})$ are equivalent to one another. Q.E.D.

It will be helpful at this point to summarize our discussion by restating in a more precise form the tentative definition of the state of $\mathcal{A}$ at time t which was given in *1.7.1*.

25 **Definition** Let $\mathcal{A}$ be characterized by the input-output-state relation

$$\mathbf{y}(t) = \mathbf{A}(\boldsymbol{\alpha}_0;\mathbf{u}_{(t_0,t]}) \qquad \boldsymbol{\alpha}_0 \in \Sigma$$

or equivalently

26 $$\mathbf{y} = \bar{\mathbf{A}}(\boldsymbol{\alpha}_0;\mathbf{u})$$

where $\boldsymbol{\alpha}_0$ denotes the state of $\mathcal{A}$ at time t_0.

Then the *state of* $\mathcal{A}$ *at time* t, $t > t_0$, is denoted by $\mathbf{s}(t)$ and is defined to be any element of the set

27 $$Q_t(\boldsymbol{\alpha}_0;\mathbf{u}) = \{\boldsymbol{\alpha}|\forall\mathbf{u}'[\bar{\mathbf{A}}(\boldsymbol{\alpha}_0;\mathbf{u})\bar{\mathbf{A}}(\boldsymbol{\alpha};\mathbf{u}') = \bar{\mathbf{A}}(\boldsymbol{\alpha}_0;\mathbf{u}\mathbf{u}')]\}$$

where $\mathbf{u} \triangleq \mathbf{u}_{(t_0,t]}$; $\mathbf{u}' \triangleq \mathbf{u}_{(t,t_1]}$; $\mathbf{u}\mathbf{u}' = \mathbf{u}_{(t_0,t_1]}$; $\bar{\mathbf{A}}(\boldsymbol{\alpha}_0;\mathbf{u}) = \mathbf{y}_{(t_0,t]} \triangleq \mathbf{y}$; $\bar{\mathbf{A}}(\boldsymbol{\alpha};\mathbf{u}') = \mathbf{y}_{(t,t_1]} \triangleq \mathbf{y}'$; $\bar{\mathbf{A}}(\boldsymbol{\alpha}_0;\mathbf{u})\bar{\mathbf{A}}(\boldsymbol{\alpha};\mathbf{u}') = \mathbf{y}\mathbf{y}'$; and $\boldsymbol{\alpha} \in \Sigma$, with the understanding that $\mathbf{u}\mathbf{u}'$ denotes a segment of the input comprised of $\mathbf{u}$ followed by $\mathbf{u}'$, and likewise for $\mathbf{y}\mathbf{y}'$ and $\bar{\mathbf{A}}(\boldsymbol{\alpha}_0;\mathbf{u})\bar{\mathbf{A}}(\boldsymbol{\alpha};\mathbf{u}')$. [Note, in particular, that $\bar{\mathbf{A}}(\boldsymbol{\alpha}_0;\mathbf{u})\bar{\mathbf{A}}(\boldsymbol{\alpha};\mathbf{u}')$ denotes the response segment $\bar{\mathbf{A}}(\boldsymbol{\alpha}_0;\mathbf{u})$ *followed* by the response segment $\bar{\mathbf{A}}(\boldsymbol{\alpha};\mathbf{u}')$ and should not be interpreted as the product of $\bar{\mathbf{A}}(\boldsymbol{\alpha}_0;\mathbf{u})$ and $\bar{\mathbf{A}}(\boldsymbol{\alpha};\mathbf{u}')$.]

28 *Comment* Despite its different appearance, the set $Q_t(\boldsymbol{\alpha}_0;\mathbf{u})$ defined by *27* is the same as the set $Q_t(\boldsymbol{\alpha}_0;\mathbf{u})$ defined by *21*. The reason is this. In the first place, we have already shown that $Q_t(\boldsymbol{\alpha}_0;\mathbf{u})$ can be expressed by *24*, in which $\mathbf{y}'$ is defined by *23*. Now the statement: for all $\mathbf{u}'$

29 $$\mathbf{y}' = \bar{\mathbf{A}}(\boldsymbol{\alpha};\mathbf{u}')$$

and

30 $$\mathbf{y}\mathbf{y}' = \bar{\mathbf{A}}(\boldsymbol{\alpha}_0;\mathbf{u}\mathbf{u}')$$

can be combined into a single statement by substituting *29* into *30*, with the result reading

31 $$\forall\mathbf{u}'[\mathbf{y}\bar{\mathbf{A}}(\boldsymbol{\alpha};\mathbf{u}') = \bar{\mathbf{A}}(\boldsymbol{\alpha}_0;\mathbf{u}\mathbf{u}')]$$

But

$$\mathbf{y} = \bar{\mathbf{A}}(\boldsymbol{\alpha}_0;\mathbf{u})$$

and hence *31* can be expressed as

$$\forall\mathbf{u}'[\bar{\mathbf{A}}(\boldsymbol{\alpha}_0;\mathbf{u})\bar{\mathbf{A}}(\boldsymbol{\alpha};\mathbf{u}) = \bar{\mathbf{A}}(\boldsymbol{\alpha}_0;\mathbf{u}\mathbf{u}')]$$

which establishes the equivalence of *27* and *21*. Q.E.D.

As was pointed out in Chap. 1 (*1.8.1 et seq.*), Definition *25* not only implies that $\mathbf{s}(t)$ is a function of $\boldsymbol{\alpha}_0$ and $\mathbf{u}_{(t_0,t]}$ but also provides, at least in principle, a means of deducing the functional dependence of $\mathbf{s}(t)$ on $\mathbf{s}(t_0)$ and $\mathbf{u}_{(t_0,t]}$ from the input-output-state relation

32 $$\mathbf{y}(t) = \bar{\mathbf{A}}(\mathbf{s}(t_0);\mathbf{u}_{(t_0,t]})$$

where $\boldsymbol{\alpha}_0 \triangleq \mathbf{s}(t_0) \triangleq$ initial state of $\mathcal{A}$. In other words, the state equation (*1.8.2*)

33 $$\mathbf{s}(t) = \mathbf{s}(\mathbf{s}(t_0);\mathbf{u}_{(t_0,t]})$$

which is the expression for $\mathbf{s}(t)$ as a function of $\mathbf{s}(t_0)$ and $\mathbf{u}_{(t_0,t]}$, is derivable from the input-output-state relation *32*. We shall establish some of the important properties of this equation and the state of $\mathcal{A}$ at time t in the following section.

3 *Basic properties of state and state equations*

A basic property of $\mathbf{s}(t)$ which is an immediate consequence of its definition is the

1 **Separation property of** $\mathbf{s}(t)$ By the definition of $\mathbf{s}(t)$ (*1.7.1*), $\mathbf{s}(t)$ is an element of the set $Q_t(\boldsymbol{\alpha}_0;\mathbf{u})$, which is the set of all $\boldsymbol{\alpha}$ satisfying the relation (*2.2.27*)

2 $$\forall \mathbf{u}'[\bar{\mathbf{A}}(\boldsymbol{\alpha}_0;\mathbf{u})\bar{\mathbf{A}}(\boldsymbol{\alpha};\mathbf{u}') = \bar{\mathbf{A}}(\boldsymbol{\alpha}_0;\mathbf{u}\mathbf{u}')]$$

On replacing $\boldsymbol{\alpha}_0$ in *2* by $\mathbf{s}(t_0)$ and $\boldsymbol{\alpha}$ by $\mathbf{s}(t)$, we obtain the identity

3 $$\bar{\mathbf{A}}(\mathbf{s}(t_0);\mathbf{u}\mathbf{u}') = \bar{\mathbf{A}}(\mathbf{s}(t_0);\mathbf{u})\bar{\mathbf{A}}(\mathbf{s}(t);\mathbf{u}') \qquad \forall \mathbf{s}(t_0)\forall \mathbf{u}\forall \mathbf{u}'$$

which, expressed in words, states: for any input consisting of a segment $\mathbf{u}$ followed by a segment $\mathbf{u}'$, the response of $\mathcal{A}$ to $\mathbf{u}\mathbf{u}'$ starting in state $\mathbf{s}(t_0)$ consists of the response segment $\bar{\mathbf{A}}(\mathbf{s}(t_0);\mathbf{u})$ followed by the response segment $\bar{\mathbf{A}}(\mathbf{s}(t);\mathbf{u}')$, where $\mathbf{s}(t)$ is the state of $\mathcal{A}$ at time t (see Fig. *2.3.1*). This basic property of $\mathbf{s}(t)$ will be referred to as the *response separation property,* since $\mathbf{s}(t)$ in a sense "separates" the response segment $\bar{\mathbf{A}}(\mathbf{s}(t_0);\mathbf{u})$ from $\bar{\mathbf{A}}(\mathbf{s}(t);\mathbf{u}')$. ◁

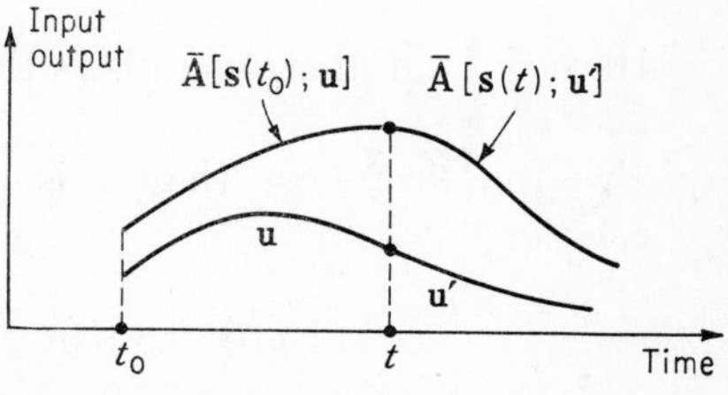

Fig. 2.3.1 Response separation property.

The response separation property of $\mathbf{s}(t)$ can be expressed more compactly by replacing $\mathbf{s}(t_0)$ in *3* by $\boldsymbol{\alpha}_0$ and regarding $\mathbf{s}(t)$ as the terminal state $\boldsymbol{\alpha}_0^*$ of $\mathcal{A}$ into which the initial state $\boldsymbol{\alpha}_0$ is taken by $\mathbf{u}$ (see *2.1.7 et seq.*). In this form, *3* reads

4 $$\bar{\mathbf{A}}(\boldsymbol{\alpha}_0;\mathbf{uu}') = \bar{\mathbf{A}}(\boldsymbol{\alpha}_0;\mathbf{u})\bar{\mathbf{A}}(\boldsymbol{\alpha}_0^*;\mathbf{u}')$$

where it is understood that *4* holds for all $\boldsymbol{\alpha}_0 \in \Sigma$, all $\mathbf{u}$, and all $\mathbf{u}'$.

Since in most cases the input-output-state relation of $\mathcal{A}$ has the form of an expression for $\mathbf{y}(t)$ as a function of $\mathbf{s}(t_0)$ and $\mathbf{u}_{(t_0,t]}$ rather than an expression for the response segment $\mathbf{y}_{(t_0,t]}$ as a function of $\mathbf{s}(t_0)$ and $\mathbf{u}_{(t_0,t]}$, it is desirable to cast *4* into a form that involves $\mathbf{A}(\boldsymbol{\alpha}_0;\mathbf{u})$ rather than $\bar{\mathbf{A}}(\boldsymbol{\alpha}_0,\mathbf{u})$. For this purpose, let τ be a time intermediate between t_0 and t. Then it is evident that the identity [for all $\mathbf{s}(t_0)$, $\mathbf{u}$, and τ]

5 $$\mathbf{A}(\mathbf{s}(t_0);\mathbf{u}_{(t_0,t]}) = \mathbf{A}(\mathbf{s}(\tau);\mathbf{u}_{(\tau,t]}) \qquad t_0 < \tau \leq t$$

where $\mathbf{A}(\mathbf{s}(\tau);\mathbf{u}_{(\tau,t]})$ denotes the response of $\mathcal{A}$ at time t to $\mathbf{u}_{(\tau,t]}$, with $\mathcal{A}$ initially in state $\mathbf{s}(\tau)$, expresses the separation property *4*. In the sequel, we shall be using for the most part *5* rather than *4* as a statement of the response separation property.

6 *Example* Consider the system of Example *1.7.19* and, for concreteness, let $t_0 = 0$, $t = 3$, $t_1 = 7$, $u_{[t_0,t_1)} = 3\ 1\ 2\ 2\ 1\ 5\ 4$ and $s(0) = 3$.[1] Then by inspection of *1.7.21*, we have

$$\bar{A}(3;\ 3\ 1\ 2\ 2\ 1\ 5\ 4) = 0\ 1\ 1\ 1\ 0\ 1\ 1$$

Now the state of $\mathcal{A}$ at time $t = 3$ is given by

$$x(3) = (3 + 3 + 1 + 2) \bmod 12 = 9$$

and hence

$$\bar{A}(3;\ 3\ 1\ 2) = 0\ 1\ 1$$
$$\bar{A}(9;\ 2\ 1\ 5\ 4) = 1\ 0\ 1\ 1$$

We have the verification

$$\bar{A}(3;\ 3\ 1\ 2\ 2\ 1\ 5\ 4) = \bar{A}(3;\ 3\ 1\ 2)\bar{A}(9;\ 2\ 1\ 5\ 4)$$

Here the initial state *3* plays the role of $\boldsymbol{\alpha}_0$ in *4*; $\mathbf{u}$ is 3 1 2, $\mathbf{u}'$ is 2 1 5 4, and $\boldsymbol{\alpha}_0^*$ is 9.

7 *Example* Suppose that $\mathcal{A}$ is characterized by the input-output-state relation

8 $$y(t) = s(t_0)e^{-(t-t_0)} + \int_{t_0}^{t} e^{-(t-\xi)}u(\xi)\,d\xi$$

where $s(t_0)$ and $u(t)$ range over the real line, and u contains no delta

[1] Note that, strictly speaking, $u_{[t_0,t_1)}$ is the set of pairs (0,3), (1,1), (2,2), (3,2), (4,1), (5,5), (6,4) (see *1.3.3*). Note also that the corresponding response segment is observed over $(t_0,t_1]$.

functions. Then we can readily verify that with $s(t)$ given by

9 $$s(t) = s(t_0)e^{-(t-t_0)} + \int_{t_0}^{t} e^{-(t-\xi)}u(\xi)\, d\xi$$

the input-output-state relation *8* has the response separation property *5*. Specifically, on letting $t_0 \le \tau \le t$, we can write *8* as

$$y(t) = s(t_0)e^{-(t-t_0)} + \int_{t_0}^{\tau} e^{-(t-\xi)}u(\xi)\, d\xi + \int_{\tau}^{t} e^{-(t-\xi)}u(\xi)\, d\xi$$

Making use of *9*, we have

10 $$s(\tau) = s(t_0)e^{-(\tau-t_0)} + \int_{t_0}^{\tau} e^{-(t-\xi)}u(\xi)\, d\xi$$

and hence the expression for $y(t)$ can be written as

11 $$y(t) = s(\tau)e^{-(t-\tau)} + \int_{\tau}^{t} e^{-(t-\xi)}u(\xi)\, d\xi$$

which is of the same form as *8*, with $s(t_0)$ replaced by $s(\tau)$. Q.E.D.

There are a number of important connections between the separation property and the self-consistency conditions discussed in Chap. *1* (see *1.6.2*). For convenience in reference, we now state the relevant facts in the form of short assertions and theorems.

12 **Assertion** If a relation of the form

13 $$\mathbf{y}(t) = \mathbf{A}(\boldsymbol{\alpha};\mathbf{u}_{(t_0,t]}) \qquad \boldsymbol{\alpha} \in \Sigma,\ \mathbf{u} \in R[\mathbf{u}]$$

in which $\mathbf{A}$ is a function defined on $\Sigma \times R[\mathbf{u}]$, has the response separation property (for all $\boldsymbol{\alpha}$ and $\mathbf{u}$)

14 $$\mathbf{A}(\boldsymbol{\alpha};\mathbf{u}_{(t_0,t]}) = \mathbf{A}(\boldsymbol{\alpha}^*;\mathbf{u}_{(\tau,t]}) \qquad t_0 < \tau \le t$$

in which $\boldsymbol{\alpha}^* \in \Sigma$ and $\boldsymbol{\alpha}^*$ depends only on $\boldsymbol{\alpha}$ and $\mathbf{u}_{(t_0,\tau]}$, then *13* satisfies the three self-consistency conditions and $\boldsymbol{\alpha}^*$ qualifies as the state of $\mathcal{A}$ at time τ, with $\boldsymbol{\alpha}$ being the state of $\mathcal{A}$ at time t_0. Also, *13* qualifies as an input-output-state relation for $\mathcal{A}$. (See *1.6.2*.) (Note that since we do not start with a characterization of $\mathcal{A}$ in terms of an input-output relation, there is no need to consider the mutual-consistency condition.)

Proof The first self-consistency condition is satisfied because $\mathbf{y}(t)$ is uniquely determined through *13* by $\boldsymbol{\alpha}$ and $\mathbf{u}_{(t_0,t]}$. As for the second self-consistency condition, the separation property *14* without the qualification "$\boldsymbol{\alpha}^*$ depends only on $\boldsymbol{\alpha}$ and $\mathbf{u}_{(t_0,\tau]}$" is in effect a statement of it (see *1.6.15*). With this qualification added, every set $Q(\boldsymbol{\alpha};\mathbf{u},\mathbf{u}')$ (*1.6.29*) will contain $\boldsymbol{\alpha}^*$ and hence the intersection $Q_\tau(\boldsymbol{\alpha};\mathbf{u})$ will be nonempty by virtue of containing $\boldsymbol{\alpha}^*$. This shows that all three self-consistency conditions are satisfied and hence by Definition *1.6.2* $\boldsymbol{\alpha}^*$ qualifies as the state of $\mathcal{A}$ at time τ and *14* qualifies as its input-output-state relation. Q.E.D.

15 *Comment* The importance of Assertion *12* stems from the fact that it reduces the verification of self-consistency conditions for a given relation of the form *13* to demonstrating that *13* has the response separation property *14*, with $\boldsymbol{\alpha}^*$ dependent only on $\boldsymbol{\alpha}$ and $\mathbf{u}_{(t_0,\tau]}$. Actually, we have already used this technique in an implicit fashion in a number of examples, among them *1.7.10*, *1.7.12*, and *1.7.19*.

16 **Theorem** If

17 $$\mathbf{y}(t) = \mathbf{A}(\mathbf{s}(t_0);\mathbf{u}_{(t_0,t]})$$

is an input-output-state relation for $\mathcal{A}$, then the state equation induced by *17* (see *1.8.2 et seq.*),

18 $$\mathbf{s}(t) = \mathbf{s}(\mathbf{s}(t_0);\mathbf{u}_{(t_0,t]})$$

has the *state separation property* expressed by

19 $$\mathbf{s}(\mathbf{s}(t_0);\mathbf{u}_{(t_0,t]}) \simeq \mathbf{s}(\mathbf{s}(\tau);\mathbf{u}_{(\tau,t]}) \qquad t_0 < \tau \leq t$$

for all $\mathbf{s}(t_0)$ and $\mathbf{u}$, with $\mathbf{s}(\tau)$ given by *18* for $\mathbf{u}_{(t_0,\tau]}$.

Proof We shall establish this result by contradiction. Specifically, with reference to Fig. *2.3.2*, assume that

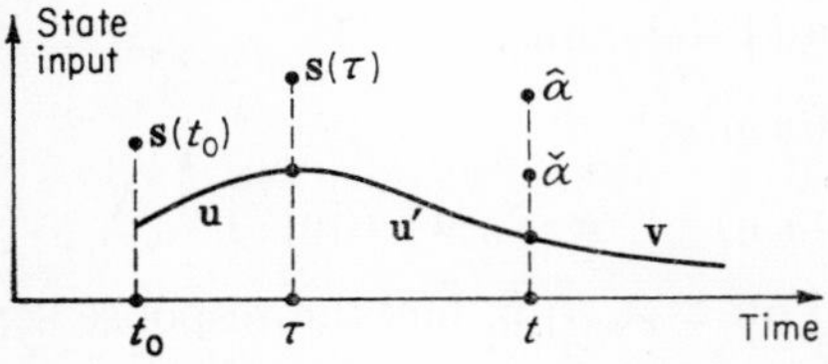

Fig. 2.3.2 State separation property.

20 $$\mathbf{s}(\mathbf{s}(t_0);\mathbf{u}_{(t_0,t]}) = \hat{\boldsymbol{\alpha}}$$

21 $$\mathbf{s}(\mathbf{s}(\tau);\mathbf{u}_{(\tau,t]}) = \check{\boldsymbol{\alpha}}$$

and $\hat{\boldsymbol{\alpha}} \not\simeq \check{\boldsymbol{\alpha}}$, that is, the state at time t yielded by *20* is not equivalent to the state at time t yielded by *21*. In that event, there will be an input, say, $\mathbf{v}_{(t,t_1]}$, that will distinguish between $\hat{\boldsymbol{\alpha}}$ and $\check{\boldsymbol{\alpha}}$ (see *2.2.3*) in the sense that

22 $$\bar{\mathbf{A}}(\hat{\boldsymbol{\alpha}};\mathbf{v}) \neq \bar{\mathbf{A}}(\check{\boldsymbol{\alpha}};\mathbf{v})$$

Now by using the response separation property *4* the response segment of $\mathcal{A}$ to $\mathbf{uu'v}$ starting in state $\mathbf{s}(t_0)$ can be split up in two ways:

23 $$\bar{\mathbf{A}}(\mathbf{s}(t_0);\mathbf{uu'v}) = \bar{\mathbf{A}}(\mathbf{s}(t_0);\mathbf{u})\bar{\mathbf{A}}(\mathbf{s}(\tau);\mathbf{u'v})$$

24 $$\bar{\mathbf{A}}(\mathbf{s}(t_0);\mathbf{uu'v}) = \bar{\mathbf{A}}(\mathbf{s}(t_0);\mathbf{uu'})\bar{\mathbf{A}}(\hat{\boldsymbol{\alpha}};\mathbf{v})$$

Applying the separation property again, we have

25 $$\bar{\mathbf{A}}(\mathbf{s}(\tau);\mathbf{u'v}) = \bar{\mathbf{A}}(\mathbf{s}(\tau);\mathbf{u'})\bar{\mathbf{A}}(\check{\boldsymbol{\alpha}};\mathbf{v})$$

26 $$\mathbf{A}(\mathbf{s}(t_0);\mathbf{uu'}) = \bar{\mathbf{A}}(\mathbf{s}(t_0);\mathbf{u})\bar{\mathbf{A}}(\mathbf{s}(\tau);\mathbf{u'})$$

On substituting *25* and *26* into *23* and *24*, respectively, and noting *22*, we arrive at the conclusion

$$\bar{\mathbf{A}}(\mathbf{s}(t_0);\mathbf{uu'v}) \neq \bar{\mathbf{A}}(\mathbf{s}(t_0);\mathbf{uu'v})$$

which violates the first self-consistency condition and hence is a contradiction. Consequently, $\hat{\alpha} \simeq \check{\alpha}$ and the theorem is proved.

27 *Comment* The state separation property of the state equation *18* is one of its key characteristics. We have already encountered special cases of it in examples and will encounter it in a more general way in Chaps. *3*, *4*, and *5*. To cite just one illustration, in Example *7* the state equation reads

$$s(t) = s(t_0)e^{-(t-t_0)} + \int_{t_0}^{t} e^{-(t-\xi)}u(\xi)\,d\xi \qquad t \geq t_0$$

and the state separation property *19* assumes the form

$$s(t) = s(\tau)e^{-(t-\tau)} + \int_{\tau}^{t} e^{-(t-\xi)}u(\xi)\,d\xi$$

28 **Theorem** If $\mathcal{A}$ is characterized by equations of the form

29 $$\mathbf{s}(t) = \mathbf{s}(\mathbf{s}(t_0);\mathbf{u}_{(t_0,t]}) \qquad t > t_0$$

30 $$\mathbf{y}(t) = \mathbf{g}(\mathbf{s}(t),\mathbf{u}(t),t)$$

where $\mathbf{s}(t_0) \in \Sigma$, $\mathbf{s}(t) \in \Sigma$, $\mathbf{s}$ is a function on $\Sigma \times R[\mathbf{u}]$, and $\mathbf{g}$ is a function on $\Sigma \times R[\mathbf{u}(t)] \times T$, and if *29* has the state separation property *19*, then $\mathbf{s}(t)$ qualifies as the state of $\mathcal{A}$ at time t and *29* and *30* constitute the state equations of $\mathcal{A}$ (see *1.8.5 et seq.*).

Proof On substituting *29* into *30* we obtain the relation

31 $$\mathbf{y}(t) = \mathbf{g}(\mathbf{s}(\mathbf{s}(t_0);\mathbf{u}_{(t_0,t]}),\mathbf{u}(t),t)$$

which is of the form

32 $$\mathbf{y}(t) = \mathbf{A}(\mathbf{s}(t_0);\mathbf{u}_{(t_0,t]})$$

Since *29* has the state separation property, we can write

33 $$\mathbf{s}(\mathbf{s}(t);\mathbf{u}_{(t_0,t]}) \simeq \mathbf{s}(\mathbf{s}(\tau);\mathbf{u}_{(\tau,t]})$$

and on substituting *33* into *31*, we have

34 $$\mathbf{y}(t) = \mathbf{g}(\mathbf{s}(\mathbf{s}(\tau);\mathbf{u}_{(\tau,t]}),\mathbf{u}(t),t)$$

Now *34* can be obtained from *31* by replacing t_0 with τ. Hence

$$\mathbf{y}(t) = \mathbf{A}(\mathbf{s}(\tau);\mathbf{u}_{(\tau,t]})$$

and

$$\mathbf{A}(\mathbf{s}(t_0);\mathbf{u}_{(t_0,t]}) = \mathbf{A}(\mathbf{s}(\tau);\mathbf{u}_{(\tau,t]}) \qquad t_0 < \tau \leq t$$

which establishes that $\mathcal{A}$ has the response separation property *5*. Furthermore, since $\mathbf{s}(\tau)$ is determined uniquely in terms of $\mathbf{s}(t_0)$ and $\mathbf{u}_{(t_0,\tau]}$ by *29*, it follows by Assertion *12* that *32* qualifies as the input-output-state relation for $\mathcal{A}$, with $\mathbf{s}(t)$ representing the state of $\mathcal{A}$ at time t and *29* and *30* constituting the state equations of $\mathcal{A}$. Q.E.D.

35 *Comment* This theorem adds insight into the key role of the state separation property of the state equation and its close relation with the self-consistency conditions introduced in Chap. 1. Together with its corollary (Corollary *36*, below), Theorem *28* provides an indirect but effective way of verifying that the self-consistency conditions are satisfied. For this reason, it will find many applications in later chapters, particularly in Chap. *4*.

It should be observed that the proof given above remains valid when the expression for $\mathbf{y}(t)$ (*30*) involves not only $\mathbf{u}(t)$ but also one or more derivatives of $\mathbf{u}$ at time t. In fact, the theorem holds true under even weaker assumptions on the form of $\mathbf{y}(t)$. However, the form assumed here will suffice for most of our purposes.

36 **Corollary** If $\mathcal{A}$ is characterized by differential state equations of the *canonical* form

37 $$\dot{\mathbf{s}}(t) = \mathbf{f}(\mathbf{s}(t),\mathbf{u}(t),t)$$

38 $$\mathbf{y}(t) = \mathbf{g}(\mathbf{s}(t),\mathbf{u}(t),t)$$

where $\mathbf{f}$ and $\mathbf{g}$ are functions on $\Sigma \times R[\mathbf{u}(t)] \times T$ such that *37* has a unique solution for $\mathbf{s}(t)$, then $\mathbf{s}(t)$ qualifies as the state of $\mathcal{A}$ at time t.

Proof. On integrating *37* between t and t_0, we have

39 $$\mathbf{s}(t) = \mathbf{s}(t_0) + \int_{t_0}^{t} \mathbf{f}(\mathbf{s}(\xi),\mathbf{u}(\xi),\xi)\, d\xi \qquad t > t_0$$

which may be regarded as an implicit form of the state equation

$$\mathbf{s}(t) = \mathbf{s}(\mathbf{s}(t_0);\mathbf{u}_{(t_0,t]})$$

Note that, by hypothesis, $\mathbf{s}(t)$ is determined uniquely by $\mathbf{s}(t_0)$ and $\mathbf{u}_{(t_0,t]}$.

Now it is trivial to verify that *39* has the separation property. Specifically, for $t_0 < \tau \leq t$ we can write *39* in the form

$$\mathbf{s}(t) = \mathbf{s}(t_0) + \int_{t_0}^{\tau} \mathbf{f}(\mathbf{s}(\xi),\mathbf{u}(\xi),\xi)\, d\xi + \int_{\tau}^{t} \mathbf{f}(\mathbf{s}(\xi),\mathbf{u}(\xi),\xi)\, d\xi$$

or

$$\mathbf{s}(t) = \mathbf{s}(\tau) + \int_{\tau}^{t} \mathbf{f}(\mathbf{s}(\xi),\mathbf{u}(\xi),\xi)\, d\xi$$

since

$$\mathbf{s}(\tau) = \mathbf{s}(t_0) + \int_{t_0}^{\tau} \mathbf{f}(\mathbf{s}(\xi),\mathbf{u}(\xi),\xi)\, d\xi$$

by *39*. The conclusion then follows from Theorem *28*.

40 **Remark** It is a well-known result in the theory of ordinary differential equations that a sufficient condition for *37* to have a unique solution (for a fixed $\mathbf{u}$) satisfying a given initial condition $\mathbf{s}(t_0) = \boldsymbol{\alpha}$ is the Lipschitz condition,[1] namely, that there exists a finite constant L

[1] See, for instance, Refs. *5* and *6*.

depending on **u** such that for all $\mathbf{s}(t)$ and $\mathbf{s}'(t) \in \Sigma$

41 $$\|\mathbf{f}(\mathbf{s}(t),\mathbf{u}(t)) - \mathbf{f}(\mathbf{s}'(t),\mathbf{u}(t))\| \leq L\|\mathbf{s}(t) - \mathbf{s}'(t)\| \qquad t \in T$$

where $\| \quad \|$ denotes the euclidean norm (see Appendix *C.16.5*). ◁

In later chapters, Corollary *36* will be applied only to linear systems. In the case of such systems, *36* and *41* lead to the following

42 **Conclusion** If $\mathcal{A}$ is characterized by linear differential state equations of the form

43 $$\begin{aligned}\dot{\mathbf{s}}(t) &= \mathbf{A}(t)\mathbf{s}(t) + \mathbf{B}(t)\mathbf{u}(t)\\ \mathbf{y}(t) &= \mathbf{C}(t)\mathbf{s}(t) + \mathbf{D}(t)\mathbf{u}(t)\end{aligned}$$

where $\mathbf{A}(t), \ldots, \mathbf{D}(t)$ are (possibly) time-dependent continuous matrices, then *41* is satisfied with

44 $$L = \sum_{i,j} \sup_{t \in T} |a_{ij}(t)|$$

where $a_{ij}(t)$ denotes the *ij*th element of $\mathbf{A}(t)$, and consequently $\mathbf{s}(t)$ qualifies as the state of $\mathcal{A}$ at time t (see also *6.2.2*).

45 *Comment* State equations of the form *43* will be referred to as the *canonical state equations* of $\mathcal{A}$. As we shall see in Chap. *4*, this is not the most general form that the state equations of a linear system can assume. ◁

As was pointed out in Chap. *1* (*1.6.44*), it may be advantageous in certain cases to relabel the points of Σ in a way that may simplify the form of the state equations of $\mathcal{A}$ or place in evidence some of their special features. In this connection, the following assertion is of relevance.

46 **Assertion** Let $\mathcal{A}$ be a system characterized by an input-output-state relation

47 $$\mathbf{y}(t) = \mathbf{A}(\boldsymbol{\alpha};\mathbf{u}) \qquad \boldsymbol{\alpha} \triangleq \mathbf{s}(t_0),\ \mathbf{u} \triangleq \mathbf{u}_{(t_0,t]}$$

which induces the state equations (see *1.8.7* and *1.8.8*)

48 $$\begin{aligned}\mathbf{s}(t) &= \mathbf{s}(\boldsymbol{\alpha};\mathbf{u})\\ \mathbf{y}(t) &= \mathbf{g}(\mathbf{s}(t),\mathbf{u}(t),t)\end{aligned}$$

Let $\mathfrak{u}$ be a one-one mapping of the state space Σ onto itself which takes $\check{\boldsymbol{\alpha}}$ into $\boldsymbol{\alpha}$. That is,

$$\mathfrak{u}(\check{\boldsymbol{\alpha}}) = \boldsymbol{\alpha} \qquad \text{and} \qquad \mathfrak{u}^{-1}(\boldsymbol{\alpha}) = \check{\boldsymbol{\alpha}}$$

where $\mathfrak{u}^{-1}$ denotes the mapping inverse to $\mathfrak{u}$. Then the relation

49 $$\mathbf{y}(t) = \check{\mathbf{A}}(\check{\boldsymbol{\alpha}};\mathbf{u}) \triangleq \mathbf{A}(\mathfrak{u}(\check{\boldsymbol{\alpha}});\mathbf{u})$$

is also an input-output-state relation for $\mathcal{A}$, with the corresponding state equations reading

50 $$\check{\mathbf{s}}(t) = \check{\mathbf{s}}(\check{\boldsymbol{\alpha}};\mathbf{u}) \triangleq \boldsymbol{\mu}^{-1}(\mathbf{s}(\boldsymbol{\mu}(\check{\boldsymbol{\alpha}});\mathbf{u}))$$
$$\mathbf{y}(t) = \check{\mathbf{g}}(\check{\mathbf{s}}(t),\mathbf{u}(t),t) \triangleq \mathbf{g}(\boldsymbol{\mu}(\check{\mathbf{s}}(t)),\mathbf{u}(t),t)$$

Proof It is obvious that all that is involved here is a relabeling of the elements of Σ via the mapping $\boldsymbol{\alpha} = \boldsymbol{\mu}(\check{\boldsymbol{\alpha}})$. Clearly, such relabeling does not affect the satisfying of self-consistency conditions; and hence if *47* is an input-output-state relation for $\mathcal{A}$, so is *49*. The same statement applies to the state equations *50* (see also *2.5.14*).

4 *Equivalent states of two or more systems*

In our discussion of the notion of equivalent states in Sec. *2* we have restricted our attention to the states of a single system $\mathcal{A}$. More generally, one can speak of equivalent states belonging to two or more different systems. Thus, consider two systems $\mathcal{A}$ and $\mathcal{B}$ having identical input function spaces and let $\boldsymbol{\alpha}$ be a state of $\mathcal{A}$ and $\boldsymbol{\beta}$ be a state of $\mathcal{B}$. Furthermore, let $\mathbf{y}$ denote the response segment of $\mathcal{A}$ and $\mathbf{w}$ that of $\mathcal{B}$ when the starting states are respectively $\boldsymbol{\alpha}$ and $\boldsymbol{\beta}$ and the common input to $\mathcal{A}$ and $\mathcal{B}$ is $\mathbf{u}$. Thus

1 $$\mathbf{y} = \bar{\mathbf{A}}(\boldsymbol{\alpha};\mathbf{u})$$

and

2 $$\mathbf{w} = \bar{\mathbf{B}}(\boldsymbol{\beta};\mathbf{u})$$

As a natural extension of the notion of equivalent states belonging to a single system $\mathcal{A}$, two states such as $\boldsymbol{\alpha}$ and $\boldsymbol{\beta}$ which belong to two systems $\mathcal{A}$ and $\mathcal{B}$ are defined to be *equivalent* if and only if for all inputs $\mathbf{u}$ in the input segment space of $\mathcal{A}$ and $\mathcal{B}$ the response of $\mathcal{A}$ starting in state $\boldsymbol{\alpha}$ is the same as the response of $\mathcal{B}$ starting in state $\boldsymbol{\beta}$.

In symbols, we have the

3 **Definition** $\{\boldsymbol{\alpha} \simeq \boldsymbol{\beta}\} \Leftrightarrow \{\bar{\mathbf{A}}(\boldsymbol{\alpha};\mathbf{u}) = \bar{\mathbf{B}}(\boldsymbol{\beta};\mathbf{u})\} \qquad \forall \mathbf{u}$

4 *Comment* We are tacitly restricting ourselves to a concept of state equivalence in which the time at which $\mathbf{u}$ is applied to $\mathcal{A}$ and $\mathcal{B}$ is immaterial. To be more general, we would have to make the qualification that $\boldsymbol{\alpha}$ and $\boldsymbol{\beta}$ are equivalent for $t_0 \geq \rho$, if $\bar{\mathbf{A}}(\boldsymbol{\alpha};\mathbf{u}) = \bar{\mathbf{B}}(\boldsymbol{\beta};\mathbf{u})$ for all $\mathbf{u}$ starting at $t_0 \geq \rho$. In this sense, when we say that $\boldsymbol{\alpha}$ and $\boldsymbol{\beta}$ are equivalent, we mean that they are equivalent for all t_0. Although we shall have no occasion to use the more general concept of equivalence

in this book, it does sometimes play a significant role in the case of time-varying systems.

5 *Example* A simple illustration of equivalent states belonging to different systems is provided by the two circuits shown in Fig. *2.4.1.*

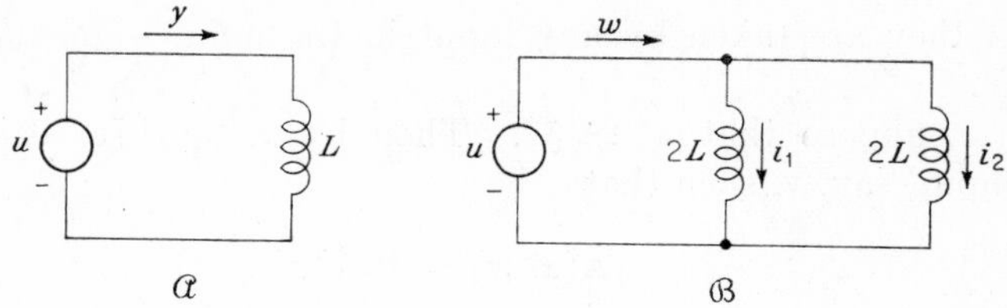

Fig. 2.4.1 Equivalent systems, $\mathcal{A} \equiv \mathcal{B}$.

Here u is the applied voltage and y and w represent the currents flowing through the terminals. The state of $\mathcal{A}$ at time t may be identified with the current through L; that is, $s(t) = y(t)$. Similarly, the state of $\mathcal{B}$ at time t is a 2-vector $\mathbf{s}(t) = (i_1(t), i_2(t))$ whose components are the currents flowing through the two inductors (see *1.7.28*). The input-output-state relations for $\mathcal{A}$ and $\mathcal{B}$ are:

6 $\mathcal{A}$: $$y(t) = y(t_0) + \frac{1}{L}\int_{t_0}^{t} u(\xi)\, d\xi \qquad s(t_0) = y(t_0)$$

7 $\mathcal{B}$: $$w(t) = i_1(t_0) + i_2(t_0) + \frac{1}{L}\int_{t_0}^{t} u(\xi)\, d\xi \qquad \mathbf{s}(t_0) = (i_1(t_0), i_2(t_0))$$

Let $y(t_0) = \alpha = 5$, say. Then $\boldsymbol{\beta} = (4,1)$ is equivalent to α. In fact, every state of $\mathcal{B}$ such that the sum of its two components is equal to 5 is equivalent to the state $\alpha = 5$.

8 *Example* Consider two systems $\mathcal{A}$ and $\mathcal{B}$ with respective state vectors (2-vectors) $\mathbf{s}(t) = (i_1(t), i_2(t))$ and $\boldsymbol{\sigma}(t) = (j_1(t), j_2(t))$ and input-output-state relations

9 $\mathcal{A}$: $$y(t) = i_1(t_0) + 2i_2(t_0) + \int_{t_0}^{t} u(\xi)\, d\xi$$

10 $\mathcal{B}$: $$w(t) = 2j_1(t_0) + 3j_2(t_0) + \int_{t_0}^{t} u(\xi)\, d\xi$$

From inspection of these relations it is clear that the state (0,0) of $\mathcal{A}$ is equivalent to the state (0,0) of $\mathcal{B}$. More generally, any two states of $\mathcal{A}$ and $\mathcal{B}$ for which the equality

11 $$i_1(t) + 2i_2(t) = 2j_1(t) + 3j_2(t)$$

holds are equivalent. For example, $(1,3) \simeq (2,1)$.

A pair of equivalent states belonging to two different systems (or, as a special case, to the same system) have an important property which is stated in the following

12 **Assertion** Let α and β be two equivalent states belonging to $\mathcal{A}$ and $\mathcal{B}$, respectively. Let α^* and β^* denote the respective states into which α and β are taken by an input $\mathbf{u}$, with $\mathcal{A}$ and $\mathcal{B}$ starting in α and β respectively. Then, for every $\mathbf{u}$ in the input segment space of $\mathcal{A}$ and $\mathcal{B}$, $\alpha^* \simeq \beta^*$. In short, if α and β are equivalent, so are the states into which they are taken by any input in the input segment space of $\mathcal{A}$ and $\mathcal{B}$.

Proof Suppose that $\alpha^* \not\simeq \beta^*$. Then by *2.2.3* there exists at least one input, say, $\mathbf{v}$, such that

13
$$\bar{\mathbf{A}}(\alpha^*;\mathbf{v}) \neq \bar{\mathbf{B}}(\beta^*;\mathbf{v})$$

By the response separation property (*2.3.4*), we can write

14
$$\bar{\mathbf{A}}(\alpha;\mathbf{uv}) = \bar{\mathbf{A}}(\alpha;\mathbf{u})\bar{\mathbf{A}}(\alpha^*;\mathbf{v})$$

and

15
$$\bar{\mathbf{B}}(\beta;\mathbf{uv}) = \bar{\mathbf{B}}(\beta;\mathbf{u})\bar{\mathbf{B}}(\beta^*;\mathbf{v})$$

and since α and β are equivalent states, we have

16
$$\bar{\mathbf{A}}(\alpha;\mathbf{uv}) = \bar{\mathbf{B}}(\beta;\mathbf{uv})$$

Clearly, *14* to *16* are inconsistent with *13*. Consequently, $\alpha^* \simeq \beta^*$ by contradiction. (Note that we are implicitly using the first part of the assumption of uniform reachability stated in *17*.)

It will be convenient for later purposes to reword Assertion *12* in terms of the notion of reachable states, which is defined below. The notion of reachability in the context of linear systems will be discussed in greater detail in Chap. *11*.

17 **Definition** A state α^* of $\mathcal{A}$ is *reachable from a state* α of $\mathcal{A}$ if and only if there exists an input segment $\mathbf{u}$ (of finite length) in the input segment space of $\mathcal{A}$ such that α is taken into α^* by $\mathbf{u}$. Unless stated to the contrary, it will be assumed that the states of $\mathcal{A}$ have the following uniform reachability property: If there exists an input segment $\mathbf{u}$ which takes a state α into a state α^*, then for each t_1 there is a t_0 and an input segment $\mathbf{v}_{(t_0,t_1]}$ which takes α $[= \mathbf{s}(t_0)]$ into α^* $[= \mathbf{s}(t_1)]$; and for each t_0 there is a t_1 and an input segment $\mathbf{w}_{(t_0,t_1]}$ which takes α into α^*.

To illustrate, in Example *1.7.19* every state is reachable from every other state in the state space. Following the terminology used by E. F. Moore in his work on sequential machines (see Ref. *3*), systems having this property will be said to be *strongly connected.*[1]

[1] In the context of linear systems, "strong connectedness" is closely related to so-called "complete controllability." A detailed discussion of controllability, observability, and related concepts is presented in Chap. *11*.

In Example *5*, in the case of system $\mathcal{A}$ every state is reachable from the state 0 (which corresponds to zero current through L). On the other hand, in the case of system $\mathcal{B}$ the state $(-1,1)$ is not reachable from the state (0,0), because on application of an input voltage $\mathbf{u}_{(t_0,t_1]}$ to $\mathcal{B}$ starting in (0,0), the resulting terminal state is the 2-vector

$$\mathbf{s}(t_1) = \left(\frac{1}{2L}\int_{t_0}^{t} u(t)\,dt, \frac{1}{2L}\int_{t_0}^{t} u(t)\,dt\right)$$

in which the first and second components are always equal to one another. Consequently, there does not exist a $\mathbf{u}_{(t_0,t_1]}$ such that $\mathbf{s}(t_1) = (-1,1)$.

An obvious and yet important property of reachable states is contained in the following

18 **Assertion** Let Σ_α denote the set of all states in the state space of $\mathcal{A}$ which are reachable from $\boldsymbol{\alpha}$. Then Σ_α is a *closed* set in the sense that if $\boldsymbol{\alpha}_0$ is any initial state in Σ_α, then every state which is reachable from $\boldsymbol{\alpha}_0$ also belongs to Σ_α. (Note that this does not necessarily imply that Σ_α is a closed set in the usual set-theoretic sense.) ◁

For convenient reference, we state in the form of an assertion a reworded version of *12* in terms of the notion of reachable states.

19 **Assertion** If $\boldsymbol{\alpha}^*$ and $\boldsymbol{\beta}^*$ are reachable from two equivalent states $\boldsymbol{\alpha}$ and $\boldsymbol{\beta}$ by the same input, then $\boldsymbol{\alpha}^*$ and $\boldsymbol{\beta}^*$ are equivalent states. ◁

The notion of reachability also helps to clarify a question concerning the transition from a free to a constrained interconnection (see Chap. *1*, *Sec. 10*). This question is discussed in the following

20 **Remark** In terms of reachable states, the state space $\Sigma(t_0,t)$ of a free interconnection of $\mathcal{A}_1, \ldots, \mathcal{A}_N$ at time t (see *1.10.26*) may be characterized as follows: $\Sigma(t_0,t)$ is the set of all states in the product space $\Sigma_1 \times \cdots \times \Sigma_N$ which are reachable (at time t), with the initial states (at time t_0) ranging over $\Sigma_1 \times \cdots \times \Sigma_N$. ◁

When we pass by a limiting process from $\Sigma(t_0,t)$ to Σ, which is the state space of the constrained interconnection of $\mathcal{A}_1, \ldots, \mathcal{A}_N$ (see *1.10.21*), the following question arises with respect to the validity of *19* in the limit as $t_0 \to -\infty$. Suppose that $\mathbf{u}$ is defined over $(-\infty,\infty)$ and that $\mathbf{u}_{(t_0,t]}$ takes $\boldsymbol{\alpha}$ and $\boldsymbol{\beta}$ (at time t_0) into $\boldsymbol{\alpha}^*(t)$ and $\boldsymbol{\beta}^*(t)$, respectively, at time t. Now if $\boldsymbol{\alpha} \simeq \boldsymbol{\beta}$ and $\boldsymbol{\alpha}^*(t)$ and $\boldsymbol{\beta}^*(t)$ converge to $\boldsymbol{\alpha}^*$ and $\boldsymbol{\beta}^*$, respectively, as $t_0 \to -\infty$, can we assert that the limit states $\boldsymbol{\alpha}^*$ and $\boldsymbol{\beta}^*$ are equivalent?

To discuss the question in more concrete terms, let us assume for simplicity that the state spaces of $\mathcal{A}$ and $\mathcal{B}$ are finite-dimensional euclidean spaces, with the norm (length) of an n-vector $\mathbf{s}(t)$ defined by (see *C.16.5 et seq.*)

21 $$\|\mathbf{s}(t)\| = \sqrt{|s_1(t)|^2 + \cdots + |s_n(t)|^2}$$

[Note that *21* is also defined for $\mathbf{s}(t)$ with complex-valued components.] Then, the statement "$\mathbf{s}(t)$ converges to $\boldsymbol{\alpha}^*$ as $t \to \infty$" means that $\|\mathbf{s}(t) - \boldsymbol{\alpha}^*\| \to 0$ as $t \to \infty$; that is, given any $\varepsilon > 0$, there exists a $T(\varepsilon)$ such that $\|\mathbf{s}(t) - \boldsymbol{\alpha}^*\| \leq \varepsilon$ for all $t \geq T(\varepsilon)$.

It is easy to show that a sufficient condition for the answer to the above question to be in the affirmative is that $\mathcal{A}$ and $\mathcal{B}$ are "well behaved" in the sense specified below for $\mathcal{A}$.

Let $\mathcal{A}$ be characterized by an input-output-state relation

22 $$\mathbf{y}(t) = \mathbf{A}(\boldsymbol{\alpha};\mathbf{u}_{(t_0,t]})$$

and let $\| \quad \|$ be a suitably defined norm (not necessarily a euclidean norm) on the space of time functions $\mathbf{y}$ over (t_0, ∞). Then $\mathcal{A}$ is *continuous* at $\boldsymbol{\alpha}$ (for a fixed $\mathbf{u}$) if, roughly speaking, "small" changes in $\boldsymbol{\alpha}$ produce "small" changes in $\mathbf{y}$, or, more precisely, if given any $\varepsilon > 0$, there exists a $\delta(\varepsilon)$ such that

23 $$\|\boldsymbol{\alpha}' - \boldsymbol{\alpha}\| \leq \delta(\varepsilon) \Rightarrow \|\mathbf{y} - \mathbf{y}'\| \leq \varepsilon \qquad \forall \boldsymbol{\alpha}'$$

where $\mathbf{y}'(t) = \mathbf{A}(\boldsymbol{\alpha}';\mathbf{u}_{(t_0,t]})$. Note that this definition is closely related to that of *stability* of $\mathcal{A}$ (see *7.2.2*).

If both $\mathcal{A}$ and $\mathcal{B}$ have this property for all inputs, then we can make the following

24 **Assertion** Let $\boldsymbol{\alpha}^*(t)$ and $\boldsymbol{\beta}^*(t)$ be the respective states of $\mathcal{A}$ and $\mathcal{B}$ into which $\boldsymbol{\alpha}$ and $\boldsymbol{\beta}$ are taken by an input $\mathbf{u}_{(t_0,t]}$. Let $\boldsymbol{\alpha}^*(t) \simeq \boldsymbol{\beta}^*(t)$ for all t_0 and let $\boldsymbol{\alpha}^*(t)$ and $\boldsymbol{\beta}^*(t)$ converge to $\boldsymbol{\alpha}^*$ and $\boldsymbol{\beta}^*$, respectively, as $t_0 \to -\infty$. Then the limit states $\boldsymbol{\alpha}^*$ and $\boldsymbol{\beta}^*$ are equivalent if $\mathcal{A}$ and $\mathcal{B}$ are continuous at $\boldsymbol{\alpha}^*$ and $\boldsymbol{\beta}^*$, respectively, for all $\mathbf{u}$ starting at t.

Proof The proof is a simple exercise in the use of ε's and δ's. Specifically, on using the subscripts a and b to identify the ε's, δ's, and outputs associated with $\mathcal{A}$ and $\mathcal{B}$, respectively, we have

25 $$t_0 \leq T_a[\delta_a(\varepsilon)] \Rightarrow \|\boldsymbol{\alpha}(t) - \boldsymbol{\alpha}^*\| \leq \delta_a(\varepsilon) \Rightarrow \|\mathbf{y} - \mathbf{y}_a^*\| \leq \varepsilon$$
$$t_0 \leq T_b[\delta_b(\varepsilon)] \Rightarrow \|\boldsymbol{\beta}(t) - \boldsymbol{\beta}^*\| \leq \delta_b(\varepsilon) \Rightarrow \|\mathbf{y} - \mathbf{y}_b^*\| \leq \varepsilon$$

where T_a has the same significance as in *21 et seq.* and $\mathbf{y}_a^* = \bar{\mathbf{A}}(\boldsymbol{\alpha}^*;\mathbf{u})$. From *25* it follows at once by using the triangle inequality (see Appendix *C.16.4*)

$$t_0 \leq \min\{T_a[\delta_a(\varepsilon)], T_b[\delta_b(\varepsilon)]\} \Rightarrow \|\mathbf{y}_a^* - \mathbf{y}_b^*\| \leq 2\varepsilon$$

which implies that $\mathbf{y}_a^* = \mathbf{y}_b^*$. Q.E.D.

This concludes for the present our discussion of the notion of equivalent states. We turn next to another notion that plays a central role in system theory—the notion of *system equivalence.*

5 *System equivalence and related concepts*

In Secs. *2* and *4* we defined the notion of state equivalence and established some of its basic properties. In this section, we shall examine a related and very important concept, namely, the concept of *system equivalence.*

As the name implies, two systems $\mathcal{A}$ and $\mathcal{B}$ are *equivalent* if, roughly speaking, they exhibit the same behavior when subjected to the same input. To lend greater precision to this idea, it is convenient to define equivalence in terms of the ability of an experimenter to distinguish between $\mathcal{A}$ and $\mathcal{B}$ on the basis of applying to a black box which is known to contain $\mathcal{A}$ or $\mathcal{B}$ an input of his choice and observing the response. If, no matter what input is applied, the experimenter cannot determine whether the black box contains $\mathcal{A}$ or $\mathcal{B}$, then $\mathcal{A}$ and $\mathcal{B}$ are *equivalent.* Otherwise, they are *nonequivalent,* or *distinguishable.*

It is clear that in order to define equivalence in more concrete terms, one must consider a variety of different situations. For example, the experimenter may have just one copy of the black box at his disposal or he may have as many as he wishes. He may know the initial state of the black box or he may not. The range of inputs which he may be permitted to apply may be limited, etc. To cover these and other situations, we need more than one concept of equivalence. In the sequel, we shall define two basic kinds of equivalence and establish some connections between them. We begin with the notion of

Weak equivalence (equivalence under a single experiment)

Let $\mathcal{A}$ and $\mathcal{B}$ be two oriented systems characterized by their input-output relations, or input-output-state relations, or as families of their respective spaces of input-output pairs (see *1.4.17 et seq.*). We assume that $\mathcal{A}$ and $\mathcal{B}$ have the same input segment space $R[\mathbf{u}]$, $\mathbf{u} \triangleq \mathbf{u}_{(t_0,t_1]}$, and we denote by W the union of their output segment spaces.

Underlying the definition given below is the assumption that the experimenter is presented with a single black box which contains either $\mathcal{A}$ or $\mathcal{B}$ and that he can choose any input $\mathbf{u}$ in $R[\mathbf{u}]$. The response of the black box to $\mathbf{u}$ is denoted by $\mathbf{w}$. The experimenter is to decide on whether the black box contains $\mathcal{A}$ or $\mathcal{B}$ from the knowledge of the pair $(\mathbf{u},\mathbf{w})$ and nothing else.

1 **Definition** $\mathcal{A}$ is said to *contain* $\mathcal{B}$, written as $\mathcal{A} \supset \mathcal{B}$, if every input-output pair for $\mathcal{B}$ is also an input-output pair for $\mathcal{A}$. Geometrically, this means that the set of points (input-output pairs) in the product space $R[\mathbf{u}] \times W$ which represents $\mathcal{B}$ is a subset of the set of points (input-output pairs) which represents $\mathcal{A}$ (see *1.4.17* and Fig. *2.5.1*). (Note that this must hold for all observation intervals $(t_0,t_1]$.)

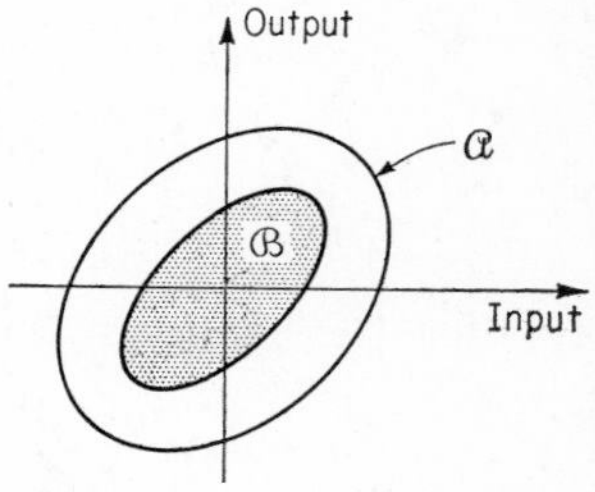

Fig. 2.5.1 Geometrical representation of "$\mathcal{A}$ contains $\mathcal{B}$."

2 *Example* Suppose that $\mathcal{A}$ and $\mathcal{B}$ are characterized by the input-output relations

3
$$\mathcal{A}: \quad \frac{dy}{dt} = \frac{d^2u}{dt^2} \qquad T = [0, \infty)$$
$$\mathcal{B}: \quad y = \frac{du}{dt}$$

where u is a real-valued time function. Clearly, every input-output pair for $\mathcal{B}$ is also an input-output pair for $\mathcal{A}$. For example, $(t,1), t > 0$, is an input-output pair for $\mathcal{B}$ as well as $\mathcal{A}$. On the other hand, $(t^2 + 2t, 2t + 1)$, $t > 0$, is an input-output pair for $\mathcal{A}$ but not for $\mathcal{B}$. Thus, $\mathcal{B}$ is contained in $\mathcal{A}$. [Note that this is a consequence of the fact that the input-output relation of $\mathcal{A}$ is the result of differentiating the input-output relation of $\mathcal{B}$. The same thing applies, more generally, when we act on both sides of an input-output relation with a differential operator (see *3.8.11*).]

4 **Definition** If $\mathcal{A}$ contains $\mathcal{B}$ and $\mathcal{B}$ contains $\mathcal{A}$, then $\mathcal{A}$ and $\mathcal{B}$ are *weakly equivalent* or *equivalent under a single experiment.* This means that every input-output pair for $\mathcal{A}$ is also an input-output pair for $\mathcal{B}$, and vice versa. Weak equivalence is denoted by $\mathcal{A} = \mathcal{B}$.

In terms of input-output-state relations rather than input-output relations, the definition of weak equivalence assumes the following form.

5 **Definition** $\mathcal{A}$ and $\mathcal{B}$ are *weakly equivalent* or *equivalent under a single experiment* if and only if to every input $\mathbf{u}$ and initial state $\boldsymbol{\alpha}$ in $\mathcal{A}$ there is a state $\boldsymbol{\beta}$ (depending on $\mathbf{u}$ and $\boldsymbol{\alpha}$) in $\mathcal{B}$ such that the response of $\mathcal{A}$ to $\mathbf{u}$ starting in state $\boldsymbol{\alpha}$ is identical with the response of $\mathcal{B}$ to $\mathbf{u}$ starting in state $\boldsymbol{\beta}$, and vice versa.

In symbols

6
$$\{\mathcal{A} = \mathcal{B}\} \Leftrightarrow \{\forall \boldsymbol{\alpha} \forall \mathbf{u} \exists \boldsymbol{\beta} [\bar{\mathbf{A}}(\boldsymbol{\alpha};\mathbf{u}) = \bar{\mathbf{B}}(\boldsymbol{\beta};\mathbf{u})]\}$$
and
$$\{\forall \boldsymbol{\beta} \forall \mathbf{u} \exists \boldsymbol{\alpha} [\bar{\mathbf{A}}(\boldsymbol{\alpha};\mathbf{u}) = \bar{\mathbf{B}}(\boldsymbol{\beta};\mathbf{u})]\}$$

Here $\exists$ denotes "there exists" and the order of the quantifiers in

$\forall\alpha\forall\mathbf{u}\exists\beta$ indicates that β depends on α and $\mathbf{u}$. Likewise, $\forall\beta\forall\mathbf{u}\exists\alpha$ indicates that α depends on β and $\mathbf{u}$.

7 *Comment* Definition *5* is equivalent to Definition *4*. This is an immediate consequence of the mutual-consistency condition—a condition which must be satisfied by an input-output-state relation (see *1.6.5*). Under this condition, to every input-output pair $(\mathbf{u},\mathbf{y})$ for $\mathcal{A}$ there corresponds at least one state α in the state space of $\mathcal{A}$ with respect to which $(\mathbf{u},\mathbf{y})$ satisfies the input-output-state relation, and conversely, every pair $(\mathbf{u},\mathbf{y})$ with $\mathbf{u} \in R[\mathbf{u}]$ and $\mathbf{y} \in R[\mathbf{y}]$ satisfying this relation is an input-output pair for $\mathcal{A}$. ◁

The justification for calling weak equivalence "equivalence under a single experiment" is provided by the following observation. If $\mathcal{A}$ and $\mathcal{B}$ have the property expressed by *6*, then no matter whether $\mathcal{A}$ or $\mathcal{B}$ is in the black box, no matter what the initial state is, and no matter what input $\mathbf{u}$ the experimenter chooses, the response $\mathbf{w}$ will always be attributable to both $\mathcal{A}$ and $\mathcal{B}$ and hence the experimenter will be unable to determine whether the black box contains $\mathcal{A}$ or $\mathcal{B}$ from the knowledge of the pair $(\mathbf{u},\mathbf{w})$. In this sense, $\mathcal{A}$ and $\mathcal{B}$ are indistinguishable by any single experiment and consequently are equivalent under a single experiment.

If $\mathcal{A}$ and $\mathcal{B}$ are indistinguishable by any single experiment, it does not follow that they could not be distinguished if the experimenter had at his disposal more than one copy of the black box, each copy containing, say, $\mathcal{A}$ in an initial state α. In that case, the experimenter could perform different experiments on the different copies of the black box and thereby base his conclusion not on just one input-output pair $(\mathbf{u},\mathbf{w})$—as in a single experiment—but on as many different input-output pairs as there are copies of the black box at his disposal. As was defined before (Chap. *1*, Sec. *8*), if the experimenter has available as many black boxes as he desires, all containing the same system in the same initial state (not known to the experimenter), then the experiment in question is said to be a *multiple experiment*. If even under such an experiment the experimenter is unable to determine whether the copies of the black box contain $\mathcal{A}$ or $\mathcal{B}$, then $\mathcal{A}$ and $\mathcal{B}$ are said to be *indistinguishable under a multiple experiment*. Clearly, indistinguishability under a multiple experiment is a stronger (i.e., more restrictive) property than indistinguishability under a single experiment.

The concept of indistinguishability under a multiple experiment underlies the

8 **Definition: system equivalence** $\mathcal{A}$ *is equivalent* to $\mathcal{B}$, written $\mathcal{A} \equiv \mathcal{B}$, if and only if to every state α in the state space of $\mathcal{A}$ there corresponds at least one equivalent state β in the state space of $\mathcal{B}$, and vice versa. ◁

To cast this definition into the form of a logical formula, observe that the statement "to every state $\boldsymbol{\alpha}$ in $\mathcal{A}$ there is an equivalent state $\boldsymbol{\beta}$ in $\mathcal{B}$" is expressed by

$$\forall \boldsymbol{\alpha} \exists \boldsymbol{\beta} \forall \mathbf{u}[\bar{\mathbf{A}}(\boldsymbol{\alpha};\mathbf{u}) = \bar{\mathbf{B}}(\boldsymbol{\beta};\mathbf{u})]$$

Making use of this observation, we have

9
$$\{\mathcal{A} \equiv \mathcal{B}\} \Leftrightarrow \{\forall \boldsymbol{\alpha} \exists \boldsymbol{\beta} \forall \mathbf{u}[\bar{\mathbf{A}}(\boldsymbol{\alpha};\mathbf{u}) = \bar{\mathbf{B}}(\boldsymbol{\beta};\mathbf{u})]\}$$

and
$$\{\forall \boldsymbol{\beta} \exists \boldsymbol{\alpha} \forall \mathbf{u}[\bar{\mathbf{A}}(\boldsymbol{\alpha};\mathbf{u}) = \bar{\mathbf{B}}(\boldsymbol{\beta};\mathbf{u})]\}$$

Note that the only difference between this definition and that of weak equivalence (Definition *6*) lies in the inversion of the order of quantifiers. Specifically, in *6* the order in the first factor in the right-hand member is $\forall \boldsymbol{\alpha} \forall \mathbf{u} \exists \boldsymbol{\beta}$ (which indicates that $\boldsymbol{\beta}$ depends on $\boldsymbol{\alpha}$ and $\mathbf{u}$), whereas in *9* it is $\forall \boldsymbol{\alpha} \exists \boldsymbol{\beta} \forall \mathbf{u}$, which signifies that $\boldsymbol{\beta}$ depends only on $\boldsymbol{\alpha}$. It is this independence of $\boldsymbol{\beta}$ of $\mathbf{u}$ that is the crux of the difference between *6* and *9*, and it is this property that makes $\boldsymbol{\beta}$ equivalent to $\boldsymbol{\alpha}$.

It remains to be shown that equivalence in the sense of Definition *8* implies and is implied by indistinguishability under a multiple experiment.

It is obvious that if *8* is satisfied, then $\mathcal{A}$ and $\mathcal{B}$ are indistinguishable under a multiple experiment. For, suppose that the copies of the black box contain, say, $\mathcal{A}$ in state $\boldsymbol{\alpha}$ and that $\boldsymbol{\beta}$ is an equivalent state in $\mathcal{B}$. Then no matter what input the experimenter applies to each copy of the black box, the observed response will be identical to what $\mathcal{B}$ would produce starting in state $\boldsymbol{\beta}$. Thus, the experimenter will be unable to distinguish between $\mathcal{A}$ and $\mathcal{B}$. The same thing is true more generally when to each state in the state space of $\mathcal{A}$ there corresponds an equivalent state in the state space of $\mathcal{B}$, and vice versa.

To show the converse requires more elaborate arguments which will be given here only for the simple case where $\mathcal{A}$ and $\mathcal{B}$ are finite-state systems, i.e., the state spaces of $\mathcal{A}$ and $\mathcal{B}$ contain a finite number of states.[1]

Specifically, suppose the right-hand side of *9* is false. Then we will have established the converse once we have shown that $\mathcal{A}$ and $\mathcal{B}$ are distinguishable under a multiple experiment.

To show that $\mathcal{A}$ and $\mathcal{B}$ are distinguishable if the right-hand side of *9* is false, we note that in this case the negation[2] of the right-hand side is true, i.e., either (I) $\exists \boldsymbol{\alpha} \forall \boldsymbol{\beta} \exists \mathbf{u}[\bar{\mathbf{A}}(\boldsymbol{\alpha};\mathbf{u}) \neq \bar{\mathbf{B}}(\boldsymbol{\beta};\mathbf{u})]$ is true or (II)

[1] A proof for continuous-state systems which makes use of Zorn's lemma was suggested by A. Chang, a student at the University of California.

[2] To negate a logical expression containing $\forall$, $\exists$, "and," "or," $\Rightarrow$, and propositions $x, y, \ldots, z$, replace $\forall$ by $\exists$, $\exists$ by $\forall$, "and" by "or," "or" by "and," $\Rightarrow$ by $\not\Leftarrow$, and every proposition by its negation. See Ref. *2* for a more detailed discussion.

$\exists \beta \forall \alpha \exists \mathbf{u}[\bar{\mathbf{A}}(\alpha;\mathbf{u}) \neq \bar{\mathbf{B}}(\beta;\mathbf{u})]$ is true. (I) means that there is a state α in $\mathcal{A}$ such that for every state β in $\mathcal{B}$ there is an input $\mathbf{u}$ which can distinguish between α and β. The same interpretation applies to (II).

Assume that $\mathcal{A}$ has n states $\alpha_1, \ldots, \alpha_n$ and $\mathcal{B}$ has m states $\beta_1, \ldots, \beta_m$ and that (I) is true for, say, α_1. Then, the experimenter may be able to distinguish between $\mathcal{A}$ and $\mathcal{B}$ if the black boxes contain $\mathcal{A}$ in a state α_1. Specifically, assume that the experimenter is presented with k black boxes $[k \geq \max(m,n)]$ numbered $1, \ldots, k$, each of which contains $\mathcal{A}$ in state α_1, with the experimenter being unaware of what object is in the black boxes. In this case, the experimenter will be able to distinguish between $\mathcal{A}$ and $\mathcal{B}$ by applying to copy i, $i = 1, \ldots, m$, an input $\mathbf{u}^i$ which distinguishes between α_1 and β_i [i.e., an input $\mathbf{u}^i$ such that $\bar{\mathbf{A}}(\alpha_1;\mathbf{u}^i) \neq \bar{\mathbf{B}}(\beta_i;\mathbf{u}^i)$]. For the observed input-output pairs $(\mathbf{u}^1,\mathbf{y}^1), \ldots, (\mathbf{u}^m,\mathbf{y}^m)$ will collectively lead the experimenter to the conclusion that the black boxes cannot contain $\mathcal{B}$ in any of its states $\beta_1, \ldots, \beta_m$. Hence the black boxes must contain $\mathcal{A}$.

10 *Comment* Note that the above reasoning is based on the tacit assumption that the definition of "distinguishability under a multiple experiment" is obtained from that of "indistinguishability under a multiple experiment" by the process of negation (see footnote on page 92). In this sense, $\mathcal{A}$ and $\mathcal{B}$ are *distinguishable under a multiple experiment* if there exists an initial state of $\mathcal{A}$ (or $\mathcal{B}$) such that if the black boxes contain $\mathcal{A}$ (or $\mathcal{B}$) in this state, then there exists a multiple experiment which will make the experimenter conclude that the black boxes contain $\mathcal{A}$ (or $\mathcal{B}$). A stronger definition of distinguishability would be one under which the experimenter can distinguish between $\mathcal{A}$ and $\mathcal{B}$ by a multiple experiment *regardless* of the initial state of the black box. It is easy to show that, in some cases, this stronger definition is implied by the weaker definition used above. One such case is that of so-called strongly connected systems (see *2.4.17 et seq*).

11 **Remark** It is obvious from the way in which system equivalence is defined by *8* that if $\mathcal{A}$ and $\mathcal{B}$ are equivalent, then they are also weakly equivalent. Although the converse is not true in general, it is true for systems that are of principal interest to us, namely, systems whose input-output relations have the form of linear differential equations. This basic property of linear systems will be established in Chap. *3*, Sec. *9*.

Before we proceed to illustrate the notion of system equivalence by an example, it will be helpful to state two basic properties of system equivalence. The first of these is the property of

12 **Transitivity** If $\mathcal{A}$ is equivalent to $\mathcal{B}$ and $\mathcal{B}$ is equivalent to $\mathcal{C}$, then $\mathcal{A}$ is equivalent to $\mathcal{C}$. In symbols,

$$\{\mathcal{A} \equiv \mathcal{B} \text{ and } \mathcal{B} \equiv \mathcal{C}\} \Rightarrow \{\mathcal{A} \equiv \mathcal{C}\}$$

This property is an immediate consequence of the transitivity of state equivalence (see *2.2.1 et seq.*).

13 *Question* Does transitivity apply to weak equivalence? ◁

The second property is

14 **Equivalence under one-one mapping** Consider a system $\mathcal{A}$ which is characterized by an input-output-state relation

$$\mathbf{y}(t) = \mathbf{A}(\boldsymbol{\alpha};\mathbf{u}) \qquad \boldsymbol{\alpha} \in \Sigma$$

Let $\boldsymbol{\mu}$ be a one-one mapping of Σ onto itself, with the image of $\boldsymbol{\alpha}$ under $\boldsymbol{\mu}$ being $\breve{\boldsymbol{\alpha}}$, that is,

$$\breve{\boldsymbol{\alpha}} = \boldsymbol{\mu}(\boldsymbol{\alpha}) \qquad \text{and} \qquad \boldsymbol{\alpha} = \boldsymbol{\mu}^{-1}(\breve{\boldsymbol{\alpha}})$$

Then the system $\breve{\mathcal{A}}$ characterized by the input-output-state relation

$$\begin{aligned}\mathbf{y} &= \mathbf{A}(\boldsymbol{\mu}^{-1}(\breve{\boldsymbol{\alpha}});\mathbf{u}) \\ &\triangleq \breve{\mathbf{A}}(\breve{\boldsymbol{\alpha}};\mathbf{u})\end{aligned}$$

is equivalent to $\mathcal{A}$. That this is true follows at once from the fact that a one-one mapping on Σ constitutes merely a relabeling of its points (see *2.3.46*).

We shall illustrate the notion of system equivalence by a simple example which is constructed by the use of *14*.

15 *Example* Consider two systems: (I) $\mathcal{A}$, characterized by the input-output-state relation

16 $$\begin{aligned}y(t) = {} & (2e^{-(t-t_0)} - e^{-2(t-t_0)})\alpha_1 + (e^{-(t-t_0)} - e^{-2(t-t_0)})\alpha_2 \\ & + \int_{t_0}^{t} (e^{-(t-\xi)} - e^{-2(t-\xi)})u(\xi)\, d\xi \qquad t > t_0\end{aligned}$$

where α_1 and α_2 are the components of $\boldsymbol{\alpha}$ and $\Sigma = \mathcal{R}^2$, and (II) $\mathcal{B}$, characterized by the input-output-state relation

17 $$\begin{aligned}y(t) = {} & (3e^{-(t-t_0)} - 5e^{-2(t-t_0)})\beta_1 + (3e^{-(t-t_0)} - 2e^{-2(t-t_0)})\beta_2 \\ & + \int_{t_0}^{t} (e^{-(t-\xi)} - e^{-2(t-\xi)})u(\xi)\, d\xi \qquad t > t_0\end{aligned}$$

where β_1 and β_2 are the components of $\boldsymbol{\beta}$.

Inspection of *16* and *17* shows that to an arbitrary $\boldsymbol{\alpha}$ there corresponds an equivalent $\boldsymbol{\beta}$ if and only if the following relation holds for all $t > t_0$:

18 $$\begin{aligned}& (2e^{-(t-t_0)} - e^{-2(t-t_0)})\alpha_1 + (e^{-(t-t_0)} - e^{-2(t-t)_0})\alpha_2 \\ & \quad = (3e^{-(t-t_0)} - 5e^{-2(t-t_0)})\beta_1 + (3e^{-(t-t_0)} - 2e^{-2(t-t_0)})\beta_2\end{aligned}$$

On equating the coefficients of like exponentials in *18*, we have

$$\alpha_1 = -2\beta_1 + \beta_2 \qquad \alpha_2 = 7\beta_1 + \beta_2$$

Clearly, this system of equations can be solved for β_1 and β_2 in terms of α_1 and α_2, and vice versa. Consequently, for every state $\boldsymbol{\alpha}$ in $\mathcal{A}$ there is one equivalent state β in $\mathcal{B}$, and vice versa. This establishes that $\mathcal{A} \equiv \mathcal{B}$. ◁

In later chapters we shall frequently be concerned with the problem of representing a given system $\mathcal{A}$ as an interconnection of components of specified types, e.g., integrators, differentiators, scalors, and adders. This motivates the following

19 **Definition** Let $\Gamma_1, \ldots, \Gamma_k$ be a set of classes of systems (for example, $\Gamma_1 \triangleq$ class of integrators with real or complex time constants, $\Gamma_2 \triangleq$ class of scalors). Then an interconnection of components $\mathcal{A}_1, \ldots, \mathcal{A}_N$ each of which belongs to one of the Γ_i, $i = 1, \ldots, k$, is a *realization of* $\mathcal{A}$ *in terms of* $\Gamma_1, \ldots, \Gamma_k$ if the interconnection in question, call it $\mathcal{B}$, is equivalent to $\mathcal{A}$. A realization of $\mathcal{A}$ need not be physically realizable. ◁

As we noted in the last section of Chap. *1*, a basic property which a given interconnection may or may not possess is that of *determinateness*. If an interconnection $\mathcal{A}$ is determinate, then a basic question is: How can one associate a state vector with $\mathcal{A}$ and what is the corresponding state space of $\mathcal{A}$? This and related questions are discussed on a general level in the following section.

6 *The state of an interconnection of systems*

Consider a system $\mathcal{A}$ which consists of an interconnection (*1.10.28*) of oriented components $\mathcal{A}_1, \ldots, \mathcal{A}_N$ (Fig. *2.6.1*) each of which is characterized by an input-output-state relation

1 $$\mathbf{y}^i(t) = \mathbf{A}_i(\mathbf{s}^i(t_0); \mathbf{u}^i_{(t_0,t]}) \qquad i = 1, \ldots, N$$

where $\mathbf{s}_i(t) \in \Sigma_i \triangleq$ state space of $\mathcal{A}_i$. Note that we use superscripts

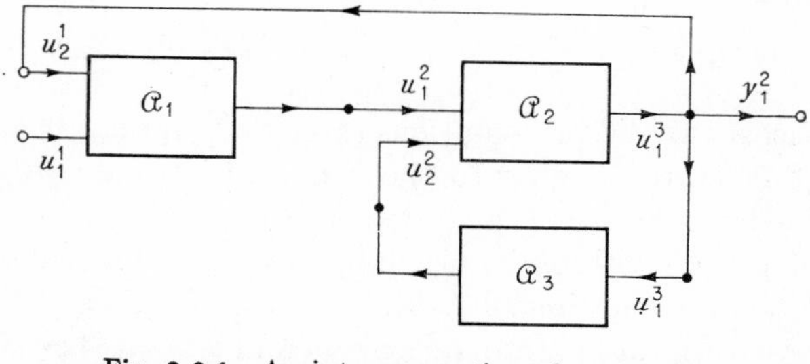

Fig. 2.6.1 An interconnection of $\mathcal{A}_1$, $\mathcal{A}_2$, $\mathcal{A}_3$.

to identify the input, output, and state vectors associated with $\mathcal{A}_i$, and we shall use subscripts to label the components of these vectors, for example, $u^i_j \triangleq j$th component of $\mathbf{u}^i$.

In accordance with *1.10.40*, the output of $\mathcal{A}$ is defined to be the composite vector

2 $$\mathbf{y} \triangleq (\mathbf{y}^1, \ldots, \mathbf{y}^N)$$

with the understanding that one or more of the components of $\mathbf{y}$ may be suppressed. As for the input to $\mathcal{A}$, it comprises all input variables of the $\mathcal{A}_i$ which are not input-output variables (*1.10.27*), and it is denoted by $\mathbf{u}$. [For example, in Fig. *2.6.1* the input to $\mathcal{A}$ is u_1^1 and the output vector is $(u_2^1, u_1^2, u_1^3, u_2^2)$.]

Let $\mathcal{A}(t_0)$ denote an initially free interconnection (*1.10.26*) which is derived from $\mathcal{A}$ by severing all connections between the $\mathcal{A}_i$ until $t = t_0$. Furthermore, let $\boldsymbol{\alpha}_0^1, \ldots, \boldsymbol{\alpha}_0^N$ denote the initial states of $\mathcal{A}_1, \ldots, \mathcal{A}_N$, with the composite initial state vector $\boldsymbol{\alpha}_0 = (\boldsymbol{\alpha}_0^1, \ldots, \boldsymbol{\alpha}_0^N)$ ranging over the product space $\Sigma_1 \times \cdots \times \Sigma_N$.

A basic property which $\mathcal{A}$ may or may not possess is that of *determinateness.* It is convenient to define this notion in terms of $\mathcal{A}(t_0)$ as follows.

3 **Definition** An interconnection $\mathcal{A}$ is *determinate* if, for all t_0, t, $\mathbf{u}$, and $\boldsymbol{\alpha}_0$, the output of $\mathcal{A}(t_0)$, $\mathbf{y}(t)$, is determined uniquely by $\mathbf{u}_{(t_0,t]}$ and $\boldsymbol{\alpha}_0$ through the input-output-state relations *1*, $i = 1, \ldots, N$ [and, of course, the interconnection relations (*1.10.28*)]. If $\mathcal{A}$ is not determinate, it is said to be *indeterminate.*

4 *Example* In the case of the system of Fig. *2.6.1*, $\mathcal{A}$ is determinate if $u_2^1(t)$, $u_1^2(t)$, $u_1^3(t)$, and $u_2^2(t)$ are determined uniquely by $\boldsymbol{\alpha}_0^1$, $\boldsymbol{\alpha}_0^2$, $\boldsymbol{\alpha}_0^3$, and $u^1_{1(t_0,t]}$. As will be shown in Chap. 3 (*3.9.12*), any linear time-invariant differential system is determinate. However, this is not generally true of nonlinear systems. For example, in the case of system $\mathcal{B}$ of Fig. *2.8.2*, if $L = -1$, $R = 2(i)^{-\frac{1}{2}}$, $t_0 = 0$, and $u(t) = 0$ for $t \geq 0$, then the differential equation

5 $$-\frac{di}{dt} + 2\sqrt{i} = 0$$

has at least two distinct solutions (I) $i(t) = 0$ for $t \geq 0$, and (II) $i(t) = t^2$ for $t \geq 0$, corresponding to the same initial state $i(0) = 0$. This is explained by the fact that *5* does not imply that if $i(0) = 0$, then all derivatives of i with respect to t are zero at $t = 0$. Note that *5* violates the Lipschitz condition (*2.3.40*).

Now let $\mathcal{A}$ be a determinate system and let $\mathcal{A}(t_0)$ be the corresponding free interconnection of the components of $\mathcal{A}$. Then given $\boldsymbol{\alpha}_0$ and $\mathbf{u}_{(t_0,t]}$ we can find $\mathbf{y}_{(t_0,t]}$ and hence the inputs $\mathbf{u}^i_{(t_0,t]}$ to the $\mathcal{A}_i$, $i = 1, \ldots, N$. From these and the $\boldsymbol{\alpha}_o^i$ we can determine through the state equations of the $\mathcal{A}_i$ the state $\mathbf{s}^i(t)$ of $\mathcal{A}_i$ at time t. The states of the $\mathcal{A}_i$ define the composite state vector

$$\mathbf{s}(t) = (\mathbf{s}^1(t), \ldots, \mathbf{s}^N(t))$$

which ranges over the space $\Sigma(t_0,t)$ (see *2.4.20*), where $\Sigma(t_0,t)$ is the set of all states in the product space $\Sigma_1 \times \cdots \times \Sigma_N$ which are reachable at time t from initial states in $\Sigma_1 \times \cdots \times \Sigma_N$ at time t_0. The state space of $\mathcal{A}$, then, is formally expressed by the limit, if it exists,

6 $$\Sigma = \lim_{t_0 \to -\infty} \Sigma(t_0,t)$$

where Σ is a subset of $\Sigma_1 \times \cdots \times \Sigma_N$. (See *1.10.21*.)

7 **Remark** Through the use of Σ, we can avoid introducing the free interconnection $\mathcal{A}(t_0)$ into the definition of a determinate system. Specifically, we can say that $\mathcal{A}$ is *determinate* if for every initial state $\boldsymbol{\alpha}_0$ in Σ and every input $\mathbf{u}$, the output $\mathbf{y}$ is uniquely determined by $\mathbf{u}$ and $\boldsymbol{\alpha}_0$. In the sequel, we shall be using for the most part this definition of determinateness rather than Definition *3*.

8 **Remark** Note that if $\mathcal{A}$ is a time-invariant system (see *1.7.6* and *3.2.36*), then clearly $\Sigma(t_0,t)$ has the inclusion property: $t_2 \geq t_1 \Rightarrow \Sigma(t_0,t_2) \subset \Sigma(t_0,t_1)$. (Why?) In this case, it may be more appropriate to define Σ by the relation

9 $$\Sigma = \bigcap_{t_0} \Sigma(t_0,t) \qquad t_0 < t$$

which differs from *6* in that every point of the space Σ defined by *9* belongs to all the $\Sigma(t_0,t)$, whereas some points of the space Σ defined by *7* may not belong to any of the $\Sigma(t_0,t)$ for finite t_0 and t.

In general, the determination of Σ—whether defined by *6* or *9*—is by no means a trivial problem. However, our primary concern in this text is with linear differential systems, and in the case of such systems Σ can be determined quite easily by virtue of the fact (which will be established in Chap. *4*) that $\mathbf{s}(t)$ is defined by a finite number of the derivatives of the input and output at time t. To illustrate, suppose that $\mathcal{A}$ comprises three components $\mathcal{A}_1$, $\mathcal{A}_2$, $\mathcal{A}_3$ (plus an adder) whose states are related to their respective inputs and outputs by the expressions

$\mathcal{A}_1$: $\qquad s^1 = y^1$

$\mathcal{A}_2$: $\qquad s^2 = y^2$

$\mathcal{A}_3$: $\qquad s^3 = u^3$

with the interconnection relation being $u^3 = y^1 + y^2$ and

$$\Sigma_1 = \Sigma_2 = \Sigma_3 = \mathcal{R}^1$$

Then Σ is a linear subspace of $\mathcal{R}^3$ defined by the relation $s^1 + s^2 = s^3$.

It should be noted that in this example the states of $\mathcal{A}_1$, $\mathcal{A}_2$, and $\mathcal{A}_3$ do not involve any derivatives of their inputs and outputs. As will be shown later, in the case of linear differential systems it is always possible to represent a system as a combination of integrators, differentiators, scalors, and adders, with the states of the integrators and differentiators at time t being, respectively, their outputs and inputs at time t (see Chap. *4*, Sec. *6*). In terms of such a representation, the expressions for the states of components have the above form and, in this sense, the simple example considered here is illustrative of the general case. However, if the system is not represented in this form and the states of the $\mathcal{A}_i$ do involve the derivatives of their respective inputs and outputs, then the constraints on the $\mathbf{s}^i$ induced by the interconnection relations will in general involve linear combinations of the $\mathbf{s}^i$ and their derivatives, inputs to the $\mathcal{A}_i$ and their derivatives, and outputs of the $\mathcal{A}_i$ and their derivatives. Of these constraints only those that are holonomic in the $\mathbf{s}^i$ (that is, involve only the $\mathbf{s}^i$ and not their derivatives) are of relevance to the determination of Σ. For example, if

$$s_1^1 = s_1^2 \qquad s_2^1 = \dot{s}_1^2 + 2s_1^2 - 3u_1^1 \qquad s_1^3 = y_1^3$$

then Σ is a three-dimensional subspace of $\mathcal{R}^4$ defined by $s_1^1 = s_1^2$. (Note that $s_j^i \triangleq j$th component of the state of $\mathcal{A}_i$.)

Determinateness theorem

We have not yet shown that the vector $\mathbf{s}(t)$ defined by *5* qualifies as the state vector of $\mathcal{A}$. This is demonstrated in the

10 **Theorem** Let $\mathcal{A}$ be a determinate interconnection of $\mathcal{A}_1, \ldots, \mathcal{A}_N$, with the input and output of $\mathcal{A}$ denoted by $\mathbf{u}$ and $\mathbf{y}$, respectively, and let $\mathbf{s}(t) = (\mathbf{s}^1(t_0), \ldots, \mathbf{s}^N(t_0))$ be an initial state vector in Σ, where Σ is a subset of $\Sigma_1 \times \cdots \times \Sigma_N$ formally defined by *6*. Furthermore, let $\mathbf{s}^i(t)$ be the state of $\mathcal{A}_i$ at time t, under the assumption that the input to $\mathcal{A}$ is $\mathbf{u}_{(t_0,t]}$ and the initial states of $\mathcal{A}_1, \ldots, \mathcal{A}_N$ are $\mathbf{s}^1(t_0), \ldots, \mathbf{s}^N(t_0)$, respectively. Then the composite vector

11 $$\mathbf{s}(t) = (\mathbf{s}^1(t), \ldots, \mathbf{s}^N(t))$$

qualifies as the state of $\mathcal{A}$ at time t, with Σ being the state space of $\mathcal{A}$. In plain words, this means that if $\mathcal{A}$ is a determinate system, then the state of $\mathcal{A}$ at time t is the aggregate of the states of its components at time t.

Proof. To say that $\mathcal{A}$ is determinate is equivalent to saying that $\mathbf{s}(t)$ satisfies the first self-consistency condition (*1.6.11*). Thus, it will suffice to show that the input-output-state relation of $\mathcal{A}$ has the response separation property, for then it will follow from Assertion *2.3.12* that $\mathbf{s}(t)$ qualifies as the state of $\mathcal{A}$ at time t. ◁

In order to avoid obscuring the essential simplicity of the argument by a multiplicity of symbols and equations, we shall establish the desired property by considering a concrete simple case such as illustrated in Fig. *2.6.6*. It will then be easy to see how the response separation property can be established in the same way for an arbitrary determinate interconnection.

The input-output-state relations for the system in question read

12 $$u^2(t) = A_1[\mathbf{s}^1(t_0); u^1_{1(t_0,t]}, u^1_{2(t_0,t]}]$$

13 $$u^1_2(t) = A_2[\mathbf{s}^2(t_0); u^2_{(t_0,t]}]$$

By hypothesis, these equations can be solved uniquely for $u^2(t)$ and $u^1_2(t)$ in terms of $u^1_{1(t_0,t]}$ and $[\mathbf{s}^1(t_0),\mathbf{s}^2(t_0)]$, yielding expressions of the form

14 $$u^2(t) = A^1[\mathbf{s}^1(t_0),\mathbf{s}^2(t_0); u^1_{1(t_0,t]}]$$

15 $$u^1_2(t) = A^2[\mathbf{s}^1(t_0),\mathbf{s}^2(t_0); u^1_{1(t_0,t]}]$$

Now since *12* and *13* are input-output-state relations, they have the response separation property (*2.3.5*) expressed by the relations

16 $$u^2(t) = A_1[\mathbf{s}^1(\tau); u^1_{1(\tau,t]}, u^1_{2(\tau,t]}]$$

17 $$u^1_2(t) = A_2[\mathbf{s}^2(\tau); u^2_{(\tau,t]}]$$

where τ is an arbitrary intermediate time between t_0 and t and $\mathbf{s}^1(\tau)$ and $\mathbf{s}^2(\tau)$ denote the states of $\mathcal{A}_1$ and $\mathcal{A}_2$, respectively, at time τ.

The fact that *12* and *13* can be solved uniquely for $u^2(t)$ and $u^1_2(t)$ in the form *14* and *15* implies that *16* and *17* can similarly be solved for $u^2(t)$ and $u^1_2(t)$, yielding expressions which differ from *14* and *15* only in that t_0 is replaced by τ. Thus

18 $$u^2(t) = A^1[\mathbf{s}^1(\tau),\mathbf{s}^2(\tau); u^1_{1(\tau,t]}]$$

19 $$u^1_2(t) = A^2[\mathbf{s}^1(\tau),\mathbf{s}^2(\tau); u^1_{1(\tau,t]}]$$

From comparison of these equations with *14* and *15* it follows that $\mathcal{A}$ has the response separation property and hence, by Assertion *2.3.12*, the composite state vector $\mathbf{s}(t)$ defined by *11* qualifies as the state vector of $\mathcal{A}$.

Special types of determinate systems

There are several types of system which are determinate by virtue of the structure of interconnections between their components or a special nature of their input-output-state relationships. In the latter category are linear differential systems, which will be defined formally in Chap. *3*. In the former category are the two types defined below.

20 **Definition** A system $\mathcal{A}$ is *cycle-free* if its signal-state graph (Chap. *1*, Sec. *9*), or, equivalently, signal-flow graph, has no cycles (loops, closed paths).[1] ◁

21 *Note* For our present purposes, it will be convenient to represent the state associated with each node in a signal-state graph as an additional branch variable which enters the node in question. This convention is illustrated in Fig. *2.6.2*, which depicts system $\mathcal{A}$ of Fig. *2.6.1*. In effect, this mode of representation amounts to nothing more than reducing the rectangular blocks in the diagrammatic representation of Fig. *1.9.1* to small circles (nodes) which serve to represent the components of $\mathcal{A}$. In this way, the structure of the interconnections of $\mathcal{A}$ (that is, the graph of $\mathcal{A}$) is placed in a clearer perspective.

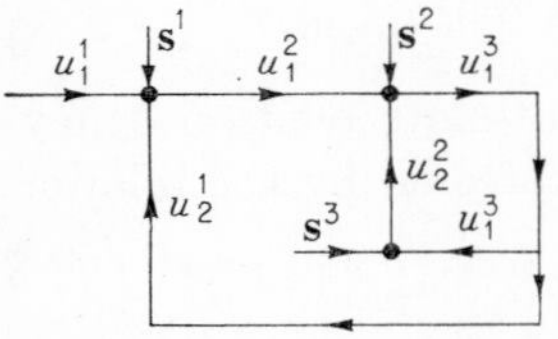

Fig. 2.6.2 Signal-state graph for the system of Fig. 2.6.1.

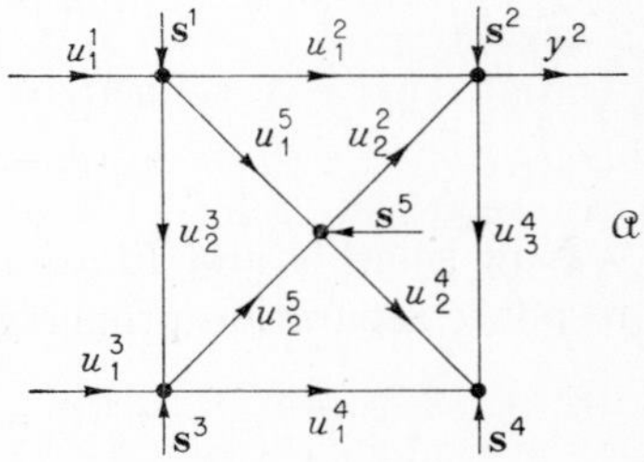

Fig. 2.6.3 A cycle-free system.

22 *Example* In Fig. *2.6.2* is illustrated the signal-state graph of a system (system $\mathcal{A}$, Fig. *2.6.1*) which has loops. In Fig. *2.6.3* is shown a cycle-free system. (Note that the labeling of branches is determined by their roles as inputs rather than outputs. For example, the branch connecting $\mathcal{A}_1$ to $\mathcal{A}_3$ represents the output of $\mathcal{A}_1$ and an input to $\mathcal{A}_3$. It is labeled u_2^3 because it is an input to $\mathcal{A}_3$; the other input to $\mathcal{A}_3$ is labeled u_1^3. Also, all the branches leaving a node are understood to represent the same output variable. For example, the branches u_1^2 and u_1^5 leaving $\mathcal{A}_1$ both represent the output of $\mathcal{A}_1$ and hence $u_1^2 = u_1^5$. Similarly, $u_2^5 = u_1^4$.)

Cycle-free systems have an intuitively obvious property which is stated in the following

[1] We assume that the reader is familiar with the elementary aspects of signal-flow graphs. An exposition of signal-flow graphs and related topics is presented in Chap. *9*, Sec. *15*.

23 **Theorem** Any cycle-free system $\mathcal{A}$ is determinate.

Proof Consider the signal-state graph of a cycle-free system $\mathcal{A}$ such as shown in Fig. *2.6.3*. Here u_1^1 and u_1^3 are the inputs to $\mathcal{A}$ and y^2 is the output. The other branch variables such as u_1^2 and u_2^2 represent the suppressed output variables. The state variables $\mathbf{s}^1, \ldots, \mathbf{s}^5$ are treated in the same way as the inputs to $\mathcal{A}$. That is, in so far as the graph-theoretic properties of the signal-state graph are concerned, all branches entering a node and not connected to other nodes are regarded as external inputs to the node, regardless of whether they are associated with input or state variables. For example, in Fig. *2.6.3*, u_1^1 and $\mathbf{s}^1$ are external inputs to node 1, $\mathbf{s}^2$ is an external input to node 2, and u_1^3 and $\mathbf{s}^3$ are external inputs to node 3. (The number of a node can be identified from the superscripts of input variables associated with it.) A node which has external inputs will be referred to as an *input node*, and all other nodes will be called *internal nodes*. [Note that internal nodes are associated with input-output variables (*1.10.27*).]

To begin with, we make the assumption that $\mathcal{A}$ is *well formed* in the sense that every internal node of $\mathcal{A}$ can be reached (via one or more oriented paths) from an input node. This ensures that there are no components of $\mathcal{A}$ which have no input applied to them.

The property that $\mathbf{s}^i$ and $\mathbf{u}^i$ determine the output of $\mathcal{A}_i$, $i = 1, \ldots, N$, translates itself into the following property of branch variables: The values of all the branches entering a node determine the values of all the branches leaving that node. (As was pointed out previously, the variables associated with the branches leaving a node have the same value, namely, the output of the component which is represented by the node in question. However, this is not relevant to the arguments which will be employed below.)

Using the terminology defined above, the statement of Theorem *23* can be restated as follows.

24 **Restatement of Theorem** *23* Let $\mathcal{A}$ be a well-formed cycle-free oriented graph in which each branch is associated with a variable, with the defining property that, for each node i, the values of branches leaving i are determined uniquely by the values of branches entering i. Furthermore, $\mathcal{A}$ contains one or more nodes (input nodes) such that at least one of the branches entering each such node is not connected to any other node (i.e., represents an external input). Then, the values of all such branches (external inputs) determine the values of all branches of $\mathcal{A}$. ◁

We establish first the following property of $\mathcal{A}$.

25 **Property** $\mathcal{A}$ has at least one input node such that all branches entering it represent external inputs. For example, in Fig. *2.6.3* node 1 is an input node with this property.

For, suppose that this is false. Then all input nodes have the property that at least one branch entering each such node leaves an internal node. But, since $\mathcal{A}$ is well formed, every internal node is reachable from at least one input node. Consequently, every input node is reachable from at least one input node.

Now let 1, 2, . . . , k, say, designate input nodes. If 1 is reachable from 1, then $\mathcal{A}$ has a cycle—which is a contradiction. Suppose that 1 is reachable from 2. Then if 2 is reachable from 1, we have a cycle—which is a contradiction. Suppose 2 is reachable from 3. Repeating this argument, we finally exhaust all nodes in the set 1, . . . , k and are forced to conclude that there must be a cycle containing one or more input nodes. Since this is a contradiction, we have shown that $\mathcal{A}$ has Property *25*.

Now we can delete from the graph every input node having this property, together with all the branches entering it, without affecting the values of other branches in the graph. (This is illustrated in Fig. *2.6.4*.) At this stage, we know the values of the branches which leave the deleted nodes and hence can regard them as external inputs with respect to the graph that remains after the removal of the input nodes in question. The remaining graph, call it $\mathcal{A}'$, is, like $\mathcal{A}$, cycle-free and well formed. On applying previously used arguments to $\mathcal{A}'$ and then repeating the process, we establish, after not more than $N - 1$ steps ($N \triangleq$ number of nodes in $\mathcal{A}$) that the values of all branches in $\mathcal{A}$ are determined by the values of its external inputs. Q.E.D.

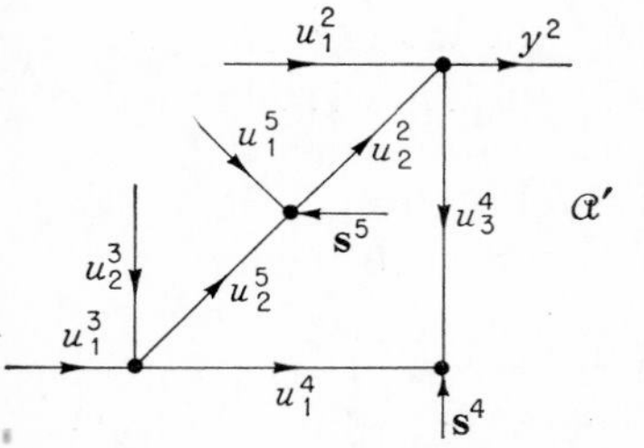

Fig. 2.6.4 Result of removing a node from the system of Fig. 2.6.3.

We turn next to the consideration of another class of determinate systems which, unlike the class discussed above, need not be cycle-free. As a preliminary, we introduce a notion which is relevant to the characterization of determinate systems.

26 **Definition** A system $\mathcal{A}$ is said to have *state-determined output* if for each t its output at time t is uniquely determined by its state at time t. This implies that the state equations of such a system have the form

27 $$\mathbf{s}(t) = \mathbf{s}(\mathbf{s}(t_0);\mathbf{u}_{(t_0,t]})$$

28 $$\mathbf{y}(t) = \mathbf{g}(\mathbf{s}(t),t)$$

where $\mathbf{g}$ is a function defined on $\Sigma \times T$.

29 *Example* A very simple example of a system with a state-determined output is an integrator (*1.9.10*), which is characterized by the input-output-state relation

30 $$y(t) = y(t_0) + \int_{t_0}^{t} u(\xi)\, d\xi \qquad t > t_0$$

or more precisely

31 $$y(t) = y(t_0-) + \int_{t_0}^{t} u(\xi)\, d\xi \qquad t \geq t_0$$

As was shown earlier (*1.7.10*), $y(t)$ qualifies as $s(t)$, the state of the integrator at time t. Thus, $s(t)$ determines $y(t)$.

More generally, as will be shown in Chap. 4 (see *4.5.19 et seq.*), any system whose input-output relation is of the form

32 $$a_n \frac{d^n y}{dt^n} + \cdots + a_1 \frac{dy}{dt} + a_0 y = b_m \frac{d^m u}{dt^m} + \cdots + b_0 u \qquad a_n \neq 0$$

has state-determined output provided $m < n$.

A simple and yet important example of a discrete-time system with state-determined output is a unit-delay element defined by the input-output relation (*1.7.25*)

33 $$y(t) = u(t-1) \qquad t \geq t_0 + 1,\ T = \{0,1,2, \cdots\}$$

As in the case of the integrator (which is in effect a continuous-time analog of the delay element), the state of the unit-delay element at time t is $y(t)$. Thus, the unit-delay element has state-determined output.

A notion which is closely related to the notion of a system with state-determined output is that of a system with state-determined input. Although this notion is not of direct relevance to the question of system determinateness, we define it for future reference.

34 **Definition** A system $\mathcal{A}$ is said to have *state-determined input* if for each t its input at time t is uniquely determined by its state at time t.

35 *Example* A very simple illustration of such a system is provided by the differentiator, i.e., a system characterized by the input-output relation

$$y = \frac{du}{dt}$$

As was pointed out previously (*1.7.10*), the state of a differentiator at time t is $u(t)$. Thus the input to the differentiator at time t is determined by $s(t)$. The same thing is true of any system whose input-output relation is of the form *32* with y and u interchanged.

Now consider a system $\mathcal{A}$ which is an interconnection of $\mathcal{A}_1, \ldots, \mathcal{A}_N$. We assume that the signal-state graph of $\mathcal{A}$ contains one or more cycles (closed paths) and that each $\mathcal{A}_i$ is characterized by differential state equations of the canonical form (see *2.3.36*)

36 $$\dot{\mathbf{s}}^i(t) = \mathbf{f}_i(\mathbf{s}^i(t),\mathbf{u}^i(t),t) \qquad i = 1, \ldots, N$$

37 $$\mathbf{y}^i(t) = \mathbf{g}_i(\mathbf{s}^i(t),\mathbf{u}^i(t),t)$$

We assume further that the $\mathbf{f}_i$ satisfy the usual sufficient conditions (*2.3.40*) which ensure the existence and uniqueness of solutions of *36* for all $\mathbf{u}^i$ in $R[\mathbf{u}^i]$.

Suppose that every cycle in $\mathcal{A}$ contains at least one node which represents a component with state-determined output. For concreteness, let $\mathcal{A}_2$ in Fig. *2.6.2* be such a component. Then, if at time t_0 we "split" the node in question in the manner illustrated in Fig. *2.6.5*, we shall know not only $\mathbf{s}^2(t_0)$ but also $\mathbf{y}^2(t_0)$, which is the output of $\mathcal{A}_2$ and an input to other nodes.

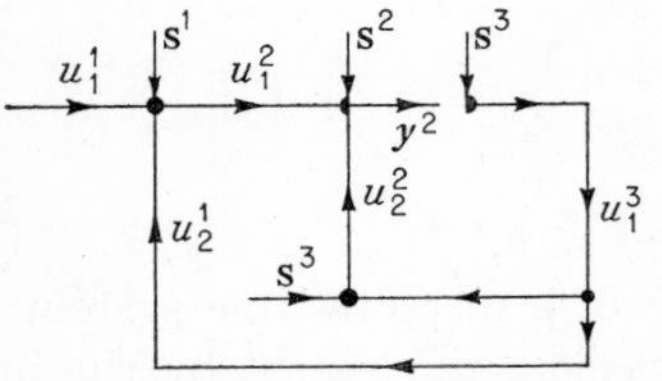

Fig. 2.6.5 Effect of node splitting.

By breaking all the cycles of $\mathcal{A}$ in this fashion, we transform the original system into a cycle-free system in which the states of all components and the values of all inputs are known at time t_0. (Note that in Fig. *2.6.5* the splitting of $\mathcal{A}_2$ breaks both cycles in $\mathcal{A}$.) On substituting these values into the state equations *36* and *37* we obtain $\dot{\mathbf{s}}^i(t_0)$ and $\mathbf{y}^i(t_0)$. Then, by using $\dot{\mathbf{s}}^i(t_0)$ and $\mathbf{s}^i(t_0)$, we can compute via *36* and *37* the value of $\mathbf{s}^i(t)$ at $t_0 + dt$, which in turn yields $\mathbf{u}^i(t_0 + dt)$ and which in combination with the known inputs at time $t_0 + dt$ makes it possible to recompute the $\mathbf{y}^i(t_0)$ and repeat the process. This heuristic argument suggests the following

38 **Theorem** Let $\mathcal{A}$ be an interconnection of $\mathcal{A}_1, \ldots, \mathcal{A}_N$ containing one or more cycles. If each $\mathcal{A}_i$ is characterized by canonical state equations of the form *36* and *37* and if each cycle in $\mathcal{A}$ contains at least one component which has state-determined output (*26*), then $\mathcal{A}$ can be characterized by canonical state equations of the form *36* and *37*.

Proof The proof is quite straightforward and is left as an exercise for the reader. To indicate how it proceeds, it will suffice to consider a simple system such as shown in Fig. *2.6.6*, in which $\mathcal{A}_2$ has state-

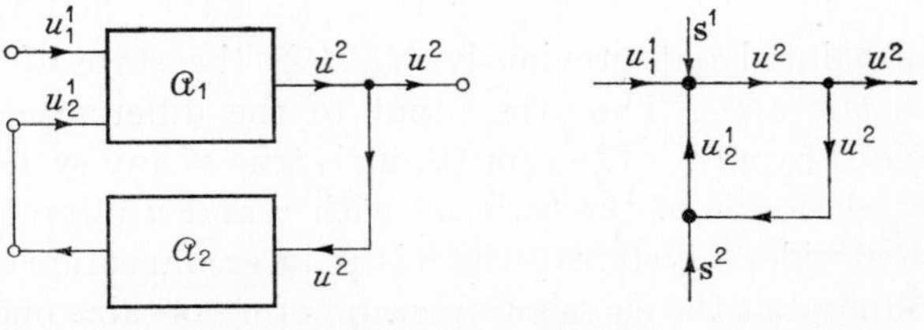

Fig. 2.6.6 Illustration for Theorem 2.6.38.

determined output, so that we have

39 $\mathcal{A}_1$:
$$\dot{\mathbf{s}}^1(t) = \mathbf{f}_1(\mathbf{s}^1(t),u_1^1(t),u_2^1(t),t)$$
$$u^2(t) = g_1(\mathbf{s}^1(t),u_1^1(t),u_2^1(t),t)$$

40 $\mathcal{A}_2$:
$$\dot{\mathbf{s}}^2(t) = \mathbf{f}_2(\mathbf{s}^2(t),u^2(t),t)$$
$$u_2^1(t) = g_2(\mathbf{s}^2(t),t)$$

Upon elimination of $u_2^1(t)$, these equations yield a pair of differential equations of the form

$$\dot{\mathbf{s}}^1(t) = \mathbf{f}_1^*(\mathbf{s}^1(t),\mathbf{s}^2(t),u_1^1(t),t)$$
$$\dot{\mathbf{s}}^2(t) = \mathbf{f}_2^*(\mathbf{s}^1(t),\mathbf{s}^2(t),u_1^1(t),t)$$

in which $\mathbf{f}_1^*$ and $\mathbf{f}_2^*$ are defined by $\mathbf{f}_1$, g_1, $\mathbf{f}_2$, and g_2, and $\mathbf{s}(t) \triangleq (\mathbf{s}^1(t),\mathbf{s}^2(t))$ plays the role of the state of $\mathcal{A}$. Thus, the state equations of $\mathcal{A}$ can be put into the canonical form

41
$$\dot{\mathbf{s}}(t) = \mathbf{f}(\mathbf{s}(t),u_1^1(t),t)$$
$$u^2(t) = g(\mathbf{s}(t),u_1^1(t),t)$$

which is what we wanted to demonstrate.

42 *Comment* Note that Theorem *38* does not assert that $\mathcal{A}$ is a determinate system. However, it follows from this theorem that $\mathcal{A}$ is determinate if the **f** and **g** functions in the canonical state equations which characterize $\mathcal{A}$ are such that the differential equation *36* has a unique solution. In particular, in the case of linear time-varying systems, it follows from Theorem *38* and Conclusion *2.3.42* that $\mathcal{A}$ is determinate if the matrices characterizing each $\mathcal{A}_i$ are continuous functions of time and every cycle in $\mathcal{A}$ has at least one component with state-determined output. More generally, in most physical systems of the feedback type every loop (cycle) contains a component which introduces some delay and which can be approximated by a delay element of the type defined in *1.7.25*. Such delay elements have state-determined output, and it is largely for this reason that most physical systems are determinate.

The question of determinateness of linear systems will be examined in greater detail in Chap. *3*, Sec. *9*. For the present, we return to the discussion of system equivalence.

7 *Further properties of system equivalence*

Equivalence of interconnections

Consider two collections of pairwise equivalent systems $\mathcal{A}_1, \ldots, \mathcal{A}_N$ and $\mathcal{B}_1, \ldots, \mathcal{B}_N$, with $\mathcal{A}_i \equiv \mathcal{B}_i$, $i = 1, \ldots, N$. Let $\mathcal{A}$ be a determinate interconnection of the $\mathcal{A}_i$ and let $\mathcal{B}$ be the same interconnection of the $\mathcal{B}_i$. On intuitive grounds we expect that, in general, $\mathcal{A} \equiv \mathcal{B}$. Indeed, we can readily deduce the equivalence of $\mathcal{A}$ and $\mathcal{B}$ in a formal way by a repeated application of the substitution principle (*1.10.35*).

There are two special cases of this property which are of frequent use in deducing the equivalence of two systems from equivalences of other systems. These properties follow from the

1 **Assertion** If $\mathcal{A} \equiv \mathcal{B}$ and $\mathcal{C} \equiv \mathcal{D}$, then (I) the free product (*1.10.10*) of $\mathcal{A}$ and $\mathcal{C}$ is equivalent to the free product of $\mathcal{B}$ and $\mathcal{D}$ and (II) the free sum (*1.10.30 et seq.*) of $\mathcal{A}$ and $\mathcal{C}$ is equivalent to the free sum of $\mathcal{B}$ and $\mathcal{D}$.

Proof It is easy to prove (I) directly, without relying on the substitution principle. The proof of (II) is left as an exercise for the reader. Let $\boldsymbol{\alpha}$, $\boldsymbol{\beta}$, $\boldsymbol{\gamma}$, $\boldsymbol{\delta}$ denote the states of $\mathcal{A}$, $\mathcal{B}$, $\mathcal{C}$, $\mathcal{D}$ at time t_0, with $\boldsymbol{\alpha}$, $\boldsymbol{\beta}$, $\boldsymbol{\gamma}$, $\boldsymbol{\delta}$ ranging over the respective state spaces Σ_a, Σ_b, Σ_c, Σ_d. Furthermore, let $\boldsymbol{\alpha}(t)$, $\boldsymbol{\beta}(t)$, $\boldsymbol{\gamma}(t)$, and $\boldsymbol{\delta}(t)$ be the states into which $\boldsymbol{\alpha}$, $\boldsymbol{\beta}$, $\boldsymbol{\gamma}$, and $\boldsymbol{\delta}$ are taken by $\mathbf{u}_{(t_0,t]}$. By *2.6.23* and *2.6.10* the composite states $[\boldsymbol{\alpha}(t),\boldsymbol{\gamma}(t)]$ and $[\boldsymbol{\beta}(t),\boldsymbol{\delta}(t)]$ qualify as the states of the free products $\mathcal{AC}$ and $\mathcal{BD}$, respectively, at time t. The state spaces of these products at time t are denoted by $\Sigma_{ac}(t_0,t)$ and $\Sigma_{bd}(t_0,t)$, and are defined by *1.10.16*.

Since $\mathcal{A} \equiv \mathcal{B}$, to every initial state $\boldsymbol{\alpha}$ of $\mathcal{A}$ there is an equivalent state, say, $\boldsymbol{\beta}$, of $\mathcal{B}$, and vice versa. Let $(\boldsymbol{\alpha},\boldsymbol{\beta})$ be such a pair of equivalent states and let $(\boldsymbol{\gamma},\boldsymbol{\delta})$ be an analogous pair for $\mathcal{C}$ and $\mathcal{D}$. Then it is obvious that the pair $(\boldsymbol{\alpha},\boldsymbol{\gamma})$, regarded as an initial state of the free product $\mathcal{AC}$, is equivalent to the pair $(\boldsymbol{\beta},\boldsymbol{\delta})$, which plays the role of the initial state of $\mathcal{BD}$. Now by hypothesis $[\boldsymbol{\alpha}(t),\boldsymbol{\gamma}(t)]$ and $[\boldsymbol{\beta}(t),\boldsymbol{\delta}(t)]$ are reachable, respectively, from $(\boldsymbol{\alpha},\boldsymbol{\gamma})$ and $(\boldsymbol{\beta},\boldsymbol{\delta})$ via $\mathbf{u}_{(t_0,t]}$. Consequently, by Assertion *2.4.19*, $[\boldsymbol{\alpha}(t),\boldsymbol{\gamma}(t)]$ and $[\boldsymbol{\beta}(t),\boldsymbol{\delta}(t)]$ are equivalent states. Furthermore, from the definitions of $\Sigma_{ac}(t_0,t)$ and $\Sigma_{bd}(t_0,t)$ it follows that the statement "to every state $(\boldsymbol{\alpha},\boldsymbol{\gamma})$ in the product space $\Sigma_a \times \Sigma_c$ there is an equivalent state $(\boldsymbol{\beta},\boldsymbol{\delta})$ in the product space $\Sigma_b \times \Sigma_d$" implies "to every state $[\boldsymbol{\alpha}(t),\boldsymbol{\gamma}(t)]$ in $\Sigma_{ac}(t_0,t)$ there is an equivalent state $[\boldsymbol{\beta}(t),\boldsymbol{\delta}(t)]$ in $\Sigma_{bd}(t_0,t)$." Now since the product of $\mathcal{A}$ and $\mathcal{C}$ is initially free, $(\boldsymbol{\alpha},\boldsymbol{\gamma})$ can be chosen arbitrarily in $\Sigma_a \times \Sigma_b$. From this and the preceding implication it follows that $\mathcal{AC} \equiv \mathcal{BD}$, with $\mathcal{AC}$ and $\mathcal{BD}$ interpreted as free products.

Having established Assertion *1*, we can deduce from it and Assertion *2.4.24* a corresponding property for constrained products (*1.10.23*). This property is stated in the

2 **Corollary** If $\mathcal{A}$, $\mathcal{B}$, $\mathcal{C}$, $\mathcal{D}$ are well behaved in the sense of *2.4.24* and if $\mathcal{A} \equiv \mathcal{B}$ and $\mathcal{C} \equiv \mathcal{D}$, then the constrained product $\mathcal{AC}$ is equivalent to the constrained product $\mathcal{BD}$.

Conditional equivalence

Consider two systems $\mathcal{A}$ and $\mathcal{B}$ such that there is a state $\boldsymbol{\alpha}_0$ in the state space of $\mathcal{A}$ which is equivalent to a state $\boldsymbol{\beta}_0$ in the state space of $\mathcal{B}$. Let Σ_{α_0} and Σ_{β_0} denote the closed sets of states (see *2.4.18*) which are reachable from $\boldsymbol{\alpha}_0$ and $\boldsymbol{\beta}_0$, respectively. Then it is obvious that Σ_{α_0} and Σ_{β_0} have the property expressed by the

3 **Assertion** To every state $\boldsymbol{\alpha}$ in Σ_{α_0} there is at least one equivalent state $\boldsymbol{\beta}$ in Σ_{β_0}, and vice versa.

Proof Let $\boldsymbol{\alpha}$ be an arbitrary state in Σ_{α_0} and let $\mathbf{u}$ be an input which takes $\boldsymbol{\alpha}_0$ into $\boldsymbol{\alpha}$. (Such an input exists because all the states in Σ_{α_0} are reachable from $\boldsymbol{\alpha}_0$.) Then by *2.4.19* the state $\boldsymbol{\beta}$ into which $\boldsymbol{\beta}_0$ is taken by $\mathbf{u}$ is equivalent to $\boldsymbol{\alpha}$, and likewise for an arbitrary state in Σ_{β_0}.

4 **Corollary** If $\boldsymbol{\alpha}_0 \simeq \boldsymbol{\beta}_0$ and all states in the state spaces of $\mathcal{A}$ and $\mathcal{B}$ are reachable from $\boldsymbol{\alpha}_0$ and $\boldsymbol{\beta}_0$, respectively, then $\mathcal{A} \equiv \mathcal{B}$. (A special instance of this is *2.9.5*.)

Based on *3*, we make the following

5 **Definition** $\mathcal{A}$ and $\mathcal{B}$ are *conditionally equivalent*, written as $\mathcal{A} \overset{*}{=} \mathcal{B}$, if there are closed subsets Σ_{α_0} and Σ_{β_0} in the state spaces of $\mathcal{A}$ and $\mathcal{B}$, respectively, such that to every state in Σ_{α_0} there is an equivalent state in Σ_{β_0}, and vice versa. $\triangleleft$

In effect, if $\mathcal{A}$ and $\mathcal{B}$ are conditionally equivalent, then they behave like equivalent systems so long as their initial states are restricted to the respective subsets Σ_{α_0} and Σ_{β_0}. This implies that, under this restriction, the various properties of system equivalence such as those expressed by *1* also apply to conditional equivalence. In particular,

6 $$\{\mathcal{A} \overset{*}{=} \mathcal{B} \text{ and } \mathcal{C} \overset{*}{=} \mathcal{D}\} \Rightarrow \{\mathcal{A}\mathcal{C} \overset{*}{=} \mathcal{B}\mathcal{D}\}$$

under the same conditions as stated in *2*. We shall use this relation later on in our discussion of zero-state equivalence and inverse systems.

8 *Zero state, ground state, and equilibrium state*

The heading of this section lists three states which by virtue of their special properties play important roles in system analysis. A given system $\mathcal{A}$ may or may not have these states and, if it has them, they may or may not be coincident. Before defining the states in question, it will be convenient to have on record the following simple

1 **Definition** A time function which has the value 0 (in scalar or vector sense) for $t \geq t_0$ is called a *null function* and is denoted by $\mathbf{0}$, or, if necessary, by $\mathbf{0}(t_0)$. If an input $\mathbf{u}$ is zero for $t \geq t_0$, then it is said to be a *zero input*. ◁

We begin with the definition of

Zero state

2 **Definition** A state $\boldsymbol{\theta}$ of $\mathcal{A}$ is a *zero state* if, for all t_0, the response of $\mathcal{A}$ to the zero input, with $\mathcal{A}$ starting in $\boldsymbol{\theta}$, is a null function. In symbols

3 $$\{\boldsymbol{\theta} \text{ is a } \textit{zero state} \text{ of } \mathcal{A}\} \Leftrightarrow \{A(\boldsymbol{\theta};\mathbf{0}) = \mathbf{0}\} \qquad \forall t_0 \qquad ◁$$

Stated informally, if $\mathcal{A}$ is initially in its zero state and no input is applied to $\mathcal{A}$ (that is, $\mathbf{u} = \mathbf{0}$), then there is no output (or, equivalently, the output is a null function). It should be noted that $\mathcal{A}$ may have no zero state, or it may have one or more nonequivalent zero states.

4 *Example* The system discussed in Example *2.2.4* has six zero states: 0, 2, 4, 6, 8, 10. However, all these states are equivalent to one another.

5 *Example* System $\mathcal{A}$ in Example *2.4.5* has a unique zero state, namely $\theta = 0$ (which corresponds to the condition where no current flows through L). In system $\mathcal{B}$, (0,0) is a zero state, as are all states of the form $(\rho, -\rho)$, where ρ is any real number. Note that all such states are equivalent to (0,0), and hence the zero state (0,0) is unique (to within equivalent states).

6 *Example* The following example demonstrates that a system can have two or more nonequivalent zero states. Consider the network $\mathcal{A}$, shown in Fig. *2.8.1*, in which the input is a voltage u, the output is a

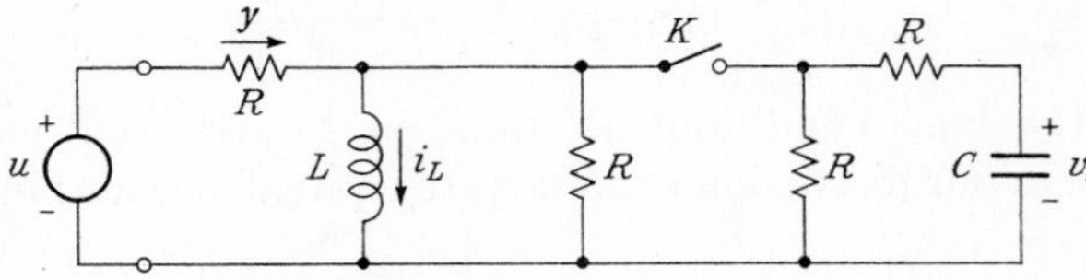

Fig. 2.8.1 A system with nonunique zero state.

current y, and K is a switch whose position is characterized by a binary variable σ, namely, $\sigma = 0$ if K is open and $\sigma = 1$ if K is closed. It is easy to verify that the state of $\mathcal{A}$ at time t can be identified with the 3-vector $\mathbf{s}(t) = (i_L(t), v_C(t), \sigma(t))$, where $i_L(t)$ is the current through L, $v_C(t)$ is the voltage across C, and $\sigma(t)$ is the value of σ at time t. Now, (0,0,0) is a zero state of $\mathcal{A}$, as is the state (0,0,1). Obviously, these two states are nonequivalent.

Ground state

A notion which frequently coincides in meaning with that of the zero state but is not coextensive with it is that of the *ground state*. Specifically, consider a system $\mathcal{A}$ in initial state $\mathbf{s}(t_0) = \boldsymbol{\alpha}$ to which a zero input is applied at t_0. Let us fix our attention on $\mathbf{s}(t)$, the state of $\mathcal{A}$ at time t, $t > t_0$, and examine what may happen to $\mathbf{s}(t)$ as $t \to \infty$.

Clearly, there are two possibilities: (I) $\mathbf{s}(t)$ may converge to a fixed state, say $\boldsymbol{\gamma}$, as $t \to \infty$; (II) $\mathbf{s}(t)$ may not converge as $t \to \infty$ (see *2.4.20 et seq.*).

Let us restrict our attention to (I). Here again we have two possibilities: (*a*) the limiting state $\boldsymbol{\gamma}$ depends on the initial state $\boldsymbol{\alpha}$; (*b*) $\boldsymbol{\gamma}$ is independent of $\boldsymbol{\alpha}$.

If (I) and (*b*) hold, the limiting terminal state $\boldsymbol{\gamma}$ is called the *ground state* of $\mathcal{A}$. Roughly, the ground state is the state into which $\mathcal{A}$ settles eventually when no input is applied. More formally, we have the

7 **Definition** The *ground state* of $\mathcal{A}$, if it exists, is the limiting terminal state of $\mathcal{A}$ when the zero input is applied to $\mathcal{A}$, provided the limiting state $\boldsymbol{\gamma}$ is the same for all initial states. In symbols,

8 $$\{\boldsymbol{\gamma} \text{ is the } \textit{ground state} \text{ of } \mathcal{A}\} \Leftrightarrow \{\boldsymbol{\gamma} = \lim_{t\to\infty} \mathbf{s}(\boldsymbol{\alpha};\mathbf{0}),\ \boldsymbol{\gamma} \text{ independent of } \boldsymbol{\alpha}\}$$

where $\mathbf{s}(\mathbf{s}(t_0);\mathbf{u}_{(t_0,t]})$ denotes the state of $\mathcal{A}$ at time t (*2.2.33*). Note that $\boldsymbol{\gamma}$, if it exists, is unique by virtue of the uniqueness of the limit. ◁

The following examples serve to illustrate the notion of the ground state and the differences between it and the zero state of a system.

9 *Example* Consider two networks $\mathcal{A}$ and $\mathcal{B}$ shown in Fig. *2.8.2*. In both cases, the state at time t can be identified with the current $i(t)$

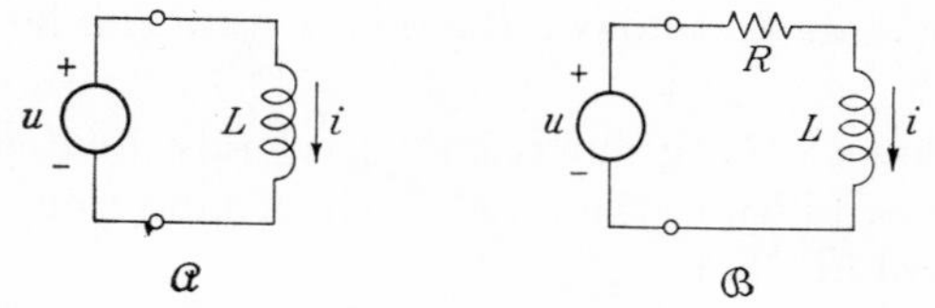

Fig. 2.8.2 $\mathcal{A}$ has zero state but not ground state; $\mathcal{B}$ has both zero state and ground state.

flowing through L. Thus, $s(t) = i(t)$. For system $\mathcal{A}$, the relation between $s(t)$ and $u(t)$ is

$$u = L\frac{ds}{dt}$$

Integrating this equation between t_0 and t, we obtain the state equation

10 $$s(t) = s(t_0) + \frac{1}{L}\int_{t_0}^{t} u(\xi)\, d\xi$$

which for the input $u(t) \equiv 0$ reduces to

11 $$s(t) = s(t_0) = \text{initial current through } L,\ t > t_0$$

Correspondingly, for system $\mathcal{B}$ we have

$$u = Rs + L\frac{ds}{dt}$$

which upon integration yields

12 $$s(t) = e^{-(R/L)(t-t_0)}s(t_0) + \frac{1}{L}\int_{t_0}^{t} e^{-(R/L)(t-\xi)}u(\xi)\,d\xi$$

and which for the zero input reduces to

13 $$s(t) = e^{-(R/L)(t-t_0)}s(t_0)$$

Inspection of *11* and *13* shows that $\mathcal{A}$ does not have a gound state—even though $s(t)$ converges to $s(t_0)$ as $t \to \infty$ [in a trivial sense, of course, since $s(t)$ is a constant] because the limiting state depends on the initial state. On the other hand, if $R/L > 0$, then $\mathcal{B}$ does have a ground state, namely $\gamma = 0$, since $s(t) \to 0$ as $t \to \infty$ for all values of $s(t_0)$. Note that both $\mathcal{A}$ and $\mathcal{B}$ have a zero state, $\theta = 0$. Thus, $\mathcal{A}$ has a zero state but not a ground state, whereas $\mathcal{B}$ has both a zero state θ and a ground state γ, with $\theta = \gamma = 0$.

14 *Example* The system shown in Fig. *2.8.1* (see Example *6*), with $R > 0$, $L > 0$, $C > 0$, does not have a ground state. The reason is that all initial states of the form $(a,b,0)$, where a and b are real numbers, tend to the limiting state $(0,0,0)$ as $t \to \infty$. On the other hand, all initial states of the form $(a,b,1)$ tend to $(0,0,1)$. Since $(0,0,0) \not\approx (0,0,1)$, the limiting state depends on the initial state and hence is not a ground state. ◁

The notion of the ground state is closely related to the notion of asymptotic stability in the large. This connection will be discussed in greater detail in Chap. 7.

Equilibrium state

Another notion which frequently coincides in meaning with the notions of the ground state and the zero state is that of the *equilibrium state*. Roughly, $\mathbf{n}$ is an *equilibrium state* of $\mathcal{A}$ if it does not change when no input is applied to $\mathcal{A}$. More formally, we have the

15 **Definition** $\mathbf{n}$ is an *equilibrium state* of $\mathcal{A}$ if on application to $\mathcal{A}$ of the zero input, with $\mathcal{A}$ initially (at t_0) in state $\mathbf{n}$, $\mathbf{s}(t)$ remains equal to $\mathbf{n}$ for all $t \geq t_0$. In symbols,

$$\{\mathbf{n} \text{ is an equilibrium state of } \mathcal{A}\} \Leftrightarrow \{\mathbf{s}(\mathbf{n};\mathbf{0}) = \mathbf{n}, t \geq t_0\}$$

where $\mathbf{s}(\mathfrak{n};\mathbf{0})$ denotes the state of $\mathcal{A}$ at time t when the state of $\mathcal{A}$ at time t_0 is $\mathfrak{n}$ and the zero input is applied starting at t_0.

16 *Example* In system $\mathcal{A}$, Example *9*, 0 is the equilibrium state as well as the zero state but not the ground state. In system $\mathcal{B}$, Example *9*, 0 is the equilibrium state, the zero state, and the ground state. In the system of Example *6*, (0,0,0) and (0,0,1) are equilibrium states. (This shows that an equilibrium state need not be unique.)

17 *Exercise* Construct an example of a system which has an equilibrium state which is neither a zero state nor a ground state.

Zero-state, zero-input, and steady-state response

In later chapters we shall frequently be dealing with various special types of responses of $\mathcal{A}$. The more important of these are defined below.

18 **Definition** The *zero-state response* of $\mathcal{A}$ to $\mathbf{u}$ ($\mathbf{u} \triangleq \mathbf{u}_{(t_0,t]}$) is the response of $\mathcal{A}$ to $\mathbf{u}$ with $\mathcal{A}$ initially in its zero state $\boldsymbol{\theta}$. The zero-state response at time t is denoted by $\mathbf{A}(\boldsymbol{\theta};\mathbf{u})$ or, for short, $\mathbf{A}(\mathbf{u})$. Correspondingly, for response segments we shall use the notation $\bar{\mathbf{A}}(\boldsymbol{\theta};\mathbf{u})$ or $\bar{\mathbf{A}}(\mathbf{u})$.

19 **Definition** The *ground-state response* of $\mathcal{A}$ to $\mathbf{u}$ has the same meaning as the zero-state response, except that the initial state is $\boldsymbol{\gamma}$ (ground state) rather than $\boldsymbol{\theta}$. The ground-state response at time t is denoted by $\mathbf{A}(\boldsymbol{\gamma};\mathbf{u})$. ◁

An important type of response which can be conveniently defined in terms of the ground-state response is the *steady-state response.* Specifically,

20 **Definition** The *steady-state response* of $\mathcal{A}$ to an input $\mathbf{u}_{(t_0,t]}$ is denoted by $\mathbf{A}_\infty(\mathbf{u})$ and is defined by the limit, if it exists, of the ground-state response of $\mathcal{A}$ to $\mathbf{u}$ as $t_0 \to -\infty$.[1] In symbols,

21
$$\mathbf{A}_\infty(\mathbf{u}) = \lim_{t_0 \to -\infty} \mathbf{A}(\boldsymbol{\gamma};\mathbf{u}_{(t_0,t]})$$

22 *Example* Consider the system $\mathcal{B}$ of Example *9*, with $R = L = 1$, and assume that $u(t) = \sin t$, $-\infty < t < \infty$. Since $\boldsymbol{\gamma} = 0$, the steady-state response is given by

$$\begin{aligned} y(t) &= \lim_{t_0 \to -\infty} \int_{t_0}^{t} e^{-(t-\xi)} \sin \xi \, d\xi \\ &= \tfrac{1}{2} (\sin t - \cos t) \end{aligned}$$

Note that the same result obtains for any initial state $\boldsymbol{\alpha}$.

[1] Usually $\mathcal{A}$ and $\mathbf{u}$ are such that, in the right-hand member of *21*, $\boldsymbol{\gamma}$ can be replaced by an arbitrary initial state $\boldsymbol{\alpha}$ without affecting the limiting value of the response as $t_0 \to -\infty$.

23 **Definition** The response of $\mathcal{A}$ to a zero input, with $\mathcal{A}$ initially in state $\mathbf{s}(t_0) = \boldsymbol{\alpha}$, is the *zero-input response* of $\mathcal{A}$ *starting in state* $\boldsymbol{\alpha}$. The zero-input response at time t is denoted by $\mathbf{A}(\boldsymbol{\alpha};\mathbf{0})$, with the corresponding response segment denoted by $\bar{\mathbf{A}}(\boldsymbol{\alpha};\mathbf{0})$. [If it is necessary to place in evidence the observation interval, the notation $\bar{\mathbf{A}}(\boldsymbol{\alpha};\mathbf{0}_{(t_0,t]})$ may be employed.]

24 *Example* The zero-input response of the system $\mathcal{B}$ of Example *9*, with $R = L = 1$, is expressed by

$$\mathbf{A}(\alpha;\mathbf{0}) = \alpha e^{-(t-t_0)} \qquad t > t_0$$

9 *Zero-state and zero-input equivalence*

There are two special types of system equivalence which will be encountered frequently in later chapters. One is the *zero-state equivalence* and the other is *zero-input equivalence.* These terms are defined below.

1 **Definition** $\mathcal{A}$ and $\mathcal{B}$ are *zero-state equivalent,* written $\mathcal{A} \doteq \mathcal{B}$, if to every zero state of $\mathcal{A}$ there corresponds an equivalent zero state of $\mathcal{B}$, and vice versa. ◁

In most of the cases with which we shall deal, $\mathcal{A}$ and $\mathcal{B}$ will have unique zero states (to within equivalent states) which will be denoted by $\boldsymbol{\theta}_a$ and $\boldsymbol{\theta}_b$, respectively. Then

$$\{\mathcal{A} \doteq \mathcal{B}\} \Leftrightarrow \{\boldsymbol{\theta}_a \simeq \boldsymbol{\theta}_b\}$$

2 **Definition** $\mathcal{A}$ and $\mathcal{B}$ are *zero-input equivalent* if to every state $\boldsymbol{\alpha}$ in $\mathcal{A}$ there corresponds a state $\boldsymbol{\beta}$ in $\mathcal{B}$, and vice versa, such that

$$\bar{\mathbf{A}}(\boldsymbol{\alpha};\mathbf{0}) = \bar{\mathbf{B}}(\boldsymbol{\beta};\mathbf{0}) \qquad \forall t_0 \forall t$$

That is, the zero-input responses of $\mathcal{A}$ and $\mathcal{B}$ starting in states $\boldsymbol{\alpha}$ and $\boldsymbol{\beta}$, respectively, are identical over all observation intervals $(t_0,t]$. ◁

The nature of these definitions suggests that two systems may be zero-state or zero-input equivalent without being equivalent in the more general sense of Definition *2.5.8*. Since this point will be discussed in detail in Chap. *3*, we confine ourselves at this juncture to a simple

3 *Example* Consider the two networks shown in Fig. *2.9.1*. Here the state space of $\mathcal{A}$ consists of a single element denoted by (1) (see *1.8.17*), while the state of $\mathcal{B}$ at time t is a 2-vector $\mathbf{s}(t) = (s_1(t),s_2(t))$ (see

1.7.28) whose components are $s_1(t)$ [$\triangleq i_L(t)$] and $s_2(t)$ [$\triangleq v_C(t)$], where $i_L(t)$ and $v_C(t)$ are respectively the current through the inductor and the voltage across the capacitor. The ground state (as well as the zero state of $\mathcal{A}$) is (1), while that of $\mathcal{B}$ is (0,0).

Now $\mathcal{B}$ is readily recognized to be a constant-resistance network (with constant input impedance of 1 ohm). This means that if $\mathcal{B}$ is initially (at t_0) in its zero state, then for an arbitrary input u the relation $y(t) = u(t)$ holds for all $t \geq t_0$. This in turn implies that $\mathcal{A}$ and $\mathcal{B}$ are zero-state equivalent.

On the other hand, $\mathcal{A}$ and $\mathcal{B}$ are not equivalent. To demonstrate this, it is sufficient to exhibit a state of $\mathcal{B}$ and an input u such that the

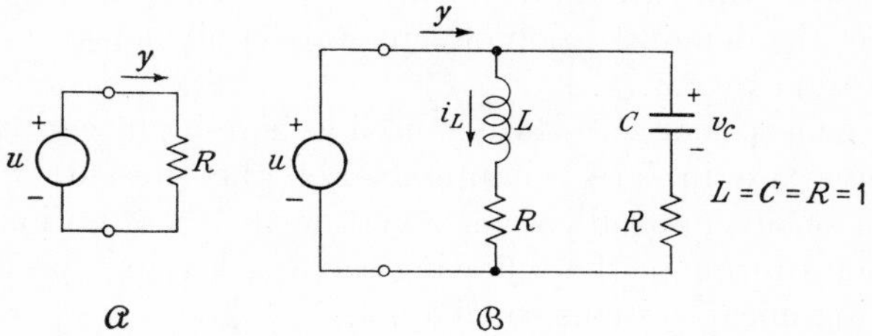

Fig. 2.9.1 $\mathcal{A}$ and $\mathcal{B}$ are zero-state equivalent although $\mathcal{A}$ and $\mathcal{B}$ are not equivalent.

response of $\mathcal{B}$ to u starting in this state is not identical with the response of $\mathcal{A}$ to u starting in state (1). Take u to be the zero input and let the initial state of $\mathcal{B}$ be $(0,-1)$. By using elementary circuit analysis techniques, the corresponding output current is readily found to be given by

$$y(t) = e^{-(t-t_0)} \qquad t \geq t_0$$

whereas in the case of $\mathcal{A}$ the corresponding output current is 0. This proves that $\mathcal{A}$ and $\mathcal{B}$ are not equivalent.

4 *Comment* The above example illustrates a general property of linear time-invariant systems which will be stated in Chap. *3*, Sec. *6*. Although we have not yet given formal definitions of some of the terms in which this property is formulated, it will be helpful to have it stated at this point, without taking the time and space to define formally the terms with which the reader is certain to have prior familiarity.

Briefly, let $\mathcal{A}$ and $\mathcal{B}$ denote linear time-invariant systems with transfer functions $H_a(s)$ and $H_b(s)$, respectively, where $s \triangleq$ complex frequency. Then $\mathcal{A}$ and $\mathcal{B}$ are zero-state equivalent if and only if $H_a(s) = H_b(s)$ for all s. For example, in Example *3* the transfer function of $\mathcal{A}$ is 1 and that of $\mathcal{B}$ is s/s, which is also 1. Thus, $\mathcal{A}$ and $\mathcal{B}$ are zero-state equivalent. It is important to note, however, that if $\mathcal{A}$ and $\mathcal{B}$ have identical transfer functions, it does not necessarily follow that $\mathcal{A}$ and $\mathcal{B}$ are equivalent in the sense of Definition *2.5.8*.

5 **Remark** Although zero-state equivalence of $\mathcal{A}$ and $\mathcal{B}$ does not imply equivalence of $\mathcal{A}$ and $\mathcal{B}$, it does imply more than just equivalence between a state of $\mathcal{A}$ and a state of $\mathcal{B}$. Specifically, it implies that $\mathcal{A}$ and $\mathcal{B}$ are conditionally equivalent in the sense of Definition *2.7.5*. Furthermore, by Corollary *2.7.4*, if $\mathcal{A} \doteq \mathcal{B}$ and all the states in the state spaces of $\mathcal{A}$ and $\mathcal{B}$ are reachable from $\boldsymbol{\theta}_a$ and $\boldsymbol{\theta}_b$, respectively, then $\mathcal{A} \equiv \mathcal{B}$.

6 *Example* The systems $\mathcal{A}$ and $\mathcal{B}$ of Example *2.5.15* have the property that all states in $\Sigma_a = \Sigma_b = \mathcal{R}^2$ are reachable from the zero state $\boldsymbol{\theta}_a = \boldsymbol{\theta}_b = (0,0)$. (This is established in a general way in Chapter *11*.) Note that in this case the verification of the equivalence $\mathcal{A} \equiv \mathcal{B}$ involves in effect the demonstration of zero-state equivalence of $\mathcal{A}$ and $\mathcal{B}$, which is expressed by *2.5.18*.

The concepts of zero-state as well as zero-input equivalence will find extensive use in later chapters. For the present, we turn to the notions of inverse and converse systems. These notions are discussed in general terms in the following section, leaving specific applications involving linear systems to Chap. *4*.

10 *Inverse and converse systems*

The concepts of inverse and converse systems are closely related to one another, with the latter being somewhat more general. We begin with the

1 **Definition** $\mathcal{A}$ and $\mathcal{B}$ are *converse systems* if every input-output pair $(\mathbf{u},\mathbf{y})$ for $\mathcal{A}$ has the property that $(\mathbf{y},\mathbf{u})$ (with $\mathbf{y}$ as input and $\mathbf{u}$ as output) is an input-output pair for $\mathcal{B}$, and vice versa.

2 *Example* Let $\mathcal{A}$ (an integrator) and $\mathcal{B}$ (a differentiator) be characterized by the input-output relations

3 $\mathcal{A}$: $$\frac{dy}{dt} = u$$

4 $\mathcal{B}$: $$y = \frac{du}{dt}$$

Clearly, $\mathcal{A}$ and $\mathcal{B}$ are converse systems. For example, $(2t,t^2)$, $t \geq t_0$, is an input-output pair for $\mathcal{A}$ and $(t^2,2t)$, $t \geq t_0$, is an input-output pair for $\mathcal{B}$; more generally, for any v in the input function space of $\mathcal{A}$, $(\dot{v},v)$ is an input-output pair for $\mathcal{A}$ and $(v,\dot{v})$ is an input-output pair for $\mathcal{B}$. Note that if $\mathcal{A}$ and $\mathcal{B}$ are converse systems, then the input function space of $\mathcal{A}$ is the output function space of $\mathcal{B}$ and, conversely, the input function space of $\mathcal{B}$ is the output function space of $\mathcal{A}$.

5 *Comment* In effect, converse systems can be regarded as opposite orientations of an object. Thus, with reference to Example *2*, let $\mathcal{C}$ be a nonoriented object characterized by the terminal relation

$$\frac{dv_2}{dt} = v_1$$

Then $\mathcal{A}$ is the result of orienting $\mathcal{C}$ by designating v_1 as the input and v_2 as the output, while $\mathcal{B}$ results from the opposite designation of v_2 as the input and v_1 as the output.

Another significant point which comes to light in Example *2* is that the state of $\mathcal{A}$ at time t has the same meaning as the state of $\mathcal{B}$ at time t, viz., in both cases $s(t)$ is $v_2(t)$. This is a special instance of a general property of linear differential systems which will be established in Chap. *4* (*4.4.27*), to the effect that the state of such systems is independent of the orientation. ◁

Looked upon from another point of view, $\mathcal{A}$ and $\mathcal{B}$ are converse systems if, roughly speaking, $\mathcal{A}$ is capable of "undoing" whatever $\mathcal{B}$ is capable of doing to its input, and vice versa. This idea is embodied in a more specific form in the concept of inverse systems which is defined below.

6 **Definition** Let $\mathcal{A}$ and $\mathcal{B}$ be characterized by input-output-state relations of the form

7 $\mathcal{A}$: $$\mathbf{y} = \bar{\mathbf{A}}(\boldsymbol{\alpha};\mathbf{u}) \qquad \boldsymbol{\alpha} \in \Sigma_a$$

8 $\mathcal{B}$: $$\mathbf{w} = \bar{\mathbf{B}}(\boldsymbol{\beta};\mathbf{v}) \qquad \boldsymbol{\beta} \in \Sigma_b$$

where $\mathbf{u}$ and $\mathbf{v}$ denote input segments to $\mathcal{A}$ and $\mathcal{B}$, respectively, and $\mathbf{y}$ and $\mathbf{w}$ represent the corresponding output segments. (The input function space of $\mathcal{A}$ is assumed to be the output function space of $\mathcal{B}$, and conversely.) Then $\mathcal{A}$ and $\mathcal{B}$ are *inverse systems* (or $\mathcal{A}$ *is inverse to* $\mathcal{B}$ or $\mathcal{A}$ *is inverse of* $\mathcal{B}$) if and only if to every state $\boldsymbol{\alpha}$ of $\mathcal{A}$ there is a state $\boldsymbol{\beta}_{\alpha}$ of $\mathcal{B}$ such that

9 $$\bar{\mathbf{B}}(\boldsymbol{\beta}_{\alpha};\bar{\mathbf{A}}(\boldsymbol{\alpha};\mathbf{u})) = \mathbf{u} \qquad \forall \mathbf{u}$$

and conversely to every state $\boldsymbol{\beta}$ of $\mathcal{B}$ there corresponds a state $\boldsymbol{\alpha}_{\beta}$ of $\mathcal{A}$ such that

10 $$\bar{\mathbf{A}}(\boldsymbol{\alpha}_{\beta};\bar{\mathbf{B}}(\boldsymbol{\beta};\mathbf{v})) = \mathbf{v} \qquad \forall \mathbf{v}$$

If $\mathcal{A}$ is inverse to $\mathcal{B}$, it is denoted by $\mathcal{B}^{-1}$, and conversely, $\mathcal{B}$ is denoted by $\mathcal{A}^{-1}$. Correspondingly, $\boldsymbol{\beta}_{\alpha}$ is denoted by $\boldsymbol{\alpha}^{-1}$. $\mathcal{A}$ will be said to be *invertible* if it has an inverse.

Note that it follows from this definition that if *9* and *10* are satisfied with the states $\boldsymbol{\alpha}$, $\boldsymbol{\beta}_\alpha$ and $\boldsymbol{\beta}$, $\boldsymbol{\alpha}_\beta$, respectively, then they are also satisfied with the states $\boldsymbol{\alpha}_\beta$, $\boldsymbol{\beta}$ and $\boldsymbol{\beta}_\alpha$, $\boldsymbol{\alpha}$.

11 *Example* Consider two systems $\mathcal{A}$ and $\mathcal{B}$ which are characterized by the input-output relations

12 $\mathcal{A}$: $$\frac{dy}{dt} + y = u$$

13 $\mathcal{B}$: $$w = \frac{dv}{dt} + v$$

Note that in the case of $\mathcal{A}$, the scalar $y(t)$, representing the output at time t, qualifies as the state of $\mathcal{A}$ at time t, that is, $s(t) = y(t)$. The state space of $\mathcal{A}$ is the real line $\Sigma_a = \mathcal{R}^1 = (-\infty, \infty)$.

On the other hand, in the case of $\mathcal{B}$, it is the input at time t, $v(t)$, that qualifies as $s(t)$ (see *1.7.10*). This is consistent with Comment *5*.

The input-output-state relations for $\mathcal{A}$ and $\mathcal{B}$ read (see *1.9.10* and *1.7.10*)

14 $\mathcal{A}$: $$y(t) = y(t_0-)e^{-(t-t_0)} + \int_{t_0}^{t} e^{-(t-\xi)}u(\xi)\, d\xi \qquad t \geq t_0$$

15 $\mathcal{B}$: $$w(t) = \frac{dv}{dt} + v - v(t_0-)\delta(t - t_0) \qquad t \geq t_0$$

Denote $y(t_0-)$ and $v(t_0-)$ by α and β, respectively. Then it is easy to verify (see Appendix A) that

16 $$B(\beta;A(\alpha;u)) = u(t) + (\alpha - \beta)\delta(t - t_0)$$

and

17 $$A(\alpha;B(\beta;u)) = v(t) + \alpha - \beta$$

Thus, *9* and *10* are satisfied with $\alpha = \beta$. This establishes that $\mathcal{A}$ and $\mathcal{B}$ are inverse systems. More generally, this same result can be established for any pair of systems which are obtained through opposite orientation of a linear differential system (see *4.4.44*). Thus, the systems $\mathcal{A}$ and $\mathcal{B}$ of Example *11* illustrate merely a special instance of this general property. [Note that *16* and *17* express the outputs of the free products (*1.10.10*) $\mathcal{B}\mathcal{A}$ and $\mathcal{A}\mathcal{B}$, respectively.]

What is the relation between the notions of converse and inverse systems? In the case of Example *11*, $\mathcal{A}$ and $\mathcal{B}$ are both converse and inverse systems. More generally, it is evident from *6* that if $\mathcal{A}$ and $\mathcal{B}$ are inverse systems, then they are also converse systems. The reverse implication, however, is not necessarily true. Specifically, from inspection of Definition *1* it is clear that to say that $\mathcal{A}$ and $\mathcal{B}$ are converse systems is the same as saying that to every input $\mathbf{u}$ and every state $\boldsymbol{\alpha}$ of $\mathcal{A}$ there corresponds a state $\boldsymbol{\beta}_{\alpha,\mathbf{u}}$ of $\mathcal{B}$ such that *9* holds, and conversely. Thus, the crux of the difference between Definition *1* and Definition *6* is that in the former $\boldsymbol{\beta}$ may depend on both $\boldsymbol{\alpha}$ and $\mathbf{u}$, whereas in the latter $\boldsymbol{\beta}$ depends only on $\boldsymbol{\alpha}$. (The same statement applies to the dependence of $\boldsymbol{\alpha}$ on $\boldsymbol{\beta}$ and $\mathbf{v}$.)

The difference between the case where $\boldsymbol{\beta}$ depends on $\boldsymbol{\alpha}$ alone and the case where $\boldsymbol{\beta}$ depends on both $\boldsymbol{\alpha}$ and $\mathbf{u}$ is essentially the difference between weak equivalence and equivalence (see *2.5.4* and *2.5.8*). As will be established in Chap. *3*, Sec. *9*, linear differential systems have the basic property that if $\mathcal{A}$ and $\mathcal{B}$ are weakly equivalent, then $\mathcal{A}$ and $\mathcal{B}$ are equivalent. Thus if $\mathcal{A}$ and $\mathcal{B}$ are linear differential systems, then the statement "$\mathcal{A}$ and $\mathcal{B}$ are inverse systems" implies and *is implied by* the statement "$\mathcal{A}$ and $\mathcal{B}$ are converse systems."

What can be said about inverse systems which are connected in tandem, as in Fig. *2.10.1*, or in reverse order? Here $\mathcal{A}^{-1}$ denotes the inverse of $\mathcal{A}$ and $\boldsymbol{\alpha}^{-1}$ represents the state $\boldsymbol{\beta}_{\alpha}$ of Definition *6*.

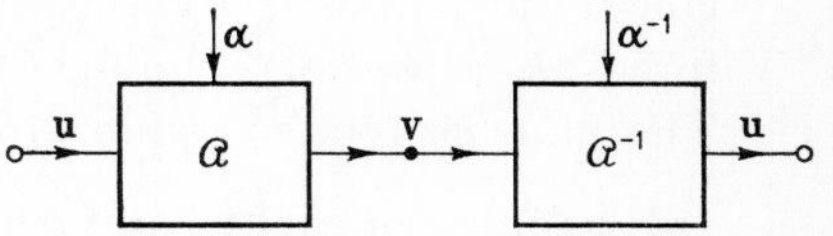

Fig. 2.10.1 Illustration of the notion of inverse.

If we restrict the initial states of the product $\mathcal{A}\mathcal{A}^{-1}$ and $\mathcal{A}^{-1}\mathcal{A}$ to states of the form $(\boldsymbol{\alpha},\boldsymbol{\alpha}^{-1})$ (note that such states form a closed set in the product space $\Sigma_a \times \Sigma_b$, where Σ_b denotes the state space of $\mathcal{A}^{-1}$), then Definition *6* implies that the systems $\mathcal{A}\mathcal{A}^{-1}$ and $\mathcal{A}^{-1}\mathcal{A}$ are equivalent to a unitor (*1.9.8*), that is, $\mathcal{A}\mathcal{A}^{-1} \equiv \mathcal{A}^{-1}\mathcal{A} \equiv I$. Conversely, if $\mathcal{A}\mathcal{A}^{-1} \equiv \mathcal{A}^{-1}\mathcal{A} \equiv I$, then it is clear that $\mathcal{A}$ and $\mathcal{A}^{-1}$ satisfy the conditions of Definition *6*. Thus, we can make the

18 **Assertion** $\{\mathcal{A}$ and $\mathcal{A}^{-1}$ are inverse systems$\} \Leftrightarrow \{\mathcal{A}\mathcal{A}^{-1} \overset{*}{=} \mathcal{A}^{-1}\mathcal{A} \overset{*}{=} I\}$ with the understanding that the initial states of $\mathcal{A}\mathcal{A}^{-1}$ and $\mathcal{A}^{-1}\mathcal{A}$ are restricted to states of the form $(\boldsymbol{\alpha},\boldsymbol{\alpha}^{-1})$, where $\boldsymbol{\alpha}$ is an arbitrary state of $\mathcal{A}$ and $\boldsymbol{\alpha}^{-1}$ is its correspondent in $\mathcal{A}^{-1}$ (see *6*). We use the symbol $\overset{*}{=}$ rather than $\equiv$ in *18* to stress that the equivalence in question is conditional in the sense of *2.7.5*.

19 *Example* In Example *11*, α^{-1} is a scalar numerically equal to α. Thus, for any initial state of the form (α,α), *16* and *17* give the following:

$$\bar{A}^{-1}(\alpha^{-1};\bar{A}(\alpha;u)) = u$$
$$\bar{A}(\alpha;\bar{A}^{-1}(\alpha^{-1};v)) = v$$

which is consistent with *18*. $\triangleleft$

Assertion *18* provides a partial answer to the question of what happens when $\mathcal{A}$ and $\mathcal{A}^{-1}$ are connected in tandem, in the sense that it shows that if $\mathcal{A}$ and $\mathcal{A}^{-1}$ are started in the respective states α and α^{-1}, then $\mathcal{A}\mathcal{A}^{-1}$ and $\mathcal{A}^{-1}\mathcal{A}$ are conditionally equivalent to a unitor. However, this question remains: Under what conditions is the product $\mathcal{A}\mathcal{A}^{-1}$ (or $\mathcal{A}^{-1}\mathcal{A}$) equivalent to I unconditionally?

It is easy to construct examples of systems which have this property in one direction only, i.e., are such that either $\mathcal{A}\mathcal{A}^{-1} \equiv I$ or $\mathcal{A}^{-1}\mathcal{A} \equiv I$ but not both simultaneously. This suggests the following

20 **Definition** $\mathcal{A}_r^{-1}$ is a *right-constrained* inverse of $\mathcal{A}$ if $\mathcal{A}_r^{-1}$ is inverse to $\mathcal{A}$ and, in addition,

21
$$\mathcal{A}\mathcal{A}_r^{-1} \equiv I$$

Similarly, $\mathcal{A}_l^{-1}$ is a *left-constrained* inverse of $\mathcal{A}$ if $\mathcal{A}_l^{-1}$ is inverse to $\mathcal{A}$ and, in addition,

22
$$\mathcal{A}_l^{-1}\mathcal{A} \equiv I$$

The adjective "constrained" serves to indicate that $\mathcal{A}_r^{-1}$, say, and $\mathcal{A}$ have the property that, when $\mathcal{A}_r^{-1}$ and $\mathcal{A}$ are connected in tandem, the constraint imposed by the interconnection (see *2.6.8*) automatically forces the states of $\mathcal{A}_r^{-1}$ and $\mathcal{A}$ to be the corresponding states α^{-1} and α. The same statement applies to $\mathcal{A}_l^{-1}$. ◁

Examples of right- and left-constrained inverses will be given in Chap. *4*, Sec. *4*. At this point, it will suffice to point out that a differentiator is a left-constrained inverse of an integrator but not vice versa. This is a special instance of a more general result which is stated in Chap. *4* (*4.4.44*).

Further properties of inverse systems

From the defining relations *9* and *10* it is a simple matter to deduce several basic properties of $\mathcal{A}^{-1}$. For convenient reference, we state them below in the form of assertions.

23 **Assertion** If $\mathcal{A}^{-1}$ exists, then it is unique (to within equivalent systems).
Proof Let $\mathcal{A}_1^{-1}$ and $\mathcal{A}_2^{-1}$ be inverse to $\mathcal{A}$. Assume that an input $\mathbf{u}$ is applied to $\mathcal{A}_1^{-1}$ starting in state $\boldsymbol{\alpha}_1^{-1}$ and that the corresponding response is $\mathbf{v}$. By *9*, there exists a state, say $\boldsymbol{\alpha}_1$, of $\mathcal{A}$ such that the response of $\mathcal{A}$ to $\mathbf{v}$ starting in state $\boldsymbol{\alpha}_1$ is $\mathbf{u}$. Now by *10*, there exists a state, say $\boldsymbol{\alpha}_2^{-1}$, of $\mathcal{A}_2^{-1}$ such that the response of $\mathcal{A}_2^{-1}$ to $\mathbf{u}$ starting in state $\boldsymbol{\alpha}_2^{-1}$ is $\mathbf{v}$. Since this is true for all $\mathbf{u}$, it follows that to every state of $\mathcal{A}_1^{-1}$ there is an equivalent state of $\mathcal{A}_2^{-1}$. Similar argument shows that to every state of $\mathcal{A}_2^{-1}$ there is an equivalent state of $\mathcal{A}_1^{-1}$. Consequently, $\mathcal{A}_1^{-1}$ and $\mathcal{A}_2^{-1}$ are equivalent in the sense of Definition *2.5.8*.

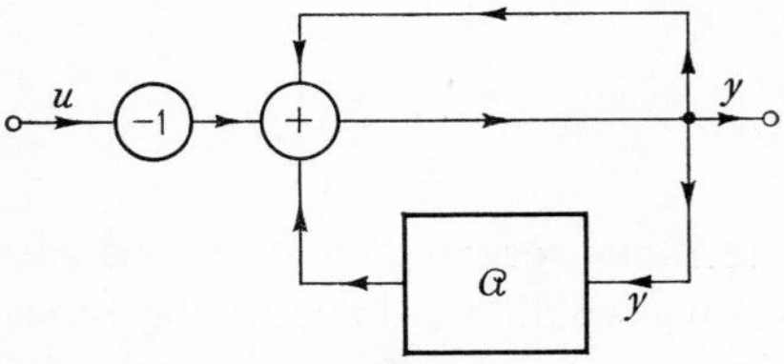

Fig. 2.10.2 Realization of the inverse of $\mathcal{A}$.

24 *Comment* It is of interest to note that the inverse of $\mathcal{A}$, if it exists, can be synthesized in the form of an interconnection of $\mathcal{A}$, an adder, and a scalor with scale factor -1, as shown in Fig. *2.10.2*. We leave it to the reader to verify that the system in question is equivalent to $\mathcal{A}^{-1}$.

25 **Assertion** If $\mathcal{A}$ is invertible and the response of $\mathcal{A}$ to an input $\mathbf{u}_1$ starting in any state $\boldsymbol{\alpha}$ is identical with the response of $\mathcal{A}$ to an input $\mathbf{u}_2$ starting in $\boldsymbol{\alpha}$, then $\mathbf{u}_1$ must be identical with $\mathbf{u}_2$. In symbols,

26 $$\{\bar{\mathbf{A}}(\boldsymbol{\alpha};\mathbf{u}_1) = \bar{\mathbf{A}}(\boldsymbol{\alpha};\mathbf{u}_2)\} \Rightarrow \{\mathbf{u}_1 = \mathbf{u}_2\} \qquad \forall \boldsymbol{\alpha}$$

for any $\mathbf{u}_1$ and $\mathbf{u}_2$ in the input segment space of $\mathcal{A}$.

This means that for each $\boldsymbol{\alpha}$ in the state space of $\mathcal{A}$, $\bar{\mathbf{A}}(\boldsymbol{\alpha};\mathbf{u})$ defines a one-one correspondence between the input segment space and the output segment space of $\mathcal{A}$.

Proof By Definition *6*, there exists a state $\boldsymbol{\alpha}^{-1}$ in $\mathcal{A}^{-1}$ such that

$$\bar{\mathbf{A}}^{-1}(\boldsymbol{\alpha}^{-1};\bar{\mathbf{A}}(\boldsymbol{\alpha};\mathbf{u}_1)) = \mathbf{u}_1 \qquad \text{and} \qquad \bar{\mathbf{A}}^{-1}(\boldsymbol{\alpha}^{-1};\bar{\mathbf{A}}(\boldsymbol{\alpha};\mathbf{u}_2)) = \mathbf{u}_2$$

and hence $\mathbf{u}_1 = \mathbf{u}_2$ by virtue of *26*.

27 **Assertion** If $\mathcal{A}$ has a unique zero state $\boldsymbol{\theta}$ and $\mathcal{A}^{-1}$ exists, then $\mathcal{A}^{-1}$ also has a unique zero state.

Proof From the definition of $\mathcal{A}^{-1}$, it follows that to the zero state $\boldsymbol{\theta}$ in $\mathcal{A}$ there corresponds a state, call it $\boldsymbol{\theta}^{-1}$, in $\mathcal{A}^{-1}$ such that

28 $$\bar{\mathbf{A}}^{-1}(\boldsymbol{\theta}^{-1};\bar{\mathbf{A}}(\boldsymbol{\theta};\mathbf{0})) = \mathbf{0}$$

Therefore $\boldsymbol{\theta}^{-1}$ is a zero state of $\mathcal{A}^{-1}$.

Next, suppose that $\mathcal{A}^{-1}$ has nonequivalent zero states, say $\boldsymbol{\theta}_1^{-1}$ and $\boldsymbol{\theta}_2^{-1}$. Then there exists a distinguishing input (see *2.2.3*), say, $\mathbf{v}$, such that

29 $$\mathbf{u}_1 = \bar{\mathbf{A}}^{-1}(\boldsymbol{\theta}_1^{-1};\mathbf{v}) \neq \bar{\mathbf{A}}^{-1}(\boldsymbol{\theta}_2^{-1};\mathbf{v}) \triangleq \mathbf{u}_2$$

But, by the definition of $\mathcal{A}^{-1}$ we must have

$$\bar{\mathbf{A}}(\boldsymbol{\theta};\mathbf{u}_1) = \bar{\mathbf{A}}(\boldsymbol{\theta};\mathbf{u}_2) = \mathbf{v}$$

which by Assertion *25* implies that $\mathbf{u}_1 = \mathbf{u}_2$. This contradicts *29* and hence proves the assertion.

30 **Assertion** If $\mathcal{A}^{-1}$ and $\mathcal{B}^{-1}$ exist, then

$$\{\mathcal{A} \equiv \mathcal{B}\} \Rightarrow \{\mathcal{A}^{-1} \equiv \mathcal{B}^{-1}\}$$

Proof Let $\mathbf{u}$ be the response of $\mathcal{A}^{-1}$ to $\mathbf{y}$ starting in state $\boldsymbol{\alpha}^{-1}$. By *10*, there exists a state $\boldsymbol{\alpha}$ of $\mathcal{A}$ such that the response of $\mathcal{A}$ to $\mathbf{u}$ starting in state $\boldsymbol{\alpha}$ is $\mathbf{y}$. Since $\mathcal{A} \equiv \mathcal{B}$, there exists a state $\boldsymbol{\beta}$ of $\mathcal{B}$ such that the response of $\mathcal{B}$ to $\mathbf{u}$ starting in state $\boldsymbol{\beta}$ is $\mathbf{y}$. Furthermore, by *9* there exists a state $\boldsymbol{\beta}^{-1}$ of $\mathcal{B}^{-1}$ such that the response of $\mathcal{B}^{-1}$ to $\mathbf{y}$ starting in state $\boldsymbol{\beta}^{-1}$ is $\mathbf{u}$. Consequently, to every state $\boldsymbol{\alpha}^{-1}$ of $\mathcal{A}$ there corresponds an equivalent state $\boldsymbol{\beta}^{-1}$ of $\mathcal{B}^{-1}$. By a similar argument, to every state $\boldsymbol{\beta}^{-1}$ of $\mathcal{B}^{-1}$ there corresponds an equivalent state $\boldsymbol{\alpha}^{-1}$ of $\mathcal{A}^{-1}$, and hence by Definition *2.5.8* $\mathcal{A}^{-1}$ and $\mathcal{B}^{-1}$ are equivalent systems.

31 **Assertion** If $\mathcal{A}^{-1}$ and $\mathcal{B}^{-1}$ exist and the product $\mathcal{A}\mathcal{B}$ is defined (see *1.10.23*), then

32 $$(\mathcal{A}\mathcal{B})^{-1} \equiv \mathcal{B}^{-1}\mathcal{A}^{-1}$$

Proof Exercise for the reader. (*Caution:* Note that the state space of $\mathcal{A}\mathcal{B}$ is not, in general, the product of the state spaces of $\mathcal{A}$ and $\mathcal{B}$.)

33 *Exercise* Construct a nontrivial example of a system which is its own inverse.

34 *Exercise* Show that $(\mathcal{A}^{-1})^{-1} \equiv \mathcal{A}$. ◁

In this as well as the preceding sections in this chapter we have presented and discussed in general terms such basic concepts as state equivalence, system equivalence, and inverse systems. Although we have illustrated the meaning of these notions with examples, their generality and abstractness may have made it somewhat difficult for the reader to concretize them in his own mind in terms of objects, devices, and concepts with which he is familiar. This is what should be expected at the present stage of our exposition. It is through the frequent use of the concepts in question in later chapters that the reader will eventually gain a clear understanding of the motivation behind them and the ways in which they can be applied to the analysis of linear systems.

REFERENCES AND SUGGESTED READING

1 Church, A.: "Introduction to Mathematical Logic," Princeton University Press, Princeton, N.J., 1956.

2 Kleene, S. C.: "Introduction to Metamathematics," D. Van Nostrand Company, Inc., Princeton, N.J., 1952.

3 Moore, E. F.: Gedanken Experiments on Sequential Machines, in "Automata Studies," Princeton University Press, Princeton, N.J., 1956.

4 Huffman, D.: The Synthesis of Sequential Switching Circuits, *J. Franklin Inst.*, vol. 257, pp. 161–190, 1954.

5 Birkhoff, G., and G. Rota: "Ordinary Differential Equations," Ginn and Company, Boston, 1962.

6 Coddington, E. A., and N. Levinson: "Theory of Ordinary Differential Equations," McGraw-Hill Book Company, Inc., New York, 1955.

7 Bellman, R.: "Adaptive Control Processes," Princeton University Press, Princeton, N.J., 1961.

8 Nemytskii, V. V., and V. V. Stepanov: "Qualitative Theory of Differential Equations," Princeton University Press, Princeton, N.J., 1960.

9 Birkhoff, G. D.: Dynamical Systems, *Amer. Math. Soc. Colloq. Publ.*, vol. 9, 1927.

10 Kalman, R. E.: On the General Theory of Control Systems, *Proc. First Intl. Cong. Automatic Cont., Moscow*, 1960, vol. 1, pp. 481–493, 1961, Butterworth & Co. (Publishers), Ltd., London.

Linearity and time invariance

3

1 *Introduction*

Like everything else, systems can be classified in a variety of ways according to their different properties. However, the more important modes of classification in system theory are dichotomies in the sense that they involve but two categories, say C and C', with C comprising all systems which have a specified property P and C' being the complement of C relative to the class of all systems. For example, in the case of the classification into linear and nonlinear systems, P is the property of *linearity* (which will be defined later in the chapter), C is the class of all *linear* systems, and C' is the class of all systems which are not linear, that is, are *nonlinear*.[1]

In the sequel, we shall focus our attention on two dichotomous modes of classification which play a particularly important role in system theory. These are summarized in the following table. As a

P	C	C'
Linearity	Linear systems	Nonlinear systems
Time invariance	Time-invariant systems	Time-varying (time-variant) systems

preliminary to defining the notions of linearity and time invariance, we begin with a brief

[1] In the literature the term "nonlinear" is sometimes used in such a broad sense that the class of nonlinear systems becomes virtually identical with the class of all systems. In this sense, the class of linear systems is merely a subclass of the class of nonlinear systems.

Recapitulation of terminology and notation

Symbols such as $\mathcal{A}$, $\mathcal{B}$, and $\mathcal{C}$ denote oriented systems. When dealing with a single system $\mathcal{A}$, its input, output, state, and state space are denoted by $\mathbf{u}$, $\mathbf{y}$, $\boldsymbol{\alpha}$, and Σ, respectively.[1] The symbol $\mathbf{s}(t)$ denotes the state of $\mathcal{A}$ at time t, and $\mathcal{A}$ is assumed to be characterized by an input-output-state relation

$$\mathbf{y}(t) = \mathbf{A}(\boldsymbol{\alpha};\mathbf{u})$$

which expresses the output at time t as a function of the initial state $\mathbf{s}(t_0) = \boldsymbol{\alpha}$ and the input segment $\mathbf{u} \triangleq \mathbf{u}_{(t_0,t]}$. In the above equation, $\boldsymbol{\alpha}$ ranges over the state space Σ and $\mathbf{u}$ ranges over the input segment space $R[\mathbf{u}]$ (see Remark *1.4.3* and Definitions *1.4.17* and *1.4.26*). When the left member of the input-output-state relation is the response segment $\mathbf{y} \triangleq \mathbf{y}_{(t_0,t]}$ rather than $\mathbf{y}(t)$, the input-output-state relation is written as

$$\mathbf{y} = \bar{\mathbf{A}}(\boldsymbol{\alpha};\mathbf{u})$$

It is understood that $\mathbf{u}$ and $\mathbf{y}$ are defined on the same observation interval and that $\boldsymbol{\alpha}$ is the state of $\mathcal{A}$ at the beginning of $\mathbf{u}$. If $\mathbf{u}$ vanishes for all $t \geq t_0$, it is said to be a zero input and is denoted by $\mathbf{0}$. The same thing applies to $\mathbf{y}$ and, more generally, to any time function $\mathbf{f}$.

If $\bar{\mathbf{A}}(\boldsymbol{\alpha};\mathbf{0}) = \mathbf{0}$, then $\boldsymbol{\alpha}$ is said to be a zero state of $\mathcal{A}$. Unless stated to the contrary, it is assumed that $\mathcal{A}$ has a unique zero state which is denoted by $\boldsymbol{\theta}$. The response segment of $\mathcal{A}$ to $\mathbf{u}$ when $\mathcal{A}$ is initially in its zero state is referred to as the zero-state response of $\mathcal{A}$ and is denoted by $\bar{\mathbf{A}}(\mathbf{u})$. Thus

$$\bar{\mathbf{A}}(\mathbf{u}) \triangleq \bar{\mathbf{A}}(\boldsymbol{\theta};\mathbf{u})$$

Note that the symbol $\mathbf{A}(\mathbf{u})$ represents $\mathbf{y}(t)$, the zero-state response of $\mathcal{A}$ at time t, whereas $\bar{\mathbf{A}}(\mathbf{u})$ denotes the zero-state response segment $\mathbf{y}_{(t_0,t]}$.

If $\boldsymbol{\alpha}$ is a state of $\mathcal{A}$ and $\boldsymbol{\beta}$ is a state of $\mathcal{B}$, then $\boldsymbol{\alpha}$ and $\boldsymbol{\beta}$ are equivalent states, written $\boldsymbol{\alpha} \simeq \boldsymbol{\beta}$, if and only if $\bar{\mathbf{A}}(\boldsymbol{\alpha};\mathbf{u}) = \bar{\mathbf{A}}(\boldsymbol{\beta};\mathbf{u})$ for all $\mathbf{u}$. $\mathcal{A}$ and $\mathcal{B}$ are equivalent systems, written $\mathcal{A} \equiv \mathcal{B}$, if to every state in the state space of $\mathcal{A}$ there is an equivalent state in the state space of $\mathcal{B}$ and vice versa. (It is understood that $\mathcal{A}$ and $\mathcal{B}$ have the same input function space.) $\mathcal{A}$ and $\mathcal{B}$ are said to be zero-state equivalent, written as $\mathcal{A} \doteq \mathcal{B}$, if the zero state of $\mathcal{A}$ is equivalent to the zero state of $\mathcal{B}$. $\mathcal{A}$ and $\mathcal{B}$ are zero-input equivalent if for every state $\boldsymbol{\alpha}$ of $\mathcal{A}$ there is a state $\boldsymbol{\beta}$ of $\mathcal{B}$, and vice versa, such that the zero-input response of $\mathcal{A}$ starting

[1] At a later point in this chapter where we begin to employ the Laplace transformation, the state of $\mathcal{A}$ will be denoted by $\mathbf{x}$ in order to avoid confusion with the complex variable s.

in state α is identical (for $t \geq t_0$) with the zero-input response of $\mathcal{B}$ starting in state β.

Unless stated to the contrary, the variable t is assumed to range over the real line $(-\infty, \infty)$. The initial time is denoted by t_0 or, when necessary, by t_0-. The input $\mathbf{u}(t)$ and output $\mathbf{y}(t)$ are usually, but not always, assumed to be vector-valued and real. When not defined in explicit terms, the input segment space $R[\mathbf{u}]$ is generally understood to be the space of time functions on $(t_0,t]$ which are finitely differentiable in the distribution sense (see *1.3.7*). Statements such as "holds for all $\mathbf{u}$" should be interpreted to mean "holds for all $\mathbf{u}$ in $R[\mathbf{u}]$, with both t_0 and t ranging over the real line." It is generally understood that the states of $\mathcal{A}$ have the following uniform reachability property: If there exists an input segment $\mathbf{u}$ which takes a state α into a state α^*, then for each t_1 there is a t_0 and an input segment $\mathbf{v}_{(t_0,t_1]}$ which takes α $(= \mathbf{s}(t_0))$ into α^* $(= \mathbf{s}(t_1))$; and for each t_0 there is a t_1 and an input segment $\mathbf{w}_{(t_0,t_1]}$ which takes α into α^*.

2 *Time invariance*

For our purposes, it will be convenient to begin our discussion with the concept of *time invariance*, which was briefly mentioned in *1.7.6* and which we shall need in our exposition of linearity and related properties in subsequent sections.

Roughly speaking, a system $\mathcal{A}$ is *time-invariant* if its characteristics do not change with time. For example, a network of fixed resistors, capacitors, and inductors is a time-invariant system. So is a system characterized by the input-output relation

1 $$y(t) = u(t) + u^2(t)$$

On the other hand, the system characterized by the input-output relation

$$y(t) = tu(t) + u^2(t)$$

is not time-invariant (i.e., is time-varying). Any system which undergoes aging (slow variation in characteristics) is, strictly speaking, a time-varying system. In fact, almost all physical systems are time-varying. Thus, the notion of a time-invariant system is essentially an idealization of a physical system whose characteristics change very slowly in relation to variations in the input.

We proceed to cast the rough definition given above into a more precise form. As a preliminary, we digress briefly to consider the notion of a translation operator.

Translation operators

2 **Definition** A *translation operator*[1] $\mathbf{T}_\delta$ is a system characterized by the input-output relation

3 $$\bar{\mathbf{T}}_\delta(\mathbf{u}_{(t_0,t]}) = \mathbf{u}_{(t_0+\delta,t+\delta]} \qquad \forall\delta\forall\mathbf{u}$$

Essentially, the action of $\mathbf{T}_\delta$ on its input $\mathbf{u}$ consists in translating $\mathbf{u}$ by a fixed amount δ along the time axis (see Fig. *3.2.1*). We write symbolically

4 $$\mathbf{y}(t) = \mathbf{T}_\delta(\mathbf{u})$$

or

5 $$\mathbf{y} = \bar{\mathbf{T}}_\delta(\mathbf{u})$$

where $\bar{\mathbf{T}}_\delta(\mathbf{u})$ denotes the response segment $\mathbf{y}_{(t_0,t]}$ and $\mathbf{u}$ is the input segment $\mathbf{u}_{(t_0,t]}$. Note that a positive shift δ corresponds to a *delay*

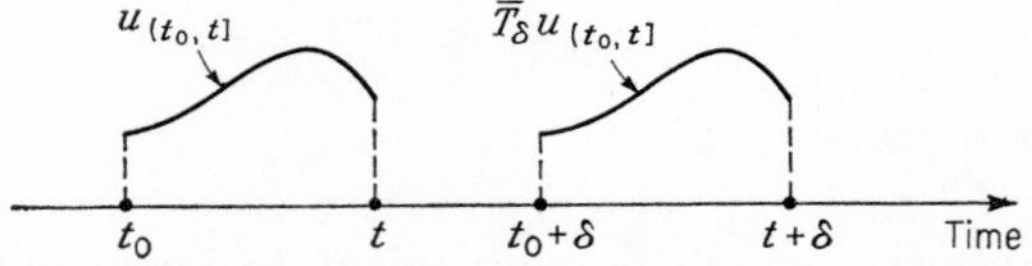

Fig. 3.2.1 $\bar{T}_\delta u_{(t_0,t]}$ denotes the translate of the segment $u_{(t_0,t]}$ by amount $\delta > 0$.

of δ units of time, whereas a negative shift δ corresponds to an *advance* of $-\delta$ units. In particular, a translation operator $\mathbf{T}_\delta$ in which δ is positive and u is scalar-valued, corresponds to a delayor (*1.7.25*) starting in its zero state. For $\delta = 0$, $\mathbf{T}_\delta$ reduces to a unitor, that is, $\mathbf{T}_0 = \mathbf{I}$ (see *1.9.8*).

From the definition of $\mathbf{T}_\delta$, it follows at once that $\mathbf{T}_\delta$ has the properties expressed by the following relations.

6 $$\bar{\mathbf{T}}_\delta(k\mathbf{u}) = k\bar{\mathbf{T}}_\delta(\mathbf{u}) \qquad \forall\delta\forall\mathbf{u} \text{ and all real constants } k$$

where $\mathbf{u}$ denotes a time function in the input function space $R[\mathbf{u}]$. This equation expresses the property of *homogeneity* defined in *3.3.5*.

7 $$\bar{\mathbf{T}}_\delta(\mathbf{u}_1 + \mathbf{u}_2) = \bar{\mathbf{T}}_\delta(\mathbf{u}_1) + \bar{\mathbf{T}}_\delta(\mathbf{u}_2) \qquad \forall\delta \text{ and all } \mathbf{u}_1,\mathbf{u}_2 \text{ in } R[\mathbf{u}]$$

where $\mathbf{u}_1$ and $\mathbf{u}_2$ denote time functions in the input function space

[1] Here and elsewhere in this book the term "operator" is usually, but not always, employed to describe a system whose only possible initial state is its zero state. We write $\mathbf{T}_\delta$ when we wish to emphasize that $\mathbf{T}_\delta$ is an operator, and, correspondingly, we write T_δ when we do not make the assumption that the initial state is restricted to be the zero state.

$R[\mathbf{u}]$. Equation *7* expresses the property of *additivity*, which is defined in *3.3.11*.

8 $$\mathbf{T}_{\delta_1}\mathbf{T}_{\delta_2} \doteq \mathbf{T}_{\delta_2}\mathbf{T}_{\delta_1} \doteq \mathbf{T}_{\delta_1+\delta_2} \qquad \forall\delta_1\forall\delta_2$$

9 $$\mathbf{T}_{\delta}\mathbf{T}_{-\delta} \doteq \mathbf{T}_0 = \mathbf{I} \qquad \forall\delta$$

These relations express the commutativity of translation operators. In mathematical terms, *8* and *9* indicate that the $\mathbf{T}_\delta, -\infty < \delta < \infty$, form a commutative group under multiplication, with $\mathbf{T}_0$ (the unitor) playing the role of the unit element.

10 *Comment* Note that in stating the above properties of translation operators we are tacitly assuming that the input function space $R[\mathbf{u}]$ has the following three characteristics: (I) if $\mathbf{u}$ belongs to $R[\mathbf{u}]$, so does every translate of $\mathbf{u}$; (II) if $\mathbf{u}$ belongs to $R[\mathbf{u}]$, then so does $k\mathbf{u}$, where k is an arbitrary real constant; and (III) if $\mathbf{u}_1$ and $\mathbf{u}_2$ belong to $R[\mathbf{u}]$, then so does their sum $\mathbf{u}_1 + \mathbf{u}_2$. The last two assumptions imply that $R[\mathbf{u}]$ is a linear vector space (see Appendix *C.2.1*). ◁

This concludes our brief digression on translation operators.

Zero-state and zero-input time invariance

As a preliminary to formulating a general definition of time invariance, it will be helpful to consider two particular forms of it, namely, *zero-state time invariance* and *zero-input time invariance.*

As these terms imply, zero-state time invariance is a form of time invariance exhibited when the system is started in its zero state. Correspondingly, zero-input time invariance is the form of time invariance associated with the zero-input response of the system.

11 *Comment* It is customary to call a system "time-invariant" if it is zero-state time-invariant in the sense defined below. The conventional definition of time invariance is not adequate for our purposes because it makes no provision for an initial state other than the zero state. Furthermore, it is easy to construct examples of time-varying systems (see Examples *33* and *38*) which are zero-state time-invariant and hence would be misclassified as time-invariant systems under the conventional definition of time invariance. ◁

The definition of zero-state time invariance is worded as follows.

12 **Definition** A system $\mathcal{A}$ is *zero-state time-invariant* if, for all inputs $\mathbf{u}$ and all time shifts δ, the zero-state response of $\mathcal{A}$ to $\mathbf{u} \triangleq \mathbf{u}_{(t_0,t]}$ is a translate (by amount $-\delta$ along the t axis) of its zero-state response to the translated input $\bar{\mathbf{T}}_\delta(\mathbf{u})$.

In symbols,

13 $$\{\mathcal{A} \text{ is } \textit{zero-state time invariant}\} \Leftrightarrow \{\bar{\mathbf{A}}(\bar{\mathbf{T}}_\delta(\mathbf{u})) = \bar{\mathbf{T}}_\delta(\bar{\mathbf{A}}(\mathbf{u}))\} \qquad \forall\delta\forall\mathbf{u}$$

In other words, $\mathcal{A}$ is zero-state time-invariant if and only if the shape of the zero-state response of $\mathcal{A}$ to any input $\mathbf{u}$ depends only on the shape of $\mathbf{u}$ and not on the time of application of $\mathbf{u}$ (that is, t_0). ◁

Definition *12* can be put into a somewhat more compact form by noting that the zero-state equivalence

$$\mathcal{A}T_\delta \doteq T_\delta\mathcal{A}$$

implies and is implied by

$$\bar{\mathbf{A}}(\bar{\mathbf{T}}_\delta(\mathbf{u})) = \bar{\mathbf{T}}_\delta(\bar{\mathbf{A}}(\mathbf{u})) \qquad \forall \mathbf{u}$$

Thus, *13* may be replaced by

14 $$\{\mathcal{A} \text{ is } \textit{zero-state time-invariant}\} \Leftrightarrow \{\mathcal{A}T_\delta \doteq T_\delta\mathcal{A}\} \qquad \forall \delta$$

the right-hand side of which signifies that $\mathcal{A}$ commutes with all translation operators $\mathbf{T}_\delta$. Note that it does not matter whether one writes $\mathbf{T}_\delta$ or T_δ in equations in which zero-state equivalence is involved.

Actually, in order to conclude that $\mathcal{A}$ is zero-state time-invariant, it suffices to verify that *14* holds for all δ in any finite closed interval. This follows from the

15 **Assertion** If the equivalence $\mathcal{A}T_\delta \doteq T_\delta\mathcal{A}$ holds for all real δ in some finite closed interval $[a,b]$, then it holds for all real values of δ.

Proof Let δ_1 and δ_2 be arbitrary time shifts in the interval $[a,b]$. Then, on postmultiplying both sides of the equivalence[1]

$$\mathcal{A}T_{\delta_1} \doteq T_{\delta_1}\mathcal{A}$$

by T_{δ_2} and making use of the equivalence $\mathcal{A}T_{\delta_2} \doteq T_{\delta_2}\mathcal{A}$, we obtain (see *8*)

16 $$\mathcal{A}T_{\delta_1+\delta_2} \doteq T_{\delta_1+\delta_2}\mathcal{A}$$

which shows that if $\mathcal{A}$ commutes with T_{δ_1} and T_{δ_2}, then it also commutes with $T_{\delta_1+\delta_2}$.

Next, starting with

17 $$\mathcal{A}T_{\delta_2} \doteq T_{\delta_2}\mathcal{A}$$

and premultiplying both sides by $T_{-\delta_2}$, we get

18 $$T_{-\delta_2}\mathcal{A}T_{\delta_2} \doteq \mathcal{A}$$

which yields

$$T_{\delta_1-\delta_2}\mathcal{A} \doteq \mathcal{A}T_{\delta_1-\delta_2}$$

[1] Note that pre- and postmultiplication is justified by *2.7.6*. Note also that we are making tacit use of the associative and substitution principles *1.10.34* and *1.10.35*.

upon postmultiplication of both sides of *18* by $T_{-\delta_2}$, premultiplication of the resulting expression by T_{δ_1}, and making use of *17*. Consequently, if $\mathcal{A}$ commutes with T_{δ_1} and T_{δ_2}, $\delta_1,\delta_2 \in [a,b]$, then it also commutes with $T_{\delta_1 \pm \delta_2}$. This implies that $\mathcal{A}$ commutes with all T_δ in which $|\delta| \leq |b - a|$, which by virtue of *16* implies that $\mathcal{A}$ commutes with all T_δ. ◁

Since there will be numerous examples of zero-state time-invariant systems in later chapters, we shall confine ourselves at this point to two simple illustrations.

19 *Example* Consider the system of Example *2.3.7*, which is characterized by the input-output-state relation

$$y(t) = e^{-(t-t_0)}y(t_0-) + \int_{t_0}^{t} e^{-(t-\xi)}u(\xi)\, d\xi \qquad t \geq t_0$$

in which $y(t_0-)$ represents the state at time t_0-. The zero-state response of this system is given by

20
$$y(t) = \int_{t_0}^{t} e^{-(t-\xi)}u(\xi)\, d\xi \qquad t \geq t_0$$

Now, if the input is shifted by δ sec in time, the value of the output at time $t + \delta$ becomes

21
$$\int_{t_0+\delta}^{t+\delta} e^{-(t-\xi+\delta)}u(\xi - \delta)\, d\xi$$

which is identical with the expression obtained by changing the variable of integration in *20* from ξ to $\xi - \delta$. Hence, the value of the zero-state response at time $t + \delta$ for the translated input is numerically equal to the value of the zero-state response at time t for the original input. Consequently, *13* is satisfied and the system in question is zero-state time-invariant.

22 *Example* By changing the time scale in a nonuniform fashion in accordance with the relation $t \to \log t$, the zero-state time-invariant system of Example *19* is transformed into a time-varying system characterized by the input-output-state relation

23
$$y(t) = \frac{t_0}{t}\, y(t_0-) + \frac{1}{t}\int_{t_0}^{t} u(\xi)\, d\xi \qquad t \geq t_0 > 0$$

This system is a special case of systems of the Euler-Cauchy type which are touched upon in *3.8.29*. ◁

A basic property of zero-state time-invariant systems is expressed by the following

24 **Theorem** Zero-state time-invariant systems form a class closed under system addition, multiplication, and inversion. More specifically, if

$\mathcal{A}$ and $\mathcal{B}$ are zero-state time-invariant, then so are $\mathcal{A} + \mathcal{B}$, $\mathcal{A}\mathcal{B}$, and, if it exists, $\mathcal{A}^{-1}$.

Proof By hypothesis,

25 $$\mathcal{A}T_\delta \doteq T_\delta\mathcal{A}$$

26 $$\mathcal{B}T_\delta \doteq T_\delta\mathcal{B}$$

for all δ. Adding *25* and *26*, we have

27 $$(\mathcal{A} + \mathcal{B})T_\delta \doteq T_\delta\mathcal{A} + T_\delta\mathcal{B} \qquad \forall\delta$$

and, on making use of *7*, *27* becomes

$$(\mathcal{A} + \mathcal{B})T_\delta \doteq T_\delta(\mathcal{A} + \mathcal{B}) \qquad \forall\delta$$

which by *14* implies that $\mathcal{A} + \mathcal{B}$ is zero-state time-invariant.

Next, replacing $\mathcal{B}T_\delta$ in $\mathcal{A}\mathcal{B}T_\delta$ by $T_\delta\mathcal{B}$ and then replacing $\mathcal{A}T_\delta$ by $T_\delta\mathcal{A}$, we obtain the equivalence

$$\mathcal{A}\mathcal{B}T_\delta \doteq T_\delta\mathcal{A}\mathcal{B} \qquad \forall\delta$$

which demonstrates that $\mathcal{A}\mathcal{B}$ is zero-state time-invariant.

Finally, assume that $\mathcal{A}$ has an inverse $\mathcal{A}^{-1}$. Then on premultiplying and postmultiplying both sides of the equivalence

28 $$\mathcal{A}^{-1}\mathcal{A} \doteq \mathrm{I}$$

by T_δ, we obtain

$$T_\delta\mathcal{A}^{-1}\mathcal{A} \doteq \mathcal{A}^{-1}\mathcal{A}T_\delta \doteq T_\delta \qquad \forall\delta$$

which, upon making use of *25*, becomes

29 $$T_\delta\mathcal{A}^{-1}\mathcal{A} \doteq \mathcal{A}^{-1}T_\delta\mathcal{A} \qquad \forall\delta$$

Postmultiplying both sides of *29* by $\mathcal{A}^{-1}$, we have

$$T_\delta\mathcal{A}^{-1} \doteq \mathcal{A}^{-1}T_\delta \qquad \forall\delta$$

which, by *14*, implies that $\mathcal{A}^{-1}$ is zero-state time-invariant.

Zero-input time invariance

We turn next to the notion of zero-input time invariance, which can be defined in a manner quite analogous to that of Definition *12*. Specifically,

30 **Definition** A system $\mathcal{A}$ is *zero-input time-invariant* if and only if for all initial states $\boldsymbol{\alpha}$ in the state space Σ, all initial times t_0, and all time shifts δ the zero-input response of $\mathcal{A}$ starting in state $\boldsymbol{\alpha}$ at time $t_0 - \delta$ is identical (to within a translation by amount δ along the time axis) with the zero-input response of $\mathcal{A}$ starting in state $\boldsymbol{\alpha}$ at time t_0.

In symbols,

31 $\{\mathcal{A} \text{ is } \textit{zero-input time-invariant}\} \Leftrightarrow \{\bar{\mathbf{A}}(\mathbf{s}(t_0 - \delta);\mathbf{0}) = \bar{\mathbf{T}}_\delta\bar{\mathbf{A}}(\mathbf{s}(t_0);\mathbf{0})\} \quad \forall\delta\forall\mathbf{s}(t_0)$

where $\bar{\mathbf{A}}(\mathbf{s}(t_0);\mathbf{0})$ denotes the zero-input response of $\mathcal{A}$ starting in state $\mathbf{s}(t_0) = \boldsymbol{\alpha}$ at time t_0, and likewise for $\bar{\mathbf{A}}(\mathbf{s}(t_0 - \delta);\mathbf{0})$, with $\mathbf{s}(t_0 - \delta) = \boldsymbol{\alpha}$.

32 *Comment* Our motive for introducing the notion of zero-input time invariance is the following. We shall see at a later point in this section that, in general, a system $\mathcal{A}$ may be zero-state time-invariant without being time-invariant in the more strict sense of Definition *36*. Furthermore, a system may be both zero-state and zero-input time-invariant without being time-invariant in the sense of Definition *36*. This is not possible, however, in the case of linear systems. Thus, if a linear system is both zero-input and zero-state time-invariant, then it is necessarily time-invariant. It is for this reason that the notion of zero-input time invariance is of significance in the case of linear systems. ◁

In general, a system may be zero-state time-invariant without being zero-input time-invariant, and vice versa. This possibility is illustrated by the following simple examples.

33 *Example* Let the input-output-state relation of $\mathcal{A}$ be of the form

$$y(t) = ts_1(t_0-) + e^{-(t-t_0)}s_2(t_0-) + \int_{t_0}^{t} e^{-(t-\xi)}u(\xi)\,d\xi \qquad t \geq t_0$$

where $\mathbf{s}(t_0-) = (s_1(t_0-),s_2(t_0-))$ represents the initial state vector of $\mathcal{A}$. Then $\mathcal{A}$ is zero-state time-invariant but not zero-input time-invariant. [Note that $\mathcal{A}$ can be realized as a parallel combination of an integrator $1/(p + 1)$ and a source (see *1.8.22*) which has the form of a grounded integrator $1/p$ in tandem with a time-varying scalor t.]

34 *Example* Consider a system $\mathcal{A}$ whose input-output relation is

$$\frac{dy}{dt} + y(t) = tu(t)$$

This system is zero-input but not zero-state time-invariant.

Time invariance

We are now ready to formulate a more general definition of time invariance which subsumes zero-state and zero-input time invariance as special cases. Specifically, suppose that the initial state of $\mathcal{A}$ is a state $\boldsymbol{\alpha}$ not necessarily equivalent to $\boldsymbol{\theta}$. Then, by analogy with the definition of zero-state time invariance, $\mathcal{A}$ will be said to be *time-invariant with respect to the initial state* $\boldsymbol{\alpha}$ if and only if

35 $$\bar{\mathbf{T}}_\delta(\bar{\mathbf{A}}(\boldsymbol{\alpha};\mathbf{u})) = \bar{\mathbf{A}}(\boldsymbol{\alpha};\bar{\mathbf{T}}_\delta(\mathbf{u})) \qquad \forall\delta\forall\mathbf{u}$$

that is, if the response segment of $\mathcal{A}$ to $\bar{\mathbf{T}}_\delta(\mathbf{u})$ ($\mathbf{u}$ shifted by δ units of time), with $\mathcal{A}$ initially in state $\boldsymbol{\alpha}$, is identical with the shifted response $\bar{\mathbf{T}}_\delta(\bar{\mathbf{A}}(\boldsymbol{\alpha};\mathbf{u}))$ of $\mathcal{A}$ to $\mathbf{u}$, with $\mathcal{A}$ initially in state $\boldsymbol{\alpha}$.

If this property holds for *all* states in the state space of $\mathcal{A}$, then $\mathcal{A}$ will be said to be *time-invariant.* More formally,

36 **Definition** $\mathcal{A}$ is *time-invariant* if and only if for all starting states $\boldsymbol{\alpha}$, all inputs $\mathbf{u}$, and all shifts δ

$$\bar{\mathbf{T}}_\delta(\bar{\mathbf{A}}(\boldsymbol{\alpha};\mathbf{u})) = \bar{\mathbf{A}}(\boldsymbol{\alpha};\bar{\mathbf{T}}_\delta(\mathbf{u}))$$

or, more compactly,

37 $$\{\mathcal{A} \text{ is } \textit{time-invariant}\} \Leftrightarrow \{\mathcal{A}\mathbf{T}_\delta \equiv \mathbf{T}_\delta\mathcal{A}\} \qquad \forall\delta$$

where the relation $\mathcal{A}\mathbf{T}_\delta \equiv \mathbf{T}_\delta\mathcal{A}$ should be interpreted as system equivalence, with $\mathbf{T}_\delta$—but not necessarily $\mathcal{A}$—starting in its zero state, and with $\mathcal{A}\mathbf{T}_\delta$ and $\mathbf{T}_\delta\mathcal{A}$ interpreted as free products (see *1.10.10*). ◁

Clearly, if $\mathcal{A}$ has a zero state and is time-invariant, then it is also zero-state time-invariant. The converse, however, is not true, as Example *33* and the less trivial example given below demonstrate.

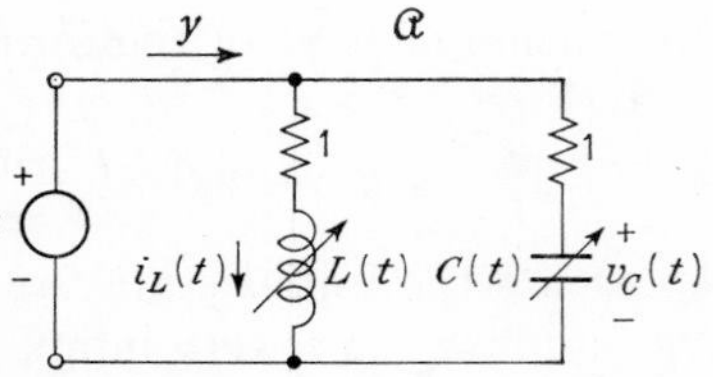

Fig. 3.2.2 $\mathcal{A}$ is a time-varying network which is zero-state time-invariant.

38 *Example* Consider the network $\mathcal{A}$ shown in Fig. *3.2.2*, in which u is the input, y is the output, and $L(t)$ and $C(t)$ are functions of time such that $L(t) = C(t) > 0$ for all t. The state of $\mathcal{A}$ at time t can be taken to be the 2-vector (see *1.7.28*)

$$\mathbf{s}(t) = (i_L(t),v_C(t))$$

where i_L is the current through L and v_C is the voltage across C. Using the well-known expression (see Ref. *1*)

$$y(t) = \exp\left[-\int_{t_0}^t a(\xi)\,d\xi\right] y(t_0) + \int_{t_0}^t d\xi\,u(\xi)\exp\left[-\int_\xi^t a(\eta)\,d\eta\right] \qquad t \geq t_0$$

for the solution of the first-order differential equation

$$\frac{dy}{dt} + a(t)y = u(t)$$

the expression for the input-output-state relation of $\mathcal{A}$ is readily found to be

39 $$y(t) = \frac{C(t)}{C(t_0)}\exp\left[-\int_{t_0}^t \frac{d\xi}{C(\xi)}\right][i_L(t_0) - v_C(t_0)] + u(t)$$

Clearly, if $\mathcal{A}$ is started in its zero state, $\boldsymbol{\theta} = (0,0)$, or in any state in which the two components are equal [which are the states reachable (*2.4.17*) from the zero state], then $y(t) = u(t)$. This implies that $\mathcal{A}$ is zero-state time-invariant. On the other hand, if the starting state is such that $i_L(t_0) \neq v_C(t_0)$, then the first term in *39* does not vanish and $\mathcal{A}$ is not time-invariant with respect to the starting state in question. Hence $\mathcal{A}$ is not time-invariant. ◁

An important connection between time invariance and zero-state time invariance is provided by the following

40 **Assertion** If $\mathcal{A}$ is zero-state time-invariant and zero-state equivalent to a time-invariant system, then $\mathcal{A}$ is time-invariant with respect to every state which is reachable from the zero state.

Proof Let $\mathcal{B}$ be a time-invariant system which is zero-state equivalent to $\mathcal{A}$. Consider an arbitrary input $\mathbf{u}$ and assume that the zero state of $\mathcal{A}$ is taken by $\mathbf{u}$ into a state $\boldsymbol{\alpha}$ in the state space of $\mathcal{A}$ and, correspondingly, the zero state of $\mathcal{B}$ is taken into a state $\boldsymbol{\beta}$ in the state space of $\mathcal{B}$. By Assertion *2.4.12*, $\boldsymbol{\alpha}$ and $\boldsymbol{\beta}$ are equivalent states. Consequently, for any input $\mathbf{v}$ applied to $\mathcal{A}$ and $\mathcal{B}$ starting in $\boldsymbol{\alpha}$ and $\boldsymbol{\beta}$, respectively, we have

41 $$\bar{\mathbf{A}}(\boldsymbol{\alpha};\mathbf{v}) = \bar{\mathbf{B}}(\boldsymbol{\beta};\mathbf{v})$$

Now since $\mathcal{B}$ is a time-invariant system, we can write (by *35*)

$$\bar{\mathbf{T}}_\delta(\bar{\mathbf{B}}(\boldsymbol{\beta};\mathbf{v})) = \bar{\mathbf{B}}(\boldsymbol{\beta};\bar{\mathbf{T}}_\delta(\mathbf{v})) \qquad \forall\delta\forall\mathbf{v}$$

which by virtue of *41* implies (see *2.4.17*)

$$\bar{\mathbf{T}}_\delta(\bar{\mathbf{A}}(\boldsymbol{\alpha};\mathbf{v})) = \bar{\mathbf{A}}(\boldsymbol{\alpha};\bar{\mathbf{T}}_\delta(\mathbf{v})) \qquad \forall\delta\forall\mathbf{v}$$

and thus shows that $\mathcal{A}$ is time-invariant with respect to $\boldsymbol{\alpha}$. Clearly, the same is true of any state which is reachable from the zero state of $\mathcal{A}$. Q.E.D.

The various types of time invariance which we have defined in the foregoing discussion all involve the initial state of $\mathcal{A}$. It is possible, however, to define still another, weaker, kind of time invariance which does not have this characteristic. Specifically, we have the

42 **Definition** Let $(\mathbf{u}_{(t_0,t]},\mathbf{y}_{(t_0,t]})$ [or $(\mathbf{u},\mathbf{y})$ for short] be an input-output pair for $\mathcal{A}$ (see *1.4.17*), with $(\mathbf{u},\mathbf{y})$ ranging over the space $R_{(t_0,t]}$ of input-output pairs. Then $\mathcal{A}$ is *weakly time-invariant* if and only if for all δ and all $(\mathbf{u},\mathbf{y})$ in $R_{(t_0,t]}$

43 $$\{(\mathbf{u},\mathbf{y}) \text{ is an input-output pair for } \mathcal{A}\} \Leftrightarrow \{(\bar{\mathbf{T}}_\delta(\mathbf{u}),\bar{\mathbf{T}}_\delta(\mathbf{y})) \text{ is an input-output pair for } \mathcal{A}\}$$

That is, if $(\mathbf{u},\mathbf{y})$ is an input-output pair for $\mathcal{A}$, then so is every translate of $(\mathbf{u},\mathbf{y})$. ◁

In general, if $\mathcal{A}$ is weakly time-invariant, then it is not necessarily time-invariant in the sense of Definition *36*. In the case of linear differential systems, however, weak time invariance implies time invariance. As will be seen in Sec. *9*, this is a consequence of the fact that in the case of linear systems weak equivalence implies equivalence (see *3.9.1*).

This concludes for the present our discussion of time invariance. We turn next to another basic concept, namely, *linearity*.

3 *Basic aspects of linearity: additivity and homogeneity*

Although our main concern in this text is with systems characterized by differential equations, our discussion of the notion of linearity and related concepts will be conducted on a considerably more general level. Though this makes it initially somewhat more difficult for the reader to relate the various assertions, theorems, etc., to those properties of linear systems with which he has prior familiarity, it does have the longer-run advantage of giving one a deeper insight into the basic properties which are common to all linear systems and not just systems governed by differential equations.

The concept of linearity

The term *linearity* connotes a relation of proportionality between the cause (input) and the effect (output). Actually, linearity implies more than proportionality—it implies the superposability of causes and their respective effects.

How can this vague statement be formulated in a more precise form? It is customary to formulate it precisely via the notions of *additivity* and *homogeneity*, under the tacit assumption that the initial state is the zero state of the system. Such an assumption has two drawbacks. In the first place, it does not provide a basis for deciding whether a given system $\mathcal{A}$ is linear or nonlinear when the initial state of $\mathcal{A}$ is not its zero state. Second, under the conventional definition of linearity a nonlinear system $\mathcal{A}$ may be misclassified as a linear system if $\mathcal{A}$ happens to behave like a linear system when its initial state is its zero state. Three such cases are cited in Examples *3.4.11*, *3.4.12*, and *3.4.24*.

In this chapter we shall formulate a definition of linearity (Definition *3.4.25*) which is not predicated on the assumption that the initial state is the zero state. However, instead of stating this definition at the outset, we shall first lay a groundwork for it by establishing the basic properties of homogeneity, additivity, and two special forms of linearity, namely zero-state linearity and zero-input linearity.

In defining these notions we shall be making the following assumptions about the system under consideration (which will be denoted by $\mathcal{A}$).

1 **Assumption** $\mathcal{A}$ has a unique zero state $\boldsymbol{\theta}$.

2 **Assumption** The input and output function spaces of $\mathcal{A}$ are *linear* function spaces. This implies that if $\mathbf{u}_1$ and $\mathbf{u}_2$ are two arbitrary time functions in $R[\mathbf{u}]$, the input function space of $\mathcal{A}$, then the time function $\mathbf{u} = a\mathbf{u}_1 + b\mathbf{u}_2$, where a and b are arbitrary constants, is likewise an element of $R[\mathbf{u}]$. The same statement applies to the output function space of $\mathcal{A}$. Beyond the assumption that the input and output function spaces of $\mathcal{A}$ are linear, we shall generally not make any restrictive assumptions on their elements other than that they are finitely differentiable in the distribution sense (see *1.3.7* and *1.4.29*).

3 **Assumption** The state space of $\mathcal{A}$ is a linear vector space. This implies that if $\boldsymbol{\alpha}_1$ and $\boldsymbol{\alpha}_2$ are arbitrary states in Σ, then any linear combination of them, $a\boldsymbol{\alpha}_1 + b\boldsymbol{\alpha}_2$, is likewise a state in Σ.

4 *Comment* The reason for Assumption *2* is the following. In the sequel, we shall frequently be comparing the response of $\mathcal{A}$ to an input $\mathbf{u}$ with the response of $\mathcal{A}$ to $k\mathbf{u}$, where k is an arbitrary constant, and also the responses of $\mathcal{A}$ to $\mathbf{u}_1$ and $\mathbf{u}_2$ with the response to the sum $\mathbf{u}_1 + \mathbf{u}_2$. Clearly, in order that both $k\mathbf{u}$ and $\mathbf{u}_1 + \mathbf{u}_2$ be admissible inputs for all $\mathbf{u}_1, \mathbf{u}_2$ in $R[\mathbf{u}]$ and all k, it is necessary that $R[\mathbf{u}]$ be a linear function space in the sense stated above. ◁

We begin with a discussion of the notion of

Homogeneity

Essentially, *homogeneity* denotes a relation of proportionality between the output and input. Stated more precisely:

5 **Definition** A system $\mathcal{A}$ is *homogeneous* if and only if for all inputs $\mathbf{u}$ in the input segment space of $\mathcal{A}$ and for all real constants k, the zero-state response of $\mathcal{A}$ to the input $k\mathbf{u}$ is k times the zero-state response of $\mathcal{A}$ to $\mathbf{u}$.

In symbols,

6 $$\{\mathcal{A} \text{ is } \textit{homogeneous}\} \Leftrightarrow \{\bar{\mathbf{A}}(k\mathbf{u}) = k\bar{\mathbf{A}}(\mathbf{u})\} \qquad \forall k \forall \mathbf{u}$$

where $\bar{\mathbf{A}}(\mathbf{u})$ denotes the zero-state response of $\mathcal{A}$ to $\mathbf{u}$ (see *2.8.18*).

Equivalently, let $\mathcal{K}$ denote a scalor with scale factor k (see *1.9.8*). Then $k\mathbf{u}$ can be regarded as the response of $\mathcal{K}$ to $\mathbf{u}$, and $\bar{\mathbf{A}}(k\mathbf{u})$ as the response of $\mathcal{A}\mathcal{K}$ (tandem combination of $\mathcal{A}$ and $\mathcal{K}$, with $\mathcal{K}$ preceding $\mathcal{A}$) to $\mathbf{u}$. In terms of these symbols, the statement "$\bar{\mathbf{A}}(k\mathbf{u}) = k\bar{\mathbf{A}}(\mathbf{u})\forall\mathbf{u}$" has the same meaning as the statement "$\mathcal{A}\mathcal{K}$ is zero-state equivalent to $\mathcal{K}\mathcal{A}$." ◁

This implies that homogeneity can also be defined as follows:

7 **Definition** A system $\mathcal{A}$ is *homogeneous* if for all real scalors $\mathcal{K}$, $\mathcal{A}\mathcal{K}$ is zero-state equivalent of $\mathcal{K}\mathcal{A}$. ◁

Actually, in order to check on whether or not the zero-state equivalence $\mathcal{A}\mathcal{K} \doteq \mathcal{K}\mathcal{A}$ holds for all real values of k, it is sufficient to verify that this equivalence holds for all values of k in any finite interval $[-a,a]$. The justification for this is provided by the following

8 **Assertion** If $\mathcal{A}\mathcal{K} \doteq \mathcal{K}\mathcal{A}$ for all scalors with k in the range $-a \leq k \leq a$, then $\mathcal{A}\mathcal{K} \doteq \mathcal{K}\mathcal{A}$ for all real k.

Proof Let $k \in [-a,a]$. Write k in the form $k = p/r$, where $p \in [-a,a]$, $p \neq 0$, and r is such that $p/r \in [-a,a]$. Then

$$\bar{\mathbf{A}}\left(\frac{p}{r}\,\mathbf{u}\right) = \frac{p}{r}\,\bar{\mathbf{A}}(\mathbf{u})$$

and on making use of $\bar{\mathbf{A}}(p\mathbf{u}) = p\bar{\mathbf{A}}(\mathbf{u})$, we have

$$p\bar{\mathbf{A}}\left(\frac{1}{r}\,\mathbf{u}\right) = \frac{p}{r}\,\bar{\mathbf{A}}(\mathbf{u})$$

or

$$\bar{\mathbf{A}}\left(\frac{1}{r}\,\mathbf{u}\right) = \frac{1}{r}\,\bar{\mathbf{A}}(\mathbf{u})$$

This shows that if $\mathcal{A}\mathcal{K} \doteq \mathcal{K}\mathcal{A}$ holds for all k in the interval $[-a,a]$, then it also holds for all k of the form $1/r$, where r is the ratio of any two numbers in $[-a,a]$. Since the range of $1/r$ is the entire real line, the assertion is proved. ◁

The following two simple examples will suffice for the present to illustrate the notion of homogeneity.

9 *Example* Consider a system $\mathcal{A}$ whose zero-state response is defined by the relation

$$y(t) = \int_{t_0}^{t} e^{-(t-\xi)}u(\xi)\,d\xi \qquad t \geq t_0$$

where u is a real-valued time function. Clearly, $\mathcal{A}$ is a homogeneous system, since if the response of $\mathcal{A}$ to u is y, then the response of $\mathcal{A}$ to ku is ky for all k and u.

10 *Example* A squarer is a memoryless system (see *1.8.17*) characterized by the input-output relation

$$y(t) = [u(t)]^2$$

where u is a real-valued time function. If y is the response of the squarer to u, then its response to ku is k^2y. Consequently, a squarer is not a homogeneous system. ◁

We turn next to the notion of

Additivity

Broadly speaking, additivity denotes the superposability of causes and effects. Thus, if a "cause" $\mathbf{u}_1$ produces the "effect" $\mathbf{y}_1$ and if a "cause" $\mathbf{u}_2$ produces the "effect" $\mathbf{y}_2$, then the superposability of causes and effects implies that the "cause" $\mathbf{u}_1 + \mathbf{u}_2$ would produce the "effect" $\mathbf{y}_1 + \mathbf{y}_2$.

This somewhat vague concept is formulated more precisely in the following

11 **Definition** A system $\mathcal{A}$ is *additive* if and only if for any pair of time functions $\mathbf{u}_1$ and $\mathbf{u}_2$ in the input segment space of $\mathcal{A}$, the zero-state response of $\mathcal{A}$ to the sum $\mathbf{u}_1 + \mathbf{u}_2$ is the sum of the zero-state responses of $\mathcal{A}$ to $\mathbf{u}_1$ and $\mathbf{u}_2$.

In symbols,

12 $$\{\mathcal{A} \text{ is } \textit{additive}\} \Leftrightarrow \{\bar{\mathbf{A}}(\mathbf{u}_1 + \mathbf{u}_2) = \bar{\mathbf{A}}(\mathbf{u}_1) + \bar{\mathbf{A}}(\mathbf{u}_2)\} \qquad \forall\mathbf{u}_1\forall\mathbf{u}_2 \quad \triangleleft$$

Let us now examine some of the implications of additivity. First, suppose that $\mathcal{A}$ is additive. Then, it is trivial to show that $\mathcal{A}$ is also *finitely additive*, in the sense that the zero-state response of $\mathcal{A}$ to any finite sum of time functions belonging to the input segment space of $\mathcal{A}$ is the sum of the respective responses. In symbols (omitting the quantifiers $\forall\mathbf{u}_1 \cdots \forall\mathbf{u}_n$ for simplicity), we have

13 $$\{\bar{\mathbf{A}}(\mathbf{u}_1 + \mathbf{u}_2) = \bar{\mathbf{A}}(\mathbf{u}_1) + \bar{\mathbf{A}}(\mathbf{u}_2)\} \Rightarrow \{\bar{\mathbf{A}}(\mathbf{u}_1 + \cdots + \mathbf{u}_n) = \bar{\mathbf{A}}(\mathbf{u}_1) + \cdots + \bar{\mathbf{A}}(\mathbf{u}_n)\}$$

For, any finite sum such as $\mathbf{v} = \mathbf{u}_1 + \cdots + \mathbf{u}_n$ can be written as $\mathbf{v} = (\mathbf{u}_1 + \cdots + \mathbf{u}_{n-1}) + \mathbf{u}_n$. Then, on applying *12* to $\mathbf{v}$, we can write

14 $$\bar{\mathbf{A}}(\mathbf{u}_1 + \cdots + \mathbf{u}_n) = \bar{\mathbf{A}}(\mathbf{u}_1 + \cdots + \mathbf{u}_{n-1}) + \bar{\mathbf{A}}(\mathbf{u}_n)$$

On repeating this process for $\mathbf{u}_1 + \cdots + \mathbf{u}_{n-1}, \mathbf{u}_1 + \cdots + \mathbf{u}_{n-2}, \ldots,$ we eventually arrive at the identity

15 $$\bar{\mathbf{A}}(\mathbf{u}_1 + \cdots + \mathbf{u}_n) = \bar{\mathbf{A}}(\mathbf{u}_1) + \cdots + \bar{\mathbf{A}}(\mathbf{u}_n) \qquad \text{Q.E.D.}$$

An important implication of additivity concerns the relation between additivity and homogeneity. This implication is contained in the

16 **Assertion** If $\mathcal{A}$ is additive, then the relation

17 $$\mathcal{A}\mathcal{K} \doteq \mathcal{K}\mathcal{A}$$

where $\mathcal{K}$ is a scalor with scale factor k, holds for all rational values of k.

Comment The significance of this property of additive systems is this: If a system is additive, then *16* implies that, for all practical purposes, it is also homogeneous, since (I) any real constant k can be approximated as closely as desired by a rational number and (II) in any physical system a small difference between k and a rational approximation to k, say, $\hat{k}$, will result in a correspondingly small difference between the responses to $k\mathbf{u}$ and $\hat{k}\mathbf{u}$.

Proof Let $\mathcal{A}$ be an additive system. Set $\mathbf{u}_1 = \mathbf{u}_2 = \cdots = \mathbf{u}_n = \mathbf{u}$ in *15*. This leads to the consequence

18 $$\{\mathcal{A} \text{ is additive}\} \Rightarrow \{\bar{\mathbf{A}}(n\mathbf{u}) = n\bar{\mathbf{A}}(\mathbf{u})\}$$

for all $\mathbf{u} \in R[\mathbf{u}]$ and all finite, nonnegative, integral values of n. Now

$$\bar{\mathbf{A}}(n\mathbf{u} - n\mathbf{u}) = \bar{\mathbf{A}}(\mathbf{0}) = \mathbf{0}$$

since the zero-state response of $\mathcal{A}$ to the zero input is $\mathbf{0}$.

On the other hand,

$$\begin{aligned}\bar{\mathbf{A}}(n\mathbf{u} - n\mathbf{u}) &= \bar{\mathbf{A}}(n\mathbf{u}) + \bar{\mathbf{A}}(-n\mathbf{u}) \\ &= n\bar{\mathbf{A}}(\mathbf{u}) + \bar{\mathbf{A}}(-n\mathbf{u})\end{aligned}$$

by additivity and *18*. Consequently,

19 $$\{\mathcal{A} \text{ is additive}\} \Rightarrow \{\bar{\mathbf{A}}(n\mathbf{u}) = n\bar{\mathbf{A}}(\mathbf{u})\}$$

for all $\mathbf{u}$ and all finite, integral values of n.

Now let

$$\mathbf{v} \triangleq \frac{n}{m}\mathbf{u}$$

where m and n are finite integers. (Note that $\mathbf{v} \in R[\mathbf{u}]$ because $R[\mathbf{u}]$ is a linear function space.) On replacing $\mathbf{u}$ by $(m/n)\mathbf{v}$ in *19*, we get

$$\{\mathcal{A} \text{ is additive}\} \Rightarrow \left\{\bar{\mathbf{A}}(m\mathbf{v}) = n\bar{\mathbf{A}}\left(\frac{m}{n}\mathbf{v}\right)\right\} \qquad \forall \mathbf{v}$$

or equivalently

$$\{\mathcal{A} \text{ is additive}\} \Rightarrow \left\{\bar{\mathbf{A}}\left(\frac{m}{n}\mathbf{v}\right) = \frac{m}{n}\bar{\mathbf{A}}(\mathbf{v})\right\} \qquad \forall \mathbf{v}$$

which shows that *16* holds for all rational values of k. Q.E.D.

20 **Remark** Since additivity "almost" implies homogeneity (in the sense of *16*), it is natural to inquire if the converse is also true in some approximate sense. That it is not is demonstrated by the following simple counterexamples. However, the artificiality of these examples indicates that it is very unlikely that a physical system picked at random would exhibit homogeneity but not additivity.

21 *Example* Let $\mathcal{A}$ be a system which in response to a time function u produces a train of pulses of the form shown in Fig. *3.3.1*. The pulses occur at the points where $u(t) = 0$, and the amplitude of the pulse occurring at, say, $t_i[u(t_i) = 0]$ is equal to $\dot{u}(t_i)$, that is, to the slope of

u at t_i. The input function space of $\mathcal{A}$ is assumed to be the class of all differentiable functions.

Clearly, $\mathcal{A}$ is a homogeneous system, since if u is multiplied by any real constant k, the output of $\mathcal{A}$ is multiplied by the same constant. On the other hand, $\mathcal{A}$ is not an additive system, as is demonstrated by the simple case where $u_1(t) \equiv t$ and $u_2(t) \equiv t^2 - 1$.

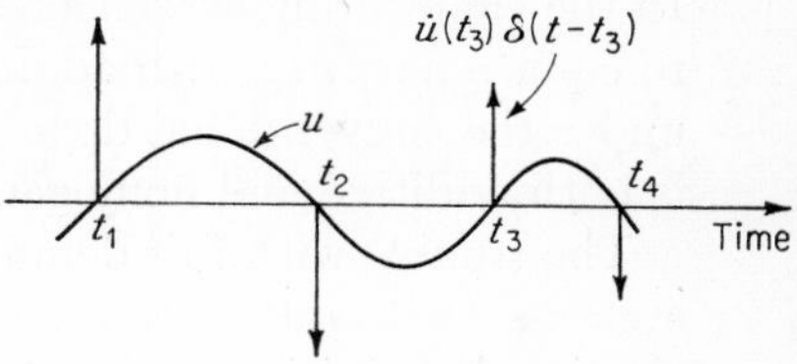

Fig. 3.3.1 Example of a system which is homogeneous but not additive.

22 *Example* Consider a memoryless system $\mathcal{A}$ whose zero-state response to an input u is given by

$$y(t) = \sqrt[3]{[u(t)]^3 + [\dot{u}(t)]^3}$$

This is a homogeneous system, since the response of $\mathcal{A}$ to ku is k times the response of $\mathcal{A}$ to u. On the other hand, $\mathcal{A}$ is clearly not additive. ◁

The following simple example exhibits a system which has the additivity property.

23 *Example* Consider the system characterized by the input-output-state relation

$$y(t) = e^{-(t-t_0)}\alpha + \int_{t_0}^{t} e^{-(t-\xi)}u(\xi)\,d\xi \qquad t \geq t_0$$

in which α is the state at time t_0-, with α ranging over $\mathcal{R}^1$ (the real line). Here the zero state is $\theta = 0$, and the zero-state response is expressed by

$$A(u) = \int_{t_0}^{t} e^{-(t-\xi)}u(\xi)\,d\xi \qquad t \geq t_0$$

Now, if $u = u_1 + u_2$, then $y = y_1 + y_2$, where

$$y_i(t) = \int_{t_0}^{t} e^{-(t-\xi)}u_i(\xi)\,d\xi \qquad i = 1, 2, t \geq t_0$$

Consequently, the system in question is additive.

This concludes our discussion of homogeneity and additivity. We shall employ these concepts in Sec. *4* to define two special cases of linearity, namely, zero-state linearity and zero-input linearity, with a view to using these cases as steppingstones to a more general definition of linearity in which no special assumptions are made about either the input or the initial state.

4 *Zero-state and zero-input linearity*

The notions of zero-state and zero-input linearity bear the same relation to one another as do the notions of zero-state and zero-input time invariance. For this reason, there are in what follows many points of parallelism with the material in Sec. *2*.

We begin with a discussion of

Zero-state linearity

In the engineering as well as the mathematical literature it is customary to equate linearity with additivity and homogeneity. In other words, under the conventional definition of linearity, a system $\mathcal{A}$ is linear if it is both additive and homogeneous.

The trouble with this definition is that one can construct examples of systems (Examples *11*, *12*, and *24*) which are linear under the conventional definition and yet exhibit clearly nonlinear behavior when started in a state other than the zero state. Thus, the conventional definition of linearity is in effect a description of a restricted type of linearity which may be appropriately called *zero-state linearity*. More formally,

1 **Definition** A system $\mathcal{A}$ is *zero-state linear* if and only if it is both additive and homogeneous. ◁

For our purposes, it will be convenient to put this definition into a somewhat different but equivalent form which is given below.

2 **Definition** Let $\mathbf{u}$ and $\mathbf{v}$ be arbitrary time functions in the input segment space of $\mathcal{A}$ and let k be an arbitrary real constant. Then $\mathcal{A}$ is *zero-state linear* if and only if the zero-state response of $\mathcal{A}$ to $k(\mathbf{u} - \mathbf{v})$ is k times the zero-state response of $\mathcal{A}$ to $\mathbf{u}$ minus k times the zero-state response of $\mathcal{A}$ to $\mathbf{v}$.

In symbols,

3 $$\{\mathcal{A} \text{ is } \textit{zero-state linear}\} \Leftrightarrow \{\bar{\mathbf{A}}(k(\mathbf{u} - \mathbf{v})) = k\bar{\mathbf{A}}(\mathbf{u}) - k\bar{\mathbf{A}}(\mathbf{v})\} \text{ for all } \mathbf{u},\mathbf{v}$$

in $R[\mathbf{u}]$ and all real k. [Note that $\bar{\mathbf{A}}(\mathbf{u})$ denotes the response segment of $\mathcal{A}$ to $\mathbf{u}$, with $\mathcal{A}$ initially in its zero state.] ◁

To demonstrate the equivalence of Definitions *1* and *2*, first set $\mathbf{v} = 0$ in *3*. It follows that $\mathcal{A}$ is homogeneous. Next, set $k = 1$ and $\mathbf{v} = -\mathbf{v}'$, where $\mathbf{v}' \in R[\mathbf{u}]$. It follows that $\mathcal{A}$ is additive. Conversely, if $\mathcal{A}$ is additive and homogeneous, it follows at once that

$$\bar{\mathbf{A}}(k(\mathbf{u} - \mathbf{v})) = k\bar{\mathbf{A}}(\mathbf{u}) - k\bar{\mathbf{A}}(\mathbf{v}) \quad \text{Q.E.D.}$$

4 *Example* The system of Example *2.2.9* is zero-state linear. So is the system of Example *2.3.7*.

Linearity with respect to an initial state

As an extension of the notion of zero-state linearity we shall say that system $\mathcal{A}$ is *linear with respect to an initial state* $\boldsymbol{\alpha}$ if *3* holds when the initial state is $\boldsymbol{\alpha}$. More specifically:

5 **Definition** A system $\mathcal{A}$ is *linear with respect to an initial state* $\boldsymbol{\alpha}$ if and only if the relation

6 $$k\bar{\mathbf{A}}(\boldsymbol{\alpha};\mathbf{u}) - k\bar{\mathbf{A}}(\boldsymbol{\alpha};\mathbf{v}) = \bar{\mathbf{A}}(\boldsymbol{\theta};k(\mathbf{u} - \mathbf{v}))$$

where $\bar{\mathbf{A}}(\boldsymbol{\alpha};\mathbf{u})$ denotes the response of $\mathcal{A}$ to $\mathbf{u}$ starting in state $\boldsymbol{\alpha}$ and $\bar{\mathbf{A}}(\boldsymbol{\theta};\mathbf{u})$ is the zero-state response of $\mathcal{A}$ to $\mathbf{u}$, holds for all real constants k and all $\mathbf{u},\mathbf{v}$ in the input segment space of $\mathcal{A}$. (Note that *6* reduces to *3* when $\boldsymbol{\alpha} = \boldsymbol{\theta}$.) ◁

Our motive in introducing this notion is the following. It is not difficult to construct examples of systems that are zero-state linear (i.e., linear in the conventional sense of the term) and yet are not linear with respect to all possible initial states. Although such systems behave like linear systems if started in the zero state, they are not "completely" linear, since there exist starting states with respect to which their behavior is nonlinear. Thus, Definition *5* serves the purpose of providing a basis for differentiating between (I) systems that are linear with respect to all possible starting states and (II) systems that are zero-state linear without being linear with respect to all possible starting states. Systems of the latter type are illustrated by Examples *11* and *12*.

A connection between zero-state linearity and linearity with respect to $\boldsymbol{\alpha}$ is provided by the following

7 **Assertion** If $\mathcal{A}$ is zero-state linear, then it is also linear with respect to all initial states which are reachable from the zero state (*2.4.17*).

Proof We have to show that if (I) $\mathcal{A}$ is zero-state linear and (II) $\boldsymbol{\alpha}$ is any state which is reachable from $\boldsymbol{\theta}$, then

$$k\bar{\mathbf{A}}(\boldsymbol{\alpha};\mathbf{u}) - k\bar{\mathbf{A}}(\boldsymbol{\alpha};\mathbf{v}) = \bar{\mathbf{A}}(\boldsymbol{\theta};k(\mathbf{u} - \mathbf{v})) \qquad \forall k \forall \mathbf{u} \forall \mathbf{v}$$

Suppose that $\boldsymbol{\alpha}$ is reachable from $\boldsymbol{\theta}$ by an input $\mathbf{w}$. Then, by the response separation property (*2.3.4*), we can write

8 $$\bar{\mathbf{A}}(\boldsymbol{\theta};\mathbf{wu}) = \bar{\mathbf{A}}(\boldsymbol{\theta};\mathbf{w}) + \bar{\mathbf{A}}(\boldsymbol{\alpha};\mathbf{u})$$
9 $$\bar{\mathbf{A}}(\boldsymbol{\theta};\mathbf{wv}) = \bar{\mathbf{A}}(\boldsymbol{\theta};\mathbf{w}) + \bar{\mathbf{A}}(\boldsymbol{\alpha};\mathbf{v})$$

where $\mathbf{wu}$ represents the segment resulting from adjoining $\mathbf{u}$ to $\mathbf{w}$ (with $\mathbf{u}$ following $\mathbf{w}$). [Note that $\bar{\mathbf{A}}(\boldsymbol{\theta};\mathbf{w})$ and $\bar{\mathbf{A}}(\boldsymbol{\alpha};\mathbf{u})$ are nonoverlapping segments.]

On subtracting *9* from *8* and multiplying both sides by k, we obtain

$$k\bar{\mathbf{A}}(\boldsymbol{\alpha};\mathbf{u}) - k\bar{\mathbf{A}}(\boldsymbol{\alpha};\mathbf{v}) = k\bar{\mathbf{A}}(\boldsymbol{\theta};\mathbf{wu}) - k\bar{\mathbf{A}}(\boldsymbol{\theta};\mathbf{wv})$$

Now, since $\mathfrak{A}$ is zero-state linear, we have

$$\begin{aligned} k\bar{\mathbf{A}}(\boldsymbol{\theta};\mathbf{wu}) - k\bar{\mathbf{A}}(\boldsymbol{\theta};\mathbf{wv}) &= \bar{\mathbf{A}}(\boldsymbol{\theta};k(\mathbf{wu} - \mathbf{wv})) \\ &= \bar{\mathbf{A}}(\boldsymbol{\theta};k(\mathbf{u} - \mathbf{v})) \end{aligned}$$

and hence

$$k\bar{\mathbf{A}}(\boldsymbol{\alpha};\mathbf{u}) - k\bar{\mathbf{A}}(\boldsymbol{\alpha};\mathbf{v}) = \bar{\mathbf{A}}(\boldsymbol{\theta};k(\mathbf{u} - \mathbf{v}))$$

for all $\mathbf{u},\mathbf{v}$ in the input segment space of $\mathfrak{A}$ and all real constants k.

10 **Corollary** If $\mathfrak{A}$ is zero-state linear and if all the states of $\mathfrak{A}$ are reachable from its zero state, then $\mathfrak{A}$ is linear with respect to all possible initial states. $\triangleleft$

The significance of Assertion *7* and its corollary is this. If a system is zero-state linear, then its nonlinearity can manifest itself only if the starting state is not the zero state or any state which is reachable from the zero state. Thus, if there are no states which are not reachable from the zero state, then zero-state linearity implies linearity with respect to all possible initial states.

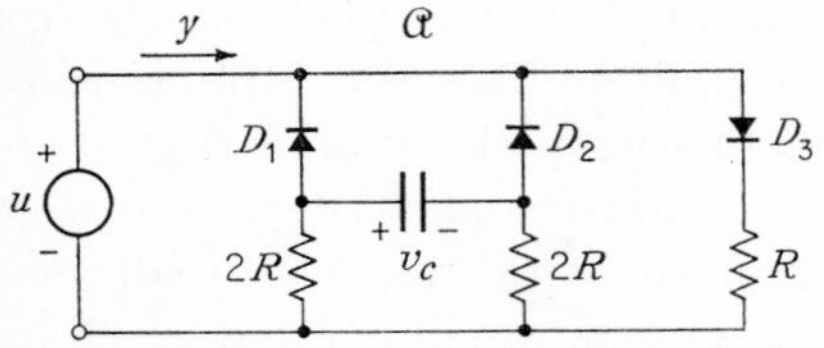

Fig. 3.4.1 Example of a nonlinear network which is zero-state linear.

11 *Example*[1] Consider the system $\mathfrak{A}$ shown in Fig. *3.4.1*. Here D_1, D_2, and D_3 are ideal diodes,[2] the voltage u is the input, and the current y is the output. The voltage v_C across the capacitor C qualifies as the state of the system, and the zero state corresponds to $v_C = 0$.

If $v_C = 0$ initially (at t_0-), then the currents through the branches containing D_1 and D_2 will be equal for $t \geq t_0$ and consequently v_C will remain equal to zero for $t \geq t_0$. By virtue of this, C can be removed from the network without affecting the current y. Thus, the system of Fig. *3.4.1* is zero-state equivalent to the networks $\mathfrak{A}',\mathfrak{A}''$ shown in Fig. *3.4.2*. These networks in turn are equivalent to a constant resistance R, which is a memoryless linear system. This implies that $\mathfrak{A}$ is zero-state linear.

[1] This simple example was suggested by D. Cargille, a student at the University of California.

[2] An ideal diode is a memoryless system characterized by the input-output relation $v(t) = 0$ for $i(t) \geq 0$ and $v(t) = \infty$ for $i(t) < 0$, where $i(t)$ is the current through the diode in the direction of the arrowhead and $v(t)$ is the voltage across the diode.

On the other hand, $\mathcal{A}$ is not linear with respect to all initial states in the sense of Definition *5*, since if it is started in any state α other than the zero state (that is, $v_C = \alpha \neq 0$ at t_0-), then the relation between u and y is not linear for the starting state α. Note also that the state $v_C = \alpha$, $\alpha \neq 0$, is not reachable from the zero state $v_C = 0$.

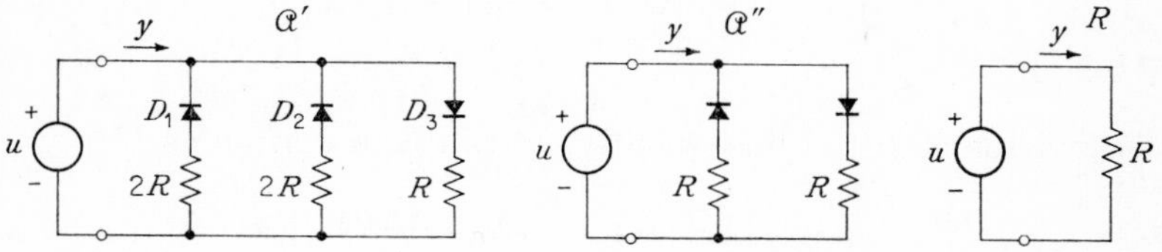

Fig. 3.4.2 $\mathcal{A}'$ is equivalent to $\mathcal{A}''$, which in turn is equivalent to R.

12 *Example* Consider the network $\mathcal{A}$, shown in Fig. *3.4.3*, in which R is a nonlinear resistance and G is a nonlinear conductance such that $R = G$ for equal values of their respective arguments and L is numerically equal to C. Essentially, this is merely a concrete instance of two networks $\mathfrak{N}$ and $\mathfrak{N}'$ (within the dashed-line rectangles) which are dual to one another in the sense that the voltages in $\mathfrak{N}$ are numerically equal to the corresponding currents in $\mathfrak{N}'$, and vice versa. Note that $\mathfrak{N}$ and $\mathfrak{N}'$ are converse to one another in the sense of Definition *2.10.1*. This implies that, if the dependence of R on the current passing through it is such that $\mathfrak{N}^{-1}$ (inverse of $\mathfrak{N}$) exists, then $\mathfrak{N}'$ is equivalent to $\mathfrak{N}^{-1}$.

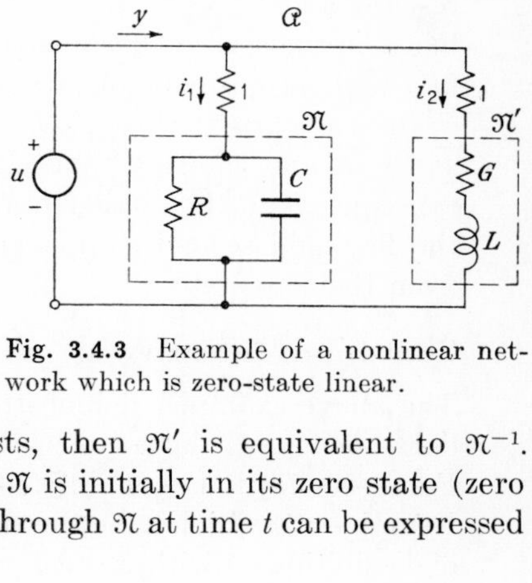

Fig. 3.4.3 Example of a nonlinear network which is zero-state linear.

Assuming that this is the case, if $\mathfrak{N}$ is initially in its zero state (zero voltage across C), then the current through $\mathfrak{N}$ at time t can be expressed symbolically as

13
$$i_1 = (I + N)^{-1}(u)$$

where $N(i_1)$ represents the zero-state response (voltage across $\mathfrak{N}$) to current i_1 and I is the identity operator. On the other hand, the current through $\mathfrak{N}'$, with $\mathfrak{N}'$ starting in its zero state (zero current through L), is given by

14
$$i_2 = (I + N^{-1})^{-1}(u)$$

Thus, the zero-state response of $\mathcal{A}$ to u is expressed by

15
$$y = [(I + N)^{-1} + (I + N^{-1})^{-1}](u)$$

Now for any $\mathcal{N}$—regardless of whether $\mathcal{N}$ is linear or nonlinear—which has a unique zero state and an inverse $\mathcal{N}^{-1}$, we can write

16 $$I + N^{-1} \doteq (I + N)N^{-1}$$

and hence

$$\begin{aligned}(I + N^{-1})^{-1} &\doteq [(I + N)N^{-1}]^{-1} \\ &\doteq N(I + N)^{-1}\end{aligned}$$

by virtue of *16*. Consequently, *15* can be rewritten as

$$\begin{aligned} y &= [(I + N)^{-1} + N(I + N)^{-1}](u) \\ &= (I + N)(1 + N)^{-1}(u) \\ &= I(u) \\ &= u \end{aligned}$$

This shows that any network of the form shown in Fig. *3.4.3*, in which $\mathcal{N}$ and $\mathcal{N}'$ are dual networks, is zero-state equivalent to a unit resistor and hence is zero-state linear. On the other hand, $\mathcal{A}$ is not linear in the sense of Definition *5* for the starting state (1,0), where the first and second components respectively represent the voltage across C and the current through L. [This is easily verified by calculating y at $t = t_0$ and showing that $y(t_0)$ is no equal to $u(t_0)$.] Note that in consequence of the duality of $\mathcal{N}$ and $\mathcal{N}'$ only those states of $\mathcal{A}$ in which the first and second components are numerically equal are reachable from the zero state.

Zero-input linearity

The above examples demonstrate that, in general, zero-state linearity does not imply linearity with respect to all possible initial states. Furthermore, it is not difficult to construct examples of systems (see Example *24*) which have the stronger property of linearity (in the sense of Definition *5*) with respect to all possible starting states and yet are clearly nonlinear. This indicates that the class of linear systems is narrower than the class of systems which are linear with respect to all possible starting states.

The additional property that we must require of a system $\mathcal{A}$ in order to justify our calling $\mathcal{A}$ "a linear system" is the property of *zero-input linearity* defined below.

17 **Definition** Let $\mathcal{A}$ be a system whose state space Σ is a linear vector space. Then $\mathcal{A}$ is *zero-input linear* if its zero-input response is a homogeneous and additive function of the initial state. That is,

18 $$\bar{\mathbf{A}}(k\boldsymbol{\alpha};\mathbf{0}) = k\bar{\mathbf{A}}(\boldsymbol{\alpha};\mathbf{0})$$

for all $\boldsymbol{\alpha}$ in Σ and all real constants k; and

19 $$\bar{\mathbf{A}}(\boldsymbol{\alpha}' + \boldsymbol{\alpha}''; \mathbf{0}) = \bar{\mathbf{A}}(\boldsymbol{\alpha}';\mathbf{0}) + \bar{\mathbf{A}}(\boldsymbol{\alpha}'';\mathbf{0})$$

for all $\boldsymbol{\alpha}'$, $\boldsymbol{\alpha}''$ in Σ, where $\bar{\mathbf{A}}(\boldsymbol{\alpha};\mathbf{0})$ denotes the zero-input response (segment) of $\mathcal{A}$ starting in state $\boldsymbol{\alpha}$. (Note that *18* and *19* can be combined into the single relation

20 $$\bar{\mathbf{A}}(k(\boldsymbol{\alpha}' - \boldsymbol{\alpha}'');\mathbf{0}) = k\bar{\mathbf{A}}(\boldsymbol{\alpha}';\mathbf{0}) - k\bar{\mathbf{A}}(\boldsymbol{\alpha}'';\mathbf{0}) \qquad \forall \boldsymbol{\alpha}' \forall \boldsymbol{\alpha}'' \forall k$$

in the manner of Definition *2*.)

21 *Comment* Since one-one mapping of the state space onto itself does not affect the character of a system (see *2.3.46 et seq.*) it is sufficient to require that the zero-input response be a homogeneous and additive function of not necessarily $\boldsymbol{\alpha}$ itself, but of some variable $\hat{\boldsymbol{\alpha}}$ which is in one-one correspondence with $\boldsymbol{\alpha}$. However, the more restrictive wording of Definition *17* is adequate for our purposes. ◁

A system may be zero-input linear without being zero-state linear, and vice versa. This possibility is illustrated by the following examples.

22 *Example* The system characterized by the input-output-state relation

23 $$y(t) = e^{-(t-t_0)}\alpha + \int_{t_0}^{t} e^{-(t-\xi)}u^2(\xi)\,d\xi \qquad t \geq t_0$$

where α represents the initial state of the system, is zero-input linear but not zero-state linear. (Here $\Sigma = \mathcal{R}^1 \triangleq$ real line.)

24 *Example* The system characterized by the input-output-state relation

$$y(t) = (e^{-(t-t_0)}\alpha_1 + e^{-2(t-t_0)}\alpha_2)^2 + \int_{t_0}^{t} (e^{-(t-\xi)} + e^{-2(t-\xi)})u(\xi)\,d\xi \qquad t \geq t_0$$

where $\boldsymbol{\alpha} = (\alpha_1,\alpha_2)$ is the initial state vector, is zero-state linear but not zero-input linear. (Here $\Sigma = \mathcal{R}^2 \triangleq$ space of pairs of real numbers.)

Definition of linearity

We are now ready to formulate a general definition of linearity which subsumes both zero-state linearity and zero-input linearity. It reads:

25 **Definition** A system $\mathcal{A}$ is *linear* if and only if:

(I) $\mathcal{A}$ is linear with respect to all possible initial states; that is

26 $$k\bar{\mathbf{A}}(\boldsymbol{\alpha};\mathbf{u}) - k\bar{\mathbf{A}}(\boldsymbol{\alpha};\mathbf{v}) = \bar{\mathbf{A}}(\boldsymbol{\theta};k(\mathbf{u} - \mathbf{v}))$$

for all $\mathbf{u},\mathbf{v}$ in $R[\mathbf{u}]$ and all real constants k (see Definition *5*); and

(II) $\mathcal{A}$ is zero-input linear; that is

27 $$k\bar{\mathbf{A}}(\boldsymbol{\alpha}';\mathbf{0}) - k\bar{\mathbf{A}}(\boldsymbol{\alpha}'';\mathbf{0}) = \bar{\mathbf{A}}(k(\boldsymbol{\alpha}' - \boldsymbol{\alpha}'');\mathbf{0})$$

for all $\boldsymbol{\alpha}',\boldsymbol{\alpha}''$ in Σ (see Definition *17*). It is understood that Σ, $R[\mathbf{u}]$, and $R[\mathbf{y}]$ are linear spaces (see *3.3.2*). ◁

This definition constitutes the starting point of our analysis of linear systems. We proceed to study some of the immediate implications of Definition *25* in the following section.

5 *Linearity and some of its implications*

The decomposition property

There are several basic properties of linear systems which can easily be deduced from Definition *3.4.25*. Specifically, on setting $k = 1$ and $\mathbf{v} = \mathbf{0}$ in *3.4.26*, we obtain the identity

1 $$\bar{\mathbf{A}}(\boldsymbol{\alpha};\mathbf{u}) = \bar{\mathbf{A}}(\boldsymbol{\alpha};\mathbf{0}) + \bar{\mathbf{A}}(\boldsymbol{\theta};\mathbf{u}) \qquad \forall\boldsymbol{\alpha}\forall\mathbf{u}$$

which, in words, means that the response of $\mathcal{A}$ to $\mathbf{u}$ starting in state $\boldsymbol{\alpha}$ is identical with the zero-input response of $\mathcal{A}$ starting in state $\boldsymbol{\alpha}$ plus the zero-state response of $\mathcal{A}$ to $\mathbf{u}$.

Any, not necessarily linear, system whose input-output-state relation admits of this representation will be said to have the *decomposition property*. More formally,

2 **Definition** A system $\mathcal{A}$ has the *decomposition property* if its response to any input $\mathbf{u}$, with $\mathcal{A}$ initially in any state $\boldsymbol{\alpha}$, can be expressed in the form *1*, that is, as the sum of the zero-input response $\bar{\mathbf{A}}(\boldsymbol{\alpha};\mathbf{0})$ and the zero-state response $\bar{\mathbf{A}}(\boldsymbol{\theta};\mathbf{u})$. ◁

Equation *1* shows that every linear system has the decomposition property. The converse, however, is not true, as is demonstrated by Examples *3.4.22* and *3.4.24*.

An alternative definition of linearity

If a system $\mathcal{A}$ is linear, then in consequence of Definition *3.4.25* it has the decomposition property, and in addition, it is zero-state and zero-input linear. Conversely, it is easy to establish that if $\mathcal{A}$ has these three properties, then it is linear in the sense of Definition *3.4.25*. Specifically, suppose that $\mathcal{A}$ has the decomposition property. Then, on writing

3 $$k\bar{\mathbf{A}}(\boldsymbol{\alpha};\mathbf{u}) = k\bar{\mathbf{A}}(\boldsymbol{\alpha};\mathbf{0}) + k\bar{\mathbf{A}}(\boldsymbol{\theta};\mathbf{u}) \qquad \forall\boldsymbol{\alpha}\forall\mathbf{u}\forall k$$

4 $$k\bar{\mathbf{A}}(\boldsymbol{\alpha};\mathbf{v}) = k\bar{\mathbf{A}}(\boldsymbol{\alpha};\mathbf{0}) + k\bar{\mathbf{A}}(\boldsymbol{\theta};\mathbf{v}) \qquad \forall\boldsymbol{\alpha}\forall\mathbf{v}\forall k$$

and subtracting *4* from *3*, we have

5 $$k\bar{\mathbf{A}}(\boldsymbol{\alpha};\mathbf{u}) - k\bar{\mathbf{A}}(\boldsymbol{\alpha};\mathbf{v}) = k\bar{\mathbf{A}}(\boldsymbol{\theta};\mathbf{u}) - k\bar{\mathbf{A}}(\boldsymbol{\theta};\mathbf{v}) \qquad \forall\boldsymbol{\alpha}\forall\mathbf{u}\forall\mathbf{v}\forall k$$

If, in addition, $\mathcal{A}$ is zero-state linear, then *5* can be replaced by

$$k\bar{\mathbf{A}}(\boldsymbol{\alpha};\mathbf{u}) - k\bar{\mathbf{A}}(\boldsymbol{\alpha};\mathbf{v}) = \bar{\mathbf{A}}(\boldsymbol{\theta};k(\mathbf{u} - \mathbf{v})) \qquad \forall\boldsymbol{\alpha}\forall\mathbf{u}\forall\mathbf{v}\forall k$$

This relation shows that if $\mathcal{A}$ has the decomposition property and is zero-state linear, then $\mathcal{A}$ is linear with respect to all possible initial states $\boldsymbol{\alpha}$. Consequently, if $\mathcal{A}$ has the decomposition property and is both zero-state and zero-input linear, then $\mathcal{A}$ qualifies as a linear system under Definition *3.4.25*.

This conclusion permits us to replace Definition *3.4.25* by the equivalent

6 **Definition** A system $\mathcal{A}$ is *linear* if and only if it has the following three properties:

Decomposition property (*2*)

7 $$\bar{\mathbf{A}}(\boldsymbol{\alpha};\mathbf{u}) = \bar{\mathbf{A}}(\boldsymbol{\alpha};\mathbf{0}) + \bar{\mathbf{A}}(\boldsymbol{\theta};\mathbf{u}) \qquad \forall\boldsymbol{\alpha}\forall\mathbf{u}$$

Zero-state linearity (*3.4.1*)

8 $$\bar{\mathbf{A}}(\boldsymbol{\theta};k(\mathbf{u} - \mathbf{v})) = k\bar{\mathbf{A}}(\boldsymbol{\theta};\mathbf{u}) - k\bar{\mathbf{A}}(\boldsymbol{\theta};\mathbf{v}) \qquad \forall\mathbf{u}\forall\mathbf{v}\forall k$$

Zero-input linearity (*3.4.17*)

9 $$\bar{\mathbf{A}}(k(\boldsymbol{\alpha}' - \boldsymbol{\alpha}'');\mathbf{0}) = k\bar{\mathbf{A}}(\boldsymbol{\alpha}';\mathbf{0}) - k\bar{\mathbf{A}}(\boldsymbol{\alpha}'';\mathbf{0}) \qquad \forall\boldsymbol{\alpha}'\forall\boldsymbol{\alpha}''\forall k \qquad \triangleleft$$

In what follows, we shall be using for the most part Definition *6*, rather than the earlier Definition *3.4.25*, as the definition of linearity. We shall forego illustrating Definition *6* at this point, since there will be numerous examples of linear systems in the sequel.

A fact concerning equivalent states and equivalent systems

Before proceeding to study various special features of linear systems, it will be helpful to establish a simple fact concerning state equivalence which will be of use later in this section and which is characteristic of systems having the decomposition property. Expressed in the form of an assertion, it reads

10 **Assertion** If $\mathcal{A}$ has the decomposition property, then two states of $\mathcal{A}$, say $\boldsymbol{\alpha}'$ and $\boldsymbol{\alpha}''$, are equivalent (*2.2.1*) if and only if the zero-input response of $\mathcal{A}$ starting in state $\boldsymbol{\alpha}'$ is identical with the zero-input response of $\mathcal{A}$ starting in state $\boldsymbol{\alpha}''$. In symbols,

11 $$\{\boldsymbol{\alpha}' \simeq \boldsymbol{\alpha}''\} \Leftrightarrow \{\bar{\mathbf{A}}(\boldsymbol{\alpha}';\mathbf{0}) = \bar{\mathbf{A}}(\boldsymbol{\alpha}'';\mathbf{0})\}$$

Comment An immediate consequence of Assertion *10* is that if $\mathcal{A}$ and $\mathcal{B}$ have the decomposition property, then $\mathcal{A} \equiv \mathcal{B}$ if $\mathcal{A}$ and $\mathcal{B}$ are both zero-input and zero-state equivalent (see *2.9.1* and *2.9.2*).

Proof We have

$$\bar{\mathbf{A}}(\boldsymbol{\alpha}';\mathbf{u}) = \bar{\mathbf{A}}(\boldsymbol{\alpha}';\mathbf{0}) + \bar{\mathbf{A}}(\boldsymbol{\theta};\mathbf{u})$$
$$\bar{\mathbf{A}}(\boldsymbol{\alpha}'';\mathbf{u}) = \bar{\mathbf{A}}(\boldsymbol{\alpha}'';\mathbf{0}) + \bar{\mathbf{A}}(\boldsymbol{\theta};\mathbf{u})$$

from which it follows at once that $\bar{\mathbf{A}}(\boldsymbol{\alpha}';\mathbf{u}) = \bar{\mathbf{A}}(\boldsymbol{\alpha}'';\mathbf{u})$ for all $\mathbf{u}$ if and only if $\bar{\mathbf{A}}(\boldsymbol{\alpha}';\mathbf{0}) = \bar{\mathbf{A}}(\boldsymbol{\alpha}'';\mathbf{0})$. Note that *11* necessitates that the zero state $\boldsymbol{\theta}$ be unique (to within equivalent states).

12 *Example* As a simple illustration of *10*, consider the network of Example *2.2.7*, for which the input-output-state relation reads

$$y(t) = i_1(t_0-) + i_2(t_0-) + \left(\frac{1}{L_1} + \frac{1}{L_2}\right)\int_{t_0}^{t} u(\xi)\, d\xi \qquad t \geq t_0$$

Here $\boldsymbol{\alpha}$ is a 2-vector with components $\alpha_1 \triangleq i_1(t_0-)$ and $\alpha_2 \triangleq i_2(t_0-)$, and the zero-input response is given by

$$\bar{\mathbf{A}}(\boldsymbol{\alpha};\mathbf{0}) = \alpha_1 + \alpha_2 \qquad t \geq t_0$$

Thus, two states $\boldsymbol{\alpha}' \triangleq (\alpha_1',\alpha_2')$ and $\boldsymbol{\alpha}'' \triangleq (\alpha_1'',\alpha_2'')$ are equivalent if and only if $\alpha_1' + \alpha_2' = \alpha_1'' + \alpha_2''$. Note that any state of the form $\boldsymbol{\alpha} = (\alpha_1, -\alpha_1)$ is equivalent to the zero state $\boldsymbol{\theta} = (0,0)$. $\triangleleft$

The following corollary of Assertion *10* follows at once from *10* and the zero-input linearity of $\mathcal{A}$.

13 **Corollary** If $\boldsymbol{\alpha}'$ and $\boldsymbol{\alpha}''$ are equivalent states of a linear system $\mathcal{A}$, then every linear combination $\boldsymbol{\alpha} = a\boldsymbol{\alpha}' + b\boldsymbol{\alpha}''$ is a state equivalent to $\boldsymbol{\alpha}'$ (and $\boldsymbol{\alpha}''$). This implies that the sets of equivalent states of $\mathcal{A}$ constitute *linear varieties* in Σ. (A linear variety is a translate of a subspace of Σ.)

Special features of linear systems

The importance of the concept of linearity stems mainly from two special features of linear systems. The first of these is the relative ease with which the response of a linear system $\mathcal{A}$ to a given input $\mathbf{u}$ can be determined. Specifically, by virtue of the decomposition property, the response can be expressed in the form

$$\mathbf{A}(\boldsymbol{\alpha};\mathbf{u}) = \mathbf{A}(\boldsymbol{\alpha};\mathbf{0}) + \mathbf{A}(\boldsymbol{\theta};\mathbf{u})$$

which separates the effect of $\mathbf{u}$ from that of the "initial excitation" represented by $\boldsymbol{\alpha}$. Furthermore, by virtue of the zero-state linearity of $\mathcal{A}$, the problem of determining the zero-state response $\mathbf{A}(\boldsymbol{\theta};\mathbf{u})$, or, for short, $\mathbf{A}(\mathbf{u})$, can be reduced to that of resolving $\mathbf{u}$ into simpler components $\boldsymbol{\phi}_1$, $\boldsymbol{\phi}_2$, . . . and determining the zero-state response to each component separately. More specifically, suppose that $\mathbf{u}$ is resolved into a set of component time functions $\boldsymbol{\phi}_1$, $\boldsymbol{\phi}_2$, . . . by expressing $\mathbf{u}$ as an infinite series

14 $$\mathbf{u} = a_1\boldsymbol{\phi}_1 + a_2\boldsymbol{\phi}_2 + \cdots$$

where the coefficients a_λ, $\lambda = 1, 2, \ldots$, are constants representing the "weights" of the component time functions $\boldsymbol{\phi}_1, \boldsymbol{\phi}_2, \ldots$ in $\mathbf{u}$. Now, if $\mathfrak{A}$ is countably additive, then the zero-state response of $\mathfrak{A}$ to $\mathbf{u}$ can be expressed as an infinite series

15 $$\mathbf{A}(\mathbf{u}) = a_1\mathbf{A}(\boldsymbol{\phi}_1) + a_2\mathbf{A}(\boldsymbol{\phi}_2) + \cdots$$

where $\mathbf{A}(\boldsymbol{\phi}_\lambda)$ represents the zero-state response of $\mathfrak{A}$ to the component $\boldsymbol{\phi}_\lambda$, $\lambda = 1, 2, \ldots$. Thus, if the $\boldsymbol{\phi}_\lambda$ are chosen in such a way that the determination of the zero-state response of $\mathfrak{A}$ to $\boldsymbol{\phi}_\lambda$, $\lambda = 1, 2, \ldots$, is a significantly simpler problem than the direct calculation of $\mathbf{A}(\mathbf{u})$, then it may be advantageous to determine $\mathbf{A}(\mathbf{u})$ indirectly by (I) resolving $\mathbf{u}$ into the $\boldsymbol{\phi}_\lambda$, (II) calculating $\mathbf{A}(\boldsymbol{\phi}_\lambda)$, $\lambda = 1, 2, \ldots$, and (III) obtaining $\mathbf{A}(\mathbf{u})$ by summing the series represented by *15*.

This basic procedure appears in various guises in many of the methods used to analyze the behavior of linear systems. In general, the set of component time functions $\{\boldsymbol{\phi}_\lambda\}$ is a continuum rather than a countable set—as is assumed in the above discussion—and the summations in *14* and *15* are integrals in which λ plays the role of the variable of integration. The basic idea, however, remains the same.

16 *Example* In the case of a complex Fourier series, the component time functions are of the form $e^{j\lambda\omega_0 t}$, where λ ranges over all integers and ω_0 is a real constant (fundamental frequency).

17 *Example* In the case of the Fourier integral representation, the component time functions form a continuum $\{e^{j\omega t}\}$, in which ω ranges over all real numbers.

18 *Example* The Laplace transform technique for the analysis of linear systems (see Appendix *B*) is based essentially on the resolution of u and y into component time functions of the form e^{st}, where s is a complex variable ranging over a line parallel to the axis of imaginaries in the s plane. Note that both the Laplace transform and the Fourier integral techniques are particularly effective in dealing with systems in which the determination of the response to $e^{j\omega t}$ or e^{st} is a simple problem. It is for this reason that the Laplace and Fourier transform techniques are used so widely in the analysis of linear time-invariant systems.

19 *Example* A particularly simple set of component time functions is the set of delta functions $\{\delta(t - \lambda)\}$, in which λ ranges over the real line. In this case, the resolution of a scalar time function u into the $\delta(t - \lambda)$ is trivially simple (see Appendix *A*), but the problem of finding the zero-state response to $\delta(t - \lambda)$ is frequently not much easier

than that of finding the zero-state response to u. Nevertheless, there is generally a distinct advantage, at least for purposes of representation of input-output relations, in resolving the input time function into the delta functions.

The closure theorem

The second special feature of linear systems finds its expression in the following

20 **Theorem** The class of linear systems is closed under the operations of system addition, multiplication, and inversion. Stated more explicitly, if $\mathcal{A}$ and $\mathcal{B}$ are linear systems, then so are $\mathcal{A} + \mathcal{B}$ and $\mathcal{A}\mathcal{B}$. Furthermore, if $\mathcal{A}$ has an inverse $\mathcal{A}^{-1}$, then $\mathcal{A}^{-1}$ is a linear system. (In effect, Theorem *20* states that any interconnection of linear systems is a linear system.)

Proof To prove this theorem, we have to establish that $\mathcal{A} + \mathcal{B}$, $\mathcal{A}\mathcal{B}$, and $\mathcal{A}^{-1}$ have the decomposition property and are both zero-state and zero-input linear. We begin with establishing this for $\mathcal{A} + \mathcal{B}$.

Let $\boldsymbol{\alpha}$ and $\boldsymbol{\beta}$ denote the states of $\mathcal{A}$ and $\mathcal{B}$, respectively. Then by Theorem *2.6.10* the state of $\mathcal{A} + \mathcal{B} \triangleq \mathcal{C}$ can be taken to be $\boldsymbol{\gamma} \triangleq (\boldsymbol{\alpha},\boldsymbol{\beta})$ (see Theorem *2.6.23*), with the zero state of $\mathcal{C}$ being $(\boldsymbol{\theta},\boldsymbol{\theta})$. (*Exercise:* Show that the zero state of $\mathcal{C}$ is unique.)

In terms of the input-output-state relations of $\mathcal{A}$ and $\mathcal{B}$, the input-output-state relation of $\mathcal{C}$ reads

21 $$\bar{\mathbf{C}}(\boldsymbol{\gamma};\mathbf{u}) = \bar{\mathbf{A}}(\boldsymbol{\alpha};\mathbf{0}) + \bar{\mathbf{B}}(\boldsymbol{\beta};\mathbf{0}) + \bar{\mathbf{A}}(\boldsymbol{\theta};\mathbf{u}) + \bar{\mathbf{B}}(\boldsymbol{\theta};\mathbf{u})$$

It is evident from inspection of *21* that $\mathcal{C}$ has the decomposition property and is both zero-state and zero-input linear. Consequently, $\mathcal{C}$ is linear.

Next, consider $\mathcal{C} \triangleq \mathcal{A}\mathcal{B}$. In this case, recalling the definition of the product of two systems (*1.10.23*) and making use of the linearity of $\mathcal{A}$ and $\mathcal{B}$, the expression for the input-output-state relation of $\mathcal{C}$ becomes

22 $$\bar{\mathbf{C}}(\boldsymbol{\gamma};\mathbf{u}) = \bar{\mathbf{A}}(\boldsymbol{\alpha};\mathbf{0}) + \bar{\mathbf{A}}(\boldsymbol{\theta};\bar{\mathbf{B}}(\boldsymbol{\beta};\mathbf{0})) + \bar{\mathbf{A}}(\boldsymbol{\theta};\bar{\mathbf{B}}(\boldsymbol{\theta};\mathbf{u}))$$

where the second term represents the zero-state response of $\mathcal{A}$ to the zero-input response of $\mathcal{B}$ and the third term represents the zero-state response of $\mathcal{A}$ to the zero-state response of $\mathcal{B}$ to $\mathbf{u}$.

Now, on setting $\mathbf{u} = \mathbf{0}$ in *22*, the expression for the zero-input response of $\mathcal{C}$ is found to be

23 $$\bar{\mathbf{C}}(\boldsymbol{\gamma};\mathbf{0}) = \bar{\mathbf{A}}(\boldsymbol{\alpha};\mathbf{0}) + \bar{\mathbf{A}}(\boldsymbol{\theta};\bar{\mathbf{B}}(\boldsymbol{\beta};\mathbf{0}))$$

To verify that $\mathcal{C}$ is zero-input linear, we note that since $\boldsymbol{\gamma} \triangleq (\boldsymbol{\alpha},\boldsymbol{\beta})$, $k\boldsymbol{\gamma} = (k\boldsymbol{\alpha},k\boldsymbol{\beta})$ for all real k. Likewise, if $\boldsymbol{\gamma}' \triangleq (\boldsymbol{\alpha}',\boldsymbol{\beta}')$ and $\boldsymbol{\gamma}'' \triangleq (\boldsymbol{\alpha}'',\boldsymbol{\beta}'')$, then $\gamma' - \gamma'' = (\alpha' - \alpha'', \beta' - \beta'')$. Thus,

24 $$\begin{aligned}\bar{\mathbf{C}}(k(\gamma' - \gamma'');\mathbf{0}) &= \bar{\mathbf{A}}(k(\alpha' - \alpha'');\mathbf{0}) + \bar{\mathbf{A}}(\boldsymbol{\theta};\bar{\mathbf{B}}(k(\beta' - \beta'');\mathbf{0}))\\ &= k\bar{\mathbf{A}}(\alpha';\mathbf{0}) - k\bar{\mathbf{A}}(\alpha'';\mathbf{0}) + k\bar{\mathbf{A}}(\boldsymbol{\theta};\bar{\mathbf{B}}(\beta';\mathbf{0}))\\ &\qquad - k\bar{\mathbf{A}}(\boldsymbol{\theta};\bar{\mathbf{B}}(\beta'';\mathbf{0}))\\ &= k\bar{\mathbf{C}}(\gamma';\mathbf{0}) - k\bar{\mathbf{C}}(\gamma'';\mathbf{0}) \qquad \forall\gamma'\ \forall\gamma''\ \forall k\end{aligned}$$

by virtue of the linearity of $\mathcal{A}$ and $\mathcal{B}$. Consequently, $\mathcal{C}$ is zero-input linear.

In a similar fashion, the zero-state response of $\mathcal{C}$ is found by setting $\gamma = \boldsymbol{\theta}_c \triangleq (\boldsymbol{\theta},\boldsymbol{\theta})$ = zero state of $\mathcal{C}$ in *22*. This yields

25 $$\bar{\mathbf{C}}(\boldsymbol{\theta}_c;\mathbf{u}) = \bar{\mathbf{A}}(\boldsymbol{\theta};\bar{\mathbf{B}}(\boldsymbol{\theta};\mathbf{u}))$$

Again, for any $\mathbf{u}',\mathbf{u}''$ in $R[\mathbf{u}]$ and any real k, we can write

26 $$\begin{aligned}\bar{\mathbf{C}}(\boldsymbol{\theta}_c;k(\mathbf{u}' - \mathbf{u}'')) &= k\bar{\mathbf{A}}(\boldsymbol{\theta};\mathbf{B}(\boldsymbol{\theta};\mathbf{u}')) - k\bar{\mathbf{A}}(\boldsymbol{\theta};\mathbf{B}(\boldsymbol{\theta};\mathbf{u}''))\\ &= k\bar{\mathbf{C}}(\boldsymbol{\theta}_c;\mathbf{u}') - k\bar{\mathbf{C}}(\boldsymbol{\theta}_c;\mathbf{u}'')\end{aligned}$$

which shows that $\mathcal{C}$ is zero-state linear. Furthermore, on comparing the expressions for $\bar{\mathbf{C}}(\gamma;\mathbf{0})$ (*23*) and $\bar{\mathbf{C}}(\boldsymbol{\theta}_c;\mathbf{u})$ (*25*) with that for $\bar{\mathbf{C}}(\gamma;\mathbf{u})$ (*22*), we can write

$$\bar{\mathbf{C}}(\gamma;\mathbf{u}) = \bar{\mathbf{C}}(\gamma;\mathbf{0}) + \bar{\mathbf{C}}(\boldsymbol{\theta}_c;\mathbf{u})$$

which implies that $\mathcal{C}$ has the decomposition property. This conclusion, together with the just established zero-state and zero-input linearity of $\mathcal{C}$, implies that $\mathcal{C}$ is linear.

Finally, consider $\mathcal{A}^{-1}$. We shall show first that $\mathcal{A}^{-1}$ is zero-state linear. For this purpose, define

27 $$\mathbf{v}' \triangleq \bar{\mathbf{A}}(\boldsymbol{\theta};\mathbf{u}') \qquad \mathbf{v}'' \triangleq \bar{\mathbf{A}}(\boldsymbol{\theta};\mathbf{u}'')$$

where $\mathbf{u}'$ and $\mathbf{u}''$ are arbitrary inputs in $R[\mathbf{u}]$, and let the input to $\mathcal{A}$ be $k(\mathbf{u}' - \mathbf{u}'')$ with $\mathcal{A}$ in its zero state. Then the input to $\mathcal{A}^{-1}$ is $k(\mathbf{v}' - \mathbf{v}'')$, and since $\mathcal{A}^{-1}$ is inverse to $\mathcal{A}$, its zero-state response to $k(\mathbf{v}' - \mathbf{v}'')$ must be $k(\mathbf{u}' - \mathbf{u}'')$. Thus,

$$\bar{\mathbf{A}}^{-1}(\boldsymbol{\theta};k(\mathbf{v}' - \mathbf{v}'')) = k\mathbf{u}' - k\mathbf{u}'' \qquad \forall\mathbf{u}'\forall\mathbf{u}''$$

where $\bar{\mathbf{A}}^{-1}(\boldsymbol{\theta};\mathbf{v})$ denotes the zero-state response of $\mathcal{A}^{-1}$ to $\mathbf{v}$, and since

28 $$\bar{\mathbf{A}}^{-1}(\boldsymbol{\theta};\mathbf{v}') = \mathbf{u}' \qquad \bar{\mathbf{A}}^{-1}(\boldsymbol{\theta};\mathbf{v}'') = \mathbf{u}''$$

we have

29 $$\bar{\mathbf{A}}^{-1}(\boldsymbol{\theta};k(\mathbf{v}' - \mathbf{v}'')) = k\bar{\mathbf{A}}^{-1}(\boldsymbol{\theta};\mathbf{v}') - k\bar{\mathbf{A}}^{-1}(\boldsymbol{\theta};\mathbf{v}'') \qquad \forall\mathbf{v}'\forall\mathbf{v}''\forall k$$

where $\mathbf{v}'$ and $\mathbf{v}''$ range over the output segment space of $\mathcal{A}$ [(which is assumed to coincide with the input segment space of $\mathcal{A}^{-1}$ (see *2.10.6*)]. This establishes that $\mathcal{A}^{-1}$ is zero-state linear.

Next, suppose that $\mathcal{A}$ is initially in state $\boldsymbol{\alpha}$ and $\mathcal{A}^{-1}$ is in a corresponding state $\boldsymbol{\alpha}^{-1}$ (see *2.10.6*). Under these conditions, let the input to $\mathcal{A}^{-1}$ be zero and let the zero-input response of $\mathcal{A}^{-1}$, which is $\bar{\mathbf{A}}^{-1}(\boldsymbol{\alpha}^{-1};\mathbf{0})$, be applied to $\mathcal{A}$. Since the output of $\mathcal{A}$ must be zero, we have

$$\bar{\mathbf{A}}(\boldsymbol{\alpha};\bar{\mathbf{A}}^{-1}(\boldsymbol{\alpha}^{-1};\mathbf{0})) = \mathbf{0}$$

which can be written as

30 $$\bar{\mathbf{A}}(\boldsymbol{\alpha};\mathbf{0}) = -\bar{\mathbf{A}}(\boldsymbol{\theta};\bar{\mathbf{A}}^{-1}(\boldsymbol{\alpha}^{-1};\mathbf{0}))$$

by virtue of the decomposition property of $\mathcal{A}$.

Under the same conditions, let the input to $\mathcal{A}$ be $\mathbf{u}$ and let the output of $\mathcal{A}$,

31 $$\mathbf{w} \triangleq \bar{\mathbf{A}}(\boldsymbol{\alpha};\mathbf{u}) = \bar{\mathbf{A}}(\boldsymbol{\alpha};\mathbf{0}) + \bar{\mathbf{A}}(\boldsymbol{\theta};\mathbf{u})$$

be applied to $\mathcal{A}^{-1}$ in state $\boldsymbol{\alpha}^{-1}$. In this case, the output of $\mathcal{A}^{-1}$ must be $\mathbf{u}$ and hence

32 $$\bar{\mathbf{A}}^{-1}(\boldsymbol{\alpha}^{-1};\bar{\mathbf{A}}(\boldsymbol{\alpha};\mathbf{0}) + \bar{\mathbf{A}}(\boldsymbol{\theta};\mathbf{u})) = \mathbf{u}$$

Now let $\mathbf{v}$ be the zero-state response of $\mathcal{A}$ to $\mathbf{u}$. Then

$$\mathbf{v} = \bar{\mathbf{A}}(\boldsymbol{\theta};\mathbf{u}) \qquad \text{and} \qquad \bar{\mathbf{A}}^{-1}(\boldsymbol{\theta};\mathbf{v}) = \mathbf{u}$$

since $\mathbf{v}$ applied to $\mathcal{A}^{-1}$ (in zero state) should yield $\mathbf{u}$. Thus, *32* may be rewritten as

33 $$\bar{\mathbf{A}}^{-1}(\boldsymbol{\alpha}^{-1};\bar{\mathbf{A}}(\boldsymbol{\alpha};\mathbf{0}) + \mathbf{v}) = \bar{\mathbf{A}}^{-1}(\boldsymbol{\theta};\mathbf{v})$$

or, in view of *31*,

$$\bar{\mathbf{A}}^{-1}(\boldsymbol{\alpha}^{-1};\mathbf{w}) = \bar{\mathbf{A}}^{-1}(\boldsymbol{\theta};\mathbf{w} - \bar{\mathbf{A}}(\boldsymbol{\alpha};\mathbf{0}))$$

which in turn may be written as

34 $$\bar{\mathbf{A}}^{-1}(\boldsymbol{\alpha}^{-1};\mathbf{w}) = \bar{\mathbf{A}}^{-1}(\boldsymbol{\theta};\mathbf{w}) - \bar{\mathbf{A}}^{-1}(\boldsymbol{\theta};\bar{\mathbf{A}}(\boldsymbol{\alpha};\mathbf{0}))$$

by virtue of the zero-state linearity of $\mathcal{A}^{-1}$.

On substituting $\bar{\mathbf{A}}(\boldsymbol{\alpha};\mathbf{0})$ as given by *30* into *34* and making use of the identity

$$\bar{\mathbf{A}}^{-1}(\boldsymbol{\theta};\bar{\mathbf{A}}(\boldsymbol{\theta};\bar{\mathbf{A}}^{-1}(\boldsymbol{\alpha}^{-1};\mathbf{0}))) = \bar{\mathbf{A}}^{-1}(\boldsymbol{\alpha}^{-1};\mathbf{0})$$

we obtain

35 $$\bar{\mathbf{A}}^{-1}(\boldsymbol{\alpha}^{-1};\mathbf{w}) = \bar{\mathbf{A}}^{-1}(\boldsymbol{\alpha}^{-1};\mathbf{0}) + \bar{\mathbf{A}}^{-1}(\boldsymbol{\theta};\mathbf{w})$$

which establishes that $\mathcal{A}^{-1}$ has the decomposition property.

It remains to be shown that $\mathcal{A}^{-1}$ is zero-input linear. To this end, let $\mathcal{A}$ be initially in state $\boldsymbol{\alpha}$ and let the input to $\mathcal{A}$ be zero. Then, on applying the output of $\mathcal{A}$, which is $\bar{\mathbf{A}}(\boldsymbol{\alpha};\mathbf{0})$, to $\mathcal{A}^{-1}$ (in state $\boldsymbol{\alpha}^{-1}$)

we should get zero output; i.e.,

36 $$\bar{\mathbf{A}}^{-1}(\boldsymbol{\alpha}^{-1};\bar{\mathbf{A}}(\boldsymbol{\alpha};\mathbf{0})) = \mathbf{0}$$

Since $\mathcal{A}^{-1}$ has the decomposition property, *36* may be written as

$$\bar{\mathbf{A}}^{-1}(\boldsymbol{\alpha}^{-1};\mathbf{0}) = -\bar{\mathbf{A}}^{-1}(\boldsymbol{\theta};\mathbf{A}(\boldsymbol{\alpha};\mathbf{0}))$$

From this relation and the zero-state linearity of $\mathcal{A}$ and $\mathcal{A}^{-1}$ it follows at once that $\mathcal{A}^{-1}$ is zero-input linear. This completes our proof of Theorem *20*. ◁

An incidental and yet interesting identity which we used in the course of proving Theorem *20* is given by *30*. In view of the importance of the property expressed by *30*, we state it as an

37 **Assertion** Let $\mathcal{A}$ be a (not necessarily linear) system having the decomposition property and let $\mathcal{A}$ have an inverse $\mathcal{A}^{-1}$. Then, given any initial state $\boldsymbol{\alpha}$ of $\mathcal{A}$, one can always find an input $\mathbf{u}$ such that the zero-state response of $\mathcal{A}$ to $\mathbf{u}$ is equal to the negative of the zero-input response of $\mathcal{A}$ starting in state $\boldsymbol{\alpha}$. Specifically, $\mathbf{u}$ is given by

38 $$\mathbf{u} = \bar{\mathbf{A}}^{-1}(\boldsymbol{\alpha}^{-1};\mathbf{0})$$

where $\boldsymbol{\alpha}^{-1}$ is the state of $\mathcal{A}^{-1}$ corresponding to the state $\boldsymbol{\alpha}$ of $\mathcal{A}$.

In plain words, this means that the initial excitation of $\mathcal{A}$, which is defined by $\boldsymbol{\alpha}$, can be traded for an input $\mathbf{u}$ given by *38*.

39 *Example* As a simple illustration, let $\mathcal{A}$ be a system characterized by the input-output relation

40 $$\frac{dy}{dt} + y = u$$

The input-output state relation of this system reads (see *2.10.14*)

41 $$y(t) = y(t_0-)e^{-(t-t_0)} + \int_{t_0}^{t} e^{-(t-\xi)}u(\xi)\,d\xi \qquad t \geq t_0$$

with $y(t_0-) = \alpha$ representing the state at time t_0-.

Correspondingly, the input-output-state relation of the inverse system is given by (see *2.10.15*)

$$y(t) = -u(t_0-)\delta(t - t_0) + \frac{dy}{dt} + u$$

and if the state of $\mathcal{A}$ is α, then the corresponding state of $\mathcal{A}^{-1}$ is $-u(t_0) = -y(t_0-) = -\alpha$.

Now the zero-input response of $\mathcal{A}$ starting in state α is

$$A(\alpha;0) = \alpha e^{-(t-t_0)} \qquad t \geq t_0$$

and by Assertion *37* the negative of this response can be obtained by applying to $\mathcal{A}$ the input

42 $$A^{-1}(\alpha^{-1};0) = -\alpha\delta(t - t_0)$$

with $\mathcal{A}$ starting in zero state. This is easily verified by substituting *42* into *41*, with $y(t_0-)$ set equal to zero.

6 *Further implications of linearity*

Representation of input-output-state relations

In this section we shall focus our attention on the properties of input-output-state relations of linear systems.

We begin by noting that in consequence of the decomposition property (*3.5.2*), the input-output-state relation of any[1] system $\mathcal{A}$ admits of the representation

1 $$\mathbf{y}(t) \triangleq \mathbf{A}(\boldsymbol{\alpha};\mathbf{u}) = \mathbf{A}(\boldsymbol{\alpha};\mathbf{0}) + \mathbf{A}(\mathbf{u}) \qquad \boldsymbol{\alpha} \in \Sigma,\ \mathbf{u} \in R[\mathbf{u}]$$

where $\mathbf{u} = \mathbf{u}_{(t_0,t]}$ is the input segment, with $\mathbf{u}$ ranging over a linear input segment space $R[\mathbf{u}]$; $\boldsymbol{\alpha}$ is the initial state (at $t = t_0-$) (see Remark *1.5.5*) of $\mathcal{A}$, with $\boldsymbol{\alpha}$ ranging over a linear state space Σ; $\mathbf{A}(\boldsymbol{\alpha};\mathbf{0})$ denotes the zero-input response of $\mathcal{A}$ at time t, with $\mathcal{A}$ starting in state $\boldsymbol{\alpha}$ at time t_0-; and $\mathbf{A}(\mathbf{u})$ is the zero-state response of $\mathcal{A}$ at time t to $\mathbf{u} \triangleq \mathbf{u}_{(t_0,t]}$. When there is need to place in evidence the fact that $\boldsymbol{\alpha}$ is the state of $\mathcal{A}$ at time t_0-, *1* will be written in the form

2 $$\mathbf{y}(t) = \mathbf{A}(\mathbf{x}(t_0-);\mathbf{0}) + \mathbf{A}(\mathbf{u})$$

where $\mathbf{x}(t_0-)$ denotes the state of $\mathcal{A}$ at time t_0-. [In this and subsequent sections we denote the state vector by $\mathbf{x}$ in place of $\mathbf{s}$ in order to avoid confusion with the Laplace transform variable s. Furthermore, we shall frequently be forced to depart from our notation for time functions in order to avoid conflict with the customary notations for delta functions and Laplace transforms (see Remark *1.3.3*).]

To simplify our analysis, we shall make the convenient but inessential assumption that $\mathbf{u}$ and $\mathbf{y}$ are scalar-valued. The results obtained under this assumption can readily be extended to the general case where $\mathbf{u}$ and $\mathbf{y}$ are vector-valued. The general case will be treated in Chaps. *5* and *6*.

Fixing our attention on *1*, we note that the second term in the right-hand member represents the result of acting on u with a linear operator

[1] Henceforth it will be understood that $\mathcal{A}$ is a linear system unless explicitly noted to the contrary.

defined on the input segment space $R[u]$. From the basic theorems of Fréchet and Riesz concerning the representation of linear functionals and the extensions of these theorems to distributions,[1] it follows that the term $A(u)$ admits of a formal representation

3 $$A(u) = \int_{t_0}^{t} h(t,\xi)u(\xi)\, d\xi$$

where the kernel $h(t,\xi)$ may contain delta functions of various orders, with the understanding that if the integrand in *3* contains delta functions at t_0 or t, then the limits of integration in *3* should be t_0- and $t+$. To express *3* in a rigorous form requires the use of the language of the theory of distributions. For our purposes, *3* will be sufficient, even though it is not well defined by mathematical standards.

Impulse response

The kernel $h(t,\xi)$ of *3* has a simple interpretation. Specifically, on applying a unit impulse (delta function) $\delta(t - \xi)$ to $\mathcal{A}$, with $\mathcal{A}$ starting in its zero state, and changing the variable of integration in *3* to ξ' in order to avoid confusion with ξ, we have

4 $$\begin{aligned} \text{zero-state response of } \mathcal{A} \text{ to } \delta(t-\xi) &= \int_{t_0}^{t} h(t,\xi')\delta(\xi' - \xi)\, d\xi' \\ &= h(t,\xi) \qquad \text{for } t \geq \xi \geq t_0 \\ &= 0 \qquad \text{for } \xi > t \geq t_0 \end{aligned}$$

by the sifting property of delta functions (*A.2.10*) and the definition of zero state. Consequently, we can make the

5 **Assertion** The zero-state response of $\mathcal{A}$ to an input u is given by

6 $$A(u) = \int_{t_0}^{t} h(t,\xi)u(\xi)\, d\xi \qquad t_0 \leq \xi \leq t$$

where $h(t,\xi)$ is the zero-state response of $\mathcal{A}$ at time t to a unit impulse $\delta(t - \xi)$ applied at time ξ. The zero-state response $h(t,\xi)$ is called the *impulse response* of $\mathcal{A}$. Note that by *4* $h(t,\xi)$ vanishes for $t < \xi$.[2] ◁

A detailed discussion of the properties of impulse response will be presented in Chap. *8*. Here we shall restrict ourselves to giving two simple examples and establishing a few elementary properties which will be needed in this chapter.

7 *Example* The zero-state response of the system of Example *3.3.23* is

[1] For an exposition of these theorems see Ref. *2*. For a discussion of distributions see Appendix *A*.

[2] It should be remembered that we have assumed throughout that $\mathcal{A}$ is a nonanticipative system (*1.8.13*). Without this assumption, $h(t,\xi)$ need not vanish for $t < \xi$.

given by

$$A(u) = \int_{t_0}^{t} e^{-(t-\xi)}u(\xi)\,d\xi$$

Consequently, the impulse response of this system reads

$$h(t,\xi) = e^{-(t-\xi)} \qquad t \geq \xi$$
$$h(t,\xi) = 0 \qquad t < \xi$$

or more compactly,

$$h(t,\xi) = 1(t-\xi)e^{-(t-\xi)}$$

where the unit step function $1(t-\xi)$ serves to truncate $h(t,\xi)$ to the left of $t = \xi$.

8 *Example* The zero-state response of the system of Example *3.2.22* is given by

$$A(u) = \frac{1}{t}\int_{t_0}^{t} u(\xi)\,d\xi \qquad t \geq t_0 > 0$$

In this case

$$h(t,\xi) = 1(t-\xi)\,\frac{1}{t} \qquad \xi > 0$$

Zero-state time invariance and equivalence

We observe that the system of Example *7* is time-invariant and that its impulse response depends only on the difference of t and ξ. This is a special case of a more general property which is now stated in the form of an

9 **Assertion** A system $\mathcal{A}$ is zero-state time-invariant (*3.2.12*) if and only if its impulse response $h(t,\xi)$ is of the form $h(t-\xi)$.

Proof To prove this assertion, it is expedient to represent $h(t,\xi)$ in the form

10 $$h(t,\xi) = w(\tau,t)$$

where $\tau \triangleq t - \xi$, and then demonstrate that $w(\tau,t)$ is independent of t. (The variable τ as defined here is sometimes referred to as the "age variable." Essentially, the age variable is reversed time with the "present" serving as the reference point.)

Now by definition, $h(t,\xi)$, or equivalently, $w(\tau,t)$, is the zero-state response of $\mathcal{A}$ to $\delta(t-\xi)$. Consequently, the zero-state response of $\mathcal{A}$ to $\delta(t-(\xi+\lambda))$, where λ is an arbitrary shift in ξ, must be $h(t, \xi+\lambda)$, or, equivalently, $w(\tau-\lambda, t)$. On the other hand, if $\mathcal{A}$ is zero-state time-invariant, then by Definition *3.2.12*, the zero-state response of $\mathcal{A}$ to $\delta(t-(\xi+\lambda))$ must be identical with $h(t-\lambda, \xi)$ or, equivalently, $w(\tau-\lambda, t-\lambda)$. This implies that

$$w(\tau-\lambda, t-\lambda) = w(\tau-\lambda, t) \qquad \forall t \forall \tau \forall \lambda$$

which in turn implies that $w(\tau,t)$ does not depend on its second argument. Conversely, if $h(t,\xi)$ is of the form $h(t-\xi)$, then by using *6* it is trivial to demonstrate that $\mathfrak{A}$ is zero-state time-invariant (see *3.2.19*). ◁

With respect to zero-state equivalence of $\mathfrak{A}$ and $\mathfrak{B}$, we have the following obvious consequence of the definition of h.

11 **Assertion** Let $\mathfrak{A}$ and $\mathfrak{B}$ be associated with impulse responses $h_{\mathfrak{A}}$ and $h_{\mathfrak{B}}$, respectively. Then $\mathfrak{A}$ and $\mathfrak{B}$ are zero-state equivalent (*2.9.1*) if and only if $h_{\mathfrak{A}} = h_{\mathfrak{B}}$.

Impulse response of sum and product

Consider two linear systems $\mathfrak{A}$ and $\mathfrak{B}$ and let $\mathfrak{S}$ and $\mathfrak{P}$ be their sum $\mathfrak{A}+\mathfrak{B}$ and product $\mathfrak{A}\mathfrak{B}$, respectively (see *1.10.23* and *1.10.30*). It is natural to raise the question: How are the impulse responses of $\mathfrak{S} \triangleq \mathfrak{A}+\mathfrak{B}$ and $\mathfrak{P} \triangleq \mathfrak{A}\mathfrak{B}$ related to those of $\mathfrak{A}$ and $\mathfrak{B}$?

Before answering this question it should be noted that, by Theorem *3.5.20*, both $\mathfrak{A}+\mathfrak{B}$ and $\mathfrak{A}\mathfrak{B}$ are linear systems and as such have unique zero states. In what follows, the zero state of $\mathfrak{A}$ and $\mathfrak{B}$ will be denoted by $\boldsymbol{\theta}'$, while that of $\mathfrak{A}+\mathfrak{B}$ and $\mathfrak{A}\mathfrak{B}$ will be denoted by $\boldsymbol{\theta}''$, with the understanding that $\boldsymbol{\theta}'' = (\boldsymbol{\theta}',\boldsymbol{\theta}')$.

First consider $\mathfrak{A}+\mathfrak{B}$. By the definition of $\mathfrak{A}+\mathfrak{B}$, we have

12
$$\bar{\mathbf{S}}(\boldsymbol{\theta}'';u) = \bar{\mathbf{A}}(\boldsymbol{\theta}';u) + \bar{\mathbf{B}}(\boldsymbol{\theta}';u) \qquad \forall u$$

and hence by the definition of the impulse response (*3.6.5*)

13
$$h_{\mathfrak{S}}(t,\xi) = h_{\mathfrak{A}}(t,\xi) + h_{\mathfrak{B}}(t,\xi) \qquad \forall t \forall \xi$$

where $h_{\mathfrak{S}}(t,\xi)$ denotes the impulse response of $\mathfrak{S}$ and likewise for $\mathfrak{A}$ and $\mathfrak{B}$.

Next consider $\mathfrak{A}\mathfrak{B}$. In this case, we have

$$\bar{\mathbf{P}}(\boldsymbol{\theta}'';u) = \bar{\mathbf{A}}(\boldsymbol{\theta}';\bar{\mathbf{B}}(\boldsymbol{\theta}';u)) \qquad \forall u$$

and upon making use of the expression for the zero-state response of $\mathfrak{A}$:

$$A(\boldsymbol{\theta}';v) = \int_{t_0}^{t} h_{\mathfrak{A}}(t,\lambda)v(\lambda)\,d\lambda \qquad t \geq t_0$$

where
$$v = B(\boldsymbol{\theta}'',u) \qquad u = \delta(t-\xi)$$

we find the desired relation

14
$$h_{\mathfrak{P}}(t,\xi) = \int_{\xi}^{t} h_{\mathfrak{A}}(t,\lambda)h_{\mathfrak{B}}(\lambda,\xi)\,d\lambda$$

For zero-state time-invariant systems, this relation reduces to

15
$$h_{\mathfrak{P}}(t) = \int_{0}^{t} h_{\mathfrak{A}}(t-\lambda)h_{\mathfrak{B}}(\lambda)\,d\lambda$$

which means that $h_{\mathcal{P}}$ is given by the convolution of $h_{\mathcal{A}}$ and $h_{\mathcal{B}}$ (see Appendix *B.3.8*).

In summary, we can make the

16 **Assertion** Let $h_{\mathcal{A}}$ and $h_{\mathcal{B}}$ be the impulse responses of $\mathcal{A}$ and $\mathcal{B}$, respectively. Then the impulse responses of $\mathcal{S} \triangleq \mathcal{A} + \mathcal{B}$ and $\mathcal{P} \triangleq \mathcal{A}\mathcal{B}$ are given by *13* and *14*.

Transfer function

It is frequently convenient in dealing with linear systems—particularly of the time-invariant type—to characterize the zero-state response in terms of the *transfer function* rather than the impulse response of the system. A detailed discussion of the notion of the transfer function and its properties will be presented in Chap. *9*. At this point, we shall merely give its definition, illustrate it by a simple example, and cite a few properties that will be needed in the interim.

17 **Definition** Let $\mathcal{A}$ be a time-invariant system with impulse response $h(t - \xi)$ and let $h(t)$ be Laplace transformable (see Appendix *B*). Then the *transfer function* of $\mathcal{A}$ is denoted by $H(s)$ and is defined to be the Laplace transform of $h(t)$. In symbols,

18
$$\begin{aligned} H(s) &\triangleq \mathcal{L}\{h(t)\} \\ &= \int_{0-}^{\infty} h(t)e^{-st}\, dt \end{aligned}$$

or equivalently

$$H(s) = \int_{-\infty}^{\infty} h(t - \xi)e^{-s(t-\xi)}\, d\xi$$

with the understanding that $h(t) = 0$ for $t < \xi$.

More generally, if $\mathcal{A}$ is a time-varying system with impulse response $h(t,\xi)$, then its transfer function is denoted by $H(s,t)$ and is defined by the relation

19
$$H(s,t) = \int_{-\infty}^{\infty} h(t,\xi)e^{-s(t-\xi)}\, d\xi$$

20 *Comment* It is customary to define the transfer function in two ways: (I) as the Laplace transform of the impulse response, which is what we have done above, and (II) in terms of the steady-state response of $\mathcal{A}$ to an input of the form $u(t) = e^{st}$. Since the latter definition is valid only under certain restrictive conditions involving the stability of $\mathcal{A}$, its formulation is deferred until Chap. *9*.

21 *Example* Let the impulse response of $\mathcal{A}$ be expressed by

$$h(t) = 1(t)(e^{-t} + e^{-2t})$$

Then the transfer function of $\mathcal{A}$ is given by

$$H(s) = \mathcal{L}\,\{h(t)\} = \frac{2s + 3}{(s + 1)(s + 2)}$$

22 **Remark** As the reader readily recognizes, this is merely a special case of the transfer function of a linear time-invariant system which is characterized by a differential equation. We shall be able to give a general expression for the transfer function of such a system once we have established the identity of its zero state, which will be done in Chap. *4*. At this point, it will suffice to state without proof that the transfer function of a system characterized by the input-output relation

$$a_n \frac{d^n y}{dt^n} + \cdots + a_0 y = b_m \frac{d^m u}{dt^m} + \cdots + b_0 u$$

where the a's and b's are constants, is given by the ratio

$$H(s) = \frac{b_m s^m + \cdots + b_0}{a_n s^n + \cdots + a_0} \quad \triangleleft$$

A basic property of the transfer function is expressed by the following

23 **Assertion** Let $\mathcal{A}$ be a time-invariant system with transfer function $H(s)$ and let y be its zero-state response to u, where u is assumed to start at $t_0 = 0$. Then the Laplace transforms of y and u (assuming that they exist) are related to one another by

24 $$Y(s) = H(s)U(s)$$

where $Y(s)$ and $U(s)$ are the Laplace transforms of y and u, respectively.

Proof By Assertion *5*, we have

$$y(t) = \int_0^t h(t - \xi)u(\xi)\, d\xi$$

and on applying the Laplace transformation to both sides of this equation we derive

$$Y(s) = H(s)U(s)$$

by the convolution property of the Laplace transforms (see Appendix *B.3.11*).

25 **Assertion** Let $\mathcal{A}$ and $\mathcal{B}$ be time-invariant systems with transfer functions $H_{\mathcal{A}}(s)$ and $H_{\mathcal{B}}(s)$, respectively. Then the transfer functions of the sum $\mathcal{S} = \mathcal{A} + \mathcal{B}$ and the product $\mathcal{P} = \mathcal{A}\mathcal{B}$ are given by

$$H_{\mathcal{S}}(s) = H_{\mathcal{A}}(s) + H_{\mathcal{B}}(s)$$
$$H_{\mathcal{P}}(s) = H_{\mathcal{A}}(s)H_{\mathcal{B}}(s)$$

We omit the proof because it is trivial.

26 **Remark** Note that the transfer function of the product of time-invariant systems is independent of the order in which the systems are connected. This implies that if $\mathcal{A}$ and $\mathcal{B}$ are time-invariant, then they are zero-state commutative in the sense that $\mathcal{A}\mathcal{B}$ is zero-state

equivalent to $\mathcal{BA}$. As we shall see in Chap. *4*, Sec. *8*, it is not always true that $\mathcal{AB}$ is equivalent to $\mathcal{BA}$ if $\mathcal{A}$ and $\mathcal{B}$ are time-invariant.

Proper, strictly proper, and improper systems

An important characteristic of a system $\mathcal{A}$ is whether or not its zero-state response contains derivatives of the input, and if so, of what order. It is convenient to define this characteristic in terms of the impulse response of $\mathcal{A}$. This motivates the following

27 **Definition** A system $\mathcal{A}$ is *strictly proper* if $h(t,\xi)$ does not contain any delta functions. $\mathcal{A}$ is *proper* if $h(t,\xi)$ contains no delta functions of order 1 or higher. That is, $h(t,\xi)$ may contain $\delta(t-\xi)$ but not $\delta^{(1)}(t-\xi)$, $\delta^{(2)}(t-\xi)$, . . . , where $\delta^{(n)}(t)$ denotes a delta function of nth order (see Appendix *A*). $\mathcal{A}$ is *improper* if it is not proper.

28 *Example* The impulse response of the system $\mathcal{A}$ characterized by the input-output relation

$$\frac{dy}{dt} + y = u(t)$$

is (see Example *7*)

$$h(t-\xi) = 1(t-\xi)e^{-(t-\xi)}$$

Clearly, $\mathcal{A}$ is a strictly proper system. On the other hand, the impulse response of the system characterized by

$$y = \frac{du}{dt} + u$$

is

$$h(t-\xi) = \delta(t-\xi) + \delta^{(1)}(t-\xi)$$

Consequently, this system is improper.

29 *Comment* In a more general way, it will be shown in Chap. *4* that if a system is characterized by an input-output relation which has the form of a differential equation

$$a_n \frac{d^n y}{dt^n} + \cdots + a_0 y = b_m \frac{d^m u}{dt^m} + \cdots + b_0 u \qquad a_n \neq 0,\ b_m \neq 0$$

in which the a's and b's are constants, then $\mathcal{A}$ is strictly proper if $m \leq n-1$, $\mathcal{A}$ is proper if $m \leq n$, and $\mathcal{A}$ is improper if $m > n$. The same result holds for systems in which the a's and b's depend on time (see *A.7.13*). ◁

This concludes for the present our brief discussion of the notions of the impulse response and the transfer function—both of which have to do with the zero-state response of $\mathcal{A}$. We turn next to the properties of the zero-input response of $\mathcal{A}$.

Properties of zero-input response

We recall that the input-output-state relation *1* comprises two terms—the zero-input response and the zero-state response of $\mathcal{A}$. The zero-input response (at time t) is expressed by $\mathbf{A}(\mathbf{x}(t_0-);\mathbf{0})$ where $\mathbf{x}(t_0-)$ denotes the initial state of $\mathcal{A}$ at time t_0-, with $\mathbf{x}(t_0-)$ ranging over the state space Σ. When needed, the zero-input response is written as $\mathbf{A}(\boldsymbol{\alpha};\mathbf{0})$ to indicate that the initial state is $\mathbf{x}(t_0-) = \boldsymbol{\alpha}$, $\boldsymbol{\alpha} \in \Sigma$.

In what follows, we shall concern ourselves exclusively with systems whose state space is finite-dimensional. Such systems will be said to be of *finite order*. Furthermore, since the components of a state vector $\mathbf{x}(t)$ are in general complex numbers, we shall identify Σ with the space of m-tuples of complex numbers, denoted by $\mathcal{C}^m$. For convenient reference, we formalize this as an

30 **Assumption** The state space Σ is the space $\mathcal{C}^m$ of ordered m-tuples of complex numbers. ◁

By the definition of zero-input linearity (Definition *3.4.17*) the (scalar-valued) zero-input response $A(\mathbf{x}(t_0-);0)$ is, for fixed t, a linear functional[1] on $\mathcal{C}^m$, which is a linear vector space of dimension m. Now any linear functional f on a finite-dimensional linear vector space such as Σ admits of the representation (see Appendix C)

$$f(\boldsymbol{\alpha}) = \gamma_1\alpha_2 + \cdots + \gamma_m\alpha_m \qquad \boldsymbol{\alpha} \in \mathcal{C}^m$$

where the γ_i, $i = 1, \ldots, m$, are scalar constants and

$$\boldsymbol{\alpha} = (\alpha_1, \ldots, \alpha_m)$$

Consequently, the zero-input response $A(\mathbf{x}(t_0-);0)$ must necessarily be of the form

31 $$A(\mathbf{x}(t_0-);0) = \phi_1(t,t_0)x_1(t_0-) + \cdots + \phi_m(t,t_0)x_m(t_0-)$$

where $\mathbf{x}(t_0-) \triangleq (x_1(t_0-), \ldots, x_m(t_0-))$ and the time functions $\phi_i(t,t_0)$, $i = 1, \ldots, m$, play the role of constants for fixed t and t_0.

The functions $\phi_1(t,t_0), \ldots, \phi_m(t,t_0)$ in *31* have a simple interpretation. Specifically, let $\boldsymbol{\alpha}^i$ be the ith coordinate vector $(0,0, \ldots, 1,0, \ldots, 0)$ in $\mathcal{C}^m$. Then from *31* we have

32 $$\phi_i(t,t_0) = A(\boldsymbol{\alpha}^i;0) \qquad i = 1, \ldots, m$$

That is, $\phi_i(t,t_0)$ is the zero-input response of $\mathcal{A}$ starting in the state $(0, \ldots, 1, \ldots, 0)$ (with 1 in the ith place) at time t_0-.

Before proceeding further, it will be helpful to summarize our conclusions up to this point in the form of an

[1] A functional is a scalar-valued function.

33 **Assertion** Let $\mathcal{A}$ be a system of finite order with a state space Σ of dimension m. Then if the input and output of $\mathcal{A}$ are scalar-valued, the input-output-state relation of $\mathcal{A}$ admits of the representation

34 $$y(t) = \langle \boldsymbol{\phi}(t,t_0), \mathbf{x}(t_0-) \rangle + \int_{t_0}^{t} h(t,\xi) u(\xi)\, d\xi \qquad t \geq t_0$$

where $\boldsymbol{\phi}(t,t_0) \triangleq (\phi_1(t,t_0), \ldots, \phi_m(t,t_0))$
$\phi_i(t,t_0) \triangleq$ zero-input response of $\mathcal{A}$ starting in the state $(0, \ldots, 1, \ldots, 0)$ at time t_0-
$\mathbf{x}(t_0-) \triangleq$ initial state of $\mathcal{A}$ at time t_0-, $\mathbf{x}(t_0-) \in \Sigma$
$h(t,\xi) \triangleq$ impulse response of $\mathcal{A} \triangleq$ zero-state response of $\mathcal{A}$ to $\delta(t-\xi)$
$\langle \mathbf{a},\mathbf{b} \rangle \triangleq$ scalar product of vectors $\mathbf{a}$ and $\mathbf{b}$[1] ◁

We have established (Assertion *9*) that $\mathcal{A}$ is zero-state time-invariant if and only if the impulse response $h(t,\xi)$ is of the form $h(t-\xi)$. In exactly the same way, it can readily be shown that $\mathcal{A}$ is zero-input time-invariant (*3.2.30*) if and only if $\boldsymbol{\phi}(t,t_0)$ is of the form $\boldsymbol{\phi}(t-t_0)$. Now by virtue of the decomposition property, $\mathcal{A}$ is time-invariant if and only if it is both zero-state and zero-input time-invariant. Combining these observations, we have the

35 **Assertion** A system $\mathcal{A}$ is time-invariant if and only if its input-output-state relation admits of the representation

36 $$y(t) = \langle \boldsymbol{\phi}(t-t_0), \mathbf{x}(t_0-) \rangle + \int_{t_0}^{t} h(t-\xi) u(\xi)\, d\xi \qquad t \geq t_0 \quad \triangleleft$$

In the following subsection we shall focus our attention on the properties of the zero-input response functions $\phi_i(t,t_0)$, $i = 1, \ldots, m$. In order to simplify our analysis, we shall assume that $\mathcal{A}$ is a time-invariant system. Then at appropriate points we shall indicate how the results obtained under the assumption of time invariance can be modified for or extended to time-varying systems.

Basis functions

Since the zero-input response functions of a time-invariant system have the form $\phi_1(t-t_0), \ldots, \phi_m(t-t_0)$, there is no loss in generality in assuming that $t_0 = 0$—which is what we shall do in the sequel.

The time functions $\phi_1(t), \ldots, \phi_m(t)$, or $\phi_1, \ldots, \phi_m$ for short, may or may not be linearly independent (see Appendix *C*). If they are not, there must be a subset of n functions, say, $\phi_1, \ldots, \phi_n$ for convenience in numbering, such that (I) $\phi_1, \ldots, \phi_n$ are linearly

[1] Strictly speaking, when $\boldsymbol{\phi}$ is complex the scalar product should be written $\langle \boldsymbol{\phi}^*, \mathbf{x} \rangle$ (see *C.5.1*), where $\boldsymbol{\phi}^*$ denotes the complex conjugate of $\boldsymbol{\phi}$. For simplicity of notation we shall omit the complex conjugate symbol in this and the following chapter since $\boldsymbol{\phi}(t_0,t)$ will usually be real-valued.

independent, (II) every time function ϕ_i, $i = 1, \ldots, m$, is expressible as a linear combination of $\phi_1, \ldots, \phi_n$. Such time functions constitute a set of *basis functions* or, more simply, a *basis set* or a *basis* for $\mathcal{A}$.

Suppose that the expressions for $\phi_{n+1}, \ldots, \phi_m$ in terms of $\phi_1, \ldots, \phi_n$ read

$$\begin{aligned} \phi_{n+1} &= a_{n+1,1}\phi_1 + \cdots + a_{n+1,n}\phi_n \\ &\cdots\cdots\cdots\cdots\cdots \\ \phi_m &= a_{m1}\phi_1 + \cdots + a_{mn}\phi_n \end{aligned}$$

where the a's are constant coefficients. On substituting these expressions into the expression for the zero-input response of $\mathcal{A}$,

$$A(\mathbf{x}(0-);0) = \phi_1(t)x_1 + \cdots + \phi_m(t)x_m$$

where for simplicity we write x_i for $x_i(0-)$, $i = 1, \ldots, m$, we obtain after minor rearrangement of terms

37 $$A(\mathbf{x}'(0-);0) = \phi_1(t)x_1' + \cdots + \phi_n(t)x_n'$$

where the vector $\mathbf{x}' = (x_1', \ldots, x_n')$ is related to the vector

$$\mathbf{x} = (x_1, \ldots, x_m)$$

by

38 $$\mathbf{x}' = \mathbf{\Gamma}\mathbf{x}$$

with $\mathbf{\Gamma}$ expressed by

$$\mathbf{\Gamma} = \begin{bmatrix} 1 & 0 & \cdots & 0 & a_{n+1,1} & \cdots & a_{m,1} \\ \cdot & \cdot & \cdot & \cdot & \cdot & \cdot & \cdot \\ 0 & 0 & \cdots & 1 & a_{n+1,n} & \cdots & a_{m,n} \end{bmatrix}$$

Since this matrix is of rank n, it follows that if $\mathbf{x}$ ranges over $\mathcal{C}^m$ then $\mathbf{x}'$ ranges over $\mathcal{C}^n$. More specifically, the fact that *36* is an input-output-state relation (see *1.6.2*) implies, in conjunction with *38*, that every zero-input response is representable as *37* and, conversely, for every $\mathbf{x}'$ in $\mathcal{C}^n$ *37* represents a zero-input response of $\mathcal{A}$. Thus, the state space of $\mathcal{A}$ may be taken to be $\mathcal{C}^n$ instead of $\mathcal{C}^m$. [A more detailed discussion of the connection between $\mathbf{x}(0-)$, $\mathbf{x}'(0-)$, as well as the connection between different basis functions for $\mathcal{A}$, is presented in Chap. *4*, Sec. *2*. In that section, the state vectors $\mathbf{x}$ and $\hat{\mathbf{x}}$ have the same significance as $\mathbf{x}'$ and $\mathbf{x}$, respectively, in the foregoing discussion.]

The observations made above lead us to the following more complete definition of basis functions.

39 **Definition** A set of (linearly independent) zero-input responses $\phi_1, \ldots, \phi_n$ constitutes a set of *basis functions* for a system $\mathcal{A}$ with state space $\Sigma = \mathcal{C}^m$, $m \geq n$, ($\mathcal{C}^m \triangleq$ space of m-tuples of complex numbers), if and only if every zero-input response of $\mathcal{A}$ is representable in the form

40 $$A(\mathbf{x}(0-);0) = \phi_1(t)\alpha_1 + \cdots + \phi_n(t)\alpha_n \qquad t \geq 0$$

where $\mathbf{x}(0-) \in \mathcal{C}^m$ and $\boldsymbol{\alpha} = (\alpha_1, \ldots, \alpha_n)$ ranges over $\mathcal{C}^n$, and, conversely, for every $\boldsymbol{\alpha}$ in $\mathcal{C}^n$ *40* expresses a zero-input response of $\mathcal{A}$. [Note that it is immaterial whether the right-hand member of *40* is expressed in terms of $\mathbf{x}'(0-)$ or $\boldsymbol{\alpha}$, since $\boldsymbol{\alpha}$ plays the role of a generic value of $\mathbf{x}'(0-)$.]

The number n is defined to be the *order* of $\mathcal{A}$. In effect, the order of $\mathcal{A}$ is the dimension of $\mathcal{C}^n$, which is the "smallest" state space that can be associated with $\mathcal{A}$. This point is discussed more fully in Chap. *4*, Sec. *2*.

41 **Remark** Definition *39* applies to time-varying systems also, provided *40* is replaced by

$$A(\mathbf{x}(t_0-);0) = \phi_1(t,t_0)\alpha_1 + \cdots + \phi_n(t,t_0)\alpha_n \qquad t \geq t_0$$

with the understanding that, in order to qualify as a set of basis functions for $\mathcal{A}$, the zero-input responses $\phi_1(t,t_0), \ldots, \phi_n(t,t_0)$ must be linearly independent for *all* values of t_0.

42 *Note* If the state space Σ is $\mathcal{R}^m$ (space of m-tuples of real numbers) rather than $\mathcal{C}^m$, then $\mathcal{C}^m$ and $\mathcal{C}^n$ in *39* are replaced by $\mathcal{R}^m$ and $\mathcal{R}^n$ respectively.

43 *Example* Consider a system $\mathcal{A}$ which is characterized by the input-output-state relation ($t_0 = 0$)

$$y(t) = e^{-t}x_1(0-) + e^{-2t}x_2(0-) + (2e^{-t} + e^{-2t})x_3(0-) + \int_{t_0}^{t} [e^{-(t-\xi)} + e^{-2(t-\xi)}]u(\xi)\, d\xi \qquad t \geq t_0$$

with $\mathbf{x}(0-)$ ranging over $\mathcal{R}^3$.

In this case, the zero-input responses are expressed by $\phi_1(t) = e^{-t}$, $\phi_2(t) = e^{-2t}$, and $\phi_3(t) = 2e^{-t} + e^{-2t}$, $t \geq 0$, and $\phi_1(t)$ and $\phi_2(t)$ qualify as basis functions for $\mathcal{A}$. In terms of these, the zero-input response reads

44 $$A(\mathbf{x}(0-);0) = e^{-t}x_1'(0-) + e^{-2t}x_2'(0-) \qquad t \geq 0$$

where $x_1'(0-) = x_1(0-) + 2x_3(0-)$ and $x_2'(0-) = x_2(0-) + x_3(0-)$. Thus, every zero-input response of $\mathcal{A}$ is of the form *44* with $\mathbf{x}'(0-) \in \mathcal{R}^2$ and, conversely, for every $\mathbf{x}'(0-) \in \mathcal{R}^2$ *44* represents a zero-input response of $\mathcal{A}$. Note that $\mathcal{A}$ is a system of order 2.

45 **Remark** The basis functions $\phi_1(t), \ldots, \phi_n(t)$ are defined by *39* only for nonnegative values of t. As we shall see in the next section, it is frequently convenient to extend the range of definition of the basis functions to the entire time axis. This can easily be done in a "natural" fashion when the basis functions are linear combinations of terms of the form $r_j(t)e^{\lambda_j t}$, $j = 1, 2, \ldots, n$, where the $r_j(t)$ are polynomials in t and the λ_j are constants. In this case—which is typical of systems characterized by constant-coefficient differential equations—the value of $\phi_i(t)$ for negative t is defined to be the value resulting from substituting the negative value in question in each term $r_j(t)e^{\lambda_j t}$ in the representation of $\phi_i(t)$. Equivalently, let $\Phi_i(s)$ denote the Laplace transform of $\phi_i(t)$. Then, $\phi_i(-t)$ is defined to be the negative of the inverse Laplace transform of $\Phi_i(-s)$ evaluated at $|t|$. For example, if $\phi_i(t) = e^{-t}$ for $t \geq 0$, then $\Phi_i(s) = 1/(s+1)$ and the value of $\phi_i(t)$ for negative t is given by $-\mathcal{L}^{-1}\{1/(1-s)\}$, which is $1(t)e^t$ evaluated at $|t|$. Thus, for $t \leq 0$, the value of $\phi_i(t)$ is defined to be $e^{|t|}$. Obviously, this is equivalent to saying that the value of $\phi_i(t)$ for negative t is e^{-t}.

In general, it will be clear from the context whether the basis functions are defined only for $t \geq 0$ or for all t. When we wish to emphasize that it is defined for all t, the basis function will be referred to as an *extended basis function*, whereas a basis function defined for only $t \geq 0$ will be said to be *one-sided*. The adjective *two-sided* will be reserved for time functions which are defined for all t, but not necessarily through an extension of their definition for $t \geq 0$.

Systems in reduced form

So far we have not made any assumptions concerning the form of the basis functions of $\mathcal{A}$. This does not mean, however, that they can be chosen in an arbitrary fashion. Indeed, as will be shown in Sec. *7*, the fact that *1* is an input-output-state relation places severe limitations on the class of functions which can serve as basis functions for $\mathcal{A}$.

As a preliminary to determining the nature of these limitations, we shall establish several equivalence properties which will be needed at later points.

To begin with, we recall that a system $\mathcal{A}$ is in *reduced form* (*2.2.11*) if no distinct states in the state space of $\mathcal{A}$ are equivalent. It is easy to verify that $\mathcal{A}$ is in reduced form if its input-output-state relation is expressed in terms of a set of basis functions of $\mathcal{A}$. More specifically:

46 **Assertion** If the input-output-state relation of $\mathcal{A}$ has the form

$$y(t) = \langle \boldsymbol{\phi}(t-t_0), \mathbf{x}(t_0-)\rangle + \int_{t_0}^{t} h(t-\xi)u(\xi)\,d\xi$$

where $\mathbf{x}(t_0-) \in \mathcal{C}^n$, $\boldsymbol{\phi}(t) = (\phi_1(t), \ldots, \phi_n(t))$, and $\phi_1(t), \ldots, \phi_n(t)$ are basis functions for $\mathcal{A}$, then $\mathcal{A}$ is in reduced form.

Proof We have to show that if $\boldsymbol{\alpha}'$ and $\boldsymbol{\alpha}''$ are distinct states (that is, $\boldsymbol{\alpha}' \neq \boldsymbol{\alpha}''$), then they cannot be equivalent. For, if $\boldsymbol{\alpha}'$ is equivalent to

$\boldsymbol{\alpha}''$, then by *3.5.10*

47 $$\langle \boldsymbol{\phi}(t - t_0), \boldsymbol{\alpha}' \rangle = \langle \boldsymbol{\phi}(t - t_0), \boldsymbol{\alpha}'' \rangle \qquad t \geq t_0$$

or $$\langle \boldsymbol{\phi}(t - t_0), (\boldsymbol{\alpha}' - \boldsymbol{\alpha}'') \rangle = 0$$

which implies $\boldsymbol{\alpha}' = \boldsymbol{\alpha}''$ by virtue of the linear independence of $\phi_1(t - t_0), \ldots, \phi_n(t - t_0)$.

48 *Note* In proving Assertion *46* we have not made any use of the time invariance of $\mathcal{A}$. Consequently, Assertion *46* is valid for time-varying systems (see Remark *41*). ◁

In addition to the property expressed by Assertion *46*, we shall need another result which concerns the connection between the basis functions of two equivalent systems. Expressed in the form of an assertion, it reads

49 **Assertion** Let $\mathcal{A}$ and $\mathcal{B}$ be zero-input equivalent systems of order n and let $\phi_1, \ldots, \phi_n$ and $\varphi_1, \ldots, \varphi_n$ be basis functions for $\mathcal{A}$ and $\mathcal{B}$, respectively. Then every basis function of $\mathcal{A}$ is expressible as a linear combination of basis functions of $\mathcal{B}$, and vice versa.

Proof By the definition of zero-input equivalence (*2.9.2*), to every state $\boldsymbol{\alpha}$ of $\mathcal{A}$ there corresponds a state $\boldsymbol{\beta}$ of $\mathcal{B}$, and vice versa, such that

50 $$\bar{A}(\boldsymbol{\alpha};0) = \bar{B}(\boldsymbol{\beta};0)$$

of which *3.5.10* is a special case.

Expressed in terms of zero-input responses, *50* implies that to every $\boldsymbol{\alpha}$ in $\mathcal{C}^n$ there is a $\boldsymbol{\beta}$ in $\mathcal{C}^n$, and vice versa, such that

51 $$\langle \boldsymbol{\phi}(t), \boldsymbol{\alpha} \rangle = \langle \boldsymbol{\varphi}(t), \boldsymbol{\beta} \rangle \qquad t \geq 0$$

From this and the linear independence of the basis functions $\phi_1, \ldots, \phi_n$ and $\varphi_1, \ldots, \varphi_n$ it follows at once that every ϕ_i, $i = 1, \ldots, n$, is a linear combination of $\varphi_1, \ldots, \varphi_n$, and vice versa. We omit the details at this point since they are given in a more general setting in *4.2.4*.

52 **Corollary** If $\phi_1, \ldots, \phi_n$ and $\varphi_1, \ldots, \varphi_n$ are two different sets of basis functions for $\mathcal{A}$, then every basis function in the first set is expressible as a linear combination of basis functions in the second set and vice versa. In symbols, this means that the row vectors $\boldsymbol{\phi} = (\phi_1, \ldots, \phi_n)$ and $\boldsymbol{\varphi} = (\varphi_1, \ldots, \varphi_n)$ are related to one another by

$$\boldsymbol{\phi} = \boldsymbol{\varphi}\boldsymbol{\Gamma}$$

where $\boldsymbol{\Gamma}$ is a nonsingular matrix.

7 *Basis functions and state equations*

As was pointed out in Sec. *6*, the fact that the relation

1 $$y(t) = \langle \boldsymbol{\phi}(t - t_0), \mathbf{x}(t_0) \rangle + \int_{t_0}^{t} h(t - \xi) u(\xi)\, d\xi$$

is an input-output-state relation for $\mathcal{A}$ and as such satisfies the self-consistency conditions *1.6.11*, *1.6.15*, and *1.6.35*, or, equivalently, has the separation properties *2.3.4* and *2.3.19*, constrains the choice of the basis functions $\phi_1, \ldots, \phi_n$ and induces a relation between them and the impulse response $h(t - \xi)$. In this section, we shall examine the nature of these constraints and, by their use, deduce the state equations for $\mathcal{A}$ in both explicit and differential forms. We shall not, however, concern ourselves at present with the solution of these equations. We shall do this in Chap. *5*.

In addition to making use of the fact that *1* is an input-output-state relation, we shall make use of the following assumptions about $\boldsymbol{\phi}$, h, and u.

I $\boldsymbol{\phi}$ is an n-vector whose components $\phi_1, \ldots, \phi_n$ are basis functions for $\mathcal{A}$ (see *3.6.39*). Note that this implies that $\mathcal{A}$ is in reduced form (*3.6.46*).

II The basis functions h, u and their derivatives of all finite orders have at most a finite number of discontinuities and delta functions over any finite observation interval.

Derived properties of basis functions

We turn our attention first to those properties of basis functions that follow from the response separation property *2.3.4* in the case of zero input.

Specifically, for each τ in $(t_0, t]$, the zero-input response of $\mathcal{A}$ at time t starting in $\mathbf{x}(t_0)$ must be identical with the zero-input response of $\mathcal{A}$ at time t starting in state $\mathbf{x}(\tau)$. Thus, the basis functions must satisfy the identity

$$\langle \boldsymbol{\phi}(t - t_0), \mathbf{x}(t_0) \rangle = \langle \boldsymbol{\phi}(t - \tau), \mathbf{x}(\tau) \rangle \qquad \forall t_0 \forall t,\ t > t_0$$

for all τ in $(t_0, t]$.

For $t_0 = 0$ and $\mathbf{x}(t_0) = (1, 0, \ldots, 0)$, this identity reduces to

2 $$\phi_1(t) = \sum_{i=1}^{n} x_i(\tau) \phi_i(t - \tau) \qquad 0 < \tau \le t$$

which implies that every basis function can be expressed as a linear combination of delayed basis functions $\phi_1(t - \tau), \ldots, \phi_n(t - \tau)$.

We shall refer to this property as the *translation property* of basis functions.

An important consequence of the translation property is contained in the following

3 **Assertion** Every basis function of $\mathcal{A}$ is infinitely differentiable (i.e., has derivatives of every finite order) for $t > 0$.

Proof Suppose that $\phi_1(t)$ has a jump at, say, $t = a$. Then by virtue of *2* at least one of the functions $\phi_1(t - \tau), \ldots, \phi_n(t - \tau)$ must have a jump at $t = a$, or, equivalently, the vector $\boldsymbol{\phi}(t)$ must have a jump at $a - \tau$. Since τ can take any value in $(0,t]$, this implies that $\boldsymbol{\phi}(t)$ will have an uncountable number of jumps in the interval $(0,t]$, which contradicts assumption (II) above. Consequently, $\phi_1(t)$ cannot have any jumps for $t > 0$, and the same statement applies to $\phi_2(t), \ldots, \phi_n(t)$. However, if $\phi_1(t)$ is a single delta function at $t = 0$, then $\mathbf{x}(\tau) = 0$ and the contradiction does not arise. Nor does it arise if $\phi_1(t)$ is a linear combination of delta functions at $t = 0$ and functions which are infinitely differentiable for $t > 0$.

Similar reasoning rules out the presence of discontinuities in the derivatives of $\phi_1(t), \ldots, \phi_n(t)$ for $t > 0$. Furthermore, on successive differentiation of both sides of *2* and repetition of the arguments used above, we conclude that $\phi_1(t)$ is infinitely differentiable for $t > 0$, with the possibility that $\phi_1(t)$ may contain delta functions at $t = 0$. The same thing holds for $\phi_2(t), \ldots, \phi_n(t)$. $\lhd$

For the present we shall assume that there are no delta functions among the basis functions of $\mathcal{A}$. [In effect, this means that we are assuming that $\mathcal{A}$ is a proper system (*3.6.27*).] This assumption will be removed at a later point in this section.

Relation between $\mathbf{x}(t_0)$ and $\mathbf{x}(\tau)$

Having established that the basis functions are infinitely differentiable, we can deduce further relations from *2* by differentiating both sides of *2* $n - 1$ times with respect to t. This yields, together with *2*, the following n relations:

4 $$\langle \boldsymbol{\phi}^{(\lambda-1)}(t - t_0), \mathbf{x}(t_0) \rangle = \langle \boldsymbol{\phi}^{(\lambda-1)}(t - \tau), \mathbf{x}(\tau) \rangle \qquad \lambda = 1, \ldots, n$$

which hold for all t_0, all $t \geq t_0$, and all τ intermediate between t_0 and t.

5 *Comment* It makes but little difference in our analysis whether the basis functions $\phi_1, \ldots, \phi_n$ are assumed to be one-sided or extended (*3.6.45*). If they are one-sided, then $\phi_i^{(\lambda)}(t)$, $i = 1, \ldots, n$, $\lambda = 0, \ldots, n - 1$, is defined for all $t > 0$ but not at $t = 0$, and hence τ must be restricted to the open interval (t_0,t). On the other hand, if the $\phi_i(t)$ are extended, then $\phi_i^{(\lambda)}(0)$ is defined. Thus, strictly speaking we must write $\phi_i^{(\lambda)}(0+)$ for one-sided basis functions and we may write $\phi_i^{(\lambda)}(0)$ for extended basis functions. This implies that, when we write $\phi_i^{(\lambda)}(0)$, we mean that either the basis functions are extended or else the basis functions are one-sided and that we have a tacit understanding that $\phi_i^{(\lambda)}(0)$ should be interpreted as $\phi_i^{(\lambda)}(0+)$, $i = 1, \ldots, n$, $\lambda = 0, \ldots, n-1$. In particular, when relations such as *4* are stated to hold for $t \geq t_0$ and $t_0 \leq \tau \leq t$ (rather than $t > t_0$ and $t_0 < \tau < t$) it is understood that either the basis functions in question are extended or, if they are not, $\phi_i^{(\lambda)}(0) \triangleq \phi_i^{(\lambda)}(0+)$, $\mathbf{h}(0) \triangleq \mathbf{h}(0+)$, and likewise for other symbols which will appear presently in our analysis. It should be noted that, since at this stage of our analysis we have not yet defined how the basis functions may be extended (this is done in *21*), the latter interpretation is more appropriate. ◁

The n relations *4* can be expressed more compactly in the matrix form

6 $$\mathbf{\Phi}(t - t_0)\mathbf{x}(t_0) = \mathbf{\Phi}(t - \tau)\mathbf{x}(\tau) \qquad \forall t_0, \forall t \geq t_0, t_0 \leq \tau \leq t$$

where $\mathbf{\Phi}$ is an $n \times n$ matrix whose rows are the vectors $\boldsymbol{\phi}(t), \ldots, \boldsymbol{\phi}^{(n-1)}(t)$. That is,

7 $$\mathbf{\Phi}(t) = \begin{bmatrix} \phi_1(t) & \cdots & \phi_n(t) \\ \phi_1^{(1)}(t) & \cdots & \phi_n^{(1)}(t) \\ \cdots & \cdots & \cdots \\ \phi_1^{(n-1)}(t) & \cdots & \phi_n^{(n-1)}(t) \end{bmatrix}$$

with the understanding that $\mathbf{\Phi}(t)$ is defined only for $t > 0$ if the basis functions are one-sided, in which case $\mathbf{\Phi}(0)$ should be interpreted as $\mathbf{\Phi}(0+)$.

On setting $\tau = t$, *6* yields

8 $$\mathbf{\Phi}(0)\mathbf{x}(t) = \mathbf{\Phi}(t - t_0)\mathbf{x}(t_0) \qquad t \geq t_0$$

which determines $\mathbf{x}(t)$ uniquely—and not just to within equivalent states—provided $\mathbf{\Phi}(0)$ is nonsingular. Note that since $\mathcal{A}$ is in reduced form, any two states $\mathbf{x}'$ and $\mathbf{x}''$ which are distinct are necessarily nonequivalent (see *3.6.46*).

9 **Remark** If $\mathbf{\Phi}(0)$ is nonsingular, then by Corollary *3.6.52* we can always "normalize" the basis functions $\phi_1(t), \ldots, \phi_n(t)$ in such a way that $\mathbf{\Phi}(0) = \mathbf{I}$. Specifically, if $\mathbf{\Phi}(0) \neq \mathbf{I}$ and $\mathbf{\Phi}(0)$ is nonsingular, then we can construct a normalized set of basis functions $\varphi_1(t), \ldots, \varphi_n(t)$ from $\phi_1(t), \ldots, \phi_n(t)$ by the linear transformation

10 $$\boldsymbol{\varphi} = \boldsymbol{\phi}\mathbf{\Phi}^{-1}(0)$$

where $\boldsymbol{\varphi}$ and $\boldsymbol{\phi}$ are the row vectors $(\varphi_1, \ldots, \varphi_n)$ and $(\phi_1, \ldots, \phi_n)$, respectively.

State transition matrix and its properties

For convenience, we shall assume hereafter that the basis functions $\phi_1(t), \ldots, \phi_n(t)$ are normalized, so that $\boldsymbol{\Phi}(0) = \mathbf{I}$. Under this assumption, *8* becomes

11 $$\mathbf{x}(t) = \boldsymbol{\Phi}(t - t_0)\mathbf{x}(t_0) \qquad \forall t_0, \forall t \geq t_0$$

In this equation, $\boldsymbol{\Phi}(t - t_0)$ plays the role of an operator which takes the initial state $\mathbf{x}(t_0)$ into the state $\mathbf{x}(t)$. For this reason, $\boldsymbol{\Phi}(t)$ is called the *state transition matrix.* We shall derive only a few of its basic properties at this point, with a fuller discussion in Chaps. *5* and *6*.

12 **Property**[1] If the basis functions are linearly independent over every subinterval of $[0, \infty)$, then $\boldsymbol{\Phi}(t)$ is nonsingular for $t \geq 0$.

Proof The determinant of $\boldsymbol{\Phi}(t)$ is the Wronskian,[2] $W(t)$, of the basis functions $\phi_1(t), \ldots, \phi_n(t)$. A basic property of the Wronskian (see Ref. *5*, p. 48) is that if $W(t) = 0$ for $t \geq 0$, then there exists a subinterval of $[0, \infty)$ over which the time functions $\phi_1, \ldots, \phi_n$ are linearly dependent. Since by hypothesis the basis functions are linearly independent over every subinterval of $[0, \infty)$, there must exist a positive value of t, say, t_1, such that $W(t_1) \neq 0$ or, equivalently, $\boldsymbol{\Phi}(t_1)$ is nonsingular. Now on letting $t - t_0 = t_1$ in *6* and noting that *6* holds for all $\mathbf{x}(t_0) \in \mathcal{C}^n$ and all $\tau \in [t_0, t_1]$, it follows that $\boldsymbol{\Phi}(t)$ is nonsingular for all $t \in [0, t_1]$ and, in particular, $\boldsymbol{\Phi}(0)$ is nonsingular. Then by *9* we can assume that $\boldsymbol{\Phi}(0) = \mathbf{I}$ and correspondingly express the state at time t as $\mathbf{x}(t) = \boldsymbol{\Phi}(t - t_0)\mathbf{x}(t_0)$.

On invoking the state separation property (*2.3.16*) of this state equation it follows that if $\boldsymbol{\Phi}(t)$ is nonsingular for $t \in [0, t_1]$ then it is nonsingular for all $t \geq 0$. Specifically, let $0 \leq \tau - t_0 \leq t_1$ and $0 \leq t - \tau \leq t_1$. Then if $\mathbf{x}(t_0)$ ranges over $\mathcal{C}^n$, so will $\mathbf{x}(\tau) = \boldsymbol{\Phi}(\tau - t_0)\mathbf{x}(t_0)$ since $\boldsymbol{\Phi}(\tau - t_0)$ is nonsingular. By the same argument

$$\mathbf{x}(t) = \boldsymbol{\Phi}(t - \tau)\mathbf{x}(\tau)$$

ranges over $\mathcal{C}^n$ if $\mathbf{x}(\tau)$ ranges over $\mathcal{C}^n$. Consequently, $\mathbf{x}(t)$ will range over $\mathcal{C}^n$ if $\mathbf{x}(t_0)$ ranges over $\mathcal{C}^n$. This implies that $\boldsymbol{\Phi}(t - t_0)$ is nonsingular for all $t - t_0$ in the interval $[0, 2t_1]$. On repeating this argument, we deduce that $\boldsymbol{\Phi}(t)$ is nonsingular for all t in the intervals $[0, 4t_1]$, $[0, 8t_1]$, ... In this way, we can demonstrate that $\boldsymbol{\Phi}(t)$ is nonsingular for all $t \geq 0$ if it is nonsingular over $[0, t_1]$.

In the sequel we shall assume, except where otherwise noted, that the basis functions $\phi_1, \ldots, \phi_n$ are linearly independent not only over $[0, \infty)$ but also over every subinterval of this interval. As shown above, under this assumption $\boldsymbol{\Phi}(t)$ is nonsingular for $t \geq 0$.

[1] A. C. Chang has shown that the nonsingularity of $\boldsymbol{\Phi}(t)$ can be deduced from the translation property (*2 et seq.*).

[2] For a discussion of the Wronskian see Ref. *1* or Ref. *5*.

13 **Property** $\mathbf{\Phi}(t)$ has the multiplicative (semigroup) property

14 $$\mathbf{\Phi}(t + \xi) = \mathbf{\Phi}(t)\mathbf{\Phi}(\xi) \qquad \forall \xi \geq 0, \forall t \geq 0$$

This follows at once from *11* by writing $\mathbf{x}(t + \xi)$ in two ways:

$$\mathbf{x}(t + \xi) = \mathbf{\Phi}(t + \xi)\mathbf{x}(0)$$

and

$$\mathbf{x}(t + \xi) = \mathbf{\Phi}(t)\mathbf{x}(\xi) = \mathbf{\Phi}(t)\mathbf{\Phi}(\xi)\mathbf{x}(0)$$

and asserting that the relation $\mathbf{\Phi}(t + \xi)\mathbf{x}(0) = \mathbf{\Phi}(t)\mathbf{\Phi}(\xi)\mathbf{x}(0)$ holds for all $\mathbf{x}(0)$.

15 **Property** $\mathbf{\Phi}(t)$ has the commutative property

$$\mathbf{\Phi}(t)\mathbf{\Phi}(\xi) = \mathbf{\Phi}(\xi)\mathbf{\Phi}(t) \qquad \forall t \geq 0, \forall \xi \geq 0$$

This follows at once from *14*.

16 **Property** $\mathbf{\Phi}(t)$ is the solution of the first-order matrix differential equation

17 $$\dot{\mathbf{\Phi}}(t) = \dot{\mathbf{\Phi}}(0)\mathbf{\Phi}(t) \qquad \mathbf{\Phi}(0) = \mathbf{I},\ t \geq 0$$

This equation follows from *14* [with the order of $\mathbf{\Phi}(t)$ and $\mathbf{\Phi}(\xi)$ interchanged] by differentiating both sides first with respect to t and then with respect to ξ. Thus

18 $$\frac{\partial}{\partial t}\mathbf{\Phi}(t + \xi) = \mathbf{\Phi}(\xi)\dot{\mathbf{\Phi}}(t)$$

$$\frac{\partial}{\partial \xi}\mathbf{\Phi}(t + \xi) = \dot{\mathbf{\Phi}}(\xi)\mathbf{\Phi}(t)$$

and since

$$\frac{\partial}{\partial t}\mathbf{\Phi}(t + \xi) = \frac{\partial}{\partial \xi}\mathbf{\Phi}(t + \xi)$$

we have

19 $$\mathbf{\Phi}(\xi)\dot{\mathbf{\Phi}}(t) = \dot{\mathbf{\Phi}}(\xi)\mathbf{\Phi}(t)$$

which becomes *17* upon setting $\xi = 0$. Note that *15* and *18* imply that $\mathbf{\Phi}(t)$ has the commutative property

20 $$\mathbf{\Phi}(t)\dot{\mathbf{\Phi}}(\xi) = \dot{\mathbf{\Phi}}(\xi)\mathbf{\Phi}(t) \qquad \forall t \geq 0, \forall \xi \geq 0$$

The extended state transition matrix

If the basis functions $\phi_1, \ldots, \phi_n$ are one-sided (*3.6.45*), then the matric differential equation *17* [in which $\dot{\mathbf{\Phi}}(0)$ should be interpreted as $\dot{\mathbf{\Phi}}(0+)$] provides a convenient means of extending the definition of $\mathbf{\Phi}(t)$ to negative values of t. Thus we have the

21 **Definition** The *(extended) state transition matrix* $\mathbf{\Phi}(t)$ is defined for all t as the solution of the differential equation

22 $$\dot{\mathbf{\Phi}}(t) = \dot{\mathbf{\Phi}}(0)\mathbf{\Phi}(t) \qquad \mathbf{\Phi}(0) = \mathbf{I}$$

Correspondingly, the extended basis functions $\phi_1(t), \ldots, \phi_n(t)$ are defined for all t by the elements of the first row of $\mathbf{\Phi}(t)$.

23 *Comment* Note that the adjective "extended" is put in parentheses to indicate that it is used only when there is a need to emphasize that $\mathbf{\Phi}(t)$ is defined for all t rather than just for $t > 0$. Note also that $\dot{\mathbf{\Phi}}(0)$ in *22* is in effect $\dot{\mathbf{\Phi}}(t)\Big]_{t=0+}$, where $\mathbf{\Phi}(t)$ is defined by *7* in terms of one-sided basis functions. ◁

There is an important relation between $\mathbf{\Phi}^{-1}(t)$ and $\mathbf{\Phi}(-t)$ that can easily be deduced from this definition. Specifically, on differentiating both sides of the identity

$$\mathbf{\Phi}^{-1}(t)\mathbf{\Phi}(t) = \mathbf{I}$$

with respect to t, we find that $\mathbf{\Phi}^{-1}(t)$ is the solution of the differential equation

24 $$\dot{\mathbf{\Phi}}^{-1}(t) = -\dot{\mathbf{\Phi}}(0)\,\mathbf{\Phi}^{-1}(t) \qquad \mathbf{\Phi}^{-1}(0) = \mathbf{I}$$

On the other hand, *22* implies that

$$\dot{\mathbf{\Phi}}(-t) = -\dot{\mathbf{\Phi}}(0)\mathbf{\Phi}(-t) \qquad \mathbf{\Phi}(0) = \mathbf{I}$$

and therefore

25 $$\mathbf{\Phi}^{-1}(t) = \mathbf{\Phi}(-t) \qquad \forall t$$

This relation can be used as an alternative means of extending the definition of $\mathbf{\Phi}(t)$ to negative t.

26 **Remark** By starting with *21* as the definition of $\mathbf{\Phi}(t)$, it is easy to show (see Chap. *5*, Sec. *2*) that Properties *12*, *13*, *15*, and *20* hold for *all* values of t_0, t, τ, and ξ. Henceforth it will be understood, unless stated to the contrary, that the state transition matrix $\mathbf{\Phi}(t)$ and the basis functions $\phi_1(t), \ldots, \phi_n(t)$ are defined for all t by *21*, and that, in consequence, Properties *12*, *13*, *15*, and *20* hold for all t.

State equations

In the preceding discussion we have obtained several basic properties of the state transition matrix $\mathbf{\Phi}(t)$ by invoking the separation and uniqueness properties of the zero-input response of $\mathfrak{a}$. By proceeding in a similar fashion in the general case of a nonzero input, we shall obtain in the sequel the state equations of $\mathfrak{a}$ and a relation between the impulse response and the state transition matrix.

Specifically, in the general case the response separation property

2.3.4 implies that the input-output-state relation *1* must satisfy the identity

$$\langle \boldsymbol{\phi}(t - t_0),\mathbf{x}(t_0)\rangle + \int_{t_0}^{t} h(t - \xi)u(\xi)\, d\xi$$
$$= \langle \boldsymbol{\phi}(t - \tau),\mathbf{x}(\tau)\rangle + \int_{\tau}^{t} h(t - \xi)u(\xi)\, d\xi$$

for all t_0, all $t \geq t_0$, and all τ, $t_0 \leq \tau \leq t$. On setting $t_0 = 0$, $u(t) = \delta(t)$, and $\mathbf{x}(t_0) = \mathbf{0}$, this identity yields

27 $$h(t) = \langle \boldsymbol{\phi}(t - \tau),\mathbf{x}(\tau)\rangle \qquad t \geq \tau,\ \tau \geq 0$$

which shows that the impulse response is expressible as a linear combination of basis functions. By *3*, this implies that, in general, the impulse response is a linear combination of delta functions and functions that are infinitely differentiable for $t > 0$. More particularly, if there are no delta functions among the basis functions of $\mathcal{A}$, then $h(t)$ is infinitely differentiable for $t > 0$. This is the case to which we shall restrict our attention in the sequel, deferring until a later point (see *45 et seq.*) the discussion of the general case.

Returning to the case where u is not a delta function and differentiating the identity with respect to τ, we have

28 $$h(t - \tau)u(\tau) = \frac{d}{d\tau}\left(\langle \boldsymbol{\phi}(t - \tau),\mathbf{x}(\tau)\rangle\right)$$

or more explicitly

$$h(t - \tau)u(\tau) = -\langle \dot{\boldsymbol{\phi}}(t - \tau),\mathbf{x}(\tau)\rangle + \langle \boldsymbol{\phi}(t - \tau),\dot{\mathbf{x}}(\tau)\rangle$$

On substituting $h(t - \tau)u(\tau)$ as given by this equation into the expression for $y(t)$,

$$y(t) = \langle \boldsymbol{\phi}(t),\mathbf{x}(0)\rangle + \int_0^t h(t - \tau)u(\tau)\, d\tau$$

we obtain after cancellation of the term $\langle \boldsymbol{\phi}(t), \mathbf{x}(0)\rangle$ the expression for the output at time t as a function of the state at time t. It reads

29 $$y(t) = \langle \boldsymbol{\phi}(0),\mathbf{x}(t)\rangle$$

(Note that the same result can be obtained by setting $t = t_0$ in *1*.)

Next, on differentiating both sides of *28* $n - 1$ times with respect to t, we obtain the following n relations:

$$h^{(\lambda-1)}(t - \tau)u(\tau) = \frac{d}{d\tau}\left(\langle \boldsymbol{\phi}^{(\lambda-1)}(t - \tau),\mathbf{x}(\tau)\rangle\right) \qquad \lambda = 1, \ldots, n$$

which may be expressed more compactly in the matrix form

30 $$\mathbf{h}(t - \tau)u(\tau) = \frac{d}{d\tau}\left[\boldsymbol{\Phi}(t - \tau)\mathbf{x}(\tau)\right] \qquad t \geq \tau$$

where $\mathbf{\Phi}(t)$ is the state transition matrix defined by *7* or, equivalently, *21*, and $\mathbf{h}(t)$ is a column n vector whose λth element is $h^{(\lambda-1)}(t)$; that is,

31
$$\mathbf{h}(t) = \begin{bmatrix} h(t) \\ h^{(1)}(t) \\ \cdot \\ \cdot \\ \cdot \\ h^{(n-1)}(t) \end{bmatrix} \qquad t \geq 0$$

with the understanding that $\mathbf{h}(0) \triangleq \mathbf{h}(0+)$. (Why? See Assertion *40* and the definition of extended impulse response.)

On integrating both sides of *30* with respect to τ between the limits t_0 and t, and making use of the fact that $\mathbf{\Phi}(0) = \mathbf{I}$ (see *9*), we obtain the relation

32
$$\mathbf{x}(t) = \mathbf{\Phi}(t - t_0)\mathbf{x}(t_0) + \int_{t_0}^{t} \mathbf{h}(t - \xi)u(\xi)\, d\xi \qquad t \geq t_0$$

which constitutes a state equation for $\mathcal{A}$ in explicit form (*1.8.8 et seq.*). Observe that it reduces to *11* when u is a zero input.

By differentiating both sides of *1* $n - 1$ times with respect to t and comparing the result with *32* (taking note of *7* and *31*), we find that the state of $\mathcal{A}$ at time t is expressed in terms of the output and its derivatives by the simple relation

33
$$\mathbf{x}(t) = (y(t), \ . \ . \ . \ , y^{(n-1)}(t))$$

However, a more careful analysis shows that *33* is valid only if $h^{(n-1)}(t)$, interpreted as the $(n - 1)$st derivative of $h(t)$ in the distribution sense, has no delta functions at $t = 0$. As we shall see in Chap. *4*, Sec. *4*, this corresponds to the case where $\mathcal{A}$ is characterized by an input-output relation of the form

$$(a_n p^n + \cdot \cdot \cdot + a_0)y = u \qquad a_n \neq 0$$

In the more general case where $\mathcal{A}$ is characterized by an input-output relation of the form

$$(a_n p^n + \cdot \cdot \cdot + a_0)y = (b_m p^m + \cdot \cdot \cdot + b_0)u$$

where $b_m \neq 0$, for some $m \geq 1$, the vector $[y(t), \ . \ . \ . \ , y^{(n-1)}(t)]$ *does not* qualify as the state of $\mathcal{A}$ at time t (see Chap. *4*, Sec. *5*).

State impulse response

The state equation *32* can be used to obtain a simple interpretation for $\mathbf{h}(t)$. Specifically, setting $t_0 = 0$, $\mathbf{x}(t_0) = \mathbf{0}$, and $u(t) = \delta(t)$ in *32* yields

34
$$\mathbf{h}(t) = \mathbf{x}(t)\Big]_{\mathbf{x}(0-)=0,\ u(t)=\delta(t)} \qquad \forall t \geq 0$$
$$\mathbf{h}(t) = 0 \qquad \text{for } t < 0$$

which means that $\mathbf{h}(t)$ is the state in which $\mathcal{a}$ is at time t given that $\mathcal{a}$ is in its zero state at time $0-$ and $u(t) = \delta(t)$. In view of this interpretation, $\mathbf{h}$ will be referred to as the *state impulse response* of $\mathcal{a}$. Note that $h(t)$, the impulse response of $\mathcal{a}$, is merely the first component of the vector $\mathbf{h}(t)$ (see *31*).

State equation in differential form

Equation *32* expresses the state of $\mathcal{a}$ at time t as a function of the initial state t_0 and the input segment $u_{(t_0,t]}$. To obtain a corresponding state equation for $\mathcal{a}$ in the differential form, it is sufficient to differentiate both sides of the identity *28* $n - 1$ times with respect to t. This yields n relations

35 $$h^{(\lambda-1)}(t - \tau)u(\tau) = -\langle \dot{\boldsymbol{\phi}}^{(\lambda-1)}(t - \tau),\mathbf{x}(\tau)\rangle + \langle \boldsymbol{\phi}^{(\lambda-1)}(t - \tau),\dot{\mathbf{x}}(\tau)\rangle \qquad \lambda = 1, \ldots, n$$

which, upon setting $\tau = t$ and noting that $\boldsymbol{\Phi}(0) = \mathbf{I}$, becomes (in matrix form)

36 $$\dot{\mathbf{x}}(t) = \dot{\boldsymbol{\Phi}}(0)\mathbf{x}(t) + \mathbf{h}(0)u(t)$$

where $\mathbf{h}$ is defined by *31*, with the understanding that $\mathbf{h}(0)$ should be interpreted as $\mathbf{h}(0+)$. Equation *36* is the desired state equation for $\mathcal{a}$ in the differential form.

37 *Comment* Strictly speaking, we should set $\tau = t-$ rather than $\tau = t$ in *35*, since $h^{(\lambda-1)}(t)$ may not be defined for $t = 0$ (see Example *43*). This yields

$$\dot{\mathbf{x}}(t-) = \dot{\boldsymbol{\Phi}}(0+)\mathbf{x}(t-) + \mathbf{h}(0+)u(t-) \qquad \forall t$$

which, upon the replacement of $t-$ with t, becomes *36*, with $\mathbf{h}(0+)$ and $\dot{\boldsymbol{\Phi}}(0+)$ in place of $\mathbf{h}(0)$ and $\dot{\boldsymbol{\Phi}}(0)$. Since $\dot{\boldsymbol{\Phi}}(0+) = \dot{\boldsymbol{\Phi}}(0)$ (by *21*), we can express the state equation in the form *36*, with the understanding that $\mathbf{h}(0)$ stands for $\mathbf{h}(0+)$. [We use $\mathbf{h}(0+)$ rather than $\mathbf{h}(0)$ because $\mathbf{h}(t)$ may contain delta functions at $t = 0$.]

Before proceeding further, it will be helpful to summarize the results obtained so far in the form of an

38 **Assertion** Let $\mathcal{a}$ be a strictly proper system (*3.6.27*) of order n characterized by the input-output-state relation

$$y(t) = \langle \boldsymbol{\phi}(t - t_0),\mathbf{x}(t_0)\rangle + \int_{t_0}^{t} h(t - \xi)u(\xi)\, d\xi \qquad t \geq t_0$$

Then the state equations of $\mathcal{a}$ in the differential form read

39 $$\begin{aligned} \dot{\mathbf{x}}(t) &= \dot{\boldsymbol{\Phi}}(0)\mathbf{x}(t) + \mathbf{h}(0+)u(t) \qquad \forall t \\ y(t) &= \langle \boldsymbol{\phi}(0),\mathbf{x}(t)\rangle \end{aligned}$$

and the state at time t is given by

$$\mathbf{x}(t) = \mathbf{\Phi}(t - t_0)\mathbf{x}(t_0) + \int_{t_0}^{t} \mathbf{h}(t - \xi)u(\xi)\,d\xi \qquad t \geq t_0$$

where $\mathbf{h}(t)$ is the state impulse response given by *31* and *34*, and $\mathbf{\Phi}(t)$ is the state transition matrix defined by *7* for $t \geq 0$ in terms of one-sided basis functions (*3.6.45*), with the extended state transition matrix defined for all t as the solution of the differential equation *22*,

$$\dot{\mathbf{\Phi}}(t) = \dot{\mathbf{\Phi}}(0)\mathbf{\Phi}(t) \qquad \mathbf{\Phi}(0) = \mathbf{I} \qquad \forall t$$

The extended state transition matrix $\mathbf{\Phi}(t)$ has the properties expressed by *12*, *13*, *15*, *20*, and *25* for all t_0, t, τ, and ξ.

Connection between the state transition matrix and the impulse response

Based on the interpretation of the state impulse response expressed by *34*, it is a simple matter to deduce an expression for $\mathbf{h}(t)$ in terms of the state transition matrix $\mathbf{\Phi}(t)$. The connection between $\mathbf{h}(t)$ and $\mathbf{\Phi}(t)$ is stated in the

40 **Assertion** The state impulse response $\mathbf{h}(t)$ is related to the state transition matrix $\mathbf{\Phi}(t)$ by the equation

41 $$\mathbf{h}(t) = 1(t)\mathbf{\Phi}(t)\mathbf{h}(0+)$$

where $1(t)$ is the unit step function.

Proof The state of $\mathcal{A}$ at time t is given by *32* or, equivalently, by the solution of the state equation

$$\dot{\mathbf{x}}(t) = \dot{\mathbf{\Phi}}(0)\mathbf{x}(t) + \mathbf{h}(0+)u(t)$$

with the state $\mathbf{x}(0-)$ serving as the prescribed initial condition at time $0-$.

From this and *34* it follows that $\mathbf{h}(t)$ is the solution of the differential equation

42 $$\dot{\mathbf{h}}(t) = \dot{\mathbf{\Phi}}(0)\mathbf{h}(t) + \mathbf{h}(0+)\delta(t)$$

subject to the initial condition $\mathbf{h}(0-) = \mathbf{0}$. Thus, to prove the assertion, it is sufficient to show that $\mathbf{h}(t)$ as expressed by *41* is the solution in question.

On substituting *41* in *42* and noting that as a result of the discontinuity at $t = 0$, the derivative of $\mathbf{h}(t)$ [in the distribution sense (*3.8.2 et seq.*)] is given by

$$\frac{d}{dt}(1(t)\mathbf{\Phi}(t)\mathbf{h}(0+)) = \mathbf{\Phi}(0)\mathbf{h}(0+)\delta(t) + 1(t)\dot{\mathbf{\Phi}}(t)\mathbf{h}(0+)$$

we have

$$\mathbf{\Phi}(0)\mathbf{h}(0+)\delta(t) + 1(t)\dot{\mathbf{\Phi}}(t)\mathbf{h}(0+) = \dot{\mathbf{\Phi}}(0)\mathbf{\Phi}(t)\mathbf{h}(0+) + \mathbf{h}(0+)\delta(t)$$

which is an identity since $\mathbf{\Phi}(0) = \mathbf{I}$ and $\dot{\mathbf{\Phi}}(0)\mathbf{\Phi}(t) = \dot{\mathbf{\Phi}}(t)$ (by *22*). Consequently, $1(t)\mathbf{\Phi}(t)\mathbf{h}(0+)$ is the solution of *42* satisfying the initial condition $\mathbf{h}(0-) = \mathbf{0}$. Q.E.D.

43 *Example* Consider the system characterized by the input-output-state relation

$$y(t) = e^{-t}x_1(0-) + e^{-2t}x_2(0-) + \int_{t_0}^{t} (e^{-(t-\xi)} + e^{-2(t-\xi)})u(\xi)\, d\xi \qquad t \geq t_0$$

In this case, $\phi_1(t) = e^{-t}$, $\phi_2(t) = e^{-2t}$, $\dot{\phi}_1(t) = -e^{-t}$, $\dot{\phi}_2(t) = -2e^{-2t}$, and

$$\mathbf{\Phi}(t) = \begin{bmatrix} e^{-t} & e^{-2t} \\ -e^{-t} & -2e^{-2t} \end{bmatrix} \qquad \mathbf{\Phi}(0) = \begin{bmatrix} 1 & 1 \\ -1 & -2 \end{bmatrix}$$

Since the basis functions are not normalized, we first form the normalized state transition matrix $\mathbf{\Phi}'(t)$ (*9*)

$$\begin{aligned} \mathbf{\Phi}'(t) &= \mathbf{\Phi}(t)\mathbf{\Phi}^{-1}(0) \\ &= \begin{bmatrix} 2e^{-t} - e^{-2t} & e^{-t} - e^{-2t} \\ -2e^{-t} + 2e^{-2t} & -e^{-t} + 2e^{-2t} \end{bmatrix} \end{aligned}$$

Now

$$\begin{aligned} h(t) &= 1(t)(e^{-t} + e^{-2t}) \\ h^{(1)}(t) &= 1(t)(-e^{-t} - 2e^{-2t}) \end{aligned}$$

and

$$\mathbf{h}(0+) = \begin{bmatrix} 2 \\ -3 \end{bmatrix}$$

It is easy to check that $\mathbf{h}(t) = 1(t)\mathbf{\Phi}'(t)\mathbf{h}(0+)$.

The state equations in differential form are expressed by

$$\begin{aligned} \dot{\mathbf{x}}(t) &= \begin{bmatrix} 0 & 1 \\ -2 & -3 \end{bmatrix} \mathbf{x}(t) + \begin{bmatrix} 2 \\ -3 \end{bmatrix} u(t) \\ y(t) &= \langle (1,0), \mathbf{x}(t) \rangle \end{aligned}$$

where $\mathbf{x}(t)$ is a column 2-vector.

44 *Comment* The relation *41* between the state transition matrix and the state impulse response provides a natural way of extending the definition of $\mathbf{h}(t)$ to negative t. Specifically, the *extended state impulse response* will be understood to be given by the relation $\mathbf{h}(t) = \mathbf{\Phi}(t)\mathbf{h}(0+)$ for all t.

Improper systems

Throughout the preceding analysis we have made the assumption that there are no delta functions among the basis functions of $\mathcal{a}$. This assumption rules out improper systems (*3.6.27*), for, as we shall see in

Chap. *4*, Sec. *5*, the basis functions of such systems include delta functions of various orders.

In what follows we shall merely sketch an extension of the results obtained so far to the case of improper systems, deferring a more detailed discussion until Chap. *4*.

By virtue of *3.7.3* and *3.7.27*, the input-output-state relation of an improper system of order r must necessarily comprise two kinds of terms: (I) infinitely differentiable basis functions and that part of the impulse response which is a linear combination of them and (II) delta functions and the remaining part of the impulse response which comprises delta functions of various orders. More specifically, $y(t)$ can be partitioned into two parts (with the subscripts p and δ identifying the proper and delta-function terms, respectively):

45 $$y(t) = y_p(t) + y_\delta(t)$$

of the form

46 $$y_p(t) = \phi_1(t - t_0)x_1(t_0) + \cdots + \phi_n(t - t_0)x_n(t_0) + \int_{t_0}^{t} h_p(t - \xi)u(\xi)\,d\xi$$

and

47 $$y_\delta(t) = \delta(t - t_0)x_{n+1}(t_0-) + \cdots + \delta^{(r-n-1)}(t - t_0)x_r(t_0-) + \int_{t_0+}^{t} h_\delta(t - \xi)u(\xi)\,d\xi$$

where $\phi_1, \ldots, \phi_n$ are infinitely differentiable basis functions, h_p is a linear combination of $\phi_1, \ldots, \phi_n$, and h_δ is a linear combination of delta functions of orders up to and including $r - n$.

This partitioning amounts essentially to representing $\mathfrak{A}$ as a sum (parallel combination) of two systems $\hat{\mathfrak{A}}$ and $\mathfrak{D}$ characterized by *46* and *47*, respectively, with $\hat{\mathfrak{A}}$ being a strictly proper system (*3.6.27*) and $\mathfrak{D}$ being a system of the differential operator type (*4.4.1*). Note that the state of $\mathfrak{A}$ has r components, the first n of which are associated with $\hat{\mathfrak{A}}$ and the rest with $\mathfrak{D}$. The corresponding state equations are given in Chap. *4*, Sec. *5*, and we shall forego reproducing them at this point.

48 *Note* All of our results concerning the state transition matrix, state equations, etc., have been obtained under the simplifying assumption that $\mathfrak{A}$ is a time-invariant system. Analogous results for time-varying systems will be established in Chap. *6*, Sec. *4*.

Validity of input-output-state relations for reversed time

In writing the input-output-state relation *1* and the state equation *32* which was derived from it, we make the usual qualification that $t \geq t_0$. Actually, it is easy to show that these equations hold for *all t* provided the state transition matrix, the state impulse response, and the impulse response which occur in these equations are assumed to be extended rather than one-sided (see *21* and *44*). This implies that we can specify the state of $\mathcal{A}$ at time t_0 and determine via these equations the state and the output of $\mathcal{A}$ at time t *before* t_0 in terms of $\mathbf{x}(t_0)$ and the values of the input over the interval $[t,t_0]$. In this case, time is, in a sense, reversed, and the state $\mathbf{x}(t_0)$ plays the role of the *terminal* (see *1.7.5 et seq.*) rather than the initial state of the system. [When we wish to distinguish between this case and the usual one where $\mathbf{x}(t_0)$ is the initial state, we shall refer to a state equation as a *backward* or *forward* state equation according as $t < t_0$ or $t \geq t_0$.]

Stated more formally, we have the

49 **Theorem** The input-output-state relation

50 $$y(t) = \langle \boldsymbol{\phi}(t - t_0),\mathbf{x}(t_0)\rangle + \int_{t_0}^{t} h(t - \xi)u(\xi)\, d\xi$$

and the state equations

51 $$\mathbf{x}(t) = \boldsymbol{\Phi}(t - t_0)\mathbf{x}(t_0) + \int_{t_0}^{t} \mathbf{h}(t - \xi)u(\xi)\, d\xi$$
$$y(t) = \langle \boldsymbol{\phi}(0),\mathbf{x}(t)\rangle$$

hold for all t and t_0 provided the basis functions $\phi_1, \ldots, \phi_n$, the state transition matrix $\boldsymbol{\Phi}(t)$, the impulse response $h(t)$, and the state impulse response $\mathbf{h}(t)$ are understood to be extended rather than one-sided. [The extended state transition matrix is defined for negative t by the relation

$$\boldsymbol{\Phi}(-t) = \boldsymbol{\Phi}^{-1}(t)$$

or, equivalently, as the solution of the differential equation *22*. The extended state impulse response is given in terms of the extended $\boldsymbol{\Phi}(t)$ by

$$\mathbf{h}(t) = \boldsymbol{\Phi}(t)\mathbf{h}(0)$$

Correspondingly, the extended basis functions and the impulse response are given by the elements of the first row of the extended $\boldsymbol{\Phi}(t)$ and $\mathbf{h}(t)$, respectively.]

Proof Since the state equations *51* are equivalent to *50*, and since $y(t)$ is a linear combination of the components of $\mathbf{x}(t)$, it will suffice to demonstrate that the theorem holds true for $\mathbf{x}(t)$.

To this end, let $t \geq t_0$ and let τ be an intermediate time between t_0 and t, $t_0 \leq \tau \leq t$. Then, the theorem is proved if we can demonstrate that the value of $\mathbf{x}(\tau)$ computed by using the forward state equation with $\mathcal{A}$ starting in state $\mathbf{x}(t_0)$ is identical with that yielded by the backward equation with $\mathbf{x}(t)$ playing the role of the terminal state.

On replacing $\mathbf{h}(t)$ by $\mathbf{\Phi}(t)\mathbf{h}(0)$, the forward state equation yields

52 $$\mathbf{x}(\tau) = \mathbf{\Phi}(\tau - t_0)\mathbf{x}(t_0) + \int_{t_0}^{\tau} \mathbf{\Phi}(\tau - \xi)\mathbf{h}(0)u(\xi)\, d\xi \qquad \tau \geq t_0$$

53 $$\mathbf{x}(t) = \mathbf{\Phi}(t - t_0)\mathbf{x}(t_0) + \int_{t_0}^{t} \mathbf{\Phi}(t - \xi)\mathbf{h}(0)u(\xi)\, d\xi \qquad t \geq t_0$$

On the other hand, the backward state equation yields the following expression for the state at time τ:

54 $$\mathbf{x}'(\tau) = \mathbf{\Phi}(\tau - t)\mathbf{x}(t) + \int_{t}^{\tau} \mathbf{\Phi}(\tau - \xi)\mathbf{h}(0)u(\xi)\, d\xi$$

so that we have to show that $\mathbf{x}'(\tau) = \mathbf{x}(\tau)$.

On substituting $\mathbf{x}(t)$ as given by *53* into *54*, we have

$$\mathbf{x}'(\tau) = \mathbf{\Phi}(\tau - t)\mathbf{\Phi}(t - t_0)\mathbf{x}(t_0) + \int_{t_0}^{t} \mathbf{\Phi}(\tau - t)\mathbf{\Phi}(t - \xi)\mathbf{h}(0)u(\xi)\, d\xi + \int_{t}^{\tau} \mathbf{\Phi}(\tau - \xi)\mathbf{h}(0)u(\xi)\, d\xi$$

and since by *14* and *36*

$$\mathbf{\Phi}(\tau - t)\mathbf{\Phi}(t - t_0) = \mathbf{\Phi}(\tau - t_0)$$
$$\mathbf{\Phi}(\tau - t)\mathbf{\Phi}(t - \xi) = \mathbf{\Phi}(\tau - \xi)$$

we have

$$\mathbf{x}'(\tau) = \mathbf{\Phi}(\tau - t_0)\mathbf{x}(t_0) + \int_{t_0}^{\tau} \mathbf{\Phi}(\tau - \xi)\mathbf{h}(0)u(\xi)\, d\xi$$

which is identical with $\mathbf{x}(\tau)$. Q.E.D.

An immediate consequence of Theorem *49* is the

55 **Corollary** If $\mathcal{A}$ is characterized by an input-output-state relation of the form *50*—which implies that $\mathcal{A}$ is in reduced form (see *3.6.46*)—then $\mathcal{A}$ is initial state determinable (*1.8.12 et seq.*) in the following sense. Given $u_{(t_0,t]}$ and $y_{(t_0,t]}$, one can uniquely determine the initial state $\mathbf{x}(t_0)$. ◁

Specifically, the knowledge of $u_{(t_0,t]}$ and $y_{(t_0,t]}$ yields the values of $u(t)$, $y(t)$, and their derivatives at $t-$. These in turn determine by *4.5.18* the state of $\mathcal{A}$ at time $t-$. Then, using *51*, we obtain

$$\mathbf{x}(t_0) = \mathbf{\Phi}(t_0 - t)\left[\mathbf{x}(t-) + \int_{t}^{t_0} \mathbf{h}(t - \xi)u(\xi)\, d\xi\right]$$

which shows that the initial state is uniquely determined by the input-output pair $(u_{(t_0,t]}, y_{(t_0,t]})$.

56 *Comment* From the results obtained in this section we can draw a significant conclusion, namely, that any linear system of finite order, subject to assumptions (I) and (II), can be characterized by state equations in the differential form. As we shall see in Chap. 4, this in turn implies that any system of finite order can be characterized by

an input-output relation having the form of a linear differential equation. Thus, by restricting ourselves to systems of finite order, we have in effect restricted ourselves to systems whose behavior is governed by linear differential equations. Such systems are the main concern of this text.

8 *Differential and discrete-time systems*

Like the class of all systems, the class of linear systems can be categorized in many different ways. In what follows, we shall focus our discussion on two principal types of linear systems, namely, *differential systems* and *discrete-time systems*, with the differential systems receiving the bulk of our attention. Actually, our main concern in this section will be with matters pertaining to terminology and notation, with more detailed analyses of the systems in question to follow in later chapters.

Linear differential systems

We begin our discussion with linear differential systems, which, as the name implies, are linear systems whose behavior is governed by differential equations. More specifically, by a *linear differential system* we mean a system whose input and output are related by one or more ordinary (rather than partial) differential equations. In the engineering literature, such systems are commonly referred to as *linear lumped-parameter systems*.

In essence, the importance of linear differential systems stems from three factors. First, most of the linear systems encountered in the physical world are of this type or can be approximated by systems of this type. Second, linear differential systems have been investigated more extensively than any other category of linear systems. And third, the study of linear differential systems serves as a convenient introduction, if not a prerequisite, to that of most other types of linear systems. For example, the properties of linear discrete-time systems parallel very closely those of linear differential systems and in many cases can be found or established by very similar techniques.

Before giving a general definition of a linear differential system, it will be helpful to observe that by a linear time-invariant differential system $\mathcal{A}$ one usually means a system characterized by a differential equation of the form

1 $$a_n \frac{d^n y}{dt^n} + \cdots + a_0 y = b_m \frac{d^m u}{dt^m} + \cdots + b_0 u$$

in which u is a scalar input time function, y is a scalar output time function, and the a_i, $i = 0, \ldots, n$, and b_j, $j = 0, \ldots, m$, are constant coefficients.

More generally, in the case of a linear differential system which is not necessarily time-invariant, the coefficients a_i and b_j may depend on time. Furthermore, u and y may be related to one another by a system of linear differential equations rather than by a single differential equation as in *1*. Also, the input u and output y may be vectors rather than scalars, in which case the a_i and b_j are matrices, possibly time-dependent.

Now as was pointed out in Chap. *1*, Sec. *4*, an input-output relation such as *1* is merely a way of defining the class of all input-output pairs which can be associated with $\mathcal{A}$. Thus, $(u_{(t_0,t]}, y_{(t_0,t]})$, or simply (u,y), is an input-output pair for $\mathcal{A}$ if and only if (u,y) satisfies the differential equation *1*. This naturally leads to the question: What do we mean—in precise terms—when we say that u and y satisfy *1*?

To answer this question, we must examine more carefully the meaning of the derivatives such as dy/dt and d^2u/dt^2 at the point at which the observation interval begins, i.e., at $t = t_0$. As a first step in this direction, let us employ the usual symbol p to denote the operation of differentiation. That is, $p\,u = du/dt$, with the understanding that $p\,u$ represents the derivative of u in the distribution sense (see Appendix *A*), which means, informally, that the derivative of a unit step function $1(t)$ is a delta function $\delta(t)$ and, more generally,

2
$$\begin{aligned} p\,1(t) &= \delta(t) \\ p\,\delta(t) &= \delta^{(1)}(t) \\ &\cdots\cdots\cdots \\ p\,\delta^{(n)}(t) &= \delta^{(n+1)}(t) \end{aligned}$$

where $\delta^{(n)}(t)$ denotes a delta function of nth order occurring at $t = 0$. This implies that, if u has a jump at, say, $t = 0$, then $p\,u$ will have a delta function at $t = 0$ expressed by $[u(0+) - u(0-)]\delta(t)$. We call $p\,u$ the "derivative in the distribution sense" for two main reasons. First, to differentiate between $p\,u$ and the derivative of u in the conventional sense—which does not exist when u has jumps or delta functions—and second, to indicate that $p\,u$ can be defined in a rigorous fashion by using the concepts and techniques of the theory of distributions. Although we shall not use the theory of distributions as such in this text, a brief self-contained exposition of it is presented in Appendix *A*.

Let us consider now what happens when p acts on a time function u which is not defined for $t < t_0$, for example, an input u which is defined for $t \geq t_0$ but not $t < t_0$. Then $p\,u$ is not uniquely defined by u. However, $p\,u$ is determined uniquely by u for $t \geq t_0$ if one has the value of u at t_0-, since the delta function in $p\,u$ at t_0 is given by $(u(t_0+) - u(t_0-))\delta(t - t_0)$ and the rest of $p\,u$ is defined by the values of u for $t \geq t_0$. These observations motivate the following

3 **Definition** If u is a time function defined for $t \geq t_0$ and u is differentiable in the distribution sense, then

4 $$p\,u(t) \triangleq -u(t_0-)\delta(t - t_0) + p\,1(t - t_0)u(t)$$

and the $p^n\,u(t)$, $n = 2, 3, \ldots$, are defined by

5 $$p^2\,u(t) = -u(t_0-)\delta^{(1)}(t - t_0) - u^{(1)}(t_0-)\delta(t - t_0) + p^2\,1(t - t_0)u(t)$$

6 $$p^3\,u(t) = -u(t_0-)\delta^{(2)}(t - t_0) - u^{(1)}(t_0-)\delta^{(1)}(t - t_0) - u^{(2)}(t_0-)\delta(t - t_0) + p^3\,1(t - t_0)u(t)$$

. . . .

Note To be consistent with our notation for time functions, we should write $p\,u$ rather than $p\,u(t)$ in *4*. Our lack of consistency in *4* is explained in Remark *1.3.3*. Note also that if $\mathbf{u}$ is a vector-valued time function, then $p\,\mathbf{u}$ is defined as above, with u replaced throughout by $\mathbf{u}$.

7 *Example* Let $u(t) = 3e^{-t}$ for $t \geq 0$ and $u(0-) = 1$, $u^{(1)}(0-) = 2$. Then,

$$\begin{aligned} p\,u(t) &= -\delta(t) + p\,1(t)3e^{-t} \\ &= -\delta(t) + 3\delta(t) - 3e^{-t} \\ &= 2\delta(t) - 3e^{-t} \qquad t \geq 0 \end{aligned}$$

Similarly,

$$p^2\,u(t) = 2\delta^{(1)}(t) - 5\delta(t) + 3e^{-t} \qquad t \geq 0$$

8 *Comment* As we shall see in Chap. *4*, Sec. *4*, p represents a differentiator $\mathfrak{D}$ which is characterized by the input-output-state relation *4*. Thus, the terms $-u(t_0-)\delta(t - t_0)$ and $p\,1(t - t_0)u(t)$ in *4* respectively represent the zero-input response and the zero-state response of $\mathfrak{D}$, with $u(t_0-)$ playing the role of the initial state of $\mathfrak{D}$.

9 *Comment* If u represents a segment $u_{(t_0,t_1]}$, then it will be understood that $p\,u$ should be interpreted as in *4*, with the delta function

$$(u(t_1+) - u(t_1-))\delta(t - t_1)$$

not included in the interval of observation $(t_0,t_1]$.

10 **Remark** In view of the fact that the symbol $p\,u$ is frequently used in many different and not always well-defined ways, it is sometimes necessary to indicate whether $p\,u$ should be understood in the sense of *4* or in the sense of *4* but with $u(t_0-)$ set equal to zero. When it is necessary to differentiate between these two cases, $p\,u$ will be referred to as an *indefinite derivative* when $p\,u$ is defined by *4* and as a *definite derivative* when $u(t_0-)$ in *4* is taken to be zero. In the sequel,

$p\,u$ and, more generally, $p^k\,u$, $k = 1, 2, \ldots$, will be understood to be indefinite derivatives unless stated otherwise. (Note that when $p\,u$ is a definite derivative, p represents a differentiator in its zero state. Note also that the notions of definite and indefinite derivatives are analogs of the notions of definite and indefinite integrals.)

Differential operators

We are now in a position to clarify what is meant by a differential equation such as *1*. For this purpose, we make the

11 **Definition** An *indefinite differential operator*, or, simply, a *differential operator of order* n, $n = 0, 1, 2, \ldots$, is a polynomial in p of the form

12 $$L(p) = a_n p^n + \cdots + a_0 \qquad a_n \neq 0$$

where p^k, $k = 0, 1, 2, \ldots$, is defined by *3* and the a_i, $i = 0, \ldots, n$, are scalar coefficients. If p in *12* is a definite derivative, then $L(p)$ is referred to as a *definite* differential operator. If the coefficients in *12* are matrices, $L(p)$ is said to be a *matric* differential operator. If $a_0, \ldots, a_n$ are time-dependent, they are written as $a_0(t), \ldots, a_n(t)$.

Note that in view of Comment *8*, a differential operator may be regarded as a parallel-series combination (*1.10.33*) of differentiators and scalors.

13 *Example* Let $L(p) = p^2 + 2p + 3$ and let $u(t) = e^{-t}$ for $t \geq 0$. Then

$$L(p)\,u = -u(0-)\delta^{(1)}(t) - (u^{(1)}(0-) + 2u(0-))\delta(t) + (p^2 + 2p + 3)1(t)e^{-t} \qquad t \geq 0$$

and

$$(p^2 + 2p + 3)1(t)e^{-t} = \delta^{(1)}(t) + \delta(t) + 2e^{-t} \qquad t \geq 0$$

14 *Comment* There is a lack of consistency in both the engineering and mathematical literature of ordinary differential equations with regard to the numbering of the coefficients in a differential operator. In many texts a differential operator is written as

15 $$L(p) = a_0 p^n + \cdots + a_n$$

rather than as in *12*, and in some both *12* and *15* are used. In what follows, we shall be somewhat inconsistent too, employing *12* in some chapters and *15* in others, depending on the purposes of the analysis.

Differential equations

Turning to the differential equation *1*, we make the following

16 **Definition** A pair (u,y), with u and y starting at t_0, *satisfies* the differential equation

17 $$a_n \frac{d^n y}{dt^n} + \cdots + a_0 y = b_m \frac{d^m u}{dt^m} + \cdots + b_0 u$$

if and only if

18 $$(a_np^n + \cdots + a_0)y = (b_mp^m + \cdots + b_0)u \qquad \text{for all } t \geq t_0$$

where

19 $$\begin{aligned} L &\triangleq L(p) \triangleq a_np^n + \cdots + a_0 \qquad a_n \neq 0 \\ M &\triangleq M(p) \triangleq b_mp^m + \cdots + b_0 \qquad b_m \neq 0 \end{aligned}$$

are indefinite differential operators in the sense of Definition *11*, with the understanding that the delta functions in Ly and Mu at t_0 are included in the interval $t \geq t_0$.

20 *Example* Suppose that

21 $$(p^2 + 3p + 2)y = (p + 3)u$$

Then a pair (u,y), with u and y starting at, say, $t_0 = 0$, satisfies *21* if there exist values of $y(0-)$, $y^{(1)}(0-)$, and $u(0-)$ such that the relation

$$\begin{aligned} -y(0-)\delta^{(1)}(t) - [3y(0-) + y^{(1)}(0-)]\delta(t) + (p^2 + 3p + 2)1(t)y(t) \\ = -u(0-)\delta(t) + (p + 3)1(t)u(t) \qquad t \geq 0 \end{aligned}$$

is satisfied by u and y, with the delta functions included in the interval $t \geq 0$. For example, the pair $(e^{-3t}, 2e^{-t} - 2e^{-2t})$, $t \geq 0$, satisfies *21* with $y(0-) = 0$, $y^{(1)}(0-) = 2$, $u(0-) = 1$. $\triangleleft$

Note that when we say that a system $\mathcal{A}$ is *characterized* by an input-output relation of the form *18*, we mean that $\mathcal{A}$ admits as input-output pairs only those time functions (u,y) (with u and y defined over an observation interval starting at t_0) which satisfy *17* in the sense of Definition *16*.

22 **Remark** In the sequel, the larger of the two numbers m,n in *19* will be referred to as the *order* of the differential equation *17*. Thus

23 $$\text{order of } \{Ly = Mu\} \triangleq \max(n,m)$$

As we shall see in Chap. *4*, the order of the differential equation $Ly = Mu$ which characterizes $\mathcal{A}$ is identical with the order of $\mathcal{A}$ in the sense of Definition *3.6.39*.

24 **Remark** Suppose that $\mathcal{A}$ is characterized by *17* as well as by its input-output-state relation

25 $$y(t) = \langle \boldsymbol{\phi}(t - t_0), \mathbf{x}(t_0-) \rangle + \int_{t_0}^{t} h(t,\xi)u(\xi)\, d\xi$$

Now by the mutual-consistency condition, every input-output pair which satisfies *17* also satisfies *25*, and vice versa. This implies that the input-output-state relation *25* constitutes what is called in the theory of differential equations a *general solution* of *17*.

Definition of a linear differential system

With these definitions as a background, we are in a position to give a precise meaning to the notion of a linear differential system.

Informally, $\mathcal{A}$ is a *linear differential system* if $\mathcal{A}$ can be represented as an interconnection of adders, scalors, and differentiators. This informal definition underlies the more general formal

26 **Definition** A system $\mathcal{A}$ with vector input $\mathbf{u}$ and vector output $\mathbf{y}$ is a *linear differential* system if and only if the input-output relation of $\mathcal{A}$ admits of the representation

27 $$\mathbf{Ly} + \mathbf{K\tilde{y}} = \mathbf{Mu}$$

where $\mathbf{L}$, $\mathbf{M}$, and $\mathbf{K}$ are, in general, matric differential operators (not necessarily with constant coefficients) and the components of $\mathbf{\tilde{y}}$ are scalar time functions playing the role of suppressed output variables of $\mathcal{A}$ (*1.10.40*). Furthermore, if $\mathbf{\tilde{y}}$ has r components, $r = 0, 1, 2, 3, \ldots$, then $\mathbf{K}$ must be a $k \times r$ matrix, $k > r$. If the matric differential operators $\mathbf{L}$, $\mathbf{M}$, and $\mathbf{K}$ have constant matrices as coefficients of powers of p, then $\mathcal{A}$ is a time-invariant linear differential system in the sense of Definitions *3.2.36* and *3.4.25*. (This will follow from the results established in Chap. *4*.)

28 *Example* A system characterized by the input-output relation

$$\frac{d^2y}{dt^2} + 3\frac{dy}{dt} + 3y = \frac{du}{dt} + 2u$$

is a linear differential time-invariant system. Here

$$L = p^2 + 3p + 3$$
$$M = p + 2$$
$$K = 0$$

29 *Example* A system characterized by the input-output relation

30 $$a_n t^n \frac{d^n y}{dt^n} + \cdots + a_1 t\frac{dy}{dt} + a_0 y = b_m t^m \frac{d^m y}{dt^m} + \cdots + b_1 tu + b_0 u$$

in which the a's and b's are constant coefficients, is a linear differential time-varying system. Here

$$L = a_n t^n p^n + \cdots + a_1 tp + a_0$$
$$M = b_m t^m p^m + \cdots + b_1 tp + b_0$$
$$K = 0$$

31 *Comment* Systems of this type are sometimes referred to as *Euler-Cauchy* systems. It is easy to verify that if in the differential equation characterizing a linear time-invariant system the variable t is replaced

by $\log t'$, the resulting system is of the Euler-Cauchy type. In other words, Euler-Cauchy systems can be derived from linear differential time-invariant systems by the change of time scale $t \to \log t$ (see Example *3.2.22* and Ref. *3*).

32 *Example* The system characterized by the system of equations

33
$$\begin{aligned}(3p^2 - 2p + 1)y_1 + 2p^2 y_2 &= -u_1 + 3u_2\\ (p^2 - p)y_1 + (p^2 + p + 1)y_2 &= 2u_1 + u_2\end{aligned}$$

in which $\mathbf{u} = (u_1,u_2)$ and $\mathbf{y} = (y_1,y_2)$ are the input and output vectors, respectively, is a linear differential time-invariant system. On rewriting *33* in the matrix form

$$\begin{bmatrix}3 & 2\\ 1 & 1\end{bmatrix}\frac{d^2\mathbf{y}}{dt^2} + \begin{bmatrix}-2 & 0\\ -1 & 1\end{bmatrix}\frac{d\mathbf{y}}{dt} + \begin{bmatrix}1 & 0\\ 0 & 1\end{bmatrix}\mathbf{y} = \begin{bmatrix}-1 & 3\\ 2 & 1\end{bmatrix}\mathbf{u}$$

it is readily seen that L and M are given by

$$\mathbf{L} = \begin{bmatrix}3p^2 - 2p + 1 & 2p^2\\ p^2 - p & p^2 + p + 1\end{bmatrix}$$

$$\mathbf{M} = \begin{bmatrix}-1 & 3\\ 2 & 1\end{bmatrix}$$

In all of the above examples the operator **K** is zero. The following example illustrates a system in which this is not the case.

34 *Example* Consider the network $\mathcal{A}$ shown in Fig. *3.8.1*, in which u is the input current, y is the output voltage, and the node voltages $\tilde{y}_1$ and $\tilde{y}_2$ are the suppressed variables. Using nodal analysis (see, for example, Ref. *6*), the equations relating u,y and $\tilde{y}_1,\tilde{y}_2$ are found to be

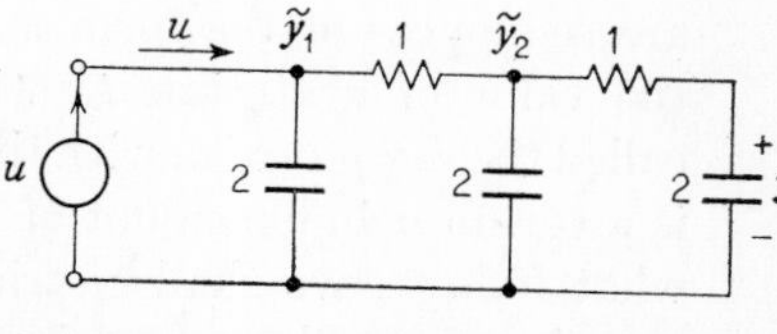

Fig. 3.8.1 Network of Example *3.8.34*.

$$\begin{aligned}0 &= u - (2p + 1)\tilde{y}_1 + \tilde{y}_2\\ y &= \qquad\qquad -\tilde{y}_1 + (2 + 2p)\tilde{y}_2\\ -(2p + 1)y &= \qquad\qquad\qquad -\tilde{y}_2\end{aligned}$$

These equations are of the general form

$$\mathbf{Ly} + \mathbf{K\tilde{y}} = \mathbf{Mu}$$

in which $\tilde{\mathbf{y}} = (\tilde{y}_1,\tilde{y}_2)$,

$$\mathbf{L} = \begin{bmatrix}0\\ 1\\ -(2p + 1)\end{bmatrix} \qquad \mathbf{M} = \begin{bmatrix}1\\ 0\\ 0\end{bmatrix} \qquad \text{and}$$

$$\mathbf{K} = \begin{bmatrix}(2p + 1) & -1\\ 1 & -(2 + 2p)\\ 0 & 1\end{bmatrix}$$

Note that **K** is a 3 × 2 matric differential operator—as it should be in order to satisfy the condition stated in Definition *26*.

35 *Comment* In Chap. *4*, Sec. *7*, it will be shown that if $\mathcal{A}$ is characterized by an input-output relation of the form *27*, then there exists an equivalent system $\mathcal{B}$ which is characterized by a single differential equation which does not involve suppressed output variables. The techniques by which a system of differential equations of the form *27* can be reduced to an equivalent single differential equation are discussed in Chaps. *4* and *6*. This remark implies that the class of linear systems characterized by *27* is no more general than that characterized by *27* with $\mathbf{K} = \mathbf{0}$.

This concludes our discussion of the terminology and notation pertaining to linear differential systems. We turn next to a closely analogous class of systems, namely, linear discrete-time systems. Because of this analogy, our discussion of linear discrete-time systems will parallel closely that of linear differential systems and will be very brief.

Discrete-time systems

As the name implies, a characteristic feature of *discrete-time systems*, or, as they are frequently called, *sampled-data systems*, is the discreteness of time. Thus, in a discrete-time system the input u and output y are sequences of the form $u_0u_1u_2 \cdots y_0y_1y_2 \cdots$, where u_λ denotes the value of u at time t_λ, with λ ranging over integers. The u_λ are called the *samples* of u, with the samples being *equispaced* if $t_\lambda - t_{\lambda-1} \triangleq T_0$ is a constant independent of λ. T_0 is called the *sampling interval*. In what follows, we shall restrict our attention to systems in which the samples of u and y are equispaced, and for convenience we shall assume that $T_0 = 1$. Under this assumption, t ranges over the integers , . . . , $-1, 0, 1, \ldots$ and the value of u at time t reads u_t.

Central to the representation and characterization of discrete-time systems is the *unit delay operator* D, which is defined below. (For simplicity we assume that $t_0 = 0$ and that u_t ranges over scalars.)

36 **Definition** Let u denote a sequence $u_0u_1u_2 \cdots$ defined for $t = 0, 1, 2, \ldots$. Then Du is a sequence y defined by

$$y_t = u_{t-1} \qquad t = 0, 1, 2, \ldots$$

and $D^k u$, $k = 1, 2, \ldots$, is defined recursively by

37 $$D^k u = D(D^{k-1}u)$$

with $D^0 = 1$. Thus

$$D^1 u = u_{-1}u_0u_1u_2 \cdots$$
$$D^2 u = u_{-2}u_{-1}u_0u_1 \cdots$$
$$D^3 u = u_{-3}u_{-2}u_{-1}u_0u_1 \cdots$$

Note that Du is not defined for all $t \geq 0$ (with t ranging over the integers) if u_{-1} is not specified. Thus D is an *indefinite* operator in the same sense as p (Remark *10*). D will be said to be *definite* if u_{-1} in Du is set equal to zero. Unless stated to the contrary, D will be understood to be indefinite.

38 *Comment* In effect, D represents a unit delayor (*1.7.25*) whose input function space is the space of sequences $u_0u_1u_2 \cdots$, with u_{t-1} playing the role of the state of D at time t. Thus, a definite D is a unit delayor which is initially in its zero state. Equivalently, a definite D is a translation operator (*3.2.2*) with delay $\delta = 1$.

39 *Example* Let $u = 3\ 1\ 2\ 2\ 0\ 1$. Then $Du = u_{-1}\ 3\ 1\ 2\ 2\ 0\ 1$, and if D is definite, $Du = 0\ 3\ 1\ 2\ 2\ 0\ 1$.

By analogy with *11* and *26*, we make the following definitions.

40 **Definition** An *indefinite delay operator*, or, simply, a *delay operator of order n*, $n = 0, 1, 2, \ldots$, is a polynomial in D of the form

41 $$L(D) = a_nD^n + \cdots + a_0 \qquad a_n \neq 0$$

where D^k, $k = 0, 1, 2, \ldots$, is defined by *36* and the a_i are scalar coefficients. If the coefficients in *41* are matrices, $L(D)$ is said to be a *matric* delay operator. If $a_0, \ldots, a_n$ are time-dependent, they are written as $a_0(t), \ldots, a_n(t)$. Essentially, $L(D)$ represents a parallel-series combination of delayors and scalors. [Note that $L(D)\mathbf{u}$ for vector-valued $\mathbf{u}$ is defined in exactly the same way as for scalar-valued u.]

42 **Definition** A system $\mathcal{A}$ with vector-valued $\mathbf{u}_t$ and $\mathbf{y}_t$ and t ranging over integers is a *linear discrete-time system* if and only if the input-output relation of $\mathcal{A}$ admits of the representation

43 $$\mathbf{Ly} + \mathbf{K\tilde{y}} = \mathbf{Mu}$$

where $\mathbf{L}$, $\mathbf{M}$, and $\mathbf{K}$ are, in general, matric delay operators (not necessarily with constant coefficients), and the components of $\mathbf{\tilde{y}}$ are suppressed output variables (*1.10.40*). As in Definition *26*, if $\mathbf{\tilde{y}}$ has r components, $r = 0, 1, 2, \ldots$, then $\mathbf{K}$ must be a $k \times r$ matrix, $k > r$. If the operators $\mathbf{L}$, $\mathbf{M}$, and $\mathbf{K}$ have constant matrices as coefficients of powers of D, then $\mathcal{A}$ is a time-invariant discrete-time system.

44 *Comment* In effect, a linear discrete-time system is an interconnection of scalors, adders, and delayors. As in the case of linear differential systems, if a linear discrete-time system is characterized by an input-output relation of the form *43* with $\mathbf{K} \neq \mathbf{0}$, then there exists an equivalent system $\mathcal{B}$ which is characterized by an input-output relation of the form *43* but with $\mathbf{K} = \mathbf{0}$. Thus, there is no loss of generality in assuming that a linear discrete-time system is characterized by an input-output relation of the form $\mathbf{Ly} = \mathbf{Mu}$.

45 *Example* Let $\mathcal{A}$ be characterized by the input-output relation

46 $$(D^2 + D + 2)y = (D + 1)u$$

Then $\mathcal{A}$ is a linear time-invariant discrete-time system with

$$L(D) = D^2 + D + 2$$

$M(D) = D + 1$, and $\mathbf{K} = \mathbf{0}$. Note that a pair (u,y) (with u and y starting at 0) satisfies *46* if and only if for some y_{-2}, y_{-1}, and u_{-1} the u_t and y_t for $t \geq 0$ satisfy the relations

$$\begin{aligned} y_{-2} + y_{-1} + 2y_0 &= u_{-1} + u_0 \\ y_{-1} + y_0 + 2y_1 &= u_0 + u_1 \\ y_0 + y_1 + 2y_2 &= u_1 + u_2 \\ &\cdots\cdots\cdots \\ y_{t-2} + y_{t-1} + 2y_t &= u_{t-1} + u_t \\ &\cdots\cdots\cdots \end{aligned}$$

These relations can be expressed more compactly by the use of z transforms, a brief exposition of which is presented in Chap. *10*. ◁

This concludes our brief discussion of the notation and basic terminology for linear discrete-time systems. We do not dwell further on systems of this type because our principal concern in the following chapters will be with differential systems.

9 *Two basic properties of linear systems*

In this final section of Chap. *3* we shall establish two basic properties of linear systems of finite order—one having to do with system equivalence and the other with determinateness (*2.6.3*). We begin with the

Connection between weak equivalence and equivalence

As was pointed out in Chap. *2* (*2.5.10*), weak equivalence does not, in general, imply equivalence. Thus, if $\mathcal{A}$ and $\mathcal{B}$ are two systems which are weakly equivalent [in the sense that every input-output pair (u,y) for $\mathcal{A}$ is also an input-output pair for $\mathcal{B}$, and vice versa (see *2.5.4*)], then it is not necessarily true that $\mathcal{A} \equiv \mathcal{B}$.

In this regard, linear systems have an important property which finds its expression in the following

1 **Theorem** Let $\mathcal{A}$ and $\mathcal{B}$ be linear differential systems of finite order. If $\mathcal{A}$ and $\mathcal{B}$ are weakly equivalent, then $\mathcal{A}$ and $\mathcal{B}$ are equivalent in the sense of Definition *2.5.8*.

Proof We shall prove this theorem under the simplifying but not essential assumptions that $\mathcal{A}$ and $\mathcal{B}$ are time-invariant and that the input and output are scalar-valued.

Let $\mathcal{A}$ and $\mathcal{B}$ be characterized by input-output-state relations of the form *3.7.1*,

2 $$\mathcal{A}: \qquad y(t) = \langle \boldsymbol{\phi}(t), \boldsymbol{\alpha} \rangle + \int_0^t h_a(t - \xi) u(\xi)\, d\xi$$

3 $$\mathcal{B}: \qquad y(t) = \langle \boldsymbol{\varphi}(t), \boldsymbol{\beta} \rangle + \int_0^t h_b(t - \xi) u(\xi)\, d\xi$$

where $t_0 = 0$, the basis functions are linearly independent over every subinterval of $[0, \infty)$ (see *3.7.12*), and h_a and h_b represent the impulse responses of $\mathcal{A}$ and $\mathcal{B}$, respectively. The state vectors $\boldsymbol{\alpha}$ and $\boldsymbol{\beta}$ are assumed to range over $\mathcal{C}^n$ (space of n-tuples of complex numbers).

First, let us consider input-output pairs of the form $(0,y)$, where y represents a zero-input response. By Assertion *3.6.49*, if every zero-input response of $\mathcal{A}$ is also a zero-input response of $\mathcal{B}$ and vice versa, then every basis function of $\mathcal{A}$ is expressible as a linear combination of basis functions of $\mathcal{B}$ and vice versa. This implies that, if $\mathcal{A}$ and $\mathcal{B}$ are weakly equivalent, then we can use the same set of basis functions, say, $\boldsymbol{\phi}(t)$, in both *2* and *3*, with the result that *3* can be replaced by a relation of the form

4 $$\mathcal{B}: \qquad y(t) = \langle \boldsymbol{\phi}(t), \boldsymbol{\beta} \rangle + \int_0^t h_b(t - \xi) u(\xi)\, d\xi$$

where $\boldsymbol{\beta}$ (which is not the same $\boldsymbol{\beta}$ as in *3*) ranges over $\mathcal{C}^n$.

The theorem is proved if we can show that $h_a(t) = h_b(t)$ for all t; for then $\mathcal{A}$ and $\mathcal{B}$ are both zero-input and zero-state equivalent, and hence are equivalent. To this end, we shall demonstrate that the statement "$\mathcal{A}$ and $\mathcal{B}$ are weakly equivalent" implies "$\mathcal{A}$ and $\mathcal{B}$ are zero-state equivalent."

Specifically, let (u,y) be an input-output pair for $\mathcal{A}$, with $\mathcal{A}$ initially in its zero state, and let

5 $$\begin{aligned} u(t) &= 0 && \text{for } 0 \leq t < T \\ u(t) &= \delta(t - T) && \text{for } t \geq T \end{aligned}$$

Then the response of $\mathcal{A}$ to u is of the form

6 $$\begin{aligned} y(t) &= 0 && \text{for } 0 \leq t < T \\ y(t) &= h_a(t - T) && \text{for } t \geq T \end{aligned}$$

By hypothesis, there must be a state in $\mathcal{B}$, say, $\boldsymbol{\beta}$, such that the response of $\mathcal{B}$ to u, with $\mathcal{B}$ initially in state $\boldsymbol{\beta}$, is identical with y. Using *2* and *4* to *6*, this condition yields

7 $$\langle \boldsymbol{\phi}(t), \boldsymbol{\beta} \rangle = 0 \qquad \text{for } 0 \leq t < T$$

8 $$\langle \boldsymbol{\phi}(t), \boldsymbol{\beta} \rangle + h_b(t - T) = h_a(t - T) \qquad \text{for } t \geq T$$

Now *7* implies that $\boldsymbol{\beta} = \mathbf{0}$, since the basis functions are assumed to be linearly independent over every subinterval of $[0, \infty)$. [For, by differentiating *7* $n - 1$ times, we get $\boldsymbol{\Phi}(t)\boldsymbol{\beta} = \mathbf{0}$ [$\boldsymbol{\Phi}(t) \triangleq$ state transition matrix (*3.7.7*)], which implies that $\boldsymbol{\beta} = \mathbf{0}$.] Therefore, on substituting $\boldsymbol{\beta} = \mathbf{0}$ in *8*, we have

9 $$h_a(t - T) = h_b(t - T) \qquad t \geq T$$

and since T is arbitrary, $h_a(t) = h_b(t)$ for all $t \geq 0$, which proves the theorem. ◁

We leave it to the reader to prove appropriately restricted forms of the following corollaries of Theorem *1*.

10 **Corollary** If $\mathcal{A}$ is weakly time-invariant (*3.2.42*), then $\mathcal{A}$ is time-invariant.

11 **Corollary** If $\mathcal{A}$ and $\mathcal{B}$ are converse systems (*2.10.1*), then $\mathcal{A}$ and $\mathcal{B}$ are inverse to one another.

Determinateness of linear systems

We turn next to another basic property of linear systems, namely the *determinateness* of linear systems (*2.6.3* and *2.6.7*).

Essentially, linear systems are determinate in the sense that if $\mathcal{A}$ is an interconnection of linear systems $\mathcal{A}_1, \ldots, \mathcal{A}_N$, with the state vector of $\mathcal{A}_i$ at time t, $\mathbf{x}^i(t)$, ranging over Σ_i, then the composite vector $\mathbf{x}(t) = (\mathbf{x}^1(t), \ldots, \mathbf{x}^N(t))$ which takes values in a subset Σ of the product space $\Sigma_1 \times \cdots \times \Sigma_N$ (see *2.6.6 et seq.*) qualifies as a state vector of $\mathcal{A}$. In practical terms, this means that the problem of associating a state vector $\mathbf{x}$ with $\mathcal{A}$ can be reduced to a number of simpler problems, each involving the association of a state vector $\mathbf{x}^i$ with a component $\mathcal{A}_i$ of $\mathcal{A}$. This approach to the problem of associating a state vector with a differential system will be discussed more fully in Chap. *4*, Sec. *6*.

We shall not attempt to establish the determinateness property of linear systems in its most general form. For our purposes, it will suffice to establish the following restricted version of it.

12 **Theorem** Let $\mathcal{A}$ be an interconnection of $\mathcal{A}_1, \ldots, \mathcal{A}_N$ and adders, where $\mathcal{A}_i$, $i = 1, \ldots, N$, is a linear time-invariant differential system of finite order with scalar input u^i and scalar output y^i. Then $\mathcal{A}$ is a determinate system in the sense of Remark *2.6.7*.

Proof Let $\boldsymbol{\alpha}^i$ denote the initial state of $\mathcal{A}_i$, $i = 1, \ldots, N$. Then by the decomposition property (*3.5.2*), the output of $\mathcal{A}_i$ can be expressed as

13 $$y^i = A_i(\boldsymbol{\alpha}^i;0) + A_i(u^i)$$

where $A_i(\boldsymbol{\alpha}^i;0)$ denotes the zero-input response of $\mathcal{A}_i$ starting in state $\boldsymbol{\alpha}^i$ and $A_i(u^i)$ is the zero-state response of $\mathcal{A}_i$ to u^i. Furthermore, by

3.6.23, the Laplace transform of $A_i(u^i)$ is given by $H_i(s)U^i(s)$, where $H_i(s)$ is the transfer function of $\mathcal{A}_i$ and $U^i(s)$ is the Laplace transform of u^i (t_0 is assumed to be 0). Thus, each $\mathcal{A}_i$ can be replaced by $\mathcal{A}_i$ in its zero state plus a source $A_i(\boldsymbol{\alpha}^i;0)$ which is connected to the output of $\mathcal{A}_i$ as shown in Fig. *3.9.1*. For convenience, the source is denoted by $A_i(s)$, where $A_i(s)$ stands for the Laplace transform of $A_i(\boldsymbol{\alpha}^i;0)$.

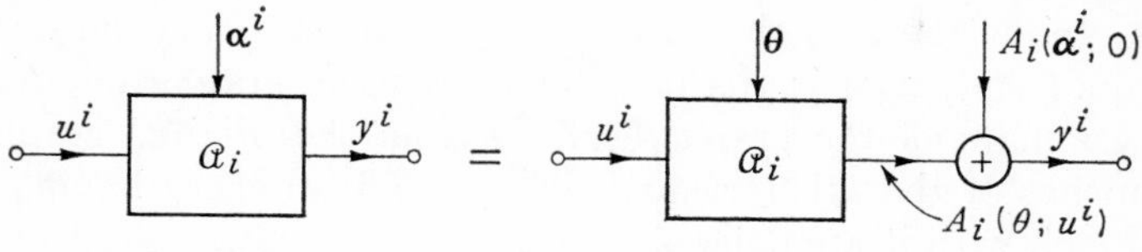

Fig. 3.9.1 Trading initial state for addition to output.

On performing the replacement for each $\mathcal{A}_i$ we obtain a signal-flow graph with branch gains $H_1(s), \ldots, H_N(s)$, a simple example of which is shown in Fig. *3.9.2*. Here $N = 4$ with the four branches labeled $H_1(s), \ldots, H_4(s)$ corresponding to $\mathcal{A}_1, \ldots, \mathcal{A}_4$, respectively. The input to $\mathcal{A}_3$, say, is the signal $V_3(s)$, which is associated with the node (node 3) from which the branch labeled $H_3(s)$ emanates. The external

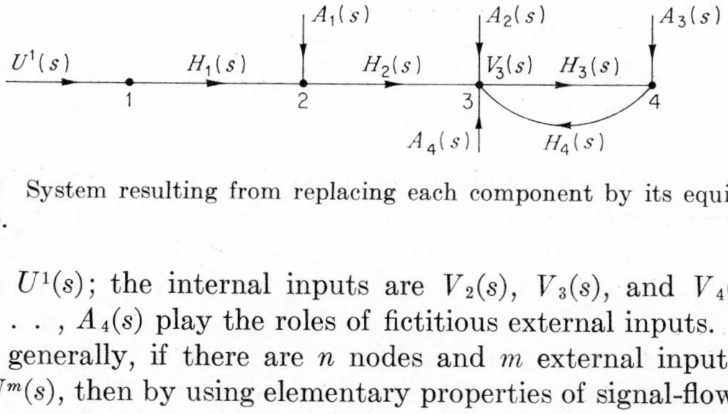

Fig. 3.9.2 System resulting from replacing each component by its equivalent in zero state.

input is $U^1(s)$; the internal inputs are $V_2(s)$, $V_3(s)$, and $V_4(s)$; and $A_1(s), \ldots, A_4(s)$ play the roles of fictitious external inputs.

More generally, if there are n nodes and m external inputs $U^1(s), \ldots, U^m(s)$, then by using elementary properties of signal-flow graphs (see Chap. *9*, Sec. *15*), we can express the V's in terms of U's by relations of the form

14
$$\begin{aligned} V_1(s) &= G_{11}(s)W_1(s) + \cdots + G_{1n}(s)W_n(s) \\ &\cdots\cdots\cdots\cdots\cdots\cdots \\ V_n(s) &= G_{n1}(s)W_1(s) + \cdots + G_{nn}(s)W_n(s) \end{aligned}$$

where $V_\lambda(s) \triangleq$ signal associated with node λ and $W_\lambda(s)$ is the sum of all external inputs applied at node λ. For example, in Fig. *3.9.2*

$$W_1(s) = U^1(s) \qquad W_2(s) = A_1(s) \qquad W_3(s) = A_2(s) + A_4(s)$$
$$\text{and} \qquad W_4(s) = A_3(s)$$

In these equations, $G_{\mu\lambda}(s)$ represents the transmission function from node λ to node μ, which is given by Mason's formula (see *9.15.14*)

15 $$G_{\mu\lambda}(s) = \frac{\sum_k G^k_{\mu\lambda}(s)\,\Delta^k_{\mu\lambda}(s)}{\Delta(s)}$$

where the summation is over all forward paths from node λ to node μ, $G^k_{\mu\lambda}(s)$, $\mu,\lambda = 1, \ldots, n$, denotes the gain of kth forward path (i.e., the product of the gains of all branches constituting the forward path in question), $\Delta(s)$ is the determinant of the graph, and $\Delta^k_{\mu\lambda}(s)$ is the determinant of the graph resulting from the original graph when all branches of the kth forward path and all branches having a node in common with it are deleted.

Since the $\mathcal{A}_i$ are linear time-invariant systems, the $H_i(s)$ are rational functions of s. Furthermore, the numerator and denominator of $G_{\mu\lambda}(s)$ are rational functions of $H_1(s), \ldots, H_N(s)$, and hence the numerator and denominator of $G_{\mu\lambda}(s)$ are likewise rational functions of s. Consequently, $G_{\mu\lambda}(s)$ is a rational function of s. This implies that, if we exclude the degenerate case where the numerator and denominator of $G_{\mu\lambda}(s)$ vanish identically for all s, the $V_i(s)$ can be expressed via *14* and *15* in terms of the inputs $U^1(s), \ldots, U^m(s)$ and the initial states $\boldsymbol{\alpha}^1, \ldots, \boldsymbol{\alpha}^N$. Consequently, $\mathcal{A}$ is a determinate system provided there is at least one value of s for which the numerator and denominator of $G_{\mu\lambda}(s)$, $\lambda,\mu = 1, \ldots, n$, do not vanish simultaneously. This minor qualification can be disregarded for all practical purposes.

16 *Comment* The proof given above involves two main points. First, by the use of the decomposition property, $\mathcal{A}$ is reduced to an interconnection of component systems $\mathcal{A}_1, \ldots, \mathcal{A}_N$, which are in their zero state, plus "fictitious" sources which are determined by the initial states of $\mathcal{A}_1, \ldots, \mathcal{A}_N$ and which are connected to the outputs of $\mathcal{A}_1, \ldots, \mathcal{A}_N$. Needless to say, this reduction is applicable to any system whose components have the decomposition property, and not just a linear system.

The second step involves showing that the reduced system is, so to speak, *zero-state determinate* in the sense that given the external as well as the fictitious inputs, one can determine the input to each of the components of $\mathcal{A}$ if they are initially in their zero state. In the case of linear time-invariant systems, this is readily established by the use of Mason's formula.

In the absence of an analogous formula for linear time-varying systems, one can regard the statement of Theorem *12* as a rule of procedure which may fail in special cases. Thus, if by associating a state vector $\mathbf{x}$ with $\mathcal{A}$ by the use of this rule we succeed in deriving the state equations (or input-output-state relations) for $\mathcal{A}$ in terms of the state equations (or input-output-state relations) of its components $\mathcal{A}_1, \ldots, \mathcal{A}_N$, then **x** qualifies as a state vector for $\mathcal{A}$, and we have solved our problem. We cannot guarantee in advance—as we can in the case of time-invariant differential systems of finite order—that the application of the rule in question will be successful. However, we can assert that a linear time-varying system is determinate if it satisfies the conditions of Comment *2.6.42*. Actually, most linear time-varying systems satisfy those conditions or can be made to satisfy them through a rearrangement of components. ◁

This concludes our discussion of general properties of linear systems. In the next chapter we shall focus our attention on various techniques for associating a state vector **x** with a given time-invariant system $\mathcal{A}$ and finding the corresponding state equations of $\mathcal{A}$.

REFERENCES AND SUGGESTED READING

1 Ince, E. L.: "Ordinary Differential Equations," Dover Publications, Inc., New York, 1926.
2 Lévy, P.: "Problèmes Concrets d'Analyse Fonctionelle," Gauthier-Villars, Paris, 1951.
3 Aseltine, J. A.: "Transform Method in Linear System Analysis," McGraw-Hill Book Company, Inc., New York, 1958.
4 Yosida, K.: "Lectures on Differential and Integral Equations," Interscience Publishers, Inc., New York, 1960.
5 Hurewicz, W.: "Lectures on Ordinary Differential Equations," John Wiley & Sons, Inc., New York, 1958.
6 Van Valkenburg, M. E.: "Network Analysis," Prentice-Hall, Inc., Englewood Cliffs, N.J., 1955.

State vectors and state equations of time-invariant differential systems 4

1 *Introduction*

Our main objective in this chapter is to develop a systematic approach to the problem of associating a state vector and state equations with a linear system characterized by a differential equation or a system of differential equations with constant coefficients. In more concrete terms, let $\mathcal{A}$ be a differential system (*3.8.26*) defined by an input-output relation of the form

1 $$\mathbf{Ly} + \mathbf{K\tilde{y}} = \mathbf{Mu}$$

where **L**, **K**, and **M** are constant-coefficient matric differential operators, **u** is the input vector, **y** is the output vector, and $\mathbf{\tilde{y}}$ is the suppressed output vector (*1.10.40*). The questions of principal interest to us are these: How can one associate with *1* a state vector **x** which satisfies the mutual- and self-consistency conditions *1.6.5*, *1.6.11*, *1.6.15*, and *1.6.35*? How can one determine the input-output-state relation and state equations of $\mathcal{A}$? How can one synthesize $\mathcal{A}$ in the form of an interconnection of adders, scalors, integrators, and differentiators? What are the forms which the state equations of $\mathcal{A}$ assume in various special cases? Is there a canonical form for the state equations of a system of finite order? How can one eliminate the suppressed output variables from *1* and thereby determine a system $\mathcal{B}$ which is equivalent to $\mathcal{A}$ and which is characterized by an input-output relation in which $\mathbf{K} = \mathbf{0}$?

In the course of answering these questions we shall solve several subsidiary problems and deduce a number of properties of input-output-state relations which bear on the main problem at hand, namely, the association of a state vector with $\mathcal{A}$. Essentially, our approach to this problem will be the following: First, by the use of the Laplace transformation or other techniques, we find an expression for the general solution (see *3.8.24*) of the differential equation in terms of which $\mathcal{A}$ is characterized. Second, we identify the constants or combinations of constants appearing in the general solution with the components of the state vector at time $0-$ and thereby obtain an expression for $\mathbf{x}(0-)$ in terms of the values at $0-$ of $\mathbf{u}$, $\mathbf{y}$, $\tilde{\mathbf{y}}$, and a finite number of their derivatives.[1] In this way the general solution in question becomes a "tentative" input-output-state relation for $\mathcal{A}$. [The adjective "tentative" is used here to emphasize that at this stage of the process it remains to be shown that the tentative input-output-state relation satisfies the self-consistency conditions or, equivalently, has the response separation property (see *2.3.12*).] Then, by replacing $0-$ in the expression for $\mathbf{x}(0-)$ by t, we obtain an expression for $\mathbf{x}(t)$ in terms of $\mathbf{u}(t)$, $\mathbf{y}(t)$, $\tilde{\mathbf{y}}(t)$, and their derivatives. Finally, on forming $\dot{\mathbf{x}}(t)$ through the differentiation of $\mathbf{x}(t)$ and eliminating $\mathbf{y}(t)$, $\tilde{\mathbf{y}}(t)$, and their derivatives from the equations defining $\mathbf{x}(t)$ and $\dot{\mathbf{x}}(t)$, we obtain the state equation of $\mathcal{A}$. Once these equations have been obtained, we invoke Corollary *2.3.36 et seq.* and thereby establish that $\mathbf{x}$ qualifies as a state vector for $\mathcal{A}$ and that the tentative input-output-state relation is indeed an input-output-state relation for $\mathcal{A}$.

This approach will serve as a basis for another, less cumbersome, technique which accomplishes the association of a state vector with $\mathcal{A}$ through the process of realizing $\mathcal{A}$ in the form of an interconnection of adders, scalors, integrators, and differentiators. In this method, we shall make use of the determinateness of linear systems (Theorem *3.9.12*) and the equivalence between $\mathcal{A}$ and its realization (see *2.5.19*), which allow us to identify the components of $\mathbf{x}$ with the state variables of the integrators and differentiators in the realization of $\mathcal{A}$. The so-called partial-fraction technique for associating a state vector with $\mathcal{A}$ is a special case of this approach.

In brief, these are the basic features of the approaches we shall employ in this chapter to associate a state vector with a system characterized by a differential equation. Before we can develop these approaches in greater detail, it will be necessary for us to establish several properties of input-output-state relations of linear time-invariant systems which bear on the question of uniqueness of $\mathbf{x}$ and the connection between different modes of associating a state vector $\mathbf{x}$ with $\mathcal{A}$.

2 *Properties of input-output-state relations*

1 *Note* In this and the following sections the initial state will be assumed to be defined at time t_0- rather than t_0. Correspondingly, the observation interval will be taken to be $[t_0,t)$ unless otherwise specified. ◁

[1] The term "derivative" is used here in its wider sense to denote a derivative of any order k, $k = 1, 2, 3, \ldots$.

In order to avoid obscuring the main lines of the argument with cumbersome notation, we shall assume for simplicity that the input u and output y of $\mathcal{A}$ are scalar-valued time functions. This assumption will not play an essential role in our discussion, and it is a simple matter to extend the results obtained under this assumption to the general case in which u and y are vector-valued.

We begin with a recapitulation of certain basic facts which were established in Chap. *3*. Specifically, it was shown in Chap. *3*, Sec. *6*, that the input-output-state relation of a time-invariant linear system $\mathcal{A}$ of order n (with scalar input u and scalar output y) admits of the representation (for $t_0 = 0$)

2 $$y(t) = \langle \boldsymbol{\phi}(t), \mathbf{x}(0-) \rangle + \int_0^t h(t-\xi)u(\xi)\,d\xi \qquad t \geq 0$$

where (I) $\mathbf{x}(0-)$ is the initial state of $\mathcal{A}$ at time $0-$.

(II) $\mathbf{x}(0-)$ ranges over $\mathcal{C}^n$, the space of n-tuples of complex numbers.

(III) $\boldsymbol{\phi}(t)$ is a basis vector whose components $\phi_1(t), \ldots, \phi_n(t)$ represent the zero-input responses of $\mathcal{A}$ starting in the initial states $(1,0, \ldots ,0)$, $(0,1,0, \ldots ,0)$, $\ldots$, $(0, \ldots ,0,1)$, respectively.

(IV) $\phi_1, \ldots, \phi_n$ are linearly independent time functions and have a nonvanishing Wronskian.

(V) $\langle \boldsymbol{\phi}(t), \mathbf{x}(0-) \rangle$ is the scalar product of $\boldsymbol{\phi}(t)$ and $\mathbf{x}(0-)$.

(VI) $h(t)$ is the impulse response of $\mathcal{A}$, that is, the zero-state response of $\mathcal{A}$ to the unit impulse $\delta(t)$.

(VII) $h(t)$ is the inverse Laplace transform of $H(s)$, the transfer function of $\mathcal{A}$.

Let us disregard for the moment *2* and assume that $\mathcal{A}$ is associated with a state vector $\hat{\mathbf{x}}$, with $\hat{\mathbf{x}}$ ranging over a linear vector space $\mathcal{C}^m$ of dimension m. By Assertion *3.6.33*, the corresponding input-output-state relation for $\mathcal{A}$ must necessarily be of the form

3 $$y(t) = \langle \hat{\boldsymbol{\phi}}(t), \hat{\mathbf{x}}(0-) \rangle + \int_0^t \hat{h}(t-\xi)u(\xi)\,d\xi \qquad t \geq 0$$

where the various symbols have the same meaning as their counterparts in *2*(I) to *2*(VII), except that the components of $\hat{\boldsymbol{\phi}}(t)$ need not be linearly independent time functions.

Comparing *3* with *2*, it is clear that $\hat{h}(t)$ and $h(t)$ must be equal for all t, since $\hat{h}$ and h represent the same time function, namely, the zero-state response of $\mathcal{A}$ to $\delta(t)$. The question is: What is the relationship, if any, between $\hat{\boldsymbol{\phi}}$, $\boldsymbol{\phi}$, $\mathbf{x}(0-)$, and $\hat{\mathbf{x}}(0-)$? This question is answered in the following

4 **Assertion** Let $\mathcal{A}$ be a linear system of order n which is associated with (I) a state vector $\mathbf{x}$ ranging over a state space $\mathcal{C}^n$ of dimension n, with the corresponding input-output-state relation having the form *2*, and (II) a state vector $\hat{\mathbf{x}}$ ranging over a state space $\mathcal{C}^m$ of dimension m, with the corresponding input-output-state relation reading

5 $$y(t) = \langle \hat{\boldsymbol{\phi}}(t), \hat{\mathbf{x}}(0-) \rangle + \int_0^t h(t - \xi)u(\xi)\, d\xi \qquad t \geq 0$$

Then $m \geq n$ and $\mathbf{x}(0-)$ is related to $\hat{\mathbf{x}}(0-)$ by

6 $$\mathbf{x}(0-) = \mathbf{\Gamma}\hat{\mathbf{x}}(0-)$$

where $\mathbf{\Gamma}$ is an $n \times m$ matrix of rank n. In particular, if $m = n$, then $\mathbf{x}(0-)$ and $\hat{\mathbf{x}}(0-)$ range over the same state space and the linear correspondence between $\mathbf{x}(0-)$ and $\hat{\mathbf{x}}(0-)$ is one-one.

Proof Since *2* and *5* are input-output-state relations for $\mathcal{A}$, they satisfy the mutual-consistency condition *1.6.5*, meaning that every input-output pair for $\mathcal{A}$ satisfies both *2* and *5* and, conversely, every pair (u,y) satisfying either *2* or *5* is an input-output pair for $\mathcal{A}$. This in turn implies that every input-output pair (u,y) satisfying *2* also satisfies *5*, and vice versa. In particular, for input-output pairs of the form $(0,y)$ (which represent zero-input responses of $\mathcal{A}$) this implies that to every vector $\mathbf{x}(0-)$ in $\mathcal{C}^n$ there corresponds a vector $\hat{\mathbf{x}}(0-)$ in $\mathcal{C}^m$, and vice versa, such that

7 $$\langle \boldsymbol{\phi}(t), \mathbf{x}(0-) \rangle = \langle \hat{\boldsymbol{\phi}}(t), \hat{\mathbf{x}}(0-) \rangle \qquad \text{for all } t \geq 0$$

Thus, let $\hat{\boldsymbol{\gamma}}^1 = (\hat{\gamma}_1^1, \ldots, \hat{\gamma}_m^1), \ldots, \hat{\boldsymbol{\gamma}}^n = (\hat{\gamma}_1^n, \ldots, \hat{\gamma}_m^n)$ be m-vectors in $\mathcal{C}^m$ corresponding to the unit n-vectors $(1, \ldots, 0), (0, 1, \ldots, 0), \ldots, (0, \ldots, 1)$ in $\mathcal{C}^n$. (Note that $\boldsymbol{\gamma}^1, \ldots, \boldsymbol{\gamma}^n$ are not necessarily unique.) For these vectors *7* yields

$$\begin{aligned} \phi_1 &= \hat{\gamma}_1^1 \hat{\phi}_1 + \cdots + \hat{\gamma}_m^1 \hat{\phi}_m \\ &\cdots\cdots\cdots\cdots\cdots \\ \phi_n &= \hat{\gamma}_1^n \hat{\phi}_1 + \cdots + \hat{\gamma}_m^n \hat{\phi}_m \end{aligned}$$

or more compactly,

8 $$\boldsymbol{\phi} = \hat{\boldsymbol{\phi}} \hat{\mathbf{\Gamma}}$$

where $\hat{\mathbf{\Gamma}}$ is a constant matrix whose ijth element is $\hat{\gamma}_i^j$ and

$$\boldsymbol{\phi} = (\phi_1, \ldots, \phi_n) \qquad \hat{\boldsymbol{\phi}} = (\hat{\phi}_1, \ldots, \hat{\phi}_m)$$

are row vectors.

Since $\phi_1, \ldots, \phi_n$ are linearly independent time functions, *8* cannot be true unless at least n of the m time functions $\hat{\phi}_1, \ldots, \hat{\phi}_m$ are linearly independent. This implies that $m \geq n$ and hence that $\mathcal{C}^m$ is of dimension $m \geq n$.

In a similar fashion, let $\boldsymbol{\gamma}^1 = (\gamma_1^1, \ldots, \gamma_n^1), \ldots, \boldsymbol{\gamma}^m = (\gamma_1^m, \ldots, \gamma_n^m)$ be m n-vectors in $\mathcal{C}^n$ corresponding to the m unit vectors $(1, \ldots, 0)$,

$(0, \ldots, 1)$ in $\mathcal{C}^m$. In this case *7* yields

$$\hat{\phi}_1 = \gamma_1^1 \phi_1 + \cdots + \gamma_n^1 \phi_n$$
$$\cdots\cdots\cdots\cdots\cdots\cdots$$
$$\hat{\phi}_m = \gamma_1^m \phi_1 + \cdots + \gamma_n^m \phi_n$$

or more compactly,

9 $$\hat{\boldsymbol{\phi}} = \boldsymbol{\phi}\boldsymbol{\Gamma}$$

where $\boldsymbol{\Gamma}$ is a constant matrix whose *ij*th element is γ_i^j.

Since $\boldsymbol{\phi}$ is an n-vector, *9* implies that not more than n of the m time functions $\hat{\phi}_1, \ldots, \hat{\phi}_m$ can be linearly independent. On the other hand, we have already shown that not fewer than n of the m time functions $\hat{\phi}_1, \ldots, \hat{\phi}_m$ are linearly independent. Consequently, we can assert that *exactly n of the m time functions* $\hat{\phi}_1, \ldots, \hat{\phi}_m$ *are linearly independent.* This leads at once to the conclusion that the matrices $\hat{\boldsymbol{\Gamma}}$ and $\boldsymbol{\Gamma}$ in *8* and *9* are of rank n; for otherwise the number of linearly independent components in the left-hand members of *8* and *9* would be less than n. (Note that the rank of $\hat{\boldsymbol{\Gamma}}$ and $\boldsymbol{\Gamma}$ cannot exceed n because they are $m \times n$ and $n \times m$ matrices, respectively.)

Next, on substituting *9* in *7*, we have

10 $$\langle \boldsymbol{\phi}, \mathbf{x}(0-) \rangle = \langle \boldsymbol{\phi}\boldsymbol{\Gamma}, \hat{\mathbf{x}}(0-) \rangle \qquad t \geq 0$$

and since the components of $\boldsymbol{\phi}$ are linearly independent time functions, *10* implies

11 $$\mathbf{x}(0-) = \boldsymbol{\Gamma}\hat{\mathbf{x}}(0-) \qquad \text{for all } \mathbf{x}(0-) \text{ in } \mathcal{C}^n \text{ and all } \hat{\mathbf{x}}(0-) \text{ in } \mathcal{C}^m$$

which is what we wanted to demonstrate.

12 **Remark** Let $\mathcal{A}$ and $\hat{\mathcal{A}}$ be systems characterized by the input-output-state relations *2* and *5*, respectively. To say that $\mathbf{x}$ and $\hat{\mathbf{x}}$ are two different representations for the state vector of $\mathcal{A}$ is the same as saying that $\mathcal{A}$ and $\hat{\mathcal{A}}$ are equivalent systems (see *2.3.46*), with $\mathbf{x}$ being the state of $\mathcal{A}$ and $\hat{\mathbf{x}}$ the state of $\hat{\mathcal{A}}$. From this point of view, *7* may be regarded as expressing the condition of zero-input equivalence of $\mathcal{A}$ and $\hat{\mathcal{A}}$ (*2.9.2*). (Note that $\mathcal{A}$ and $\hat{\mathcal{A}}$ are zero-state equivalent by virtue of the relation $h = \hat{h}$.) Also, the condition $m \geq n$ means that the dimension of the state space of any system equivalent to $\mathcal{A}$ cannot be less than n. If $m > n$, then the correspondence between $\mathcal{C}^m$ and $\mathcal{C}^n$ is not one-one, which implies that some of the states in $\mathcal{C}^m$ are equivalent to one another and hence that $\hat{\mathcal{A}}$ is not in reduced form (see *2.2.11*). This is consistent with the result that $\mathbf{x}(0-) = \boldsymbol{\Gamma}\hat{\mathbf{x}}(0-)$ and that $\hat{\mathbf{x}}(0-)$ cannot be similarly expressed in terms of $\mathbf{x}(0-)$ when $m > n$.

Relation between x and x̂ when $m = n$

The case that is of particular interest to us is that where $\mathbf{x}(0-)$ and $\hat{\mathbf{x}}(0-)$ are vectors of the same dimension n. In this case, $\mathbf{\Gamma}$ and $\hat{\mathbf{\Gamma}}$ are $n \times n$ matrices of rank n. Furthermore, to the relation

13 $$\mathbf{x}(0-) = \mathbf{\Gamma}\hat{\mathbf{x}}(0-) \qquad \forall \mathbf{x} \forall \hat{\mathbf{x}}$$

which was derived from *7* and *9* by invoking the linear independence of $\phi_1, \ldots, \phi_n$, we can add the relation

14 $$\hat{\mathbf{x}}(0-) = \hat{\mathbf{\Gamma}}\mathbf{x}(0-) \qquad \forall \mathbf{x} \forall \hat{\mathbf{x}}$$

which follows in the same way from *7*, *8*, and the linear independence of $\hat{\phi}_1, \ldots, \hat{\phi}_n$. Equations *13* and *14* taken together imply that $\mathbf{\Gamma}$ is nonsingular and that $\hat{\mathbf{\Gamma}}$ and $\mathbf{\Gamma}$ are inverse to one another, i.e.,

15 $$\hat{\mathbf{\Gamma}} = \mathbf{\Gamma}^{-1}$$

Note that the nonsingularity of $\mathbf{\Gamma}$ follows also from the fact that $\mathbf{\Gamma}$ is of rank n. This result enables us to state the following corollary of Assertion *4*.

16 **Corollary** If a linear system $\mathcal{A}$ of order n is associated with a state vector $\mathbf{x}$ ranging over a linear vector space $\mathcal{C}^n$ of dimension n, then any other way of associating with $\mathcal{A}$ a state vector of the same dimension as $\mathbf{x}$ must necessarily lead to a vector $\hat{\mathbf{x}}$ such that

17 $$\mathbf{x}(0-) = \mathbf{\Gamma}\hat{\mathbf{x}}(0-)$$

where $\mathbf{\Gamma}$ is a constant nonsingular $n \times n$ matrix defined by *9*. ◁

We can strengthen this result by showing that if *17* holds at $t = 0-$, then it holds for all $t \geq 0$. This is done in the following

18 **Lemma** If the basis functions $\boldsymbol{\phi}$ and $\hat{\boldsymbol{\phi}}$ in *2* and *3* are related by

$$\hat{\boldsymbol{\phi}} = \boldsymbol{\phi}\mathbf{\Gamma}$$

and the initial state vectors are related by

$$\mathbf{x}(0-) = \mathbf{\Gamma}\hat{\mathbf{x}}(0-)$$

where $\mathbf{\Gamma}$ is a nonsingular $n \times n$ matrix, then for all inputs u in the input segment space of $\mathcal{A}$ the states $\mathbf{x}$ and $\hat{\mathbf{x}}$ at time t are related by

$$\mathbf{x}(t) = \mathbf{\Gamma}\hat{\mathbf{x}}(t) \qquad \forall t \geq 0$$

Proof It is easy to verify that when the basis functions are not normalized, the differential state equation satisfied by $\mathbf{x}$ (see *3.7.9*) assumes the form (see *3.7.36*)

19 $$\mathbf{\Phi}(0)\dot{\mathbf{x}}(t) = \dot{\mathbf{\Phi}}(0)\mathbf{x}(t) + \mathbf{h}(0)u(t)$$

where, as in *3.7.7*, $\mathbf{\Phi}(t)$ is expressed by

$$\mathbf{\Phi}(t) = \begin{bmatrix} \phi_1(t) & \cdots & \phi_n(t) \\ \cdot & \cdots & \cdot \\ \phi_1^{(n-1)}(t) & \cdots & \phi_n^{(n-1)}(t) \end{bmatrix} \qquad t \geq 0$$

and $\mathbf{h}(t)$ is an n-vector whose ith element is the $(i - 1)$st derivative of the impulse response $h(t)$; that is,

20
$$\mathbf{h}(t) = \begin{bmatrix} h(t) \\ \cdots \\ h^{(n-1)}(t) \end{bmatrix} \qquad t \geq 0$$

Since $\hat{\mathbf{x}}$, like $\mathbf{x}$, is a state vector for $\mathcal{A}$, it too must satisfy an equation of the same form as *19*:

21
$$\hat{\mathbf{\Phi}}(0)\dot{\hat{\mathbf{x}}}(t) = \dot{\hat{\mathbf{\Phi}}}(0)\hat{\mathbf{x}}(t) + \mathbf{h}(0)u(t)$$

[Note that $\hat{\mathbf{h}}(0) = \mathbf{h}(0)$ because $\hat{\mathbf{h}}(t) \equiv \mathbf{h}(t)$.]

Furthermore, since the relation $\hat{\boldsymbol{\phi}} = \boldsymbol{\phi}\mathbf{\Gamma}$ holds for all $t \geq 0$, we have [with the understanding that $\boldsymbol{\phi}^{(i-1)}(0) \triangleq \boldsymbol{\phi}^{(i-1)}(0+)$ and likewise for $\hat{\boldsymbol{\phi}}$]

$$\hat{\boldsymbol{\phi}}^{(i-1)} = \boldsymbol{\phi}^{(i-1)}\mathbf{\Gamma} \qquad t \geq 0, i = 1, \ldots, n$$

and therefore

22
$$\hat{\mathbf{\Phi}}(t) = \mathbf{\Phi}(t)\mathbf{\Gamma} \qquad t \geq 0$$

On replacing $\hat{\mathbf{\Phi}}(0)$ in *19* by $\mathbf{\Phi}(0)\mathbf{\Gamma}$, eliminating $\mathbf{h}(0)u(t)$ from *19* and *21*, and defining

$$\mathbf{z}(t) = \mathbf{x}(t) - \mathbf{\Gamma}\hat{\mathbf{x}}(t)$$

we have

$$\mathbf{\Phi}(0)\dot{\mathbf{z}}(t) = \dot{\mathbf{\Phi}}(0)\mathbf{z}$$

or

23
$$\dot{\mathbf{z}}(t) = \mathbf{\Phi}^{-1}(0)\dot{\mathbf{\Phi}}(0)\mathbf{z}$$

since $\mathbf{\Phi}(0)$ is a nonsingular matrix.

Now by hypothesis

$$\mathbf{z}(0-) = \mathbf{x}(0-) - \mathbf{\Gamma}\hat{\mathbf{x}}(0-) = \mathbf{0}$$

and since $\mathbf{z}(t)$ is the solution of *23* with $\mathbf{z}(0-) = \mathbf{0}$, it follows that[1] $\mathbf{z}(t) = \mathbf{0}$ for $t \geq 0$ and hence

24
$$\mathbf{x}(t) = \mathbf{\Gamma}\hat{\mathbf{x}}(t) \qquad \forall t \geq 0$$

which is what we set out to demonstrate.

[1] The solution of vector differential equations of first order is discussed in greater detail in Chap. *5*, Sec. *2*.

Relation between x and $\hat{\mathbf{x}}$

The foregoing analysis leads us to an important conclusion, namely, that the different ways of associating a state vector with $\mathcal{A}$ amount merely to attaching different labels (connected by a one-one linear mapping) to the points of the state space $\mathcal{C}^n$ (see *2.3.46*). This conclusion is stated more precisely in the following

25 **Theorem** If a linear time-invariant system $\mathcal{A}$ of order n is associated with a state vector $\mathbf{x}$ ranging over $\mathcal{C}^n$, then any other way of associating a state vector with $\mathcal{A}$ of the same dimension as $\mathbf{x}$ must necessarily lead to a vector $\hat{\mathbf{x}}$ which is related to $\mathbf{x}$ by

$$\mathbf{x} = \mathbf{\Gamma}\hat{\mathbf{x}} \qquad \forall t$$

where $\mathbf{\Gamma}$ is a nonsingular constant $n \times n$ matrix defined by *9*.

From this it follows (see *2.3.46*) that if the state equations of $\mathcal{A}$ corresponding to $\mathbf{x}$ are of the canonical form (*2.3.45*)

26
$$\begin{aligned}\dot{\mathbf{x}} &= \mathbf{A}\mathbf{x} + \mathbf{b}u \\ y &= \langle \mathbf{c},\mathbf{x} \rangle + d_0 u\end{aligned}$$

where $\mathbf{A}$ is a constant matrix, $\mathbf{b}$ and $\mathbf{c}$ are constant vectors, and d_0 is a constant scalar, then the state equations of $\mathcal{A}$ corresponding to $\hat{\mathbf{x}}$ are

27
$$\begin{aligned}\dot{\hat{\mathbf{x}}} &= \hat{\mathbf{A}}\hat{\mathbf{x}} + \hat{\mathbf{b}}u \\ y &= \langle \hat{\mathbf{c}},\hat{\mathbf{x}} \rangle + d_0 u\end{aligned}$$

where

28
$$\begin{aligned}\hat{\mathbf{A}} &= \mathbf{\Gamma}^{-1}\mathbf{A}\mathbf{\Gamma} \\ \hat{\mathbf{b}} &= \mathbf{\Gamma}^{-1}\mathbf{b} \\ \hat{\mathbf{c}} &= \mathbf{c}\mathbf{\Gamma}\end{aligned}$$

29 *Comment* The form of the relation between $\hat{\mathbf{A}}$ and $\mathbf{A}$ in *28* suggests that by a suitable choice of the state vector $\hat{\mathbf{x}}$ it may be possible to make $\hat{\mathbf{A}}$ a diagonal matrix or, at least, put it into the Jordan canonical form (see *D.5.21*). As will be shown in Sec. *9*, the partial-fraction technique for associating a state vector with $\mathcal{A}$ leads to state equations in which $\hat{\mathbf{A}}$ has the Jordan canonical form.

30 *Comment* Theorem *25* remains valid when $\hat{\mathbf{x}}$ ranges over a space $\mathcal{C}^m$ of dimension $m > n$. However, in this case $\mathbf{\Gamma}$ is not a square matrix and the correspondence between $\mathbf{x}$ and $\hat{\mathbf{x}}$ is not one-one (see Assertion *4*).

31 **Remark** In deducing Theorem *25* we have not used in any essential way the assumption that $\mathcal{A}$ is a time-invariant system. Consequently, Theorem *25* holds true when $\mathcal{A}$ is a time-varying system, provided the following replacements of symbols are made in the statement of Theorem *25* as well as in the analysis which precedes it (see *3.6.33*).

(I)	$0 \rightarrow t_0$
(II)	$\boldsymbol{\phi}(t) \rightarrow \boldsymbol{\phi}(t,t_0)$
(III)	$\boldsymbol{\Phi}(t) \rightarrow \boldsymbol{\Phi}(t,t_0)$
(IV)	$h(t - \xi) \rightarrow h(t,\xi)$
(V)	$\mathbf{h}(t - \xi) \rightarrow \mathbf{h}(t,\xi)$
(VI)	$\mathbf{A} \rightarrow \mathbf{A}(t)$, $\mathbf{b} \rightarrow \mathbf{b}(t)$, $\mathbf{c} \rightarrow \mathbf{c}(t)$, $\mathbf{d}_0 \rightarrow \mathbf{d}_0(t)$

It is important to note that $\boldsymbol{\Phi}(t_0,t)$ must be nonsingular for all t_0 and all $t \geq t_0$.

Association of a state vector with $\mathcal{A}$

By exhibiting the connection between all possible ways in which a state vector can be associated with $\mathcal{A}$ and by showing that, in effect, the different ways of defining $\mathbf{x}$ involve merely different ways of expressing the zero-input response of $\mathcal{A}$ as a linear combination of some set of basis functions of $\mathcal{A}$, Theorem *25* provides a base for constructing systematic approaches to the problem of associating a state vector with any given system of finite order. One such approach will be developed in the following sections along the lines sketched in Sec. *1*. In more detailed terms, given a linear time-invariant system $\mathcal{A}$, we shall associate a state vector $\mathbf{x}$ with $\mathcal{A}$ through the following steps.

1. A general solution to the differential equation which characterizes $\mathcal{A}$ is found by the use of the Laplace transformation (or other techniques if $\mathcal{A}$ is not time-invariant).[1]

2. The constants appearing in the general solution are identified with the components of $\mathbf{x}(0-)$. This yields an expression for $\mathbf{x}(0-)$ [or $\mathbf{x}(t_0-)$ if $t_0 \neq 0$], in terms of the initial values of the input, output, and the suppressed output vectors, and, at the same time, identifies the basis functions $\phi_1, \ldots, \phi_n$ (which must be linearly independent).

3. With the components of $\mathbf{x}(0-)$ substituted for the constants in the general solution and $0-$ replaced by t_0-, the general solution becomes a tentative input-output-state relation—"tentative" in the sense that at this stage of the process it remains to be shown that it qualifies as an input-output-state relation under the mutual- and self-consistency conditions (*1.6.2*). (It should be emphasized that the function of the first three steps is merely that of leading to a likely candidate for the state vector of $\mathcal{A}$ rather than that of proving that the expression for $\mathbf{x}(t)$ in terms of u, y, $\tilde{\mathbf{y}}$, and their derivatives qualifies as a state vector for $\mathcal{A}$.)

[1] Actually, all that we need to determine $\mathbf{x}$ are the terms which represent the initial conditions. This point is elaborated upon in *4.5.58*.

4. In the relations between $\mathbf{x}(0-)$ and the initial values of u, y, the suppressed output vector $\tilde{\mathbf{y}}$, and their derivatives, the initial time $0-$ is replaced by t. This yields a tentative expression for the state of $\mathcal{A}$ at time t in terms of $u(t)$, $y(t)$, $\tilde{\mathbf{y}}(t)$, and the derivatives. Again, this expression for $\mathbf{x}(t)$ is "tentative" in the sense that $\mathbf{x}(t)$ cannot be claimed to represent the state of $\mathcal{A}$ at time t (for all $t \geq 0$) until it has been demonstrated directly or indirectly that $\mathbf{x}(t)$ qualifies as the state of $\mathcal{A}$ under Definition *1.6.2*.

5. The state equations of $\mathcal{A}$ are obtained by forming the expressions for $\dot{\mathbf{x}}(t)$ and $y(t)$ and eliminating all variables other than $\mathbf{x}(t)$ and $u(t)$ from these expressions. If the state equations have the canonical form (*2.3.45*)

32
$$\dot{\mathbf{x}} = \mathbf{A}\mathbf{x} + \mathbf{B}\mathbf{u}$$
$$\mathbf{y} = \mathbf{C}\mathbf{x} + \mathbf{D}\mathbf{u}$$

then $\mathbf{x}(t)$ qualifies as the state of the system at time t by virtue of Corollary *2.3.36 et seq.*, which imply that $\mathbf{x}$ satisfies the mutual- and self-consistency conditions. If the state equations do not have the canonical form [e.g., in the case of systems of the differential operator type (see *4.4.17*)], then it is necessary to show by direct means that $\mathbf{x}$ satisfies the mutual- and self-consistency conditions or, equivalently, that $\mathbf{x}$ has the state separation property *2.3.19*.

We now proceed to develop this approach in greater detail, deferring until Sec. *9* the description of an alternative and very effective technique which is based on the determinateness of linear systems. We begin with a simple class of systems, namely, systems of the *reciprocal differential operator type* which will be used in subsequent sections as a prototype for systems of more general form.

3 *Systems of the reciprocal differential operator type*

Consider a nonoriented object $\mathcal{B}$ with scalar-valued terminal variables v_1 and v_2 (*1.4.1*) which is characterized by a differential equation of the form (see *3.8.11*)

1
$$L(p)v_1 = v_2$$

where $L(p) = a_n p^n + \cdots + a_0$, $a_n \neq 0$, and the a_λ, $\lambda = 1, \ldots, n$, are real or complex constants. Such an object can be oriented in but two ways: (I) by letting $v_1 \triangleq y \triangleq$ output and $v_2 \triangleq u \triangleq$ input, and (II) by letting $v_1 \triangleq u \triangleq$ input and $v_2 \triangleq y =$ output. By the first mode of orientation we obtain what we call a *reciprocal differential operator system* $\mathcal{R}$, which is characterized by the input-output relation

$$L(p)y = u \qquad L(p) = a_n p^n + \cdot \cdot \cdot + a_0$$

and which for convenience will be denoted by $1/L(p)$, while by the second mode we obtain a *differential operator system* $\mathfrak{D}$, denoted by $L(p)$, which is characterized by the input-output relation

$$y = L(p)u \qquad L(p) = a_n p^n + \cdot \cdot \cdot + a_0$$

In this section, we shall focus our attention on systems of the reciprocal differential operator type. Systems of the differential operator type and their relation to systems of the reciprocal differential operator type will be considered in Sec. *4*.

Input-output-state relations

As was pointed out in Sec. *2*, the first step toward associating a state vector with and finding the corresponding input-output-state relation for a system characterized by a differential equation consists in finding the general solution of this equation. Thus, our first task is to find a general solution of the differential equation

2 $$L(p)y = u \qquad L(p) = a_n p^n + \cdot \cdot \cdot + a_0 \qquad a_n \neq 0$$

which characterizes $\mathcal{R}$. This can be done by drawing on the well-known facts in the theory of ordinary differential equations. For our purposes, however, it will be more convenient not to rely on the classical theory and instead derive the expression for the general solution directly through the use of the Laplace transformation.

Specifically, suppose that a pair of time functions $u_{(t_0,\infty)}, y_{(t_0,\infty)}$, or (u,y) for short, satisfies (see *3.8.16*) the differential equation *2*; that is, (u,y) is an input-output pair for $\mathcal{R}$. Then, by virtue of the constancy of the coefficients of *2*, every pair of the form $(T_\delta u, T_\delta y)$, where T_δ is a translation operator (*3.2.2*) with arbitrary shift δ, will also satisfy *2*. With this in mind, we can—without any loss in generality—set $t_0 = 0$ in order to make it convenient to apply the Laplace transformation to the determination of the general solution of *2*.

Thus, let $u_{(0,\infty)}, y_{(0,\infty)}$, or (u,y) for short, be an input-output pair satisfying *2*. On applying the Laplace transformation to both sides of *2* and making use of the formula (see *B.3.19*)

3 $$\mathfrak{L}\{p^r f\} = s^r F(s) - s^{r-1} f(0-) - \cdot \cdot \cdot - f^{(r-1)}(0-) \qquad r = 1, 2, \ldots$$

where $F(s)$ is the Laplace transform of $f(t)$[1] and $f^{(\lambda)}(0-)$, $\lambda = 1, 2, \ldots,$

[1] Note that to be consistent with our notation for functions, we should say "F is the Laplace transform of f" rather than "$F(s)$ is the Laplace transform of $f(t)$." This and other departures from consistency in notation in this text are dictated either by expediency or by the desirability of avoiding conflict with standard notation (see Remark *1.3.3*).

is the initial value of the λth derivative of f at $t = 0-$, we obtain the relation

4 $$(a_n s^n + \cdots + a_0)Y(s) = U(s) + a_n y^{(n-1)}(0-) + (a_n s + a_{n-1})y^{(n-2)}(0-) + \cdots + (a_n s^{n-1} + \cdots + a_1)y(0-)$$

Upon replacing $a_n s^n + \cdots + a_0$ by $L(s)$, dividing both sides by $L(s)$, and rearranging terms, *4* becomes

5 $$Y(s) = \frac{U(s)}{L(s)} + \sum_{\lambda=1}^{n} \frac{(a_n s^{n-\lambda} + \cdots + a_\lambda)}{L(s)} y^{(\lambda-1)}(0-)$$

where $Y(s) = \mathcal{L}\{y(t)\}$ and $U(s) = \mathcal{L}\{u(t)\}$. At this point, we can assert that if (u,y) is an input-output pair satisfying *2*, then the pair of their respective Laplace transforms $(U(s),Y(s))$ satisfies *5*. Furthermore, since the correspondence between a time function and its Laplace transform is one-one, the inverse Laplace transforms of $U(s)$ and $Y(s)$ are $u(t)$ and $y(t)$, respectively. Consequently, on applying the inverse Laplace transformation to both sides of *5* and making use of the convolution property (*B.3.11*), we obtain

6 $$y(t) = \sum_{\lambda=1}^{n} y^{(\lambda-1)}(0-)\phi_\lambda(t) + \int_0^t h(t - \xi)u(\xi)\, d\xi \qquad t \geq 0$$

where

$$h(t) = \mathcal{L}^{-1}\left\{\frac{1}{L(s)}\right\} = \text{impulse response of } \mathcal{R} \text{ (see } 3.6.5\text{)}$$

7 $$\frac{1}{L(s)} \triangleq H(s) = \text{transfer function of } \mathcal{R} \text{ (see } 3.6.17\text{)}$$

$$\phi_\lambda(t) = \mathcal{L}^{-1}\left\{\frac{a_n s^{n-\lambda} + \cdots + a_\lambda}{L(s)}\right\} \qquad \lambda = 1, \ldots, n$$

$$= \text{zero-input response of } \mathcal{R} \text{ (see } 3.6.32\text{)}$$

Thus, if (u,y) is an input-output pair satisfying *2*, then (u,y) also satisfies *6*. This implies, more specifically, that to every input-output pair (u,y) for *2* there corresponds a (not necessarily unique) n-tuple of complex numbers $(\alpha_1, \ldots, \alpha_n)$ in $\mathcal{C}^n$ ($\mathcal{C}^n \triangleq$ space of n-tuples of complex numbers) such that (u,y) satisfies *6* for $t \geq 0$ with

$$y^{(\lambda-1)}(0-) = \alpha_\lambda \qquad \lambda = 1, \ldots, n$$

Next, we must show that for every n-tuple $(\alpha_1, \ldots, \alpha_n)$ in $\mathcal{C}^n$, the expression for y given by *6* with $y^{(\lambda-1)}(0-)$ replaced by α_λ, $\lambda = 1, \ldots, n$, defines an input-output pair for *2*, that is, *6* is a solution of *2* for each $(\alpha_1, \ldots, \alpha_n)$ in $\mathcal{C}^n$. As a preliminary, we establish that the ϕ_λ and h in *6* have the properties asserted below.

8 **Assertion** The functions ϕ_λ, $\lambda = 1, \ldots, n$, are linearly independent solutions of the homogeneous differential equation

9 $$L(p)\phi_\lambda = 0 \qquad t \geq 0, \lambda = 1, \ldots, n$$

satisfying the initial conditions

10 $$\phi_\lambda^{(\lambda-1)}(0-) = 1$$

11 $$\phi_\lambda^{(\mu-1)}(0-) = 0 \qquad \text{for } \mu \neq \lambda,\ \mu,\lambda = 1, \ldots, n$$

Proof On applying the Laplace transformation to both sides of *9* and making use of *10* and *11*, we obtain the following expression for the Laplace transform of ϕ_λ:

12 $$\Phi_\lambda(s) = \mathcal{L}\{\phi_\lambda(t)\} = \frac{a_n s^{n-\lambda} + \cdots + a_\lambda}{L(s)}$$

Since *12* is identical with the expression for $\mathcal{L}\{\phi_\lambda(t)\}$ in *7*, it follows that ϕ_λ as defined by *7* is a solution of *9* satisfying the initial conditions *10* and *11*.

The linear independence of the ϕ_λ is an immediate consequence of the linear independence of their respective Laplace transforms. To establish the latter, suppose that the $\Phi_\lambda(s)$ are not linearly independent. Then there exist constants $\rho_1, \ldots, \rho_n$ not all zero such that

13 $$\rho_1\Phi_1(s) + \cdots + \rho_n\Phi_n(s) \equiv 0$$

Now on substituting the $\Phi_\lambda(s)$ into *13*, multiplying both sides by $L(s)$ [note that $L(s) \not\equiv 0$ by virtue of the assumption that $a_n \neq 0$], and setting the coefficients of powers of s equal to zero, we obtain the system of linear equations

$$\begin{aligned} \rho_1 a_n &= 0 \\ \rho_1 a_{n-1} + \rho_2 a_n &= 0 \\ \cdots\cdots\cdots\cdots \\ \rho_1 a_1 + \cdots + \rho_n a_n &= 0 \end{aligned}$$

which implies $\rho_1 = \rho_2 = \cdots = \rho_n = 0$ (since $a_n \neq 0$). This contradicts the assumption that not all $\rho_1, \ldots, \rho_n$ are zero and thus establishes the linear independence of the $\Phi_\lambda(s)$. Q.E.D.

14 **Assertion** The function h is the solution of the differential equation

15 $$L(p)h(t) = \delta(t)$$

satisfying the initial conditions

16 $$h^{(\lambda-1)}(0-) = 0 \qquad \lambda = 1, \ldots, n$$

Proof By applying the Laplace transformation to both sides of *15* and making use of the initial conditions *16*, we obtain

$$\mathcal{L}\{h(t)\} = \frac{1}{L(s)}$$

which agrees with *7*. This verifies that h is the impulse response of $\mathcal{R}$ [zero-state response of $\mathcal{R}$ to $\delta(t)$] and that the transfer function of $\mathcal{R}$ is given by

$$H(s) = \mathcal{L}\{h(t)\} = \frac{1}{L(s)} \qquad \triangleleft$$

We are now ready to verify by direct substitution that for every $(\alpha_1, \ldots, \alpha_n)$ in $\mathcal{C}^n$ the expression

17 $$y(t) = \sum_{\lambda=1}^{n} \alpha_\lambda \phi_\lambda(t) + \int_0^t h(t - \xi)u(\xi)\, d\xi$$

satisfies *2*. Specifically, on substituting *17* into *2* and making use of *9*, *2* reduces to

$$L(p) \int_0^t h(t - \xi)u(\xi)\, d\xi = u(t) \qquad t \geq 0$$

We can readily verify that this is an identity by applying *B.3.24*. Thus, we have

$$\begin{aligned} L(p) \int_0^t h(t - \xi)u(\xi)\, d\xi &= \int_0^t [L(p)h(t - \xi)]u(\xi)\, d\xi \\ &= \int_0^t \delta(t - \xi)u(\xi)\, d\xi \\ &= u(t) \qquad t \geq 0 \end{aligned}$$

by virtue of *15* and the sifting property of delta functions (see *A.2.11*).

Expression for the general solution for arbitrary t_0

We have established that every input-output pair (u,y) (starting at $t_0 = 0$) which satisfies the input-output relation *2* also satisfies *6* and, conversely, every pair (u,y) (starting at $t_0 = 0$) which satisfies *6* also satisfies *2*. This implies that *6* is the general solution of *2*, or, equivalently, that *6* satisfies the mutual-consistency condition (*1.6.5*).

To obtain the form of the general solution for arbitrary t_0, let $(u_{(t_0,\infty)}, y_{(t_0,\infty)})$ be any input-output pair satisfying *2*. Then by virtue of the constancy of the coefficients in *2*, the shifted pair $(T_{-t_0}u_{(t_0,\infty)}, T_{-t_0}y_{(t_0,\infty)})$ will satisfy *2* (as well as *6*) since $T_{-t_0}u_{(t_0,\infty)}$ and $T_{-t_0}y_{(t_0,\infty)}$ start at $t = 0$. More specifically, let (see *3.2.2*)

$$\hat{u} \triangleq T_{-t_0}u_{(t_0,\infty)}$$
$$\hat{y} \triangleq T_{-t_0}y_{(t_0,\infty)}$$

to simplify the notation. Then

18 $$\hat{y}(t) = \sum_{\lambda=1}^{n} \hat{y}^{(\lambda-1)}(0-)\phi_\lambda(t) + \int_0^t h(t-\xi)\hat{u}(\xi)\,d\xi \qquad t \geq 0$$

and since

$$\hat{u}(t) = u(t_0 + t) \qquad \forall t$$
$$\hat{y}(t) = y(t_0 + t) \qquad \forall t$$

18 may be written as

$$y(t_0 + t) = \sum_{\lambda=1}^{n} y^{(\lambda-1)}(t_0-)\phi_\lambda(t) + \int_0^t h(t-\xi)u(t_0+\xi)\,d\xi$$

which upon the change of variables $t \to t - t_0$, $\xi \to \xi - t_0$, yields

19 $$y(t) = \sum_{\lambda=1}^{n} y^{(\lambda-1)}(t_0-)\phi_\lambda(t-t_0) + \int_{t_0}^t h(t-\xi)u(\xi)\,d\xi \qquad t \geq t_0$$

This is the desired expression for the general solution of *2* for arbitrary t_0.

Expression for the input-output-state relation

It will be helpful at this point to summarize the results of the foregoing analysis in the form of an

20 **Assertion** Let $\mathcal{R}$ be a system characterized by the input-output relation

21 $$L(p)y = u$$

in which

$$L(p) = a_n p^n + \cdots + a_0 \qquad a_n \neq 0$$

and the a_i, $i = 1, \ldots, n$, are constants, not necessarily real.

Then, the expression for the general solution of *21* is

22 $$y(t) = \sum_{\lambda=1}^{n} y^{(\lambda-1)}(t_0-)\phi_\lambda(t-t_0) + \int_{t_0}^t h(t-\xi)u(\xi)\,d\xi \qquad t \geq t_0$$

where

23 $$h(t) = \mathcal{L}^{-1}\left\{\frac{1}{L(s)}\right\} = \text{impulse response of } \mathcal{R}$$

$$H(s) = \frac{1}{L(s)} = \text{transfer function of } \mathcal{R}$$

$$\phi_\lambda(t) = \mathcal{L}^{-1}\left\{\frac{a_n s^{n-\lambda} + \cdots + a_\lambda}{L(s)}\right\} \qquad \lambda = 1, \ldots, n$$

The time functions $\phi_1, \ldots, \phi_n$ are linearly independent and satisfy the differential equation

$$L(p)\phi_\lambda(t) = 0 \qquad \lambda = 1, \ldots, n$$

under the initial conditions *10* and *11*. Thus they qualify as a set of (one-sided) basis functions for $\mathfrak{R}$ (see *3.6.39*). ◁

This completes step 1. Turning to step 2, we have to identify the constants appearing in *21* with the components of $\mathbf{x}(t_0-)$, the state of $\mathfrak{R}$ at time t_0-. This can be done in an infinite variety of ways, depending on the choice of the basis functions (see *4.2.25*) in *22*. A natural, though not necessarily the most advantageous, way (as will be seen later) is to identify the basis functions with the functions $\phi_1, \ldots, \phi_n$ in *23*. In this case, the components of $\mathbf{x}(t_0-)$, which are the coefficients of the basis functions, are given by

$$x_1(t_0-) = y(t_0-)$$
$$\cdots\cdots\cdots$$
$$x_n(t_0-) = y^{(n-1)}(t_0-)$$

or, more compactly,

24 $$\mathbf{x}(t_0-) = (y(t_0-), \ldots, y^{(n-1)}(t_0-))$$

Another natural way is to let the basis functions—or rather, their Laplace transforms—be

25 $$\frac{s^{n-1}}{L(s)}, \ldots, \frac{s}{L(s)}, \frac{1}{L(s)}$$

In this case, the components of $\mathbf{x}(t_0-)$ are given by

26 $$\begin{aligned} x_1(t_0-) &= a_n y(t_0-) \\ x_2(t_0-) &= a_n y^{(1)}(t_0-) + a_{n-1} y(t_0-) \\ &\cdots\cdots\cdots \\ x_n(t_0-) &= a_n y^{(n-1)}(t_0-) + \cdots + a_1 y(t_0-) \end{aligned}$$

In the sequel, we shall focus our attention on the case where the first component of the initial state vector is equated to the output of $\mathfrak{R}$ at t_0-, the second component to the first derivative of the output, etc. This implies that the state vector at time t is expressed by

27 $$\mathbf{x}(t) = (y(t), \ldots, y^{(n-1)}(t))$$

For convenience in referring to this case, we shall call $\mathbf{x}(t)$, as given by *27*, the *normal state vector of* $\mathfrak{R}$ and the corresponding state equations the *normal state equations for* $\mathfrak{R}$ (compare with *3.7.33*). The state space over which $\mathbf{x}$ ranges is $\mathcal{C}^n$, the space of n-tuples of complex numbers.

On replacing the initial values $y^{(\lambda-1)}(t_0-)$ in *22* by their expressions in terms of the components of $\mathbf{x}(t_0-)$, the general solution *22* becomes

28 $$y(t) = \langle \boldsymbol{\phi}(t - t_0), \mathbf{x}(t_0-) \rangle + \int_{t_0}^{t} h(t - \xi)u(\xi)\, d\xi \qquad t \geq t_0$$

where h is the impulse response of $\mathcal{R}$, $\boldsymbol{\phi}(t)$ represents the vector

29 $$\boldsymbol{\phi}(t) = (\phi_1(t), \ldots, \phi_n(t))$$

whose components are the basis functions

30 $$\phi_\lambda(t) = \mathcal{L}^{-1}\left\{\frac{a_n s^{n-\lambda} + \cdots + a_\lambda}{L(s)}\right\}$$

and $\langle \boldsymbol{\phi}(t - t_0), \mathbf{x}(t_0-) \rangle$ denotes the scalar product of the basis vector $\boldsymbol{\phi}(t - t_0)$ and the initial state vector $\mathbf{x}(t_0-)$. Equation *28* constitutes a tentative input-output-state relation for $\mathcal{R}$, since it remains to be shown that $\mathbf{x}(t)$ as defined by *27* qualifies as a state vector for $\mathcal{R}$.

State equations

To derive the state equations of $\mathcal{R}$, we form the expression for $\dot{\mathbf{x}}(t)$ by differentiating both sides of *27*. This yields

31 $$\dot{\mathbf{x}}(t) = (y^{(1)}(t), y^{(2)}(t), \ldots, y^{(n)}(t))$$

On the other hand, the differential equation *21* gives

$$y^{(n)}(t) = \frac{1}{a_n}(u(t) - a_0 y(t) - \cdots - a_{n-1}y^{(n-1)}(t))$$

and hence

$$\dot{\mathbf{x}}(t) = \left(y^{(1)}(t), y^{(2)}(t), \ldots, \frac{1}{a_n}(u(t) - a_0 y(t) - \cdots - a_{n-1}y^{(n-1)}(t))\right)$$

This relation shows that the components of $\dot{\mathbf{x}}(t)$ are linear combinations of the components of $\mathbf{x}(t)$ and $u(t)$. To exhibit these relations in a matrix form, let $x_i(t)$ and $\dot{x}_i(t)$, $i = 1, \ldots, n$, denote the ith components of $\mathbf{x}(t)$ and $\dot{\mathbf{x}}(t)$, respectively. Then *31* implies

$$\begin{aligned}
\dot{x}_1(t) &= x_2(t) \\
\dot{x}_2(t) &= x_3(t) \\
&\cdots\cdots \\
\dot{x}_n(t) &= -\frac{a_0}{a_n}x_1(t) - \cdots - \frac{a_{n-1}}{a_n}x_n(t) + \frac{1}{a_n}u(t)
\end{aligned}$$

or in matrix form,

32 $$\begin{bmatrix} \dot{x}_1(t) \\ \cdots \\ \cdots \\ \dot{x}_n(t) \end{bmatrix} = \begin{bmatrix} 0 & 1 & 0 & \cdots & 0 \\ 0 & 0 & 1 & \cdots & 0 \\ \cdot & \cdot & \cdot & \cdots & \cdot \\ -\frac{a_0}{a_n} & \cdots & \cdot & \cdots & -\frac{a_{n-1}}{a_n} \end{bmatrix} \begin{bmatrix} x_1(t) \\ \cdots \\ \cdots \\ x_n(t) \end{bmatrix} + \begin{bmatrix} 0 \\ 0 \\ \cdots \\ \frac{1}{a_n} \end{bmatrix} u(t)$$

which is a state equation of the canonical form $\dot{\mathbf{x}} = \mathbf{A}\mathbf{x} + \mathbf{b}u$, where $\mathbf{A}$ and $\mathbf{b}$ are a constant $n \times n$ matrix and an n-vector, respectively.

We have thus established that if $\mathbf{x}(t)$ is defined as in *27*, with $\mathbf{x}(t)$ ranging over $\mathcal{C}^n$, then $\mathbf{x}(t)$ satisfies the state equation *32*. This result, in conjunction with the relation

$$y(t) = x_1(t)$$

or, in matrix form,

$$y(t) = [1 \quad 0 \quad \cdots \quad 0] \begin{bmatrix} x_1(t) \\ \cdots \\ x_n(t) \end{bmatrix}$$

permits us to conclude by *2.3.42* that $\mathbf{x}(t)$ and the input-output-state relation *28* satisfy the mutual- and self-consistency conditions *1.6.5*, *1.6.11*, *1.6.15*, and *1.6.35*.

We summarize this and previous conclusions in the form of an

33 **Assertion** Let $\mathcal{R}$ be a system of the reciprocal differential operator type characterized by the input-output relation

$$L(p)y = u \qquad L(p) = a_n p^n + \cdots + a_0 \qquad a_n \neq 0$$

Then the vector

$$\mathbf{x}(t) = (y(t), \ldots, y^{(n-1)}(t))$$

qualifies as a state vector of $\mathcal{R}$ at time t. With this choice of $\mathbf{x}(t)$ (called the *normal state vector*), the state equations of $\mathcal{R}$ read

34
$$\dot{\mathbf{x}}(t) = \mathbf{A}\mathbf{x}(t) + \mathbf{b}u(t)$$
$$y(t) = \langle \mathbf{c}, \mathbf{x}(t) \rangle$$

where

$$\mathbf{A} = \begin{bmatrix} 0 & 1 & 0 & \cdots & 0 \\ 0 & 0 & 1 & \cdots & 0 \\ \cdot & \cdot & \cdot & \cdots & \cdot \\ -\dfrac{a_0}{a_n} & \cdot & \cdot & \cdots & -\dfrac{a_{n-1}}{a_n} \end{bmatrix} \qquad \mathbf{b} = \begin{bmatrix} 0 \\ \cdots \\ \dfrac{1}{a_n} \end{bmatrix}$$

$$\mathbf{c} = [1 \quad 0 \quad \cdots \quad 0]$$

The input-output-state relation of $\mathcal{R}$ is given by

35
$$y(t) = \langle \boldsymbol{\phi}(t - t_0), \mathbf{x}(t_0-) \rangle + \int_{t_0}^{t} h(t - \xi)u(\xi)\, d\xi \qquad t \geq t_0$$

where, to recapitulate,

$$h(t) = \mathcal{L}^{-1}\left\{\frac{1}{L(s)}\right\}$$

$$\boldsymbol{\phi}(t) = (\phi_1(t), \ldots, \phi_n(t))$$

$$\phi_\lambda(t) = \mathcal{L}^{-1}\left\{\frac{a_n s^{n-\lambda} + \cdots + a_\lambda}{L(s)}\right\} \qquad \lambda = 1, \ldots, n$$

$$\mathbf{x}(t_0-) = (y(t_0-), \ldots, y^{(n-1)}(t_0-))$$

36 *Example* Suppose that $\mathcal{R}$ is characterized by

$$\frac{d^2y}{dt^2} + 3\frac{dy}{dt} + 2y = u$$

Then

$$L(s) = s^2 + 3s + 2 = (s+1)(s+2)$$

and

$$h(t) = \mathfrak{L}^{-1}\left\{\frac{1}{(s+1)(s+2)}\right\} = 1(t)(e^{-t} - e^{-2t})$$

$$\phi_1(t) = \mathfrak{L}^{-1}\left\{\frac{s+3}{(s+1)(s+2)}\right\} = 1(t)(2e^{-t} - e^{-2t})$$

$$\phi_2(t) = \mathfrak{L}^{-1}\left\{\frac{1}{(s+1)(s+2)}\right\} = 1(t)(e^{-t} - e^{-2t})$$

where $1(t)$ denotes the unit step function.

The components of the state vector at time t are

$$x_1(t) = y(t)$$
$$x_2(t) = \dot{y}(t)$$

Correspondingly, the input-output-state relation is given by

$$y(t) = (2e^{-(t-t_0)} - e^{-2(t-t_0)})x_1(t_0-) + (e^{-(t-t_0)} - e^{-2(t-t_0)})x_2(t_0-) + \int_{t_0}^{t} [e^{-(t-\xi)} - e^{-2(t-\xi)}]u(\xi)\, d\xi \qquad t \geq t_0$$

and the matrices and vectors which appear in the normal state equations *34* read

$$\mathbf{A} = \begin{bmatrix} 0 & 1 \\ -2 & -3 \end{bmatrix} \qquad \mathbf{b} = \begin{bmatrix} 0 \\ 1 \end{bmatrix} \qquad \mathbf{c} = [1 \quad 0]$$

37 *Exercise* Determine the input-output-state relation and the state equations for the system of Example *36* for the case where the state is defined by *26*. Find the matrix $\mathbf{\Gamma}$ (*4.2.9*) which relates the state defined by *26* to the normal state vector.

Some properties of $\mathcal{R}$

The input-output-state relation *35* provides us with a complete characterization of $\mathcal{R}$. Having this characterization in hand, it is a simple matter to deduce the several basic properties of $\mathcal{R}$ which are listed below.

38 **Property** $\mathcal{R}$ is a system of order n in the sense of Definition *3.6.39*. This follows at once from the fact that the number of (linearly independent) basis functions in the input-output-state relation *35* is n.

39 **Property** No matter how the state vector of $\mathcal{R}$ is defined, the dimension of the state space of $\mathcal{R}$ cannot be lower than n. This follows from Assertion *4.2.4*.

40 **Property** $\mathcal{R}$ is a linear system in the sense of Definition *3.5.6*.

41 **Property** $\mathcal{R}$ is a time-invariant system in the sense of Definition *3.2.36*. This follows from Assertion *3.6.35*.

42 **Property** The normal state equations are in reduced form (see *3.6.46*), which means that there are no distinct equivalent states in the state space $\mathcal{C}^n$.

43 **Property** The basis functions $\phi_1, \ldots, \phi_n$ defined by *30* are the zero-input responses of $\mathcal{R}$ starting, respectively, in the initial (unit vector) states $(1,0, \ldots ,0)$, $(0,1, \ldots ,0)$, $\ldots$, $(0,0, \ldots ,1)$. This follows from Assertion *8* and the way in which $\mathbf{x}$ is defined in terms of the initial values of y and its derivatives.

44 **Remark** Most of the results and conclusions arrived at in the preceding discussion apply with but minor modifications to the case where $\mathcal{R}$ is a time-varying system. Specifically, if the coefficients in $L(p)$ are functions of time rather than constants, that is, $L(p)$ is of the form

45 $$L(p,t) = a_n(t)p^n + \cdots + a_0(t) \qquad a_n(t) \neq 0 \qquad \forall t$$

then the vector

46 $$\mathbf{x}(t) = (y(t), \ldots ,y^{(n-1)}(t))$$

qualifies as a normal state vector for $\mathcal{R}$, just as it does in the time-invariant case. The normal state equations for $\mathcal{R}$ read

47 $$\dot{\mathbf{x}}(t) = \mathbf{A}(t)\mathbf{x}(t) + \mathbf{b}(t)u(t)$$
$$y(t) = \langle \mathbf{c}(t), \mathbf{x}(t) \rangle$$

where $\mathbf{A}(t)$, $\mathbf{b}(t)$, and $\mathbf{c}(t)$ have exactly the same form *32* as their counterparts in the time-invariant case, with the $a_i(t)$ taking the place of a_i, $i = 0, \ldots, n$.

Special case: an integrator

A special and yet very important form of a system of the reciprocal differential operator type is an *integrator*, a system which we have used for illustrative purposes on many previous occasions. Our earlier definition of the notion of an integrator was informal in nature (*1.9.10*). We are now in a position to define it more precisely and associate an integrator with a state vector and state equations.

In its wide sense—which is the sense in which the term will be used in the sequel—an integrator is essentially a reciprocal differential operator system of order 1. More specifically,

48 **Definition** An *integrator* is a system characterized by an input-output relation of the form

49 $$(p + a)y = u$$

where a is a constant, not necessarily real. The reciprocal of a is called the *time constant* of the integrator. A *pure integrator* is one in which $a = 0$. In this case *49* becomes

50 $$p\,y = u$$

(Since the term "integrator" is commonly used to denote a device defined by *50* rather than *49*, we shall on occasion use the term "*impure, or imperfect, integrator*" to make it clear that the device we have in mind is characterized by *49* rather than *50*.) An integrator characterized by an input-output relation of the form *49* is denoted by $1/(p + a)$. ◁

Since an integrator is a system of the reciprocal differential operator type of order 1, its normal state vector has just one component, $y(t)$, which is the output of the integrator at time t. Furthermore, by Theorem *4.2.25*, this is the only way (to within a constant factor) in which a one-dimensional state vector can be associated with an integrator. Thus, we can make the

51 **Assertion** The state of an integrator at time t is necessarily of the form

$$x(t) = ky(t)$$

where k is a constant. Unless indicated to the contrary, k will be understood to be unity. ◁

The input-output-state relation and the state equations for an integrator are special cases of *34* and *35*, with $a_1 = 1$ and $a_0 = a$. They read

52 $$y(t) = x(t_0-)e^{-a(t-t_0)} + \int_{t_0}^{t} e^{-a(t-\xi)}u(\xi)\,d\xi \qquad t \geq t_0$$

and

53 $$\begin{aligned} \dot{x} &= -ax + u \\ y &= x \end{aligned}$$

This concludes for the present our discussion of systems of the reciprocal differential operator type. We shall return to them in Sec. *4* and again in Sec. *9*, where an alternative technique for associating a state vector with $\mathcal{R}$ will be described.

4 *Systems of the differential operator type*

In this section, we consider systems of the differential operator type denoted by $\mathfrak{D}$ and characterized by an input-output relation of the form

1
$$y(t) = M(p)u$$

where $M(p) = b_m p^m + \cdots + b_0$, $b_m \neq 0$, and $b_0, \ldots, b_m$ are constants, not necessarily real. For brevity, a system characterized by *1* will be denoted by $M(p)$.

Our interest in systems of this type stems from two reasons: First, as will be shown in Secs. *5* and *6*, any differential system can be realized as a combination of systems of the reciprocal differential and differential operator type and, second, the systems characterized by $L(p)y = u$ and $y = L(p)u$ are inverse to each other in the sense of Definition *2.10.6*. This will be established at a later point in the present section.

In Sec. *3* we found the input-output-state relation and state equations for $\mathfrak{R}$. In this section we shall do the same for $\mathfrak{D}$, omitting the details of derivations and arguments which are parallel to those of Sec. *3*. We begin with the derivation of the general solution of *1*.

General solution

By applying the Laplace transformation to both sides of *1*, we obtain the following expression for the Laplace transform of the general solution:

2
$$Y(s) = M(s)U(s) - \sum_{\lambda=1}^{m} (b_m s^{m-\lambda} + \cdots + b_\lambda)u^{(\lambda-1)}(0-)$$

where $M(s) = b_m s^m + \cdots + b_0$ and $u^{(\lambda)}(0-) \triangleq$ initial value of the λth derivative of the input at $t = 0-$. Consequently, the general solution itself (for $t_0 = 0$) may be written as

3
$$y(t) = \sum_{\lambda=1}^{m} \phi_\lambda(t)u^{(\lambda-1)}(0-) + \int_0^t h(t-\xi)u(\xi)\,d\xi \qquad t \geq 0$$

where

4
$$\phi_\lambda(t) = \mathfrak{L}^{-1}\{b_m s^{m-\lambda} + \cdots + b_\lambda\} = b_m \delta^{(m-\lambda)}(t) + \cdots + b_\lambda \delta(t) \qquad \lambda = 1, \ldots, m$$

$$h(t) = \mathfrak{L}^{-1}\{M(s)\} = b_m \delta^{(m)}(t) + \cdots + b_0 \delta(t)$$

with $\delta^{(\lambda)}(t)$ representing a delta function of λth order (see *A.2.5*). By using exactly the same arguments as in Sec. *3*, we can easily establish the following facts about *3*.

(I) The basis functions $\phi_\lambda(t)$ are linearly independent, which implies that $\mathfrak{D}$ is a differential system of order m.

(II) The $\phi_\lambda(t)$ represent zero-input responses of $\mathfrak{D}$, with $\phi_\lambda(t)$ given by

5 $$\phi_\lambda(t) = M(p)u \qquad \lambda = 1, \ldots, m$$

where $u = 0$ for $t \geq 0$, and

6 $$\begin{aligned} &u^{(\lambda-1)}(0-) = 1 \\ &u^{(\mu-1)}(0-) = 0 \qquad \text{for all } \mu \ (\mu = 1, \ldots, m) \text{ different from } \lambda \end{aligned}$$

(III) $h(t)$ is the impulse response of $\mathfrak{D}$; that is,

7 $$h(t) = M(p)u$$

where $u = \delta(t)$ and $u(0-) = \cdots = u^{(m-1)}(0-) = 0$.

We are now ready to associate a state vector $\mathbf{x} = (x_1, \ldots, x_m)$ with $\mathfrak{D}$. We do this in a manner analogous to that used in Sec. *3*; that is, we let

$$x_1(0-) \triangleq u(0-),\ x_2(0-) \triangleq u^{(1)}(0-),\ \ldots,\ x_m(0-) \triangleq u^{(m-1)}(0-)$$

and call such a state vector the *normal* state vector of $\mathfrak{D}$. Under this mode of identification of the components of $\mathbf{x}(0-)$ with the constants appearing in the general solution, the expression for the state at time t becomes

8 $$\mathbf{x}(t) = (u(t), \ldots, u^{(m-1)}(t))$$

with the state space Σ being $\mathfrak{C}^m$, the space of m-tuples of complex numbers. [Note that this implies that $u(t)$ may be complex-valued.]

Input-output-state relation

If the normal state vector of $\mathfrak{D}$ is defined to be the vector $\mathbf{x}(t)$ given by *8*, then the corresponding normal input-output-state relation for $\mathfrak{D}$ (for arbitrary t_0) is obtained by substituting $x_\lambda(0-)$ for each $u^{(\lambda-1)}(0-)$ in the general solution *3* and replacing $0-$ with t_0-. The result reads

9 $$y(t) = \langle \boldsymbol{\phi}(t - t_0), \mathbf{x}(t_0-) \rangle + \int_{t_0}^{t} h(t - \xi)u(\xi)\, d\xi \qquad t \geq t_0$$

where

10 $$\begin{aligned} &\mathbf{x}(t) = (u(t), \ldots, u^{(m-1)}(t)) \\ &\boldsymbol{\phi}(t) \triangleq (\phi_1(t), \ldots, \phi_m(t)) \\ &\phi_\lambda(t) \text{ is given by } 4,\ \lambda = 1, \ldots, m \\ &h(t) \text{ is given by } 4 \end{aligned}$$

11 *Comment* A question which suggests itself at this point is this: what is the connection between the input-output relation

12
$$\begin{aligned} y(t) &= M(p)u \\ &= (b_m p^m + \cdots + b_0)u \\ &= b_m u^{(m)}(t) + \cdots + b_0 u(t) \end{aligned}$$

and the input-output-state relation *9*?

On writing the latter relation in full, we have

13
$$y(t) = -\sum_{\lambda=1}^{m} u^{(\lambda-1)}(t_0-)[b_m \delta^{(m-\lambda)}(t - t_0) + \cdots + b_\lambda \delta(t - t_0)] + \int_{t_0}^{t} [b_m \delta^{(m)}(t - \xi) + \cdots + b_0 \delta(t - \xi)]u(\xi)\, d\xi$$

Now, a delta function $\delta^{(\lambda)}(t - \xi)$ of order λ has the property

14
$$\int_{t_0}^{t} \delta^{(\lambda)}(t - \xi)u(\xi)\, d\xi = p^\lambda 1(t - t_0)u(t)$$

where $1(t - t_0)$ is a unit step function which serves to truncate u to the left of the point $t = t_0$. Thus, *13* may be written as

15
$$y(t) = \sum_{\lambda=1}^{m} u^{(\lambda-1)}(t_0-)[b_m \delta^{(m-\lambda)}(t - t_0) + \cdots + b_\lambda \delta(t - t_0)] + M(p)1(t - t_0)u(t)$$

Now we recall (see *3.8.3 et seq.*) that when p acts on a time function u which may have a discontinuity at $t = t_0$, we have

16
$$\begin{aligned} p\,u &= -\,u(t_0-)\delta(t - t_0) + p\,1(t - t_0)u(t) \\ p^2 u &= -u^{(1)}(t_0-)\delta(t - t_0) - u(t_0-)\delta^{(1)}(t - t_0) + p^2\,1(t - t_0)u(t) \\ &\cdots\cdots\cdots\cdots\cdots\cdots \\ p^m u &= -u^{(m-1)}(t_0-)\delta(t - t_0) - \cdots - u(t_0-)\delta^{(m-1)}(t - t_0) + p^m\,1(t - t_0)u(t) \end{aligned}$$

Furthermore, we note that *15* results when the right-hand members of *16* are substituted for $p\,u, \ldots, p^m u$, respectively, in the input-output relation *12*. This shows that the input-output-state relation *13* can be derived directly from the input-output relation *12* merely by replacing $p\,u, p^2 u, \ldots, p^m u$ in *12* with the equivalent expressions *16*. In effect, then, the input-output-state relation *9* serves merely to place in evidence the effect of a discontinuity in u or its derivatives at $t = t_0$.

It will be helpful at this point to summarize our conclusions in the form of an

17 **Assertion** Let $\mathfrak{D}$ be a system of the differential operator type

18
$$y = M(p)u \qquad M(p) = b_m p^m + \cdots + b_0 \qquad b_m \neq 0$$

and let the normal state vector of $\mathfrak{D}$ at time t be defined by

19 $$\mathbf{x}(t) = (u(t), \ldots, u^{(m-1)}(t))$$

Then the input-output-state relation of $\mathfrak{D}$ reads

20 $$y(t) = \langle \boldsymbol{\phi}(t - t_0), \mathbf{x}(t_0-) \rangle + \int_{t_0}^{t} h(t - \xi) u(\xi)\, d\xi \qquad t \geq t_0$$

or, more explicitly,

21 $$y(t) = \langle \boldsymbol{\phi}(t - t_0), \mathbf{x}(t_0-) \rangle + M(p)[1(t - t_0)u(t)]$$

where, to recapitulate,

22 $$\boldsymbol{\phi}(t) = (\phi_1(t), \ldots, \phi_n(t))$$

23 $$\phi_\lambda(t) = \mathfrak{L}^{-1}\{b_m s^{m-\lambda} + \cdots + b_\lambda\} = b_m \delta^{(m-\lambda)}(t) + \cdots + b_\lambda \delta(t) \qquad \lambda = 1, \ldots, m$$

24 $$h(t) = \mathfrak{L}^{-1}\{M(s)\} = b_m \delta^{(m)}(t) + \cdots + b_0 \delta(t)$$

25 *Comment* It is understood that any delta functions which u may have at $t = t_0$ are included in the term $1(t - t_0)u(t)$ and are acted upon by $M(p)$ in the usual fashion (see *A.2.5*).

26 *Comment* Note that at this step of our analysis *9* must be regarded as a tentative input-output-state relation since we have not yet verified that $\mathbf{x}$ as defined by *19* qualifies as a state vector for $\mathfrak{D}$ under the self-consistency conditions. We shall establish this after deriving the state equations for $\mathfrak{D}$.

27 **Remark** It is of interest to observe that the normal state vector associated with $\mathfrak{D}$ has exactly the same intrinsic significance as the normal state vector associated with $\mathfrak{R}$. Specifically, if we write the input-output relations of $\mathfrak{R}$ and $\mathfrak{D}$ in the nonoriented form

$$L(p)v_1 = v_2 \qquad L(p) = a_n p^n + \cdots + a_0 \qquad a_0 \neq 0$$

then the state vector $\mathbf{x}$ is expressed in both cases by

28 $$\mathbf{x} = (v_1, \ldots, v_1^{(n-1)})$$

regardless of which orientation is used. This implies that the definition of the state vector in terms of the variables entering into the differential equations which characterize a system is independent of the manner in which the system is oriented, i.e., independent of whether a particular variable is labeled as input or output. The reason for this lies in the fact that, in the process of deriving the input-output-state relation from the general solution, we make no real use of the assumption that u is the input and y is the output. This is true not only of systems of the reciprocal differential and differential types considered above but, more generally, of any linear differential system. It should be noted, however, that, although the definition of $\mathbf{x}$ is independent of the orientation, the form of the state equations satisfied by $\mathbf{x}$ depends very strongly on the orientation of the system.

Setting up the state equations

The state equations of $\mathfrak{D}$ corresponding to the normal state vector

$$\mathbf{x}(t) = (u(t), \ldots, u^{(m-1)}(t))$$

can readily be set up by following the procedure of Sec. *3*. Specifically, on forming the expression for $\dot{\mathbf{x}}(t)$ and comparing it with that for $\mathbf{x}(t)$, we obtain

29
$$\begin{aligned} x_1 &= u \\ \dot{x}_1 &= x_2 \\ \dot{x}_2 &= x_3 \\ &\cdots\cdots \\ \dot{x}_{m-1} &= x_m \end{aligned}$$

Furthermore, from the input-output relation

30
$$y = b_0 u + b_1 u^{(1)} + \cdots + b_m u^{(m)}$$

and *29*, we deduce

31
$$y = b_0 x_1 + \cdots + b_{m-1} x_m + b_m \dot{x}_m$$

Equations *29*, together with *31*, constitute the desired state equations of $\mathfrak{D}$. We shall refer to them as the *normal state equations* corresponding to the normal state vector *19*.

32 *Example* Suppose that $\mathfrak{D}$ is characterized by the input-output relation

$$y = \frac{d^2u}{dt^2} + 3\frac{du}{dt} + 2u$$

In this case, the normal state vector is expressed by

$$\mathbf{x} = (u, \dot{u})$$

and the normal state equations *29* and *31* become

$$\begin{aligned} x_1 &= u \\ \dot{x}_1 &= x_2 \\ y &= 2x_1 + 3x_2 + \dot{x}_2 \end{aligned}$$

The input-output-state relation for $\mathfrak{D}$ reads

$$y(t) = (\delta^{(1)}(t - t_0) + 3\delta(t - t_0))x_1(t_0-) + \delta(t - t_0)x_2(t_0-) + (p^2 + 3p + 2)1(t - t_0)u(t) \quad \triangleleft$$

We observe that the state equations *29* and *31* are not of the same form as the state equations of a system of the reciprocal differential operator type (*4.3.32*), nor are they of the canonical form

$$\dot{\mathbf{x}} = \mathbf{Ax} + \mathbf{Bu}$$
$$\mathbf{y} = \mathbf{Cx} + \mathbf{Du}$$

Consequently, we cannot use Corollary *2.3.36*, as in Sec. 3, to show that $\mathbf{x}$ qualifies as a state vector of $\mathfrak{D}$.

Although it is an easy matter to verify that $\mathbf{x}$ as defined by *19* has the state separation property *2.3.19*, it will be instructive to demonstrate directly that $\mathbf{x}$ satisfies the four consistency conditions *1.6.5*, *1.6.11*, *1.6.15*, and *1.6.35*. This is what we shall do in the sequel.

Direct verification that x qualifies as a state vector

We have to verify that *21* is an input-output-state relation for the system characterized by the input-output relation

33 $$y(t) = (b_m p^m + \cdots + b_0)u$$

To avoid being influenced by notation, let us express *21* in the form

34 $$y(t) = \langle \boldsymbol{\phi}(t - t_0), \boldsymbol{\alpha} \rangle + M(p)[1(t - t_0)u(t)] \qquad t \geq t_0$$

where $\boldsymbol{\alpha}$ is an m-vector, $\boldsymbol{\alpha} = (\alpha_1, \ldots, \alpha_m)$, ranging over $\mathcal{C}^m$. [In effect, $\boldsymbol{\alpha}$ represents a point (state) in the state space Σ of $\mathfrak{D}$.] We employ the symbol $\boldsymbol{\alpha}$ rather than $\mathbf{x}(t_0-)$ in *34* because at this stage of our argument we have not yet demonstrated that the components of $\boldsymbol{\alpha}$ are the values of u and its derivatives at t_0-.

Since *34* is a general solution for *33*, it follows that *34* satisfies the mutual-consistency condition (see *3.8.24*). Furthermore, since the response is uniquely determined by $\boldsymbol{\alpha}$ and $u_{(t_0,t]}$, it follows that *34* satisfies the first self-consistency condition also. Thus, it will suffice to show that *34* satisfies the third self-consistency condition, since this condition implies the second self-consistency condition (see *1.6.39*).

We can simplify the argument without losing its essential features by carrying out the verification for the case where $m = 1$. Actually, this is all that we shall need at a later point (Secs. *8* and *9*) to develop an effective general technique for associating a state vector with a differential system of any finite order.

For $m = 1$, *33* and *34* become respectively

35 $$y = p\,u$$

36 $$y(t) = \alpha\delta(t - t_0) + p\,1(t - t_0)u(t)$$

where for simplicity we have set $b_0 = 0$, $b_1 = 1$. We assume furthermore that $u(t)$ is real-valued, which implies that α ranges over the real line $(-\infty, \infty)$.

Suppose that, starting at $t = 0$ with $\alpha = 0$, we apply to $\mathfrak{D}$ an input of the form shown in Fig. *4.4.1a* and observe the corresponding response y. Then u and y constitute an input-output pair (u,y) for *35* starting at $t = 0$ with $\alpha = 0$.

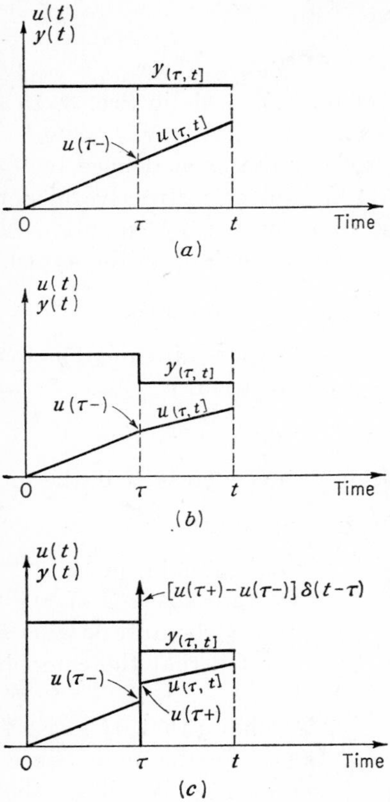

Fig. 4.4.1 Response of p. (*a*) u and $\dot{u}$ are continuous at τ; (*b*) u is continuous at τ; (*c*) u is discontinuous at τ.

Now let τ be a fixed intermediate time between 0 and t and consider the segments $u_{(\tau,t]}$ and $y_{(\tau,t]}$ of u and y, respectively, over the observation interval $(\tau,t]$. By the second self-consistency condition, there must be a value of α in $(-\infty,\infty)$ such that $(u_{(\tau,t]},y_{(\tau,t]})$ is an input-output pair starting at time τ. Indeed, we note that the term $p\ 1(t-\tau)u(t)$ in *36* contributes a delta function $u(\tau+)\delta(t-\tau)$ to the response at time τ. Since y does not contain a delta function at time τ, it follows that the term $u(\tau+)\delta(t-\tau)$ must be canceled by the term $\alpha\delta(t-\tau)$. This in turn implies that $\alpha = u(\tau+)$ or, equivalently, $\alpha = u(\tau-)$, since u is continuous at τ. This, then, is the value of α in *36* with respect to which $(u_{(\tau,t]},y_{(\tau,t]})$ is an input-output pair for *35*.

Next, assume that u is kept fixed over the interval $(0,\tau]$ and is varied over the interval $(\tau,t]$ in such a way as to preserve the continuity of u at τ. For example, a "new" u may have the appearance shown in Fig. *4.4.1b*. Again, the same argument shows that the "new" pair $(u_{(\tau,t]},y_{(\tau,t]})$ is an input-output pair for *35* starting at τ with $\alpha = u(\tau-)$. More generally, we can draw the same conclusion for any "new" pair $(u_{(\tau,t]},y_{(\tau,t]})$ so long as u is continuous at τ.

Next, consider the case where u is not continuous at τ, as is illustrated in Fig. *4.4.1c*. In this case, the response y will contain a delta function at τ whose magnitude is equal to the value of the jump in u at τ. Specifically, the delta function in question is expressed by

$$(u(\tau+) - u(\tau-))\delta(t - \tau)$$

To account for this delta function in y, the value of α in *36* must be

$u(\tau-)$. Thus, we can conclude that even when we allow the "new" input u to have a discontinuity at τ, the value of α with respect to which $(u_{(\tau,t]},y_{(\tau,t]})$ is an input-output pair remains equal to $u(\tau-)$.

The same thing holds true when we allow u to have not only a discontinuity but also a delta function at τ. In sum, then, no matter what $u_{(\tau,t]}$ is, the value of α with respect to which $(u_{(\tau,t]},y_{(\tau,t]})$ is an input-output pair remains fixed and equal to $u(\tau-)$. This shows that *36* satisfies the third self-consistency condition, since $u(\tau-)$ belongs to all the sets $Q(\alpha;u_{(0,\tau]}u_{(\tau,t]})$ and hence to the intersection of these sets (see *1.6.35*). This in turn implies that $u(\tau-)$ is the state of $\mathfrak{D}$ (for $m = 1$) at time $\tau-$.

We have thus demonstrated in a direct fashion that the expression

$$y(t) = \alpha\delta(t - t_0) + p\,1(t - t_0)u(t)$$

in which α ranges over $\mathbb{R}^1 \triangleq (-\infty, \infty)$, qualifies as an input-output-state relation for the system characterized by the input-output relation

$$y = p\,u$$

Furthermore, we have shown that $u(t)$ qualifies as the state of the system at time t. Note that, by Theorem *4.2.25*, any other way of associating a state vector with the system in question cannot lead to anything other than $ku(t)$ [that is, a constant times $u(t)$] as the expression for the state of the system at time t.

More generally, we can demonstrate in the same fashion that *34*, with $\Sigma = \mathcal{C}^m$, satisfies the third self-consistency condition and that $\mathbf{x}(t) = (u(t), \ldots, u^{(m-1)}(t))$ qualifies as the state of $\mathfrak{D}$ at time t. It is much simpler, however, to arrive at the same conclusion by employing a technique described in Sec. *6*, which makes use of the determinateness theorem for linear systems (Theorem *3.9.12*) and the fact that the state of a differential operator system of order 1 can be identified with its input—which is what we have just demonstrated.

Special case: a differentiator

In Sec. *3* we defined an integrator as a reciprocal differential operator system of order 1. In a parallel manner, we can define a differentiator as a differential operator system of order 1. More precisely,

37 **Definition** A *differentiator* is a system characterized by an input-output relation of the form

38 $$y = (p + b)u$$

where b is a constant, not necessarily real. A *pure* differentiator is one in which $b = 0$. A differentiator which is characterized by an input-output relation of the form *38* is denoted by $(p + b)$. ◁

As in the case of an integrator, the normal state vector of a differentiator has just one component, $u(t)$, which is the input to the differentiator at time t. Again, we can make the

39 **Assertion** The state of a differentiator at time t is necessarily of the form

$$x(t) = ku(t)$$

where k is a constant. Unless indicated to the contrary, k will be assumed to be unity. ◁

The input-output-state relation and the state equations for a differentiator are special cases of *29* and *31*, with $b_1 = 1$ and $b_0 = b$. They read

40 $$y(t) = x(t_0-)\delta(t - t_0) + p\,1(t - t_0)u(t) + bu(t)$$

41 $$x = u$$
$$y = \dot{x} + bu$$

A connection between systems of differential and reciprocal differential type

Consider a system $\mathcal{R}$ of the reciprocal differential operator type which is characterized by an input-output relation

42 $$L(p)y = u \qquad L(p) = a_n p^n + \cdots + a_0 \qquad a_n \neq 0$$

Correspondingly, let $\mathfrak{D}$ be a system of the differential operator type characterized by the input-output relation ($w \triangleq$ output, $v \triangleq$ input)

43 $$w = L(p)v \qquad L(p) = a_n p^n + \cdots + a_0 \qquad a_n \neq 0$$

Obviously, $\mathcal{R}$ and $\mathfrak{D}$ are converse systems in the sense of Definition *2.10.1*, since if a pair of time functions (f,g) is an input-output pair for $\mathcal{R}$, then (g,f) is an input-output pair for $\mathfrak{D}$, and vice versa.

By using the expressions for the input-output-state relations for $\mathcal{R}$ and $\mathfrak{D}$, it is easy to show that $\mathcal{R}$ and $\mathfrak{D}$ are not only converse but also inverse to one another (*2.10.6*). Furthermore, we can show that $\mathfrak{D}$ is a left- but not right-constrained inverse of $\mathcal{R}$ (see *2.10.20*). More specifically, we can make the

44 **Assertion** Let $\mathcal{R}$ be a system of the reciprocal differential operator type characterized by *42* and let $\mathfrak{D}$ be a system of the differential operator type characterized by *43*. Then $\mathcal{R}$ and $\mathfrak{D}$ are inverse systems in the sense of Definition *2.10.6* and $\mathfrak{D}$ is a left- but not right-constrained inverse of $\mathcal{R}$ in the sense of Definition *2.10.20*.

Proof Let $\bar{R}(\boldsymbol{\alpha};u)$ denote the response segment of $\mathcal{R}$ to u (see *1.6.2*) starting in a state $\boldsymbol{\alpha} \in \mathcal{C}^n$ ($\mathcal{C}^n$ = state space of $\mathcal{R}$ = state space of $\mathfrak{D}$) and let $\bar{D}(\boldsymbol{\beta};v)$ denote the response segment of $\mathfrak{D}$ to v starting in a state

$\boldsymbol{\beta}$ in $\mathcal{C}^n$. To demonstrate that $\mathcal{R}$ and $\mathcal{D}$ are inverse to one another, we have to show that (I) to every state $\boldsymbol{\alpha}$ in $\mathcal{C}^n$ there corresponds a state $\boldsymbol{\beta}(\boldsymbol{\alpha})$ in $\mathcal{C}^n$ such that if $\bar{R}(\boldsymbol{\alpha};u)$ is applied to $\mathcal{D}$ starting in $\boldsymbol{\beta}(\boldsymbol{\alpha})$, then the response of $\mathcal{D}$ is u, for all u in the input segment space of $\mathcal{R}$, and (II) to every state $\boldsymbol{\beta}$ in $\mathcal{C}^n$ there corresponds a state $\boldsymbol{\alpha}(\boldsymbol{\beta})$ in $\mathcal{C}^n$ such that if $\bar{D}(\boldsymbol{\beta};v)$ is applied to $\mathcal{R}$ starting in $\boldsymbol{\alpha}(\boldsymbol{\beta})$, then the response of $\mathcal{R}$ is v, for all v in the input segment space of $\mathcal{D}$.

Now the input-output-state relations of $\mathcal{R}$ and $\mathcal{D}$ in the Laplace transform form read (see *4.3.5* and *4.4.2*)

45 $$\mathcal{R}: \qquad Y(s) = \frac{U(s)}{L(s)} + \frac{\sum_{\lambda=1}^{n} (a_n s^{n-\lambda} + \cdots + a_\lambda) y^{(\lambda-1)}(0-)}{L(s)}$$

46 $$\mathcal{D}: \qquad W(s) = L(s)V(s) - \sum_{\lambda=1}^{n} (a_n s^{n-\lambda} + \cdots + a_\lambda) v^{(\lambda-1)}(0-)$$

where $W(s) \triangleq \mathcal{L}\{w(t)\}$ and $V(s) \triangleq \mathcal{L}\{v(t)\}$. If the initial state of $\mathcal{R}$ is $\boldsymbol{\alpha} = (\alpha_1, \ldots, \alpha_n)$, that is,

$$(y(0-), \ldots, y^{(n-1)}(0-)) \triangleq \boldsymbol{\alpha}$$

and the initial state of $\mathcal{D}$ is $\boldsymbol{\beta} = (\beta_1, \ldots, \beta_n)$, that is,

$$(v(0-), \ldots, v^{(n-1)}(0-)) \triangleq \boldsymbol{\beta}$$

then on setting $V(s) = Y(s)$ [which signifies that $\bar{R}(\boldsymbol{\alpha};u)$ is applied to $\mathcal{D}$] and substituting $Y(s)$ in place of $V(s)$ in *46*, we obtain the following expression for the Laplace transform of the response of $\mathcal{D}$:

47 $$W(s) = U(s) + \sum_{\lambda=1}^{n} (a_n s^{n-\lambda} + \cdots + a_\lambda)(\alpha_\lambda - \beta_\lambda)$$

Clearly, $W(s) \equiv U(s)$ if and only if $\alpha_\lambda = \beta_\lambda$, $\lambda = 1, \ldots, n$, that is, if $\boldsymbol{\alpha} = \boldsymbol{\beta}$. Furthermore, we obtain the same result on applying $\bar{D}(\boldsymbol{\beta};v)$ to $\mathcal{R}$ starting in state $\boldsymbol{\alpha}$.

This shows that (I) and (II) are satisfied when $\boldsymbol{\alpha} = \boldsymbol{\beta}$, that is, when both $\mathcal{R}$ and $\mathcal{D}$ are started at the same point in the state space $\mathcal{C}^n$. Consequently, $\mathcal{R}$ and $\mathcal{D}$ are inverse systems in the sense of Definition *2.10.6*.

Now suppose that $\mathcal{R}$ and $\mathcal{D}$ are connected in tandem as shown in Fig. *4.4.2a*. Then, since $\mathcal{R}$ has output-determined state and $\mathcal{D}$ has input-determined state (see *2.6.26* and *2.6.34*), the equality $y = v$ which is imposed by the connection implies the equality $\boldsymbol{\alpha} = \boldsymbol{\beta}$ of the states of $\mathcal{R}$ and $\mathcal{D}$. From this and *47* it follows that $\mathcal{D}$ is a left-constrained inverse of $\mathcal{R}$.

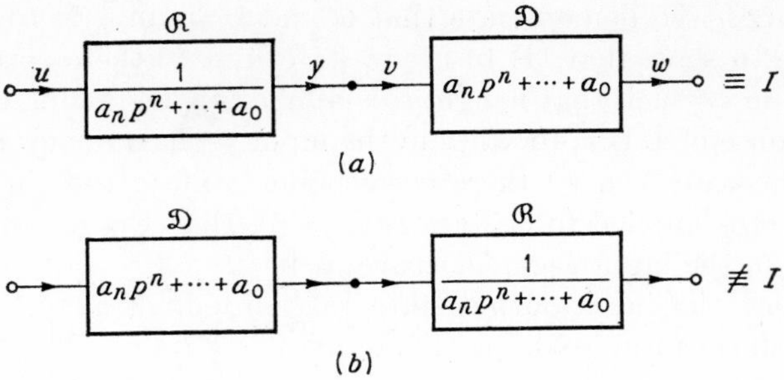

Fig. 4.4.2 Inverse systems. (*a*) $\mathfrak{D}\mathfrak{R} \equiv I$; (*b*) $\mathfrak{R}\mathfrak{D} \not\equiv I$. $\mathfrak{R}$ is a right-constrained inverse of $\mathfrak{D}$.

On the other hand, $\mathfrak{D}$ is not a right-constrained inverse of $\mathfrak{R}$ (Fig. *4.4.2b*), since in this case $\boldsymbol{\alpha}$ is not constrained to be equal to $\boldsymbol{\beta}$ by the tandem connection and $W(s) \not\equiv U(s)$ by *47*. (We disregard, of course, the trivial case where $n = 0$.)

48 **Remark** An important special case of Assertion *44* is one where $\mathfrak{R}$ is an integrator defined by

$$p\,y = u$$

and denoted by $1/p$, and $\mathfrak{D}$ is a differentiator defined by

$$w = p\,u$$

and denoted by p. By Assertion *44*, $1/p$ and p are inverse to one another. Furthermore, p is a left-constrained inverse of $1/p$, which in operational notation signifies that the constrained product $p \cdot \frac{1}{p}$ [which represents a tandem combination of $1/p$ and p, with p acting on the output of $1/p$ (see *1.10.23*)] is equivalent to the identity operator [i.e., a unitor (*1.9.8*)]. On the other hand, $\frac{1}{p} \cdot p$ *is not* equivalent to the identity operator, since p is not a right-constrained inverse of $1/p$. This observation clarifies the results obtained previously in Example *2.10.11*. (Specifically, the delta-function term in *2.10.16* vanishes when $\mathfrak{B}\mathfrak{A}$ is interpreted as a constrained product.) ◁

Another useful relation that can be drawn at once from *45* and *46* provides a rule for "trading" a time function added to the output of $\mathfrak{R}$ for one added to the input to $\mathfrak{R}$. The rule in question is contained in the

49 **Assertion** Let $\mathfrak{R}$ denote the system $1/L(p)$, with the initial state of $\mathfrak{R}$ at time t_0 being $\boldsymbol{\alpha} = (\alpha_1, \ldots, \alpha_n)$. Suppose that the response of $\mathfrak{R}$ to $\mathbf{u}$ starting in state $\boldsymbol{\alpha}$ is $\mathbf{y}$. Then to produce an output $\mathbf{y} + \mathbf{w}$, where $\mathbf{w}$ is a specified time function (defined for $t \geq t_0$), it is sufficient to (I) add to the input the time function

$$\mathbf{v} = L(p)\mathbf{w}$$

where $L(p)$ should be interpreted as an indefinite differential operator (*3.8.11*), and (II) subtract from the initial state of $\mathcal{R}$ the vector $(w(t_0-), \ldots, w^{(n-1)}(t_0-))$. ◁

We turn next to the consideration of a more general type of differential system which subsumes both the differential and reciprocal differential operator types of systems as special cases.

5 *State vectors and state equations for general differential systems*

By a general differential system (with scalar input u and scalar output y) we mean here a system characterized by an input-output relation of the form

1 $$\mathbf{L}(p)y + \mathbf{K}(p)\tilde{\mathbf{y}} = \mathbf{M}(p)u$$

where $\mathbf{L}(p)$ and $\mathbf{M}(p)$ are vector differential operators, $\mathbf{K}(p)$ is a matrix differential operator, and $\tilde{\mathbf{y}}$ is the suppressed output vector.

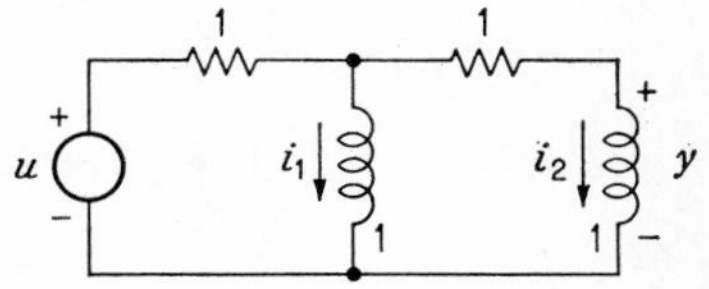

Fig. 4.5.1 Network of Example *4.5.2*.

2 *Example* Consider the network $\mathcal{A}$ shown in Fig. *4.5.1* in which u is the input voltage, y is the output voltage, and the currents i_1 and i_2 play the role of suppressed output variables. For simplicity, the element values are assumed to be unity.

The circuit equations for $\mathcal{R}$ read

$$u = p\,i_1 + i_1 + i_2$$
$$0 = p\,i_1 - p\,i_2 - i_2$$
$$y = p\,i_2$$

Upon rearranging these equations to put them into the form of *1*, we have

$$-\begin{bmatrix}0\\0\\1\end{bmatrix} y + \left[\begin{bmatrix}1 & 0\\1 & -1\\0 & 1\end{bmatrix} p + \begin{bmatrix}1 & 1\\0 & -1\\0 & 0\end{bmatrix}\right]\begin{bmatrix}i_1\\i_2\end{bmatrix} = \begin{bmatrix}1\\0\\0\end{bmatrix} u$$

In this case,

$$\mathbf{L}(p) = -\begin{bmatrix}0\\0\\1\end{bmatrix} \qquad \mathbf{K}(p) = \begin{bmatrix}1 & 0\\1 & -1\\0 & 1\end{bmatrix} p + \begin{bmatrix}1 & 1\\0 & -1\\0 & 0\end{bmatrix} \qquad \mathbf{M}(p) = \begin{bmatrix}1\\0\\0\end{bmatrix}$$

3 *Example* Consider a system $\mathcal{R}$ characterized by an integrodifferential equation of the form

4
$$\left(p^2 + 2p + 3 + \frac{1}{p}\right) y = \left(p + \frac{2}{p}\right) u$$

where $1/p$ represents an integrator (*4.3.48*).

Let

5
$$\tilde{y}_1 = \frac{1}{p}\, y$$
$$\tilde{y}_2 = \frac{1}{p}\, u$$

Then

$$p\,\tilde{y}_1 = y$$
$$p\,\tilde{y}_2 = u$$

by the definition of an integrator. [This follows also from operating on both sides of *5* with p and making use of the fact that $p \cdot \frac{1}{p} = 1$ (see *4.4.48*).] Thus, *4* may be replaced by the system of equations

6
$$(p^2 + 2p + 3)y + \tilde{y}_1 = p\,u + 2\tilde{y}_2$$
$$p\,\tilde{y}_1 = y$$
$$p\,\tilde{y}_2 = u$$

which is of the general form *1*, with

$$\mathbf{L}(p) = \begin{bmatrix} 1 \\ 0 \\ 0 \end{bmatrix} p^2 + \begin{bmatrix} 2 \\ 0 \\ 0 \end{bmatrix} p + \begin{bmatrix} 3 \\ -1 \\ 0 \end{bmatrix}$$

$$\mathbf{K}(p) = \begin{bmatrix} 0 & 0 \\ 1 & 0 \\ 0 & 1 \end{bmatrix} p + \begin{bmatrix} 1 & -2 \\ 0 & 0 \\ 0 & 0 \end{bmatrix}$$

$$\mathbf{M}(p) = \begin{bmatrix} 1 \\ 0 \\ 0 \end{bmatrix} p + \begin{bmatrix} 0 \\ 0 \\ 1 \end{bmatrix}$$

In Sec. 7 we shall establish an important fact: that, given any general differential system $\mathcal{G}$, one can always find a system $\mathcal{A}$ equivalent to $\mathcal{G}$ which is characterized by an input-output relation of the form

7
$$L(p)y = M(p)u$$

where

8
$$L(p) = a_n p^n + \cdots + a_0 \qquad a_n \neq 0$$
$$M(p) = b_m p^m + \cdots + b_0 \qquad b_m \neq 0$$

and the a's and b's are constant coefficients, not necessarily real. Thus, the class of systems defined by *1* is no more and no less general than that defined by *7*.

In view of this fact, we can focus our attention on differential systems characterized by *7*. This does not mean, however, that our approach to the problem of associating a state vector with a system $\mathcal{G}$ characterized by *1* will always involve—as a first step—the replacement of $\mathcal{G}$ with an equivalent system $\mathcal{A}$ characterized by *7*. We shall be able to associate a state vector with $\mathcal{G}$ in a direct fashion by the use of techniques developed in Secs. *6* to *8*.

State vectors and state equations

Let $\mathcal{A}$ denote a system characterized by an input-output relation of the form *7*. Our problem is to associate a state vector with $\mathcal{A}$ and find the corresponding state equations.

Before applying our standard approach (Sec. *2*), let us note that *7* may be replaced by two relations

9
$$L(p)y - v = 0$$
$$v = M(p)u$$

which is of the general form *1*, with v playing the role of a suppressed output variable. Consequently, $\mathcal{A}$ may be regarded as a tandem combination (Fig. *4.5.2*) of the differential operator system $M(p)$,

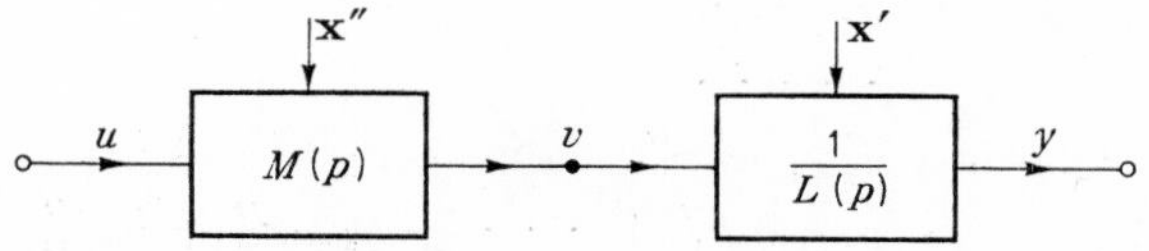

Fig. 4.5.2 A general system regarded as a tandem combination of $M(p)$ and $1/L(p)$.

followed by the reciprocal differential operator system $1/L(p)$ or, equivalently, as the product of $1/L(p)$ and $M(p)$. Accordingly, we can (and frequently shall) denote $\mathcal{A}$ by $\frac{1}{L(p)} \cdot M(p)$. [Note that this notation does not permit us, without additional justification, to treat $\frac{1}{L(p)} \cdot M(p)$ as if it were an ordinary ratio of two polynomials in p.]

We can make an immediate use of this observation to derive a way of associating a state vector with $\mathcal{A}$. Specifically, by the determinateness of linear systems (Theorem *3.9.12*), the vector

10
$$\mathbf{x} = (\mathbf{x}',\mathbf{x}'')$$

in which $\mathbf{x}'$ is the state vector for $1/L(p)$ and $\mathbf{x}''$ is the state vector for $M(p)$, qualifies as a state vector for $\mathcal{A}$. Thus, taking $\mathbf{x}'$ and $\mathbf{x}''$ to be the normal state vectors (*4.3.27* and *4.4.19*) of $1/L(p)$ and $M(p)$, respectively, we have

11 $$\mathbf{x}(t) = (y(t), \ldots, y^{(n-1)}(t); u(t), \ldots, u^{(m-1)}(t))$$

as the expression for the state of $\mathcal{A}$ at time t. Since $\mathbf{x}'$ ranges over $\mathcal{C}^n$ and $\mathbf{x}''$ ranges over $\mathcal{C}^m$, $\mathbf{x}$ ranges over $\mathcal{C}^{n+m}$. Thus, when the state vector of $\mathcal{A}$ is defined by *11*, the state space of $\mathcal{A}$ is $\mathcal{C}^{n+m}$, the space of all $(m + n)$-tuples of complex numbers.

The corresponding state equations of $\mathcal{A}$ can readily be set up by adjoining the state equations of $1/L(p)$ to those of $M(p)$. Specifically, we have for $1/L(p)$ (see *4.3.34*)

12 $$\begin{aligned} \dot{\mathbf{x}}' &= \mathbf{A}\mathbf{x}' + \mathbf{b}v \\ y &= \langle \mathbf{c}, \mathbf{x}' \rangle \end{aligned}$$

where

$$\mathbf{A} = \begin{bmatrix} 0 & 1 & 0 & \cdots & 0 \\ 0 & 0 & 1 & \cdots & 0 \\ \cdot & \cdot & \cdot & \cdots & \cdot \\ -\dfrac{a_0}{a_n} & \cdots & \cdots & \cdots & -\dfrac{a_{n-1}}{a_n} \end{bmatrix} \qquad \mathbf{b} = \begin{bmatrix} 0 \\ 0 \\ \cdots \\ \dfrac{1}{a_n} \end{bmatrix} \qquad \mathbf{c} = [1 \quad 0 \quad \cdots \quad 0]$$

and for $M(p)$ (see *4.4.17*)

13 $$\begin{aligned} x_1'' &= u \\ \dot{x}_1'' &= x_2'' \\ &\cdots\cdots \\ \dot{x}_{m-1}'' &= x_m'' \\ v &= b_0 x_1'' + \cdots + b_{m-1} x_m'' + b_m \dot{x}_m'' \end{aligned}$$

On eliminating v from these equations, we obtain

14 $$\begin{aligned} \dot{\mathbf{x}}' &= \mathbf{A}\mathbf{x}' + \mathbf{b}(b_0 x_1'' + \cdots + b_{m-1} x_m'' + b_m \dot{x}_m'') \\ x_1'' &= u \\ \dot{x}_1'' &= x_2'' \\ &\cdots\cdots \\ \dot{x}_{m-1}'' &= x_m'' \\ y &= \langle \mathbf{c}, \mathbf{x}' \rangle \end{aligned}$$

which are the desired state equations of $\mathcal{A}$.

A disadvantage of this way of associating a state vector with $\mathcal{A}$ is that it leads to a system which is not in reduced form (*3.6.46*). This manifests itself in the dimension of the state space $\mathcal{C}^{n+m}$ being equal to $n + m$ rather than max (m,n), which, as we shall see presently, is the order (*3.6.39*) of $\mathcal{A}$.

We can obtain a reduced form of $\mathcal{A}$ by employing the approach used in Secs. *3* and *4*, which starts with the derivation of the general solution of *7*. This is what we shall do in the sequel.

General solution

It will be convenient to consider first the case where $\mathcal{A}$ is a proper system in the sense of Definition *3.6.27*. This is equivalent to assuming that $\mathcal{A}$ is characterized by the input-output relation

15 $$L(p)y = M(p)u$$

where $L(p) = a_n p^n + \cdots + a_0$, $M(p) = b_n p^n + \cdots + b_0$, $a_n \neq 0$.

On applying the Laplace transformation to both sides of *15* we obtain after rearrangement of terms the following expression for the Laplace transform of the general solution (for $t_0 = 0$):

16 $$\begin{aligned} Y(s) = \frac{1}{L(s)} \{ & s^{n-1}[a_n y(0-) - b_n u(0-)] \\ & + s^{n-2}[a_n y^{(1)}(0-) - b_n u^{(1)}(0-) + a_{n-1}y(0-) - b_{n-1}u(0-)] \\ & + \cdots \\ & + [a_n y^{(n-1)}(0-) - b_n u^{(n-1)}(0-) \\ & \qquad + \cdots + a_1 y(0-) - b_1 u(0-)]\} \\ & + H(s)U(s) \end{aligned}$$

where

17 $$H(s) = \frac{M(s)}{L(s)} = \text{transfer function of } \mathcal{A} \text{ (see } 3.6.17)$$

Expression for the state vector

At this stage we are ready to associate a state vector $\mathbf{x}$ with $\mathcal{A}$ by identifying the components of $\mathbf{x}(0-)$ with the constants appearing in the general solution *16*. One way of doing this is to equate $x_1(0-)$ to the coefficient of s^{n-1}, $x_2(0-)$ to the coefficient of s^{n-2}, etc. In this way, we arrive at the following expression for $\mathbf{x}(t)$ in terms of $u(t)$, $y(t)$, and their derivatives. [Alternative expressions for $\mathbf{x}(t)$ will be given in Sec. *9*.]

18 $$\begin{aligned} x_1 &= a_n y - b_n u \\ x_2 &= a_n y^{(1)} - b_n u^{(1)} + a_{n-1}y - b_{n-1}u \\ &\cdots\cdots\cdots\cdots \\ x_n &= a_n y^{(n-1)} - b_n u^{(n-1)} + \cdots + a_1 y - b_1 u \end{aligned}$$

State equations

To show that $\mathbf{x}$ defined in this manner qualifies as a state vector for $\mathcal{A}$, it is sufficient to show (by Conclusion *2.3.42*) that $\dot{\mathbf{x}}$, $\mathbf{x}$, u, and y satisfy state equations of the canonical form

19
$$\dot{\mathbf{x}} = \mathbf{A}\mathbf{x} + \mathbf{B}u$$
$$y = \mathbf{C}\mathbf{x} + \mathbf{D}u$$

This is easy to demonstrate. Specifically, on forming the expression for $\dot{\mathbf{x}}$ and comparing it with $\mathbf{x}$, we arrive at once at the following relations:

20
$$\begin{aligned} x_1 &= a_n y - b_n u \\ x_2 &= \dot{x}_1 + a_{n-1}y - b_{n-1}u \\ x_3 &= \dot{x}_2 + a_{n-2}y - b_{n-2}u \\ &\cdots\cdots\cdots\cdots \\ x_n &= \dot{x}_{n-1} + a_1 y - b_1 u \end{aligned}$$

In addition, the differential equation *15* yields

$$\dot{x}_n = -(a_0 y - b_0 u)$$

Solving these equations for $\dot{\mathbf{x}}$ and y in terms of $\mathbf{x}$ and u, we have

21
$$\begin{aligned} \dot{x}_1 &= \frac{1}{a_n}(-a_{n-1}x_1 + a_n x_2 + (a_n b_{n-1} - a_{n-1}b_n)u) \\ \dot{x}_2 &= \frac{1}{a_n}(-a_{n-2}x_1 + a_n x_3 + (a_n b_{n-2} - a_{n-2}b_n)u) \\ &\cdots\cdots\cdots\cdots\cdots\cdots \\ \dot{x}_{n-1} &= \frac{1}{a_n}(-a_1 x_1 + a_n x_n + (a_n b_1 - a_1 b_n)u) \\ \dot{x}_n &= \frac{1}{a_n}(-a_0 x_1 + (a_n b_0 - a_0 b_n)u) \end{aligned}$$

and
$$y = \frac{1}{a_n}(x_1 + b_n u)$$

These are the desired state equations of $\mathcal{a}$. We note that they have the canonical form *19*, with

22
$$\mathbf{A} = \frac{1}{a_n}\begin{bmatrix} -a_{n-1} & a_n & 0 & \cdots & 0 \\ -a_{n-2} & 0 & a_n & \cdots & 0 \\ \cdots & \cdots & \cdots & \cdots & \cdots \\ -a_1 & 0 & 0 & \cdots & a_n \\ -a_0 & 0 & 0 & \cdots & 0 \end{bmatrix} \qquad \mathbf{B} = \frac{1}{a_n}\begin{bmatrix} a_n b_{n-1} - a_{n-1}b_n \\ a_n b_{n-2} - a_{n-2}b_n \\ \cdots\cdots \\ \cdots\cdots \\ a_n b_0 - a_0 b_n \end{bmatrix}$$

$$\mathbf{C} = \begin{bmatrix} \frac{1}{a_n} & 0 & \cdots & 0 \end{bmatrix} \qquad \mathbf{D} = \begin{bmatrix} \frac{b_n}{a_n} \end{bmatrix}$$

23 *Comment* The expression for $\mathbf{x}$ and the state equations derived above correspond to the choice of basis functions defined by

$$\phi_\lambda(t) = \mathcal{L}^{-1}\left\{\frac{s^{n-\lambda}}{L(s)}\right\} \qquad \lambda = 1, \ldots, n$$

This choice is different from that which leads to the normal state vector in the case of systems of the reciprocal differential operator type, namely (see *4.3.30*)

$$\phi_\lambda(t) = \mathfrak{L}^{-1}\left\{\frac{a_n s^{n-\lambda} + \cdots + a_\lambda}{L(s)}\right\} \qquad \lambda = 1, \ldots, n$$

With the latter choice, the **A** matrix in the state equations *19* is expressed by *4.3.32*; that is, it is identical with the **A** matrix of the reciprocal differential operator system $1/L(p)$. The corresponding realization of $\mathfrak{A}$ is shown in Fig. *4.9.7*. We leave it as an exercise for the reader to set up the expression for the state vector and determine the state equations for this case (see *4.9.15 et seq.*).

Input-output-state relation

To obtain the expression for the input-output-state relation for $\mathfrak{A}$, we invert $Y(s)$ as given by *16* and replace $0-$ by t_0-. The result reads

24 $$y(t) = \langle \boldsymbol{\phi}(t - t_0), \mathbf{x}(t_0-)\rangle + \int_{t_0}^{t} h(t - \xi)u(\xi)\, d\xi$$

where

25 $$\boldsymbol{\phi}(t) = (\phi_1(t), \ldots, \phi_n(t)) = \text{basis function vector}$$

$$\phi_\lambda(t) = \mathfrak{L}^{-1}\left\{\frac{s^{n-\lambda}}{L(s)}\right\} \qquad \lambda = 1, \ldots, n$$

$$= \text{zero-input responses of } \mathfrak{A}$$

$$h(t) = \mathfrak{L}^{-1}\{H(s)\} = \text{impulse response of } \mathfrak{A}$$

$$H(s) = \frac{M(s)}{L(s)} = \text{transfer function of } \mathfrak{A}$$

$$\mathbf{x}(t) = (x_1(t), \ldots, x_n(t)) = \text{state vector of } \mathfrak{A}$$

$$x_\lambda(t) = a_n y^{(\lambda-1)}(t) - b_n u^{(\lambda-1)}(t) + \cdots + a_{n-\lambda+1}y(t) - b_{n-\lambda+1}u(t) \qquad \lambda = 1, \ldots, n$$

From inspection of these relations we can draw the following conclusions.

26 **Conclusion** The zero-input responses $\phi_1(t), \ldots, \phi_n(t)$ are linearly independent and hence constitute a set of basis functions for $\mathfrak{A}$. This follows at once from the linear independence of the Laplace transforms of $\phi_1(t), \ldots, \phi_n(t)$, which are, respectively, $\frac{s^{n-1}}{L(s)}, \ldots, \frac{1}{L(s)}$.

27 **Conclusion** $\mathfrak{A}$ is a system of order n. This is a consequence of Conclusion *26* and Definition *3.6.39*.

28 **Conclusion** $\mathfrak{A}$ is in reduced form; i.e., there are no distinct states in the state space of $\mathfrak{A}$ which are equivalent to one another. This is a consequence of Conclusion *26* and Assertion *3.6.46*.

29 **Conclusion** $\mathcal{A}$ is a linear system in the sense of Definition *3.5.6* and a time-invariant system in the sense of Definition *3.2.36*. (The latter follows from *3.6.35*.)

30 **Conclusion** $\mathcal{A}$ is a proper system in the sense of Definition *3.6.27*. This follows from the fact that $h(t)$ is the inverse Laplace transform of a rational function $M(s)/L(s)$ in which the degree of the numerator does not exceed the degree of the denominator.

It will be helpful to summarize the main results of the foregoing analysis in the form of an

31 **Assertion** Let $\mathcal{A}$ be a proper differential system of order n which is characterized by an input-output relation of the form

$$L(p)y = M(p)u$$

$$L(p) = a_n p^n + \cdots + a_0 \qquad M(p) = b_n p^n + \cdots + b_n \qquad a_n \neq 0$$

Then the vector $\mathbf{x} = (x_1, \ldots, x_n)$ ranging over $\mathcal{C}^n$ and defined by

32 $$x_\lambda = a_n y^{(\lambda-1)} - b_n u^{(\lambda-1)} + \cdots + a_{n-\lambda+1} y - b_{n-\lambda+1} u \qquad \lambda = 1, \ldots, n$$

qualifies as a state vector for $\mathcal{A}$. Correspondingly, the input-output-state relation of $\mathcal{A}$ is given by *24* and the state equations of $\mathcal{A}$ are of the canonical form

$$\dot{\mathbf{x}} = \mathbf{Ax} + \mathbf{Bu}$$
$$\mathbf{y} = \mathbf{Cx} + \mathbf{Du}$$

where **A**, **B**, **C**, and **D** are given by *22*. ◁

As we shall see in Sec. *9*, the results derived above through the determination of the general solution of $\mathcal{A}$ can be obtained much more expeditiously by the use of the so-called realization technique. For this reason, we defer until Sec. *9* the discussion of alternative choices for the state vector **x** and the state equations to which they lead.

The case of improper $\mathcal{A}$

We turn next to the more general case where $\mathcal{A}$ is not necessarily a proper system. Specifically, let $\mathcal{A}$ be characterized by

33 $$L(p)y = M(p)u$$
$$L(p) = a_n p^n + \cdots + a_n \qquad M(p) = b_m p^m + \cdots + b_0$$

where m may be greater than n. For concreteness, we assume that $m > n$.

We can treat this case by using the standard approach employed in previous cases, i.e., by finding the general solution of *33* and identifying the constants appearing in this solution with the components of the initial state vector $\mathbf{x}(0-)$. It will be much simpler, however, to proceed indirectly, reducing the case in question to the case of a proper system through the use of a theorem which is proved below.

34 **Theorem** Let $\mathfrak{A}$ be an improper system characterized by *33*, with $m > n$. By using long division, express $M(p)$ in the form

35 $$M(p) \equiv (d_k p^k + \cdots + d_1 p)L(p) + \hat{M}(p)$$

where $k = m - n$, $\hat{M}(p)$ is a polynomial of degree n, and the d's are constants. Then

$$\mathfrak{A} \equiv \hat{\mathfrak{D}} + \hat{\mathfrak{A}}$$

(which, in words, means that $\mathfrak{A}$ is equivalent to a parallel combination of $\hat{\mathfrak{D}}$ and $\hat{\mathfrak{A}}$), where $\hat{\mathfrak{D}}$ is a system of the differential operator type characterized by the input-output relation

$$w = (d_k p^k + \cdots + d_1 p)u \qquad w \triangleq \text{output of } \hat{\mathfrak{D}}$$

and $\hat{\mathfrak{A}}$ is a proper system characterized by the input-output relation

$$L(p)v = \hat{M}(p)u \qquad v \triangleq \text{output of } \hat{\mathfrak{A}}$$

The statement of this theorem is illustrated in Fig. *4.5.3*.

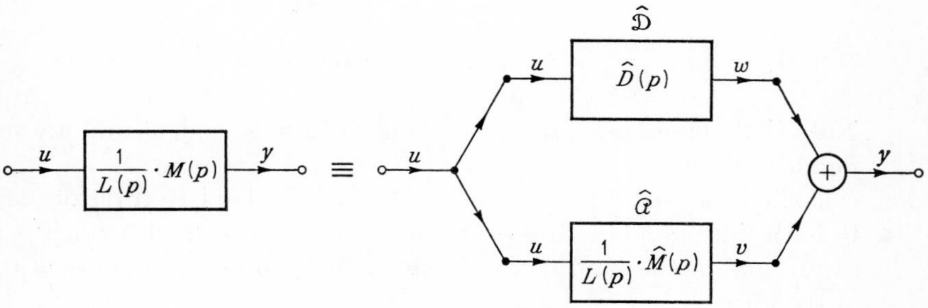

Fig. 4.5.3 Decomposition of an improper system into a proper system and a system of the differential operator type.

Proof It was shown in Chap. *3* (*3.5.10* and *3.6.49*) that two systems $\mathfrak{A}$ and $\mathfrak{B}$ are equivalent if they have the same basis functions and are zero-state equivalent. We shall show that this is true of $\mathfrak{A}$ and $\hat{\mathfrak{D}} + \hat{\mathfrak{A}}$.

Specifically, the transfer function of $\mathfrak{A}$ is

36 $$H_{\mathfrak{A}}(s) = \frac{M(s)}{L(s)}$$

On the other hand, the transfer function of $\hat{\mathfrak{D}} + \hat{\mathfrak{A}}$ is (by *3.6.25*) the sum of transfer functions of $\hat{\mathfrak{D}}$ and $\hat{\mathfrak{A}}$, that is,

$$\begin{aligned} H_{\hat{\mathfrak{D}}+\hat{\mathfrak{A}}}(s) &= \frac{\hat{M}(s)}{L(s)} + d_k s^k + \cdots + d_1 s \\ &= \frac{\hat{M}(s) + L(s)(d_k s^k + \cdots + d_1 s)}{L(s)} \\ &= \frac{M(s)}{L(s)} \\ &= H_{\mathfrak{A}}(s) \end{aligned}$$

by *35* and *36*. Thus, $\mathfrak{A}$ and $\hat{\mathfrak{D}} + \hat{\mathfrak{A}}$ have identical transfer functions and hence are zero-state equivalent (*3.6.11*).

Turning to the basis functions of $\mathfrak{A}$ and $\hat{\mathfrak{D}} + \hat{\mathfrak{A}}$, we recall from our earlier analyses of proper systems and systems of the differential operator type that the basis functions in question are given (in the Laplace transform form) by

$\hat{\mathfrak{A}}$: $$\frac{s^{n-1}}{L(s)}, \frac{s^{n-2}}{L(s)}, \ldots, \frac{1}{L(s)} \qquad \text{(see 23)}$$

and

$\hat{\mathfrak{D}}$: $$1, s, \ldots, s^{k-1} \qquad \text{(see 4.4.17[1])}$$

Hence the basis functions of $\hat{\mathfrak{D}} + \hat{\mathfrak{A}}$ are

$\hat{\mathfrak{D}} + \hat{\mathfrak{A}}$: $$\frac{s^{n-1}}{L(s)}, \ldots, \frac{s}{L(s)}, \frac{1}{L(s)}, 1, s, \ldots, s^{k-1}$$

Note that these basis functions are linearly independent and are m in number, since $k = m - n$.

To find the basis functions of $\mathfrak{A}$, we apply the Laplace transformation to both sides of *33*, with u set equal to zero. The result, which is the expression for the Laplace transform of the zero-input response of $\mathfrak{A}$, is of the form

37 $$Y(s) = \frac{c_{m-1}s^{m-1} + \cdots + c_0}{L(s)}$$

where the c's are constants involving the initial values of u, y, and their derivatives. Writing *37* as

$$Y(s) = \beta_k s^{k-1} + \cdots + \beta_1 s + \beta_0 + \frac{\gamma_0}{L(s)} + \gamma_1 \frac{s}{L(s)} + \cdots + \gamma_{n-1}\frac{s^{n-1}}{L(s)}$$

where the β's and γ's are constants, shows that the Laplace transforms

[1] Note that the basis functions in *4.4.17* are linear combinations of $1, s, \ldots, s^{m-1}$.

of the basis functions of $\mathfrak{A}$ are

38 $$\frac{s^{n-1}}{L(s)}, \ldots, \frac{s}{L(s)}, \frac{1}{L(s)}, 1, s, \ldots, s^{k-1}$$

and hence are identical with those of $\hat{\mathfrak{D}} + \hat{\mathfrak{A}}$. This concludes the proof of Theorem *34*.

39 **Remark** In the course of proving Theorem *34* we have established that $\mathfrak{A}$ has m basis functions if $m > n$. Previously we have shown (see *4.5.27*) that if $m \leq n$, then $\mathfrak{A}$ has n basis functions. Consequently, the number of basis functions of $\mathfrak{A}$ is given by max (m,n), regardless of which of these conditions holds. Thus, we can assert that the order (in the sense of Definition *3.6.39*) of a linear differential system characterized by an input-output relation of the form *33* is max (m,n). Note that this agrees with the definition of the order of a differential equation (*3.8.22*). $\lhd$

Having established Theorem *34*, we can make an immediate application of it to the problem of associating a state vector and setting up the state equations of an improper system $\mathfrak{A}$ characterized by an input-output relation of the form

40 $$L(p)y = M(p)u$$
$$L(p) = a_n p^n + \cdots + a_0 \qquad M(p) = b_m p^m + \cdots + b_0$$

Specifically, on replacing $\mathfrak{A}$ by $\hat{\mathfrak{D}} + \hat{\mathfrak{A}}$ in the manner illustrated in Fig. *4.5.3* and making use of the determinateness of linear systems (*3.9.12*), we reduce the problem of associating a state vector $\mathbf{x}$ with $\mathfrak{A}$ to that of associating a state vector $\mathbf{x}'$ with $\hat{\mathfrak{A}}$ and a state vector $\mathbf{x}''$ with $\hat{\mathfrak{D}}$. Then $\mathbf{x}$ is expressed as the composite vector

$$\mathbf{x} = (\mathbf{x}',\mathbf{x}'')$$

Since we know how to associate a state vector with a proper system such as $\hat{\mathfrak{A}}$ as well as with a system of the differential operator type such as $\hat{\mathfrak{D}}$, the problem of associating a state vector with $\mathfrak{A}$ may be regarded as solved. It is, however, actually more convenient not to associate a state vector with $\hat{\mathfrak{D}}$ and to use instead a hybrid type of representation for the output of $\mathfrak{A}$ which is described below.

Hybrid state equations

Essentially, we do this: Let v denote the output of $\hat{\mathfrak{A}}$ in Fig. *4.5.3* and let $\hat{D}(p)$ denote the differential operator $d_k p^k + \cdots + d_1 p$ which characterizes $\hat{\mathfrak{D}}$; that is,

41 $$\hat{D}(p) = d_k p^k + \cdots + d_1 p$$

Then the output of $\mathcal{A}$ can be written as

42 $$y = \hat{D}(p)u + v$$

Now $\hat{\mathcal{A}}$ is characterized by the input-output relation

43 $$L(p)v = \hat{M}(p)u$$

where

$$L(p) = a_n p^n + \cdots + a_0 \qquad \hat{M}(p) = \hat{b}_n p^n + \cdots + \hat{b}_0$$

with the $\hat{b}$'s determined by *35*. Let $\mathbf{x}$ denote the state vector of $\hat{\mathcal{A}}$ (rather than $\mathcal{A}$), defined in terms of v, u, and their derivatives via *32*, with b's in *32* replaced by $\hat{b}$'s. In terms of $\mathbf{x}$, the state equations of $\hat{\mathcal{A}}$ can be written as

44 $$\dot{\mathbf{x}} = \mathbf{A}\mathbf{x} + \mathbf{b}u$$
$$v = \langle \mathbf{c},\mathbf{x} \rangle + d_0 u$$

where $\mathbf{A}$, $\mathbf{b}$, $\mathbf{c}$, and d_0 are given by *22*, with $d_0 = \hat{b}_n/a_n$.

On substituting v from *44* into *42*, we have

$$y = \hat{D}(p)u + \langle \mathbf{c},\mathbf{x} \rangle + d_0 u$$

and on adjoining this relation to *44*, we obtain the equations

45 $$\dot{\mathbf{x}} = \mathbf{A}\mathbf{x} + \mathbf{b}u$$

46 $$y = \langle \mathbf{c},\mathbf{x} \rangle + d_0 u + \hat{D}(p)u$$

which, strictly speaking, are not the state equations of $\mathcal{A}$ since $\mathbf{x}$ is the state vector of $\hat{\mathcal{A}}$ rather than $\mathcal{A}$. Nevertheless, since *45* and *46* serve the same purpose as the usual state equations, we shall refer to *45* and *46* as the *hybrid state equations* of $\mathcal{A}$, with the adjective "hybrid" indicating that $\mathbf{x}$ is the state vector of a part of $\mathcal{A}$, namely, $\hat{\mathcal{A}}$, and that *45* and *46* are in effect a mixture of state equations for $\hat{\mathcal{A}}$ and the input-output relation ($w = \hat{D}(p)u$) for $\hat{\mathfrak{D}}$.

When no confusion is likely to result, we shall drop the adjective "hybrid" and refer to *45* and *46* simply as the *state equations* of $\mathcal{A}$.

47 **Remark** Note that *46* can be expressed in a somewhat neater form by absorbing the term $d_0 u$ in $\hat{D}(p)$. (This is equivalent to transferring the scalar d_0 from $\hat{\mathcal{A}}$ to $\hat{\mathfrak{D}}$.) Thus, if we define

48 $$D(p) = d_k p^k + \cdots + d_1 p + d_0$$
$$= \hat{D}(p) + d_0$$

then the hybrid state equations become

49 $$\dot{\mathbf{x}} = \mathbf{A}\mathbf{x} + \mathbf{b}u$$
$$y = \langle \mathbf{c},\mathbf{x} \rangle + D(p)u$$

This is the form in which the state equations of an improper system will usually be written in the sequel. ◁

It will be helpful at this point to summarize our conclusions in the form of an

50 **Assertion** Let $\mathcal{A}$ be an improper differential system characterized by the input-output relation

$$L(p)y = M(p)u$$

$$L(p) = a_n p^n + \cdots + a_0 \quad M(p) = b_m p^m + \cdots + b_0 \quad m - n \triangleq k > 0$$

By using long division write $M(p)$ in the form

$$M(p) = D(p)L(p) + \hat{M}(p)$$

where $D(p)$ is a polynomial in p of degree k and $\hat{M}(p)$ is a polynomial of degree $n - 1$. Let $\mathcal{D}$ be a system of the differential operator type characterized by the input-output relation

$$w = D(p)u$$

and let $\hat{\mathcal{A}}$ be the proper system characterized by the input-output relation

$$L(p)v = \hat{M}(p)u$$

Then $\mathcal{A}$ is equivalent to the sum (i.e., parallel combination) of $\mathcal{D}$ and $\hat{\mathcal{A}}$ (Fig. *4.5.3*) and is a system of order m.

Let $\mathbf{x}$ be a state vector associated with $\hat{\mathcal{A}}$ (for example, via *32*) and let the corresponding canonical state equations of $\hat{\mathcal{A}}$ be

$$\dot{\mathbf{x}} = \mathbf{A}\mathbf{x} + \mathbf{b}u$$
$$y = \langle \mathbf{c}, \mathbf{x} \rangle$$

where, if $\mathbf{x}$ is defined by *32*, $\mathbf{A}$, $\mathbf{b}$, and $\mathbf{c}$ are given by *22*. Then the relations between the input to $\mathcal{A}$, the output of $\mathcal{A}$, and the state vector of $\hat{\mathcal{A}}$ are given by

51
$$\dot{\mathbf{x}} = \mathbf{A}\mathbf{x} + \mathbf{b}u$$
$$y = \langle \mathbf{c}, \mathbf{x} \rangle + D(p)u$$

where $D(p)$ is a differential operator of the form

52
$$D(p) = d_k p^k + \cdots + d_1 p + d_0 \qquad k = m - n$$

These relations constitute the hybrid state equations or simply state equations of $\mathcal{A}$.

53 *Comment* Note that in Assertion *50* we state that $\hat{M}(p)$ is a polynomial of degree $n - 1$, whereas in Theorem *34* $\hat{M}(p)$ is stated to be of degree n. This difference is accounted for by our transferring the scalar d_0 from

$\hat{\mathcal{A}}$ to $\hat{\mathcal{D}}$ (see Remark *47*). This transfer does not affect the expressions for **A**, **b**, and the coefficients in $\hat{D}(p)$ (apart from d_0).

54 *Example* Consider an improper system $\mathcal{A}$ which is characterized by the input-output relation

55 $$(p^2 + 3p + 2)y = (p^3 + 4p^2 + 6p + 5)u$$

In this case, we have

$$p^3 + 4p^2 + 6p + 5 = (p^2 + 3p + 2)(p + 1) + p + 3$$

and hence $\mathcal{A}$ is equivalent to the parallel combination of $\hat{\mathcal{A}}$ and $\hat{\mathcal{D}}$ which are characterized by the input-output relations

$$\hat{\mathcal{A}}: \qquad (p^2 + 3p + 2)v = (p + 3)u$$
$$\hat{\mathcal{D}}: \qquad w = (p + 1)u$$

Using *32*, the expression for the state vector of $\hat{\mathcal{A}}$ in terms of u, v, and their derivatives is found to be

56 $$\mathbf{x} = (v, \dot{v} + 3v - u)$$

and the corresponding state equations are given by (see *21*)

$$\begin{aligned} \dot{x}_1 &= -3x_1 + x_2 + u \\ \dot{x}_2 &= -2x_1 + 3u \\ v &= x_1 \end{aligned}$$

In terms of these equations, the hybrid state equations of $\mathcal{A}$ read

57 $$\begin{aligned} \dot{x}_1 &= -3x_1 + x_2 + u \\ \dot{x}_2 &= -2x_1 + 3u \\ y &= x_1 + (p + 1)u \end{aligned}$$

58 **Remark** Some (but not all) of the expressions for the state vector and the state equations derived above carry over with minor modifications to the case where $\mathcal{A}$ is a time-varying system characterized by an input-output relation of the form

$$L(p,t)y = M(p,t)u$$

where

59 $$\begin{aligned} L(p,t) &= a_n(t)\, p^n + \cdots + a_0(t) \\ M(p,t) &= b_n(t)\, p^n + \cdots + b_0(t) \end{aligned}$$

with $a_n(t) \neq 0$ for all t.

The time-varying case will be treated in detail in Chap. *6*. Here we shall merely sketch a direct technique for associating a state vector with $\mathfrak{A}$ which does not require the determination of the general solution, as does the approach used in the foregoing analysis.

The basic idea of the method is this. By replacing p and its powers in the differential equation by the expressions given by *3.8.3*, we place in evidence the initial conditions needed to determine the response. Then we group these in a suitable manner to form the components of an initial state vector $\mathbf{x}(t_0-)$ and thereafter use the usual procedure to determine the corresponding state equations. To illustrate, suppose that $n = 2$ and that the a's and b's are continuous time functions. Then, on using *3.8.3* and transferring the terms involving the initial values to the right-hand side, we have

60 $$L(p,t)1(t - t_0)y(t) = M(p,t)1(t - t_0)u(t) + \delta^{(1)}(t - t_0)[a_2(t)y(t_0-) - b_2(t)u(t_0-)] + \delta(t - t_0)[a_2(t)\dot{y}(t_0-) - b_2(t)\dot{u}(t_0-) + a_1(t)y(t_0-) - b_1(t)u(t_0-)]$$

Now by *A.5.17*

61 $$\delta^{(1)}(t - t_0)a_2(t) = \delta^{(1)}(t - t_0)a_2(t_0) - \delta(t - t_0)\dot{a}_2(t_0)$$

and likewise for $b_2(t)$. Consequently, *60* can be rewritten as

62 $$L(p,t)1(t - t_0)y(t) = M(p,t)1(t - t_0)u(t) + \delta^{(1)}(t - t_0)[a_2(t_0)y(t_0-) - b_2(t_0)u(t_0-)] + \delta(t - t_0)[a_2(t_0)\dot{y}(t_0-) - \dot{a}_2(t_0)y(t_0-) + a_1(t_0)y(t_0-) - b_2(t_0)\dot{u}(t_0-) + \dot{b}_2(t_0)u(t_0-) - b_1(t_0)u(t_0-)]$$

which suggests that $\mathbf{x}(t)$ be defined by

63 $$\begin{aligned} x_1(t) &= a_2(t)y(t) - b_2(t)u(t) \\ x_2(t) &= a_2(t)\dot{y}(t) - \dot{a}_2(t)y(t) + a_1(t)y(t) \\ &\qquad - b_2(t)\dot{u}(t) + \dot{b}_2(t)u(t) - b_1(t)u(t) \end{aligned}$$

Because of the presence of the derivatives of the coefficients, the expressions for the components of $\mathbf{x}(t)$ rapidly gain in complexity with increase in n. However, as will be shown in Chap. *6* (*6.4.12*), it is possible to define the state vector in such a way that the corresponding state equations have the same form as they have in the time-invariant case (see *4.9.15*).

64 *Note* If $\mathfrak{A}$ is improper, then, as in the time-invariant case, $\mathfrak{A}$ can be represented as a parallel combination of a proper system and a system of the differential operator type $\hat{\mathfrak{D}}$. However, $\hat{M}(p)$ and $\hat{D}(p)$ cannot be found by the use of long division—as they can be in the time-invariant case.

This concludes for the present our discussion of systems characterized by a single differential equation. We turn next to the analysis of systems represented by an interconnection of adders, scalors, integrators, and differentiators.

6 State vectors and state equations for an interconnection of adders, scalors, integrators, and differentiators

Systems having the form of an interconnection of adders, scalors, integrators, and differentiators are of interest to us for two related reasons. First, as we shall see in Sec. *9*, given any linear system $\mathcal{A}$ characterized by a single differential equation $L(p)y = M(p)u$ or by its state equations, one can always construct an interconnection of adders, scalors, integrators, and differentiators, call it $\mathcal{B}$, such that $\mathcal{B}$ and $\mathcal{A}$ are equivalent systems. Second, on the basis of this equivalence, we can develop an effective and intuitively appealing technique for associating a state vector with $\mathcal{A}$ which consists essentially in realizing $\mathcal{A}$ in the form of an interconnection of adders, scalors, integrators, and differentiators and then associating a state vector with and finding the state equations for the latter system. This technique will be described in detail in Sec. *9*.

Associating a state vector

Consider an interconnection of scalors, adders, integrators, and differentiators, an example of which is shown in Fig. *4.6.1*.

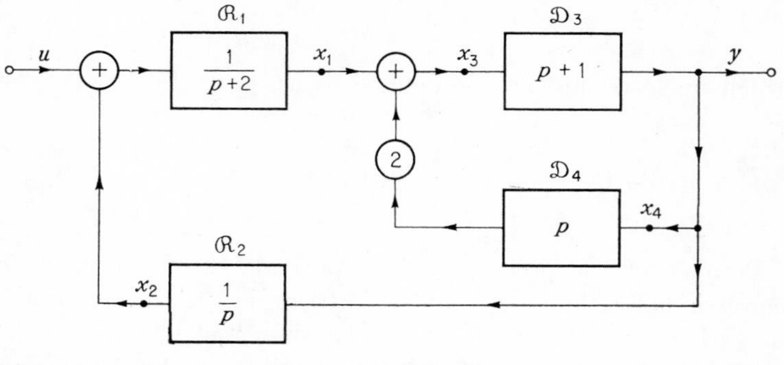

Fig. 4.6.1 A system comprising integrators, differentiators, adders, and scalors.

By Theorem *3.9.12*, such a system, call it $\mathcal{B}$, is determinate. Consequently, its state $\mathbf{x}$ can be identified with a vector $\mathbf{x} = (x_1, \ldots, x_n)$ whose components are the state vectors of those elements of $\mathcal{B}$ which are not memoryless, i.e., the integrators and differentiators. Now by Assertions *4.3.51* and *4.4.39*, the state of an integrator at time t is its output or, more generally, a constant times its output at t, while the state of a differentiator at time t is its input or, more generally, a constant times its input at t. From this it follows that a vector $\mathbf{x}$ whose components are the outputs of the integrators and the inputs to the differentiators qualifies as a state vector for $\mathcal{B}$.

1 **Remark** If $\mathcal{B}$ contains integrators and differentiators connected in tandem as illustrated in Fig. *4.6.2*, then, in order to reduce the dimension of $\mathbf{x}$, it is expedient to let the output of the integrator serve in the dual role of the state of both the integrator and the differentiator. For example, in Fig. *4.6.2* the component x_1 of $\mathbf{x}$ is the state of the integrator as well as that of the differentiator. ◁

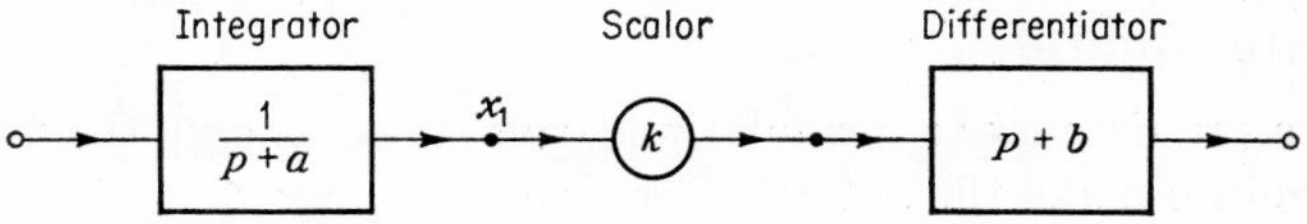

Fig. 4.6.2 Reduction of dimension of $\mathbf{x}$ by choosing x_1 to be the state of both $1/(p+a)$ and $p+b$.

The above observations lead us to the following simple rule for associating a state vector with $\mathcal{B}$.

2 **Rule** Let $\mathcal{B}$ be a system comprising scalors, adders, integrators, and differentiators. To associate a state vector $\mathbf{x} = (x_1, \ldots, x_n)$ with $\mathcal{B}$, assign a component of $\mathbf{x}$ to (I) the output of each integrator and (II) to the input of each differentiator which is not connected to the output of an integrator through a scalor.

3 *Note* For convenience in numbering, we assign the first l components of $\mathbf{x}$ ($l \triangleq$ number of integrators in $\mathcal{B}$) to the outputs of the integrators in $\mathcal{B}$ and the remaining $n - l$ components $x_{l+1}, \ldots, x_n$ to the inputs of those differentiators which are not connected to an integrator in the manner illustrated in Fig. *4.6.2*.

4 *Example* By applying this rule to the system of Fig. *4.6.1* we obtain $\mathbf{x} = (x_1,x_2,x_3,x_4)$, where $x_1 \triangleq$ output of integrator $\mathcal{R}_1$, $x_2 \triangleq$ output of $\mathcal{R}_2$, $x_3 \triangleq$ input to differentiator $\mathfrak{D}_3$, $x_4 \triangleq$ input to $\mathfrak{D}_4$.

5 *Example* For the system of Fig. *4.6.3* (which differs from that of Fig. *4.6.1* in the interchange of $\mathcal{R}_2$ and $\mathfrak{D}_4$), we have $\mathbf{x} = (x_1,x_2,x_3,x_4)$, with the x_i, $i = 1, \ldots, n$, having the same significance as in Example *4*.

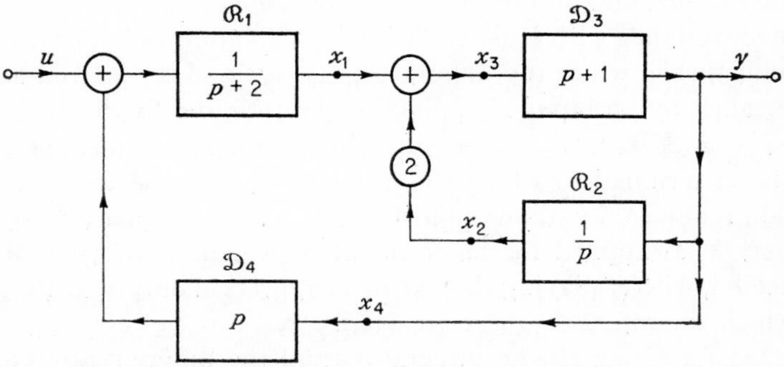

Fig. 4.6.3 System of Example *4.6.5*.

6 *Example* For the system of Fig. *4.6.4*, we have $\mathbf{x} = (x_1,x_2,x_3)$.

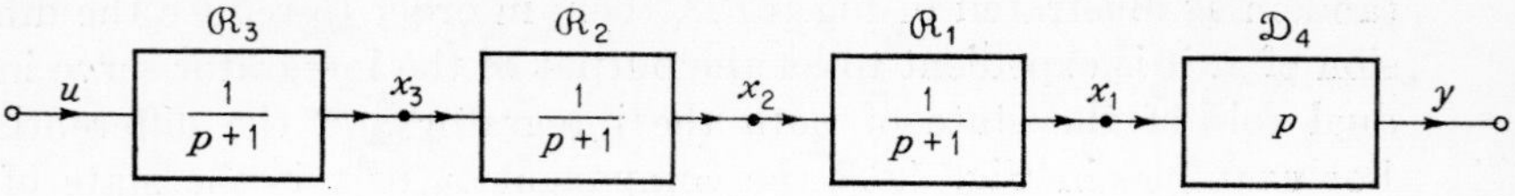

Fig. 4.6.4 System of Example *4.6.6*.

State equations

As a preliminary to formulating a rule for setting up the state equations for $\mathcal{B}$ we make the following obvious

7 *Observation* Let $\mathcal{R}_i$ be an integrator in $\mathcal{B}$ characterized by the input-output relation

$$(p + \gamma_i)y = u$$

where γ_i is a constant, not necessarily real. Then if the output of $\mathcal{R}_i$ is identified with x_i, the ith component of $\mathbf{x}$, we have

8
$$\begin{aligned} \text{output of } \mathcal{R}_i &= x_i \\ \text{input to } \mathcal{R}_i &= (p + \gamma_i)x_i \\ &= \dot{x}_i + \gamma_i x_i \end{aligned}$$

Similarly, let $\mathcal{D}_j$ denote a differentiator defined by

$$y = (p + \gamma_j)u$$

Then if the input to $\mathcal{D}_j$ is identified with x_j, we have

9
$$\begin{aligned} \text{input to } \mathcal{D}_j &= x_j \\ \text{output of } \mathcal{D}_j &= (p + \gamma_j)x_j \\ &= \dot{x}_j + \gamma_j x_j \end{aligned}$$

We are now ready to formulate a simple procedure for setting up the state equations.

10 **Procedure** Suppose that $\mathcal{B}$ is an interconnection of scalors, adders, integrators, and differentiators with which a state vector $\mathbf{x}$ is associated in accordance with Rule *2*. Clearly, the input and output of $\mathcal{B}$ remain undisturbed when any integrator, say $\mathcal{R}_i$, in $\mathcal{B}$ is removed and its place is taken by an input x_i applied to the terminal to which the output of $\mathcal{R}_i$ is connected, with $(p + \gamma_i)x_i$ playing the role of a suppressed output at the terminal to which the input of $\mathcal{R}_i$ is connected. Similarly, we can remove any differentiator, say $\mathcal{D}_j$, and replace it by an input $(p + \gamma_j)x_j$ applied to the terminal to which the output of $\mathcal{D}_j$ is connected, with x_j playing the role of a suppressed output at the terminal to which the input of $\mathcal{D}_j$ is connected.

On removing all the integrators and the differentiators in $\mathcal{B}$ in this fashion we are left with a system $\hat{\mathcal{B}}$ which contains only adders and scalors. This is illustrated in Figs. *4.6.5* and *4.6.6*, which show the systems remaining after the removal of integrators and differentiators from the systems of Figs. *4.6.1* and *4.6.4*, respectively.

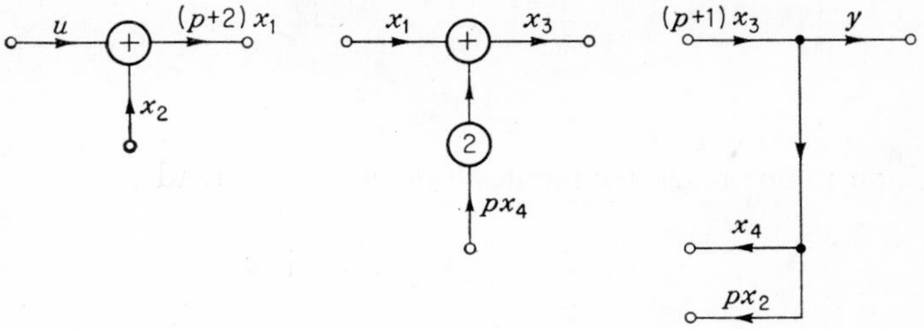

Fig. 4.6.5 System remaining after removal of integrators and differentiators from system of Fig. *4.6.1*.

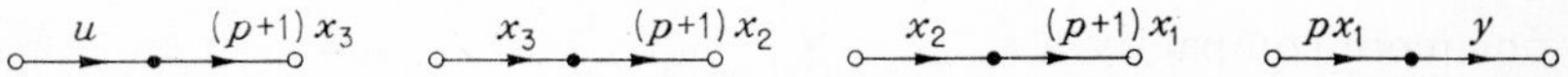

Fig. 4.6.6 System remaining after removal of integrators and differentiators from system of Fig. *4.6.4*.

In accordance with Note *3*, let $x_1, \ldots, x_l$ denote the outputs of the integrators in $\mathcal{B}$ and let $x_{l+1}, \ldots, x_n$ denote the inputs to the differentiators in $\mathcal{B}$, excluding those whose input terminals are connected directly or through scalors to the output terminals of an integrator (see Remark *1*). In terms of these variables, the inputs to $\hat{\mathcal{B}}$ are u, $x_1, \ldots, x_l$, $(p + \gamma_{l+1})x_{l+1}, \ldots, (p + \gamma_n)x_n$ and the outputs of $\hat{\mathcal{B}}$ are y, $(p + \gamma_1)x_1, \ldots, (p + \gamma_l)x_l$, $x_{l+1}, \ldots, x_n$. This is represented diagrammatically in Fig. *4.6.7*.

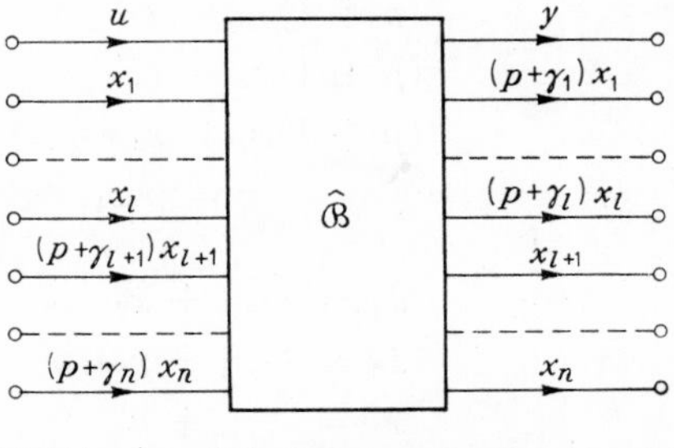

Fig. 4.6.7 $\hat{\mathcal{B}}$ and its input and output variables.

By this construction, we obtain from $\mathcal{B}$ a memoryless linear system $\hat{\mathcal{B}}$ such that the relations between the inputs and outputs of $\hat{\mathcal{B}}$ are exactly the same as the relations between u, y, and the components of $\mathbf{x}$ and their derivatives in $\mathcal{B}$. Having obtained $\hat{\mathcal{B}}$, the state equations of $\mathcal{B}$ can then be set up by inspection. For example, from Fig. *4.6.5* we obtain in this manner

$$(p+2)x_1 = x_2 + u$$
$$x_3 = 2p\,x_4 + x_1$$
$$p\,x_2 = x_4$$
$$x_4 = (p+1)x_3$$
$$y = (p+1)x_3$$

Upon minor rearrangement, these equations read

11
$$\begin{aligned}\dot{x}_1 &= -2x_1 + x_2 + u\\ \dot{x}_2 &= x_4\\ \dot{x}_4 &= \tfrac{1}{2}(x_3 - x_1)\\ \dot{x}_3 &= -x_3 + x_4\\ y &= x_4\end{aligned}$$

or more compactly,

$$\dot{\mathbf{x}} = \mathbf{A}\mathbf{x} + \mathbf{b}u$$
$$y = \langle \mathbf{c},\mathbf{x}\rangle$$

where

$$\mathbf{A} = \begin{bmatrix} -2 & 1 & 0 & 0\\ 0 & 0 & 0 & 1\\ 0 & 0 & -1 & 1\\ -0.5 & 0 & 0.5 & 0\end{bmatrix} \qquad \mathbf{b} = \begin{bmatrix}1\\0\\0\\0\end{bmatrix} \qquad \mathbf{c} = [0\ \ 0\ \ 0\ \ 1]$$

Equations *11* are the desired state equations for the system of Fig. *4.6.1*.

In a similar fashion, for the system of Fig. *4.6.4* we derive from inspection of Fig. *4.6.6*

$$(p+1)x_3 = u$$
$$(p+1)x_2 = x_3$$
$$(p+1)x_1 = x_2$$
$$y = p\,x_1$$

or

$$\dot{x}_1 = -x_1 + x_2$$
$$\dot{x}_2 = -x_2 + x_3$$
$$\dot{x}_3 = -x_3 + u$$
$$y = x_2 - x_1$$

Again, these equations are of the form *11*, with

$$\mathbf{A} = \begin{bmatrix} -1 & 1 & 0\\ 0 & -1 & 1\\ 0 & 0 & -1\end{bmatrix} \qquad \mathbf{b} = \begin{bmatrix}0\\0\\1\end{bmatrix} \qquad \mathbf{c} = [-1\ \ 1\ \ 0]$$

General form of state equations

To find the general form of state equations, we note that $\hat{\mathcal{B}}$ is a memoryless linear system (see *1.8.17*) and hence the input variables $u, x_1, \ldots, x_l, (\dot{x}_{l+1} + \gamma_{l+1}x_{l+1}), \ldots, (\dot{x}_n + \gamma_n x_n)$ and the output variables $y, (\dot{x}_1 + \gamma_1 x_1), \ldots, (\dot{x}_l + \gamma_l x_l), x_{l+1}, \ldots, x_n$ must be related to one another by linear algebraic equations. For compactness, let $\mathbf{x}_{\mathcal{R}}$ and $\mathbf{x}_{\mathfrak{D}}$ denote the vectors

12 $$\mathbf{x}_{\mathcal{R}} = (x_1, \ldots, x_l)$$

and

13 $$\mathbf{x}_{\mathfrak{D}} = (x_{l+1}, \ldots, x_n)$$

respectively, in terms of which the state vector $\mathbf{x}$ can be represented in partitioned form as

$$\mathbf{x} = (\mathbf{x}_{\mathcal{R}}, \mathbf{x}_{\mathfrak{D}})$$

Then, the relations between the variables in question can be written as

14 $$\begin{aligned} \dot{\mathbf{x}}_{\mathcal{R}} &= \mathbf{A}\mathbf{x}_{\mathcal{R}} + \mathbf{A}'\mathbf{x}_{\mathfrak{D}} + \mathbf{A}''\dot{\mathbf{x}}_{\mathfrak{D}} + \mathbf{b}u \\ \mathbf{x}_{\mathfrak{D}} &= \mathbf{F}\mathbf{x}_{\mathcal{R}} + \mathbf{F}'\mathbf{x}_{\mathfrak{D}} + \mathbf{F}''\dot{\mathbf{x}}_{\mathfrak{D}} + \mathbf{g}u \\ y &= \langle \mathbf{c}, \mathbf{x}_{\mathcal{R}} \rangle + \langle \mathbf{c}', \mathbf{x}_{\mathfrak{D}} \rangle + \langle \mathbf{c}'', \dot{\mathbf{x}}_{\mathfrak{D}} \rangle + d_0 u \end{aligned}$$

where the coefficients on the right are constant matrices, vectors, and scalars. These equations express the general form of the state equations of an interconnection of adders, scalors, differentiators, and integrators.[1]

15 *Example* Consider the system $\mathcal{B}$ shown in Fig. *4.6.8*. Here x_1 is the output of $\mathcal{R}_1$ and $(p + 1)x_1$ is the corresponding input; x_2 is the output of $\mathcal{R}_2$, as well as the input to $\mathfrak{D}_3$, and $p\, x_2$ is the corresponding input to $\mathcal{R}_2$ and $(p + 2)x_2$ is the corresponding output of $\mathfrak{D}_3$; x_3 is the input to $\mathfrak{D}_4$ and $p\, x_3$ is the corresponding output. By inspection, we have

$$\begin{aligned} (p + 1)x_1 &= u \\ p\, x_2 &= x_1 + u \\ x_3 &= (p + 2)x_2 + u \\ y &= x_1 + 3x_2 + (p + 2)x_2 + p\, x_3 \end{aligned}$$

which after rearrangement read

$$\begin{aligned} \dot{x}_1 &= -x_1 + u \\ \dot{x}_2 &= x_1 + u \\ x_3 &= \dot{x}_2 + 2x_2 + u = x_1 + 2x_2 + 2u \\ y &= x_1 + 3x_2 + \dot{x}_2 + 2x_2 + \dot{x}_3 = 2x_1 + 3x_2 + \dot{x}_3 + u \end{aligned}$$

[1] It should be noted that when $\mathcal{B}$ contains one or more scalors with infinite gain (*1.9.8*), the inputs to these scalors are constrained to be zero (so long as their outputs are finite), which is equivalent to "grounding" the system at the terminals in question. Such constraints give rise to additional linear relations between the components of $\mathbf{x}$ which are not exhibited explicitly in *14*.

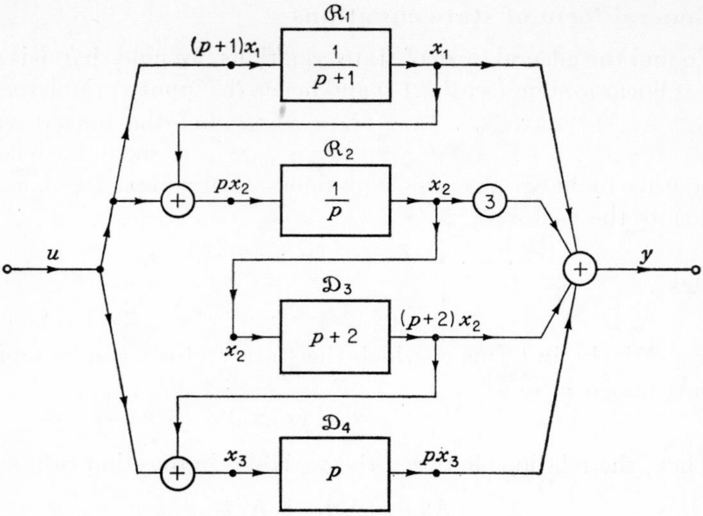

Fig. 4.6.8 System of Example *4.6.15.*

These are the desired state equations of $\mathcal{B}$. Note that they are of the general form *14.* ◁

As they stand, Eqs. *14* do not have the canonical form

16
$$\dot{\mathbf{x}} = \mathbf{A}\mathbf{x} + \mathbf{b}u$$
$$y = \langle \mathbf{c},\mathbf{x} \rangle + d_0 u$$

nor are they in the hybrid form

17
$$\dot{\mathbf{x}} = \mathbf{A}\mathbf{x} + \mathbf{b}u$$
$$y = \langle \mathbf{c},\mathbf{x} \rangle + D(p)u$$

Thus, the question arises: Can Eqs. *14* be put into the canonical form *16* or the hybrid form *17*, and, if so, by what means?

In the first place, it is evident that there are special cases in which Eqs. *14* have the canonical form *16*. For example, if $\mathcal{B}$ contains no differentiators, then $\mathbf{x} = \mathbf{x}_{\mathcal{R}}$ and *14* reduces to

18
$$\dot{\mathbf{x}} = \mathbf{A}'\mathbf{x} + \mathbf{b}u$$
$$y = \langle \mathbf{c},\mathbf{x} \rangle + d_0 u$$

Furthermore, it is easy to construct examples of systems (e.g., the system of Fig. *4.6.1*) which contain both integrators and differentiators and yet lead to state equations of the form *16* (see *11*) either directly or after the elimination of one or more of the components of $\mathbf{x}_{\mathcal{R}}$ and $\mathbf{x}_{\mathcal{D}}$ from *14.* However, it is also easy to demonstrate that it is not always possible to reduce *14* to *16* merely by solving the state equations *14* for $\dot{\mathbf{x}}$ and y in terms of $\mathbf{x}$ and u. For example, if the state equations

14 read

19
$$\begin{aligned} \dot{x}_1 &= x_1 + \dot{x}_2 + u \\ x_2 &= 2x_1 - 2u \\ y &= x_1 \end{aligned}$$

then on eliminating x_2, we have

$$\begin{aligned} \dot{x}_1 &= -x_1 + 2\dot{u} - u \\ y &= x_1 \end{aligned}$$

which are not of the form *16*. Similarly, on eliminating x_1 we obtain

$$\begin{aligned} \dot{x}_2 &= -x_2 + 2\dot{u} - 4u \\ y &= \tfrac{1}{2}(x_2 + 2u) \end{aligned}$$

which likewise do not have the form in question.

In citing this example we tacitly assume that there exists an interconnection of adders, scalors, integrators, and differentiators such that equations *19* are its state equations. The assumption is justified by the following

20 **Assertion** Given any set of equations of the form *14*, one can always construct an interconnection of adders, scalors, integrators, and differentiators whose state equations are given by *14*. ◁

The manner in which such an interconnection can be constructed is easily understood from the

21 *Example* Consider the set of equations

22
$$\begin{aligned} \dot{x}_1 &= x_1 + x_2 + \dot{x}_2 + u \\ \dot{x}_2 &= 2x_1 + 3x_2 + x_3 \\ x_3 &= 2x_1 + \dot{x}_3 - \dot{x}_4 \\ x_4 &= 2x_1 + u \\ y &= x_1 + \dot{x}_3 + \dot{x}_4 + u \end{aligned}$$

By inspection of the structure of the system $\mathfrak{B}$ shown in Fig. *4.6.9*, it is easy to verify that the state equations of $\mathfrak{B}$ are given by *22*. The reason for this lies in the nature of the procedure which we use to construct $\mathfrak{B}$. Essentially, it amounts to the following simple rule. With each equation in *14* associate a pure integrator or a pure differentiator according as the left-hand member is a component of $\dot{\mathbf{x}}_{\mathfrak{R}}$ or $\mathbf{x}_{\mathfrak{D}}$. Label the input of the ith integrator $\dot{x}_i$ and its output x_i. Similarly, label the input of the jth differentiator x_j and its output $\dot{x}_j$. Let the input to each differentiator and integrator be the output of an adder, the inputs to which are weighted combinations of $x_1, \ldots, x_n$ and $\dot{x}_1, \ldots, \dot{x}_n$, with each combination representing a row on the

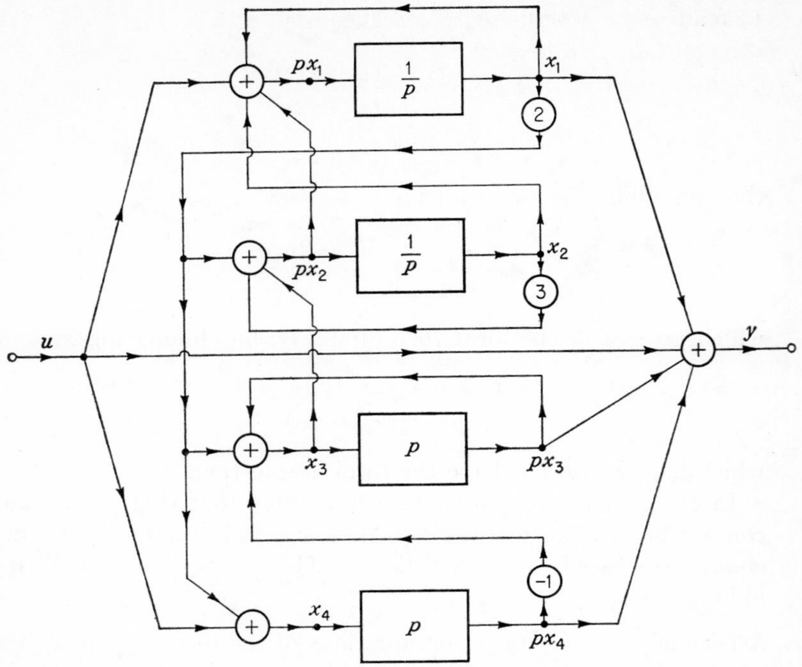

Fig. 4.6.9 System of Example *4.6.21*.

right-hand side of *14*. Finally, obtain y by forming the linear combination defined by the expression for y in *14*. ◁

In summary, Eqs. *14* cannot always be reduced to the canonical form merely by solving for $\dot{\mathbf{x}}$ and y in terms of $\mathbf{x}$ and u. However, as we shall see in Secs. *7* and *8*, it is always possible to replace $\mathcal{B}$ by an equivalent interconnection of adders, scalors, integrators, and differentiators whose state equations have the hybrid form (*4.5.45 et seq.*). Such a replacement can be interpreted as a linear change of variables $\mathbf{x} \rightarrow \mathbf{\Gamma x}'$ in which $\mathbf{x}$, $\mathbf{x}'$, and $\mathbf{\Gamma}$ play, respectively, the roles of $\mathbf{x}$, $\hat{\mathbf{x}}$, and $\mathbf{\Gamma}$ in *4.2.18*.

State equations for *RLC* networks

An *RLC* network, i.e., an electrical network comprising resistors, inductors, and capacitors, is a special case of an interconnection of adders, scalors, integrators and differentiators. Indeed, as will be shown in the sequel, any *RLC* network can be represented as an interconnection of adders, scalors, and integrators.[1]

More specifically, consider a network $\mathcal{A}$ such as is shown in Fig. *4.6.10*,

[1] We are tacitly assuming that the network in question is such that the corresponding interconnection does not contain scalors with infinite gain (see footnote on page 247). For more general treatment see Refs. *3* and *4*.

in which u ($\triangleq$ input voltage) is the input and y ($\triangleq$ output voltage) is the output. Note that $\mathcal{A}$ is an oriented system even though its components L_1, L_2, C_3, C_4, R_5, and R_6 are nonoriented.

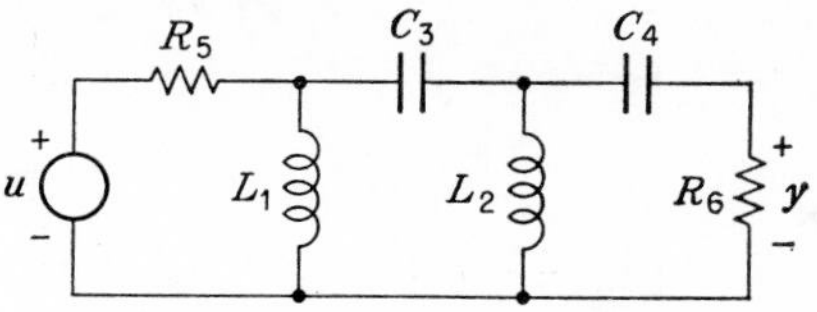

Fig. 4.6.10 An *RLC* network.

As was noted previously, the state equations *14* of an interconnection of scalors, adders, integrators, and differentiators assume the canonical form *18* when the interconnection in question does not contain differentiators. To achieve this condition in an electrical network comprising R's, L's, and C's, it is expedient to orient the L's and C's in such a way as to make them integrators. In concrete terms, this means that an inductor L characterized by

$$v = L\frac{di}{dt}$$

is oriented by identifying v with its input and i with its output. Similarly, a capacitor C defined by

$$i = C\frac{dv}{dt}$$

is oriented by making i its input and v its output. Correspondingly, the state of L at time t is taken to be $i(t)$ and that of C is taken to be $v(t)$.

Once $\mathcal{A}$ is oriented in this fashion, it becomes an interconnection of adders, scalors, and integrators to which we can apply Rule *2* and Procedure *10*. Rewording these in network terminology, we obtain the following rule for setting up the state equations of $\mathcal{A}$.

23 **Procedure** (I) Associate a state vector $\mathbf{x}$ with $\mathcal{A}$ by assigning components of $\mathbf{x}$ to the currents flowing through the inductors and the voltages appearing across the capacitors. (II) Replace each inductor L in $\mathcal{A}$ with a fictitious current source i_L, where $i_L \triangleq$ current flowing through L = state of L (Fig. *4.6.11a*). (III) Replace each capacitor C in $\mathcal{A}$ with a fictitious voltage source v_C, where $v_C \triangleq$ voltage across C = state of C (Fig. *4.6.11b*). (IV) As a result of these replacements, $\mathcal{A}$ is transformed into a network $\hat{\mathcal{A}}$ comprising only resistors, current sources, and voltage sources. (Observe that $\hat{\mathcal{A}}$ has the same significance as $\hat{\mathcal{B}}$ in *10*.) Find the output voltage appearing at the terminals of each fictitious current source i_L in $\mathcal{A}$ and equate it to $-Lpi_L$. Similarly, find the output current flowing through the terminals of each fictitious voltage source v_C in $\mathcal{A}$ and equate it to $-Cpv_C$. Finally, express the output y of $\mathcal{A}$ as a linear combination of all the voltage and

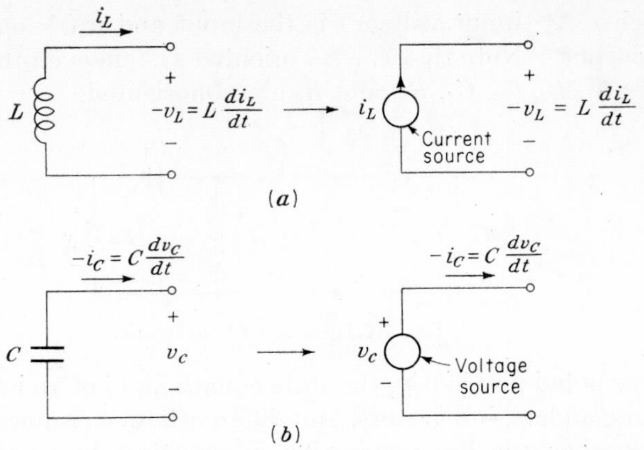

Fig. 4.6.11 (*a*) Replacement of an inductor by a current source, (*b*) replacement of a capacitor by a voltage source. (Note the polarities.)

current sources in 𝒜 (i.e., including both the fictitious and external sources). The resulting equations are the state equations of 𝒜.

24 *Example* Applying this procedure to the network of Fig. *4.6.10*, we associate with 𝒜 the state vector $\mathbf{x} = (i_1, i_2, v_3, v_4)$. Then, on replacing L's and C's by the corresponding current and voltage sources, we obtain the structure shown in Fig. *4.6.12*. Finally, using elementary

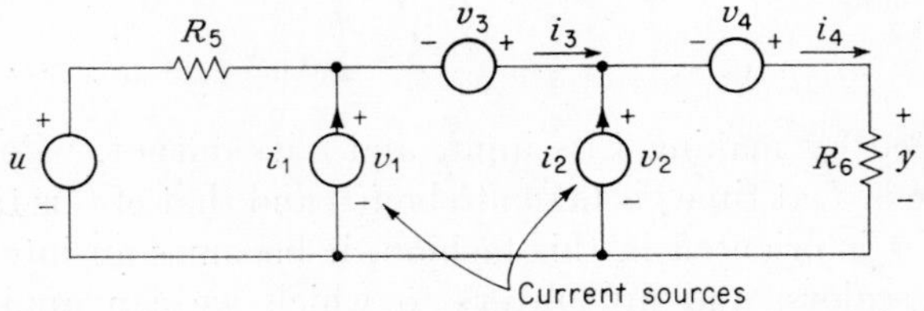

Fig. 4.6.12 The result of replacing inductors and capacitors in Fig. *4.6.10* by current and voltage sources.

circuit analysis techniques, we derive the following expressions for v_1, v_2, i_3, i_4, y:

$$-L_1 p i_1 = v_1 = \frac{1}{R_5 + R_6}(R_5R_6 i_1 + R_5R_6 i_2 - R_5 v_3 - R_5 v_4 + R_6 u)$$

$$-L_2 p i_2 = v_2 = \frac{1}{R_5 + R_6}(R_5R_6 i_1 + R_5R_6 i_2 + R_6 v_3 - R_5 v_4 + R_6 u)$$

$$-C_3 p v_3 = i_3 = \frac{1}{R_5 + R_6}(R_5 i_1 - R_6 i_2 + v_3 + v_4 + u)$$

$$-C_4 p v_4 = i_4 = \frac{1}{R_5 + R_6}(R_5 i_1 + R_5 i_2 + v_3 + v_4 + u)$$

$$y = \frac{1}{R_5 + R_6}(R_5R_6 i_1 + R_5R_6 i_2 + R_6 v_3 + R_6 v_4 + R_6 u)$$

which when equated to $-L_1pi_1, \ldots, y$, respectively, yield the desired state equations for $\mathcal{A}$.

25 **Remark** The technique described above is applicable also to time-varying networks. However, it should be noted that when L and C depend on time, their terminal relations assume the following form:

26 L: $$v(t) = \frac{d}{dt}(L(t)i(t))$$

27 C: $$i(t) = \frac{d}{dt}(C(t)v(t))$$

28 *Exercise* Extend Procedure 23 to the case of networks containing mutual inductors, in addition to R's, L's, and C's. (A mutual inductor is a nonoriented 4-pole characterized by the terminal relations

29 $$\begin{aligned} v_1 &= L_{11}pi_1 + L_{12}pi_2 \\ v_2 &= L_{21}pi_1 + L_{22}pi_2 \end{aligned}$$

where $L_{11}, \ldots, L_{22}$ are constants.)

7 *Equivalence relations and properties of zero-input response*

Suppose that we are given a system $\mathcal{A}$ which is characterized by a differential equation or a system of differential equations, or is represented as an interconnection of systems of simpler types such as scalors, adders, integrators, and differentiators. Assume that our problem is to associate a state vector $\mathbf{x}$ with $\mathcal{A}$ and find the corresponding state equations for $\mathcal{A}$. Instead of attacking this problem directly, it is frequently expedient to replace $\mathcal{A}$ by an equivalent system, say $\mathcal{B}$, and then associate a state vector $\hat{\mathbf{x}}$ with, and find the corresponding state equations for, $\mathcal{B}$ rather than $\mathcal{A}$. By virtue of the equivalence of $\mathcal{A}$ and $\mathcal{B}$, the state vector $\hat{\mathbf{x}}$ will also qualify as a state vector for $\mathcal{A}$, and so will the state equations satisfied by it. Clearly, if $\mathcal{B}$ is easier to deal with than $\mathcal{A}$ or if it is of a type with which we know how to associate a state vector—whereas $\mathcal{A}$ is not—then there may be a distinct advantage in using this approach over trying to associate a state vector with $\mathcal{A}$ by direct means.

To cite an example, suppose that $\mathcal{A}$ is characterized by a differential equation of the form $Ly = Mu$. As an alternative to the approach described in Sec. 5, one may try to find a realization for $\mathcal{A}$ in the form of an interconnection of adders, scalors, integrators, and differentiators and then associate a state vector with this realization by the use of the techniques of Sec. *6*. This is the basis for the so-called partial-fraction expansion technique which will be taken up in Sec. *9*.

For this as well as other reasons, it is important to have in hand a set of working rules for replacing a given system with one equivalent to it. The development of such rules is our main objective in this section.

A basic theorem

In Chap. *3* we established an important fact (*3.7.38*), namely, that a strictly proper time-invariant system $\mathcal{A}$ of finite order n admits the representation

1
$$\dot{\mathbf{x}} = \mathbf{A}\mathbf{x} + \mathbf{b}u$$
$$y = \langle \mathbf{c},\mathbf{x} \rangle$$

where $\mathbf{A}$ is a constant $n \times n$ matrix, $\mathbf{b}$ and $\mathbf{c}$ are constant vectors, and $\mathbf{x}$ is a state vector ranging over $\mathcal{C}^n$ ($\triangleq$ space of n-tuples of complex numbers). In what follows, we shall establish another important fact, namely, that any system characterized by *1* or, more generally, by the hybrid state equations (*4.5.45 et seq.*)

2
$$\dot{\mathbf{x}} = \mathbf{A}\mathbf{x} + \mathbf{b}u$$
$$y = \langle \mathbf{c},\mathbf{x} \rangle + D(p)u$$

where $D(p)$ is a differential operator, is equivalent to a system characterized by a single differential equation of the form $L(p)y = M(p)u$. These two facts add up to the conclusion that, *given any strictly proper*[1] *time-invariant system $\mathcal{A}$ of finite order, one can always find a differential system $\mathcal{B}$ which is equivalent to $\mathcal{A}$ and which is characterized by a single differential equation $L(p)y = M(p)u$.*

Our proof of the existence of such a $\mathcal{B}$ will be constructive in nature, i.e., given any $\mathcal{A}$, we shall be able to determine $L(p)$ and $M(p)$ such that the system $\frac{1}{L(p)} \cdot M(p)$ (see *4.5.9 et seq.*) is equivalent to $\mathcal{A}$. As a preliminary, we shall derive the expression for the transfer function and the Laplace transform of the zero-input response of a system characterized by *1* and establish a connection between them.

Relation between the transfer function and zero-input response

Let $\mathcal{A}$ be a system characterized by state equations of the form *1*, with $\mathbf{x}$ ranging over $\mathcal{C}^m$. To obtain the expression for the general solution

[1] The restriction to strictly proper systems is made here merely because *1* is proved in Chap. *3* only for such systems. Actually, as is pointed out there, it is not difficult to extend the result to improper systems.

of *1*, we apply the Laplace transformation to both sides of *1*, which yields

3 $$(s\mathbf{I} - \mathbf{A})\mathbf{X}(s) = \mathbf{x}(0-) + \mathbf{b}U(s)$$

4 $$Y(s) = \langle \mathbf{c}, \mathbf{X}(s) \rangle$$

where $\mathbf{I}$ is the $m \times m$ identity matrix, $U(s)$, $Y(s)$, and $\mathbf{X}(s)$ are the Laplace transforms of $u(t)$, $y(t)$, and $\mathbf{x}(t)$, respectively, and $\mathbf{x}(0-)$ is the initial state vector.

On eliminating $\mathbf{X}(s)$ from *3* and *4*, we obtain

5 $$Y(s) = \langle \mathbf{c}, (s\mathbf{I} - \mathbf{A})^{-1}\mathbf{x}(0-) \rangle + \langle \mathbf{c}, (s\mathbf{I} - \mathbf{A})^{-1}\mathbf{b}U(s) \rangle$$

where $(s\mathbf{I} - \mathbf{A})^{-1}$ denotes the inverse of the matrix $(s\mathbf{I} - \mathbf{A})$. This relation is in effect the desired expression for the general solution of *1* in the Laplace transform form. From *5*, the input-output-state relation for $\mathcal{A}$ can readily be derived by using the inverse Laplace transformation. For our present purposes, however, *5* will be sufficient. The input-output-state relation and the solution of state equations of the form *1* will be considered in detail in Chaps. *5* and *6*.

We note that the first term in *5* represents the Laplace transform of the zero-input response of $\mathcal{A}$. For convenience, we denote it by $Z(s;\mathbf{x}(0-))$:

6 $$Z(s;\mathbf{x}(0-)) = \langle \mathbf{c}, (s\mathbf{I} - \mathbf{A})^{-1}\mathbf{x}(0-) \rangle$$

The second term in *5* represents the Laplace transform of the zero-state response of $\mathcal{A}$ to u. Since the transfer function of $\mathcal{A}$ is the Laplace transform of the impulse response of $\mathcal{A}$—which in turn is the zero-state response of $\mathcal{A}$ to $\delta(t)$—and since $\mathcal{L}\{\delta(t)\} = 1$, it follows that the expression for the transfer function of $\mathcal{A}$ is[1]

7 $$H(s) = \langle \mathbf{c}, (s\mathbf{I} - \mathbf{A})^{-1}\mathbf{b} \rangle$$

We observe that $H(s)$ is related to $Z(s;\mathbf{x}(0-))$ in a very simple manner, namely,

8 $$H(s) = Z(s;\mathbf{b})$$

Thus, we can make the

9 **Assertion** Let $\mathcal{A}$ be a system characterized by the state equations

10 $$\dot{\mathbf{x}} = \mathbf{A}\mathbf{x} + \mathbf{b}u$$
$$y = \langle \mathbf{c}, \mathbf{x} \rangle$$

Then the transfer function of $\mathcal{A}$, $H(s)$, is the Laplace transform of the

[1] Our treatment of transfer functions in this section has the restricted objective of making it possible for us to formulate certain equivalence criteria for $\mathcal{A}$. A more general treatment of transfer functions and related questions is presented in Chap. *9*.

zero-input response of $\mathcal{A}$ starting in the state $\mathbf{x}(0-) = \mathbf{b}$. [Equivalently, the impulse response of $\mathcal{A}$, $h(t)$, is the zero-input response of $\mathcal{A}$ starting in $\mathbf{x}(0-) = \mathbf{b}$ (see also *45*).]

11 **Remark** Note that if $\mathcal{A}$ is a time-varying system in which $\mathbf{A}$ or $\mathbf{b}$ or $\mathbf{c}$ is time-dependent, it is still true that the *impulse response of* $\mathcal{A}$, $h(t,\xi)$ (see *3.6.5*), *is the zero-input response of* $\mathcal{A}$ *starting in* $\mathbf{x}(\xi-) = \mathbf{b}(\xi-)$. This is easily demonstrated without the use of the Laplace transformation by expressing $\dot{\mathbf{x}}$ as $-\mathbf{x}(\xi-)\delta(t-\xi) + p\,1(t-\xi)\mathbf{x}(t)$ (see *3.8.3 et seq.*) and noting that the impulse response $h(t,\xi)$ results when u is set equal to zero and $\mathbf{x}(\xi-) = \mathbf{b}(\xi-)$. ◁

We can draw useful results from Assertion *9* by examining $Z(s;\mathbf{x}(0-))$ and $H(s)$ in greater detail. Specifically, the matrix $(s\mathbf{I} - \mathbf{A})^{-1}$ has the form (before the cancellation of common factors in the numerator and denominator)

$$(s\mathbf{I} - \mathbf{A})^{-1} = \frac{\text{polynomial in } s \text{ of degree } m-1}{\det\,(s\mathbf{I} - \mathbf{A})}$$

where $\det\,(s\mathbf{I} - \mathbf{A})$ is $(-1)^m$ times the characteristic polynomial of $\mathbf{A}$ (see *C.18.1*). Consequently, $Z(s;\mathbf{x}(0-))$ and $H(s)$ must be of the form (before cancellation)

12 $$Z(s;\mathbf{x}(0-)) = \frac{r(s;\mathbf{x}(0-))}{d(s)}$$

13 $$H(s) = \frac{q(s)}{d(s)}$$

where $d(s) = \det\,(s\mathbf{I} - \mathbf{A})$, $q(s)$ is a polynomial of degree $m-1$, and $r(s;\mathbf{x}(0-))$ is a polynomial of degree $m-1$ whose coefficients are linear combinations of the components of $\mathbf{x}(0-)$. Furthermore, $r(s;\mathbf{b}) = q(s)$.

Let us reduce H and Z by canceling all common factors in $q(s)$ and $d(s)$, and $r(s;\mathbf{x}(0-))$ and $d(s)$, respectively, with the understanding that in Z we cancel only those factors which are common to $r(s;\mathbf{x}(0-))$ and $d(s)$ for all values of $\mathbf{x}(0-)$. In this way, Z and H are reduced to expressions of the form

14 $$Z(s;\mathbf{x}(0-)) = \frac{r'(s;\mathbf{x}(0-))}{d'(s)}$$

15 $$H(s) = \frac{q''(s)}{d''(s)}$$

where the primed and double-primed polynomials represent what is left of the original polynomials after cancellation.

16 **Remark** If the minimal polynomial of $\mathbf{A}$ (see *D.2.1*) is not identical with the characteristic polynomial of $\mathbf{A}$, then the ratio of the two will

be the greatest common divisor of $r(s;\mathbf{x}(0-))$ and $d(s)$ for all $\mathbf{x}(0-)$ (see *D.2.6*).

A basic lemma

The reduced form of $Z(s;\mathbf{x}(0-))$ has a basic property which is characteristic of time-invariant systems and which is frequently assumed to be true without proof. The statement and proof of this property are contained in the

17 **Lemma** Let $Z(s;\mathbf{x}(0-))$ be the Laplace transform of the zero-input response starting in state $\mathbf{x}(0-)$ of any linear time-invariant system $\mathcal{A}$. Suppose that after the cancellation of all factors common [for all $\mathbf{x}(0-)$] to the numerator and denominator of Z, the expression for $Z(s;\mathbf{x}(0-))$ in reduced form reads

18
$$Z(s;\mathbf{x}(0-)) = \frac{\alpha_1 s^{n-1} + \cdots + \alpha_{n-1}s + \alpha_n}{d'(s)} \triangleq Z'(s;\boldsymbol{\alpha})$$

where $d'(s)$ is a polynomial of degree n, the α_i, $i = 1, \ldots, n$, are coefficients dependent on $\mathbf{x}(0-)$, and the symbol $Z'(s;\boldsymbol{\alpha})$ is introduced to indicate that $Z(s;\mathbf{x}(0-))$ is in reduced form and that $Z(s;\mathbf{x}(0-))$ is expressed as a function of s and $\boldsymbol{\alpha} \triangleq (\alpha_1, \ldots, \alpha_n)$.

Then, for *every* $\boldsymbol{\alpha}$ in $\mathcal{C}^n$, $Z'(s;\boldsymbol{\alpha})$ is the Laplace transform of a zero-input response of $\mathcal{A}$. In other words, the α_i in *18* cannot be constrained to a subspace of $\mathcal{C}^n$ and, in particular, the numerator polynomial in *18* cannot have any of its powers missing for all values of $\boldsymbol{\alpha}$.

Proof The property in question is essentially a consequence of the time invariance of $\mathcal{A}$ and the superposability of zero-input responses (see *3.4.17*).

Specifically, the time invariance of $\mathcal{A}$ implies that, if z is a zero-input response of $\mathcal{A}$, then so is $\dot{z}$. To show this, write

19
$$\dot{\mathbf{x}} = \mathbf{A}\mathbf{x} \qquad u \equiv 0$$
$$z = \langle \mathbf{c},\mathbf{x} \rangle$$

which defines z to be a zero-input response $\mathcal{A}$. On differentiating both sides of *19* and denoting $\dot{\mathbf{x}}$ by $\mathbf{w}$, we have

$$\dot{\mathbf{w}} = \mathbf{A}\mathbf{w}$$
$$\dot{z} = \langle \mathbf{c},\mathbf{w} \rangle$$

which shows that $\dot{z}$ also satisfies *19* and hence, like z, is a zero-input response of $\mathcal{A}$. It is understood that, if z is interpreted as a one-sided response (see *3.6.45*), we do not include in $\dot{z}$ the delta function resulting from the differentiation of z at $t = 0$.

Consider now $Z'(s;\boldsymbol{\alpha})$. By the definition of $Z'(s;\boldsymbol{\alpha})$, *every* zero-input response of $\mathcal{A}$ can be obtained by assigning a particular value to $\boldsymbol{\alpha}$ in

$\mathcal{C}^n$. [For, $Z'(s;\boldsymbol{\alpha})$ is merely $Z(s;\mathbf{x}(0-))$, which in turn is the zero-input part of the Laplace transform of the general solution (see *4.5.16*).] What we want to show is the converse, namely, that for *every* $\boldsymbol{\alpha}$ in $\mathcal{C}^n$, $Z'(s;\boldsymbol{\alpha})$ is the Laplace transform of a zero-input response.

Suppose that this is not true, that is, $\boldsymbol{\alpha}$ is restricted to a subspace of $\mathcal{C}^n$, say $\mathcal{C}^k$, $k < n$. Then we can select a subset of components of $\boldsymbol{\alpha}$, say $\alpha_1, \ldots, \alpha_k$, such that all the components of $\boldsymbol{\alpha}$ can be represented as linear combinations of $\alpha_1, \ldots, \alpha_k$ and, furthermore, for *every* $\boldsymbol{\alpha} \triangleq (\alpha_1, \ldots, \alpha_k)$ in $\mathcal{C}^k$, $Z'(s;\boldsymbol{\alpha})$ is a zero-input response of $\mathcal{a}$.

Written out in terms of $\alpha_1, \ldots, \alpha_k$, $Z'(s;\boldsymbol{\alpha})$ assumes the following form:

20 $$Z'(s;\boldsymbol{\alpha}) = \frac{\alpha_1 p_1(s) + \alpha_2 p_2(s) + \cdots + \alpha_k p_k(s)}{d'(s)}$$

where $p_1(s), \ldots, p_k(s)$ are linearly independent polynomials in s of degree not exceeding $n - 1$. [Note that if the $p_i(s)$ were not linearly independent, then we could reduce k still further—which by hypothesis cannot be done.] Since $Z'(s;\boldsymbol{\alpha})$ is a zero-input response (in the Laplace transform form) for every $\boldsymbol{\alpha}' = (\alpha_1, \ldots, \alpha_k)$ in $\mathcal{C}^k$, it follows that

$$\frac{p_1(s)}{d'(s)}, \ldots, \frac{p_k(s)}{d'(s)}$$

are also zero-input responses [corresponding to

$$\boldsymbol{\alpha}' = (1,0, \ldots, 0), \ldots, (0,0, \ldots, 1)$$

respectively].

Let $z_j(t)$, $j = 1, \ldots, k$, denote the zero-input response of which $p_j(s)/d'(s)$ is the Laplace transform. Since $p_j(s)$ is a polynomial of degree not exceeding $n - 1$ [where n is the degree of $d'(s)$], we can always write by long division

21 $$\frac{sp_j(s)}{d'(s)} = \gamma_j + \frac{q_j(s)}{d'(s)}$$

where $q_j(s)$, the remainder, is a polynomial of degree not exceeding $n - 1$ and γ_j is a constant which vanishes when the degree of $p_j(s)$ is lower than $n - 1$.

We can interpret *21* as follows. $q_j(s)/d'(s)$ is the Laplace transform of the derivative of $z_j(t)$, with the delta-function term $\gamma_j\delta(t)$ not included. In accordance with our understanding, then (see *19 et seq.*), $q_j(s)/d'(s)$ is the Laplace transform of $\dot{z}_j(t)$, $j = 1, \ldots, k$.

Since $\dot{z}_j(t)$ is a zero-input response of $\mathcal{a}$ and since the Laplace transform of every zero-input response of $\mathcal{a}$ is of the form *20*, we must have

22 $$\frac{q_j(s)}{d'(s)} = \frac{\alpha_1^j p_1(s) + \cdots + \alpha_k^j p_k(s)}{d'(s)} \qquad j = 1, \ldots, k$$

On replacing $q_j(s)$ in *22* by

$$q_j(s) = sp_j(s) - \gamma_j d'(s)$$

(which results from *21*), and clearing $d'(s)$, we obtain a set of relations between the $p_j(s)$ and $d'(s)$ which read

23
$$\begin{aligned}(s - \alpha_1^1)p_1(s) - \alpha_2^1 p_2(s) - \cdots - \alpha_k^1 p_k(s) &= \gamma_1 d'(s) \\ \cdots\cdots\cdots\cdots\cdots\cdots\cdots\cdots\cdots\cdots\cdots\cdots \\ -\alpha_1^k p_1(s) - \alpha_2^k p_2(s) - \cdots + (s - \alpha_k^k)p_k(s) &= \gamma_k d'(s)\end{aligned}$$

We note that not all $\gamma_1, \ldots, \gamma_k$ can be zero in *23*, for this would be inconsistent with the linear independence of the $p_j(s)$ (see *20*). Thus, on solving these equations for the $p_j(s)$ by the Cramer rule, we obtain expressions of the form

24
$$p_j(s) = d'(s)\,\frac{r_j(s)}{\Delta(s)}$$

where

25
$$\Delta(s) = \begin{vmatrix} s - \alpha_1^1 & -\alpha_2^1 & \cdots & -\alpha_k^1 \\ \cdots & \cdots & \cdots & \cdots \\ -\alpha_1^k & -\alpha_2^k & \cdots & (s - \alpha_k^k) \end{vmatrix}$$

is a polynomial of degree not exceeding k and $r_j(s)$ is a polynomial of degree not exceeding $k - 1$.

Finally, on substituting *24* and *25* in *20*, and canceling $d'(s)$, we obtain the following expression for the Laplace transform of the zero-input response:

26
$$Z'(s;\boldsymbol{\alpha}) = \frac{(\alpha_1 r_1(s) + \cdots + \alpha_k r_k(s))}{\Delta(s)}$$

in which the degree of the numerator does not exceed $k - 1$ and hence is lower than $n - 1$ (since $k < n$) and the degree of the denominator does not exceed k and hence is lower than n. This implies that there is a common factor in the numerator and denominator of $Z'(s;\boldsymbol{\alpha})$ (as given by *20*) which upon cancellation leads to *26*. This contradicts the hypothesis that $Z'(s;\boldsymbol{\alpha})$ is in reduced form and thus proves the lemma.

An immediate consequence of Lemma *17* is the

27 **Corollary** The basis functions of $\mathcal{A}$ (see *4.5.23*) can be taken to be (in the Laplace transform form)

$$\frac{s^{n-1}}{d'(s)}, \ \ldots, \ \frac{s}{d'(s)}, \frac{1}{d'(s)}$$

where $d'(s)$ is the denominator of the reduced form of the Laplace transform of the zero-input response of $\mathcal{A}$ and n is the degree of $d'(s)$.

[This follows from the linear independence of the functions in question and the fact just established, namely, that for every $\boldsymbol{\alpha} \in \mathcal{C}^n$, $Z'(s;\boldsymbol{\alpha})$ is a zero-input response function (in the Laplace transform form).] [Note that we could not have made this assertion before proving Lemma *17*, for we could not rule out the possibility that some of the powers of s might be missing in the numerator of $Z'(s;\mathbf{x}(0-))$ (*18*) for all values of $\mathbf{x}(0-)$.] ◁

In changing from these basis functions to another set, say $\Phi_1(s)$, . . . , $\Phi_n(s)$, it is frequently helpful to invoke the following

28 **Assertion** Let $Z'(s;\boldsymbol{\alpha})$ be the Laplace transform (in reduced form) of the zero-input response of $\mathfrak{a}$ starting from a state $\boldsymbol{\alpha}$ in $\mathcal{C}^n$. If for every $\boldsymbol{\alpha} \in \mathcal{C}^n$ we can represent $Z'(s;\boldsymbol{\alpha})$ in the form

29
$$Z'(s;\boldsymbol{\alpha}) = \beta_1\Phi_1(s) + \cdots + \beta_n\Phi_n(s)$$

where $\Phi_1(s)$, . . . , $\Phi_n(s)$ are linearly independent functions of s, then $\Phi_1(s)$, . . . , $\Phi_n(s)$ qualify as a set of basis functions for $\mathfrak{a}$ (in the Laplace transform form) and the vectors $\boldsymbol{\beta} = (\beta_1, \ldots, \beta_n)$ and $\boldsymbol{\alpha} = (\alpha_1, \ldots, \alpha_n)$ are in one-one correspondence with each other.

Proof By hypothesis, every zero-input response of $\mathfrak{a}$ can be written (in the Laplace transform form)

30
$$Z'(s;\boldsymbol{\alpha}) = \alpha_1 \frac{s^{n-1}}{d'(s)} + \cdots + \alpha_n \frac{1}{d'(s)}$$

Consequently, to every n-tuple $(\beta_1, \ldots, \beta_n)$ which can result from the expansion of $Z'(s;\boldsymbol{\alpha})$ in the form *29* there will correspond an $\boldsymbol{\alpha}$ in $\mathcal{C}^n$ such that

31
$$\alpha_1 \frac{s^{n-1}}{d'(s)} + \cdots + \alpha_n \frac{1}{d'(s)} \equiv \beta_1\Phi_1(s) + \cdots + \beta_n\Phi_n(s)$$

Conversely, by Lemma *17*, for every $\boldsymbol{\alpha}$ in $\mathcal{C}^n$, *30* represents the Laplace transform of a zero-input response of $\mathfrak{a}$; therefore, to every $\boldsymbol{\alpha}$ in $\mathcal{C}^n$ there corresponds a $\boldsymbol{\beta}$ in $\mathcal{C}^n$ such that *31* is satisfied. This implies that

32
$$\boldsymbol{\beta} = \boldsymbol{\alpha}\boldsymbol{\Gamma} \qquad \forall \boldsymbol{\alpha} \in \mathcal{C}^n$$

where $\boldsymbol{\Gamma}$ is an $n \times n$ constant matrix which associates a $\boldsymbol{\beta}$ to each $\boldsymbol{\alpha}$. (Note that this $\boldsymbol{\Gamma}$ has the same significance as in *4.2.25*.)

On denoting

33
$$\boldsymbol{\phi}(s) \triangleq (\Phi_1(s), \ldots, \Phi_n(s))$$
$$\hat{\boldsymbol{\phi}}(s) \triangleq \left(\frac{s^{n-1}}{d'(s)}, \ldots, \frac{1}{d'(s)}\right)$$

and substituting *32* in *31*, we have

$$\langle \boldsymbol{\alpha}, (\hat{\boldsymbol{\phi}}(s) - \boldsymbol{\Gamma}\boldsymbol{\phi}(s)) \rangle \equiv 0 \qquad \forall \boldsymbol{\alpha} \in \mathcal{C}^n$$

which implies that

34 $$\hat{\boldsymbol{\phi}}(s) - \boldsymbol{\Gamma}\Phi(s) \equiv 0$$

Now both $\Phi_1(s), \ldots, \Phi_n(s)$ and $s^{n-1}/d'(s), \ldots, 1/d'(s)$ are linearly independent sets of functions. Consequently, the matrix $\boldsymbol{\Gamma}$ in *32* must be of rank n. This implies that the correspondence between $\boldsymbol{\alpha}$ and $\boldsymbol{\beta}$ is one-one and hence that, for *every* $\boldsymbol{\beta}$ in $\mathcal{C}^n$, *29* represents the Laplace transform of a zero-input response of $\mathcal{A}$. Furthermore, from *34* and the nonsingularity of $\boldsymbol{\Gamma}$ it follows that every basis function $s^{\lambda-1}/d'(s)$ is a linear combination of $\Phi_1(s), \ldots, \Phi_n(s)$ and, conversely, every $\Phi_i(s)$ is a linear combination of $s^{n-1}/d'(s), \ldots, 1/d'(s)$. Consequently, $\Phi_1(s), \ldots, \Phi_n(s)$ qualify as a set of basis functions for $\mathcal{A}$. Q.E.D.

We can make an immediate application of this result to the partial-fraction expansion of $Z'(s;\boldsymbol{\alpha})$. Thus, suppose that

35 $$Z'(s;\boldsymbol{\alpha}) = \frac{\alpha_1 s^{n-1} + \cdots + \alpha_n}{(s-\lambda_1)^{\mu_1} \cdots (s-\lambda_p)^{\mu_p}} \qquad \mu_1 + \cdots + \mu_p = n$$

where the λ's denote the zeros of $d'(s)$ and the μ's are their multiplicities.

On expanding $Z'(s;\boldsymbol{\alpha})$ into partial fractions, we obtain an expression of the general form

36 $$\begin{aligned} Z'(s;\boldsymbol{\alpha}) = {} & \frac{\beta_1^1}{(s-\lambda_1)^{\mu_1}} + \frac{\beta_2^1}{(s-\lambda_1)^{\mu_1-1}} + \cdots + \frac{\beta_{\mu_1}^1}{(s-\lambda_1)} \\ & + \cdots\cdots\cdots\cdots\cdots\cdots \\ & + \frac{\beta_1^p}{(s-\lambda_p)^{\mu_p}} + \frac{\beta_2^p}{(s-\lambda_p)^{\mu_p-1}} + \cdots + \frac{\beta_{\mu_p}^p}{(s-\lambda_p)} \end{aligned}$$

Clearly, the n functions

37 $$\begin{gathered} \frac{1}{(s-\lambda_1)^{\mu_1}}, \ldots, \frac{1}{(s-\lambda_1)} \\ \cdots\cdots\cdots\cdots \\ \frac{1}{(s-\lambda_p)^{\mu_p}}, \ldots, \frac{1}{(s-\lambda_p)} \end{gathered}$$

are linearly independent. Hence by Assertion *28* they qualify as a set of basis functions (in the Laplace transform form) for $\mathcal{A}$.

38 *Example* Suppose that $Z'(s;\boldsymbol{\alpha})$ is given by

$$Z'(s;\boldsymbol{\alpha}) = \frac{\alpha_1 s^4 + \alpha_2 s^3 + \alpha_3 s^2 + \alpha_4 s + \alpha_5}{(s+1)^2(s+2)^2(s+3)}$$

Then the functions

$$\frac{1}{(s+1)^2}, \frac{1}{(s+1)}, \frac{1}{(s+2)^2}, \frac{1}{(s+2)}, \frac{1}{(s+3)}$$

qualify as a set of basis functions for $\mathcal{A}$.

Relation between $Z(s;\mathbf{x}(0-))$ and $H(s)$

We are now prepared to resume our discussion of the relation between $Z(s;\mathbf{x}(0-))$ (*12*) and the transfer function $H(s)$ (*13*). Specifically, we note that if a factor, say $(s - a)$, is canceled from the numerator and denominator of $Z(s;\mathbf{x}(0-))$, then it will also be canceled from the numerator and denominator of $H(s)$, since (I) the numerator of $H(s)$ ($\triangleq q(s)$) is merely the numerator of $Z(s;\mathbf{x}(0-))$ ($\triangleq r(s;\mathbf{x}(0-))$) with $\mathbf{x}(0-)$ replaced by $\mathbf{b}$; and (II) no factor is canceled in Z unless it is a common factor for *all* values of $\mathbf{x}(0-)$. This observation leads to the following

39 **Lemma** If the transfer function $H(s)$ and the Laplace transform of the zero-input response $Z(s)$ are in reduced form, then the denominator of $H(s)$ divides the denominator of $Z(s)$. In symbols, this means that

40 $$d'(s) = \rho(s)d''(s)$$

where $\rho(s)$ is a polynomial in s. For reasons that will become clear later, we shall refer to $\rho(s)$ as the *restoring factor*. ◁

We can use this lemma to derive a somewhat more explicit relation between the impulse response and the zero-input response than we did previously (*9*). Specifically, we had found that the impulse response, $h(t)$, may be identified with the zero-input response of $\mathcal{A}$ starting in state $\mathbf{b}$. We have also found (Lemma *17*) that, after reduction, the Laplace transform of the zero-input response admits the representation

41 $$Z'(s;\boldsymbol{\alpha}) = \alpha_1\Phi_1(s) + \cdots + \alpha_n\Phi_n(s)$$

where $\Phi_1(s), \ldots, \Phi_n(s)$ are a set of basis functions of $\mathcal{A}$ (in the Laplace transform form) and the vector $\boldsymbol{\alpha} = (\alpha_1, \ldots, \alpha_n)$ ranges over $\mathcal{C}^n$. [Correspondingly, the zero-input response $z(t)$ reads

42 $$z(t) = \alpha_1\phi_1(t) + \cdots + \alpha_n\phi_n(t) \qquad t \geq 0$$

where the basis functions $\phi_1(t), \ldots, \phi_n(t)$ are the inverse Laplace transforms of $\Phi_1(s), \ldots, \Phi_n(s)$, respectively.]

Now we can choose $\Phi_1(s), \ldots, \Phi_n(s)$ to be the functions given by *37*. Then, Lemma *39* implies that the partial-fraction expansion of the transfer function $H(s)$ must necessarily be of the form

43 $$H(s) = \gamma_1\Phi_1(s) + \cdots + \gamma_n\Phi_n(s)$$

where the γ_i, $i = 1, \ldots, n$, are constants such that $\gamma_i = 0$ if the factor corresponding to $\Phi_i(s)$ is present in $d'(s)$ but not in $d''(s)$ (see *39*). On the basis of this conclusion, we can make the

44 **Assertion** Let $\phi_1(t), \ldots, \phi_n(t)$ be the set of basis functions of a proper system $\mathcal{A}$ which are yielded by the partial-fraction expansion of $Z(s;\mathbf{x}(0-))$, the Laplace transform of the zero-input response of $\mathcal{A}$. Then the impulse response of $\mathcal{A}$ admits the representation

45 $$h(t) = \gamma_1\phi_1(t) + \cdots + \gamma_n\phi_n(t)$$

where the γ_i, $i = 1, \ldots, n$, are constants, with $\gamma_i = 0$ if $\Phi_i(s)$ is present in the partial-fraction expansion of $Z(s;\mathbf{x}(0-))$ but not in $H(s)$. [Note that the partial-fraction expansions of $Z(s;\mathbf{x}(0-))$ and $Z'(s;\boldsymbol{\alpha})$ are identical. The same statement applies to $H(s)$ and $H'(s)$.]

46 *Comment* To extend this assertion to an improper system, it is necessary to make a modification in *45*. Specifically, if $\mathcal{A}$ is an improper system, it can be decomposed into a strictly proper system $\hat{\mathcal{A}}$ and a system of the differential operator type $\mathfrak{D}$ which is characterized by an input-output relation of the form (see *4.5.50*)

47 $$w = (d_0 + d_1p + \cdots + d_kp^k)u$$

Now let $\phi_1(t), \ldots, \phi_n(t)$ be a set of basis functions for $\hat{\mathcal{A}}$. Then, using Assertion *44* and *47*, the impulse response of $\mathcal{A}$ can be expressed as

48 $$h(t) = \gamma_1\phi_1(t) + \cdots + \gamma_n\phi_n(t) + d_0\delta(t) + d_1\delta^{(1)}(t) + \cdots + d_k\delta^{(k)}(t)$$

By Assertion *28* and Assertion *44*, the functions $\phi_1(t), \ldots, \phi_n(t)$, $\delta(t), \ldots, \delta^{(k-1)}(t)$ constitute a set of basis functions for $\mathcal{A}$. In terms of these functions, *48* is an expression of the same general form as *45*, except for the last term $\delta^{(k)}(t)$—which is the derivative of the basis function $\delta^{(k-1)}(t)$. Consequently, we can conclude that when $\mathcal{A}$ is an improper system, its impulse response admits of the representation

49 $$h(t) = \gamma_1\phi_1(t) + \cdots + \gamma_n\phi_n(t) + d_0\phi_{n+1}(t) + \cdots + d_{k-1}\phi_{n+k}(t) + d_k\dot{\phi}_{n+k}(t)$$

where $\phi_\lambda(t) = \delta^{(\lambda-n-1)}(t)$, $\lambda = n+1, \ldots, n+k$.

Determination of a system equivalent to $\mathcal{A}$

We are now ready to apply the results derived above to the following basic

50 *Problem* Let $\mathcal{A}$ be a system characterized by the state equations

51 $$\dot{\mathbf{x}} = \mathbf{A}\mathbf{x} + \mathbf{b}u$$
$$y = \langle \mathbf{c},\mathbf{x} \rangle$$

Find a system $\mathcal{B}$ characterized by a single differential equation of the form

$$L(p)y = M(p)u$$

such that $\mathcal{B}$ is equivalent to $\mathcal{A}$.

To solve this problem, we recall (*3.5.10*) that two linear systems $\mathcal{A}$ and $\mathcal{B}$ are equivalent if (I) $\mathcal{A}$ and $\mathcal{B}$ are zero-state equivalent—i.e., have the same transfer function—and (II) $\mathcal{A}$ and $\mathcal{B}$ are zero-input equivalent—i.e., have the same basis functions (or, more generally, are such that every basis function of $\mathcal{A}$ is expressible as a linear combination of basis functions of $\mathcal{B}$, and vice versa).

This fact, in conjunction with the results derived in the preceding subsection, leads us to a theorem which constitutes a solution to the problem before us.

52 **Theorem** Let $\mathcal{A}$ be a system characterized by *51* and let its transfer function $H_a(s)$ be (in reduced form)

53
$$H_a(s) = \frac{\tilde{M}(s)}{\tilde{L}(s)}$$

[Note that $\tilde{M}(s)$ and $\tilde{L}(s)$ correspond to $q''(s)$ and $d''(s)$ in *15*.] Furthermore, let the denominator of the Laplace transform of the zero-input response of $\mathcal{A}$ (in reduced form) be $\rho(s)\tilde{L}(s)$, where $\rho(s)$ is a polynomial in s (see *39*) and $\rho(s)\tilde{L}(s)$ is a polynomial of degree n in s. Then the system $\mathcal{B}$ characterized by the input-output relation

54
$$L(p)y = M(p)u$$

in which $L(p)$ and $M(p)$ are polynomials in p given by the products

55
$$L(p) = \rho(p)\tilde{L}(p)$$
$$M(p) = \rho(p)\tilde{M}(p)$$

is equivalent to $\mathcal{A}$.

Proof In the first place, $\mathcal{A}$ and $\mathcal{B}$ are zero-state equivalent, since, by construction, the transfer function of $\mathcal{B}$ is

$$\begin{aligned} H_b(s) &= \frac{M(s)}{L(s)} \\ &= \frac{\rho(s)\tilde{L}(s)}{\rho(s)\tilde{M}(s)} = \frac{\tilde{L}(s)}{\tilde{M}(s)} \\ &= H_a(s) \end{aligned}$$

In the second place, the basis functions of $\mathcal{B}$ can be taken to be (in the Laplace transform form) (see *4.5.26*)

$$\frac{s^{n-1}}{L(s)}, \ldots, \frac{s}{L(s)}, \frac{1}{L(s)}$$

But these are also the basis functions of $\mathcal{A}$ (see *27*): thus, $\mathcal{A}$ and $\mathcal{B}$ are both zero-input equivalent and zero-state equivalent, and hence are equivalent. Q.E.D.

56 *Comment* The importance of this theorem stems from the fact that it provides us with an effective technique for replacing a given differential system $\mathcal{A}$ with an equivalent system $\mathcal{B}$ which is characterized by a single differential equation.

The crux of the idea behind the technique in question is this. Given a system $\mathcal{A}$, it is generally a simple matter to find its transfer function $H_a(s)$. Now suppose that after determining $H_a(s)$ (in reduced form) as the ratio of two polynomials $\tilde{L}(s)$ and $\tilde{M}(s)$, we define a system $\tilde{\mathcal{B}}$ by the input-output relation

57 $$\tilde{L}(p)y = \tilde{M}(p)u$$

Clearly, the transfer function of $\tilde{\mathcal{B}}$ is identical with that of $\mathcal{A}$. However, this in itself does not allow us to conclude that $\tilde{\mathcal{B}}$ is equivalent to $\mathcal{A}$, since the basis functions of $\mathcal{A}$ and $\tilde{\mathcal{B}}$ may be different. Thus, our problem is to modify $\tilde{\mathcal{B}}$ in such a way as to leave its transfer function unchanged, while at the same time making its basis functions identical with those of $\mathcal{A}$.

We achieve this result by finding the "restoring factor" $\rho(s)$ which accounts for the canceled factors in $H_a(s)$. Once $\rho(s)$ is determined, we form the "restored" transfer function

$$H_b(s) = \frac{\rho(s)}{\rho(s)} H_a(s) = \frac{\rho(s)\tilde{M}(s)}{\rho(s)\tilde{L}(s)}$$

and define a corresponding differential system $\mathcal{B}$ by the input-output relation

$$L(p)y = M(p)u$$

where

58 $$L(p) = \rho(p)\tilde{L}(p)$$
$$M(p) = \rho(p)\tilde{M}(p)$$

In this way, we obtain a system $\mathcal{B}$ which has both the same transfer function and the same basis functions as $\mathcal{A}$ and hence is equivalent to $\mathcal{A}$.

This explains the reason for calling $\rho(s)$ the restoring factor for $\mathcal{A}$. For the same reason, the technique provided by Theorem *52* for finding a system $\mathcal{B}$ which is characterized by a single differential equation and which is equivalent to a given system $\mathcal{A}$ will be termed the "restoration technique."

Although in the statement of Theorem *52* $\mathcal{A}$ is assumed to be a strictly proper system, both the theorem and the restoration technique which is based on it are applicable to any type of differential system.

The way in which the restoration technique is applied in various situations is illustrated by the following examples.

59 *Example* Consider a system $\mathcal{A}$ which is characterized by the state equations *51*, with

$$\mathbf{A} = \begin{bmatrix} -1 & 0 & 0 \\ 1 & -2 & 0 \\ 0 & 0 & -4 \end{bmatrix} \qquad \mathbf{b} = \begin{bmatrix} 1 \\ 0 \\ 0 \end{bmatrix} \qquad \mathbf{c} = [1 \quad -2 \quad 1]$$

In this case,

$$(s\mathbf{I} - \mathbf{A})^{-1} = \frac{1}{(s+1)(s+2)(s+4)} \begin{bmatrix} (s+2)(s+4) & 0 & 0 \\ s+4 & (s+1)(s+4) & 0 \\ 0 & 0 & (s+1)(s+2) \end{bmatrix}$$

and the Laplace transform of the zero-input response is given by

$$\begin{aligned} Z(s;\mathbf{x}(0-)) &= \langle \mathbf{c}, (s\mathbf{I} - \mathbf{A})^{-1}\mathbf{x}(0-) \rangle \\ &= \frac{s}{(s+1)(s+2)} x_1(0-) - \frac{2}{(s+2)} x_2(0-) \\ &\qquad + \frac{1}{(s+4)} x_3(0-) \\ &= \frac{\alpha_1 s^2 + \alpha_2 s + \alpha_3}{(s+1)(s+2)(s+4)} \\ &= Z'(s;\boldsymbol{\alpha}) \end{aligned}$$

Note that the numerator and the denominator of $Z(s;\mathbf{x}(0-))$ have no common factors for all $\mathbf{x}(0-)$ and hence $Z(s;\mathbf{x}(0-))$ is in reduced form.

Now the transfer function $H(s)$ is expressed by

$$\begin{aligned} H(s) &= Z(s;\mathbf{b}) \qquad \mathbf{b} = (1,0,0) \\ &= \frac{s}{(s+1)(s+2)} \end{aligned}$$

and hence the restoring factor $\rho(s)$ is given by

$$\rho(s) = (s+4)$$

Making use of *55*, the differential equation characterizing the equivalent system $\mathcal{B}$ is found to be

$$(p+1)(p+2)(p+4)y = (p+4)u$$

60 *Example* Consider an improper system $\mathcal{A}$ which is characterized by state equations of the form

$$\begin{aligned} x_1 &= u \\ \dot{x}_2 &= 0 \\ \dot{x}_3 &= x_2 - x_3 \\ y &= \dot{x}_1 + x_3 \end{aligned}$$

On applying the Laplace transformation to these equations and setting $u = 0$, we find the following expression for the Laplace transform of the zero-input response:

$$Z(s;\boldsymbol{\alpha}) = \frac{\alpha_1 s + \alpha_2}{s(s+1)}$$

where α_1 and α_2 are constants depending on $x_1(0-)$, $x_2(0-)$, and $x_3(0-)$.

On the other hand, on setting $x_1(0-) = x_2(0-) = x_3(0-) = 0$ and forming the ratio

$$H(s) = \frac{Y(s)}{U(s)}$$

where $Y(s)$ and $U(s)$ are the Laplace transforms of y and u, respectively, we have

$$H(s) = s$$

In this case, the restoring factor is given by

$$\rho(s) = s(s+1)$$

and hence the equivalent system $\mathfrak{B}$ is characterized by the differential equation

$$p(p+1)y = p^2(p+1)u$$

61 *Example* Let $\mathfrak{A}$ be represented by an interconnection of scalors, adders, integrators, and differentiators such as shown in Fig. *4.7.1*. The

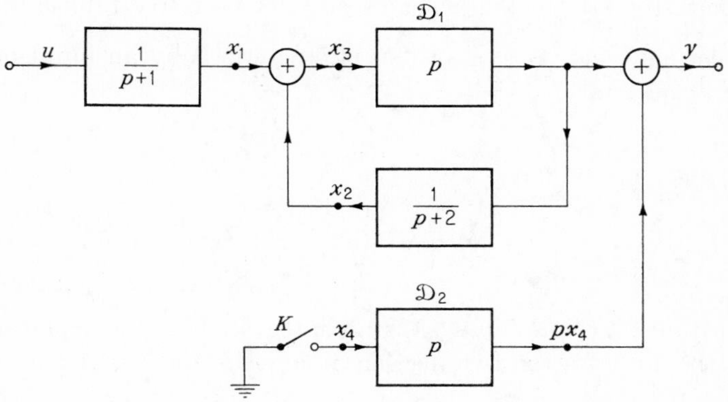

Fig. 4.7.1 System of Example *4.7.61*.

problem is to find an equivalent system $\mathfrak{B}$ which is characterized by a single differential equation.

We associate a state vector $\mathbf{x} \triangleq (x_1,x_2,x_3,x_4)$ with $\mathfrak{A}$ by the use of Rule *4.6.2*. The input to $\mathfrak{D}_2$ is assumed to be $x_4(0-)$ at $t = 0-$ and zero for $t \geq 0$. This is represented graphically by the switch K which "grounds" the input to $\mathfrak{D}_2$ starting at $t = 0$.

By using Procedure *4.6.10*, the state equations of $\mathfrak{A}$ are readily found to be

$$\begin{aligned} \dot{x}_1 &= -x_1 + u \\ x_3 &= x_1 + x_2 \\ \dot{x}_2 &= -2x_2 + \dot{x}_3 \\ x_4 &= 0 \qquad t \geq 0 \\ y &= \dot{x}_4 + \dot{x}_3 \end{aligned}$$

On applying the Laplace transformation to these equations (with $u = 0$ for $t \geq 0$), and solving for the Laplace transform of the zero-input response, we have

$$Z(s;\mathbf{x}(0-)) = -\frac{x_1(0-)}{2(s+1)} + \tfrac{1}{2}x_1(0-) - x_3(0-) - x_4(0-)$$

On the other hand,

$$H(s) = \left.\frac{Y(s)}{U(s)}\right]_{\mathbf{x}(0-)=0} = \frac{s(s+2)}{2(s+1)}$$

In this case $\rho(s) = 1$ and hence $\mathfrak{B}$ is characterized by

$$2(p+1)y = p(p+2)u$$

Note that $\mathfrak{A}$ is an improper system.

Equivalence between integrodifferential and differential systems

The restoration technique can readily be used to establish the following

62 **Assertion** Let $\mathfrak{A}$ be a system characterized by an input-output relation of the form

63
$$\left(a_n p^n + \cdots + a_0 + \frac{a'_0}{p} + \cdots + \frac{a'_{n'}}{p^{n'}}\right) y = \left(b_m p^m + \cdots + b_0 + \frac{b'_0}{p} + \cdots + \frac{b'_{m'}}{p^{m'}}\right) u$$

where $a_n, \ldots, a_0, a'_0, \ldots, a'_{n'}$ and $b_m, \ldots, b_0, b'_0, \ldots, b'_{m'}$ are constants. (Note that *63* is an integrodifferential equation.) Let r be the larger of the two integers n' and m', that is,

64
$$r \triangleq \max(n',m')$$

Then $\mathfrak{A}$ is a system of order $r + \max(m,n)$ (see *3.6.39*), and $\mathfrak{A}$ is equivalent to the system $\mathfrak{B}$ characterized by the single differential equation

65
$$(a_n p^{n+r} + \cdots + a'_{n'} p^{r-n'})y = (b_m p^{m+r} + \cdots + b'_{m'} p^{r-m'})u$$

66 *Comment* In effect, this assertion legitimizes the commonly used procedure of acting on both sides of an integrodifferential equation with the operator p^r and replacing the product $p^r \cdot \frac{1}{p^\lambda}$ by $p^{r-\lambda}$. While it is true (by *4.4.48*) that $p^r \cdot \frac{1}{p^\lambda}$ is equivalent to $p^{r-\lambda}$ (in the sense of system equivalence), this in itself does not prove that $\mathcal{B}$ is equivalent to $\mathcal{A}$. The reason for this is that when we act on both sides of a differential or an integrodifferential equation with, say, p, the resulting equation characterizes a system which contains the original system (in the sense of Definition *2.5.1*) but is not necessarily equivalent to it.

Assertion *62* can be proved in several ways. A straightforward way is to apply the Laplace transformation to both sides of *63* and *65* and verify that the input-output-state relations of $\mathcal{A}$ and $\mathcal{B}$ (in the Laplace transform form) are identical. It is simpler, however, to use the restoration technique in the manner of Example *59*.

We leave the details of the proof as an exercise for the reader. ◁

In addition to the results concerning system equivalence which were established in the foregoing presentation, we shall need several more bearing on the equivalence between a system $\mathcal{A}$ and an interconnection of adders, scalors, integrators, and differentiators. These results are deduced in the following section.

8 *Further equivalence properties of time-invariant systems*

Let $\mathcal{A}$ be a system of order r characterized by an input-output relation of the form

1 $$L(p)y = M(p)u$$

where

2 $$\begin{aligned} L(p) &= a_n p^n + \cdots + a_0 \\ M(p) &= b_m p^m + \cdots + b_0 \\ r &= \max(m,n) \end{aligned}$$

Let $\mathcal{B}$ be a realization of $\mathcal{A}$ in the form of an interconnection of adders, scalors, integrators, and differentiators. Then, by the definition of a realization of $\mathcal{A}$, $\mathcal{A}$ and $\mathcal{B}$ are equivalent systems (see *2.5.19*).

To show that $\mathcal{B}$ is a realization of $\mathcal{A}$, we have to demonstrate that (I) $\mathcal{A}$ and $\mathcal{B}$ are zero-state equivalent and (II) $\mathcal{A}$ and $\mathcal{B}$ are zero-input equivalent. The verification of (I) is, in general, a simple matter, since to show that $\mathcal{A}$ and $\mathcal{B}$ are zero-state equivalent, it suffices to verify that $H_a(s)$, the transfer function of $\mathcal{A}$, is identical with $H_b(s)$, the transfer function of $\mathcal{B}$. The verification of (II), on the other hand, is a relatively cumbersome and not altogether straightforward problem. Thus, it is desirable to have criteria under which $\mathcal{B}$ can be asserted to be a realization of $\mathcal{A}$ without the necessity of demonstrating that $\mathcal{A}$ and $\mathcal{B}$ are zero-input equivalent.

One such criterion and several related results are established in the sequel. As a preliminary, we derive a simple bound on the number of integrators and differentiators in $\mathcal{B}$.

3 **Assertion** If $\mathcal{A}$ is of order r and $\mathcal{B}$ is a realization of $\mathcal{A}$ in the form of an interconnection of adders, scalors, integrators, and differentiators, then $\mathcal{B}$ must contain at least r integrators and differentiators.

Proof In Sec. *6* we have shown that the vector $\mathbf{x}$, whose components are the outputs of the integrators and the inputs to the differentiators in $\mathcal{B}$, qualifies as a state vector for $\mathcal{B}$. Thus, if m is the total number of integrators and differentiators in $\mathcal{B}$ and dim Σ is the dimension of the state space of $\mathcal{B}$, then

4
$$\dim \Sigma \leq m$$

since the dimension of the state space of $\mathcal{B}$ is bounded by the number of components in $\mathbf{x}$.

On the other hand, by Assertion *4.2.4* and Remark *4.2.12*, the dimension of the state space of any system equivalent to $\mathcal{A}$ cannot be lower than r, that is,

5
$$r \leq \dim \Sigma$$

Consequently,

6
$$m \geq r$$

which is what we wanted to establish.

A criterion of equivalence between $\mathcal{A}$ and $\mathcal{B}$

Consider now a system $\mathcal{A}$ characterized by an input-output relation of the form

7
$$L(p)y = M(p)u$$

where

$$L(p) = a_n p^n + \cdots + a_0 \qquad M(p) = b_m p^m + \cdots + b_0$$

with the order of $\mathcal{A}$ being $r \triangleq \max(m,n)$. Suppose that $\mathcal{B}$ is an interconnection of scalors, adders, integrators, and differentiators which satisfies the condition stated in Assertion *3* with the equality sign, that is, $\mathcal{B}$ has r integrators and differentiators. Furthermore, suppose that $\mathcal{B}$ is zero-state equivalent to $\mathcal{A}$, which implies that the transfer function of $\mathcal{B}$, $H_b(s)$, is identical with that of $\mathcal{A}$, or, more concretely,

$$H_b(s) = H_a(s) = \frac{M(s)}{L(s)}$$

Are these conditions sufficient to ensure that $\mathcal{B}$ is a realization of $\mathcal{A}$ or, in other words, that $\mathcal{B}$ is equivalent to $\mathcal{A}$? The answer to this question is in the negative, as the following simple counterexample demonstrates.

8 *Example* Let $\mathcal{A}$ be defined by

9 $$p(p+1)y = (p+1)u$$

and let $\mathcal{B}$ be a realization of the system characterized by the input-output relation

$$p^2 y = p u$$

Clearly, both $\mathcal{A}$ and $\mathcal{B}$ are of order 2 and $\mathcal{A}$ is zero-state equivalent to $\mathcal{B}$, since $H_a(s) = H_b(s) = 1/s$. A realization of $\mathcal{B}$ comprising two integrators is shown in Fig. *4.8.1*. (Note that the first integrator is

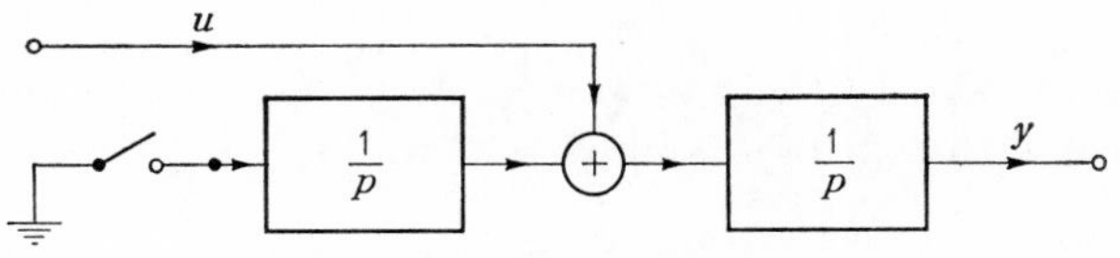

Fig. 4.8.1 System of Example *4.8.8*.

grounded through a switch, which means that its input is zero for $t \geq 0$. Such realizations will be treated in greater detail in Sec. *9*.)

Now $\mathcal{B}$ is not equivalent to $\mathcal{A}$ because it is not zero-input equivalent to $\mathcal{A}$, which in turn follows from the fact that the basis functions of $\mathcal{A}$ are $1/s(s+1)$ and $1/(s+1)$, whereas those of $\mathcal{B}$ are $1/s^2$ and $1/s$. Thus, the system of Fig. *4.8.1* is not equivalent to $\mathcal{A}$ even though it contains two integrators and is zero-state equivalent to $\mathcal{A}$.

We note that, in the case of the input-output relation *9*, $L(p)$ and $M(p)$ have a common factor $p+1$. Is it possible to construct a counterexample in which $L(p)$ and $M(p)$ do not have a factor in common? The answer to this question as well as a very useful criterion of equivalence between $\mathcal{A}$ and $\mathcal{B}$ is provided by the following

10 **Theorem** Let $\mathcal{A}$ be a system of order r characterized by an input-output relation of the form

$$L(p)y = M(p)u$$

in which the polynomials $L(p)$ and $M(p)$ do not have common factors (i.e., do not have one or more common zeros).

Let $\mathcal{B}$ be an interconnection of scalors, adders, integrators, and differentiators which is zero-state equivalent to $\mathcal{A}$ and which contains exactly r integrators and differentiators. Then $\mathcal{B}$ is a realization of $\mathcal{A}$; that is, $\mathcal{B}$ is equivalent to $\mathcal{A}$.

Proof It is easy to prove this theorem by contradiction. Specifically, suppose that (I) $\mathcal{B}$ is zero-state equivalent to $\mathcal{A}$, (II) $\mathcal{B}$ contains exactly r integrators and differentiators, (III) $L(p)$ and $M(p)$ have no common factors, and (IV) $\mathcal{B}$ is not equivalent to $\mathcal{A}$. We proceed to show that (I), . . . , (IV) are inconsistent.

By Theorem *4.7.52*, there exists a system, call it $\hat{\mathcal{B}}$, which is equivalent to $\mathcal{B}$ and which is characterized by a single differential equation of the form

11 $$\tilde{L}(p)y = \tilde{M}(p)u$$

where $\tilde{L}(p)$ and $\tilde{M}(p)$ are polynomials in p. Since $\mathcal{B}$ is zero-state equivalent to $\mathcal{A}$, so $\hat{\mathcal{B}}$ must be. Consequently, the operators $\tilde{L}(p)$ and $\tilde{M}(p)$ in *11* must necessarily be such that

12 $$\frac{\tilde{M}(s)}{\tilde{L}(s)} = \frac{M(s)}{L(s)}$$

in order to satisfy the requirement that the transfer function of $\mathcal{A}$ be identical with that of $\mathcal{B}$ and $\hat{\mathcal{B}}$, that is,

$$H_a(s) = \frac{M(s)}{L(s)}$$

$$= H_b(s) = H_{\hat{b}}(s) = \frac{\tilde{L}(s)}{\tilde{M}(s)}$$

Now since $M(s)$ and $L(s)$ have no factors in common, *11* implies that $\tilde{L}(p)$ and $\tilde{M}(p)$ must be of the form

13 $$\tilde{L}(p) = Q(p)L(p)$$
$$\tilde{M}(p) = Q(p)M(p)$$

where $Q(p)$ is a polynomial in p. Furthermore, by (IV), $\mathcal{A}$ is not equivalent to $\mathcal{B}$ and hence $\mathcal{A}$ is not equivalent to $\hat{\mathcal{B}}$. This implies that $Q(p)$ in *13* is a polynomial of degree not less than 1. [For, if $Q(p)$ were a constant, $\mathcal{A}$ and $\mathcal{B}$ would be characterized by the same input-output relation and hence would be equivalent.] This in turn implies that $\hat{r}$, the order of $\hat{\mathcal{B}}$ [which is equal to the highest power of p in $\tilde{L}(p)$ and $\tilde{M}(p)$], is greater than r, the order of $\mathcal{A}$.

Now $\mathcal{B}$ is a realization of $\hat{\mathcal{B}}$, since $\mathcal{B}$ is equivalent to $\hat{\mathcal{B}}$. By Assertion *3*, $\mathcal{B}$ must contain at least $\hat{r}$ integrators and differentiators. This contradicts the assumption that $\mathcal{B}$ contains exactly r integrators and differentiators and thus proves the theorem. ◁

We shall make extensive use of Theorem *10* in Sec. *9*, where it will play a key role in the development of a simple and yet effective technique for associating a state vector with a given differential system $\mathcal{A}$. For this reason, we limit its illustration at this point to one simple

14 *Example* Let $\mathcal{A}$ be a system of order 2 characterized by the input-output relation

$$(p + 1)(p + 2)y = p\,u$$

The system $\mathcal{B}$ shown in Fig. *4.8.2* comprises two integrators and is zero-state equivalent to $\mathcal{A}$. Therefore, by Theorem *10*, $\mathcal{B}$ is equivalent to $\mathcal{A}$.

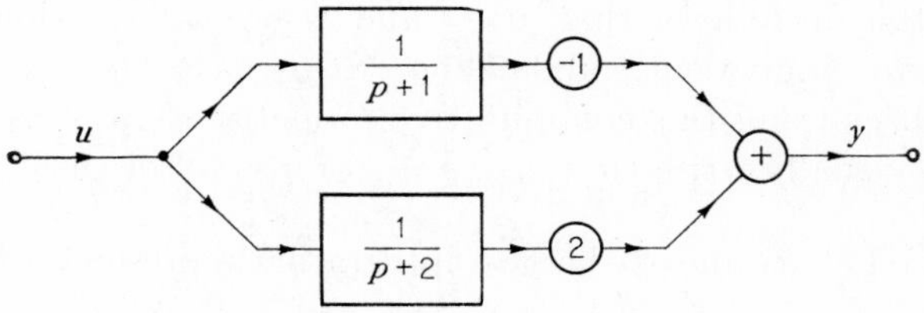

Fig. 4.8.2 System of Example *4.8.14*.

Commutativity

One of the most basic equivalence properties of linear time-invariant systems is the property of *commutativity*, which is expressed by the following

15 **Theorem** Let $\mathcal{A}_1$ and $\mathcal{A}_2$ be two systems characterized by $\frac{1}{L_1(p)} \cdot M_1(p)$ and $\frac{1}{L_2(p)} \cdot M_2(p)$, respectively, where L_1 and M_1 have no factors in common, and likewise for L_2 and M_2. [This notation signifies that $\mathcal{A}_1$ and $\mathcal{A}_2$ are characterized by input-output relations of the form $L_1(p)y = M_1(p)u$ and $L_2(p)y = M_2(p)u$, respectively (see *4.5.9 et seq.*).] Then $\mathcal{A}_1$ and $\mathcal{A}_2$ commute, i.e.,

$$\mathcal{A}_1\mathcal{A}_2 \equiv \mathcal{A}_2\mathcal{A}_1$$

(meaning that the tandem combination of $\mathcal{A}_1$ and $\mathcal{A}_2$, with $\mathcal{A}_1$ following $\mathcal{A}_2$, is equivalent to the tandem combination of $\mathcal{A}_1$ and $\mathcal{A}_2$ with $\mathcal{A}_1$ preceding $\mathcal{A}_2$) if and only if $M_1(p)$ has no factors in common with $L_2(p)$ and $M_2(p)$ has no factors in common with $L_1(p)$. ◁

We shall first establish three special cases of this theorem and then use them to prove the theorem itself.

Case 1 Let $\mathcal{A}_1$ and $\mathcal{A}_2$ be two differentiators represented by $(p + \gamma_1)$ and $(p + \gamma_2)$, respectively. Then $(p + \gamma_1) \cdot (p + \gamma_2)$ is equivalent to $(p + \gamma_2) \cdot (p + \gamma_1)$ for all γ_1, γ_2. [Here $(p + \gamma_1) \cdot (p + \gamma_2)$ and $(p + \gamma_2) \cdot (p + \gamma_1)$ represent the systems $\mathcal{A}_1\mathcal{A}_2$ and $\mathcal{A}_2\mathcal{A}_1$, respectively.]

Proof In Sec. *4* we have shown that the basis functions of a system of the differential operator type

$$y = (b_m p^m + \cdots + b_0)u \qquad b_m \neq 0$$

are given by 1, $s, \ldots, s^{m-1}$. Consequently, the systems $\mathcal{A}_1\mathcal{A}_2$ and $\mathcal{A}_2\mathcal{A}_1$ have identical basis functions, namely, 1, s. Furthermore, $\mathcal{A}_1\mathcal{A}_2$ and $\mathcal{A}_2\mathcal{A}_1$ have the same transfer function

16 $$H_{12}(s) = H_{21}(s) = (s + \gamma_1)(s + \gamma_2)$$

From this it follows that $\mathcal{A}_1\mathcal{A}_2$ and $\mathcal{A}_2\mathcal{A}_1$ are zero-input as well as zero-state equivalent, and hence $\mathcal{A}_1\mathcal{A}_2 \equiv \mathcal{A}_2\mathcal{A}_1$. [Note that it is partly because of this commutative property of $(p + \gamma_1)$ and $(p + \gamma_2)$ that we usually write $(p + \gamma_1)(p + \gamma_2)$ instead of $(p + \gamma_1) \cdot (p + \gamma_2)$.]

Case 2 Let $\mathcal{A}_1$ and $\mathcal{A}_2$ be two integrators represented by $\dfrac{1}{p + \gamma_1}$ and $\dfrac{1}{p + \gamma_2}$, respectively. Then for all γ_1 and γ_2

17 $$\frac{1}{(p + \gamma_1)} \cdot \frac{1}{(p + \gamma_2)} \equiv \frac{1}{(p + \gamma_2)} \cdot \frac{1}{(p + \gamma_1)}$$

Note that, as in the case of differentiators, we usually write

$$\frac{1}{(p + \gamma_1)(p + \gamma_2)} \qquad \text{instead of} \qquad \frac{1}{(p + \gamma_1)} \cdot \frac{1}{(p + \gamma_2)}$$

Proof We repeat the arguments used in Case 1. Specifically, in Sec. *3* it was shown that the basis functions of a system of the reciprocal differential operator type

$$L(p)y = u$$

where

$$L(p) = a_n p^n + \cdots + a_0 \qquad a_n \neq 0$$

are given by

$$\frac{s^{n-1}}{L(s)}, \ldots, \frac{1}{L(s)}$$

Consequently, the systems $\mathcal{A}_1\mathcal{A}_2$ and $\mathcal{A}_2\mathcal{A}_1$ have identical basis functions, namely,

$$\frac{s}{s^2 + (\gamma_1 + \gamma_2)s + \gamma_1\gamma_2}, \frac{1}{s^2 + (\gamma_1 + \gamma_2)s + \gamma_1\gamma_2}$$

Furthermore, $\mathcal{A}_1\mathcal{A}_2$ and $\mathcal{A}_2\mathcal{A}_1$ have the same transfer function

$$H_{12}(s) = H_{21}(s) = \frac{1}{s^2 + (\gamma_1 + \gamma_2)s + \gamma_1\gamma_2}$$

Therefore, $\mathcal{A}_1\mathcal{A}_2$ and $\mathcal{A}_2\mathcal{A}_1$ are equivalent systems.

Case 3 Let $\mathfrak{A}_1$ be a differentiator represented by $p + \gamma_1$ and let $\mathfrak{A}_2$ be an integrator represented by $\frac{1}{p + \gamma_2}$. Then

18
$$(p + \gamma_1) \cdot \frac{1}{(p + \gamma_2)} \equiv \frac{1}{(p + \gamma_2)} \cdot (p + \gamma_1)$$

if and only if $\gamma_1 \neq \gamma_2$.

Proof To say that $\mathfrak{A}_2\mathfrak{A}_1$ is represented by $\frac{1}{(p + \gamma_2)} \cdot (p + \gamma_1)$ is equivalent to saying that $\mathfrak{A}_2\mathfrak{A}_1$ is characterized by the input-output relation

$$(p + \gamma_2)y = (p + \gamma_1)u$$

Such a system has a single basis function (see *4.5.26*) $\frac{1}{s + \gamma_2}$.

Next, let us determine the basis functions of $(p + \gamma_1) \cdot \frac{1}{(p + \gamma_2)}$, that is, $\mathfrak{A}_1\mathfrak{A}_2$. If the output of $\mathfrak{A}_2$ is denoted by v, then $\mathfrak{A}_1\mathfrak{A}_2$ is characterized by the equations

19
$$\begin{aligned} y &= (p + \gamma_1)v \\ (p + \gamma_2)v &= u \end{aligned}$$

in which v plays the role of a suppressed output variable (see *3.8.26*). On applying the Laplace transformation to both sides of *19* (with u set equal to zero for $t \geq 0$), the expression for the Laplace transform of the zero-input response is found to be

20
$$Z(s;v(0-)) = \frac{v(0-)(\gamma_1 - \gamma_2)}{s + \gamma_2}$$

Thus, $\mathfrak{A}_1\mathfrak{A}_2$ has just one basis function, $\frac{1}{s + \gamma_2}$, which is identical with that of $\mathfrak{A}_2\mathfrak{A}_1$, *provided* $\gamma_1 \neq \gamma_2$. ◁

A somewhat more illuminating (but also less convincing) way of deriving the same result is this: by the argument used in Case 2, $\frac{1}{p + \gamma_2}$ has just one basis function $\frac{1}{s + \gamma_2}$ or, as a function of time, $1(t)e^{-\gamma_2 t}$. Consequently, the basis function of $(p + \gamma_1) \cdot \frac{1}{(p + \gamma_2)}$ is given by the result of acting with the differential operator $p + \gamma_1$ on $1(t)e^{-\gamma_2 t}$. Deleting the delta function due to the discontinuity at $t = 0$ (see *4.7.19 et seq.*), the basis function in question is seen to be $1(t)e^{-\gamma_2 t}$ *provided* $\gamma_2 \neq \gamma_1$, for otherwise the time function resulting from acting with $p + \gamma_1$ on $1(t)e^{-\gamma_2 t}$ vanishes for $t > 0$.

We have shown so far that $\frac{1}{(p + \gamma_2)} \cdot (p + \gamma_1)$ and $(p + \gamma_1) \cdot \frac{1}{(p + \gamma_2)}$

have the same set of basis functions $\left(\text{namely, the function } \frac{1}{s+\gamma_2}\right)$ for all values of γ_1 and γ_2 excluding $\gamma_1 = \gamma_2$. Now the transfer functions of these two systems are identical for all values of γ_1 and γ_2, for

$$H_{12}(s) = \frac{s+\gamma_1}{s+\gamma_2} = H_{21}(s)$$

Consequently, $\mathcal{A}_1\mathcal{A}_2$ is equivalent to $\mathcal{A}_2\mathcal{A}_1$ if and only if $\gamma_1 \neq \gamma_2$, which is what we wanted to demonstrate. [Note that this result is in agreement with the conclusion reached in *4.4.44*, namely, that $(p + \gamma_1)$ is a left-constrained inverse of $\frac{1}{p+\gamma_1}$ but not vice versa.] ◁

Having established Cases 1, 2, and 3, it is a simple matter to reduce any given case to these special cases by repeated transposition of the first-order factors in $\mathcal{A}_1$ and $\mathcal{A}_2$. Specifically, suppose that $\mathcal{A}_1$ and $\mathcal{A}_2$ are represented by

$$\mathcal{A}_1: \qquad \frac{1}{(p+1)(p+2)} \cdot (p+4)$$

$$\mathcal{A}_2: \qquad \frac{1}{(p+3)} \cdot p$$

Then $\mathcal{A}_1\mathcal{A}_2$ is represented by

21 $$\mathcal{A}_1\mathcal{A}_2: \qquad \frac{1}{(p+1)(p+2)} \cdot (p+4) \cdot \frac{1}{(p+3)} \cdot p$$

By making use of the substitution principle (*1.10.35*), we can replace *21* with the successive equivalent expressions

$$\frac{1}{(p+1)(p+2)} \cdot (p+4)p \cdot \frac{1}{(p+3)}$$

$$\frac{1}{(p+1)(p+2)} \cdot p(p+4) \cdot \frac{1}{(p+3)}$$

$$p \cdot \frac{1}{(p+1)(p+2)} \cdot (p+4) \cdot \frac{1}{(p+3)}$$

. . . .

$$\frac{1}{(p+3)} \cdot p \cdot \frac{1}{(p+1)(p+2)} \cdot (p+4)$$

with the last expression representing $\mathcal{A}_2\mathcal{A}_1$.

To prove the converse, suppose that the conditions of Theorem *15* are violated in that either $M_1(p)$ and $L_2(p)$ or $M_2(p)$ and $L_1(p)$ or both have factors in common. Then by successive transposition of factors which are not in common, we can put $\mathcal{A}_1\mathcal{A}_2$ and $\mathcal{A}_2\mathcal{A}_1$ into the forms $\mathcal{B}\mathcal{C}$ and $\mathcal{B}^*\mathcal{C}$, respectively, where $\mathcal{B}$, $\mathcal{B}^*$, and $\mathcal{C}$ are products of integrators and differentiators, with $\mathcal{B}$ and $\mathcal{B}^*$ containing the same factors but in reverse order. For example, if $\mathcal{A}_1$ and $\mathcal{A}_2$ are represented by

$\mathcal{A}_1$: $$\frac{1}{(p+1)(p+2)}\cdot p$$

$\mathcal{A}_2$: $$\frac{1}{p(p+3)}$$

then

22 $$\mathcal{A}_1\mathcal{A}_2 \equiv \mathcal{B}\mathcal{C} \equiv p\cdot\frac{1}{p}\,\frac{1}{(p+1)(p+2)(p+3)}$$

and

23 $$\mathcal{A}_2\mathcal{A}_1 \equiv \mathcal{B}^*\mathcal{C} \equiv \frac{1}{p}\cdot p\,\frac{1}{(p+1)(p+2)(p+3)}$$

where

24 $$\mathcal{C} \equiv \frac{1}{(p+1)(p+2)(p+3)}$$
$$\mathcal{B} \equiv p\cdot\frac{1}{p}$$
$$\mathcal{B}^* \equiv \frac{1}{p}\cdot p$$

25 **Remark** Note that $\mathcal{B}$ (or $\mathcal{B}^*$) can always be put into the form of a product $\mathfrak{D}\mathcal{R}$, where $\mathfrak{D}$ is a differential operator system and $\mathcal{R}$ is a reciprocal differential operator system. Thus, if $\mathcal{B} \equiv \mathfrak{D}\mathcal{R}$, then $\mathcal{B}^* \equiv \mathcal{R}\mathfrak{D}$, and vice versa. Furthermore, $\mathfrak{D}$ and $\mathcal{R}$ are inverse to one another (see *4.4.44*) if the common factors in $L_1(p)$ and $M_2(p)$, and $L_2(p)$ and $M_1(p)$, are of multiplicity 1. ◁

The nonequivalence of $\mathcal{A}_1\mathcal{A}_2$ and $\mathcal{A}_2\mathcal{A}_1$ follows from the nonequivalence of $\mathcal{B}$ and $\mathcal{B}^*$. Specifically, if $\mathcal{B}$ is a product of factors of the form

26 $$(p+\gamma)^\mu\cdot\frac{1}{(p+\gamma)^\lambda}$$

then $\mathcal{B}^*$ is a product of the same factors in reverse order:

27 $$\frac{1}{(p+\gamma)^\lambda}\cdot(p+\gamma)^\mu$$

Now *26* and *27* are necessarily nonequivalent because the basis functions of *26* form a proper subset of the basis functions of *27*. [That is, every basis function of *26* is also a basis function of *27*, but there are basis functions of *27* which are not in the set of basis function of *26*. This is due to the fact that the operator $(p+\gamma)^\mu$ in *26* "annihilates" one or more of the basis functions of *27*. Note that this argument is similar to that used in Case 3.] This implies that the basis functions of either

$\mathcal{A}_1\mathcal{A}_2$ or $\mathcal{A}_2\mathcal{A}_1$—according as it is $\mathcal{B}$ or $\mathcal{B}^*$ that is of the form $\mathcal{R}\mathcal{D}$—form a proper subset of the basis functions of either $\mathcal{A}_2\mathcal{A}_1$ or $\mathcal{A}_1\mathcal{A}_2$, and this demonstrates that $\mathcal{A}_1\mathcal{A}_2$ and $\mathcal{A}_2\mathcal{A}_1$ are nonequivalent if $L_1(p)$ and $M_2(p)$ or $L_2(p)$ and $M_1(p)$ have factors in common. Q.E.D.

We are now ready to apply the equivalence properties established in this and the preceding section to the problem of associating a state vector with a given differential system. This forms the subject of the following section.

9 *Determination of state vector and state equations by the realization technique*

The various equivalence properties derived in the preceding sections and, in particular, Theorem *4.8.10*, provide us with a basis for an alternative approach to the problem of associating a state vector with a given differential system $\mathcal{A}$. For convenience, the approach in question will be referred to as the *realization technique.*

The essence of the realization technique is this: given a system $\mathcal{A}$ characterized by, say, an input-output relation of the form

$$L(p)y = M(p)u$$

where

$$L(p) = a_np^n + \cdots + a_0$$
$$M(p) = b_mp^m + \cdots + b_0$$

we construct an equivalent system $\mathcal{B}$ which is a realization of $\mathcal{A}$ in the form of an interconnection of adders, scalors, integrators, and differentiators. Then we associate a state vector $\mathbf{x}$ with $\mathcal{B}$ by the use of Rule *4.6.2* and find the corresponding state equations for $\mathcal{A}$ by the techniques of Sec. *6*. Since $\mathcal{B}$ and $\mathcal{A}$ are equivalent systems, $\mathbf{x}$ qualifies as a state vector for $\mathcal{A}$ and the state equations of $\mathcal{B}$ may be regarded as being also the state equations of $\mathcal{A}$.

This approach is particularly effective when $L(p)$ and $M(p)$ have no factors in common, for in that case we can construct $\mathcal{B}$ simply by synthesizing the transfer function $H(s)$ through the usual techniques of circuit theory (which yield a system that is zero-state equivalent to $\mathcal{A}$) and then invoking Theorem *4.8.10* (assuming the number of integrators and differentiators in $\mathcal{B}$ is equal to the order of $\mathcal{A}$) to verify that $\mathcal{B}$ is equivalent to $\mathcal{A}$.

For purposes of comparison, we shall first apply the realization technique to the various types of systems which we have already studied in Secs. *3* to *5*. Then we shall develop a special version of the realization technique, namely, the so-called partial-fraction expansion technique, an important feature of which is that it yields state equations of the form *4.7.51* in which the matrix **A** is in the Jordan canonical form.

We begin with an analysis of

Systems of the reciprocal differential type

Let $\mathcal{A}$ be a system of the reciprocal differential type characterized by

1 $$(a_n p^n + \cdots + a_0)y = u \qquad a_n \neq 0$$

The transfer function of $\mathcal{A}$ is given by

2 $$H(s) = \frac{1}{a_n s^n + \cdots + a_0}$$

and it is easy to verify that the network $\mathcal{B}$ shown in Fig. *4.9.1* has the

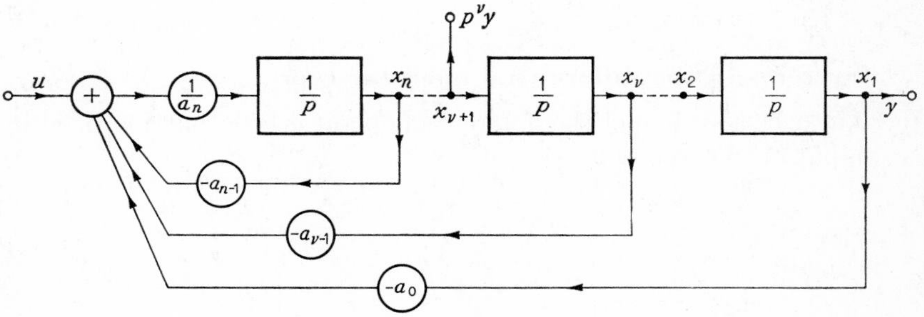

Fig. 4.9.1 Realization of $\dfrac{1}{a_n p^n + \cdots + a_0}$.

same transfer function and hence is zero-state equivalent to $\mathcal{A}$. Furthermore, $\mathcal{B}$ has exactly n integrators. Therefore, by Theorem *4.8.10*, $\mathcal{B}$ is a realization of $\mathcal{A}$.

To associate a state vector with $\mathcal{B}$, we use Rule *4.6.2*, with the results shown in Fig. *4.9.1*. The defining relations for **x** are

$$\begin{aligned} x_1 &= y \\ x_2 &= y^{(1)} \\ &\cdots\cdots \\ x_n &= y^{(n-1)} \end{aligned}$$

In this way, we arrive at what we previously called the normal state vector for $\mathcal{A}$ (see *4.3.27*). Needless to say, the corresponding state equations for $\mathcal{B}$ are identical with the normal state equations obtained previously (*4.3.33*).

As an illustration of what happens when we realize $\mathcal{A}$ in a different way, consider the following

3 *Example* Let $\mathfrak{A}$ be characterized by the input-output relation

$$(p + 1)(p + 2)^2 y = u$$

In this case, it is trivial to verify that the system $\mathfrak{B}$ shown in Fig. 4.9.2

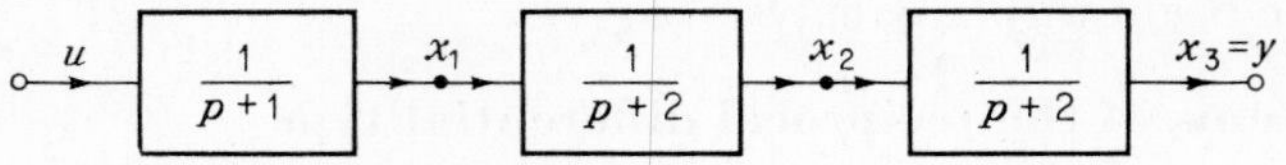

Fig. 4.9.2 Realization of the system of Example 4.9.3.

constitutes a realization of $\mathfrak{A}$. Choosing **x** as indicated, the state equations of $\mathfrak{B}$ (and hence $\mathfrak{A}$) are easily found by inspection of Fig. 4.9.2:

$$\begin{aligned} \dot{x}_1 &= -x_1 + u \\ \dot{x}_2 &= -2x_2 + x_1 \\ \dot{x}_3 &= -2x_3 + x_2 \\ y &= x_3 \end{aligned}$$

We turn next to

Systems of the differential operator type

Let $\mathfrak{A}$ be a system of the differential operator type characterized by the input-output relation

4 $$y = (b_m p^m + \cdots + b_0)u \qquad b_m \neq 0$$

A simple realization of $\mathfrak{A}$ is shown in Fig. 4.9.3.

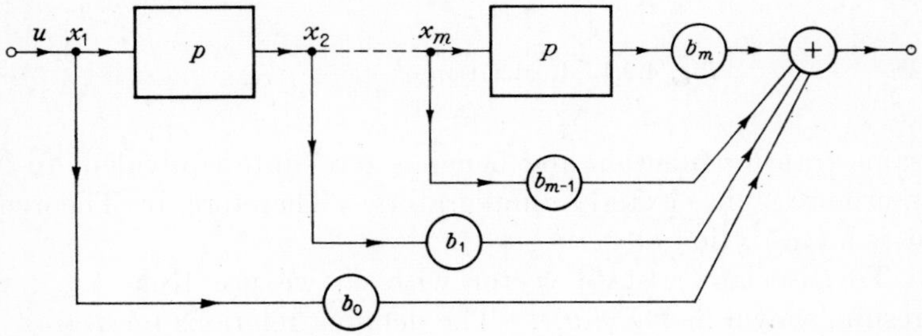

Fig. 4.9.3 Realization of $b_m p^m + \cdots + b_0$.

Associating a component of **x** with the input of each differentiator in $\mathfrak{B}$, we have

5 $$\begin{aligned} x_1 &= u \\ x_2 &= u^{(1)} \\ &\cdots\cdots \\ x_m &= u^{(m-1)} \end{aligned}$$

which coincides with the definition of the normal state vector for $\mathfrak{A}$ (see 4.4.8). The corresponding state equations have the normal form 4.4.29.

Systems of the general type

Let 𝒜 be a system characterized by the input-output relation

6 $$(a_n p^n + \cdots + a_0)y = (b_n p^n + \cdots + b_0)u$$

and let us assume, to begin with, that 𝒜 is a proper system of order n—which means that a_n, but not necessarily b_n, is different from zero.

Again, using Theorem *4.8.10* it is easy to verify that the system ℬ shown in Fig. *4.9.4* constitutes a realization of 𝒜. (Actually, this is true

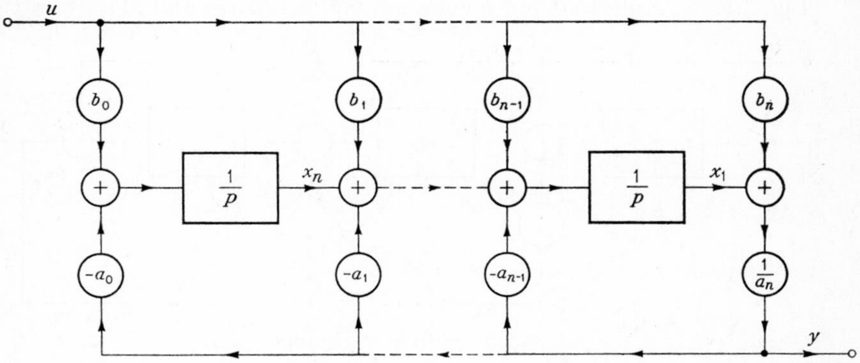

Fig. 4.9.4 Realization of $\frac{1}{(a_n p^n + \cdots + a_0)} \cdot (b_n p^n + \cdots + b_0)$, $a_n \neq 0$.

even when the left- and right-hand operators in *6* have one or more factors in common.)

Choosing $\mathbf{x}$ in accordance with Rule *4.6.2*, we obtain by inspection of Fig. *4.9.4* the following relations:

7 $$\begin{aligned} x_1 &= a_n y - b_n u \\ x_2 &= \dot{x}_1 + a_{n-1} y - b_{n-1} u \\ &\cdots\cdots\cdots\cdots \\ x_n &= \dot{x}_{n-1} + a_1 y - b_1 u \\ \dot{x}_n &= -a_0 y + b_0 u \end{aligned}$$

which are identical with the expressions found previously by the approach of Sec. *5* (see *4.5.18 et seq.*). Clearly, the technique used above is much simpler, since it does not require the determination of the general solution. However, a difficulty arises when $L(p)$ and $M(p)$ in *6* have factors in common, since in this event we cannot draw upon Theorem *4.8.10* to establish the equivalence between 𝒜 and its realization ℬ. In such cases, we generally rely on a somewhat vague "continuity" argument to reason that if a structure such as ℬ in Fig. *4.9.4* is equivalent to 𝒜 for all values of a's and b's for which $L(p)$ and $M(p)$

have no factors in common, then $\mathcal{B}$ is equivalent to $\mathcal{A}$ for all values of a's and b's.

8 *Example* Consider a system $\mathcal{A}$ characterized by the input-output relation

$$p(p + 1)(p + 2)y = p(p^2 + 1)u$$

or equivalently

9 $$(p^3 + 3p^2 + 2p)y = (p^3 + p)u$$

In this case, system $\mathcal{B}$ of Fig. *4.9.4* reduces to the system shown in Fig. *4.9.5*. Note that p is a common factor in $L(p)$ and $M(p)$ and that

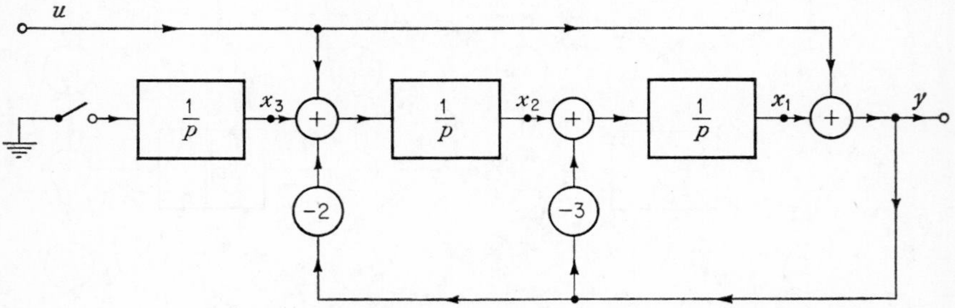

Fig. 4.9.5 System of Example *4.9.8*.

as a result of the absence of the coefficients a_0 and b_0 in *9*, the input to the first integrator in Fig. *4.9.5* is zero for $t \geq 0$. This is indicated in the diagram by a switch which "grounds" the first integrator for $t \geq 0$.

Alternative realizations

There are many alternative realizations of the system $\mathcal{A}$ characterized by *6*, of which the two structures described below are worthy of special attention because of the close relation between them and the structure of Fig. *4.9.1*, which constitutes a realization of a system of the reciprocal differential type which is characterized by *1*. [For convenient reference, we shall denote the latter system by $1/L(p)$ and $\mathcal{A}$ by $\frac{1}{L(p)} \cdot M(p)$.]

Specifically, by inspection of the structure of Fig. *4.9.1*, it is clear that if the output of $1/L(p)$ is y, then the input to the νth integrator (counting from right to left) is $p^\nu y$. From this it follows that we can obtain any linear combination of $y, \ldots, p^{n-1}y$ by "tapping" the inputs to the integrators and, more specifically, we can realize the system characterized by the operational expression

10 $$\mathcal{A}': \qquad (b_n p^n + \cdots + b_0) \cdot \frac{1}{(a_n p^n + \cdots + a_0)}$$

or, more simply, $M(p) \cdot \frac{1}{L(p)}$, by using the structure of Fig. *4.9.6*.

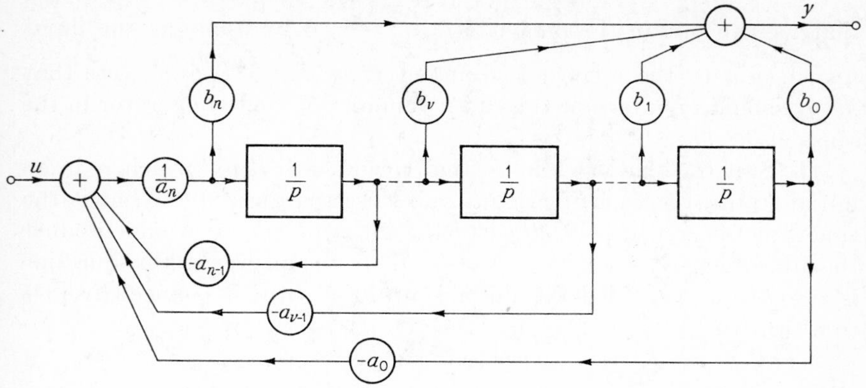

Fig. 4.9.6 Realization of $(b_n p^n + \cdots + b_0) \cdot \dfrac{1}{(a_n p^n + \cdots + a_0)}$.

It should be noted, however, that by virtue of Theorem *4.8.15*, $\mathcal{A}'$ is *not* equivalent to $\mathcal{A}$ $\left[\text{which is defined by } \dfrac{1}{L(p)} \cdot M(p) \text{ rather than } M(p) \cdot \dfrac{1}{L(p)}\right]$ unless $L(p)$ and $M(p)$ have no common factors. If this condition is satisfied, then the structure of Fig. *4.9.6* constitutes a realization of $\mathcal{A}$, with the property (which is also possessed by the structure of Fig. *4.9.7*) that the corresponding **A** matrix in the state equations *4.7.51* has exactly the same form for this structure as it has for the realization of $1/L(p)$ in Fig. *4.9.1*.

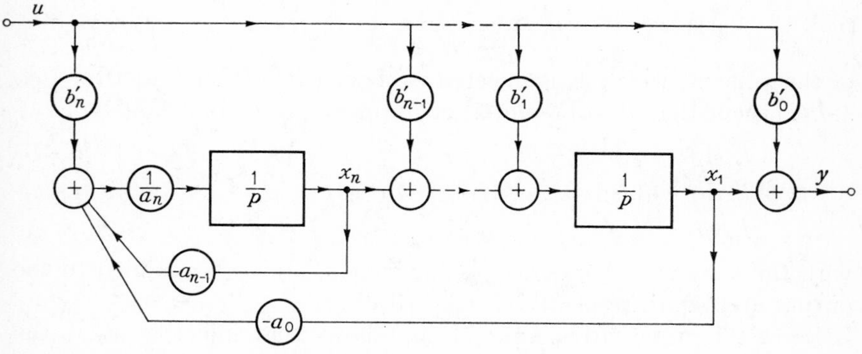

Fig. 4.9.7 Alternative realization of

$$\frac{1}{(a_n p^n + \cdots + b_0)} \cdot (b_n p^n + \cdots + b_0) \qquad a_n \neq 0$$

The second structure, which is shown in Fig. *4.9.7*, follows from the following observations.

(I) We can write *6* as $L(p)y = \tilde{u}$, where $\tilde{u} = M(p)u$. This implies that we can obtain the output of $\frac{1}{L(p)} \cdot M(p)$ by applying the input $\tilde{u} = M(p)u$ to the reciprocal differential system $1/L(p)$. Note that $M(p)$ should be interpreted as an indefinite differential operator in the sense of *3.8.11*.

(II) Suppose that we add to the output of $1/L(p)$ (which is in an initial state $\boldsymbol{\alpha}$) a time function w and raise the question: What is the time function v which if added to the input of $1/L(p)$ would produce the added output w? By Assertion *4.4.49*, the answer to this question is $v = L(p)w$, provided the initial state of $1/L(p)$ is changed from $\boldsymbol{\alpha}$ to $\boldsymbol{\alpha}'$, where

11 $$\boldsymbol{\alpha}' = \boldsymbol{\alpha} - [w(t_0-), \ldots, w^{(n-1)}(t_0-)]$$

(III) Suppose we take the structure of Fig. *4.9.1* and add a time function u_ν to the output of the νth integrator (counting from right to left), as shown in Fig. *4.9.8*. We observe that the structure to the left

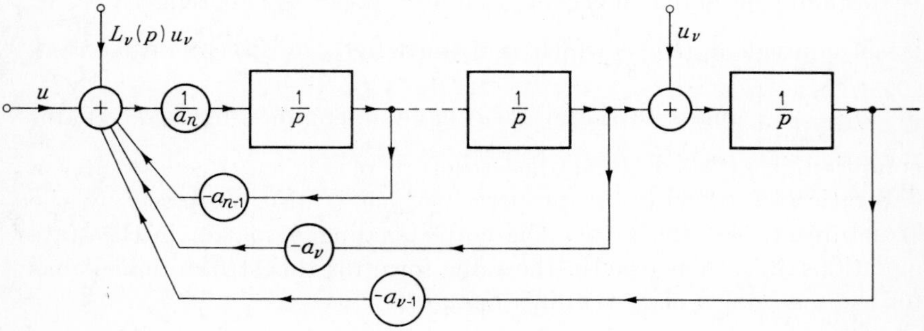

Fig. 4.9.8 Replacement of u_ν by an input applied at the input of $\frac{1}{(a_np^n + \cdots + a_0)}$.

of the point at which u_ν is injected is of the same form as that of Fig. *4.9.1*, except that the differential operator corresponding to it is

12 $$L_\nu(p) = a_np^{n-\nu} + \cdots + a_\nu \qquad \nu = 1, \ldots, n-1$$
$$L_0(p) = L(p)$$
$$L_n(p) = 1$$

with the last two relations signifying that u_0 and u_n are added to the output and input, respectively, of $1/L(p)$.

From this observation and (II) it follows that injecting u_ν at the input of the νth integrator is equivalent to adding the time function $L_\nu(p)u_\nu$ to the input of $1/L(p)$, as illustrated in Fig. *4.9.8*. It is understood, of course, that when we replace u_ν by $L_\nu(p)u_\nu$, we should also modify the states of the first $n - \nu$ integrators (from left to right) in Fig. *4.9.8* in accordance with *11*.

(IV) Finally, suppose that we make u_ν proportional to u, that is, $u_\nu = b'_\nu u$, $\nu = 0, \ldots, n$, where the b'_ν are as yet undetermined constants. By (III), this is equivalent to adding to the input of $1/L(p)$ the time function

$$b'_0L_0(p)u + b'_1L_1(p)u + \cdots + b'_nL_n(p)u$$

Thus, if we can choose the b'_ν in such a way as to make this time function identical with $\tilde{u}$ [see (I)], that is,

13 $$[b'_0L_0(p) + \cdots + b'_nL_n(p)]u = (b_np^n + \cdots + b_0)u$$

then the structure of Fig. *4.9.8* will have the same output as $\frac{1}{L(p)} \cdot M(p)$ for all u and hence will constitute a realization of $\mathcal{A}$.

It is easy to show that such b'_ν, $\nu = 0, \ldots, n$, can always be found. Specifically, on substituting *12* into *13* and equating the coefficients of like terms, we obtain the following triangular system of equations:

14 $$\begin{aligned} b_n &= b'_0a_n \\ b_{n-1} &= b'_0a_{n-1} + b'_1a_n \\ &\cdots\cdots\cdots\cdots \\ b_0 &= b'_0a_0 + \cdots + b'_{n-1}a_{n-1} + b'_n \end{aligned}$$

which can always be solved for the b'_ν in terms of the b_ν and the a_ν, since $a_n \neq 0$.

On identifying the components of $\mathbf{x} = (x_1, \ldots, x_n)$ with the outputs of integrators in Fig. *4.9.7*, the state equations of $\mathcal{A}$ become

15 $$\begin{aligned} \dot{x}_1 &= x_2 + b'_1u \\ &\cdots\cdots\cdots \\ \dot{x}_{n-1} &= x_n + b'_{n-1}u \\ \dot{x}_n &= \frac{1}{a_n}(-a_0x_1 - \cdots - a_{n-1}x_n + b'_nu) \\ y &= x_1 + b'_0u \end{aligned}$$

with the components of the state vector expressed in terms of u, y, and their derivatives by

16 $$\begin{aligned} x_1 &= y - b'_0u \\ x_2 &= y^{(1)} - b'_0u^{(1)} - b'_1u \\ &\cdots\cdots\cdots\cdots\cdots \\ x_n &= y^{(n-1)} - b'_0u^{(n-1)} - \cdots - b'_{n-1}u \end{aligned}$$

For the time-varying case, equations analogous to *15* will be derived by a somewhat different technique in Chap. *6*, Sec. *4*.

Case of improper $\mathcal{A}$

The case of improper $\mathcal{A}$ can readily be reduced to the cases treated above by using the decomposition technique stated in Theorem *4.5.34*. In this way, $\mathcal{A}$ is realized as a parallel combination of a proper system

$\hat{\mathfrak{A}}$ which comprises scalors, adders, and integrators, and a system $\mathfrak{D}$ of the differential operator type whose realization comprises scalors, adders, and differentiators.

17 **Remark** It is possible to realize an improper $\mathfrak{A}$ as a system $\mathfrak{B}$ which does not contain any differentiators. One way of doing this is based on the observation (see *4.4.48*) that a differentiator represented by $(p + \gamma)$ is inverse to the integrator represented by $1/(p + \gamma)$ and hence can be realized in terms of the latter by the scheme of Comment *2.10.24* which is illustrated in Fig. *4.9.9*. (The triangular block represents an infinite gain amplifier.) Using the substitution described

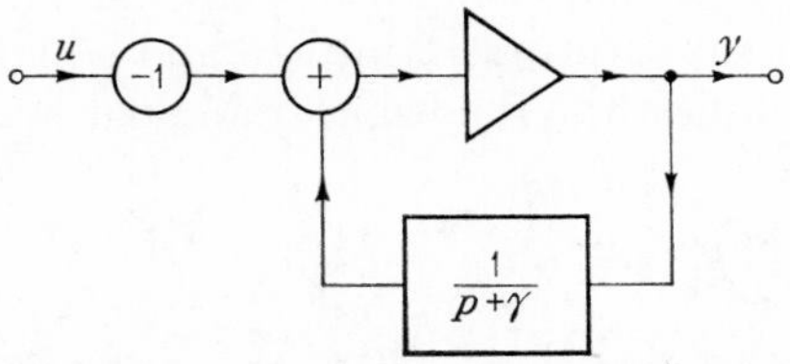

Fig. 4.9.9 Realization of $p + \gamma$. (The triangular block represents an amplifier with infinite gain.)

above in $\mathfrak{D}$, $\mathfrak{B}$ becomes a system comprising scalors, adders, integrators, and infinite gain amplifiers. It is more convenient, however, to realize $\mathfrak{A}$ in the form shown in Fig. *4.9.10*, which employs a single infinite gain amplifier. By the use of Theorem *4.8.10*, it is easy to

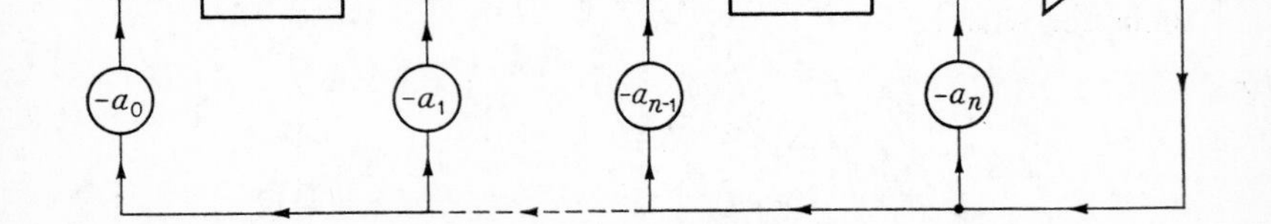

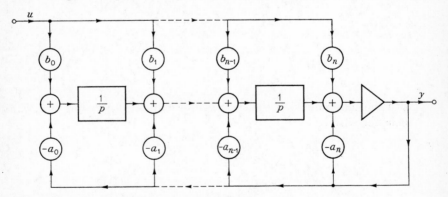

Fig. 4.9.10 Realization of a not necessarily proper system

$$\frac{1}{(a_n p^n + \cdots + a_0)} \cdot (b_n p^n + \cdots + b_0).$$

verify that this structure is equivalent to $\mathfrak{A}$. Note that for $a_n = 0$, the realization of Fig. *4.9.4* reduces to that of Fig. *4.9.10*.

Partial-fraction expansion technique

The technique to be described below is merely a special case of the realization technique. Its most significant feature is that it leads to state equations in which the **A** matrix has a diagonal or, more generally, a Jordan canonical form (see *D.5.21*). Its main disadvantage is that it requires the factorization of $L(p)$.

Specifically, let $\mathcal{A}$ be a proper system characterized by an input-output relation

18 $$L(p)y = M(p)u$$

in which $L(p)$ has, or can be put into, the form

$$L(p) = (p - \lambda_1)^{\mu_1} \cdots (p - \lambda_q)^{\mu_q} \qquad \mu_1 + \cdots + \mu_q = n$$

in which $\lambda_1, \ldots, \lambda_q$ are the (distinct) zeros of $L(p)$ and $\mu_1, \ldots, \mu_q$ are their respective multiplicities. We assume that $M(p)$ and $L(p)$ have no factors in common.

If $\mathcal{A}$ is an improper system, then by Theorem *4.5.34* we can decompose it into a proper system $\hat{\mathcal{A}}$ and a system of the differential operator type $\hat{\mathcal{D}}$. The procedure described below will then apply to $\hat{\mathcal{A}}$.

For simplicity, we consider first the case where $\mu_1 = \cdots = \mu_q = 1$, that is, all the zeros of $L(p)$ are simple.

Case of simple zeros

In this case, $\mathcal{A}$ is characterized by the input-output relation

$$(p - \lambda_1) \cdots (p - \lambda_n)y = M(p)u$$

where the λ_i, $i = 1, \ldots, n$, are distinct, the degree of $M(p)$ does not exceed n, and $(p - \lambda_i)$ is not a factor of $M(p)$, $i = 1, \ldots, n$.

The transfer function of $\mathcal{A}$ is given by

$$H(s) = \frac{M(s)}{(s - \lambda_1) \cdots (s - \lambda_n)}$$

and on expanding $H(s)$ in partial fractions, we have

$$H(s) = \frac{c_1}{s - \lambda_1} + \cdots + \frac{c_n}{s - \lambda_n} + d_0$$

where the c_i and d_0, $i = 1, \ldots, n$, are constants depending on $\lambda_1, \ldots, \lambda_n$ and the coefficients of $M(p)$, and where $d_0 = 0$ if $\mathcal{A}$ is a strictly proper system [i.e., if the degree of $M(p)$ does not exceed $n - 1$].

Now it is easy to verify by inspection that the system $\mathcal{B}$ shown in Fig. *4.9.11* has this transfer function and hence by Theorem *4.8.10* is a realization of $\mathcal{A}$.

On associating the components of **x** with the outputs of integrators in $\mathcal{B}$, the state equations of $\mathcal{B}$ are easily found by inspection. They read

$$\dot{x}_1 = \lambda_1 x_1 + u$$
$$\cdots\cdots\cdots$$
$$\dot{x}_n = \lambda_n x_n + u$$
$$y = c_1 x_1 + \cdots + c_n x_n + d_0 u$$

For convenient reference, these results are summarized in the

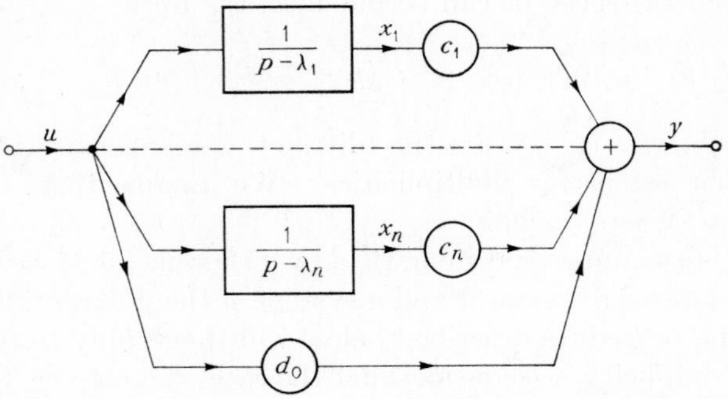

Fig. 4.9.11 Partial-fraction expansion in the case of simple poles.

19 **Assertion** Let $\mathcal{A}$ be a proper system characterized by the input-output relation

$$(p - \lambda_1) \cdots (p - \lambda_n)y = M(p)u$$

in which the λ_i, $i = 1, \ldots, n$, are distinct and no $(p - \lambda_i)$ is a factor of $M(p)$. Furthermore, let the partial-fraction expansion of the transfer function $H(s)$ be

20 $$H(s) = \frac{c_1}{s - \lambda_1} + \cdots + \frac{c_n}{s - \lambda_n} + d_0$$

Then the system $\mathcal{B}$ shown in Fig. *4.9.11* is a realization of $\mathcal{A}$ and the vector $\mathbf{x} = (x_1, \ldots, x_n)$ defined by

$$\dot{x}_i = \lambda_i x_i + u \qquad i = 1, \ldots, n$$

qualifies as a state vector for $\mathcal{A}$. The corresponding state equations of $\mathcal{A}$ read (in matrix form)

21 $$\dot{\mathbf{x}} = \mathbf{A}\mathbf{x} + \mathbf{b}u$$
$$y = \langle \mathbf{c},\mathbf{x} \rangle + d_0 u$$

where

22 $$\mathbf{A} = \begin{bmatrix} \lambda_1 & 0 & \cdots & 0 \\ 0 & \lambda_2 & \cdots & 0 \\ \cdot & \cdot & \cdots & \cdot \\ 0 & 0 & \cdots & \lambda_n \end{bmatrix} \qquad \mathbf{b} = \begin{bmatrix} 1 \\ 1 \\ \cdots \\ 1 \end{bmatrix} \qquad \mathbf{c} = [c_1 c_2 \cdots c_n]$$

Note that under the assumption that the zeros of $L(p)$ are simple, the partial-fraction technique leads to state equations *21* in which the $\mathbf{A}$ matrix is in diagonal form.

Case of multiple zeros

For simplicity, we assume that $L(p)$ has just one multiple zero of order μ, in which case we write

$$L(p) = (p - \lambda_1)^\mu (p - \lambda_{\mu+1}) \cdots (p - \lambda_n)$$

[It is a trivial matter to extend the results obtained under this simplifying assumption to the case where $L(p)$ has more than one zero of multiplicity higher than 1.]

Proceeding as in the case of simple zeros, we expand the transfer function $H(s)$:

23 $$H(s) = \frac{M(s)}{(s - \lambda_1)^\mu (s - \lambda_{\mu+1}) \cdots (s - \lambda_n)}$$

into the partial fractions

24 $$H(s) = \frac{c_1}{(s - \lambda_1)^\mu} + \frac{c_2}{(s - \lambda_1)^{\mu-1}} + \cdots + \frac{c_\mu}{s - \lambda_1} + \frac{c_{\mu+1}}{s - \lambda_{\mu+1}} + \cdots + \frac{c_n}{s - \lambda_n} + d_0$$

The system $\mathcal{B}$ shown in Fig. *4.9.12* has this transfer function and hence, by Theorem *4.8.10*, is a realization of $\mathcal{A}$.

Associating the components of $\mathbf{x} = (x_1, \ldots, x_n)$ with the outputs of integrators in the manner indicated in Fig. *4.9.12*, the state equations

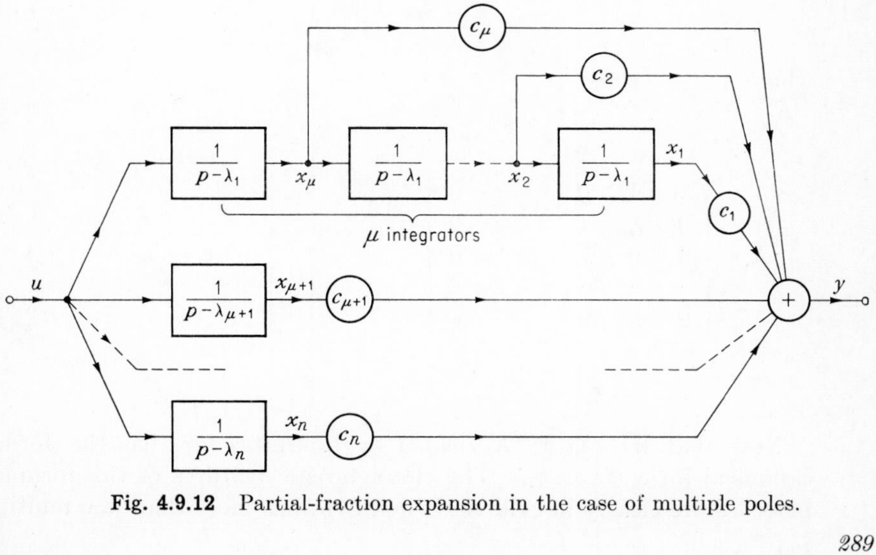

Fig. 4.9.12 Partial-fraction expansion in the case of multiple poles.

of $\mathcal{A}$ become

25
$$\begin{aligned}\dot{x}_1 &= \lambda_1 x_1 + x_2\\ &\cdots\cdots\cdots\\ \dot{x}_{\mu-1} &= \lambda_1 x_{\mu-1} + x_\mu\\ \dot{x}_\mu &= \lambda_1 x_\mu + u\\ &\cdots\cdots\cdots\\ \dot{x}_n &= \lambda_n x_n + u\\ y &= c_1 x_1 + \cdots + c_n x_n + d_0\end{aligned}$$

These results are summarized in the

26 **Assertion** Let $\mathcal{A}$ be a proper system characterized by the input-output relation

27
$$(p - \lambda_1)^\mu (p - \lambda_{\mu+1}) \cdots (p - \lambda_n) y = M(p) u$$

in which $\lambda_1, \lambda_{\mu+1}, \ldots, \lambda_n$ are distinct and no $(p - \lambda_i)$, $i = 1, \mu + 1, \ldots, n$, is a factor of $M(p)$. Furthermore, let the partial-fraction expansion of the transfer function of $\mathcal{A}$ be

28
$$H(s) = \frac{c_1}{(s - \lambda_1)^\mu} + \cdots + \frac{c_\mu}{s - \lambda_1} + \frac{c_{\mu+1}}{s - \lambda_{\mu+1}} + \cdots + \frac{c_n}{s - \lambda_n} + d_0$$

Then the system $\mathcal{B}$ shown in Fig. *4.9.12* is a realization of $\mathcal{A}$ and the vector $\mathbf{x} = (x_1, \ldots, x_n)$ defined as in Fig. *4.9.12* qualifies as a state vector for $\mathcal{A}$. The corresponding state equations of $\mathcal{A}$ read (in matrix form)

29
$$\begin{aligned}\dot{\mathbf{x}} &= \mathbf{A}\mathbf{x} + \mathbf{b}u\\ y &= \langle \mathbf{c}, \mathbf{x} \rangle + d_0 u\end{aligned}$$

where

$$\mathbf{A} = \begin{bmatrix} \lambda_1 & 1 & 0 & \cdots & 0 \\ 0 & \lambda_1 & 1 & \cdots & 0 \\ 0 & 0 & \lambda_1 & \cdots & 0 \\ \cdot & \cdot & \cdot & \cdots & \cdot \\ 0 & 0 & 0 & \cdots & \lambda_n \end{bmatrix} \qquad \mathbf{b} = \begin{bmatrix} 0 \\ \cdot \\ \cdot \\ \cdot \\ 0 \\ 1 \\ \cdot \\ \cdot \\ \cdot \\ 1 \end{bmatrix} \qquad \mathbf{c} = [c_1 \cdots c_n]$$

Note that the matrix **A** yielded by this procedure has the Jordan canonical form (*D.5.21*). The characteristic features of this form are placed more clearly in evidence when $L(p)$ has more than one multiple zero. For example, suppose that

$$L(p) = (p+2)^4(p+4)^2(p+1)(p+3)$$

Then **A** has the following form:

30
$$\mathbf{A} = \begin{bmatrix} -2 & 1 & 0 & 0 & 0 & 0 & 0 & 0 \\ 0 & -2 & 1 & 0 & 0 & 0 & 0 & 0 \\ 0 & 0 & -2 & 1 & 0 & 0 & 0 & 0 \\ 0 & 0 & 0 & -2 & 0 & 0 & 0 & 0 \\ 0 & 0 & 0 & 0 & -4 & 1 & 0 & 0 \\ 0 & 0 & 0 & 0 & 0 & -4 & 0 & 0 \\ 0 & 0 & 0 & 0 & 0 & 0 & -1 & 0 \\ 0 & 0 & 0 & 0 & 0 & 0 & 0 & -3 \end{bmatrix}$$

As was already stated, the main advantage of the partial-fraction expansion technique is that it leads to state equations in which the **A** matrix is in the Jordan canonical form or, when $L(p)$ has no multiple zeros, in the diagonal form. Its disadvantages are: (I) it requires the expansion of $1/L(p)$ into partial fractions—a process which is by no means trivial for high-order polynomials, (II) it leads to complex-valued state vectors when $\lambda_1, \ldots, \lambda_n$ are not all real, and (III) the relationship between the components of the state vector and the values of the output and its derivatives is considerably more complicated than in the case of the state vector defined by *7* or *16*.

31 *Example* Assume that $\mathcal{A}$ is characterized by the input-output relation

$$L(p)y = u$$

where

$$L(p) = (p+1)^2(p^2+1)$$

and hence

$$H(s) = \frac{1}{(s+1)^2(s^2+1)}$$

On expanding $H(s)$ into partial fractions, we have

$$H(s) = \frac{1}{2}\frac{1}{(s+1)^2} + \frac{1}{2}\frac{1}{(s+1)} - \frac{1}{4}\frac{1}{(s+j)} - \frac{1}{4}\frac{1}{(s-j)}$$

Correspondingly, the state equations read

$$\dot{\mathbf{x}} = \mathbf{A}\mathbf{x} + \mathbf{b}u$$
$$y = \langle \mathbf{c},\mathbf{x} \rangle$$

where

$$\mathbf{A} = \begin{bmatrix} -1 & 1 & 0 & 0 \\ 0 & -1 & 0 & 0 \\ 0 & 0 & -j & 0 \\ 0 & 0 & 0 & j \end{bmatrix} \qquad \mathbf{b} = \begin{bmatrix} 0 \\ 1 \\ 1 \\ 1 \end{bmatrix} \qquad \mathbf{c} = [\tfrac{1}{2}, \ \tfrac{1}{2}, \ -\tfrac{1}{4}, \ -\tfrac{1}{4}]$$

It is instructive to compare these matrices with their counterparts in the state equations *4.3.32*. On writing

$$L(p) = p^4 + 2p^3 + 2p^2 + 2p + 1$$

and making use of *4.3.32* we obtain for the latter

$$\mathbf{A} = \begin{bmatrix} 0 & 1 & 0 & 0 \\ 0 & 0 & 1 & 0 \\ 0 & 0 & 0 & 1 \\ -1 & -2 & -2 & -2 \end{bmatrix} \qquad \mathbf{b} = \begin{bmatrix} 0 \\ 0 \\ 0 \\ 1 \end{bmatrix} \qquad \mathbf{c} = [1, \quad 0, \quad 0, \quad 0]$$

This concludes our discussion of various techniques for associating a state vector with a differential system and determining the corresponding state equations of the system. We are now ready to proceed to study the behavior of differential systems in greater detail, based on the characterization of such systems by their state equations rather than input-output relations having the form of a single differential equation.

REFERENCES AND SUGGESTED READING

1 Laning, J. H., Jr., and R. H. Battin: "Random Processes in Automatic Control," McGraw-Hill Book Company, Inc., New York, 1956.
2 Lur'e, A. I.: Some Nonlinear Problems in the Theory of Automatic Control, *Gos. Izdat. Teh. Teo. Lit.*, Moscow, 1951.
3 Bashkow, T.: The *A* Matrix, New Network Description, *I.R.E. Trans. on Circuit Theory*, vol. CT-4, pp. 117–119, September, 1957.
4 Bryant, P. R.: The Explicit Form of Bashkow's *A* Matrix, *I.R.E. Trans. on Circuit Theory*, vol. CT-9, no. 3, pp. 303–306, 1962.

Linear time-invariant differential systems 5

1 *Introduction*

In the preceding chapters, we have introduced and discussed in general terms such basic concepts as state, linearity, time invariance, system equivalence, and differential systems. In what follows, we shall enter a new phase in our analysis. Specifically, we shall place greater stress on detail in our study of the relations between input, output, and state, with a view to developing a body of concrete analytical as well as computational techniques for the analysis and design of linear systems of various types.

The present chapter is concerned in the main with the development of methods for computing the response of time-invariant systems, with the discussion of time-varying systems deferred until the next chapter. In the first two sections we consider time-invariant systems described by their canonical state equations (*2.3.45*) $\dot{\mathbf{x}} = \mathbf{Ax} + \mathbf{Bu}$, $\mathbf{y} = \mathbf{Cx} + \mathbf{Du}$. Since the main problem in determining the dependence of $\mathbf{y}$ on $\mathbf{u}$ lies in solving the differential equation $\dot{\mathbf{x}} = \mathbf{Ax} + \mathbf{Bu}$, we shall focus our attention primarily on this problem, treating first the zero-input (free-motion) case and then the forced-motion ($\mathbf{u} \neq 0$) case. In particular, in Sec. *3*, a Laplace transform technique is developed for computing $\exp(\mathbf{A}t)$—a matrix which plays a central role in relating the state at time t to an initial state $\mathbf{x}(t_0)$. In Secs. *4* and *5* we present the mode interpretation of the motion in state space; this mode interpretation is a generalization of the concept of "normal modes" usually encountered in the study of small vibrations about an equilibrium point of a conservative dynamical system. Our interpretation, however, is applicable to all linear time-invariant systems. In the final sections we focus our attention on the properties and methods of solution for systems represented by higher-order differential equations of the form

$$\sum_j L_{ij}(p)x_j(t) = F_i(p)u(t)$$

$i = 1, 2, \ldots, n$, because such systems occur frequently in practice.

Since our main concern in this and the following three chapters is with the solution of systems of differential equations, we shall find it expedient in some instances to modify our notations and terminology in order to bring them into closer conformity with those commonly used in the theory of ordinary differential equations. In most cases, these modifications will be minor and self-explanatory. For example, the initial state at time t_0 will be denoted by $\mathbf{x}_0$ rather than $\boldsymbol{\alpha}_0$ or $\boldsymbol{\alpha}$, and the state at time t (in the absence of input) will be expressed as $\mathbf{x}(t;\mathbf{x}_0,t_0)$. The observation interval will frequently be taken to be $[t_0,t]$ rather than $(t_0,t]$. The zero-input response (for the case where $\mathbf{y} = \mathbf{x}$) will be referred to as *free motion* to stress its physical significance, etc. As a rule, we shall not comment on minor changes in terminology and notations when their motivation is clear from the context.

2 *Linear time-invariant systems described by their state equations*

In this section we consider linear time-invariant systems represented by their state equations in differential form. As explained in the introduction, we can simplify our analysis by assuming that the output of the system is its state. Thus, our primary concern will be with computing the solutions of state equations and interpreting their properties.

Zero-input response (free motion)

Since the output is the state $\mathbf{x}$ of the system, and since the input is identically zero, the system is described by a vector differential equation

1 $$\dot{\mathbf{x}} = \mathbf{A}\mathbf{x} \qquad \mathbf{x}(t_0) = \mathbf{x}_0$$

where $\mathbf{A}$ is an $n \times n$ matrix with constant elements that are real or complex numbers, $\mathbf{x}(t)$ is an n-rowed column vector representing the state of the system at time t, and $\mathbf{x}_0$ is the initial state of the system. It is well known that the differential equation *1* has a unique solution (see *2.3.40 et seq.*). We shall denote by $\mathbf{x}(t;\mathbf{x}_0,t_0)$ the value at time t of the solution which reduces to $\mathbf{x}_0$ at t_0. As a first step giving an analytic expression for $\mathbf{x}(t;\mathbf{x}_0,0)$ we introduce the

2 **Lemma** Let $\mathbf{A}$ be a constant $n \times n$ matrix whose elements are real or complex numbers. Define

3 $$\exp(\mathbf{A}t) = \mathbf{I} + \mathbf{A}t + \cdots + \mathbf{A}^k \frac{t^k}{k!} + \cdots$$

Then the series converges absolutely for all finite t and uniformly in any finite interval.

Proof The assertion is equivalent to stating that the sequence of matrices $\mathbf{S}_N$, where

$$\mathbf{S}_N = \sum_{k=0}^{N} \mathbf{A}^k \frac{t^k}{k!}$$

converges absolutely and uniformly to a finite-sum matrix. Let $a_{ij}^{(k)}$ be the (i,j) element of $\mathbf{A}^k$, $k = 0, 1, 2, \ldots$; then the (i,j) element of $\mathbf{S}_N$ is $\sum_{k=0}^{N} a_{ij}^{(k)} \frac{t^k}{k!}$. We have to establish the absolute convergence of this series for all $i, j = 1, 2, \ldots, n$. In other words, we have to show that

4 $$\sum_{k=0}^{\infty} \left| a_{ij}^{(k)} \frac{t^k}{k!} \right| < \infty \qquad \forall t \text{ finite}, \forall i,j$$

Let $m = \max_i \left(\sum_{j=1}^{n} |a_{ij}| \right)$; m is a finite number which depends only on $\mathbf{A}$. Since $\mathbf{A}^{k+1} = \mathbf{A}\mathbf{A}^k$, we have

$$\max_{i,j} |a_{ij}^{(k+1)}| = \max_{i,j} \left| \sum_{l=1}^{n} a_{il} a_{lj}^{(k)} \right| \leq \max_{i,j} \left(\sum_{l=1}^{n} |a_{il}|\,|a_{lj}^{(k)}| \right)$$
$$\leq \left(\max_i \sum_{l=1}^{n} |a_{il}| \right) \left(\max_{l,j} |a_{lj}^{(k)}| \right)$$

Hence

$$\max_{i,j} |a_{ij}^{(k+1)}| \leq m \max_{i,j} |a_{ij}^{(k)}| \qquad k = 1, 2, \ldots$$

Since for $k = 0$, by the definition of m, $\max_{i,j} |a_{ij}| \leq m$, we get, by induction on k,

$$\max_{i,j} |a_{ij}^{(k)}| \leq m^k \qquad k = 1, 2, \ldots$$

Thus the series *4* is dominated by $\sum_{k=0}^{\infty} m^k \frac{|t|^k}{k!} = e^{m|t|}$; hence it converges absolutely for any finite t. Futhermore, by the Weierstrass M test it converges uniformly over any finite interval $[-T, +T]$.

5 *Exercise* Let

$$\mathbf{A} = \begin{bmatrix} \lambda_1 & 0 \\ 0 & \lambda_2 \end{bmatrix} \qquad \mathbf{B} = \begin{pmatrix} \lambda & 1 \\ 0 & \lambda \end{pmatrix} \qquad \mathbf{C} = \begin{bmatrix} \lambda & 1 & 0 & \cdot & \cdots & 0 \\ 0 & \lambda & 1 & 0 & \cdots & 0 \\ \cdot & \cdot & \cdot & \cdot & \cdot & \cdot \\ \cdot & \cdot & \cdot & \cdot & \lambda & 1 \\ 0 & \cdot & \cdot & \cdot & 0 & \lambda \end{bmatrix}$$

Use the defining power series *3* to show that

$$\exp(\mathbf{A}t) = \operatorname{diag}(e^{\lambda_1 t}, e^{\lambda_2 t}) \qquad \exp(\mathbf{B}t) = \begin{pmatrix} e^{\lambda t} & te^{\lambda t} \\ 0 & e^{\lambda t} \end{pmatrix}$$

$$\exp(\mathbf{C}t) = e^{\lambda t}\begin{bmatrix} 1 & t & \frac{t^2}{2!} & \cdots & \frac{t^{n-1}}{(n-1)!} \\ 0 & 1 & t & \cdots & \frac{t^{n-2}}{(n-2)!} \\ \cdots & \cdots & \cdots & \cdots & \cdots \\ 0 & 0 & 0 & \cdots & 1 \end{bmatrix}$$

6 *Exercise* Show that $\mathbf{AB} = \mathbf{BA} \Rightarrow [\exp(\mathbf{A}t)]\,[\exp(\mathbf{B}t)] = [\exp(\mathbf{B}t)]\,[\exp(\mathbf{A}t)]$, $\forall t$. Find an example to show that if $\mathbf{AB} \neq \mathbf{BA}$, the above conclusion need not hold.

7 **Lemma** Let $\mathbf{A}$ be an $n \times n$ constant matrix whose elements are real or complex numbers. Let $\mathbf{\Phi}(t)$ be the solution to the matrix differential equation

8 $$\dot{\mathbf{\Phi}}(t) = \mathbf{A}\mathbf{\Phi}(t) \qquad \mathbf{\Phi}(0) = \mathbf{I}$$

Then

$$\mathbf{\Phi}(t) = \exp(\mathbf{A}t)$$

Proof Since $\mathbf{A}$ is constant, the solution is unique. The initial condition is satisfied by $\exp(\mathbf{A}t)$. Equation *3* is a power series in t which converges over any finite interval; therefore, it can be differentiated term by term. The resulting series is the derivative of $\exp(\mathbf{A}t)$, viz.:

$$\frac{d}{dt}\exp(\mathbf{A}t) = \mathbf{A} + \mathbf{A}^2 t + \mathbf{A}^3\frac{t^2}{2!} + \cdots + \mathbf{A}^{k+1}\frac{t^k}{k!} + \cdots = \mathbf{A}\exp(\mathbf{A}t)$$

Therefore, $\exp(\mathbf{A}t)$ is a solution of *8*. $\triangleleft$

Lemma *7* can also be proved easily by considering $\exp(\mathbf{A}t)$ as a function of a matrix (see *D.6.12*).

9 **Theorem** Let $\mathbf{A}$ be an $n \times n$ constant matrix whose elements are real or complex numbers. Let the system be described by its state equation

10 $$\dot{\mathbf{x}}(t) = \mathbf{A}\mathbf{x}(t) \qquad \mathbf{x}(t_0) = \mathbf{x}_0$$

where $\mathbf{x}_0$ is the prescribed state at time t_0. The resulting free motion is given by

11 $$\mathbf{x}(t;\mathbf{x}_0,t_0) = \exp[\mathbf{A}(t-t_0)]\mathbf{x}_0 \qquad -\infty < t < \infty$$

12 *Comment* The expression *11* gives, for all t in $(-\infty, \infty)$, the state at time t which is on the trajectory going through $\mathbf{x}_0$ at time t_0. A useful interpretation of *11* in the more general context of time-varying systems is the following. Let the matrix $\mathbf{\Phi}(t,t_0)$ be the solution of *8* such that $\mathbf{\Phi}(t_0,t_0) = \mathbf{I}$; that is, from *7*, $\mathbf{\Phi}(t,t_0) = \exp[\mathbf{A}(t-t_0)]$. Then by *11*,

$\mathbf{x}(t;\mathbf{x}_0,t_0)$ is the product of $\mathbf{\Phi}(t,t_0)$ and $\mathbf{x}_0$, that is, $\mathbf{\Phi}(t,t_0)$ is a linear transformation (see *C.9.1*) which maps the initial state $\mathbf{x}_0$ at t_0 into the state at time t. For this reason, $\mathbf{\Phi}(t,t_0)$ is called the *state transition matrix.* This point of view leads to another important fact: let $\bar{\mathbf{x}}(\mathbf{x}_0,t_0)$ be the trajectory going through $\mathbf{x}_0$ at time t_0 (that is, the vector-valued function defined for each t by *11*). The set of all solutions of *10* constitutes an n-dimensional linear vector space (see *C.2.1* and *C.4.11*); indeed, let $\mathbf{a}_1, \mathbf{a}_2, \ldots, \mathbf{a}_n$ constitute a basis for the state space and let $\mathbf{x}_0 = \sum_{i=1}^{n} \xi_i \mathbf{a}_i$ be the (unique) representation of $\mathbf{x}_0$ in that basis. Then

13
$$\mathbf{x}(t;\mathbf{x}_0,t_0) = \sum_{i=1}^{n} \xi_i \mathbf{x}(t;\mathbf{a}_i,t_0)$$

In other words, any solution of *10* can be uniquely represented by a suitable linear combination of $\mathbf{x}(t;\mathbf{a}_i,t_0)$, $i = 1, 2, \ldots, n$. It is relation *13* which is the basis for the mode interpretation which is developed in Sec. *4*.

Properties of exp $(\mathbf{A}t)$

14 **Assertion** The matrix exp $(\mathbf{A}t)$ is nonsingular for all finite t's. More precisely, let α be the trace of $\mathbf{A}$, that is, $\alpha = \sum_{i=1}^{n} a_{ii}$; then

15
$$\det [\exp (\mathbf{A}t)] = e^{\alpha t} \qquad -\infty < t < \infty$$

Proof Exercise for the reader (see *6.2.10*).

16 **Assertion** $\exp (\mathbf{A}t_1) \cdot \exp (\mathbf{A}t_2) = \exp [\mathbf{A}(t_1 + t_2)] \qquad \forall t_1, t_2$

Proof From *3*, we have

$$\exp (\mathbf{A}t_1) \cdot \exp (\mathbf{A}t_2) = \left(\sum_{k=0}^{\infty} \frac{\mathbf{A}^k t_1^k}{k!}\right)\left(\sum_{l=0}^{\infty} \frac{\mathbf{A}^l t_2^l}{l!}\right) = \sum_{k,l=0}^{\infty} \mathbf{A}^{k+l} \frac{t_1^k t_2^l}{k!\,l!}$$

where we used the fact that the two power series are absolutely convergent. Now, reorder the summation by putting $k + l = n$; thus

$$\exp (\mathbf{A}t_1) \cdot \exp (\mathbf{A}t_2) = \sum_{n=0}^{\infty} \mathbf{A}^n \frac{1}{n!}\left[\sum_{l=0}^{n} \frac{n!}{(n-l)!\,l!} t_1^{n-l} t_2^l\right] = \sum_{n=0}^{\infty} \mathbf{A}^n \frac{(t_1 + t_2)^n}{n!}$$

which is recognized to be exp $[\mathbf{A}(t_1 + t_2)]$ by Definition *3*.

17 *Comment* Since the R.H.S. of *16* is invariant under an interchange of t_1 and t_2, it follows that $\exp(\mathbf{A}t_1)$ and $\exp(\mathbf{A}t_2)$ commute for all t_1, t_2. Now let $t_2 = -t_1$; then together with *14* we get

18 $$[\exp(\mathbf{A}t)]^{-1} = \exp(-\mathbf{A}t)$$

Forced response

Let us now allow the input to differ from zero; we then have to consider the equation $\dot{\mathbf{x}}(t) = \mathbf{A}\mathbf{x}(t) + \mathbf{B}\mathbf{u}(t)$, where $\mathbf{B}$ is an $n \times r$ constant matrix and $\mathbf{u}(t)$ is an $r \times 1$ vector representing r scalar inputs. We shall simplify the notation and write $\mathbf{a}(t)$ for $\mathbf{B}\mathbf{u}(t)$.

19 **Theorem** Let the system be described by its equation in the state form

20 $$\dot{\mathbf{x}}(t) = \mathbf{A}\mathbf{x}(t) + \mathbf{a}(t)$$

where $\mathbf{A}$ is an $n \times n$ constant matrix and $\mathbf{a}(t)$ represents the effect of the input to the system. If the state at time t_0 is $\mathbf{x}_0$, then the state at time t is given by (see *6.2.22*)

21 $$\mathbf{x}(t;\mathbf{x}_0,t_0;\mathbf{a}_{(t_0,t]}) = \{\exp[\mathbf{A}(t - t_0)]\}\mathbf{x}_0 + \int_{t_0}^{t} \{\exp[\mathbf{A}(t-\tau)]\}\mathbf{a}(\tau)\, d\tau \qquad -\infty < t < \infty$$

or equivalently

22 $$\mathbf{x}(t;\mathbf{x}_0,t_0;\mathbf{a}_{(t_0,t]}) = \{\exp[\mathbf{A}(t - t_0)]\}\mathbf{x}_0 + \exp(\mathbf{A}t) \int_{t_0}^{t} [\exp(-\mathbf{A}\tau)]\mathbf{a}(\tau)\, d\tau \qquad -\infty < t < \infty$$

Proof The equivalence of *21* and *22* follows directly from *16* and *18*. To establish *22*, observe that for $t = t_0$ the R.H.S. reduces to $\mathbf{x}_0$, as it should. Next, differentiate the R.H.S. of *22*:

$$\mathbf{A}\{\exp[\mathbf{A}(t - t_0)]\}\mathbf{x}_0 + \mathbf{A}[\exp(\mathbf{A}t)] \int_{t_0}^{t} [\exp(-\mathbf{A}\tau)]\mathbf{a}(\tau)\, d\tau + [\exp(\mathbf{A}t)\exp(-\mathbf{A}t)]\mathbf{a}(t)$$

The last term reduces to $\mathbf{a}(t)$ by *18*. By comparison with *22*, we see that the expression above is of the form $\mathbf{A}\mathbf{x}(t;\mathbf{x}_0,t_0;\mathbf{a}_{(t_0,t]}) + \mathbf{a}(t)$. Therefore, the R.H.S. of *22* satisfies the differential equation *1* and the initial condition.

23 *Exercise* Consider the multiple-input linear time-invariant system described by

$$\dot{\mathbf{x}}(t) = \mathbf{A}\mathbf{x}(t) + \mathbf{B}\mathbf{u}(t)$$

where $\mathbf{A}$ is $n \times n$ and $\mathbf{B}$ is $n \times r$. Show that the control $\tilde{\mathbf{u}}_{(t_0,t_1]}$ will bring the system from the state $\mathbf{x}_0$ at time t_0 to the state $\mathbf{x}_1$ at time t_1 if and only if

$$\int_{t_0}^{t_1} [\exp(-\mathbf{A}\tau)]\mathbf{B}\tilde{\mathbf{u}}(\tau)\,d\tau = [\exp(-\mathbf{A}t_1)]\mathbf{x}_1 - [\exp(-\mathbf{A}t_0)]\mathbf{x}_0 \quad \triangleleft$$

We should like to give an interpretation of the second term of *21* and *22*. Let us introduce the notation

24 $$\mathbf{G}(t,\tau) = [\exp(\mathbf{A}t)] \cdot [\exp(-\mathbf{A}\tau)] \cdot 1(t-\tau) = 1(t-\tau)\exp[\mathbf{A}(t-\tau)]$$

$\mathbf{G}(t,\tau)$ is the Green function of the system *20*; because it is a matrix in the present case, we shall adopt the language of the physicist and refer to it as the *Green dyadic* of the system *20* (compare with *3.7.34 et seq.*). $\mathbf{G}(t,\tau)$ allows us to calculate the effect at time t of the input $\mathbf{a}$ acting in the interval $[\tau, \tau + \Delta\tau]$: for $\Delta\tau$ very small, this contribution is (see *21*)

$$\mathbf{G}(t,\tau)\mathbf{a}(\tau)\,d\tau$$

Another way of looking at this fact is to consider the case where $\mathbf{a}(t)$ is an impulse $\mathbf{c}$ occurring at time τ, that is, $\mathbf{a}(t) = \mathbf{c}\delta(t-\tau)$. The contribution to $\mathbf{x}(t)$ of this forcing function is given by the second term of *21*, namely

25 $$\mathbf{G}(t,\tau)\mathbf{c}$$

where t is the time at which the contribution is computed and τ is the time at which the impulse is applied.

The presence of the factor $1(t-\tau)$ in *24* is necessitated by the nonanticipative character of the system *20*; without this factor, an impulse $\mathbf{c}$ occurring at time τ would have some effect on $\mathbf{x}(t)$, according to *25*, even though τ might be later than t, that is, even though the input was applied later than the instant of observation.

With the notation *24* in mind, *21* may be rewritten for the case $\mathbf{x}_0 = \mathbf{0}$:

26 $$\mathbf{x}(t) = \int_{t_0}^{t} \mathbf{G}(t,\tau)\mathbf{a}(\tau)\,d\tau \qquad t \geq t_0$$

27 *Comment* Equation *24* can also be written in the form

$$\mathbf{G}(t,\tau) = [\exp(\mathbf{A}t)][\exp(\mathbf{A}\tau)^{-1}]1(t-\tau)$$

which is a form very close to the Green dyadic of time-varying systems (see *6.2.18*). The fact that the integral in *21* expresses the superposition property may be brought to light by an example borrowed from physics. Consider a uniform medium in which the electric charge density ρ is specified. The electrostatic potential ϕ at point $\mathbf{r}$ is given by

28 $$\phi(\mathbf{r}) = \int \frac{\rho(\mathbf{r}')}{4\pi\epsilon_0|\mathbf{r} - \mathbf{r}'|}\, d\mathbf{r}'$$

where the integral is carried over the whole space. There is a rough analogy between *26* and *28* in the sense that they both express the superposition property: $1/(4\pi\epsilon_0|\mathbf{r} - \mathbf{r}'|)$ is the potential at $\mathbf{r}$ due to a *unit* point change at $\mathbf{r}'$; $\mathbf{G}(t,\tau)\mathbf{c}$ gives the response at time t due to a "point" excitation $\mathbf{c}\delta(t - \tau)$.

3 *The computation of* exp (**A***t*)

It is not practicable to compute the matrix exp $(\mathbf{A}t)$ by the power series *5.2.3* except in very special cases or for small values of t. We can derive a closed-form expression for exp $(\mathbf{A}t)$ either as a special case of the study of the functions of a matrix or by a purely algebraic method based on the Laplace transform. The first method has the advantage of using the geometric insight resulting from the study of Appendixes *C* and *D*. We shall present it first. The second method, purely algebraic in its spirit, needs no special background, and we shall develop it to the extent of deriving all the important relationships obtained by the first method. From a practical computational point of view either method is effective.

exp (A*t*) as a particular case of a function of a matrix

The exponential function e^z is analytic everywhere in the finite complex plane; therefore, the fundamental formula for the function of a matrix is directly applicable (see *D.6.5*) and yields

1 $$\exp(\mathbf{A}t) = \sum_{k=1}^{\sigma} \sum_{l=0}^{m_k - 1} t^l e^{\lambda_k t} \mathbf{Z}_{kl}$$

where $\lambda_1, \lambda_2, \ldots, \lambda_\sigma$ are the distinct eigenvalues of $\mathbf{A}$ (hence $\lambda_i \neq \lambda_j$, $i,j = 1, 2, \ldots, \sigma$), m_k is the multiplicity of the eigenvalue λ_k as a zero of the minimal polynomial of $\mathbf{A}$ (see *18* below *et seq.* or *D.2.1*), and the matrices $\mathbf{Z}_{kl}$ have constant elements and depend exclusively on $\mathbf{A}$. The computation of the matrices $\mathbf{Z}_{kl}$ from $\mathbf{A}$ is presented in detail, together with an example, in Appendix *D*, Sec. *8*.

It should be stressed that if the minimal polynomial of $\mathbf{A}$ is not known, one may use for m_k the multiplicity of λ_k as a zero of the characteristic polynomial of $\mathbf{A}$, that is, the polynomial $\Delta(\lambda) = \det(\mathbf{A} - \lambda\mathbf{I})$. The only possible penalty for doing so is, in some cases, a certain amount of unnecessary computation, but the final result is the same (*D.8.27*). Whenever $\Delta(\lambda)$ has distinct zeros, then $m_k = 1$ for $k = 1, 2, \ldots, n$ and the minimal polynomial is identical with characteristic polynomial.

exp (A*t*) from the Laplace transform point of view

For very simple cases, say 2×2 matrices, the theoretical developments that follow are unnecessary. Consider *5.2.8*; take its Laplace transform. Clearly, $\exp(\mathbf{A}t)$, for $t \geq 0$, is the inverse Laplace transform of $(s\mathbf{I} - \mathbf{A})^{-1}$. This is easily computed to be of the form $\mathbf{B}(s)/d(s)$, where $\mathbf{B}(s)$ is a matrix whose elements are polynomials in s of degree $n - 1$ at most, and $d(s) = \det(s\mathbf{I} - \mathbf{A})$. By dividing all elements of $\mathbf{B}$ by the polynomial d, one obtains a matrix $\mathbf{R}$ whose elements are rational functions of s. [All elements have a common denominator $d(s)$.] Now perform a partial-fraction expansion on all elements of $\mathbf{R}$. The result is a sum of the form

$$\sum_{k=1}^{\sigma} \sum_{l=0}^{m_k - 1} \mathbf{Y}_{kl} \frac{1}{(s - s_k)^{l+1}}$$

where the matrices $\mathbf{Y}_{kl}$ have constant elements. The inverse transform of this sum gives

2 $$\exp(\mathbf{A}t) = \sum_{k=1}^{\sigma} \sum_{l=0}^{m_k - 1} \mathbf{Y}_{kl} \frac{t^l}{l!} e^{\lambda_k t}$$

This approach is satisfactory for very simple cases; however, when n is large, it is important to be able to organize the computation more systematically (especially for machine computation) and to have enough insight into the results to be able to check them. For this reason we present a more systematic approach to the question. The reader interested in only the practical computation of $\exp(\mathbf{A}t)$ is referred to *31* below.

Let us first deduce some results that follow from Cramer's rule.[1] Consider the matrix $\mathbf{\Phi}(t)$ (which is the state transition matrix with $t_0 = 0$) defined in *5.2.8*. Let $\hat{\mathbf{\Phi}}(s) = \mathcal{L}\{\mathbf{\Phi}(t)\}$, that is, $\hat{\mathbf{\Phi}}(s)$ is the matrix each element of which is the Laplace transform of the corresponding element of $\mathbf{\Phi}(t)$. Taking the $\mathcal{L}$ transform of both sides of *5.2.8*, we get

$$(s\mathbf{I} - \mathbf{A})\hat{\mathbf{\Phi}}(s) = \mathbf{I}$$

Since we know that each element of $\mathbf{\Phi}(t)$ can be bounded by $ke^{\sigma_0 t}$ for

[1] G. Birkhoff and S. MacLane, "A Survey of Modern Algebra," p. 306, The Macmillan Company, New York, 1953.

some k and σ_0, the above relation holds for all s such that Re $(s) > \sigma_0$ (*B.2.2* and *B.2.4*). Furthermore, this relation suggests to identify $\hat{\mathbf{\Phi}}(s)$ with the inverse of the matrix $(s\mathbf{I} - \mathbf{A})$. Since the determinant of this matrix is zero only for those s that are eigenvalues of $\mathbf{A}$, we are led to

$$\hat{\mathbf{\Phi}}(s) = (s\mathbf{I} - \mathbf{A})^{-1} \qquad \forall s \notin \mathcal{E}$$

where $\mathcal{E}$ is the set of all eigenvalues of $\mathbf{A}$. The first result we wish to consider is the

3 **Lemma** Let $\mathbf{A}$ be an $n \times n$ constant matrix; then

4 $$(s\mathbf{I} - \mathbf{A})^{-1} = \frac{\mathbf{B}(s)}{d(s)}$$

where[1]

5 $$d(s) = \det (s\mathbf{I} - \mathbf{A}) = s^n + d_1 s^{n-1} + \cdots + d_{n-1}s + d_n$$

and

6 $$\mathbf{B}(s) = s^{n-1}\mathbf{B}_0 + s^{n-2}\mathbf{B}_1 + \cdots + s\mathbf{B}_{n-2} + \mathbf{B}_{n-1}$$

with $\mathbf{B}_0, \mathbf{B}_1, \ldots, \mathbf{B}_{n-1}$ $n \times n$ matrices with constant elements.

Proof Cramer's rule establishes immediately that the (i,k) element of $(s\mathbf{I} - \mathbf{A})^{-1}$ is equal to $M_{ki}(s)/d(s)$, where $M_{ki}(s)$ is the cofactor of the (k,i) element of $(s\mathbf{I} - \mathbf{A})$. Now $M_{ki}(s)$ is $(-1)^{i+k}$ times the determinant of the matrix obtained from $(s\mathbf{I} - \mathbf{A})$ by deleting row k and column i; hence $M_{ki}(s)$ is a polynomial in s of degree $n - 1$ at most. Let $\mathbf{B}_l$ be the matrix whose (i,k) element is the coefficient of s^{n-1-l} in $M_{ki}(s)$ $(l = 0, 1, \ldots, n - 1)$; then *4* and *6* follow.

7 *Comment* This procedure for computing $\mathbf{B}(s)$ suggested by Cramer's rule is not a practical procedure when n is more than 2 or 3: it requires the evaluation of n^2 determinants of order $n - 1$, each of which requires the evaluation of $(n - 1)!$ products of $n - 1$ numbers, i.e., a total of $n^2(n - 1)(n - 1)!$ multiplications! In many instances, the problem of obtaining the polynomial $d(s)$ [let alone the matrix $\mathbf{B}(s)$] is not trivial. ◁

Let us establish a couple of facts which will turn out to be useful in the general development that follows.

8 **Corollary**

$$d_{n-1} = (-1)^{n-1} \sum_{i=1}^{n} A_{ii}$$

where A_{ii} is the cofactor of the element a_{ii} of $\mathbf{A}$.

[1] Usually one considers the characteristic polynomial $\Delta(s) = \det (\mathbf{A} - s\mathbf{I})$ instead of $d(s)$. Note that $\Delta(s) = (-1)^n d(s)$, since multiplying each row of $\mathbf{A} - s\mathbf{I}$ by -1 multiplies the determinant by $(-1)^n$.

Proof *5* implies that

$$d_{n-1} = \lim_{s \to 0} \frac{d}{ds}[d(s)]$$

Now $\frac{d}{ds} \det (s\mathbf{I} - \mathbf{A}) \Big|_{s=0}$ is a sum of n determinants whose ith term is the determinant obtained by differentiating the ith column of $(s\mathbf{I} - \mathbf{A})$ with respect to s and then setting s to zero; the resulting ith determinant is

$$i\text{th row} \rightarrow \begin{vmatrix} -a_{11} & -a_{12} & \cdots & 0 & -a_{1,i+1} & \cdots & -a_{1n} \\ -a_{21} & -a_{22} & \cdots & 0 & -a_{2,i+1} & \cdots & \cdot \\ \cdot & \cdot & \cdots & 0 & \cdot & \cdots & \cdot \\ \cdot & \cdot & \cdots & 1 & \cdot & \cdots & \cdot \\ & & & 0 & -a_{i+1,i+1} & & \\ & & & \cdot & & & \\ & & & \cdot & & & \\ & & & \cdot & & & \\ -a_{n1} & & \cdots & 0 & -a_{n,i+1} & \cdots & -a_{nn} \end{vmatrix}$$

$$\uparrow$$
$$i\text{th column}$$

Clearly, this determinant is $(-1)^{n-1}A_{ii}$. Hence *8* follows. ◁

Let us consider *8* again. From *6*, $\mathbf{B}(0) = \mathbf{B}_{n-1}$, and since the (i,i) element of $\mathbf{B}_{n-1}$ is $(-1)^{n-1}A_{ii}$, we have immediately, by comparing *5* and *8*,

9 $$d_{n-1} = \operatorname{tr} \mathbf{B}(s) \Big|_{s=0}$$

In principle, Cramer's rule suffices to compute the state transition matrix $\mathbf{\Phi}(t)$. We proceed now to show (I) that there is a more convenient method for evaluating $\hat{\mathbf{\Phi}}(s) = (s\mathbf{I} - \mathbf{A})^{-1}$ than Cramer's rule and (II) that the usual method of expanding a rational function in partial fractions can readily be extended to matrices [such as $\hat{\mathbf{\Phi}}(s)$] whose elements are rational functions. This procedure will give us tools to establish some facts that can be proved only by a detailed study of linear transformations as in Appendices *C* and *D*.

The technique for computing the coefficient matrices $\mathbf{B}_i$ of $\hat{\mathbf{\Phi}}(s)$ is given in the form of a

10 **Theorem**[1] Given an $n \times n$ constant matrix $\mathbf{A}$, then the coefficients d_i of the polynomial $d(s)$ defined in *5* and the matrix coefficients $\mathbf{B}_j$ of the matrix polynomial $\mathbf{B}(s)$ defined in *6* are given by

[1] J. M. Souriau, *C. R. Acad. Sci. Paris,* vol. 227, pp. 1010, 1011, 1948. Also called Fadeeva's method, in V. N. Fadeeva, "Computational Methods in Linear Algebra," Dover Publications, Inc., New York, 1959.

11
$$
\begin{aligned}
d_1 &= -\operatorname{tr}(\mathbf{A}) & \mathbf{B}_0 &= \mathbf{I}\\
d_2 &= -\tfrac{1}{2}\operatorname{tr}(\mathbf{B}_1\mathbf{A}) & \mathbf{B}_1 &= \mathbf{B}_0\mathbf{A} + d_1\mathbf{I}\\
d_3 &= -\tfrac{1}{3}\operatorname{tr}(\mathbf{B}_2\mathbf{A}) & \mathbf{B}_2 &= \mathbf{B}_1\mathbf{A} + d_2\mathbf{I}\\
&\cdots\cdots\cdots & &\cdots\cdots\cdots\\
d_k &= -\frac{1}{k}\operatorname{tr}(\mathbf{B}_{k-1}\mathbf{A}) & \mathbf{B}_k &= \mathbf{B}_{k-1}\mathbf{A} + d_k\mathbf{I}\\
&\cdots\cdots\cdots & &\cdots\cdots\cdots\\
d_{n-1} &= -\frac{1}{n-1}\operatorname{tr}(\mathbf{B}_{n-2}\mathbf{A}) & \mathbf{B}_{n-1} &= \mathbf{B}_{n-2}\mathbf{A} + d_{n-1}\mathbf{I}\\
d_n &= -\frac{1}{n}\operatorname{tr}(\mathbf{B}_{n-1}\mathbf{A}) & 0 &= \mathbf{B}_{n-1}\mathbf{A} + d_n\mathbf{I}
\end{aligned}
$$

12 *Comment* This iterative technique for successively computing the d_i's and the $\mathbf{B}_i$'s determines the characteristic polynomial by *5* and $(s\mathbf{I} - \mathbf{A})^{-1}$ by *6* and *4*. Therefore, it is an alternative method to Cramer's rule. It is of interest to note that the last equation of *11* serves as a check: the extent to which $\mathbf{B}_{n-1}\mathbf{A}$ differs from the diagonal matrix $-d_n\mathbf{I}$ gives an estimate of the magnitude of the round-off errors.

Proof First clear the denominator in *4* and take into account *5* and *6*; then, for all s,

13
$$(s^{n-1}\mathbf{B}_0 + s^{n-2}\mathbf{B}_1 + \cdots + s\mathbf{B}_{n-2} + \mathbf{B}_{n-1})(s\mathbf{I} - \mathbf{A}) = (s^n + d_1 s^{n-1} + \cdots + d_{n-1}s + d_n)\mathbf{I}$$

This equality between matrix polynomials will hold if and only if coefficients of like powers of s are equal; i.e.,

14
$$
\begin{aligned}
\mathbf{B}_0 &= \mathbf{I}\\
\mathbf{B}_1 &= \mathbf{B}_0\mathbf{A} + d_1\mathbf{I}\\
&\cdots\cdots\cdots\\
\mathbf{B}_k &= \mathbf{B}_{k-1}\mathbf{A} + d_k\mathbf{I}\\
&\cdots\cdots\cdots\\
\mathbf{B}_{n-1} &= \mathbf{B}_{n-2}\mathbf{A} + d_{n-1}\mathbf{I}\\
0 &= \mathbf{B}_{n-1}\mathbf{A} + d_n\mathbf{I}
\end{aligned}
$$

If the coefficients $d_1, d_2, \ldots, d_n$ of $d(s)$ were known, *14* would constitute an algorithm for computing the $\mathbf{B}_k$'s. Suppose now that the d_i's are unknown. Let σ be an arbitrary complex number; then, remembering that $d(s + \sigma)$ is a polynomial in s of degree n, we have successively

$$
\begin{aligned}
d(s+\sigma) &= \det((s+\sigma)\mathbf{I} - \mathbf{A})\\
&= d(\sigma) + sd'(\sigma) + \frac{s^2}{2!}d''(\sigma) + \cdots + \frac{s^n}{n!}d^{(n)}(\sigma)
\end{aligned}
$$

From *9* the coefficient of s in the above relation is

$$\operatorname{tr} \mathbf{B}(s+\sigma)\Big|_{s=0} = \operatorname{tr} \mathbf{B}(\sigma)$$

In other words, changing σ into s,

$$d'(s) = \operatorname{tr}(\mathbf{B}(s))$$

Hence from *5* and *6*

$$\operatorname{tr}(s^{n-1}\mathbf{B}_0 + s^{n-2}\mathbf{B}_1 + \cdots + s\mathbf{B}_{n-2} + \mathbf{B}_{n-1}) = \sum_{k=0}^{n} k d_{n-k} s^{k-1} \qquad \forall s$$

where $d_0 = 1$. These polynomials in s will be equal if and only if the coefficients of like powers of s are equal; i.e.,

15
$$\begin{aligned} \operatorname{tr}(\mathbf{B}_0) &= n \\ \operatorname{tr}(\mathbf{B}_1) &= (n-1)d_1 \\ &\cdots\cdots\cdots \\ \operatorname{tr}(\mathbf{B}_k) &= (n-k)d_k \\ &\cdots\cdots\cdots \\ \operatorname{tr}(\mathbf{B}_{n-1}) &= d_{n-1} \end{aligned}$$

Let us take the trace of the matrix equations *14* and use $\mathbf{B}_0 = \mathbf{I}$:

16
$$\begin{aligned} \operatorname{tr}(\mathbf{B}_1) &= \operatorname{tr}(\mathbf{A}) + nd_1 \\ &\cdots\cdots\cdots \\ \operatorname{tr}(\mathbf{B}_k) &= \operatorname{tr}(\mathbf{B}_{k-1}\mathbf{A}) + nd_k \\ &\cdots\cdots\cdots \\ \operatorname{tr}(\mathbf{B}_{n-1}) &= \operatorname{tr}(\mathbf{B}_{n-2}\mathbf{A}) + nd_{n-1} \\ 0 &= \operatorname{tr}(\mathbf{B}_{n-1}\mathbf{A}) + nd_n \end{aligned}$$

Subtracting each equation of *15* from the corresponding one of *16*, we get the first set of equations *11*. The second set is identical with *14*. Therefore, *11* is established. Q.E.D.

17 *Comment* In practical cases, it often happens that the numerator and denominator polynomials of a transfer function have common factors. In the present case where we deal with the matrix $(s\mathbf{I} - \mathbf{A})^{-1}$ whose elements are rational functions with the common denominator $d(s)$ (see *4*), a similar phenomenon may occur: it may happen that *all* elements of the matric polynomial $\mathbf{B}(s)$ have one or more factors in common with $d(s)$. When this happens, these common factors may be canceled from both the numerator and denominator of all the elements of $(s\mathbf{I} - \mathbf{A})^{-1}$ in *4*: more explicitly, since $\mathbf{B}(s)$ is an $n \times n$ matrix with polynomial elements, all the n^2 elements of $\mathbf{B}(s)/d(s)$ are rational functions in which the same common factors can be canceled.

This leads to a simplified expression, namely,

18 $$(s\mathbf{I} - \mathbf{A})^{-1} = \frac{\mathbf{P}(s)}{m(s)}$$

where the polynomial $m(s)$ and the matric polynomial $\mathbf{P}(s)$ are the result of these cancellations. Clearly, it is always true that $m(s)$ is a factor of $\Delta(s) = (-1)^n d(s)$ and degree $(m) \leq$ degree (Δ). When all possible cancellations common to all the n^2 rational functions that are elements of $(s\mathbf{I} - \mathbf{A})^{-1}$ have been performed, then the resulting denominator polynomial $m(s)$ is called the *minimal polynomial of the matrix* **A**. This minimal polynomial is identical with the minimal polynomial[1] defined in Appendix *D*, Sec. *2* (see in particular *D.2.1* to *D.2.6*). For our purposes here it is of interest to note that (I) $m(s)$ is the polynomial of least degree such that the matrix $m(\mathbf{A}) = \mathbf{0}$ and (II) every eigenvalue of **A** [that is, a zero of $\Delta(s)$] is a zero of $m(s)$. ◁

From the set of equations *11* the celebrated Cayley-Hamilton theorem is easily derived. Consider the system *11*: successively, from the bottom up, substitute for the successive $\mathbf{B}_k$'s the values assigned to them by the equation just above; then

$$\mathbf{0} = \mathbf{A}^n + d_1\mathbf{A}^{n-1} + \cdots + d_{n-1}\mathbf{A} + d_n\mathbf{I}$$

In other words, by referring to *5*,

$$d(\mathbf{A}) = \mathbf{0} \qquad \text{and} \qquad \Delta(\mathbf{A}) = \mathbf{0}$$

Therefore, we have the

19 **Cayley-Hamilton theorem** Let **A** be a matrix whose elements are real or complex numbers. Let the characteristic polynomial of **A** be denoted by Δ [that is, $\Delta(\lambda) = \det(\mathbf{A} - \lambda\mathbf{I})$]. Then the matrix $\Delta(\mathbf{A})$ is the zero matrix **0**. ◁

For the purpose of computing $(s\mathbf{I} - \mathbf{A})^{-1}$, Theorem *11* is a more efficient procedure than Cramer's rule because it requires only n matrix multiplications. The next step is to compute the inverse Laplace transform of $(s\mathbf{I} - \mathbf{A})^{-1}$. Since the n^2 elements of $(s\mathbf{I} - \mathbf{A})^{-1}$ are rational functions of s, the obvious procedure is to perform a partial-fraction expansion of each term of the matrix. Since from *18* every term of $(s\mathbf{I} - \mathbf{A})^{-1}$ has the same denominator, it seems reasonable to expect that this partial-fraction expansion can be carried out by matrix operations. That is, for the case of a simple pole at s_1, we can compute directly the matrix of residues at that pole, etc. The procedure is described by the

[1] In Appendix *D*, the minimal polynomial had to be labeled ψ in order to avoid conflicts of notation.

20 **Theorem** Let $\mathbf{A}$ be an arbitrary $n \times n$ matrix whose elements are real or complex numbers. Then

(I)

21 $$(s\mathbf{I} - \mathbf{A})^{-1} = \frac{\mathbf{P}(s)}{m(s)} = \sum_{k=1}^{\sigma} \sum_{l=0}^{m_k - 1} \frac{\mathbf{Y}_{kl}}{(s - \lambda_k)^{l+1}}$$

where the minimal polynomial of $\mathbf{A}$ is written as

22 $$m(s) = \prod_{k=1}^{\sigma} (s - \lambda_k)^{m_k}$$

(II) In addition, for $k = 1, 2, \ldots,$

23 $$\sum_k \mathbf{Y}_{k0} = \mathbf{I}$$
$$\mathbf{Y}_{k,l+1} = \mathbf{Y}_{kl}(\mathbf{A} - \lambda_k \mathbf{I}) \qquad l = 0, 1, 2, \ldots, m_k - 2$$
$$\mathbf{Y}_{k,m_k-1}(\mathbf{A} - \lambda_k \mathbf{I}) = \mathbf{0}$$

(III) Finally,

24 $$\exp(\mathbf{A}t) = \sum_{k=1}^{\sigma} \sum_{l=0}^{m_k - 1} \mathbf{Y}_{kl} \frac{t^l}{l!} e^{\lambda_k t} \qquad t \geq 0$$

25 *Comment* The matrices $\mathbf{Y}_{kl}$ defined in *21* are related to the $\mathbf{Z}_{kl}$ which appear in *1* as follows:

$$(l!)^{-1}\mathbf{Y}_{kl} = \mathbf{Z}_{kl}$$

Proof The proof of the theorem is very simple although somewhat detailed. The basic idea is to perform the partial-fraction expansion of $\mathbf{P}(s)/m(s)$ exactly as it is done in the scalar case. The next step is to study its properties.

(I) It is obvious from *21* and *22* that the elements of $(s\mathbf{I} - \mathbf{A})^{-1}$ have a pole of order $\leq m_k$ at λ_k. Let us therefore define the constant matrix $\mathbf{Y}_{k,m_k-1}$ by the relation

$$\mathbf{Y}_{k,m_k-1} \triangleq \lim_{s \to \lambda_k} \left[(s - \lambda_k)^{m_k} \frac{\mathbf{P}(s)}{m(s)} \right] \qquad k = 1, \ldots, \sigma$$

From *22* it follows that if we put $m(s) = (s - \lambda_k)^{m_k} p_k(s)$, we have $p_k(\lambda_k) \neq 0$ and

$$\mathbf{Y}_{k,m_k-1} = \frac{\mathbf{P}(\lambda_k)}{p_k(\lambda_k)}$$

This equality implies that

$$\mathbf{P}(s) - \mathbf{Y}_{k,m_k-1} p_k(s) = \mathbf{0} \qquad \text{for } s = \lambda_k$$

Therefore, the left-hand side is of the form

$$\mathbf{P}(s) - \mathbf{Y}_{k,m_k-1} p_k(s) = (s - \lambda_k)\mathbf{D}_1(s)$$

where each element of $\mathbf{D}_1(s)$ is obtained by factoring out $(s - \lambda_k)$ from the corresponding element of the left-hand side. Dividing this equation by $m(s)$ gives

$$(s\mathbf{I} - \mathbf{A})^{-1} = \frac{\mathbf{P}(s)}{m(s)} = \frac{\mathbf{Y}_{k,m_k-1}}{(s - \lambda_k)^{m_k}} + \frac{\mathbf{D}_1(s)}{(s - \lambda_k)^{m_k-1}p_k(s)} \qquad \forall s \notin \mathcal{E}$$

The last term of this expression is a matrix which has a pole of order $m_k - 1$ at λ_k. Therefore, define the constant matrix $\mathbf{Y}_{k,m_k-2}$ by the relation

$$\mathbf{Y}_{k,m_k-2} \triangleq \lim_{s \to \lambda_k} \left[(s - \lambda_k)^{m_k-1} \frac{\mathbf{D}_1(s)}{(s - \lambda_k)^{m_k-1}p_k(s)} \right]$$

Hence we can write

$$\frac{\mathbf{D}_1(s)}{(s - \lambda_k)^{m_k-1}p_k(s)} = \frac{\mathbf{Y}_{k,m_k-2}}{(s - \lambda_k)^{m_k-1}} + \frac{\mathbf{D}_2(s)}{(s - \lambda_k)^{m_k-2}p_k(s)} \qquad \forall s \notin \mathcal{E}$$

Iterating the procedure, we exhaust the pole at λ_k and get

$$(s\mathbf{I} - \mathbf{A})^{-1} = \sum_{l=0}^{m_k-1} \frac{\mathbf{Y}_{kl}}{(s - \lambda_k)^{l+1}} + \frac{\mathbf{C}_k(s)}{p_k(s)} \qquad \forall s \notin \mathcal{E}$$

where $\mathbf{C}_k(s)$ is the matrix with polynomials in s as elements resulting from these operations and, as above, $p_k(\lambda_k) \neq 0$. The summation in the above equation constitutes the contribution to $(s\mathbf{I} - \mathbf{A})^{-1}$ of the m_kth-order pole at λ_k.

Repeating this procedure at each eigenvalue of $\mathbf{A}$, one obtains *21*, thus establishing the statement (I) of the theorem.

(II) Define for $k = 1, 2, \ldots,$

26
$$\mathbf{Y}_k(s) = \sum_{l=0}^{m_k-1} \frac{\mathbf{Y}_{kl}}{(s - \lambda_k)^{l+1}}$$

Hence

27
$$(s\mathbf{I} - \mathbf{A})^{-1} = \sum_{k=1}^{\sigma} \mathbf{Y}_k(s)$$

and

28
$$\sum_{k=1}^{\sigma} \mathbf{Y}_k(s)(s\mathbf{I} - \mathbf{A}) = \mathbf{I}$$

Now

$$\begin{aligned}\mathbf{Y}_k(s)(s\mathbf{I} - \mathbf{A}) &= \mathbf{Y}_k(s)[(s - \lambda_k)\mathbf{I} + (\lambda_k\mathbf{I} - \mathbf{A})] \\ &= \mathbf{Y}_{k0} + \frac{[\mathbf{Y}_{k1} + \mathbf{Y}_{k0}(\lambda_k\mathbf{I} - \mathbf{A})]}{(s - \lambda_k)} + \cdots \\ &\quad + \frac{[\mathbf{Y}_{kl+1} + \mathbf{Y}_{kl}(\lambda_k\mathbf{I} - \mathbf{A})]}{(s - \lambda_k)^{l+1}} + \cdots \\ &\quad + \frac{\mathbf{Y}_{k,m_k-1}(\lambda_k\mathbf{I} - \mathbf{A})}{(s - \lambda_k)^{m_k}}\end{aligned}$$

If we substitute the above equation into *28*, we obtain a sum of the form

$$\sum_{k=1}^{\sigma} \sum_{l=0}^{m_k} \frac{\mathbf{N}_{kl}}{(s - \lambda_k)^l} = \mathbf{I} \qquad \forall s \notin \mathcal{E}$$

where the matrices $\mathbf{N}_{kl}$ have constant elements. Since this equality holds for all $s \notin \mathcal{E}$, each matrix $\mathbf{N}_{kl}$ must be zero for $l \geq 1$ and $\sum_{k=1} \mathbf{N}_{k0} = \mathbf{I}$. Hence,

$$\sum_{k=1}^{\sigma} \mathbf{Y}_{k0} = \mathbf{I}$$

$$\mathbf{Y}_{k,l+1} = \mathbf{Y}_{kl}(\mathbf{A} - \lambda_k\mathbf{I}) = \mathbf{Y}_{k0}(\mathbf{A} - \lambda_k\mathbf{I})^{l+1} \qquad l = 0, 1, 2, \ldots, m_k - 2 \quad k = 1, \ldots, \sigma$$

$$\mathbf{Y}_{k,m_k-1}(\mathbf{A} - \lambda_k\mathbf{I}) = \mathbf{0} \qquad k = 1, \ldots, \sigma$$

Thus *23* is established.

(III) This follows directly from taking the inverse transform of *21*.

29 *Comment* Observe that *23* implies that each term of *28* reduces as follows:

30 $$\mathbf{Y}_k(s)(s\mathbf{I} - \mathbf{A}) = \mathbf{Y}_{k0}$$

which is a constant matrix.

31 **Computational procedure** The computation of exp $(\mathbf{A}t)$ involves the following sequence of steps:

(I) Compute $\mathbf{B}(s)$ from $(s\mathbf{I} - \mathbf{A})$ by *11* or any other suitable method.

(II) Remove any known common factor between $d(s)$ and all the elements of $\mathbf{B}(s)$. The result is the numerator $\mathbf{P}(s)$ and the denominator $m(s)$. [If a common factor is overlooked, general theory shows that this will cause no erroneous result, only unnecessary computations (see *D.8.27*).] Let

$$m(s) = \prod_{k=1}^{\sigma} (s - \lambda_k)^{m_k}$$

(III) Compute the matrices $\mathbf{Y}_{k0}, \mathbf{Y}_{k1}, \ldots, \mathbf{Y}_{k,m_k-1}$, for

$$k = 1, 2, \ldots, \sigma$$

as follows: let $p_{ij}(s)$ be the (i,j) element of $\mathbf{P}(s)$; let $p_k(s)$ be defined by $m(s) = (s - \lambda_k)^{m_k} p_k(s)$ [note that $p_k(\lambda_k) \neq 0$]. Expand $p_{ij}(s)$ in Taylor series around λ_k, viz.:

$$\frac{p_{ij}(s)}{p_k(s)} = \alpha_0 + \alpha_1(s - \lambda_k) + \alpha_2(s - \lambda_k)^2 + \cdots + \alpha_{m_k-1}(s - \lambda_k)^{m_k-1} + \cdots$$

where

$$\alpha_l = \frac{1}{l!}\frac{d^l}{ds^l}\left[\frac{p_{ij}(s)}{p_k(s)}\right]\Bigg|_{s=\lambda_k}$$

Then $\mathbf{Y}_{k0}$ is the matrix whose (i,j) element is α_{m_k-1}

$\mathbf{Y}_{k1}$ is the matrix whose (i,j) element is α_{m_k-2}

$\mathbf{Y}_{k,m_k-1}$ is the matrix whose (i,j) element is α_0

(IV) Check that $\sum\limits_{k=1} \mathbf{Y}_{k0} = \mathbf{I}$

$$\mathbf{Y}_{k,m_k-1}(\mathbf{A} - \lambda_k\mathbf{I}) = \mathbf{0} \qquad k = 1, 2, \ldots, \sigma$$

The knowledge of the $\mathbf{Y}_{kl}$'s leads directly to exp $(\mathbf{A}t)$ by *24*. ◁

This ends the description of the computational procedure for finding exp $(\mathbf{A}t)$ based on the Laplace transform method. However, let us use the results obtained above to establish a basic fact that can also be derived by techniques of linear algebra.

Consider the residue matrices $\mathbf{Y}_{k0}$. From *30* we have

$$\mathbf{Y}_k(s) = \mathbf{Y}_{k0}(s\mathbf{I} - \mathbf{A})^{-1} \qquad \forall s \notin \mathcal{E}$$

and, from *27*,

$$\mathbf{Y}_k(s) = \mathbf{Y}_{k0} \sum_{j=1}^{\sigma} \mathbf{Y}_j(s)$$

Hence, by rearranging terms,

$$(\mathbf{Y}_{k0} - \mathbf{I})\mathbf{Y}_k(s) + \mathbf{Y}_{k0} \sum_{j \neq k} \mathbf{Y}_j(s) = \mathbf{0} \qquad \forall s \notin \mathcal{E}$$

Since $\mathbf{Y}_j(s)$ is the contribution to $(s\mathbf{I} - \mathbf{A})^{-1}$ of the pole at λ_j, the left-hand side is a sum of terms of a partial-fraction expansion which is identically zero. Hence, with the notation of *26*, we get

$$\mathbf{Y}_{k0}^2 = \mathbf{Y}_{k0} \qquad k = 1, \ldots, \sigma$$

$$\mathbf{Y}_{k0}\mathbf{Y}_{j0} = 0 \qquad j, k = 1, \ldots, \sigma; j \neq k$$

The first of the relations above implies that $\mathbf{Y}_{k0}$ represents a projection (see *C.12.4*). We express these results in the form of a

32 **Theorem** The residue matrices $\mathbf{Y}_{10}, \mathbf{Y}_{20}, \ldots, \mathbf{Y}_{\sigma 0}$ at the poles of $(s\mathbf{I} - \mathbf{A})^{-1}$ represent *projections* with the following properties:

$$\sum_{k=0}^{\sigma} \mathbf{Y}_{k0} = \mathbf{I}$$

$$\mathbf{Y}_{k0}\mathbf{Y}_{j0} = \mathbf{0} \qquad k \neq j \quad ◁$$

In the language of linear vector spaces, this implies that the range spaces of the residue matrices constitute a partition of the state space into direct sum of subspaces (see *D.5.6* and *15*). In Appendix *D*, the projections $\mathbf{Y}_{k0}$ are denoted by $\mathbf{E}_k$ (*D.5.6*).

4 *Modes in linear time-invariant systems (distinct eigenvalues)*

Any book on classical mechanics includes a chapter dealing with the study of small vibrations of *conservative* systems about an equilibrium point. It is shown that once the equations are linearized, any (small) free motion of the system can be thought of as a superposition of modes of vibration. Each mode of vibration is sinusoidal and is characterized by its frequency. This interpretation of the free motions in terms of modes is extremely important for understanding many engineering vibration problems. It is, however, less well known that this concept of modes can be extended to any linear system without requiring that it be conservative. Therefore, the mode concept that is presented below will apply, for example, to any linear time-invariant differential system, be it electrical, mechanical, or electromechanical, reciprocal or nonreciprocal, lossy or lossless, passive or active.

As a first step we must introduce a few preliminary ideas. Although these ideas are presented much more thoroughly in Appendix *C*, the account that follows is sufficient for our present purposes.

Eigenvalues, eigenvectors, basis, reciprocal basis, spectral expansion

For simplicity, consider a *single-input* linear time-invariant system described by its state equation[1]

1 $$\dot{\mathbf{x}}(t) = \mathbf{A}\mathbf{x}(t) + \mathbf{a}u(t)$$

where $\mathbf{A}$ is an $n \times n$ constant matrix, $\mathbf{a}$ is a constant n-vector, $u(t)$ is the (scalar) input, and $\mathbf{x}(t)$ ranges over $\mathcal{C}^n$ (space of n-tuples of complex numbers; see *3.7.36*). Let us first define a number of terms.

2 **Definition** The number λ is said to be an *eigenvalue* of $\mathbf{A}$ if $\Delta(\lambda) = \det(\mathbf{A} - \lambda\mathbf{I}) = 0$. $\Delta(\lambda)$ is called the *characteristic polynomial.* It is a polynomial of degree n in λ; therefore, there are at most n distinct eigenvalues. When $\mathbf{A}$ is real and λ is a complex eigenvalue, then λ^* is also an eigenvalue because $\Delta(\lambda)$ is a polynomial with real coefficients.

3 **Assumption** Throughout Sec. *4* the eigenvalues of $\mathbf{A}$ are assumed to be *distinct;* they are denoted by $\lambda_1, \lambda_2, \ldots, \lambda_n$.

4 **Definition** Any nonzero vector $\mathbf{u}_i$ such that

5 $$\mathbf{A}\mathbf{u}_i = \lambda_i\mathbf{u}_i$$

is called an *eigenvector* of $\mathbf{A}$; more precisely, it is an eigenvector associated with the eigenvalue λ_i. ◁

[1] The vector $\mathbf{a}$ in *1* is used in a sense which is different from that of *5.2.20*.

Since the components of $\mathbf{u}_i$ are the solutions of the system of n linear homogeneous algebraic equations, they are determined only within a constant factor: if $\mathbf{u}_i$ is an eigenvector, so is $\alpha\mathbf{u}_i$, where α is an arbitrary constant. This constant factor α is usually so selected that the "length" of the eigenvector is unity: the eigenvector is then said to be *normalized*. More precisely, let $\mathbf{u}_i = (u_{1i}, u_{2i}, \ldots, u_{ni})$; then $\mathbf{u}_i$ is normalized if $\sum_{j=1}^{n} |u_{ji}|^2 = 1$.

6 **Lemma** If the eigenvalues of $\mathbf{A}$ are distinct (i.e., if Assumption *3* holds), the n eigenvectors of $\mathbf{A}$ are linearly independent and hence constitute a basis for the state space $\mathcal{C}^n$ of *1*.

Proof By contradiction. Suppose the eigenvectors are not linearly independent; then there are n constants, $\alpha_1, \alpha_2, \ldots, \alpha_n$, not all zero, such that $\sum_{k=1}^{n} \alpha_k \mathbf{u}_k = \mathbf{0}$. Let i be the index of one of the nonzero constants. Let us premultiply the above relation by the matrix

$$(\mathbf{A} - \lambda_1\mathbf{I})(\mathbf{A} - \lambda_2\mathbf{I}) \cdots (\mathbf{A} - \lambda_{i-1}\mathbf{I})(\mathbf{A} - \lambda_{i+1}\mathbf{I}) \cdots (\mathbf{A} - \lambda_n\mathbf{I})$$

Observe that the matrix $(\mathbf{A} - \lambda_i\mathbf{I})$ is not a factor of this product. Clearly, since the factors of this product commute and since

$$(\mathbf{A} - \lambda_k\mathbf{I})\mathbf{u}_k = 0$$

for $k = 1, \ldots, n$, the result is

$$\alpha_i(\lambda_i - \lambda_1)(\lambda_i - \lambda_2) \cdots (\lambda_i - \lambda_{i-1})(\lambda_i - \lambda_{i+1}) \cdots (\lambda_i - \lambda_n)\mathbf{u}_i = \mathbf{0}$$

Since $\mathbf{u}_i \neq \mathbf{0}$ by *4* and since, for any $k \neq i$, $\lambda_i - \lambda_k \neq 0$ by Assumption *3*, the above equality implies $\alpha_i = 0$. This contradicts the assumption; therefore, the $\mathbf{u}_i$'s are linearly independent. Since there are n distinct eigenvectors and since the state space of *1* is of dimension n, the set of vectors $\mathbf{u}_1, \mathbf{u}_2, \ldots, \mathbf{u}_n$ constitutes a basis for the state space (see *C.4.9* to *C.4.11*).

7 **Definition** Let $\mathbf{a} = (\alpha_1, \alpha_2, \ldots, \alpha_n)$, $\mathbf{b} = (\beta_1, \beta_2, \ldots, \beta_n)$. The scalar product of $\mathbf{a}$ and $\mathbf{b}$ is written $\langle \mathbf{a}, \mathbf{b} \rangle$ and is by definition the complex number

8
$$\sum_{i=1}^{n} \alpha_i^* \beta_i = \langle \mathbf{a}, \mathbf{b} \rangle$$

This form of scalar product is called the *complex scalar product*. In most cases the vectors we are considering have real components. However, there are still many instances in which they have complex components. For this reason it is more convenient to use the complex scalar product throughout.

9 **Definition** Given a basis $\{\mathbf{u}_i\}_{i=1}^n$, the set of vectors $\{\mathbf{v}_i\}_{i=1}^n$ is said to be the *reciprocal basis* of the basis $\{\mathbf{u}_i\}$ if

10 $$\langle \mathbf{v}_i,\mathbf{u}_j\rangle = \delta_{ij} \qquad i, j = 1, 2, \ldots, n$$

11 *Comment* (I) Given the n^2 components of $\mathbf{u}_1, \ldots, \mathbf{u}_n$, *10* is a set of n^2 linear algebraic equations in the n^2 components of $\mathbf{v}_1, \ldots, \mathbf{v}_n$. The system splits easily into n systems with n unknowns: consider $\mathbf{v}_1$; its n components are the solutions of the n linear algebraic equations $\langle \mathbf{v}_1,\mathbf{u}_i\rangle = \delta_{1i}$. The determinant of this system has as elements of its ith row the components of $\mathbf{u}_i$. Since the $\mathbf{u}_i$'s are linearly independent, the determinant is different from zero and hence $\mathbf{v}_1$ is uniquely determined: *any basis has one and only one reciprocal basis.*

(II) Consider the two-dimensional case illustrated in Fig. *5.4.1*. Let $\mathbf{u}_1$ and $\mathbf{u}_2$ be specified. The direction of $\mathbf{v}_1$ is determined by the fact that $\langle \mathbf{v}_1,\mathbf{u}_2\rangle = 0$, that is, $\mathbf{v}_1$ is perpendicular to $\mathbf{u}_2$; its length is determined by $\langle \mathbf{v}_1,\mathbf{u}_1\rangle = 1$.

(III) If all the vectors of the basis $\{\mathbf{u}_i\}_{i=1}^n$ are normalized to a unit length, then the $\mathbf{v}_i$'s will in general not be normalized.

(IV) If the basis $\{\mathbf{u}_i\}_{i=1}^n$ is orthonormal, that is, $\langle \mathbf{u}_i,\mathbf{u}_j\rangle = \delta_{ij}$, then the basis is itself its own reciprocal basis. ◁

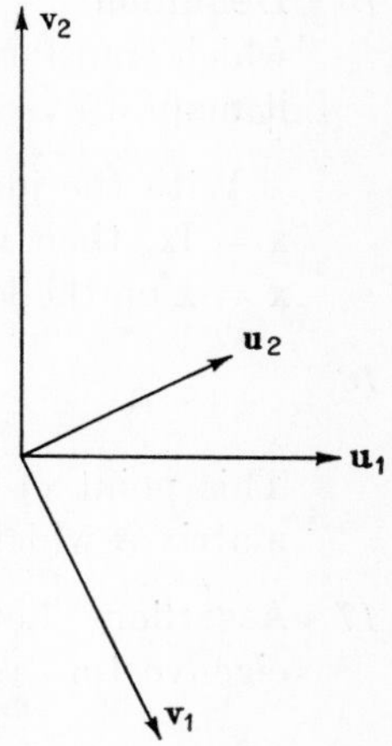

Fig. 5.4.1 The vectors $\mathbf{u}_1$, $\mathbf{u}_2$ constitute a basis for $\mathcal{C}^2$. The vectors $\mathbf{v}_1$, $\mathbf{v}_2$ are the vectors of the corresponding reciprocal basis.

The usefulness of the reciprocal basis follows from the

12 **Lemma** Let $\{\mathbf{u}_i\}_{i=1}^n$ be a basis. Let the (unique) representation of $\mathbf{x}$ be $\sum_{i=1}^{n} \xi_i \mathbf{u}_i$. Then

13 $$\xi_k = \langle \mathbf{v}_k,\mathbf{x}\rangle \qquad k = 1, 2, \ldots, n$$

and

14 $$\mathbf{x} = \sum_{i=1}^{n} \langle \mathbf{v}_i,\mathbf{x}\rangle \mathbf{u}_i$$

Proof *13* and *14* follow directly by taking the scalar product of $\mathbf{x} = \sum_{i=1}^{n} \xi_i \mathbf{u}_i$ with $\mathbf{v}_k$: that is, multiply the lth scalar equation by the complex conjugate of the lth component of $\mathbf{v}_k$ ($l = 1, 2, \ldots, n$) and sum; the result is *13* if we make use of *10*. *14* follows directly by substitution. ◁

At this point we need to introduce a convenient notation: consider the expression $\mathbf{a}\rangle\langle\mathbf{b}$ and call it a *dyad*. Given any vector $\mathbf{x}$, the product of the dyad $\mathbf{a}\rangle\langle\mathbf{b}$ and $\mathbf{x}$ is the vector $\mathbf{a}\langle\mathbf{b},\mathbf{x}\rangle$, that is, the vector $\mathbf{a}$ times the scalar $\langle\mathbf{b},\mathbf{x}\rangle$. The result may also be written $\langle\mathbf{b},\mathbf{x}\rangle\mathbf{a}$. Another way of looking at this definition is to observe that $\mathbf{a}\rangle\langle\mathbf{b}$, considered as a linear transformation operating on the vector $\mathbf{x}$, has a one-dimensional *range* (see *C.9.6*) which is spanned by $\mathbf{a}$, that is, all vectors $(\mathbf{a}\rangle\langle\mathbf{b})\mathbf{x}$ are proportional to $\mathbf{a}$. More precisely, we have the

15 **Definition** A *dyad* is a linear transformation denoted by $\mathbf{a}\rangle\langle\mathbf{b}$ which transforms the vector $\mathbf{x}$ into the vector $\langle\mathbf{b},\mathbf{x}\rangle\mathbf{a}$. In other words, it maps all vectors of $\mathcal{C}^n$ into vectors proportional to $\mathbf{a}$.

With the idea of the dyad in mind, if we look at *14* and note that $\mathbf{x} = \mathbf{I}\mathbf{x}$, then we may say that *14* has been obtained by multiplying $\mathbf{x} = \mathbf{x}$ on the left by

16
$$\mathbf{I} = \sum_{i=1}^{n} \mathbf{u}_i\rangle\langle\mathbf{v}_i$$

This point of view leads to a very important representation of any matrix $\mathbf{A}$ which satisfies Assumption *3*.

17 **Assertion** Let $\mathbf{A}$ have n distinct eigenvalues λ_i. Let $\{\mathbf{u}_i\}$ be its eigenvectors and $\{\mathbf{v}_i\}$ the reciprocal basis of the $\mathbf{u}_i$'s (see *9*). Then

18
$$\mathbf{A} = \sum_{i=1}^{n} \lambda_i\mathbf{u}_i\rangle\langle\mathbf{v}_i$$

Proof It follows by direct computation that for any $\mathbf{x}$, we have

$$\mathbf{A}\mathbf{x} = \mathbf{A}\Big(\sum_{i=1}^{n} \langle\mathbf{v}_i,\mathbf{x}\rangle\mathbf{u}_i\Big) = \sum_{i=1}^{n} \langle\mathbf{v}_i,\mathbf{x}\rangle\mathbf{A}\mathbf{u}_i$$
$$= \sum_{i=1}^{n} \langle\mathbf{v}_i,\mathbf{x}\rangle\lambda_i\mathbf{u}_i = \Big(\sum_{i=1}^{n} \lambda_i\mathbf{u}_i\rangle\langle\mathbf{v}_i\Big)\mathbf{x}$$

Note that in these steps we used *14*, the linearity of $\mathbf{A}$ and *5*. ◁

Expression *18* is called the *spectral representation* of $\mathbf{A}$: it gives a geometric interpretation of the effect of the linear transformation $\mathbf{A}$ on the vector $\mathbf{x}$. Consider all vectors with their components with respect to the basis $\{\mathbf{u}_i\}$; the ith component of $\mathbf{A}\mathbf{x}$ is equal to λ_i times the ith component of $\mathbf{x}$ ($i = 1, 2, \ldots, n$).

19 *Exercise* Define the product of two dyads by $(\mathbf{a}\rangle\langle\mathbf{b})(\mathbf{c}\rangle\langle d) = \langle\mathbf{b},\mathbf{c}\rangle\mathbf{a}\rangle\langle\mathbf{d}$. Let $\mathbf{E}_i = \mathbf{u}_i\rangle\langle\mathbf{v}_i$, in the notation of *10*. Show that $\mathbf{E}_i\mathbf{E}_j = \mathbf{0}$, $\mathbf{E}_i^2 = \mathbf{E}_i$, and $\sum_{i=1}^{n} \mathbf{E}_i = \mathbf{I}$.

20 *Exercise* Use the notation and assumptions of *17*. Let $\mathbf{P}$ be the matrix whose ith column is the components of $\mathbf{u}_i$. Let $\mathbf{Q}$ be the matrix whose ith row is the complex conjugates of the components of $\mathbf{v}_i$. (Remember we use the complex scalar product *7*.) (I) Show that $\mathbf{QP} = \mathbf{I}$.

(II) Show that both **P** and **Q** are nonsingular. (III) In the equation $\dot{\mathbf{x}} = \mathbf{A}\mathbf{x}$, change variable, put $\mathbf{x} = \mathbf{P}\mathbf{y}$. Put $\mathbf{y} = (\eta_1, \ldots, \eta_n)$. Show that the resulting equations are $\dot{\eta}_i = \lambda_i \eta_i$, $i = 1, 2, \ldots, n$. In other words if we pick as basis vectors the eigenvectors of **A**, the system $\dot{\mathbf{x}} = \mathbf{A}\mathbf{x}$ is diagonalized.

Mode interpretation of free motions

We now develop the mode interpretation of the free motions[1] of the system *1*; that is, throughout this subsection the input **u** is zero for all t. We use the same notation as above and we restrict ourselves to the case where Assumption *3* holds, that is, **A** has distinct eigenvalues.

To start the analysis, let us express the free motion $\mathbf{x}(t;\mathbf{x}_0,0)$ in terms of its components along the eigenvectors of **A**, viz.:

21 $$\mathbf{x}(t;\mathbf{x}_0,0) = \sum_{i=1}^{n} \alpha_i(t)\mathbf{u}_i \qquad -\infty < t < \infty$$

This is always possible, since by *6* the $\mathbf{u}_i$'s constitute a basis for the state space. Considering *21* at $t = 0$ and using *13*, we get

22 $$\alpha_i(0) = \langle \mathbf{v}_i, \mathbf{x}_0 \rangle \qquad i = 1, 2, \ldots, n$$

In order to calculate the functions $\alpha_i(t)$, substitute *21* into *1* and obtain successively

$$\sum_{i=1}^{n} \dot{\alpha}_i(t)\mathbf{u}_i = \mathbf{A}\left[\sum_{i=1}^{n} \alpha_i(t)\mathbf{u}_i\right] = \sum_{i=1}^{n} \alpha_i(t)\mathbf{A}\mathbf{u}_i$$
$$= \sum_{i=1}^{n} \alpha_i(t)\lambda_i\mathbf{u}_i$$

The resulting equality is one between two vectors, both expressed as a linear combination of the basis vectors. Since such representation is unique,

23 $$\dot{\alpha}_i(t) = \lambda_i \alpha_i(t) \qquad i = 1, 2, \ldots, n$$

The solution of *23* subject to the initial conditions *22* is

$$\alpha_i(t) = e^{\lambda_i t}\langle \mathbf{v}_i, \mathbf{x}_0 \rangle \qquad i = 1, 2, \ldots, n$$

Hence

24 $$\mathbf{x}(t;\mathbf{x}_0,0) = \sum_{i=1}^{n} e^{\lambda_i t}\langle \mathbf{v}_i, \mathbf{x}_0 \rangle \mathbf{u}_i$$

Comparing this with *5.2.11*, we are led to the expression

25 $$\exp(\mathbf{A}t) = \sum_{i=1}^{n} e^{\lambda_i t}\mathbf{u}_i \rangle \langle \mathbf{v}_i$$

[1] We could also call these free motions "zero-input state responses" since we are considering the case where the state itself is the output.

the *spectral representation* of exp $(\mathbf{A}t)$. Note that in order to derive *25* we had to assume that $\mathbf{A}$ has distinct eigenvalues. In general, *25* holds if and only if $\mathbf{A}$ is a simple linear transformation (see *41* below).

26 *Exercise* Derive *24* by using the point of view of Comment *5.2.12*, especially Eq. *5.2.13*. ◁

We are now ready to introduce some interpretations. First let us define the concept of mode for systems satisfying Assumption *3*.

27 **Definition** The free system $\dot{\mathbf{x}} = \mathbf{A}\mathbf{x}$ will be said to have one and only one *mode* excited if its free motion (zero-input response) is of the form

$$\mathbf{x}(t) = \mathbf{c}e^{\lambda t}$$

where $\mathbf{c}$ is a constant vector and λ is a constant scalar. ◁

Clearly, since *24* represents all possible free motions of the system, the constant λ in the factor $e^{\lambda t}$ must be an eigenvalue of $\mathbf{A}$. To emphasize the ideas associated with the mode concept, we express them in terms of assertions.

28 **Assertion** Any free motion of the system *1* can be represented in one and only one way as the superposition of a certain number of modes of the system. ◁

The uniqueness follows from the fact that the eigenvectors of $\mathbf{A}$ constitute a basis for the state space (see *6*).

29 **Assertion** Each mode is excited independently of the other modes. ◁

Here by the "excitation" of the ith mode we mean $\langle \mathbf{v}_i, \mathbf{x}_0 \rangle$. The assertion follows immediately: the excitation of the ith mode is computed directly from $\mathbf{x}_0$ without regard to the values of $\langle \mathbf{v}_k, \mathbf{x}_0 \rangle$ for $k \neq i$. Another way of illustrating this fact is the following: suppose $\mathbf{x}_0 = \beta \mathbf{u}_i$, where β is a constant; geometrically the initial state is on the line supported by the ith eigenvector. By *10*, $\langle \mathbf{v}_k, \mathbf{x}_0 \rangle = 0$ for $k \neq i$; hence $\mathbf{x}(t;\beta\mathbf{u}_i,0) = \beta e^{\lambda_i t}\mathbf{u}_i$. Similarly, it is easy to find the initial state required for having the first mode excited by β_1, the second by β_2, . . . ; simply pick $\mathbf{x}_0 = \beta_1\mathbf{u}_1 + \beta_2\mathbf{u}_2 + \cdots + \beta_n\mathbf{u}_n$.

30 **Assertion** The excitation of each mode in the free motion depends only on the initial state. This is obvious from *24*. ◁

The interesting fact about these results is that the concept of modes applies to any linear time-invariant system with distinct eigenvalues. These concepts apply whether the system is active or passive, lossless or lossy, reciprocal or nonreciprocal. These concepts, of course, apply to a wide variety of physical systems: the only requirement is that the mathematical model satisfy *1* and *3*.

31 *Example*[1] We now illustrate these ideas by a simple example, namely, the *RC* circuit shown in Fig. *5.4.2*. Let us label the voltages across each

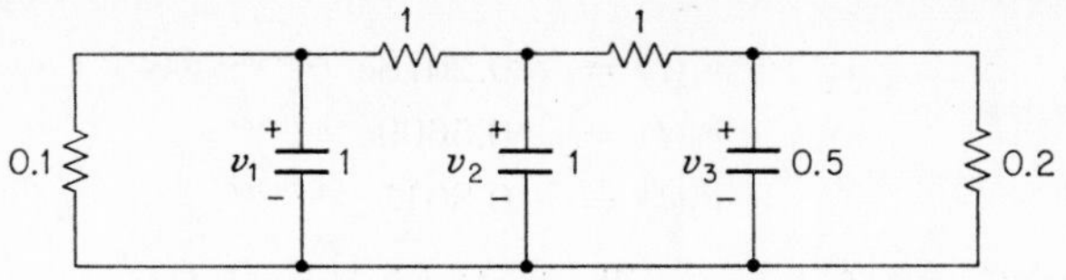

Fig. 5.4.2 Third-order system used in Example *5.4.31*. The element values are in mhos and darafs.

capacitance v_1, v_2, and v_3 and call $\mathbf{x}$ the vector whose components are v_1, v_2, and v_3. The three node equations read

$$\begin{aligned} \dot{v}_1 + 1.1v_1 - v_2 &= 0 \\ \dot{v}_2 - v_1 + 2v_2 - v_3 &= 0 \\ (\tfrac{1}{2})\dot{v}_3 - v_2 + 1.2v_3 &= 0 \end{aligned}$$

In matrix form, after multiplying the last equation by 2, we have

$$\dot{\mathbf{x}} = \mathbf{A}\mathbf{x} \qquad \text{where } \mathbf{A} = \begin{bmatrix} -1.1 & 1 & 0 \\ 1 & -2 & 1 \\ 0 & 2 & -2.4 \end{bmatrix}$$

The third-degree characteristic equation det $(\mathbf{A} - \lambda\mathbf{I}) = 0$ has three

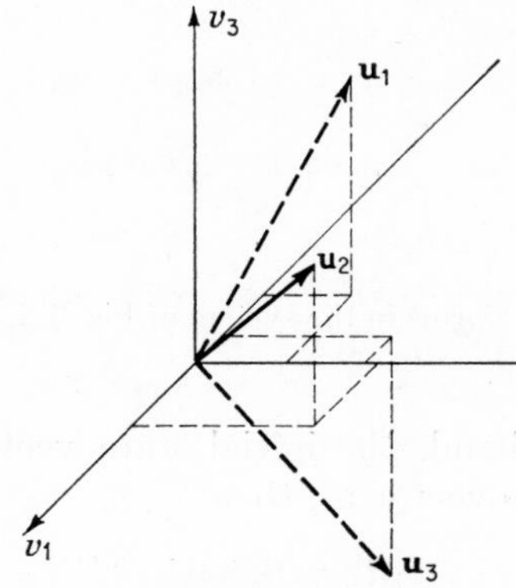

Fig. 5.4.3 Perspective view of the eigenvectors of the system shown in Fig. *5.4.2*.

roots: $\lambda_1 = -1.5878$, $\lambda_2 = -0.1126$, $\lambda_3 = -3.7996$. Solving Eq. *5* with these eigenvalues, we obtain the following normalized eigenvectors:

$$\mathbf{u}_1 = \begin{bmatrix} -0.6108 \\ 0.2980 \\ 0.7337 \end{bmatrix} \qquad \mathbf{u}_2 = \begin{bmatrix} 0.6064 \\ 0.5986 \\ 0.5235 \end{bmatrix} \qquad \mathbf{u}_3 = \begin{bmatrix} -0.2078 \\ 0.5609 \\ -0.8015 \end{bmatrix}$$

These eigenvectors are illustrated in Fig. *5.4.3*. If the initial conditions

[1] C. A. Desoer, Modes in Linear Circuits, *I.R.E. Trans. Circuit Theory*, vol. CT-7, no. 3, pp. 211–223, 1960.

are $v_1(0) = -0.2078$, $v_2(0) = 0.5609$, $v_3(0) = -0.8015$ (or any set of numbers proportional to the components of $\mathbf{u}_3$), the resulting behavior is

$$v_1(t) = -0.2078e^{-3.7996t}$$
$$v_2(t) = 0.5609e^{-3.7996t}$$
$$v_3(t) = -0.8015e^{-3.7996t}$$

These three waveforms are illustrated in Fig. *5.4.4*.

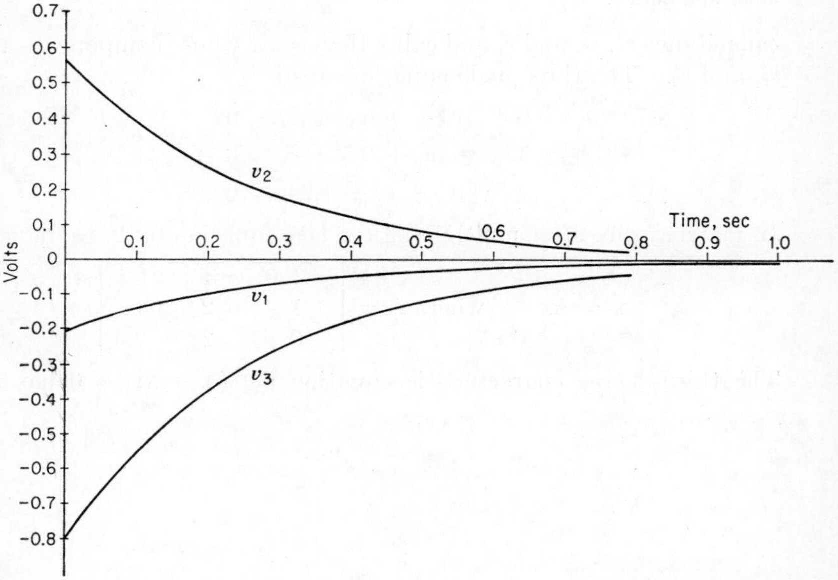

Fig. 5.4.4 Voltage waveforms in the system of Fig. *5.4.2* when only the third mode is excited.

If, on the other hand, the initial state vector $\mathbf{x}(0)$ had been proportional to the eigenvector $\mathbf{u}_2$, then

$$v_1(t) = 0.6064e^{-0.1126t}$$
$$v_2(t) = 0.5986e^{-0.1126t}$$
$$v_3(t) = 0.5235e^{-0.1126t}$$

Free motion (complex eigenvalues)

The analytical developments above apply in all cases where $\mathbf{A}$ is a constant matrix with distinct eigenvalues. In most applications the elements of $\mathbf{A}$, as well as those of $\mathbf{x}$, are real. However, the application of the formula *24* may lead to complex terms if some eigenvalues are complex. We propose here to consider this case in more detail.

We assume that $\mathbf{A}$ is real and $\mathbf{x}_0$ is real. Let $\lambda_1 = \alpha_1 + j\omega_1$ be a complex eigenvalue of **A**. Since the characteristic polynomial det $(\mathbf{A} - \lambda\mathbf{I})$ has real coefficients, $\lambda_1^* = \alpha_1 - j\omega_1$ is also an eigenvalue. Let us call it λ_2. The eigenvector $\mathbf{u}_1$, corresponding to λ_1, has complex elements; we shall write it

$$\mathbf{u}_1 = \mathbf{u}_1' + j\mathbf{u}_1'' \qquad \mathbf{u}_1', \mathbf{u}_1'' \text{ real}$$

Similarly, $\mathbf{u}_2$, the eigenvector corresponding to λ_2, is of the form (see *5*)

$$\mathbf{u}_2 = \mathbf{u}_1' - j\mathbf{u}_1''$$

It is easily verified that $\mathbf{v}_1$ and $\mathbf{v}_2$, the elements of the reciprocal basis corresponding to $\mathbf{u}_1$ and $\mathbf{u}_2$, are complex conjugates of one another. Let us put

$$\mathbf{v}_1 = \tfrac{1}{2}\mathbf{v}_1' + j\tfrac{1}{2}\mathbf{v}_1'' \qquad \mathbf{v}_2 = \tfrac{1}{2}\mathbf{v}_1' - j\tfrac{1}{2}\mathbf{v}_1'' \qquad \mathbf{v}_1', \mathbf{v}_1'' \text{ real}$$

The relations

$$\langle \mathbf{v}_1,\mathbf{u}_1\rangle = 1 \qquad \langle \mathbf{v}_1,\mathbf{u}_2\rangle = 0$$

become four scalar relations involving real vectors $\mathbf{u}_1'$, $\mathbf{v}_1'$, $\mathbf{u}_1''$, and $\mathbf{v}_1''$:

$$\langle \mathbf{v}_1',\mathbf{u}_1'\rangle = 1 \qquad \langle \mathbf{v}_1'',\mathbf{u}_1'\rangle = 0$$
$$\langle \mathbf{v}_1',\mathbf{u}_1''\rangle = 0 \qquad \langle \mathbf{v}_1'',\mathbf{u}_1''\rangle = 1$$

With these notations, the first two terms of *24* become

32 $$e^{\alpha_1 t}[\langle \mathbf{v}_1',\mathbf{x}_0\rangle \cos \omega_1 t + \langle \mathbf{v}_1'',\mathbf{x}_0\rangle \sin \omega_1 t]\mathbf{u}_1' + e^{\alpha_1 t}[\langle \mathbf{v}_1'',\mathbf{x}_0\rangle \cos \omega_1 t - \langle \mathbf{v}_1',\mathbf{x}_0\rangle \sin \omega_1 t]\mathbf{u}_1''$$

or, in its equivalent polar form,

33 $$e^{\alpha_1 t}[\gamma \cos(\omega_1 t - \varphi)\,\mathbf{u}_1' - \gamma \sin(\omega_1 t - \varphi)\,\mathbf{u}_1'']$$

where γ and φ are given by

$$\gamma \cos \varphi = \langle \mathbf{v}_1',\mathbf{x}_0\rangle \qquad \gamma \sin \varphi = \langle \mathbf{v}_1'',\mathbf{x}_0\rangle$$

The bracketed quantity is the superposition of two sinusoidal oscillations along the directions $\mathbf{u}_1'$, $\mathbf{u}_1''$. The amplitude and phase of the oscillations depend only on the initial state $\mathbf{x}_0$. The whole motion occurs in the plane (more precisely, two-dimensional subspace), supported by $\mathbf{u}_1'$ and $\mathbf{u}_1''$. In order to better illustrate *32* and *33*, consider two special cases:

(I) $\mathbf{x}_0 = \mathbf{u}_1'$. Then $\gamma = 1$ and $\varphi = 0$.

$$\mathbf{x}(t) = e^{\alpha_1 t} \cos \omega_1 t\,\mathbf{u}_1' - e^{\alpha_1 t} \sin \omega_1 t\,\mathbf{u}_1''$$

(II) $\mathbf{x}_0 = \mathbf{u}_1''$. Then $\gamma = 1$ and $\varphi = \pi/2$.

$$\mathbf{x}(t) = e^{\alpha_1 t} \sin \omega_1 t\,\mathbf{u}_1' + e^{\alpha_1 t} \cos \omega_1 t\,\mathbf{u}_1''$$

These two cases are illustrated in Fig. *5.4.5*, where we have assumed $\alpha_1 < 0$ so that the state slides along the exponential spiral toward the origin.

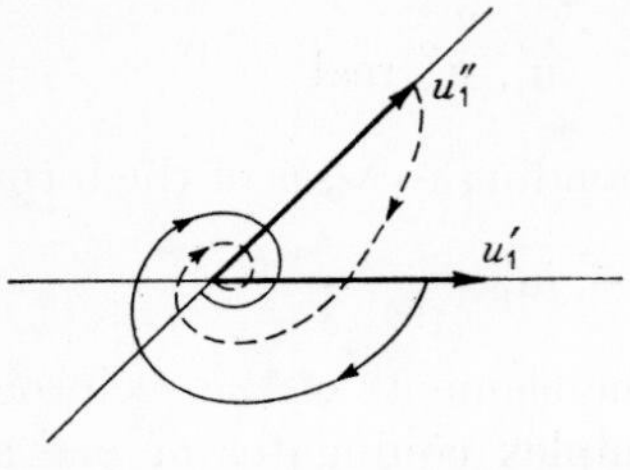

Fig. 5.4.5 Illustration of the spiral motions in the plane $\mathbf{u}_1'$, $\mathbf{u}_1''$ resulting from a mode with complex eigenvalue.

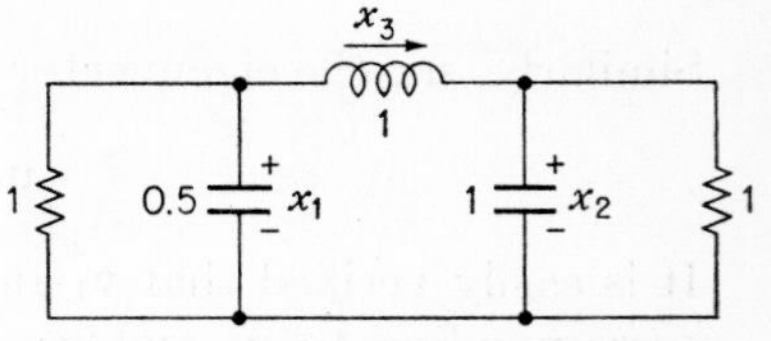

Fig. 5.4.6 Third-order system of Example *5.4.34*.

34 *Example*[1] Consider the *RLC* circuit shown in Fig. *5.4.6*. Writing two node equations and one loop equation, one gets

$$\begin{bmatrix} \dot{x}_1 \\ \dot{x}_2 \\ \dot{x}_3 \end{bmatrix} = \begin{bmatrix} -2 & 0 & -2 \\ 0 & -1 & +1 \\ 1 & -1 & 0 \end{bmatrix} \begin{bmatrix} x_1 \\ x_2 \\ x_3 \end{bmatrix}$$

where x_1, x_2, and x_3 are defined in the figure.

The matrix of this circuit has three eigenvalues, one real and a pair of complex conjugate ones. The corresponding eigenvectors are given in the table

$$\lambda_1 = -1.4534 \qquad \lambda_2 = -0.7733 + j1.468 \qquad \lambda_3 = \lambda_2^*$$

$$\mathbf{u}_1 = \begin{bmatrix} 0.834 \\ 0.503 \\ -2.228 \end{bmatrix} \qquad \mathbf{u}_2 = \begin{bmatrix} -0.100 - j0.646 \\ 0.268 + j0.322 \\ -0.4118 + j0.468 \end{bmatrix}$$

For example, if the initial conditions are along $\mathbf{u}_1$ [say, $x_1(0) = 0.834$, $x_2(0) = 0.503$, and $x_3(0) = -2.228$], only the exponentially damped mode is excited and the resulting voltages and currents are very similar to those of the *RC* circuit of the previous example. On the other hand, if the vector representing the initial conditions lies in the plane defined by $\mathbf{u}_2'$ and $\mathbf{u}_2''$ [where $\mathbf{u}_2' = (-0.100, 0.268, -0.4118)$ and $\mathbf{u}_2'' = (-0.646, 0.322, 0.468)$], then only the oscillatory mode is excited. Throughout the circuit the voltages and the currents are damped sinusoids of different amplitudes and phases, but they all have in common the decrement -0.7733 and the angular frequency 1.468 rad/sec. For such initial conditions, although this circuit is a three-reactance circuit, the voltages and currents have the simple waveforms of the standard *RLC* resonant circuit.

[1] *Ibid.*

Forced oscillations

Consider for simplicity a *single-input,* linear, time-invariant system represented by

$$\dot{\mathbf{x}} = \mathbf{A}\mathbf{x} + \mathbf{a}u(t)$$

where $\mathbf{a}$ is a constant vector and u is the input. From *5.2.21* the state of the system at time t, assuming that the state at $t = 0$ is $\mathbf{x}_0$, is given by

$$\mathbf{x}(t) = [\exp{(\mathbf{A}t)}]\mathbf{x}_0 + \int_0^t \{\exp{[\mathbf{A}(t-\tau)]}\}\mathbf{a}u(\tau)\,d\tau$$

Assuming that $\mathbf{A}$ has distinct eigenvalues, the spectral representation *25* is valid and

35 $$\mathbf{x}(t) = \sum_{i=1}^{n} e^{\lambda_i t}\mathbf{u}_i\left[\langle \mathbf{v}_i,\mathbf{x}_0\rangle + \int_0^t e^{-\lambda_i\tau}\langle \mathbf{v}_i,\mathbf{a}\rangle u(\tau)\,d\tau\right]$$

Thus, for any t, the state $\mathbf{x}(t)$ is a linear combination of the modes of the system; however, the time behavior of the coefficients of the linear combination is more complicated: compare the brackets of *35* and *24*. The excitation of the ith mode due to the input u is

$$e^{\lambda_i t}\langle \mathbf{v}_i,\mathbf{a}\rangle \int_0^t e^{-\lambda_i\tau}u(\tau)\,d\tau$$

For all t, this term is proportional to the constant $\langle \mathbf{v}_i,\mathbf{a}\rangle$ which is the component of $\mathbf{a}$ along $\mathbf{u}_i$ in the basis $\{\mathbf{u}_k\}$. Equation *35* and the above call for the following comments which we present in the form of an

36 **Assertion** Irrespective of the input u, each mode is excited independently of the others. ◁

The amount of excitation of any particular mode does not depend on the amount of excitation of the other modes.

37 **Assertion** The forcing vector $\mathbf{a}$ may be so chosen that, for all possible inputs u, a particular mode is never affected by the input. ◁

In such a case, its excitation, if any, is due exclusively to the initial state. For example, let $\langle \mathbf{v}_i,\mathbf{a}\rangle = 0$, that is, the vector $\mathbf{a}$ has no component along $\mathbf{u}_i$; then *35* shows that the input u will never affect the ith mode. We say that the *input u is uncoupled to the ith mode.*

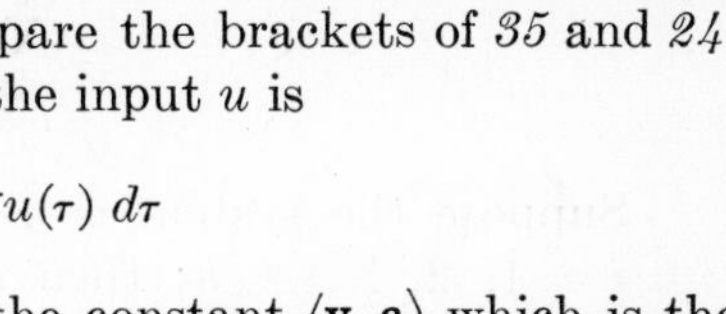

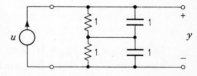

Fig. 5.4.7 Circuit considered in Exercise *5.4.38*. The element values are in ohms and farads.

38 *Exercise* Given the circuit shown in Fig. *5.4.7*, derive its equations in state form. Is the input coupled to all the modes of the circuit?

39 *Exercise* Suppose $\lambda_k = \alpha_k + j\omega_k$ and $\mathbf{u}_k = \mathbf{u}_k' + j\mathbf{u}_k''$, $\mathbf{u}_k'$ and $\mathbf{u}_k''$ real.

Show that if $\mathbf{a} = \mathbf{u}_k'$ and $\mathbf{x}_0 = \mathbf{0}$, then

$$\mathbf{x}(t) = \left[\int_0^t u(\tau)e^{\alpha_k(t-\tau)} \cos \omega_k(t-\tau)\, d\tau\right] \mathbf{u}_k' - \left[\int_0^t u(\tau)e^{\alpha_k(t-\tau)} \sin \omega_k(t-\tau)\, d\tau\right] \mathbf{u}_k''$$

and, if $\mathbf{a} = \mathbf{u}_k''$,

$$\mathbf{x}(t) = \left[\int_0^t u(\tau)e^{\alpha_k(t-\tau)} \sin \omega_k(t-\tau)\, d\tau\right] \mathbf{u}_k' + \left[\int_0^t u(\tau)e^{\alpha_k(t-\tau)} \cos \omega_k(t-\tau)\, d\tau\right] \mathbf{u}_k''$$

Resonance

Let the input be $u = e^{j\omega t}$. Assuming that the system is in the zero state at $t = 0$, we have

$$\begin{aligned}\mathbf{x}(t) &= \sum_{i=1}^{n} \langle \mathbf{v}_i,\mathbf{a}\rangle \left[\int_0^t e^{j\omega(t-\tau)}e^{\lambda_i\tau}\, d\tau\right] \mathbf{u}_i \\ &= \sum_{i=1}^{n} \frac{\langle \mathbf{v}_i,\mathbf{a}\rangle}{\lambda_i - j\omega} (e^{\lambda_i t} - e^{j\omega t})\mathbf{u}_i\end{aligned}$$

Suppose the system is asymptotically stable, that is, $\operatorname{Re} \lambda_i < 0$ for $i = 1, 2, \ldots, n$; then as $t \to \infty$, $e^{\lambda_i t} \to 0$.[1] Thus as $t \to \infty$, the motion of $\mathbf{x}(t)$ becomes asymptotic to the sinusoidal steady state

$$\mathbf{x}(t) \to \sum_{i=1}^{n} \frac{\langle \mathbf{v}_i,\mathbf{a}\rangle}{j\omega - \lambda_i} e^{j\omega t}\mathbf{u}_i \qquad \text{as } t \to \infty$$

The excitation of the ith mode has a peak amplitude:

$$\left|\frac{\langle \mathbf{v}_i,\mathbf{a}\rangle}{j\omega - \lambda_i}\right|$$

if λ_i is real. When λ_i is complex, we must consider both $\mathbf{u}_i$ and $\mathbf{u}_i^*$; the oscillation of the ith mode in the $\mathbf{u}_i'$, $\mathbf{u}_i''$ plane has an amplitude

$$\left|\frac{\langle \mathbf{v}_i,\mathbf{a}\rangle}{j\omega - \lambda_i} + \frac{\langle \mathbf{v}_i^*,\mathbf{a}\rangle}{j\omega - \lambda_i^*}\right|$$

Let $\lambda_i = \alpha_i + j\omega_i$. If $\omega \simeq \omega_i$ and if $\alpha_i \ll \omega_i$ (that is, if the ith mode has very little damping and if the input frequency is close to the frequency of the mode), then in the above expression the first term dominates and the amplitude of oscillation is approximately

$$\left|\frac{\langle \mathbf{v}_i,\mathbf{a}\rangle}{j\omega - \lambda_i}\right|$$

[1] Definition and characterization of asymptotic stability are found in Chap. 7, Secs. 2 and 3.

40 *Comment* We are thus led to the following conclusion. In the sinusoidal steady state the amplitude of oscillation of a particular mode depends on (I) the magnitude and direction of the forcing vector **a** and on (II) the distance between λ_i and $j\omega$ in the s plane. The first dependence is measured by $|\langle \mathbf{v}_i, \mathbf{a} \rangle|$; this scalar product is a measure of the coupling between the input and the ith mode. The second dependence is such that the amplitude of oscillation is inversely proportional to $|j\omega - \lambda_i|$, the distance in the s plane between the frequency of the excitation, $j\omega$, and that of the ith mode, $\alpha_i + j\omega_i$. This fact is well known from the Laplace transform approach: the residue at the pole $j\omega$ of the forcing function contains in its denominator the factor $|j\omega - \lambda_i|$.

Thus, in order to obtain the largest amplitude of oscillation in a particular mode, say, the ith, one should pick **a** so that $|\langle \mathbf{v}_i, \mathbf{a} \rangle|$ is as large as possible and use ω_i as the excitation frequency.

Remark on simple linear transformations[1]

In n-dimensional space, a matrix **A** represents, with respect to a given basis, a linear transformation which associates to each vector **x** a vector **y** given by $\mathbf{y} = \mathbf{A}\mathbf{x}$. In *C.18.6* we define a *simple* linear transformation as one whose eigenvectors constitute a basis for the space. From *6* it follows that a matrix whose eigenvalues are distinct represents a simple linear transformation. However, the class of simple linear transformations is much broader: it may include matrices with multiple eigenvalues; for example, when

$$\mathbf{A} = \begin{bmatrix} 1 & 0 \\ 0 & 1 \end{bmatrix}$$

$\det(\mathbf{A} - \lambda \mathbf{I}) = (\lambda - 1)^2$ and $\lambda = 1$ is a second-order zero of the characteristic equation. But the eigenvectors $\mathbf{u}_1 = (1,0)$, $\mathbf{u}_2 = (0,1)$ span the space.

The point we wish to make is the following: let $\lambda_1, \lambda_2, \ldots, \lambda_n$ be the (not necessarily distinct) eigenvalues of **A**. Let $\mathbf{u}_1, \mathbf{u}_2, \ldots, \mathbf{u}_n$ be the corresponding eigenvectors. If the eigenvectors constitute a basis for the space, then we still have the spectral representations

$$\mathbf{A} = \sum_{i=1}^{n} \lambda_i \mathbf{u}_i\rangle\ \langle \mathbf{v}_i$$

$$\exp(\mathbf{A}t) = \sum_{i=1}^{n} e^{\lambda_i t} \mathbf{u}_i\rangle\ \langle \mathbf{v}_i$$

where $\{\mathbf{v}_i, \mathbf{v}_2, \ldots, \mathbf{v}_n\}$ constitute the reciprocal basis of the basis $\{\mathbf{u}_1, \ldots, \mathbf{u}_n\}$. Therefore we have the

[1] For a more complete treatment see Appendix *C*, Sec. *18*.

41 **Assertion** The mode theory developed above is valid also when the matrix $\mathbf{A}$ represents a simple linear transformation. $\lhd$

These statements are justified by the following observation. The only place where the assumption that the eigenvalues of $\mathbf{A}$ are distinct was used was in proving that the eigenvectors spanned the space. Under our present assumptions, this fact is true by assumption irrespective of whether the eigenvalues are distinct or not.

42 *Exercise* Let $\mathbf{A}^t$ be the transpose of $\mathbf{A}$, that is, the matrix whose element of the ith row and jth column is a_{ji}. Show that, if $\mathbf{A}$ represents a simple linear transformation, $\mathbf{A}^t$ also represents a simple linear transformation; furthermore, that the spectral representations of $\mathbf{A}^t$ and $\exp(\mathbf{A}^t t)$ can be obtained from those of $\mathbf{A}$ and $\exp(\mathbf{A}t)$ by interchanging the $\mathbf{u}_i$'s and $\mathbf{v}_i$'s.

5 *Modes in linear time-invariant systems (general case)*

The mode picture in the case where $\mathbf{A}$ is not a simple linear transformation is very involved. In order to keep the discussion within reason, we assume that the reader is familiar with most of the ideas of Appendix *D*, Sec. *5*. This will allow us to describe the situation precisely and briefly. We shall consider only the free motion of the system described by

1 $$\dot{\mathbf{x}} = \mathbf{A}\mathbf{x} \qquad \mathbf{x}(0) = \mathbf{x}_0$$

If $\mathbf{A}$ is not a simple linear transformation, some zeros of the characteristic polynomial $\Delta(\lambda)$ are not simple. Let us label its *distinct* zeros (eigenvalues) as $\lambda_1, \lambda_2, \ldots, \lambda_\sigma$; clearly, $\sigma < n$. Let m_k be the multiplicity of λ_k as a zero of the *minimal* polynomial of $\mathbf{A}$ (see *D.2.1*) Let

2 $$\mathfrak{N}_k^l = \{\mathbf{x} \mid (\mathbf{A} - \lambda_k \mathbf{I})^l \mathbf{x} = 0\} \qquad l = 1, 2, \ldots ; k = 1, \ldots, \sigma$$

$\mathfrak{N}_k^l$ is a linear vector space which is a subset of the state space $\mathcal{C}^n$. The following facts are either immediate or established in Appendix *D*.

(I) The subspaces $\mathfrak{N}_k^l$ are invariant subspaces of $\mathbf{A}$; that is,

3 $$\mathbf{x} \in \mathfrak{N}_k^l \Rightarrow \mathbf{A}\mathbf{x} \in \mathfrak{N}_k^l$$

4 $$\text{(II)} \quad \mathfrak{N}_k^1 \subset \mathfrak{N}_k^2 \subset \cdots \subset \mathfrak{N}_k^{m_k} = \mathfrak{N}_k^{m_k+i} \qquad i = 1, 2, \ldots$$

For convenience, we write $\mathfrak{N}_k$ instead of $\mathfrak{N}_k^{m_k}$.

(III) The state space $\mathcal{C}^n$ is the direct sum of the $\mathfrak{N}_k$'s:

5 $$\mathcal{C}^n = \mathfrak{N}_1 \oplus \mathfrak{N}_2 \oplus \cdots \oplus \mathfrak{N}_\sigma$$

(IV) In the notation of *5.3.1*,

6 $$\mathbf{Z}_{kl}\mathbf{x} \in \mathfrak{N}_k \qquad \forall \mathbf{x} \in \mathcal{C}^n,\ l = 0, 1, \ldots, m_k - 1 \quad k = 1, 2, \ldots, \sigma$$

7 $$k \neq m \Rightarrow \mathbf{Z}_{kl}\mathbf{Z}_{mj} = 0 \qquad l = 0, 1, \ldots, m_k - 1 \quad j = 0, 1, \ldots, m_m - 1$$

From these properties of **A** we deduce the following conclusions.

8 **Assertion** If $\mathbf{x}_0 \in \mathfrak{N}_k$, then $\mathbf{x}(t) \in \mathfrak{N}_k$ for all $t > 0$; that is, if the initial state lies in subspace $\mathfrak{N}_k$, the state will remain in that subspace for all subsequent times.

This follows immediately from the fundamental formula for exp $(\mathbf{A}t)$ (*5.3.1*) and from *6* and *7*. Heuristically, it is obvious, because $\mathbf{x}_0 \in \mathfrak{N}_k \Rightarrow \mathbf{A}\mathbf{x}_0 \in \mathfrak{N}_k$; hence, by *1*, $\mathbf{x}_0 + \dot{\mathbf{x}}_0\, dt \in \mathfrak{N}_k$, since $\mathfrak{N}_k$ is itself a linear vector space, in fact, a subspace of the state space $\mathcal{C}^n$. Since this reasoning applies for all times, the conclusion follows.

9 **Assertion** Any initial state can be written in one and only one way as

$$\mathbf{x}_0 = \mathbf{y}_1 + \mathbf{y}_2 + \cdots + \mathbf{y}_\sigma$$

where $$\mathbf{y}_i \in \mathfrak{N}_i \qquad i = 1, 2, \ldots, \sigma$$

This follows immediately from *5*. Thus, the initial state can be considered as the superposition of σ initial states and, in view of *8*, the resulting free motion $\mathbf{x}(t)$ is a unique superposition of the free motions $\mathbf{y}_i(t)$, for all t.

Thus if we call $\mathbf{y}_i(t)$ the ith mode, we have the three properties: (I) any free motion can be represented in one and only one way as a superposition of a certain number of modes of the system, (II) each mode is excited independently of the other modes, and (III) the amount of excitation of each mode depends only on the initial conditions. These properties are identical with those valid for the case of simple operators; however, the time behavior of each mode is much more complicated. From *6* and the fundamental formula for exp $(\mathbf{A}t)$ we have

$$\mathbf{y}_i(t) = \sum_{l=0}^{m_i - 1} t^l e^{\lambda_i t}\mathbf{Z}_{il}\mathbf{x}_0$$

The following special cases will illustrate the time behavior of the ith mode:

(I) If $\mathbf{y}_i(0) \in \mathfrak{N}_i^1$, then $\mathbf{y}_i(t) = e^{\lambda_i t}\mathbf{y}_i(0)$

(II) If $\mathbf{y}_i(0) \in \mathfrak{N}_i^2$, but $\mathbf{y}_i(0) \notin \mathfrak{N}_i^1$, then

$$\mathbf{y}_i(t) = e^{\lambda_i t}\mathbf{y}_i(0) + te^{\lambda_i t}(\mathbf{A} - \lambda_i\mathbf{I})\mathbf{y}_i(0)$$

(III) If $\mathbf{y}_i(0) \in \mathfrak{N}_i^{m_i}$, but $\mathbf{y}_i(0) \notin \mathfrak{N}_i^{m_i-1}$, then

$$\mathbf{y}_i(t) = e^{\lambda_i t}\mathbf{y}_i(0) + \sum_{k=1}^{m_i-1} t^k e^{\lambda_i t}(\mathbf{A} - \lambda_i \mathbf{I})^k \mathbf{y}_i(0)$$

Thus we arrive at the final

10 **Assertion** Any initial state that excites a free motion of the form $t^l e^{\lambda_i t}$ also excites motions of the form $t^{l-1}e^{\lambda_i t}, \ldots, te^{\lambda_i t}, e^{\lambda_i t}$. ◁

We conclude our discussion at this point. It is, however, obvious that the forced response can also be interpreted in terms of modes.

11 *Exercise* Consider the system $\dot{\mathbf{x}} = \mathbf{A}\mathbf{x} + \mathbf{a}u(t)$. Pick an input u and a constant forcing vector $\mathbf{a}$ such that the state of the system (assumed to be starting from rest at $t = 0$) is described by $\mathbf{x}(t) = t^N e^{\lambda_i t}\mathbf{d}$ for all $t > 0$, where $\mathbf{d}$ is some constant vector (not prescribed in advance) and N is some prescribed arbitrary positive integer. [*Hint:* Take $\mathbf{a}$ to be an eigenvector of $\mathbf{A}$ corresponding to λ_i and take u such that $\mathcal{L}\{u\} = N!/(s - \lambda_i)^N$.]

6 *Systems of differential equations*

In the preceding sections we focused our attention on the solution of first-order vector differential equations of the form $\dot{\mathbf{x}} = \mathbf{A}\mathbf{x} + \mathbf{B}u$. In this section, we shall consider vector differential equations (not necessarily state equations) of the more general form

1 $$\mathbf{L}(p)\mathbf{x}(t) = \mathbf{M}(p)u(t)$$

or more explicitly

2 $$\sum_{j=1}^{n} L_{ij}(p)x_j(t) = M_i(p)u(t) \qquad i = 1, 2, \ldots, n$$

where the $L_{ij}(p)$ and $M_i(p)$ are differential operators (*3.8.11*) with constant coefficients, u is a scalar input, and the dependent variable $\mathbf{x}(t)$ plays the role of a vector-valued output. In effect, *1* may be regarded as an input-output relation which differs from the relations considered in Chap. *4* in that $\mathbf{L}(p)$ and $\mathbf{M}(p)$ are matric rather than scalar differential operators. Equations of the form *1* are encountered quite frequently in practice as a result of direct application of the laws of physics. For example, in the analysis of linear time-invariant circuits Kirchhoff laws lead directly to a system of the form *1*; the components of $\mathbf{x}(t)$ are then either loop currents or node pair voltages.

In the analysis of the small vibrations of mechanical or electromechanical systems Lagrange's equations also lead to such equations.

Input-output-state relations

As usual, one of the first questions we raise in connection with *1* is: How can one associate a state vector with *1* and what is the corresponding input-output-state relation? To solve this problem, we can employ a slightly extended version of the Laplace transform technique described in Chap. *4*. A simple example will suffice to illustrate its use.

3 *Example* Consider the system

$$\begin{bmatrix} p^2 + p + 1 & 1 \\ p & p + 2 \end{bmatrix} \begin{bmatrix} x_1(t) \\ x_2(t) \end{bmatrix} = \begin{bmatrix} p + 1 \\ 1 \end{bmatrix} u(t)$$

On applying the Laplace transformation to both sides of this system, we obtain after a rearrangement of terms

4
$$\begin{bmatrix} s^2 + s + 1 & 1 \\ s & s + 2 \end{bmatrix} \begin{bmatrix} X_1(s) \\ X_2(s) \end{bmatrix} = \begin{bmatrix} (s + 1)U(s) + sx_1(0-) + \dot{x}_1(0-) + x_1(0-) - u(0-) \\ U(s) + x_1(0-) + x_2(0-) \end{bmatrix}$$

On inspection of these relations and recalling the procedure used in Chap. *4* (see Sec. *5*), it is evident that the 3-vector

$$\mathbf{z}(t) = \begin{bmatrix} x_1(t) \\ \dot{x}_1(t) + x_1(t) - u(t) \\ x_1(t) + x_2(t) \end{bmatrix}$$

qualifies as the state of the system at time t. Then, on solving *4* for $X_1(s)$ and $X_2(s)$, the desired input-output-state relation (in the Laplace transform form) is found to be

$$X_1(s) = \frac{N_1(s)}{D(s)} U(s) + \frac{s(s + 2)z_1(0-) + (s + 2)z_2(0-) - z_3(0-)}{D(s)}$$

$$X_2(s) = \frac{N_2(s)}{D(s)} U(s) + \frac{-s^2 z_1(0-) - sz_2(0-) + (s^2 + s + 1)z_3(0-)}{D(s)}$$

where $D(s) = (s^2 + s + 1)(s + 2) - s$, $N_1(s) = (s^2 + 3s + 1)$, and $N_2(s) = 1$.

The next step is to obtain the time responses x_1 and x_2 from the above Laplace transform equations. It is obvious that the value of the output at time t will consist of two terms, one depending on $u_{[0,t]}$ and the other on the initial state $\mathbf{z}(0-)$. The first term is the zero-state response of the system and the second is its zero-input response. (*Question:* What is the state equation satisfied by $\mathbf{z}$?)

The elimination method

A different approach, which has the advantage of being applicable not only to time-invariant but also to time-varying systems, is based on a reduction of the system of equations *1* to a triangular system which can be solved as a succession of scalar differential equations in a single unknown function. The reduction technique in question is analogous to the Gauss elimination procedure used in solving systems of linear algebraic equations. It is based on the following

5 **Theorem** Consider the system $\mathcal{S}$ of differential equations defined by *1* and the system $\mathcal{S}'$ obtained from $\mathcal{S}$ as follows: all the equations of $\mathcal{S}'$ are identical to their corresponding ones in $\mathcal{S}$ except for the kth equation, which is given by

$$\sum_{j=1}^{n} [L_{kj}(p) + M(p)L_{ij}(p)]x_j(t) = [F_k(p) + M(p)F_i(p)]u(t)$$

where $M(p)$ is an arbitrary differential operator, say $\sum_{k=0}^{N'} m_k p^k$, with the m_k's constant. Then $\hat{\mathbf{x}}(t) = (\hat{x}_1(t), \ldots, \hat{x}_n(t))$ is a solution of $\mathcal{S}$ if and only if $\hat{\mathbf{x}}(t)$ is a solution of $\mathcal{S}'$. $\lhd$

6 *Comment* The systems $\mathcal{S}$ and $\mathcal{S}'$ are equivalent in the sense that any solution of $\mathcal{S}$ is a solution of $\mathcal{S}'$ and conversely (see *2.5.4* and *3.9.1*). More specifically, the transformation of $\mathcal{S}$ into $\mathcal{S}'$ introduces no spurious solutions and hence $\mathcal{S} \equiv \mathcal{S}'$ rather than $\mathcal{S} \subset \mathcal{S}'$ (see *2.5.1*).

Proof (I) The direct statement $\Rightarrow$ is obvious from the relation between $\mathcal{S}$ and $\mathcal{S}'$. (II) The proof of $\Leftarrow$ is as follows: If $\hat{\mathbf{x}}(t)$ is a solution of $\mathcal{S}'$, then it is a solution of the system obtained from $\mathcal{S}'$ by replacing the kth equation of $\mathcal{S}'$ by a new one resulting from the addition to the kth equation of $\mathcal{S}'$ of the ith equation of $\mathcal{S}'$, multiplied by $-M(p)$. Note that this is the kth equation of $\mathcal{S}$. Thus $\hat{\mathbf{x}}(t)$ is a solution of $\mathcal{S}$.

7 **Corollary** The theorem is still true if the L_{ij}'s and M are linear time-varying differential operators. In other words, the theorem also applies to linear time-varying systems of differential equations.

8 **Corollary** The same statement holds if $\mathcal{S}'$ is obtained from $\mathcal{S}$ by multiplying the kth equation of $\mathcal{S}$ by a *nonzero constant.* Let us call *an elementary row operation* any operation on the system of equations of the kind described in Theorem *5* or Corollary *8*.

9 **Corollary** By a succession of elementary row operations, any two rows of the matrix $\mathbf{L}(p)$ may be interchanged. In other words, by a succession of elementary row operations, any two equations of the system $\mathcal{S}$ may be interchanged.

Proof Let us interchange the ith row with the first row. The procedure can be best explained by showing the successive states of the first column after each elementary row operation:

$$\begin{bmatrix} L_{11} \\ \cdot \\ \cdot \\ \cdot \\ L_{i1} \\ \cdot \end{bmatrix} \to \begin{bmatrix} L_{11} \\ \cdot \\ \cdot \\ \cdot \\ L_{11} + L_{i1} \\ \cdot \end{bmatrix} \to \begin{bmatrix} L_{11} \\ \cdot \\ \cdot \\ \cdot \\ -L_{11} - L_{i1} \\ \cdot \end{bmatrix} \to \begin{bmatrix} -L_{i1} \\ \cdot \\ \cdot \\ \cdot \\ -L_{11} - L_{i1} \\ \cdot \end{bmatrix}$$

$$\to \begin{bmatrix} L_{i1} \\ \cdot \\ \cdot \\ \cdot \\ -L_{11} - L_{i1} \\ \cdot \end{bmatrix} \to \begin{bmatrix} L_{i1} \\ \cdot \\ \cdot \\ \cdot \\ -L_{11} \\ \cdot \end{bmatrix} \to \begin{bmatrix} L_{i1} \\ \cdot \\ \cdot \\ \cdot \\ L_{11} \\ \cdot \end{bmatrix}$$

We shall now use a succession of elementary row operations to bring the system *1* to the required form. The procedure is described as a sequence of steps.

10 **Procedure**

Step 1. Among all elements of the first column (which consists of $L_{11}, L_{21}, \ldots, L_{n1}$), pick the polynomial which has the least degree and which is not identical to zero; by a succession of elementary row operations bring this polynomial to the (1,1) position.

Step 2. Let $\hat{L}_{k1}$ be the polynomial in the $(k,1)$ position resulting from step 1 ($k = 1, 2, \ldots, n$). Divide each polynomial $\hat{L}_{k1}$ by $\hat{L}_{11}$, viz.:

$$\hat{L}_{k1}(p) = q_{k1}\hat{L}_{11}(p) + r_{k1}(p)$$

where $d^0 r_{k1} < d^0 \hat{L}_{11}$.[1] For $k = 2, 3, \ldots, n$, subtract from the kth equation the first one multiplied by $q_{k1}(p)$. As a result of these elementary row operations, the first column is now $(\hat{L}_{11}, r_{21}, r_{31}, \ldots, r_{n1})$. The right-hand side of the kth equation is $[\hat{F}_k - q_{k1}(p)\hat{F}_1(p)]u(t)$, for $k = 1, 2, \ldots, n$.

Step 3. If all the remainders of the divisions of step 2 are identically zero, this cycle of elementary operations terminates and the matrix is in the form *11* below. If some remainders r_{k1} are not identically zero, bring to the (1,1) position the remainder which is of least degree not identically zero. Repeat step 2 until all the elements of the first column [except the one in the (1,1) position] are identically zero. These iterations require a finite number of operations, since each

[1] $d^0 r_{k1}$ = degree of the polynomial r_{k1}.

cycle of divisions reduces the degree of the polynomials by at least 1. The resulting matrix is of the form

11
$$\begin{bmatrix} L_{11} & L_{12} & L_{13} & \cdots & L_{1n} \\ 0 & L_{22} & L_{23} & \cdots & \cdot \\ \cdot & \cdot & \cdot & \cdots & \cdot \\ 0 & L_{2n} & L_{4n} & \cdots & L_{nn} \end{bmatrix}$$

where the L_{ij}'s are, in general, polynomials different from those of *1*.

Step 4. Perform the steps 1, 2, 3 on the $(n-1) \times (n-1)$ matrix formed by the rows and columns numbered 2 to n of *11*.

Step 5. Repeat step 4 on the successively obtained smaller matrices of order $n-2$, $n-3$, ... The final result is a system $\tilde{S}$ of equations of the form

12
$$\begin{bmatrix} \tilde{L}_{11} & \tilde{L}_{12} & \cdots & \cdot & \tilde{L}_{1n} \\ 0 & \tilde{L}_{22} & \cdots & \cdot & \tilde{L}_{2n} \\ \cdot & \cdot & \cdots & \cdot & \cdot \\ 0 & \cdot & & \tilde{L}_{n-1n-1} & \tilde{L}_{n-1n} \\ 0 & \cdot & & 0 & \tilde{L}_{nn} \end{bmatrix} \begin{bmatrix} \tilde{x}_1 \\ \tilde{x}_2 \\ \cdots \\ \tilde{x}_{n-1} \\ \tilde{x}_n \end{bmatrix} = \begin{bmatrix} \tilde{F}_1(p) \\ \tilde{F}_2(p) \\ \cdots \\ \cdot \\ \tilde{F}_n(p) \end{bmatrix} u(t)$$

where the $\tilde{x}_i$'s are identical to the x_i because these functions have not been affected by the sequence of elementary row operations.

13 **Conclusion** By a succession of elementary row operations, any system of differential equations such as *1* can be changed into an equivalent system which is in the triangular form *12*. ◁

The solution of *12* amounts to solving a succession of high-order differential equations in one unknown function: the nth equation determines $\tilde{x}_n$ and the $(n-1)$st then reads

$$\tilde{L}_{n-1,n-1}\tilde{x}_{n-1} + \tilde{L}_{n-1,n}\tilde{x}_n = F_{n-1}u$$

where both u and $\tilde{x}_n$ are known; therefore, it can be solved for $\tilde{x}_{n-1}$, etc.

14 *Comment* The procedure above which leads to *12* is also a convenient procedure for computing the characteristic polynomial of the system *1*. This characteristic polynomial is equal to the determinant, say Δ, of the matrix $\mathbf{L}(p)$ in *1*. It will be shown below that Δ is, within a constant factor, equal to the determinant of the matrix $(\tilde{L}_{ij}(p))$ in *12*. In other words,

$$\Delta = k \prod_{i=1}^{n} \tilde{L}_{ii}(p) \qquad k \text{ constant independent of } p$$

15 *Comment* The system *12* can be further simplified by the further use of the elementary row operation defined in *5*. Start by considering the second column: adding to the first row the second row multiplied

by a suitable factor, we can make the degree of $\tilde{L}_{12}$ become smaller than that of $\tilde{L}_{22}$. Next, operating on the third column, we make the degree of $\tilde{L}_{13}$ and $\tilde{L}_{23}$ smaller than that of $\tilde{L}_{33}$. Thus by a succession of elementary row operations the matrix $\tilde{L}$ may be brought into a form such that, for $k = 2, \ldots, n$, the degrees of $\tilde{L}_{1k}, \tilde{L}_{2k}, \ldots, \tilde{L}_{k-1,k}$ are smaller than the degree of $\tilde{L}_{kk}$. In particular, if $\tilde{L}_{kk}$ is a constant, all the elements of the kth column, except for the diagonal element, can be reduced to zero.

Matrix interpretation of the elimination method

The elementary row operation described in Theorem *5* is equivalent to multiplying *1* on the left by the matrix whose (α,β) element is $\delta_{\alpha,\beta} + \delta_{\alpha k}\delta_{\beta i}M(p)$, $\alpha,\beta = 1, 2, \ldots, n$, in other words, by a matrix all of whose elements are zero except the diagonal elements, which are equal to 1, and the element in position (k,i), which is equal to $M(p)$. Note that this matrix is obtained from the unit matrix by adding to its kth row the ith row multiplied by the differential operator $M(p)$, that is, by applying to the unit matrix the operation that we wish to apply to $\mathbf{L}$.

To multiply the kth row by a nonzero constant K, as in *8*, is equivalent to multiplying *1* on the left by the matrix whose (α,β) element is $\delta_{\alpha\beta} + \delta_{\alpha k}\delta_{\beta k}(K-1)$, that is, by the diagonal matrix all of whose diagonal elements are unity except that in the kth row which is equal to K. Note again that this matrix is obtained from the unit matrix by multiplying its kth row by the constant K, that is, by applying to the unit matrix the operation that we wish to apply to $\mathbf{L}$.

In these two cases the determinants of the multiplying matrices are equal to 1 or K, respectively. Therefore $\det \mathbf{L}(p) = \gamma \det \tilde{\mathbf{L}}(p)$, where γ is a nonzero constant. Therefore, the determinant of the matrix $(\tilde{L}_{ij}(p))$ in *12* is equal to a nonzero constant times the determinant of the matrix $\mathbf{L}(p)$ of *1*.

16 *Example* An example is particularly useful to illustrate the simplicity of the procedure and to show how the required initial conditions are obtained. Consider the circuit shown in Fig. *5.6.1*. The voltage

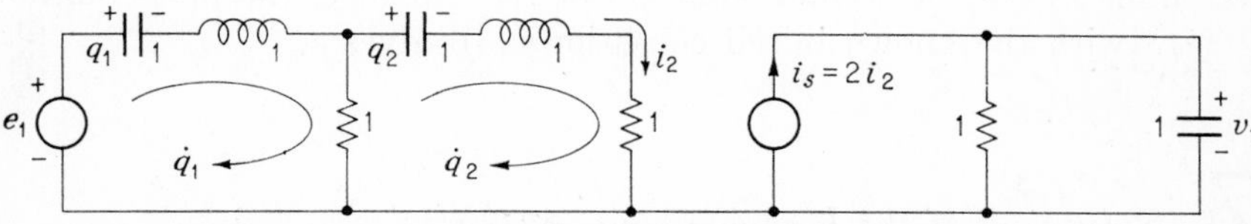

Fig. 5.6.1 Circuit studied in Example *5.6.16*. The element values are in ohms, farads, and henrys.

source e_1 is the input. Let us pick as variables the charges q_1, q_2 and the capacitor voltage v_1. If we write the current law for the parallel

RC circuit and the voltage laws for the loops defined in the figure, we obtain

17 $$\begin{bmatrix} p+1 & 0 & -2p \\ 0 & p^2+p+1 & -p \\ 0 & -p & p^2+2p+1 \end{bmatrix} \begin{bmatrix} v_1 \\ q_1 \\ q_2 \end{bmatrix} = \begin{bmatrix} 0 \\ e_1 \\ 0 \end{bmatrix}$$

This is a system of equations of the form *1*. Let us apply the elimination procedure *10*. The first column of *17* already fits the triangular pattern of *12*; we consider therefore the 2×2 submatrix formed by the second and third rows and columns. Step 1: interchange rows 2 and 3. Step 2: multiply row 2 by $(p+1)$ and add to row 3. Thus

$$\begin{bmatrix} p+1 & 0 & -2p \\ 0 & -p & (p+1)^2 \\ 0 & 1 & (p+1)^3 - p \end{bmatrix} \begin{bmatrix} v_1 \\ q_1 \\ q_2 \end{bmatrix} = \begin{bmatrix} 0 \\ 0 \\ e_1 \end{bmatrix}$$

Since the second column is not in the required form, repeat the procedure. Step 1: interchange rows 2 and 3. Step 2: multiply row 2 by p and add to row 3. Thus

18 $$\begin{bmatrix} p+1 & 0 & -2p \\ 0 & 1 & p^3+3p^2+2p+1 \\ 0 & 0 & p^4+3p^3+3p^2+3p+1 \end{bmatrix} \begin{bmatrix} v_1 \\ q_1 \\ q_2 \end{bmatrix} = \begin{bmatrix} 0 \\ e_1 \\ pe_1 \end{bmatrix}$$

This is the required form.

Now consider the initial conditions: The initial charges on the capacitors and the initial current in the inductances define the initial state of the system (see Chap. *4*, Sec. *6*). Thus the initial state prescribes $q_1(0)$, $\dot{q}_1(0)$, $q_2(0)$, $\dot{q}_2(0)$, $v_1(0)$ and the input specifies $e_{1[0,\infty)}$. Now the last equation in *18* requires $q_2(0)$, $\dot{q}_2(0)$, $\ddot{q}_2(0)$, and $\dddot{q}_2(0)$ in order to define $q_{2[0,\infty)}$ uniquely. In order to find $\ddot{q}_2(0)$ and $\dddot{q}_2(0)$, one has to go back to the original system, *17* in this case. From the second and third equations of *17* evaluated at $t = 0$, and from the initial state, one gets $\ddot{q}_1(0)$ and $\ddot{q}_2(0)$. Differentiating the third equation, one then gets $\dddot{q}_2(0)$. The solution of the last equation in *18* requires $e_1(0)$, which is known since $e_{1[0,\infty)}$ is given; thus the last equation defines q_2 uniquely. The solution q_2 and the input e_1 determine q_1 by the second equation of *18*. Finally, the first equation of *18* with the known initial condition $v_1(0)$ gives v_1.

7 *Solutions of the homogeneous system*

Consider a system described by the equations *5.6.1*, which represent a linear time-invariant system whose outputs are $x_1, x_2, \ldots, x_n$. Let us consider the zero-input response of this system, in other words, the differential equation

1 $$\mathbf{L}(p)\mathbf{x}(t) = \mathbf{0}$$

where $\mathbf{L}(p)$ is the matrix of differential operators defined in *5.6.1*. Suppose we write the state equations of this system and carry out a mode analysis of the free motions. Since each component of $\mathbf{x}(t)$ is a linear function of the state of the system, it will usually happen that some of the x_i's are uncoupled to some of the modes. Thus we may set ourselves the following problem: Find the differential operator of least order, Δ_i, such that all free motions of *1* are such that the ith component of the output satisfies the differential equation $\Delta_i(p)x_i = 0$. The purpose of this section is to answer the question without using the device of performing the mode analysis.

Let $\mathbf{\Gamma}(p)$ be the adjoint matrix of $\mathbf{L}(p)$; that is, by definition, $\Gamma_{ij}(p)$ is the cofactor of $L_{ji}(p)$.[1] Both $\mathbf{\Gamma}(p)$ and $\mathbf{L}(p)$ are matrices whose elements are polynomials in p. From elementary properties of determinants,

2 $$\mathbf{L}(p)\mathbf{\Gamma}(p) = \mathbf{\Gamma}(p)\mathbf{L}(p) = \Delta(p)\mathbf{I}$$

where $\Delta(p) = \det \mathbf{L}(p)$. As a first step we shall establish two facts which relate the columns of $\mathbf{\Gamma}$ with the solutions of *1*.

3 **Assertion** If s_1 is a simple zero of $\Delta(s)$, then any column of the matrix $\mathbf{\Gamma}(s_1)e^{s_1t}$ is a solution of *1* and at least one column is a nontrivial solution of *1*.

Proof By direct calculation, using *2*, we get

$$\mathbf{L}(p)\mathbf{\Gamma}(s_1)e^{s_1t} = e^{s_1t}\mathbf{L}(s_1)\mathbf{\Gamma}(s_1) = e^{s_1t}\,\Delta(s_1)\mathbf{I} = 0 \qquad \forall t$$

In other words, every column of $\mathbf{\Gamma}(s_1)e^{s_1t}$ is a solution of *1*. It remains to show that some column of $\mathbf{\Gamma}(s_1)$ is not identically zero.

Now, from the rule of differentiation of a determinant, $\Delta^{(1)}(s) \triangleq \frac{d}{ds}\Delta(s)$ is a linear combination of all minors of $\Delta(s)$. Since s_1 is a simple zero of $\Delta(s)$, $\Delta^{(1)}(s_1) \neq 0$ and not all minors of $\Delta(s)$ are zero. In other words, not all columns of $\mathbf{\Gamma}(s_1)$ are identical to zero. Therefore, at least one column of $\mathbf{\Gamma}(s_1)e^{s_1t}$ is a nontrivial solution of *1*.

4 **Assertion** Let $\mathbf{\Gamma}^{(k)}(s)$ be the kth derivative of the matrix $\mathbf{\Gamma}(s)$. If s_1 is a zero of order $m + 1$ of $\Delta(s)$, then any column of the matrix

5 $$e^{s_1t}\left[\mathbf{\Gamma}^{(m)}(s_1) + \binom{m}{1}\mathbf{\Gamma}^{(m-1)}(s_1)t + \binom{m}{2}\mathbf{\Gamma}^{(m-2)}(s_1)t^2 + \cdots + \binom{m}{m-1}\mathbf{\Gamma}^{(1)}(s_1)t^{m-1} + \mathbf{\Gamma}(s_1)t^m\right]$$

[1] This adjoint matrix should not be confused with the matrix of the adjoint of the linear transformation represented by $\mathbf{L}$ (see *C.14.1*). Note that the cofactor of L_{ij} is $(-1)^{i+j}$ times the minor of L_{ij} and the minor of L_{ij} is the determinant of the matrix obtained by deleting the ith row and jth column of $\mathbf{L}$.

is a solution of *1* and at least one column of this matrix is not identically zero.

Proof Let us prove the assertion for $m = 1$, that is, s_1 is a double zero of $\Delta(s)$. Consider the matrix $\frac{\partial}{\partial s}[e^{st}\Gamma(s)]$; then successively we obtain

$$\begin{aligned}\mathbf{L}(p)\cdot\frac{\partial}{\partial s}[e^{st}\mathbf{\Gamma}(s)] &= \mathbf{L}\left(\frac{\partial}{\partial t}\right)\cdot\frac{\partial}{\partial s}[e^{st}\mathbf{\Gamma}(s)] \\ &= \frac{\partial}{\partial s}\cdot\mathbf{L}\left(\frac{\partial}{\partial t}\right)[e^{st}\mathbf{\Gamma}(s)] \\ &= \frac{\partial}{\partial s}[e^{st}\mathbf{L}(s)\mathbf{\Gamma}(s)] \\ &= \frac{\partial}{\partial s}[e^{st}\,\Delta(s)\mathbf{I}] = e^{st}\left[t+\frac{\partial}{\partial s}\right]\Delta(s)\mathbf{I} \\ &= e^{st}[t\,\Delta(s) + \Delta^{(1)}(s)]\mathbf{I}\end{aligned}$$

Since s_1 is a double zero of Δ, $\Delta(s_1) = \Delta^{(1)}(s_1) = 0$; and consequently the matrix $\frac{\partial}{\partial s}[e^{st}\mathbf{\Gamma}(s)]\Big|_{s=s_1}$ and every one of its column vectors satisfy *1*.

When $m > 1$, then every column of the $m + 1$ matrices

$$\frac{\partial^k}{\partial s^k}[e^{st}\mathbf{\Gamma}(s)]\Big|_{s=s_1} = e^{s_1t}\left(t+\frac{\partial}{\partial s}\right)^k\mathbf{\Gamma}(s)\Big|_{s=s_1} \qquad k = 0, 1, \ldots, m$$

satisfies *1*. Next we show that not all columns of $\mathbf{\Gamma}(s_1), \mathbf{\Gamma}^{(1)}(s_1), \ldots, \mathbf{\Gamma}^{(m)}(s_1)$ are identically zero. If these $(m + 1)$ matrices were identically zero, then every minor of $\Delta(s)$, say, $q(s)$, would satisfy the conditions $q(s_1) = q^{(1)}(s_1) = \cdots = q^{(m)}(s_1) = 0$; hence, every minor would have $(s - s_1)^{m+1}$ as a factor and, by the argument used in the preceding proof, $\Delta(s)$ would have, at s_1, a zero of order greater than $m + 1$. This contradicts the definition of m, the order of the zero s_1 of Δ. Therefore, at least one column of the matrices $\mathbf{\Gamma}^{(k)}(s_1)$,

$$k = 0, 1, \ldots, m$$

is not identically zero. ◁

From *2* it follows immediately that if $\mathbf{x}(t)$ is a solution of *1*, any of its components, say, $x_i(t)$, satisfies the differential equation

6 $$\Delta(p)x_i(t) = 0$$

The converse, however, is not true, i.e., there are cases where some solutions of *6* are not the ith component of any solution, $\mathbf{x}(t)$, of *1*. To wit, let

7 $$\mathbf{L}(p) = \begin{bmatrix} p+1 & 0 & 0 \\ 0 & p & 0 \\ 0 & 0 & p \end{bmatrix}$$

Clearly, $x_2(t)$ and $x_3(t)$ are required by *1* to be constants. However, *6* reads in this case $p^2(p+1)x_i(t) = 0$, $i = 1, 2, 3$, and its linearly independent solutions are k_1, k_2t, k_3e^{-t}. In this case, k_2t and k_3e^{-t}, although solutions of *6*, cannot appear in the second and third components of any vector solution, $\mathbf{x}(t)$, of *1*. The following theorem gives the differential operator $\Delta_i(p)$ of least order such that the ith component of every solution $\mathbf{x}(t)$ of *1* satisfies $\Delta_i(p)x_i = 0$ and, conversely, every solution of that differential equation is the ith component of a vector solution of *1*.

8 **Theorem**[1] Let $\mathbf{x}(t) = (x_1(t), x_2(t), \ldots, x_n(t))$ be a solution of *1*. The differential equation of least order satisfied by its ith component $x_i(t)$, $i = 1, 2, \ldots, n$, is

9 $$\Delta_i(p)x_i(t) = 0$$

where $\Delta_i(s)$ is the quotient of $\Delta(s)$ by $g_i(s)$, the greatest common divisor of the ith row of $\mathbf{\Gamma}(s)$.

10 *Comment* $\Delta_i(s)$ is a polynomial in s. Consider the expansion of $\Delta(s)$ according to the elements of its ith column; the result is a linear combination of the elements of the ith row of $\mathbf{\Gamma}(s)$. Hence, by definition of $g_i(s)$, that polynomial can be factored.

Proof *Case 1* Let s_1 be a zero of order $m+1$ of both $g_i(s)$ and $\Delta(s)$. Hence $\Delta_i(s_1) \neq 0$, $g_i(s_1) = g_1'(s_1) = \cdots = g_i^{(m)}(s_1) = 0$. All the elements of the ith row of the matrices in the sum *5* are identically zero because all the elements of the ith row of $\mathbf{\Gamma}(s)$ have the common factor $(s - s_1)^{m+1}$. The ith components of all vector solutions of *1* associated with s_1 are identically zero. Hence any zero of Δ which is not a zero of Δ_i plays no role in the ith component of any solution $\mathbf{x}(t)$ of *1*.

Case 2 Let s_2 be a zero of order $m+1$ of $\Delta(s)$ but a zero of order $k+1$ of $g_i(s)$ ($m \geq k$ by definition of g_i). It is therefore a zero of order $m-k$ of $\Delta_i(s)$. By the same argument as above, the ith rows of $\mathbf{\Gamma}(s_2)$, $\mathbf{\Gamma}^{(1)}(s_2), \ldots, \mathbf{\Gamma}^{(k)}(s_2)$ are identically zero. Furthermore, the ith row of $\mathbf{\Gamma}^{(k+1)}(s_2)$ cannot be identically zero, for otherwise $g_i(s)$ would contain the factor $(s - s_2)^{k+2}$. Let ${}^i\mathbf{\Gamma}(s)$ be the ith row of $\mathbf{\Gamma}(s)$. Hence any component of the row vector

$$e^{s_2t}\left[{}^i\mathbf{\Gamma}^{(m)}_{(s_2)} + \binom{m}{1}{}^i\mathbf{\Gamma}^{(m-1)}_{(s_2)}t + \cdots + \binom{m}{m-k-1}{}^i\mathbf{\Gamma}^{(k+1)}_{(s_2)}t^{m-k-1}\right]$$

is a solution of *1* and there is at least one vector solution of *1* whose ith component behaves like $(\alpha_0 + \alpha_1t + \cdots + \alpha_{m-k-1}t^{m-k-1})e^{s_2t}$ with $\alpha_{m-k-1} \neq 0$. From these two cases, it follows that the order of the differential operator of *9* cannot be reduced further. ◁

[1] C. A. Desoer, and E. Polak, A Note on Lumped Time Invariant Systems, *I.R.E. Trans. Circuit Theory,* CT-9, no. 3, pp 282–283, September, 1962.

This concludes our study of linear time-invariant differential systems. The next chapter is devoted to linear time-varying systems.

REFERENCES AND SUGGESTED READING

1 Bellman, R.: "Stability Theory of Differential Equations," McGraw-Hill Book Company, Inc., New York, 1953.

2 Coddington, E. A., and N. Levinson: "Theory of Ordinary Differential Equations," McGraw-Hill Book Company, Inc., 1955.

3 Desoer, C. A.: Modes in Linear Circuits, *I.R.E. Trans. Circuit Theory,* vol. CT-7, no. 3, pp. 211–223, 1960.

4 Fadeeva, V. N.: "Computational Methods of Linear Algebra," Dover Publications, Inc., New York, 1959.

5 Gantmacher, F. R.: "The Theory of Matrices," vols. 1 and 2, Chelsea Publishing Company, New York, 1959.

6 Ince, E. L.: "Ordinary Differential Equations," Dover Publications, Inc., New York, 1956.

7 Kaplan, W.: "Operational Methods for Linear Systems," Addison-Wesley Publishing Company, Inc., Reading, Mass., 1962.

8 Kaplan, W.: "Ordinary Differential Equations," Addison-Wesley Publishing Company, Inc., Reading, Mass., 1958.

9 Lefschetz, S.: "Differential Equations: Geometric Theory," Interscience Publishers, Inc., New York, 1957.

10 Souriau, J. M.: Une méthode pour la décomposition spectrale et l'inversion des matrices, *C. R. Acad. Sci. Paris,* vol. 227, pp. 1010, 1011, 1948.

Linear time-varying differential systems 6

1 *Introduction*

In this chapter we investigate in detail the properties of the responses of linear time-varying systems. This chapter will, therefore, bear a strong resemblance to the preceding one. There will be, however, a striking difference: in the present chapter we have little to say about computational techniques because, except for a few special cases of some practical interest, the only effective means for computing the response of time-varying systems is the digital computer. In Sec. *2* we consider systems described by their equations in state form. This section bears great similarity to that of Chap. *5*, except for the fact that here the adjoint system (which is not even mentioned in Chap. *5*) plays a very important role. Sections *3* and *4* are devoted to the study of the relation between the impulse response of systems described by $L(p,t)x = u$ and $L(p,t)x = M(p,t)u$. In particular we investigate the relation between the impulse response and the basis functions of the operator $L(p,t)$ and its adjoint $L^*(p,t)$. Section *5* is devoted to the study of the tandem connection of two time-varying differential systems. In Sec. *6* the elimination procedure for solving high-order systems of differential equations (see Chap. *5*, Sec. *6*) is used to transform a time-varying system into one of simpler form. Finally, in Sec. *7* the very important practical case of periodically varying systems is considered, and the Poincaré-Lyapunov theory of such systems is developed.

2 *Linear time-varying systems described by their state equations*

As in the case of time-invariant systems, instead of considering a general differential system described by its state equations $\dot{\mathbf{x}} = \mathbf{A}(t)\mathbf{x} + \mathbf{B}(t)\mathbf{u}$

and $\mathbf{y} = \mathbf{C}(t)\mathbf{x} + \mathbf{D}(t)\mathbf{u}$, we shall restrict ourselves to the consideration of the first equation. To put it another way, we restrict ourselves to systems whose output is the state vector, for the reason that, once the properties of the trajectory in state space are known, the properties of an output $\mathbf{y}$ given by $\mathbf{C}(t)\mathbf{x} + \mathbf{D}(t)\mathbf{u}$ are easy to deduce. More specifically, in this section we shall investigate the zero-input response and the forced response of systems described by

$$\dot{\mathbf{x}}(t) = \mathbf{A}(t)\mathbf{x}(t) + \mathbf{B}(t)\mathbf{u}(t)$$

where $\mathbf{A}(t)$ is an $n \times n$ matrix of scalar functions assumed to be continuous for all t; similarly, $\mathbf{B}(t)$ is assumed to be an $n \times r$ continuous matrix, $\mathbf{x}(t)$ is the state vector, and $\mathbf{u}$ is the input.

Zero-input response (free motion)

First we consider the case where the input is identically zero; that is, we have, for all t,

1 $$\dot{\mathbf{x}}(t) = \mathbf{A}(t)\mathbf{x}(t)$$

We shall first derive a formula for $\mathbf{x}(t;\mathbf{x}_0,t_0)$, which is, by definition, the state of the system at time t given that the system was in state $\mathbf{x}_0$ at time t_0. Let us first quote a uniqueness result:

2 **Lemma**[1] For the linear system *1*, where the elements $a_{ij}(t)$ of $\mathbf{A}(t)$ are continuous on $[t_0,t_1]$, there is one and only one solution $\mathbf{x}(t;\mathbf{x}_0,t_0)$ of *1* on $[t_0,t_1]$ passing through the state $\mathbf{x}_0$ at time t_0. If $\mathbf{A}(t)$ is continuous for all $t \in (-\infty,\infty)$, then the system *1* has a unique solution $\mathbf{x}(t;\mathbf{x}_0,t_0)$ which is defined for all $t \in (-\infty,\infty)$ and which passes through $\mathbf{x}_0$ at t_0.

3 *Comment* In some applications, such as linear circuits with switches, linear pulse systems, etc., $\mathbf{A}(t)$ is not continuous. The following result is pertinent.[2] Let $\mathbf{A}(t)$ be an integrable function of t such that $\|\mathbf{A}(t)\| < \alpha(t)$ and $\int_{t_0}^{t_1} \alpha(t)\,dt < \infty$. Then there is a unique solution $\mathbf{x}(t;\mathbf{x}_0,t_0)$ over $[t_0,t_1]$ in the sense that $\mathbf{x}(t;\mathbf{x}_0,t_0)$ is continuous in t and satisfies the integral equation

$$\mathbf{x}(t;\mathbf{x}_0,t_0) = \mathbf{x}_0 + \int_{t_0}^{t} \mathbf{A}(\tau)\mathbf{x}(\tau;\mathbf{x}_0,t_0)\,d\tau$$

Sometimes[3] the theory of linear differential equations is developed for the case where $\mathbf{A}(t)$ is a *regulated* function of t; that is, each element $a_{ij}(t)$ of the matrix has at every point a right-hand limit and a left-

[1] E. A. Coddington and N. Levinson, "Theory of Ordinary Differential Equations," p. 20, McGraw-Hill Book Company, Inc., New York, 1955.

[2] *Ibid.*, p. 97, prob. 1.

[3] N. Bourbaki, "Fonctions d'une variable réelle," chap. IV, Hermann & Cie, Paris, 1961.

hand limit. This implies that, on every finite interval, the set of discontinuity points of $\mathbf{A}$ is countable and that $\mathbf{A}$ is integrable. Under these conditions, the differential equation *1* has a unique solution $\mathbf{x}(t;\mathbf{x}_0,t_0)$ which is a continuous function of t. It satisfies the above integral equation for every t but satisfies the differential equation *1* only for t outside an at most countable set of values of t. ◁

The expression for the zero-input response of the system *1* is given in the following

4 **Theorem** Let $\mathbf{A}(t)$ be an $n \times n$ matrix whose elements are continuous functions of time. Let $\mathbf{\Phi}(t,t_0)$ be the $n \times n$ matrix which is the solution of the equations

5 $$\frac{d}{dt}\mathbf{\Phi}(t,t_0) = \mathbf{A}(t)\mathbf{\Phi}(t,t_0) \qquad \mathbf{\Phi}(t_0,t_0) = \mathbf{I}$$

Then the solution to the equation

6 $$\dot{\mathbf{x}}(t) = \mathbf{A}(t)\mathbf{x}(t) \qquad \mathbf{x}(t_0) = \mathbf{x}_0$$

is denoted by $\mathbf{x}(t;\mathbf{x}_0,t)$ and is given by

7 $$\mathbf{x}(t;\mathbf{x}_0,t_0) = \mathbf{\Phi}(t,t_0)\mathbf{x}_0 \qquad \forall t,\ \forall \mathbf{x}_0$$

Proof By the definition of $\mathbf{\Phi}(t,t_0)$, observe that *7* reduces to $\mathbf{x}_0$ for $t = t_0$. Finally, on differentiating *7* we see that it satisfies the differential equation *6*.

8 **Definition** The matrix $\mathbf{\Phi}(t,t_0)$ is called the *state transition matrix.* ◁

Equation *7* can be interpreted as follows: $\mathbf{\Phi}(t,t_0)$ is a linear transformation which maps the state $\mathbf{x}_0$ at t_0 into the state $\mathbf{x}(t)$ at time t. This linear dependence of $\mathbf{x}(t)$ on $\mathbf{x}_0$ (exhibited by *7*) is a direct consequence of the zero-input linearity property of linear systems (see *3.4.17*). Another consequence is that all zero-input responses of *1* constitute an n-dimensional linear vector space (see *C.2.1* and *C.4.9*). Let $\mathcal{C}^n$ be the state space of *1*. These zero-input responses satisfy the requirements of additivity and homogeneity since, from *7*, $\mathbf{x}(t;\ \mathbf{x}_1 + \mathbf{x}_2,\ t_0) = \mathbf{x}(t;\mathbf{x}_1,t_0) + \mathbf{x}(t;\mathbf{x}_2,t_0)$, and $\mathbf{x}(t;\alpha\mathbf{x}_0,t_0) = \alpha\mathbf{x}(t;\mathbf{x}_0,t_0)$ for all $\mathbf{x}_1$, $\mathbf{x}_2$, $\mathbf{x}_0 \in \mathcal{C}^n$ and all complex numbers α. Let $\{\mathbf{a}_i\}_1^n$ be a basis for the state space $\mathcal{C}^n$ of *1* and let $\mathbf{x}_0 = \sum_1^n \xi_i\mathbf{a}_i$ be the (unique) representation of $\mathbf{x}_0$ in that basis; then the linearity of *7* with respect to $\mathbf{x}_0$ implies that

$$\mathbf{x}(t;\mathbf{x}_0,t_0) = \sum_{i=1}^{n} \xi_i\mathbf{x}(t;\mathbf{a}_i,t_0)$$

Thus any zero-input response of *1* can be expressed as a linear combination of n particular zero-input responses; hence, the dimension of the linear vector space is no greater than n. Let us pick as basis vectors the vectors $\mathbf{e}_i$ defined as follows: for $i = 1, 2, \ldots, n$, $\mathbf{e}_i$ has all its components equal to zero except the ith component, which is unity. From *7*, $\mathbf{x}(t;\mathbf{e}_i,t_0)$ is the ith column vector of $\mathbf{\Phi}(t,t_0)$. We shall show below (see *11*) that these n vectors are linearly independent for all t. Hence the dimension of the linear vector space of all zero-input responses of *1* is actually n.

Properties of $\mathbf{\Phi}(t,t_0)$

By analogy with the time-invariant case one might be tempted to write $\exp \int_{t_0}^{t} \mathbf{A}(\tau)\, d\tau$ for $\mathbf{\Phi}(t,t_0)$. In general this is erroneous because

$$\frac{d}{dt}[\mathbf{B}(t)]^2 = \dot{\mathbf{B}}(t)\mathbf{B}(t) + \mathbf{B}(t)\dot{\mathbf{B}}(t)$$

whereas the relation

$$\frac{d}{dt}[\mathbf{B}(t)]^2 = 2\mathbf{B}(t)\dot{\mathbf{B}}(t) = 2\dot{\mathbf{B}}(t)\mathbf{B}(t) \qquad \forall t$$

is true only if $\mathbf{B}(t)$ and $\dot{\mathbf{B}}(t)$ commute for all t. Thus referring to the series expansion definition of the exponential of a matrix (*5.2.3*), we have the

9 **Assertion** If, for all t, $\int_{t_0}^{t} \mathbf{A}(\tau)\, d\tau$ and $\mathbf{A}(t)$ commute, then

$$\mathbf{\Phi}(t,t_0) = \exp\left[\int_{t_0}^{t} \mathbf{A}(\tau)\, d\tau\right]$$

10 **Assertion** Let $\mathbf{\Phi}(t,t_0)$ be the state transition matrix of *1* defined by *5*. Then

$$\det \mathbf{\Phi}(t,t_0) = \exp\left[\int_{t_0}^{t} \alpha(\tau)\, d\tau\right]$$

where $\alpha(\tau) \triangleq \sum_{i=1}^{n} a_{ii}(\tau) \triangleq \operatorname{tr} \mathbf{A}(\tau)$.

The above assertion implies that

11 **Corollary** If $\mathbf{A}(t)$ is continuous over every finite time interval, then $\mathbf{\Phi}(t,t_0)$ is nonsingular for all finite t. (Therefore, for all t_0, the column vectors of $\mathbf{\Phi}(t,t_0)$ are linearly independent for all finite t.)

Proof of Assertion 10 Consider the time derivative of det $\mathbf{\Phi}$: it is a sum of n determinants $d_1, d_2, \ldots, d_n$, where d_i is the determinant all of whose elements are identical to those of $\mathbf{\Phi}$ except for the ith row, whose elements are the time derivatives of the corresponding ones in $\mathbf{\Phi}$. Let ϕ_{ij} be the general element of $\mathbf{\Phi}$. Then, by *5*

$$\dot{\phi}_{ij}(t) = \sum_{k=1}^{n} a_{ik}(t)\phi_{kj}(t)$$

Using some obvious row operations, one gets $d_i = a_{ii}(t) \det \mathbf{\Phi}$. Thus,

$$\frac{d}{dt}(\det \mathbf{\Phi}) = \left(\sum_{i=1}^{n} a_{ii}(t) \right) \det \mathbf{\Phi}$$

Since $\det \mathbf{\Phi}\Big|_{t_0} = \det \mathbf{\Phi}(t_0,t_0) = 1$, *10* follows by integrating this first-order differential equation in $\det \mathbf{\Phi}$.

12 **Assertion** Let $\mathbf{A}(t)$ be an $n \times n$ matrix whose elements are continuous functions of time. Then the solution of the matric differential equation

13 $$\dot{\mathbf{X}}(t) = \mathbf{A}(t)\mathbf{X}(t) \qquad \mathbf{X}(t_0) = \mathbf{C}$$

where $\mathbf{C}$ is an arbitrarily prescribed constant matrix, is given by

14 $$\mathbf{X}(t) = \mathbf{\Phi}(t,t_0)\mathbf{C}$$

Conversely, any solution of the above matric differential equation is of that form.

Proof Identical to that of Theorem *4* except for obvious modifications.

15 *Comment* Any nonsingular matrix which satisfies the matric differential equation *13* is called a *fundamental matrix* of the system *1*. Thus any fundamental matrix is of the form *14* for some nonsingular constant matrix $\mathbf{C}$. Also, the n columns of any fundamental matrix are n linearly independent solutions of *1*.

16 **Assertion** The state transition matrix has the group property

$$\mathbf{\Phi}(t_1,t_2)\mathbf{\Phi}(t_2,t_3) = \mathbf{\Phi}(t_1,t_3) \qquad \forall t_1, t_2, t_3$$

An immediate consequence of this property is

17 $$\mathbf{\Phi}(t_1,t_2)^{-1} = \mathbf{\Phi}(t_2,t_1)$$

Proof Exercise for the reader. (*Hint:* Use *12*.)

18 *Exercise* Show that the state transition matrix may be written as

$$\mathbf{\Phi}(t,t_0) = \mathbf{X}(t)\mathbf{X}^{-1}(t_0)$$

where $\mathbf{X}(t)$ is a nonsingular matrix which is differentiable for all t. [*Hint:* $\mathbf{X}(t) = \mathbf{\Phi}(t,0)$ and use *16*.]

Forced response

In many applications a linear system has an n-dimensional state space, has r inputs which are represented by the r-rowed vector $\mathbf{u}$, and has state equations of the form

$$\dot{\mathbf{x}}(t) = \mathbf{A}(t)\mathbf{x}(t) + \mathbf{B}(t)\mathbf{u}(t)$$

where $\mathbf{A}(t)$ and $\mathbf{B}(t)$ are known $n \times n$ and $n \times r$ matrices whose elements are continuous in t, $\mathbf{u}(t)$ is the input, and $\mathbf{x}(t)$ is the state.

For our purposes we adopt the simpler notation

19 $$\dot{\mathbf{x}}(t) = \mathbf{A}(t)\mathbf{x}(t) + \mathbf{a}(t)$$

where $\mathbf{a}(t) = \mathbf{B}(t)\mathbf{u}(t)$ is considered to be the input.

20 **Theorem** Consider the system *19* where $\mathbf{A}(t)$ is a continuous function of time. The solution that goes through the state $\mathbf{x}_0$ at t_0 is given by

21 $$\mathbf{x}(t;\mathbf{x}_0,t_0;\mathbf{a}_{[t_0,t]}) = \mathbf{\Phi}(t,t_0)\mathbf{x}_0 + \int_{t_0}^{t} \mathbf{\Phi}(t,\xi)\mathbf{a}(\xi)\,d\xi$$

Proof Immediate by direct verification of the initial condition and direct substitution into *19*. To effect this substitution note that

$$\frac{d}{dt}\int_{t_0}^{t} \mathbf{\Phi}(t,\xi)\mathbf{a}(\xi)\,d\xi = \mathbf{\Phi}(t,t)\mathbf{a}(t) + \int_{t_0}^{t} \frac{d}{dt}\mathbf{\Phi}(t,\xi)\mathbf{a}(\xi)\,d\xi$$
$$= \mathbf{a}(t) + \mathbf{A}(t)\int_{t_0}^{t} \mathbf{\Phi}(t,\xi)\mathbf{a}(\xi)\,d\xi$$

22 *Comment* The notation $\mathbf{x}(t;\mathbf{x}_0,t_0;\mathbf{a}_{[t_0,t]})$ is used to exhibit the fact that the state at time t depends on the initial conditions $\mathbf{x}_0$, t_0 and on the values of the forcing vector $\mathbf{a}(\xi)$ over the interval $[t_0,t]$. Understanding of this triple dependence is the key to many control problems. Of course, later on we shall drop the unwieldy notation $\mathbf{x}(t;\mathbf{x}_0,t_0;\mathbf{a}_{[t_0,t]})$ and write $\mathbf{x}(t)$ for the state at time t.

23 *Comment* Let us give an interpretation of *21*. Suppose that the input $\mathbf{a}$ differs from zero only on the infinitesimal interval $[\tau, \tau + d\tau]$. Then, by *7*,

$$\mathbf{x}(t) = \mathbf{\Phi}(t,t_0)\mathbf{x}_0 \qquad \text{for } t_0 \le t < \tau$$

but from *19*

$$\mathbf{x}(\tau + d\tau) = \mathbf{x}(\tau) + \mathbf{A}(\tau)\mathbf{x}(\tau)\,d\tau + \mathbf{a}(\tau)\,d\tau$$
$$= \mathbf{\Phi}(\tau + d\tau, t_0)\mathbf{x}_0 + \mathbf{a}(\tau)\,d\tau$$

Therefore, considering the expression above for the initial state at time $\tau + d\tau$ and observing that the system is in free motion for $t > \tau + d\tau$, we have

$$\mathbf{x}(t) = \mathbf{\Phi}(t,t_0)\mathbf{x}_0 + \mathbf{\Phi}(t, \tau + d\tau)\mathbf{a}(\tau)\,d\tau \qquad t > \tau + d\tau$$

where we use the group property *16* to simplify the first term. Dropping second-order terms in $d\tau$, we get

$$\mathbf{x}(t) = \mathbf{\Phi}(t,t_0)\mathbf{x}_0 + \mathbf{\Phi}(t,\tau)\mathbf{a}(\tau)\,d\tau$$

Thus we see that the second term of *21* is simply the *superposition* of the effects *observed at time t* of the forcing function acting during $[\tau, \tau + d\tau]$. In the time-invariant case the superposition integral of *21* reduces to a convolution integral because $\mathbf{\Phi}(t,\tau) = \exp[\mathbf{A}(t - \tau)]$, that is, is a function of the difference $t - \tau$.

24 *Exercise* Consider a system described by *19* where

$$\mathbf{A}(t) = \begin{bmatrix} 2 & -e^{-t} \\ e^{-t} & 1 \end{bmatrix}$$

Show that $\mathbf{x}_1 = (e^{2t}\cos t,\ e^t \sin t)$, $\mathbf{x}_2 = (-e^{2t}\sin t,\ e^t \cos t)$ are two linearly independent solutions of *19* when $\mathbf{a} = \mathbf{0}$. Show that

$$\mathbf{\Phi}(t,t_0) = \begin{bmatrix} e^{2(t-t_0)}\cos(t-t_0) & -e^{(2t-t_0)}\sin(t-t_0) \\ e^{(t-2t_0)}\sin(t-t_0) & e^{(t-t_0)}\cos(t-t_0) \end{bmatrix}$$

Check that this matrix obeys Assertion *12* and the group property *16*. Write the general solution of *19* when $\mathbf{a} \neq \mathbf{0}$ for this $\mathbf{A}(t)$.

The adjoint system

In order to understand the structure of the properties of time-varying systems, it is very important to consider the adjoint system, which is a system closely related to the system *1*. In time-invariant systems, the adjoint system is never mentioned because to obtain the adjoint system one need only change t into $-t$: roughly speaking, in the time-invariant case, the adjoint of a given system is simply the given system running backward in time. For the time-invariant case, the two systems are different.

25 **Definition** The two systems of equations

26 $$\dot{\mathbf{x}} = \mathbf{A}(t)\mathbf{x}$$

and

27 $$\dot{\mathbf{y}} = -\mathbf{A}^*(t)\mathbf{y}$$

where $\mathbf{A}^*(t)$ is the conjugate transpose of $\mathbf{A}(t)$, are said to be *adjoint* to one another. ◁

In *27*, $\mathbf{A}^*(t)$ is the matrix representation of the adjoint linear transformation of the transformation represented by $\mathbf{A}(t)$ (see *C.14.1*).

The importance and usefulness of the adjoint system is based on the following lemma.

28 **Lemma** Let $\mathbf{x}(t)$ and $\mathbf{y}(t)$ be any solutions of *1* and *27*, respectively. Then

$$\langle \mathbf{x}(t), \mathbf{y}(t) \rangle \equiv \text{constant}$$

Furthermore, if we denote by $\mathbf{\Psi}(t,t_0)$ the state transition matrix of the adjoint system, that is,

29 $$\frac{d}{dt}\mathbf{\Psi}(t,t_0) = -\mathbf{A}^*(t)\mathbf{\Psi}(t,t_0) \qquad \mathbf{\Psi}(t_0,t_0) = \mathbf{I}$$

then

30 $$\mathbf{\Psi}^*(t,t_0)\mathbf{\Phi}(t,t_0) = \mathbf{I} \qquad \text{for all } t \text{ and } t_0$$

31 *Comment* Note that *30* and *17* imply that

32 $$\mathbf{\Psi}^*(t,t_0) = \mathbf{\Phi}(t,t_0)^{-1} = \mathbf{\Phi}(t_0,t) \qquad \forall t,t_0$$

Conversely, if *32* holds, then the corresponding systems are related to one another as *1* and *27*. For this reason *32* can be used as an alternative way of defining adjointness of systems of the form *1* (see also Theorem *6.3.16*).

Proof To prove *28*, note that

$$\begin{aligned}\frac{d}{dt}\langle \mathbf{x}(t),\mathbf{y}(t)\rangle &= \langle \dot{\mathbf{x}}(t),\mathbf{y}(t)\rangle + \langle \mathbf{x}(t),\dot{\mathbf{y}}(t)\rangle \\ &= \langle \mathbf{A}(t)\mathbf{x}(t),\mathbf{y}(t)\rangle + \langle \mathbf{x}(t),-\mathbf{A}^*(t)\mathbf{y}(t)\rangle \\ &= \langle \mathbf{A}(t)\mathbf{x}(t),\mathbf{y}(t)\rangle + \langle -\mathbf{A}(t)\mathbf{x}(t),\mathbf{y}(t)\rangle \\ &= \langle [\mathbf{A}(t) - \mathbf{A}(t)]\mathbf{x}(t),\mathbf{y}(t)\rangle = 0\end{aligned}$$

where we used the fact that $\langle \mathbf{u},\mathbf{A}\mathbf{v}\rangle = \langle \mathbf{A}^*\mathbf{u},\mathbf{v}\rangle$, $\forall \mathbf{u},\mathbf{v}$ (see *C.14.2*). *30* is proved in a similar manner: for $t = t_0$, the relation holds by the initial conditions imposed on $\mathbf{\Phi}$ and $\mathbf{\Psi}$. Differentiate the left-hand side of *30*, and use *29* and *5* to obtain

$$\begin{aligned}&\dot{\mathbf{\Psi}}^*(t,t_0)\mathbf{\Phi}(t,t_0) + \mathbf{\Psi}^*(t,t_0)\dot{\mathbf{\Phi}}(t,t_0) \\ &\qquad = \mathbf{\Psi}^*(t,t_0)\mathbf{A}(t)\mathbf{\Phi}(t,t_0) - \mathbf{\Psi}^*(t,t_0)\mathbf{A}(t)\mathbf{\Phi}(t,t_0) = \mathbf{0}\end{aligned}$$

Note that we also used the fact that $[\mathbf{A}^*(t)]^* = \mathbf{A}(t)$ (see *C.14.5*). Hence the left-hand side of *30* is always equal to $\mathbf{I}$.

33 *Comment* Let us interpret *30* geometrically. Let $\boldsymbol{\phi}_i(t,t_0)$ be the *i*th column of $\mathbf{\Phi}(t,t_0)$: $\boldsymbol{\phi}_i(t,t_0)$ is the solution of *1* such that all its components at t_0 are zero except the *i*th, which is unity. Let $\boldsymbol{\psi}_i(t,t_0)$ be the *i*th column of $\mathbf{\Psi}(t,t_0)$: $\boldsymbol{\psi}_i(t,t_0)$ is the solution of *27* such that all its components at t_0 are zero except the *i*th, which is unity. Remembering that we use the complex scalar product (see *5.4.7* and *C.5.1*), i.e., if $\mathbf{x} = (\xi_1, \ldots, \xi_n)$ and $\mathbf{y} = (\eta_1, \ldots, \eta_n)$, then $\langle \mathbf{x},\mathbf{y}\rangle = \sum_{i=1}^{n} \xi_i^*\eta_i$, let us observe that the (i,j) element of the product of *30* is the scalar product of $\boldsymbol{\psi}_i$ with $\boldsymbol{\phi}_j$; hence *30* implies

34 $$\langle \boldsymbol{\psi}_i(t,t_0),\boldsymbol{\phi}_j(t,t_0)\rangle = \delta_{ij} \qquad i, j = 1, 2, \ldots, n$$

Now, by *11*, the *n* column vectors of $\mathbf{\Phi}(t,t_0)$ are linearly independent for all *t*; that is, for all *t*, the set of vectors $\{\boldsymbol{\phi}_i(t,t_0)\}$ constitutes a basis for the state space $\mathcal{C}^n$. Thus *34* implies that (see *C.8.1* and *5.4.9*) for any *t*, the set of vectors $\{\boldsymbol{\psi}_i(t,t_0)\}$ constitutes the *reciprocal basis* of the basis $\{\boldsymbol{\phi}_i(t,t_0)\}$ of the state space $\mathcal{C}^n$ of *1*. Thus, for example, for any vector $\mathbf{c}$, for all *t*, and for all t_0

35 $$\mathbf{c} = \sum_{i=1}^{n} \langle \boldsymbol{\psi}_i(t,t_0),\mathbf{c}\rangle \boldsymbol{\phi}_i(t,t_0)$$

Therefore we also have

36 $$\mathbf{I} = \sum_{i=1}^{n} \boldsymbol{\phi}_i(t,t_0)\rangle \langle \boldsymbol{\psi}_i(t,t_0) \qquad \forall t,t_0$$

which is analogous to *5.4.16* and which occurred in the time-invariant case. In *36*, the vectors of the basis and those of the reciprocal basis vary with time.

37 **Remark: alternate forms for Eq. *21*** It is important to be able to write the expression for $\mathbf{x}(t;\mathbf{x}_0,t_0;\mathbf{a}_{[t_0,t]})$ in several ways. We have given the basic formula *21*. Let us now use successively *16, 17, 32,* and *36* to obtain four additional expressions for $\mathbf{x}$:

38 $$\mathbf{x}(t;\mathbf{x}_0,t_0;\mathbf{a}_{(t_0,t]}) = \begin{cases} \boldsymbol{\Phi}(t,t_0)\mathbf{x}_0 + \int_{t_0}^{t} \boldsymbol{\Phi}(t,\xi)\mathbf{a}(\xi)\, d\xi \\ \boldsymbol{\Phi}(t,t_0)\left[\mathbf{x}_0 + \int_{t_0}^{t} \boldsymbol{\Phi}(t_0,\xi)\mathbf{a}(\xi)\, d\xi\right] \\ \boldsymbol{\Phi}(t,t_0)\left\{\mathbf{x}_0 + \int_{t_0}^{t} [\boldsymbol{\Phi}(\xi,t_0)]^{-1}\mathbf{a}(\xi)\, d\xi\right\} \\ \boldsymbol{\Phi}(t,t_0)\left[\mathbf{x}_0 + \int_{t_0}^{t} \boldsymbol{\Psi}^*(\xi,t_0)\mathbf{a}(\xi)\, d\xi\right] \\ \sum_{i=1}^{n} \boldsymbol{\phi}_i(t,t_0)\left[\langle \boldsymbol{\psi}_i(t_0,t_0),\mathbf{x}_0\rangle + \int_{t_0}^{t} \langle \boldsymbol{\psi}_i(\tau,t_0),\mathbf{a}(\tau)\rangle\, d\tau\right] \end{cases}$$

39 *Comment* The last equation can be given an interpretation based on comment *33*: for any t, the response $\mathbf{x}(t)$ is a linear combination of the n linearly independent solutions $\boldsymbol{\phi}_i(t,t_0)$ of the homogeneous equation *1*. Each coefficient of this linear combination is a sum of two terms. The first term is a constant [$\langle \boldsymbol{\psi}_i(t_0,t_0),\mathbf{x}_0\rangle$, the ith component of $\mathbf{x}_0$] which depends only on the initial state $\mathbf{x}_0$; it measures the component of $\mathbf{x}_0$ along $\boldsymbol{\phi}_i(t_0,t_0)$. The second term of the sum is a time-varying term which takes into account the effect of the input $\mathbf{a}(t)$; it is the time integral over $[t_0,t]$ of the component of the input $\mathbf{a}(\tau)$ along the vector $\boldsymbol{\phi}_i(\tau,t_0)$ (compare the second term in the brackets of the last equation *38* and the expansion *35*). In other words, at every instant τ, one computes the components of $\mathbf{a}(\tau)$ along the instantaneous basis $\{\boldsymbol{\phi}_i(\tau,t_0)\}$, and the contribution of the input $\mathbf{a}(\tau)$ to the component of the state at time t along $\boldsymbol{\phi}_i(t,t_0)$, which is due to the input acting during the infinitesimal interval $(\tau, \tau + d\tau)$, is $\langle \boldsymbol{\psi}_i(\tau,t_0),a(\tau)\rangle\, d\tau$.

Another way of expressing this idea is the following. Let the response of *19* be written as $\mathbf{x}(t) = \sum_{i=1}^{n} \xi_i(t)\boldsymbol{\phi}_i(t,t_0)$, where the $\xi_i(t)$ are the components of $\mathbf{x}(t)$ with respect to the basis $\{\boldsymbol{\phi}_i(t,t_0)\}$ at time t. Then from the last equation *38* we see that

40 $$\dot{\xi}_i(t) = \langle \boldsymbol{\psi}_i(t,t_0),\mathbf{a}(t)\rangle \qquad \xi_i(t_0) = \langle \boldsymbol{\psi}_i(t_0,t_0),\mathbf{x}_0\rangle$$

Geometrically, the basis $\{\phi_i(t,t_0)\}$ is a "moving set of basis vectors" ("a moving reference frame," a physicist would say) because the vectors $\phi_i(t,t_0)$ change in both length and direction. If the input $\mathbf{a}$ is identically zero, then from the equation above the components ξ_i of $\mathbf{x}(t;\mathbf{x}_0,t_0)$ are constant! Also we could say that the set of basis vectors $\{\phi_i(t,t_0)\}$ "diagonalizes" the system in the sense that for $\mathbf{a} \equiv \mathbf{0}$ the equations with respect to that basis read $\dot{\xi}_i = 0$ or $\dot{\xi} = \mathbf{0}\xi$, where $\mathbf{0}$ is the zero matrix which is a special case of a diagonal matrix. In the time-invariant case, when $\mathbf{A}$ is a simple linear transformation (see *C.18.6*), we could pick a *fixed* basis with respect to which the equations of motion were diagonalized. In the time-varying case this can be done only by using a moving basis.

41 *Exercise* Write the solution of *19* as $\mathbf{x}(t;\mathbf{x}_0,t_0;\mathbf{a}_{[t_0,t]}) = \Sigma\xi_i(t)\phi_i(t;t_0)$. Find by direct substitution into *19* the differential equations obeyed by the $\xi_i(t)$'s and their initial conditions. (This is the method of variation of parameters.)

42 *Comment* The set of basis vectors $\{\phi_i(t,t_0)\}$ is not unique. For if $\mathbf{C}$ is an arbitrary nonsingular matrix and if $\hat{\mathbf{\Phi}}(t,t_0)$ and $\hat{\mathbf{\Psi}}^*(t,t_0)$ obey the same differential equations (*5* and *29*, respectively) but with the initial conditions $\hat{\mathbf{\Phi}}(t_0,t_0) = \mathbf{C}$, $\hat{\mathbf{\Psi}}^*(t_0,t_0) = \mathbf{C}^{-1}$, then *30* still holds and the $\{\psi_i(t,t_0)\}$ constitute for all t a reciprocal basis to the $\{\hat{\phi}_i(t,t_0)\}$. Thus equation *38* needs no modification if ^'s are put on all the ϕ_i's and ψ_i's.

43 *Exercise* For the time-varying case one may also introduce a *Green dyadic* and set

44
$$\mathbf{G}(t,\tau) \triangleq \mathbf{\Phi}(t,\tau)1(t-\tau) = 1(t-\tau)\sum_{i=1}^{n} \phi_i(t,t_0)\rangle\langle\psi_i(t,t_0)$$

Show that

$$\mathbf{x}(t;\mathbf{x}_0,t_0;\mathbf{a}_{[t_0,t]}) = \mathbf{\Phi}(t,t_0)\mathbf{x}_0 + \int_{t_0}^{t} \mathbf{G}(t,\tau)\mathbf{a}(\tau)\,d\tau$$

Comment on the relation between the nonanticipative character of the system *19* and the presence of $1(t-\tau)$ in *44*.

45 **Remark** *The use of the adjoint in engineering problems* In many communication and control problems, either linear or nonlinear, systems of time-varying differential equations appear naturally. Optimization problems, in particular, often require the consideration of the adjoint system. The basic reasons for this will become clear by considering in detail a specific though grossly simplified control problem. Suppose that the system we wish to control is described by a set of known nonlinear differential equations $\dot{\mathbf{x}} = \mathbf{f}(\mathbf{x},\mathbf{u},t)$. The n-vector $\mathbf{x}$ is the state, and the r-vector $\mathbf{u}$ is the control. We are given the initial state $\mathbf{x}_0$ and the initial time t_0. Let us denote by $\mathbf{x}(t_1)$ the state at a specified time t_1: $\mathbf{x}(t_1)$ is the state reached from $\mathbf{x}_0$ at time t_0 as a result of a control $\mathbf{u}_{[t_0,t_1]}$. The problem is to maximize the value that a given payoff function ϕ takes at $\mathbf{x}(t_1)$. Suppose that an approximate analysis or some intuitive argument suggests that a certain control $\hat{\mathbf{u}}_{[t_0,t_1]}$ would be a good first guess. Call $\hat{\mathbf{x}}(t_1)$ the resulting state at time t_1. Consider now the problem of improving the initial guess by a perturbation technique. If, starting from $\mathbf{x}_0$ at t_0, we apply a control $\hat{\mathbf{u}}_{[t_0,t_1]} + \delta\mathbf{u}_{[t_0,t_1]}$, then the corresponding solution of the nonlinear differential equations may be written as $\hat{\mathbf{x}}_{[t_0,t_1]} + \delta\mathbf{x}_{[t_0,t_1]}$. Furthermore, if $\mathbf{f}$ be sufficiently smooth and if $\delta\mathbf{u}_{[t_0,t_1]}$ is sufficiently small, then $\delta\mathbf{x}(t)$ will be small for all t in $[t_0,t_1]$. Under these assumptions, by performing a Taylor expansion of the original differential equation and by dropping the second-order terms, we arrive at the approximate differential equation for $\delta\mathbf{x}$:

$$\frac{d}{dt}\,\delta\mathbf{x} = \mathbf{A}(t)\delta\mathbf{x}(t) + \mathbf{B}(t)\delta\mathbf{u}(t) \qquad \delta\mathbf{x}(t_0) = \mathbf{0}$$

where $\mathbf{A}(t)$ is the $n \times n$ matrix whose i,j element is the partial derivative $\partial f_i/\partial x_j$ and $\mathbf{B}(t)$ is the $n \times r$ matrix whose i,k element is $\partial f_i/\partial u_k$. In both cases, the partial derivatives are evaluated along the original trajectory $\hat{\mathbf{x}}_{[t_0,t_1]}$ and the original control $\hat{\mathbf{u}}_{[t_0,t_1]}$; they are therefore known functions of time. The change in the state at time t_1 resulting from a small change of control $\delta\mathbf{u}_{[t_0,t_1]}$ is then given by

$$\delta\mathbf{x}(t_1) = \int_{t_0}^{t_1} \mathbf{\Phi}(t_1,\xi)\mathbf{B}(\xi)\delta\mathbf{u}(\xi)\,d\xi$$

This expression calls for a comment: the effect of $\delta\mathbf{u}_{[t_0,t_1]}$ on $\delta\mathbf{x}(t_1)$ depends on the behavior of $\mathbf{\Phi}(t_1,\xi)$ as a function of ξ, that is, as a function of its *second* argument. However, the defining equation of the state transition matrix, Eq. *5*, specifies the rate of change of $\mathbf{\Phi}$ with respect to its *first* argument. Equations *32* and *29* suggest that consideration of the state transition matrix of the adjoint system is called for because

$$\frac{d}{d\xi}\,\mathbf{\Phi}^*(t_1,\xi) = \frac{d}{d\xi}\,\mathbf{\Psi}(\xi,t_1) = -\mathbf{A}^*(\xi)\mathbf{\Psi}(\xi,t_1)$$

A little further analysis will, however, bring us directly to the adjoint system. Going back to the problem, recall that we should maximize ϕ at the final state. Again neglecting second-order terms, we see that the increase in ϕ is

$$\begin{aligned}\delta\phi &\triangleq \phi(\hat{\mathbf{x}}(t_1) + \delta\mathbf{x}(t_1)) - \phi(\hat{\mathbf{x}}(t_1))\\ &= \langle \mathbf{c},\delta\mathbf{x}(t_1)\rangle\end{aligned}$$

where the vector $\mathbf{c}$ is the gradient of ϕ evaluated at $\hat{\mathbf{x}}(t_1)$; in other words, $\mathbf{c}$ is a known vector. Now we obtain successively

$$\begin{aligned}\delta\phi &= \left\langle \mathbf{c}, \int_{t_0}^{t_1} \mathbf{\Phi}(t_1,\xi)\mathbf{B}(\xi)\delta\mathbf{u}(\xi)\,d\xi \right\rangle \\ &= \int_{t_0}^{t_1} \langle \mathbf{c}, \mathbf{\Phi}(t_1,\xi)\mathbf{B}(\xi)\delta\mathbf{u}(\xi)\rangle\,d\xi \\ &= \int_{t_0}^{t_1} \langle \mathbf{B}^*(\xi)\mathbf{\Phi}^*(t_1,\xi)\mathbf{c}, \delta\mathbf{u}(\xi)\rangle\,d\xi\end{aligned}$$

Since, by *32*, $\mathbf{\Phi}^*(t_1,\xi)\mathbf{c} = \mathbf{\Psi}(\xi,t_1)\mathbf{c}$, we see that this vector function of ξ is the solution of the adjoint differential equation $\dot{\mathbf{z}}(t) = -\mathbf{A}^*(t)\mathbf{z}(t)$ subject to the "initial" condition $\mathbf{z}(t_1) = \mathbf{c}$. (The adjoint system must be integrated backward in time starting at t_1 and ending at the prior time t_0!) Call $\boldsymbol{\lambda}(\xi)$ the solution just defined; then

$$\delta\phi = \int_{t_0}^{t_1} \langle \mathbf{B}^*(\xi)\boldsymbol{\lambda}(\xi), \delta\mathbf{u}(\xi)\rangle\,d\xi$$

Observe that the functions $\mathbf{B}^*_{[t_0,t_1]}$ and $\boldsymbol{\lambda}_{[t_0,t_1]}$ can be computed on the basis of the known data, so that the expression above allows us to compute $\delta\phi$ for any $\delta\mathbf{u}_{[t_0,t_1]}$ provided the latter is small. In order to keep $\delta\mathbf{u}_{[t_0,t_1]}$ small, it is convenient to require that

46 $$\int_{t_0}^{t_1} \langle \delta\mathbf{u}(\xi), \delta\mathbf{u}(\xi)\rangle\,d\xi = \eta$$

where η is a small number chosen in advance. With this constraint the problem of maximizing $\delta\phi$ is the same as that of maximizing

$$\frac{\delta\phi}{\eta} = \frac{\int_{t_0}^{t_1} \langle \mathbf{B}^*(\xi)\boldsymbol{\lambda}(\xi), \delta\mathbf{u}(\xi)\rangle\,d\xi}{\int_{t_0}^{t_1} \langle \delta\mathbf{u}(\xi), \delta\mathbf{u}(\xi)\rangle\,d\xi}$$

The denominator may be interpreted as the scalar product of the vector-valued function $\delta\mathbf{u}$, defined on $[t_0,t_1]$, with itself. Similarly, the numerator is the scalar product of $\mathbf{B}^*\boldsymbol{\lambda}$ with $\delta\mathbf{u}$ (see *C.5.1* and *C.5.3*). By the method used to prove *C.5.8*, it can easily be shown that Schwarz's inequality still holds in this case and that the above ratio will reach its maximum if and only if the change in control $\delta\mathbf{u}$ is given by

$$\delta\mathbf{u}(\xi) = k\mathbf{B}^*(\xi)\boldsymbol{\lambda}(\xi) \qquad t_0 \le \xi \le t_1$$

where the constant k is so chosen that the constraint *46* is satisfied.

Let us recapitulate the steps required to perform one iteration: (I) given $\hat{\mathbf{u}}_{[t_0,t_1]}$ and $\hat{\mathbf{x}}(t_1)$, calculate $\mathbf{A}(t)$, $\mathbf{B}(t)$, and $\mathbf{c}$; (II) integrate the adjoint differential equation to obtain $\boldsymbol{\lambda}(\xi)$; (III) determine $\delta\mathbf{u}$ by the expression above in which the unspecified constant k is determined through the constraint *46*.

The adjoint of a system represented by $L(p,t)y = u$

Consider the nth-order ordinary differential equation $L(p,t)y = u$ in which

47 $$L(p,t) = p^n + a_1(t)p^{n-1} + \cdots + a_{n-1}(t)p + a_n(t)$$

where p is the differential operator d/dt and $a_k(t) \in C^{n-k}$, $k = 1, 2, \ldots, n$. To start with, let us consider the homogeneous equation

48 $$p^n y + a_1(t)p^{n-1}y + \cdots + a_{n-1}(t)py + a_n(t)y = 0$$

If we use as state vector the vector $\mathbf{y} = (y,\dot{y},\ddot{y}, \ldots ,y^{(n-1)})$, then we can write (see *4.3.33 et seq.*)

49 $$\dot{\mathbf{y}} = \mathbf{A}(t)\mathbf{y}$$

with

50 $$\mathbf{A}(t) = \begin{bmatrix} 0 & 1 & 0 & \cdots & \cdots & 0 \\ 0 & 0 & 1 & \cdots & \cdots & \cdots \\ \cdots & \cdots & 0 & 1 & \cdots & \cdots \\ \cdots & \cdots & \cdots & 0 & \cdots & \cdots \\ \cdots & \cdots & \cdots & \cdots & \cdots & 0 \\ 0 & 0 & \cdots & \cdots & 0 & 1 \\ -a_n & -a_{n-1} & \cdots & \cdots & -a_2 & -a_1 \end{bmatrix}$$

The adjoint state equation is, according to the Definition *27*,

$$\dot{\mathbf{z}} = -\mathbf{A}^*(t)\mathbf{z}$$

where the matrix $\mathbf{A}^*(t)$ is the conjugate transpose of the matrix $\mathbf{A}(t)$, namely,

51 $$-\mathbf{A}^*(t) = \begin{bmatrix} 0 & 0 & \cdots & \cdots & \cdots & 0 & a_n^* \\ -1 & 0 & \cdots & \cdots & \cdots & 0 & a_{n-1}^* \\ 0 & -1 & 0 & \cdots & \cdots & \cdots & \cdots \\ \cdots & 0 & -1 & 0 & \cdots & \cdots & \cdots \\ \cdots & \cdots & \cdots & \cdots & \cdots & \cdots & \cdots \\ \cdots & \cdots & \cdots & \cdots & 0 & 0 & \cdots \\ \cdots & \cdots & \cdots & \cdots & -1 & 0 & a_2^* \\ 0 & 0 & \cdots & \cdots & 0 & -1 & a_1^* \end{bmatrix}$$

Let the components of $\mathbf{z}$ be $z_1, z_2, \ldots, z_n$; then the adjoint system reads

52 $$\begin{aligned} p\,z_1 &= a_n^* z_n \\ p\,z_2 &= a_{n-1}^* z_n - z_1 \\ p\,z_3 &= a_{n-2}^* z_n - z_2 \\ &\cdots\cdots\cdots \\ p\,z_n &= a_1^* z_n - z_{n-1} \end{aligned}$$

If we multiply in the above system the kth equation by $(-1)^{k-1}p^{k-1}$ and add the resulting equations, we have

$$(-1)^n p^n z_n + (-1)^{n-1}p^{n-1}(a_1^* z_n) + \cdots + (-1)p(a_{n-1}^* z_n) + a_n^* z_n = 0$$

Therefore, it is reasonable to call the operator

53 $$L^*(p,t) \triangleq (-1)^n p^n \cdot + (-1)^{n-1}p^{n-1}(a_1^* \cdot) + \cdots + (-1)p(a_{n-1}^* \cdot) + a_n^* \cdot$$

the *adjoint of the operator*

54 $$L(p,t) \triangleq p^n \cdot + a_1(t)p^{n-1} \cdot + a_2(t)p^{n-1} \cdot + \cdots + a_{n-1}(t)p \cdot + a_n(t) \cdot$$

where the dots indicate the operand.

55 *Comment* It is very important to observe that the solution of $Ly = 0$ is the *first* component of the vector solution of *49*, whereas the solution $z(t)$ of $L^*z = 0$ is the nth component of the vector solution of

$$\dot{\mathbf{z}} = -\mathbf{A}^*(t)\mathbf{z}$$

This observation will be useful in some later developments.

56 *Exercise* Write $Ly = u$, with L given by *54*, in state equation form. Let $\mathbf{y} = (y,\dot{y}, \ldots ,y^{(n-1)})$.
[*Ans.:* $\dot{\mathbf{y}} = \mathbf{A}(t)\mathbf{y} + \mathbf{b}u$, where $\mathbf{b} = (0,0, \ldots ,0,1)$ and $\mathbf{A}(t)$ is given by *50*.]

57 *Exercise* Write $L^*z_n = r$, where L is given by *54*, in state equation form. Let $\mathbf{z} = (z_1,z_2, \ldots ,z_n)$.
[*Ans.:* $\dot{\mathbf{z}} = -\mathbf{A}^*(t)\mathbf{z} - \mathbf{c}r$, where $\mathbf{c} = (1,0, \ldots ,0)$ and $\mathbf{A}^*(t)$ is given by *51*.]

3 *System represented by $Ly = u$*

In this section we consider a single-input single-output linear time-varying differential system described by $Ly = u$.

The impulse response

We consider a nonanticipative system $\mathcal{S}_L$ represented by

1 $$L(p,t)y = \sum_{k=0}^{n} a_k(t)p^{n-k}y(t) = u$$

where y is the output and u the input. We assume that the $(n + 1)$ functions $a_k(t)$ are continuous functions of time and that $a_0(t) \neq 0$ for all t. Since this representation directly relates the output y to the input u, it is natural to consider the impulse response of the system. Recall that we use the

2 **Definition** The unit-impulse response of the nonanticipative system $\mathcal{S}_L$ is denoted by $h(t,\xi)$; it is the zero-state response of the system at time t to a unit impulse applied at time ξ. ◁

Figure *6.3.1* illustrates the behavior of $h(t,\xi)$. Note that $h(t,\xi) = 0$ for all $t < \xi$, because the system is in the zero state at time $\xi-$ and

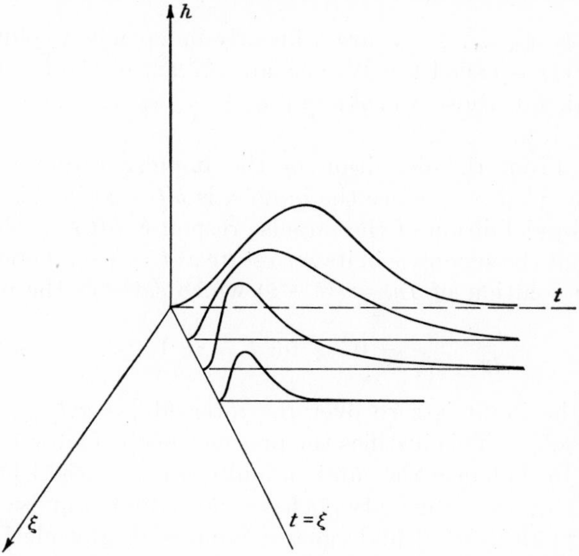

Fig. 6.3.1 The behavior of $h(t,\xi)$, the impulse response of the system represented by $L(p,t)y = u$.

because the system is nonanticipative [i.e., it does not respond prior to the application of the impulse (see *1.8.13*)]. The figure shows that the function $h(\cdot,0)$ delayed by one second is definitely different from the function $h(\cdot,1)$, thus exhibiting the fact that the properties of the system vary with time.

The relation between the impulse response and the differential equation *1* is given by the following

3 **Theorem** $h(t,\xi)$, the impulse response of the system $\mathcal{S}_L$ described by *1*, is such that[1]

4 (I) $$L_t h(t,\xi) = \delta(t-\xi) \qquad \text{for all } t \text{ and } \xi$$

(II) $$\left.\frac{\partial^k h(t,\xi)}{\partial t^k}\right|_{t=\xi+} = 0 \qquad k = 0, 1, \ldots, n-2$$

5 $$\left.\frac{\partial^{n-1} h(t,\xi)}{\partial t^{n-1}}\right|_{t=\xi+} = \frac{1}{a_0(\xi)}$$

[1] The subscript t attached to L in *4* is to specify that the differential operator p, which appears in the expression for L, operates on the variable t and not on the variable ξ.

(III)

6 $$h(t,\xi) = \frac{1(t-\xi)}{a_0(\xi)W(\xi)} \begin{vmatrix} \phi_1(\xi) & \phi_2(\xi) & \cdots & \phi_n(\xi) \\ \phi_1^{(1)}(\xi) & \phi_2^{(1)}(\xi) & \cdots & \phi_n^{(1)}(\xi) \\ \cdots & \cdots & \cdots & \cdots \\ \phi_1^{(n-2)}(\xi) & \phi_2^{(n-2)}(\xi) & \cdots & \phi_n^{(n-2)}(\xi) \\ \phi_1(t) & \phi_2(t) & \cdots & \phi_n(t) \end{vmatrix}$$

where $\phi_1, \phi_2, \ldots, \phi_n$ are n linearly independent solutions of $Ly = 0$ and $W(\xi)$ is called the Wronskian (*3.7.12*) of these solutions [i.e., the determinant whose ith column is $\phi_i(\xi), \phi_i^{(1)}(\xi), \ldots, \phi_i^{(n-2)}(\xi), \phi_i^{(n-1)}(\xi)$, for $i = 1, 2, \ldots, n$].

Proof From the definition of the impulse response, $h(t,\xi)$ satisfies $L_t h(t,\xi) = \delta(t-\xi)$ since the input u is $\delta(t-\xi)$ in this case. Furthermore, by definition of the impulse response, $h(t,\xi)$ is that solution of *4* such that the system is in its zero state at $t = \xi-$; therefore, $h(t,\xi)$ is the unique solution of $Ly = \delta(t-\xi)$ which satisfies the initial conditions

$$\left.\frac{d^k y}{dt^k}\right|_{t=\xi-} = 0 \qquad \text{for } k = 0, 1, 2, \ldots, n-1$$

Since the input is zero over the interval $(-\infty,\xi-)$, $y(t) = 0$ for all $t \in (-\infty,\xi)$. This justifies the presence of the factor $1(t-\xi)$ in *6*. In order to balance the unit impulse in the right-hand side of *4*, $a_0(t)\partial^n h(t,\xi)/\partial t^n$ must also behave like a unit impulse at $t = \xi$; therefore, $\partial^{n-1}h(t,\xi)/\partial t^{n-1}$ undergoes a jump of magnitude $1/a_0(\xi)$ at $t = \xi$.[1] Thus (I) and (II) are established. To prove (III), we show that *6* is an explicit expression of the solution of *4* with the initial conditions *5*. First compute $\partial^k h(t,\xi)/\partial t^k$ for some $t > \xi$; note that the kth derivative is obtained for $t > \xi$ by differentiating k times the last row of the determinant. Now for $t \to \xi+$ (in view of the continuity of $\phi_i^{(k)}$, $i = 1, 2, \ldots, n$, $k = 0, 1, \ldots, n-2$), the determinant vanishes since it has in the limit two identical rows. For $k = n-1$, in view of the continuity of the $\phi_i^{(n-1)}$, the determinant becomes identical to the Wronskian $W(\xi)$. Therefore, expression *6* satisfies the appropriate initial conditions at $\xi+$. Finally, it is a solution of $Ly = 0$ for $t > \xi$, since *6* is a linear combination of the $\phi_i(t)$. This completes the proof of (III).

7 *Comment* Note that *6* implies that $h(t,\xi)$ has the form

$$h(t,\xi) = 1(t-\xi)\sum_{i=1}^{n} \varphi_i(t)\alpha_i(\xi)$$

where $\alpha_i(\xi)$ is the cofactor of $\phi_i(\xi)$ in $W(\xi)$ divided by $a_0(\xi)W(\xi)$. It is easy to show (see Exercise *12*) that the $\alpha_i(t)$ are basis functions for the adjoint differential operator L^*.

[1] For a more detailed discussion of this point see *A.7.9* and *A.7.11*.

8 *Exercise* Let $a_0(t) = 1$ for all t. Prove Theorem *3* by considering the state equations of the system. [*Hint:* Use $(y, \dot{y}, \ldots, y^{(n-1)})$ as the state vector; show that the nth column of $\mathbf{\Phi}(t,\xi)$, for $t \geq \xi$, is $(h(t,\xi), h^{(1)}(t,\xi), \ldots, h^{(n-1)}(t,\xi))$, where the indicated differentiations are partial differentiations with respect to t.]

The basis functions

9 **Definition** Any set of n linearly independent solutions of $Ly = 0$ is called a set of *basis functions* of the operator L.

10 *Comment* The reason for calling such sets of solutions basis functions is that any such set constitutes a *basis* for the linear vector space whose elements are all the solutions of $Ly = 0$ (see *C.2.1* and *C.2.5*). Note also that this definition is equivalent to that given previously (see *3.6.39* and *3.6.41*).

Given the time-varying operator $L(p,t)$, there are no general methods for obtaining a set of basis functions. However, the converse problem —given n functions, find a linear differential operator L of order n such that these functions are basis functions of L—is easily solved.

11 **Theorem** Let $\phi_1(t), \phi_2(t), \ldots, \phi_n(t)$ be n functions having n continuous derivatives (i.e., belonging to the class C^n) over some interval $t_0 \leq t \leq t_1$. Let their Wronskian vanish nowhere in this interval. Then, these functions are n linearly independent solutions of the differential equation

$$W(\phi_1, \phi_2, \ldots, \phi_n, x) = 0$$

where W is the Wronskian of $\phi_1, \phi_2, \ldots, \phi_n, x$.
Proof Exercise for the reader.

12 *Exercise* Let the unit-impulse response be written as

$$h(t,\xi) = 1(t - \xi) \sum_{i=1}^{n} \phi_i(t)\alpha_i(\xi)$$

where the $\alpha_i(\xi)$ are defined by comparison with *6*. Let $a_0(t) = 1$, for all t, for convenience. From the above theorem show that $h(t,\xi)$, considered as a function of ξ, is such that

13 $$L_\xi^* h(t,\xi) = \delta(t - \xi)$$

14 $$\left.\frac{\partial^k h(t,\xi)}{\partial \xi^k}\right|_{\xi \to t-} = 0 \qquad k = 0, 1, \ldots, n-2$$
$$\left.\frac{\partial^{n-1} h(t,\xi)}{\partial \xi^{n-1}}\right|_{\xi \to t-} = (-1)^n$$

[*Hint:* Write the coefficient of $1(t - \xi)\phi_k(t)$ in *6* as $W_k(\xi)/W(\xi)$. Show that W_k/W are linearly independent solutions of $L^*y = 0$.]

The important facts concerning the forced response of the system *1* are summarized in the

15 **Theorem** The response of the system $\mathcal{S}_L$ described by *1* to the input $u_{[t_0,t]}$, given the initial state $y(t_0-)$, $\dot{y}(t_0-)$, . . . , $y^{(n-1)}(t_0-)$ of $\mathcal{S}_L$, is

$$y(t) = \sum_{i=1}^{n} \gamma_i \phi_i(t) + \int_{t_0}^{t} h(t,\xi)u(\xi)\, d\xi$$

where $\phi_1, \ldots, \phi_n$ are n basis functions of L and the constants $\gamma_1, \ldots, \gamma_n$ are determined by the prescribed initial state.
Proof Exercise for the reader.

The adjoint system

The following theorem exhibits a very important relation between the impulse response of the nonanticipative system $\mathcal{S}_L$ and that of the purely anticipative adjoint system $\mathcal{S}_L^*$. Observe the close analogy between the following and Remark *6.2.45*.

16 **Theorem** Consider the nonanticipative system $\mathcal{S}_L$ (see *1.8.13*) described by *1* [with $a_0(t) = 1$, $\forall t$; $a_k(t) \in C^{n-k}$] and whose impulse response is $h(t,\xi)$. Let $\mathcal{S}_L^*$ be a purely anticipative system (see *1.8.13*) described by

17 $$L^*z = u$$

Let $h^a(t,\xi)$ be the solution of $L_t^* h^a(t,\xi) = \delta(t-\xi)$ such that

$$\left.\frac{\partial^k h^a(t,\xi)}{\partial t^k}\right|_{t=\xi+} = 0 \qquad k = 0, 1, 2, \ldots, n-1$$

Then

18 $$h^a(t,\xi) = h^*(\xi,t)$$

Proof For $\mathcal{S}_L$ pick $(y,\dot{y}, \ldots, y^{n-1})$ as state vector. Then $\mathcal{S}_L$ is represented by the state equation

19 $$\dot{\mathbf{y}} = \mathbf{A}(t)\mathbf{y} + \mathbf{b}u$$

where $\mathbf{b} = (0,0, \ldots, 0,1)$. Let $\mathbf{\Phi}(t,\xi)$ be the state transition matrix of *19*. In order to represent the adjoint system $\mathcal{S}_L^*$ described by *17*, pick a state vector $\mathbf{z} = (z_1,z_2, \ldots, z_n)$ related to z as follows:

$$z_n = z \qquad z_{n-1} = a_1^* z_n - \dot{z}_n \qquad z_{n-2} = a_2^* z_n - \dot{z}_{n-1} \qquad \cdots$$
$$z_2 = a_{n-2}^* z_n - \dot{z}_3 \qquad z_1 = a_{n-1}^* z_n - \dot{z}_2$$

Then (see Exercise *6.2.57*)

20 $$\dot{\mathbf{z}} = -\mathbf{A}^*(t)\mathbf{z}(t) - \mathbf{c}u$$

where $\mathbf{c} = (1,0, \ldots ,0)$. Let $\mathbf{\Psi}(t,\xi)$ be the state transition matrix of *20*.

Let us make three observations: (I) In the case where $\mathbf{b} = \mathbf{c} = \mathbf{0}$, the homogeneous systems *19* and *20* are adjoints of one another (see *6.2.25*); hence we have, by *6.2.32*,

21 $$\mathbf{\Phi}(\xi,t) = \mathbf{\Phi}(t,\xi)^{-1} = \mathbf{\Psi}^*(t,\xi)$$

(II) From the definition of the impulse response and the choice of state vector in *19*, $h(t,\xi) = \phi_{1n}(t,\xi)$ for $t \geq \xi$. [Note that the function $\phi_{1n}(t,\xi)$ is not identically zero for $t < \xi$, but $h(t,\xi) = 0$ for such t's since $\mathcal{S}_L$ is nonanticipative.] (III) From the definition of $h^a(t,\xi)$ and from the choice of the state vector of *20*, we have $h^a(t,\xi) = \psi_{n1}(t,\xi)$ for all $t \leq \xi$.

Finally, by considering the $(1,n)$ element of the matrix equation *21*, we obtain $h^a(t,\xi)^* = h(\xi,t)$ for all $t \leq \xi$. Since both sides are identical to zero for $t > \xi$, the complex conjugate of the above equation gives *18*.

4 *System represented by $Lx = Mu$*

Consider a nonanticipative linear time-varying system $\mathcal{S}$ which has a single input u and a single output x. Let $\mathcal{S}$ be represented by a linear differential equation of the form

1 $$\mathcal{S}: \quad u \rightarrow x \qquad\qquad L(p,t)x = M(p,t)u$$

where the symbol $\mathcal{S}: u \rightarrow x$ is used to indicate that u is the input and x is the output of $\mathcal{S}$. Let λ and μ be the orders of the differential operators L and M, respectively. Again we assume that the coefficients of the differential operator L satisfy the conditions $a_k \in C^{\lambda-k}$, $k = 0, 1, \ldots , \lambda$, and $a_0(t) \neq 0$ for all t.

By analogy with *6.3.9*, any set of λ linearly independent solutions of $L(p,t)y = 0$ will be referred to as a *set of basis functions of the system* $\mathcal{S}$. In addition, we define the set of zero-response functions of $\mathcal{S}$: any set of μ linearly independent solutions of $M(p,t)y = 0$ will be called a *set of zero-response functions of* $\mathcal{S}$. [Note that the basis functions as defined here coincide in meaning with those defined in Chaps. *3* and *4* (see *3.6.39*, *4.5.31*, and *4.5.50*) so long as $\mathcal{S}$ is a strictly proper system (*3.6.27*). If $\mathcal{S}$ is not strictly proper, then the basis functions of $\mathcal{S}$ (in the sense of *3.6.39*) will comprise the basis functions in the sense defined here together with a set of delta functions of orders up to and including $\mu - \lambda$]

2 *Exercise* Consider the time-invariant case. Suppose that the polynomials $L(s)$ and $M(s)$ have distinct roots. Call them s_i and z_j, respectively. Show that the sets $\{e^{s_it}\}_1^\lambda$, $\{e^{z_jt}\}_1^\mu$ are respectively a set of

basis functions and a set of zero-response functions of $\mathcal{S}$. What happens if L or M has multiple zeros?

3 *Comment* If ψ is a nontrivial zero-response function of the system $\mathcal{S}$ defined by *1*, and if $\mu \geq 1$, then, in general, $1(t - t_0)\psi(t)$ is not a zero-response function of $\mathcal{S}$. Indeed by *6.3.15* the zero-state response of $\mathcal{S}$ to $1(t - t_0)\psi(t)$ is given by

4 $$x(t) = \int_{t_0}^{t} h(t,\xi)M(q,\xi)[1(\xi - t_0)\psi(\xi)]\, d\xi \qquad t \geq t_0$$

where $h(t,\xi)$ is the impulse response of the system $Ly = 0$ and $q = d/d\xi$. For simplicity let us consider an example: let $\mathcal{S}$ be specified by

$$(p^2 + a_1(t)p + 1)x(t) = (p + 1)u(t)$$

Clearly we can take ψ to be e^{-t}. For simplicity let $t_0 = 0$ and let $u(t) = 1(t)e^{-t}$. Then $M(p,t)u(t) = (p + 1)u(t) = \delta(t)e^{-t} = \delta(t)$ (see *A.5.12*). Therefore, from *4*, the zero-state response of that system to $1(t)e^{-t}$ is $h(t,0)$.

5 *Exercise* For the system and the input $u(t)$ just considered find the state $\mathbf{s}_0$ at time $0-$ such that $x(t;\mathbf{s}_0,0-;1(t)e^{-t}) = 0$ for all $t \geq 0$.

The relation between the impulse response of the system described by *1* and that described by *6.3.1* is given by the following

6 **Theorem** Consider the two systems

$$\mathcal{S}_M\colon \quad u \to x \qquad\qquad L(p,t)x = M(p,t)u$$

7 $$\mathcal{S}_1\colon \quad v \to x \qquad\qquad L(p,t)x = v$$

Let $h_M(t,\xi)$, $h_1(t,\xi)$ be the impulse response of $\mathcal{S}_M$ and $\mathcal{S}_1$, respectively. Then

8 $$h_M(t,\xi) = M^*(q,\xi)h_1(t,\xi)$$

where $M^*(q,\xi)$ is the adjoint operator of $M(q,\xi)$ and $q = d/d\xi$.

Proof From the definitions of $h_1(t,\xi)$ and $h_M(t,\xi)$, the response of $\mathcal{S}_M$, starting from the zero state at t_0-, may be written in two ways:

9 $$x(t) = \int_{t_0-}^{t} h_M(t,\xi)u(\xi)\, d\xi$$

10 $$x(t) = \int_{t_0-}^{t} h_1(t,\xi)M(q,\xi)u(\xi)\, d\xi$$

Since the state of $\mathcal{S}_M$ is specified at t_0- and since as a result of differentiations of the input u the integrand of *10* may include delta functions at t_0, we must carry out the integration from t_0- to t. By successive integrations by parts, we may bring *10* into the form

11 $$x(t) = \int_{t_0-}^{t} [M^*\!:(q,\xi)h_1(t,\xi)]u(\xi)\, d\xi$$

which by comparison with *9* leads to the conclusion that *8* holds because both *9* and *11* hold for all $u_{[t_0,t]}$. To illustrate the procedure, let $M(q,\xi) = \sum_{k=0}^{\mu} m_k(\xi)\, q^{\mu-k}$ and consider the contribution to *10* of the term $m_{\mu-1}(\xi)\, q$.

$$\int_{t_0-}^{t} h_1(t,\xi)m_{\mu-1}(\xi)\, q\, u(\xi)\, d\xi = [m_{\mu-1}(\xi)h_1(t,\xi)u(\xi)]\Big|_{t_0-}^{t} - \int_{t_0-}^{t+} q\,[m_{\mu-1}(\xi)h_1(t,\xi)]r(\xi)\, d\xi$$

Now $u(t_0-) = 0$ and $h_1(t,t) = 0$, by *6.3.5*; therefore,

$$\int_{t_0-}^{t} h_1(t,\xi)m_{\mu-1}(\xi)\, q\, r(\xi)\, d\xi = \int_{t_0-}^{t} -q\,[m_{\mu-1}(\xi)h_1(t,\xi)]r(\xi)\, d\xi$$

Observe that to the term $m_{\mu-1}(\xi)\, q$ of $M(q,\xi)$ there corresponds the term $-q\,[m_{\mu-1}(\xi)]$ of its adjoint $M^*(q,\xi)$. By performing the appropriate number of integrations by parts, a similar conclusion may be established for all terms of $M(q,\xi)$. In other words, this procedure transforms *10* into *11*. Therefore *8* is established. ◁

Let us close this section by giving a realization of the system $\mathcal{S}_M$, which is similar to that given for the time-invariant case in *4.9.15*.

12 **Assertion** Consider the system $\mathcal{S}_M$ defined by

13 $$L(p,t)y = M(p,t)u$$

where

$$L(p,t) = \sum_{k=0}^{n} a_{n-k}(t)p^k \qquad M(p,t)u = \sum_{k=0}^{n} b_{n-k}(t)p^k$$

Let $a_0(t) = 1$ for all t (some of the $b_0, b_1, \ldots$ may be identically zero), so that the order of the system *13* is n. If, for $i = 0, 1, \ldots, n$, a_i and $b_i \in C^{n-i}$, then the system *13* has the following state equations:

14 $$\begin{bmatrix} \dot{x}_1 \\ \dot{x}_2 \\ \cdot \\ \cdot \\ \cdot \\ x_n \end{bmatrix} = \begin{bmatrix} 0 & 1 & 0 & \cdot & \cdot & 0 \\ 0 & 0 & 1 & & & \\ \cdot & \cdot & \cdot & \cdot & \cdot & \cdot \\ \cdot & \cdot & \cdot & \cdot & \cdot & 0 \\ \cdot & \cdot & \cdot & \cdot & \cdot & 1 \\ -a_n & -a_{n-1} & & \cdot & \cdot & -a_1 \end{bmatrix} \begin{bmatrix} x_1 \\ x_2 \\ \cdot \\ \cdot \\ \cdot \\ x_n \end{bmatrix} + \begin{bmatrix} \phi_1 \\ \phi_2 \\ \cdot \\ \cdot \\ \cdot \\ \phi_n \end{bmatrix} u$$

and

15 $$y = x_1 + \phi_0 u$$

where the ϕ_i may be computed successively in terms of the a_i's and b_i's by the relations

16 $$\phi_0(t) = b_0(t)$$
$$\phi_i(t) = b_i(t) - \sum_{r=0}^{i-1} \sum_{m=0}^{i-r} \binom{n+m-i}{n-i} a_{i-r-m}(t) p^m \phi_r(t)$$

Proof The proof is purely computational; so we shall only outline the steps: (I) use *14* and *15* to evaluate $y, \dot{y}, \ddot{y}, \ldots, y^{(n-1)}$: viz., $y = x_1 + \phi_0 u$, $\dot{y} = x_2 + \phi_1 u + p(\phi_0 u), \ldots$; (II) substitute in *13*; (III) reorder the summations so that both sides consist of weighted sums of successive derivatives of u; and (IV) equate coefficients of like derivatives of u. Then *16* follows.

17 *Comment* From *14* to *16* it is a simple matter to derive expressions for $x_1, x_2, \ldots, x_n$ in terms of u and y and their derivatives. The expres-

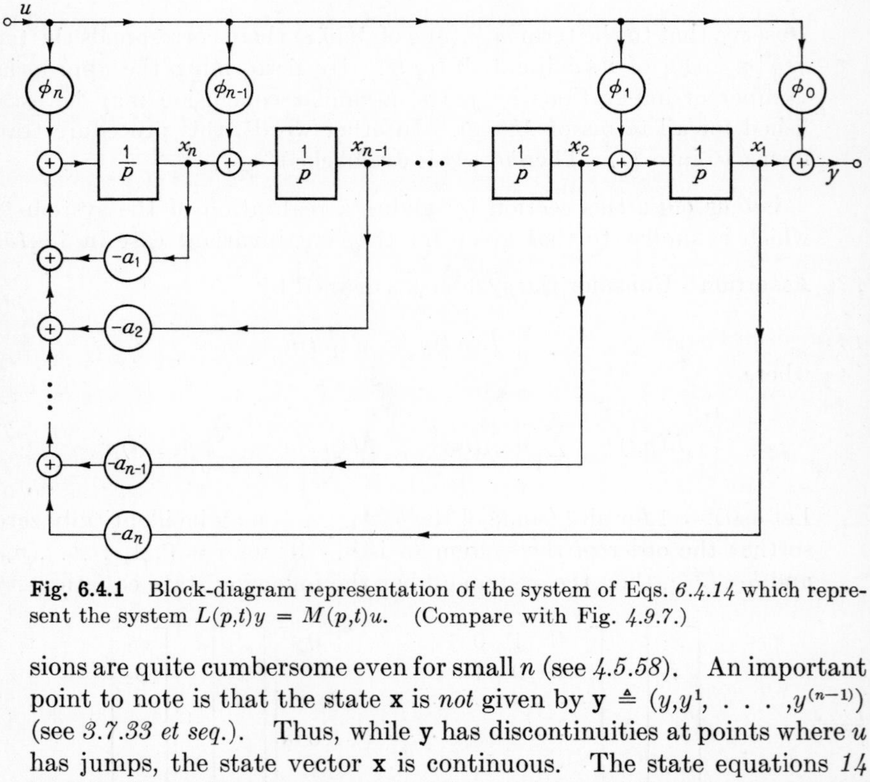

Fig. 6.4.1 Block-diagram representation of the system of Eqs. *6.4.14* which represent the system $L(p,t)y = M(p,t)u$. (Compare with Fig. *4.9.7*.)

sions are quite cumbersome even for small n (see *4.5.58*). An important point to note is that the state $\mathbf{x}$ is *not* given by $\mathbf{y} \triangleq (y, y^1, \ldots, y^{(n-1)})$ (see *3.7.33 et seq.*). Thus, while $\mathbf{y}$ has discontinuities at points where u has jumps, the state vector $\mathbf{x}$ is continuous. The state equations *14* lead to the realization shown in Fig. *6.4.1* in which there are n integrators and, in general, $2n$ time-varying scalors. A useful interpretation of the ϕ_i's is stated in the following

18 *Exercise* Suppose the system $\mathcal{S}_M$ is time-invariant; therefore, the a_i's and b_i's in *13* are constant. If any of the $b_i \neq 0$ $(i \geq 1)$, and if

$u(t) = 1(t)$, then the vector $\mathbf{y} = (y,y, \ldots ,y^{n-1})$ is singular at $t = 0$. Using the techniques of Appendix A, show that

$$\mathbf{y}(0+) - \mathbf{y}(0-) = (\phi_0,\phi_1, \ldots ,\phi_{n-1})$$

5 *Tandem connection*

First consider two time-invariant linear systems $\mathcal{A}_1$ and $\mathcal{A}_2$ described by

$$\mathcal{A}_1\colon\ u \to y \qquad L_1(p)y = M_1(p)u$$
$$\mathcal{A}_2\colon\ u \to y \qquad L_2(p)y = M_2(p)u$$

where L_1, L_2, M_1, and M_2 are time-invariant differential operators, i.e., polynomials in p with constant coefficients. We know that the tandem combination $\mathcal{A}_1\mathcal{A}_2$ ($\mathcal{A}_2$ preceding $\mathcal{A}_1$) is zero-state equivalent to $\mathcal{A}_2\mathcal{A}_1$ ($\mathcal{A}_1$ preceding $\mathcal{A}_2$) (see *3.6.26*) and that $\mathcal{A}_1\mathcal{A}_2$ is equivalent to $\mathcal{A}_2\mathcal{A}_1$ if and only if M_1 has no common factors with L_2 and M_2 has no common factors with L_1 (see *4.8.15*).

Let us now consider the time-varying case. Here the systems are characterized by

1 $$\mathcal{B}_1\colon\ u \to y \qquad L_1(p,t)y = M_1(p,t)u$$
2 $$\mathcal{B}_2\colon\ u \to y \qquad L_2(p,t)y = M_2(p,t)u$$

where L_1, L_2, M_1, and M_2 are time-varying differential operators, i.e., polynomials in p with coefficients that are known functions of time. Let the degrees of these polynomials be respectively λ_1, λ_2, μ_1, μ_2. We assume that the leading coefficients of L_1, L_2, M_1, and M_2 differ from zero for all t, so that the orders of these differential operators do not vary with time.

Consider now the tandem connection of $\mathcal{B}_1$ preceding $\mathcal{B}_2$, that is, the product $\mathcal{B}_2\mathcal{B}_1$. Let u be the input and y_i be the output of $\mathcal{B}_i$ in the tandem connection.

The equations of the tandem connection are then

3 $$L_1(p,t)y_1 = M_1(p,t)u$$
4 $$L_2(p,t)y_2 = M_2(p,t)y_1$$

We want to find the differential operators of least order, $L(p,t)$ and $M(p,t)$, such that the differential equation

5 $$L(p,t)y_2 = M(p,t)u$$

is satisfied by all the input-output pairs (u,y_2) of $\mathcal{B}_2\mathcal{B}_1$.

For the analysis to follow we introduce the following notations:

$\{\varphi_{i1}\}$, $i = 1, 2, \ldots, \lambda_1$, is a set of basis functions for $L_1(p,t)$.
$\{\varphi_{i2}\}$, $i = 1, 2, \ldots, \lambda_2$, is a set of basis functions for $L_2(p,t)$.
$\{\psi_{ij}\}$, $i = 1, 2, \ldots, \mu_j$, is a set of basis functions for $M_j(p,t)$, $j = 1, 2$.

Suppose we have found differential operators of minimal order $P_1(p,t)$ and $P_2(p,t)$ such that (note the order of the factors; see Comment *6.6.5*)

6 $$P_1(p,t)L_1(p,t) = P_2(p,t)M_2(p,t) \triangleq P(p,t)$$

where $P(p,t)$ is, by definition, the common value of the products. From this relation it is obvious that any basis function of $L_1(p,t)$ is a basis function of $P(p,t)$ and any basis function of $M_2(p,t)$ is a basis function of $P(p,t)$. Therefore, if we denote by π_{i1} and π_{i2} the basis functions of P_1 and P_2, respectively, we conclude that the basis functions of P_2 are

7 $$\pi_{i2} = M_2(p,t)\varphi_{i1} \qquad i = 1, 2, \ldots, \lambda_1$$

and those of P_1 are

8 $$\pi_{i1} = L_1(p,t)\varphi_{i2} \qquad i = 1, 2, \ldots, \lambda_2$$

9 **Assumption** It is assumed that the sets $\{\pi_{i1}\}$ and $\{\pi_{i2}\}$ are two sets of linearly independent functions.[1] $\triangleleft$

This assumption justifies our calling these sets basis functions (see Definition *6.3.9*). Given these sets of basis functions of P_1 and P_2, it is easy to construct the differential operators P_1 and P_2 by use of *6.3.11*. Let us now operate on the left of *3* by P_1 and on the left of *4* by P_i. As a result of *6*, we obtain

$$P_2(p,t)L_2(p,t)y_2 = P_1(p,t)M_1(p,t)u$$

Therefore,

10 $$L(p,t) = P_2(p,t)L_2(p,t) \qquad M(p,t) = P_1(p,t)M_1(p,t)$$

We conclude this discussion by an

11 **Assertion** Given two time-varying differential systems $\mathcal{B}_1$ and $\mathcal{B}_2$ characterized by *1* and *2*, the product $\mathcal{B}_2\mathcal{B}_1$ (i.e., the tandem connection of $\mathcal{B}_1$ preceding $\mathcal{B}_2$) has all its input-output pairs (u,y_2) satisfying the

[1] Suppose Assumption *9* is not satisfied; suppose, in particular, that the π_{i2} are not linearly independent. We would like to point out the analogy between this situation and that of the time-invariant case where L_1 and M_2 have one or more factors in common. Indeed, if the π_{i2} are linearly dependent, there is a linear combination (with constant coefficients) of the π_{i2} that sums to zero for all t. Hence, by *7*, the same linear combination of the φ_{i1} is a solution of $M_2(p,t)z = 0$. Thus there is at least one basis function of $L_1(p,t)$ (the linear combination of the φ_{i1}) which is a zero-response function of $\mathcal{B}_2$, that is, is a solution of $M_2(p,t)z = 0$.

differential equation $L(p,t)y_2 = M(p,t)u$. If Assumption *9* is satisfied, L and M are given by *10*, where $P_1(p,t)$ and $P_2(p,t)$ are the differential operators which have $\{\pi_{i1}\}$ and $\{\pi_{i2}\}$ as sets of basis functions (see *7* and *8*). The arbitrary nonzero factors in P_1 and P_2 must be so selected that *6* holds.

6 *Systems of higher-order differential equations*

Let us consider a system described by a system of higher-order differential equations of the form

1 $$\mathbf{L}(p,t)\mathbf{x}(t) = \mathbf{M}(p,t)u(t)$$

or more explicitly

2 $$\sum_{j=1}^{n} L_{ij}(p,t)x_j(t) = M_i(p,t)u(t) \qquad i = 1, 2, \ldots, n$$

where the $L_{ij}(p,t)$ and $M_i(p,t)$ are differential operators with time-varying coefficients, u is a scalar input, and the dependent variable $\mathbf{x}$ is the vector-valued output. It is *assumed* that in each L_{ij} the non-identically zero coefficient of the highest power of p differs from zero for all t: thus, for each pair (i,j), the order of the differential operator does not change with t.

The first question one would like to answer in connection with *1* is: How can one associate a state vector with *1* and what is the corresponding input-output-state relation? In the case of time-invariant systems this question could easily be answered by the use of the Laplace transform technique. Since in the case of differential equations with time-varying coefficients the Laplace transformation does not lead to a set of linear *algebraic* equations in the transformed variable, it is no longer an effective tool for answering this question. Our first step will be to present the elimination method, which will bring the system *1* to a triangular form. Later we shall use this form to determine the state of the system.

The elimination method

The basic idea is identical with that of the method described in *5.6.10*: the idea is to reduce the system *1* to a form such that the matrix of the differential operators L_{ij} is triangular; consequently, the system can be solved as a succession of differential equations in one unknown function. The procedure is based on the

3 **Lemma** Let $L(p,t)$, $N(p,t)$ be two differential operators of order λ and ν, respectively, with $\lambda \geq \nu$; let $p = d/dt$. Let the coefficient of the highest power of p in L and N be distinct from zero for all t. Then there are two uniquely defined operators $M(p,t)$, $R(p,t)$, of orders μ and ρ, respectively, such that

4 $$L(p,t) = M(p,t)N(p,t) + R(p,t)$$

with $\lambda = \mu + \nu$ and $\rho < \nu$.

5 *Comment* The operation above is analogous to the "division" of $L(p,t)$ by $N(p,t)$; $M(p,t)$ is the "quotient" and $R(p,t)$ is the "remainder." It should be stressed, however, that, whereas time-invariant linear differential operators can be treated as if they were polynomials in the variable p, this is not the case for time-varying differential operators. The addition of time-varying differential operators is associative and commutative; the multiplication of time-varying differential operators is associative and distributive with respect to addition:

$$[L_1(p,t)L_2(p,t)]L_3(p,t) = L_1(p,t)[L_2(p,t)L_3(p,t)]$$

and

$$L_1(p,t)[L_2(p,t) + L_3(p,t)] = L_1(p,t)L_2(p,t) + L_1(p,t)L_3(p,t)$$

But the multiplication of such operators is *not commutative*. For example, let $L_1(p,t) = p$, $L_2(p,t) = e^{-t}p$; then $L_1L_2 = p(e^{-t}p) = e^{-t}p^2 - e^{-t}p$; $L_2L_1 = e^{-t}p^2$; hence $L_1L_2 \neq L_2L_1$. ◁

Proof To show that the coefficients $m_k(t)$ and $r_k(t)$ of the operators $M(p,t)$ and $R(p,t)$ defined in 4 are uniquely defined, let us consider the case where

$$L(p,t) = \sum_{k=0}^{4} a_{4-k}p^k \qquad N(p,t) = n_0p + n_1$$

Equation 4 gives

$$(m_0p^3 + m_1p^2 + m_2p + m_3)(n_0p + n_1) + r_0 = a_0p^4 + a_1p^3 + a_2p^2 + a_3p + a_4$$

A direct computation and identification of like powers of p gives

$$\begin{array}{lllll}
n_0m_0 & & & & = a_0 \\
(\dot n_0 + n_1)m_0 + & n_0m_1 & & & = a_1 \\
(\ddot n_0 + \dot n_1)m_0 + & (\dot n_0 + n_1)m_1 + & n_0m_2 & & = a_2 \\
(\dddot n_0 + \ddot n_1)m_0 + & (\ddot n_0 + \dot n_1)m_1 + & (\dot n_0 + n_1)m_2 + n_0m_3 & & = a_3 \\
\dddot n_1m_0 + & \ddot n_1m_1 + & \dot n_1m_2 + n_1m_3 + r_0 & & = a_4
\end{array}$$

By assumption $n_0(t) \neq 0$ for all t, the system may be solved from the top down by successive substitution for m_0, m_1, m_2, m_3, and r_0. Since the determinant of the system is $n_0^3(t)$, hence $\neq 0$ for all t, the solution is unique. This completes the proof of the assertion. ◁

As in *5.6.8* we define two types of *elementary row operations:*

(I) Replace in the system $\mathcal{S}$ of differential equations, given in *1*, the kth equation by the sum of the kth equation and the ith equation multiplied by $-M(p,t)$.

(II) Replace, in the system $\mathcal{S}$ of differential equations, the kth equations by K times the kth equation, where K is a nonzero constant.

As in *5.6.10,* we can show that by a succession of elementary row operations we can replace $\mathcal{S}$ by another system $\mathcal{S}'$ given by

6 $$\sum_{j=1}^{n} \tilde{L}_{ij}(p,t)x_j(t) = \tilde{F}_i(p,t)r(t) \qquad i = 1, 2, \ldots, n$$

where $\tilde{L}_{ij} \equiv 0$ for $i < j$. From the previously given arguments it follows that $\mathbf{x}(t) \equiv (x_1,x_2, \ldots, x_n)$ is a solution of *1* if and only if it is a solution of *6*. In view of the triangular form of the matrix $(\tilde{L}_{ij})$, the system *6* can be solved by successive substitutions from the bottom equation up. At each step, one has to solve a linear differential equation with time-varying coefficients in one unknown.

Let us now consider the problem of assigning a state to the system *1*. As a first step let us make the following

7 *Comment* It is always possible to use elementary row operations to cause the system *6* to have the property that in the matric differential operator in the left-hand side, each diagonal element has an order larger than that of all other elements of the same column, i.e., for all j, the order of $\tilde{L}_{jj}(p,t)$ is larger than the order of $\tilde{L}_{ij}(p,t)$ for $i = 1, 2, \ldots, n$. The procedure is as follows: Consider the columns of the matric differential operator $\tilde{\mathbf{L}}$ of *6*, starting from the left. Suppose the jth column is the first column for which an off-diagonal element, say, $\tilde{L}_{i'j}$, has an order higher than that of the diagonal element L_{jj}. Since *6* is already in triangular form, $i' < j$. Let us now add to the i'th row the jth row premultiplied by a suitable $M(p,t)$ as in Lemma *3*: the order of the resulting (i',j) element is now smaller than that of $\tilde{L}_{jj}$. Since *6* is in the triangular form, this procedure does not affect the columns preceding the jth column; therefore, by successively operating on each column starting from the left, we shall end up with a matric differential operator $\hat{\mathbf{L}}$ in which each diagonal element has an order higher than that of all the elements of the same column.

Let us assume that the system is brought into this form and let us illustrate the selection of a state by considering a simple

8 *Example* Suppose that the methods described above lead to the following system of differential equations:

9 $$\begin{bmatrix} p^2 + \cos t\, p + 1 & p + 1 \\ 0 & p^2 + e^t p + 1 \end{bmatrix} \begin{bmatrix} x_1(t) \\ x_2(t) \end{bmatrix} = \begin{bmatrix} p^2 + p + 1 \\ 1 \end{bmatrix} u(t)$$

In the present case, the state at time t_0 is a collection of numbers such that the knowledge of the state at time t_0, the vector differential equation *9*, and the input $u_{(t_0,t]}$ is sufficient to determine the output over the interval $(t_0,t]$, that is, $x_1(\xi)$ and $x_2(\xi)$ for $t_0 < \xi \leq t$. Recalling the definition of $p\,u(t)$ (see *3.8.4*), and assuming that $u_{(t_0,t]}$ is a time function, we obtain from *9* the system

10 $$\begin{bmatrix} p^2 + \cos t\, p + 1 & p + 1 \\ 0 & p^2 + e^t p + 1 \end{bmatrix} \begin{bmatrix} 1(t - t_0)x_1(t) \\ 1(t - t_0)x_2(t) \end{bmatrix} = \begin{bmatrix} p^2 + p + 1 \\ 1 \end{bmatrix} 1(t - t_0)u(t) + \begin{bmatrix} \varphi_1(t) \\ \varphi_2(t) \end{bmatrix}$$

where

$$\varphi_1(t) = [x_1(t_0-) - u(t_0-)]\delta^{(1)}(t - t_0) + [x_1^{(1)}(t_0-) + \cos t_0\, x_1(t_0-) + x_2(t_0-) - u(t_0-) - u^{(1)}(t_0-)]\delta(t - t_0)$$

$$\varphi_2(t) = x_2(t_0-)\delta^{(1)}(t - t_0) + [x_2^{(1)}(t_0-) + e^{t_0}x_2(t_0-)]\delta(t - t_0)$$

It is easy to see that the vector

$$\boldsymbol{\alpha}(t_0) \triangleq \begin{bmatrix} x_1(t_0-) - u(t_0-) \\ x_1^{(1)}(t_0-) + \cos t_0\, x_1(t_0-) - u'(t_0-) - u(t_0-) \\ x_2(t_0-) \\ x_2^{(1)}(t_0-) \end{bmatrix}$$

qualifies for the state at time t_0 of the system described by *9*: in particular, given $\boldsymbol{\alpha}(t_0)$ and $u_{(t_0,t]}$, the uniqueness theorem of systems of differential equations guarantees that the output $\mathbf{x}_{(t_0,t]}$ is uniquely defined.

7 *Periodically varying systems*

Periodically varying linear systems are very important in engineering for two reasons: first, there are linear periodically varying systems in the real world, e.g., parametric amplifiers where the pump imposes a periodic variation on some circuit element; second, in the consideration of the stability of periodic solutions of nonlinear differential equations one has to consider the equations of the first variation which constitute a system of linear differential equations with periodically varying coefficients. In this case the period is the period of the oscillation whose stability is under study.

We consider in this section the free motion of a system described by

1 $$\dot{\mathbf{x}} = \mathbf{A}(t)\mathbf{x}$$

where $\mathbf{A}(t)$ depends continuously on t and is periodic with period T_0.

More precisely, $\mathbf{A}(t) = \mathbf{A}(t + T_0)$ for all t. Let us observe that if $\mathbf{\Phi}(t,t_0)$ is the state transition matrix of *1*, then $\mathbf{\Phi}(t + T_0, t_0)$ is also a fundamental matrix of *1*, that is, for all t its n columns are linearly independent solutions of *1* (see *6.2.15*). This is checked by direct verification:

$$\dot{\mathbf{\Phi}}(t + T_0, t_0) = \mathbf{A}(t + T_0)\mathbf{\Phi}(t + T_0, t_0) = \mathbf{A}(t)\mathbf{\Phi}(t + T_0, t_0)$$

Thus, $\mathbf{\Phi}(t + T_0, t_0)$ satisfies *1*. It is a fundamental matrix by *6.2.15*. The main result to be established is the

2 **Theorem** Let $\mathbf{A}(t)$ be continuous and periodic with period T_0. Then (I) the state transition matrix of *1* can always be written as

3 $$\mathbf{\Phi}(t,t_0) = \mathbf{P}(t,t_0) \exp [(t - t_0)\mathbf{B}] \qquad \mathbf{P}(t_0,t_0) = \mathbf{I}$$

where $\mathbf{P}(t,t_0)$ is a nonsingular periodic matrix with period T_0 and $\mathbf{B}$ is a constant matrix.

(II) By changing coordinates to a periodically varying system of coordinates such that the state is represented in the new system by $\mathbf{y}(t) = \mathbf{P}^{-1}(t,t_0)\mathbf{x}(t)$, the new representation of the state satisfies the equation

4 $$\dot{\mathbf{y}}(t) = \mathbf{B}\mathbf{y}(t)$$

which is an equation with constant coefficients.

Proof As we have seen, if $\mathbf{\Phi}(t,t_0)$ is the state transition matrix of the system *1*, then $\mathbf{\Phi}(t + T_0, t_0)$ is a fundamental matrix of *1*. Its ith column, $\boldsymbol{\phi}_i(t + T_0, t_0)$, is then of the form $\mathbf{\Phi}(t,t_0)\boldsymbol{\gamma}_i$, where $\boldsymbol{\gamma}_i$ is a suitably chosen constant vector since the vector $\boldsymbol{\phi}_i(t + T_0, t_0)$ can be represented as a linear combination of the basis vectors $\{\boldsymbol{\phi}_i(t,t_0)\}$. Let $\mathbf{C}$ be the matrix whose columns are the constant vectors $\boldsymbol{\gamma}_i$; $\mathbf{C}$ is nonsingular since it is equal to $\mathbf{\Phi}^{-1}(t,t_0)\mathbf{\Phi}(t + T_0, t_0)$, the product of two nonsingular matrices. Define $\mathbf{B}$ by $\exp (T_0\mathbf{B}) = \mathbf{C}$; $\mathbf{B}$ is a constant matrix. (However, if $\mathbf{C}$ is real, it does not follow that $\mathbf{B}$ is real.[1]) Now

$$\mathbf{\Phi}(t + T_0, t_0) = \mathbf{\Phi}(t,t_0)\mathbf{C} = \mathbf{\Phi}(t,t_0) \exp (T_0\mathbf{B})$$

Define

5 $$\mathbf{P}(t,t_0) \triangleq \mathbf{\Phi}(t,t_0) \exp [-(t - t_0)\mathbf{B}]$$

The matrix $\mathbf{P}(t,t_0)$ is nonsingular, since both $\mathbf{\Phi}(t,t_0)$ and $\exp [-(t - t_0)\mathbf{B}]$ are nonsingular. Furthermore $\mathbf{P}$ is periodic with period T_0 because,

[1] $\mathbf{B} = (1/T_0) \log \mathbf{C}$; now by *D.6.1*, if $\mathbf{C}$ has a negative real eigenvalue, say, λ_i, $\log \lambda_i$ is complex; hence $\mathbf{B}$ is complex.

for all t,

$$\begin{aligned}\mathbf{P}(t + T_0, t_0) &= \mathbf{\Phi}(t + T_0, t_0) \exp[-(t + T_0 - t_0)\mathbf{B}] \\ &= \mathbf{\Phi}(t + T_0, t_0)[\exp(-T_0\mathbf{B})]\{\exp[-(t - t_0)\mathbf{B}]\} \\ &= \mathbf{\Phi}(t,t_0)\{\exp[-(t - t_0)\mathbf{B}]\} \triangleq \mathbf{P}(t,t_0)\end{aligned}$$

From the last relation, *3* follows. Now let

6 $$\mathbf{Y}(t,t_0) \triangleq \mathbf{P}^{-1}(t,t_0)\mathbf{\Phi}(t,t_0)$$

By *5*,

$$\mathbf{Y}(t,t_0) = \exp[(t - t_0)\mathbf{B}]$$

Hence $\mathbf{Y}(t,t_0)$ is the solution of the equation $\dot{\mathbf{Y}} = \mathbf{BY}$ such that

$$\mathbf{Y}(t_0,t_0) = \mathbf{I}$$

Finally, let $\mathbf{z}(t)$ be any solution of *1*; then $\mathbf{z}(t) = \mathbf{\Phi}(t_0,t)\mathbf{z}(t_0)$, and using the definition of $\mathbf{y}(t)$, we observe that

$$\mathbf{y}(t) \triangleq \mathbf{P}^{-1}(t,t_0)\mathbf{z}(t) = \mathbf{P}^{-1}(t,t_0)\mathbf{\Phi}(t,t_0)\mathbf{z}(t_0) = \mathbf{Y}(t,t_0)\mathbf{z}(t_0)$$

is the solution of *4*, with the initial condition $\mathbf{y}(t_0) = \mathbf{z}(t_0)$.

7 *Comment* There is no general method for determining $\mathbf{P}(t,t_0)$ or $\mathbf{C}$, except numerical integration of *1* over an interval of length T_0.

8 *Comment* The eigenvalues of $\mathbf{B}$ are called *characteristic exponents* of $\mathbf{A}$, and the eigenvalues of $\mathbf{C}$ are called the *characteristic multipliers* of $\mathbf{A}$.

9 *Comment* The importance of the assertion (II) of *2* is that theoretical consideration of periodically varying systems often reduces to consideration of the time-invariant system *4*.

10 *Comment* Let $\mathbf{b}_1, \mathbf{b}_2, \ldots, \mathbf{b}_n$ be the columns of $\exp(t\mathbf{B})$ and let $\mathbf{p}_1, \ldots, \mathbf{p}_n$ be the complex conjugate of the rows of $\mathbf{P}(t)$ (for simplicity, we put $t_0 = 0$ and drop the second argument t_0). Then the ith column of $\mathbf{\Phi}(t)$ has the form

$$\begin{matrix}\langle \mathbf{p}_1(t),\mathbf{b}_i(t)\rangle \\ \langle \mathbf{p}_2(t),\mathbf{b}_i(t)\rangle \\ \cdot \\ \cdot \\ \cdot \\ \langle \mathbf{p}_n(t),\mathbf{b}_i(t)\rangle\end{matrix}$$

where the vectors $\mathbf{p}_i(t)$ are periodic in t and the $\mathbf{b}_i(t)$ have components that are linear combinations of $e^{\lambda_j t}, te^{\lambda_j t}, \ldots, t^{k_j-1}e^{\lambda_j t}, j = 1, 2, \ldots,$ where λ_j's are eigenvalues of $\mathbf{B}$ and k_j is the multiplicity of λ_j as a zero of the minimal polynomial of $\mathbf{B}$. Thus *3* imposes a strong constraint on the form of the solutions of *1*.

REFERENCES AND SUGGESTED READING

1 Bellman, R.: "Stability Theory of Differential Equations," McGraw-Hill Book Company, Inc., New York, 1953.

2 Bourbaki, N.: "Fonctions d'une variable réelle," chap. IV, Hermann & Cie, Paris, 1961.

3 Cesari, L.: "Asymptotic Behavior and Stability Problems in Ordinary Differential Equations," Springer Verlag, OHG, Berlin, 1959.

4 Coddington, E. A., and N. Levinson: "Theory of Ordinary Differential Equations," McGraw-Hill Book Company, Inc., New York, 1955.

5 Darlington, S.: Nonstationary Smoothing and Prediction Using Network Theory Concepts, *I.R.E. Trans. Circuit Theory,* vol. CT-6, pp. 1–13, 1959.

6 Ince, E. L.: "Ordinary Differential Equations," Dover Publications, Inc., New York, 1956.

7 Kaplan, W.: "Operational Methods for Linear Systems," Addison-Wesley Publishing Company, Inc., Reading, Mass., 1962.

8 Laning, J. H., Jr., and R. H. Battin: "Random Processes in Automatic Control," McGraw-Hill Book Company, Inc., New York, 1956.

9 Lefschetz, S.: "Differential Equations: Geometric Theory," Interscience Publishers, Inc., New York, 1957.

10 *I.R.E. Trans. Circuit Theory,* vol. CT-2, no. 1, 1955. (Special issue on linear time-varying systems.)

11. Zadeh, L. A.: Time-varying Networks, I, *Proc. I.R.E.*, vol. 49, pp. 1488-1503, October, 1961.

Stability of linear differential systems 7

1 *Introduction*

In Chaps. *5* and *6* we have investigated various basic properties of time-invariant and time-varying differential systems. In particular, we have seen that the state at time t is expressed in terms of the initial state $\mathbf{x}_0$ and the input $\mathbf{u}_{[t_0,t]}$ by an expression of the form

$$\mathbf{x}(t;\mathbf{x}_0,t_0;\mathbf{u}_{[t_0,t]}) = \mathbf{\Phi}(t,t_0)\mathbf{x}_0 + \int_{t_0}^{t} \mathbf{\Phi}(t,t')\mathbf{B}(t')\mathbf{u}(t')\,dt'$$

and we studied in detail the properties of the state transition matrix $\mathbf{\Phi}$, its relation to those of the adjoint system, and the relation between $\mathbf{\Phi}$ and the impulse response of the system. Now we turn to the study of the behavior of $\mathbf{x}$ as a function of t. In most practical systems, it is required that the system be "stable," i.e., when $\mathbf{u} = \mathbf{0}$, $\mathbf{x}(t)$ must remain bounded for all subsequent times; otherwise, some internal component of the system may burn out or break down. Section *2* will be devoted to the precise formulation of this concept of stability. We shall see that we shall have to distinguish between stability in the sense of Lyapunov and asymptotic stability. In Secs. *3* and *4* we shall present necessary and sufficient conditions for stability based on these concepts. In the case of time-varying systems, this characterization is based on the behavior of the state transition matrix which in most practical cases can be obtained only by numerical computation. For this reason we give in Sec. *5* some sufficiency tests for asymptotic stability which do not require the knowledge of $\mathbf{\Phi}(t,t_0)$. In Sec. *6* we develop the idea of reducible systems, systems that have the property that, when considered from a suitably chosen moving reference frame, they look like time-invariant systems. In the final section, we turn to another concept of stability. Roughly speaking, this concept is that a system is stable whenever any bounded input produces a bounded output; we must first formulate this idea precisely and then give its characterization. For the case of time-invariant systems whose output is actually the state of the system, the concept of asymptotic stability and the last concept are equivalent.

2 *Definition of stability based on the free motion of the state*

Let us consider a linear differential system $\mathcal{A}$ characterized by $\dot{\mathbf{x}} = \mathbf{A}\mathbf{x} + \mathbf{B}\mathbf{u}$. For simplicity we shall assume that the output of $\mathcal{A}$ is actually the state rather than a linear function of the state and the input. For the next three sections we shall restrict ourselves to consideration of the free motion of the state, i.e., we shall assume that $\mathbf{u}(t) = \mathbf{0}$ for all t, or equivalently we consider the system

1 $$\dot{\mathbf{x}}(t) = \mathbf{A}(t)\mathbf{x}(t)$$

where $\mathbf{A}$ is an $n \times n$ matrix whose elements are continuous functions of time on (t_0, ∞).

The first concept to be defined is that of *stability of the zero state* of $\mathcal{A}$ or, as it will occasionally be referred to, *zero-input stability* of $\mathcal{A}$, since it involves the free motion (zero-input response) of $\mathcal{A}$. Roughly speaking, the zero state $\mathbf{x} = \mathbf{0}$ is stable if, for every initial state $\mathbf{x}_0$ which is sufficiently close to $\mathbf{0}$, the corresponding free motion $\mathbf{x}(t;\mathbf{x}_0,t_0)$ remains close to zero for all $t \geq t_0$. A familiar example of a physical system which has a stable zero state [which is also its equilibrium state (*2.8.15*)] is a ball bearing in a teacup. There any sufficiently small displacement of the ball bearing from its equilibrium position results in a trajectory which remains close to the equilibrium position forever after.

2 **Definition** The zero state $\mathbf{x} = \mathbf{0}$ is said to be *stable in the sense of Lyapunov* or, equivalently, $\mathcal{A}$ is said to be *zero-input stable in the sense of Lyapunov*, if for any t_0 and any $\varepsilon > 0$, there is a $\delta > 0$ depending on ε and t_0 such that[1]

$$\|\mathbf{x}_0\| < \delta \Rightarrow \|\mathbf{x}(t;\mathbf{x}_0,t_0)\| < \varepsilon \qquad \forall t \geq t_0$$

For brevity, we shall write $\mathbf{x} = 0$ is stable i.s.L. (in the sense of Lyapunov).

If the zero state is stable i.s.L. and if, for every t_0 and every $\varepsilon > 0$ there is a $\delta > 0$ *independent of* t_0 such that the above inequality holds, then the zero state is said to be *uniformly stable i.s.L.* ◁

[1] In view of the fact that the norms in $\mathcal{C}^n$ are equivalent (*C.16.8 et seq.*), we have the freedom of picking the norm that is most convenient for the case at hand. Whenever in the course of a proof a specific norm is used, we shall so indicate.

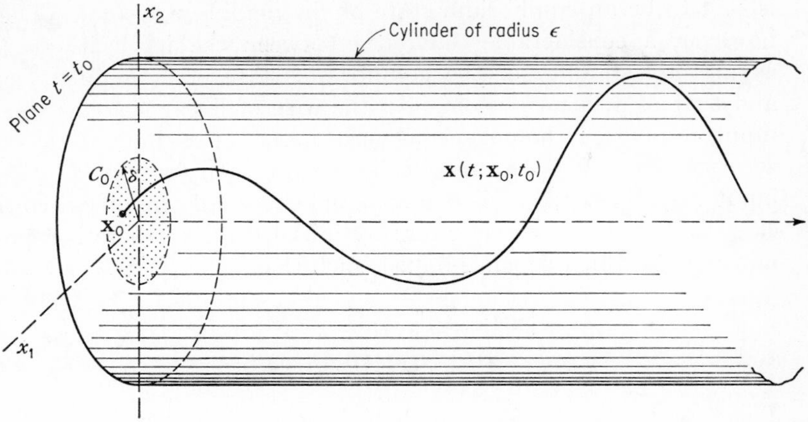

Fig. 7.2.1 The concept of stability in the sense of Lyapunov.

The concept of stability i.s.L. is illustrated in Fig. *7.2.1* for a second-order system: if $\mathbf{x}_0$ is in the interior of the circle C_0 of radius δ, then the trajectory $\mathbf{x}(t;\mathbf{x}_0,t_0)$ remains for all future times inside the cylinder of radius ε.

In most engineering applications we require that the response eventually go to zero. Since this requirement is not implied by the stability i.s.L., we must introduce a further

3 **Definition** The zero state $\mathbf{x} = 0$ is said to be *asymptotically stable* if (I) it is stable i.s.L. and (II) for any t_0 and for any $\mathbf{x}_0$ *sufficiently close to* $\mathbf{0}$, $\mathbf{x}(t;\mathbf{x}_0,t_0) \to \mathbf{0}$ as $t \to \infty$.

4 *Comment* The conditions (I) and (II) are equivalent to the following: For any $\varepsilon_1 > 0$ and $\varepsilon_2 > 0$ there are a $\delta > 0$ and a T sufficiently large that $\|\mathbf{x}_0\| < \delta$ implies that

$$\|\mathbf{x}(t;\mathbf{x}_0,t_0)\| < \varepsilon_1 \qquad \text{for all } t \geq t_0$$

and also that

$$\|\mathbf{x}(t;\mathbf{x}_0,t_0)\| < \varepsilon_2 \qquad \text{for all } t \geq t_0 + T$$

Both δ and T depend in general on t_0, ε_1, and ε_2.

5 *Comment* These concepts of the stability of the zero state consider exclusively the zero-input response (free motion) of the system. It should be stressed, in particular, that asymptotic stability of the zero state does not imply that any bounded input will produce a bounded output (see *7.7.2* and *7.7.13*).

6 **Remark: stability in the large** It is apparent that Definitions *2* and *3* may be applied to nonlinear systems, say, to a differential system defined by $\dot{\mathbf{x}} = \mathbf{f}(\mathbf{x})$, where $\mathbf{f}(\mathbf{0}) = \mathbf{0}$. In such cases the state $\mathbf{x} = \mathbf{0}$

is said to be an equilibrium state of the nonlinear system. There is, however, a considerable difference between the implications of the asymptotic stability of the equilibrium state of a nonlinear system and that of a linear system. In the case of linear systems the zero-input response is homogeneous (see *3.4.17*); this implies that if the zero state $\mathbf{x} = \mathbf{0}$ is asymptotically stable, then for any $\mathbf{x}_0$, the zero input response $\mathbf{x}(t;\mathbf{x}_0,t_0)$ is bounded and eventually becomes arbitrarily close to $\mathbf{0}$. More precisely, for any initial state $\mathbf{x}_0$, there is a positive number M (which depends on $\mathbf{x}_0$), such that

$$\|\mathbf{x}(t;\mathbf{x}_0,t_0)\| < M \qquad \forall t \geq t_0$$

and

$$\mathbf{x}(t;\mathbf{x}_0,t_0) \to \mathbf{0} \qquad \text{as } t \to \infty$$

This follows directly from the homogeneity of the zero-input response. We need only take $M = (\epsilon_1/\delta)\|\mathbf{x}_0\|$ in the expressions of Comment *4*. This fact is expressed as follows: If the linear system *1* has its zero state asymptotically stable, then it is *asymptotically stable in the large.* The expression "in the large" is used to indicate that the asymptotic stability holds for all initial states and is not restricted to states sufficiently close to the zero state. As a consequence we shall use the

7 **Definition** The linear system *1* is said to be *stable i.s.L.* (asymptotically stable) whenever its zero state is stable (asymptotically stable) i.s.L. ◁

For nonlinear systems, an equilibrium state may be asymptotically stable without being asymptotically stable in the large. This is illustrated by an example. Consider the second-order nonlinear system specified by the differential equations which define the motion of its state in terms of the polar coordinates of the state:

$$\dot{r} = r^2 - r \qquad r \geq 0$$

$$\dot{\theta} = r$$

The point $r = 0$, $\theta = 0$ is an equilibrium point since at $(r = 0, \theta = 0)$ the derivatives $\dot{r}$, $\dot{\theta}$ are both zero. Now, for any $r(t_0) < 1$ and any $\theta(t_0)$, the point $(r(t),\theta(t))$ spirals into the origin. Therefore, we say that the equilibrium point $(r = 0, \theta = 0)$ is asymptotically stable. However, for $r(t_0) > 1$ and arbitrary $\theta(t_0)$, the point $(r(t),\theta(t))$ spirals outward, and eventually the point gets arbitrarily far away from the origin. Therefore, the equilibrium point $(r = 0, \theta = 0)$ is not asymptotically stable in the large. This idea is sometimes expressed by saying that the asymptotic stability of $(r = 0, \theta = 0)$ is valid only *locally*.

3 *Characterization of stable systems*

In this section we state two theorems that characterize stable and asymptotically stable systems.

1 **Theorem** The system described by *7.2.1* is stable i.s.L. $\Leftrightarrow$ there exists a constant M, which may depend on t_0, such that

$$\|\mathbf{\Phi}(t,t_0)\| \leq M \qquad \forall t \geq t_0$$

Proof $\Leftarrow$ Observe that the zero-input response of *1* is always given by (see *6.2.7*)

$$\mathbf{x}(t;\mathbf{x}_0,t_0) = \mathbf{\Phi}(t,t_0)\mathbf{x}_0$$

Therefore (see *C.16.10*)

$$\begin{aligned}\|\mathbf{x}(t;\mathbf{x}_0,t_0)\| &\leq \|\mathbf{\Phi}(t,t_0)\| \, \|\mathbf{x}_0\| \\ &\leq M\|\mathbf{x}_0\|\end{aligned}$$

Thus

$$\|\mathbf{x}_0\| < \frac{\varepsilon}{M} \Rightarrow \|\mathbf{x}(t;\mathbf{x}_0,t_0)\| \leq \varepsilon \qquad \text{for all } t \geq t_0$$

and the system is stable i.s.L. in view of Definition *7.2.2*.

$\Rightarrow$ We prove it by contradiction. If $\mathbf{\Phi}$ is not uniformly bounded for $t \geq t_0$, there is at least one element, say, ϕ_{ik}, which takes arbitrarily large values as $t \to \infty$. Let us pick the initial state $\mathbf{x}_0$ to have all components zero except the kth component, which is equal to ξ. Then the ith component of the state vector $\mathbf{x}(t;\mathbf{x}_0,t_0)$ is

$$x_i(t) = \phi_{ik}(t)\xi$$

Now, however small ξ may be, since ϕ_{ik} takes arbitrarily large values at $t \to \infty$, $x_i(t)$ will also take arbitrarily large values as $t \to \infty$. Therefore, the system is unstable, which contradicts the hypothesis. Consequently, $\mathbf{\Phi}$ must be uniformly bounded for all $t \geq t_0$. ◁

To characterize the asymptotic stability, we have the

2 **Theorem** The linear system *7.2.1* is asymptotically stable if and only if (I) there is a constant M such that

$$\|\mathbf{\Phi}(t,t_0)\| \leq \mathrm{M} \qquad \forall t \geq t_0$$

and (II)

$$\lim_{t\to\infty} \|\mathbf{\Phi}(t,t_0)\| = 0 \qquad \forall t_0$$

Proof The proof follows easily from that of *1* by a few easy modifications; it is therefore left as an exercise for the reader. ◁

We know that the state vector of a time-invariant system cannot grow faster than an exponential. For time-varying systems, this is still true provided $\mathbf{A}(t)$ remains bounded for all $t \geq t_0$. This fact is a consequence of the following

3 **Assertion** Any solution of *7.2.1* satisfies

$$\|\mathbf{x}(t;\mathbf{x}_0,t_0)\| \leq \|\mathbf{x}_0\| \exp\left[\int_{t_0}^{t} \|\mathbf{A}(\xi)\| \, d\xi\right] \qquad \forall t \geq t_0$$

Proof Let us integrate *6.2.1* between t_0 and t and obtain

$$\mathbf{x}(t;\mathbf{x}_0,t_0) = \mathbf{x}_0 + \int_{t_0}^{t} \mathbf{A}(\xi)\mathbf{x}(\xi;\mathbf{x}_0,t_0) \, d\xi$$

Let us take the norm of both sides and use the properties of the norm (*C.16.10* and *C.16.12*) to get

$$\|\mathbf{x}(t;\mathbf{x}_0,t_0)\| \leq \|\mathbf{x}_0\| + \int_{t_0}^{t} \|\mathbf{A}(\xi)\| \quad \|\mathbf{x}(\xi;\mathbf{x}_0,t_0)\| \, d\xi$$

Assertion *3* follows directly from this inequality by virtue of the inequality established in the next exercise.

4 *Exercise Bellman-Gronwall inequality* Let $k \geq 0$ and w be real-valued continuous functions on $[t_0, \infty)$ and let c be a constant. If

$$w(t) \leq c + \int_{t_0}^{t} k(\xi)w(\xi) \, d\xi \qquad \forall t \geq t_0$$

then

$$w(t) \leq c \exp \int_{t_0}^{t} k(\xi) \, d\xi \qquad \forall t \leq t_0$$

(*Hint:* Call the integral in the given inequality $y(t)$: then, $w(t) \leq y(t) + c$. Multiply this inequality by $k(t) \exp\left[-\int_{t_0}^{t} k(\xi) \, d\xi.\right]$ Observe that $\dot{y} = kw$; hence

$$\frac{d}{dt}\left\{y(t) \exp\left[-\int_{t_0}^{t} k(\xi) \, d\xi\right]\right\} \leq c \exp\left[-\int_{t_0}^{t} k(\xi) \, d\xi\right]$$

Integrate both sides of the inequality between t_0 and t, observe that $y(t_0) = 0$, and cancel the common exponential factor to finally obtain the claimed inequality.)

5 *Comment* If $\|\mathbf{A}(t)\| \leq M$ for all t, then

$$\|\mathbf{x}(t;\mathbf{x}_0,t_0)\| \leq \|\mathbf{x}_0\| \exp\left[M(t - t_0)\right] \qquad \forall \mathbf{x}_0, \forall t \geq t_0$$

4 *Special cases*

Linear time-invariant systems

The questions of stability of linear time-invariant systems are important not only because such systems occur so frequently in practice but also because their stability implies, in some cases, the local stability of the zero state of a nonlinear system. For example, the following theorem plays a very important role in the theory of nonlinear systems:[1]

1 **Theorem** Let $\dot{\mathbf{x}} = \mathbf{Ax} + \mathbf{f}(\mathbf{x},t)$, where $\mathbf{A}$ is a real constant matrix all of whose eigenvalues have negative real parts. Let $\mathbf{f}$ be real, continuous for small $\|\mathbf{x}\|$ and for all $t \geq 0$, and

$$\mathbf{f}(\mathbf{x},t) = o(\|\mathbf{x}\|) \qquad \|\mathbf{x}\| \to 0$$

uniformly in t, $t \geq 0$. Then the zero state, $\mathbf{x} = \mathbf{0}$, is asymptotically stable. ◁

It is important to emphasize that this result concerning the nonlinear system is purely local: it asserts that states sufficiently close to $\mathbf{0}$ will remain close to $\mathbf{0}$ and approach $\mathbf{0}$ arbitrarily closely as $t \to \infty$.

The necessary and sufficient conditions for the stability and asymptotic stability of linear time-invariant systems follow easily from the general formula for $\mathbf{x}(t;\mathbf{x}_0,t_0)$ (see *5.2.9*) and from the fundamental formula for exp $(\mathbf{A}t)$ (*5.3.1*). The characterization of stability i.s.L. is given by the

2 **Theorem** The system described by the state transition equation $\dot{\mathbf{x}} = \mathbf{Ax}$, where $\mathbf{A}$ is a constant matrix, is stable i.s.L. $\Leftrightarrow$ (I) all the eigenvalues of $\mathbf{A}$ have nonpositive real parts and (II) those eigenvalues of $\mathbf{A}$ that lie on the imaginary axis are simple zeros of the *minimal polynomial* of $\mathbf{A}$.

Proof From *5.2.11*, we have $\mathbf{x}(t;\mathbf{x}_0,t_0) = [\exp \mathbf{A}(t - t_0)]\mathbf{x}_0$. Therefore, we need only show that $\|\exp \mathbf{A}(t - t_0)\| < M$, $\forall t \geq t_0 \Leftrightarrow$ conditions (I) and (II) hold. For convenience we take $t_0 = 0$, which is justified since the system is time-invariant (*3.2.26*).

$\Leftarrow$ Consider the fundamental formula applied to exp $(\mathbf{A}t)$ (*5.3.1*). We obtain successively (using *C.16.12*)

$$\|\exp(\mathbf{A}t)\| = \left\| \sum_{k=1}^{\sigma} \sum_{l=0}^{m_k-1} t^l e^{\lambda_k t} \mathbf{Z}_{kl} \right\|$$

$$\leq \sum_{k=1}^{\sigma} \sum_{l=0}^{m_k-1} t^l e^{\alpha_k t} \|\mathbf{Z}_{kl}\| \qquad t \geq 0$$

where $\alpha_k = \text{Re}(\lambda_k)$, $k = 1, 2, \ldots, \sigma$.

Let

$$M = \sum_{k=1}^{\sigma} \sum_{l=0}^{m_k-1} \|\mathbf{Z}_{kl}\| \sup (t^l e^{\alpha_k t})$$

where the supremum is taken over $[0, \infty)$.

[1] E. A. Coddington and N. Levinson, "Theory of Ordinary Differential Equations," McGraw-Hill Book Company, Inc., New York, 1955.

If conditions (I) and (II) of the theorem are satisfied, then for all k, l, sup $(t^l e^{\alpha_k t})$ is finite. Since the matrices $\mathbf{Z}_{kl}$ are constant, the same is true of the numbers $\|\mathbf{Z}_{kl}\|$. Therefore M is a finite number and the stability i.s.L. follows.

$\Rightarrow$ Let us use a contradiction proof to establish that the stability i.s.L. implies (I) and (II). First suppose that some eigenvalue, say, λ_1, has a positive real part: that is, $\alpha_1 > 0$. Pick as an initial state $\mathbf{x}_0$ an eigenvector associated with the eigenvalue λ_1; then (*5.4.5*)

$$\mathbf{x}(t;\mathbf{u}_1,0) = e^{\lambda_1 t}\mathbf{u}_1$$

Since Re $(\lambda_1) = \alpha_1 > 0$, $\|\mathbf{x}(t;\mathbf{u}_1,0\| \to \infty$ exponentially, irrespective of how small $\|\mathbf{x}_0\|$ has been chosen. Therefore, stability i.s.L. implies that no eigenvalue of $\mathbf{A}$ can have a positive real part.

Suppose now that the minimal polynomial has a zero of order $m_1 > 1$ on the imaginary axis. Let λ_1 be this zero and $\lambda_1 = j\omega_1$. Since $m_1 > 1$ let us pick $\mathbf{x}_0 \in \mathfrak{N}_1^2$ (see *D.3.1*), but $\mathbf{x}_0 \notin \mathfrak{N}_1^1 \triangleq \mathfrak{N}(\mathbf{A} - \lambda_1\mathbf{I})$. Thus $(\mathbf{A} - j\omega_1\mathbf{I})\mathbf{x}_0 \neq \mathbf{0}$. The state at time t is then, by *D.6.2*,

$$\mathbf{x}(t;\mathbf{x}_0,0) = e^{j\omega_1 t}\mathbf{x}_0 + te^{j\omega_1 t}(\mathbf{A} - j\omega_1\mathbf{I})\mathbf{x}_0$$

Again $\|\mathbf{x}(t;\mathbf{x}_0,0)\| \to \infty$ (linearly with time in this case) irrespective of how small $\mathbf{x}_0$ has been chosen. Therefore stability i.s.L. implies that the minimal polynomial of $\mathbf{A}$ cannot have multiple zeros with zero real parts. $\triangleleft$

The characterization of asymptotic stability is very similar and is stated as a

3 **Theorem** The system described by its state transition equation $\dot{\mathbf{x}} = \mathbf{A}\mathbf{x}$, where $\mathbf{A}$ is a constant matrix, is asymptotically stable if and only if all the eigenvalues of $\mathbf{A}$ have negative (<0) real parts.

Proof The proof is similar to that of *2* and is left as an exercise for the reader.

4 *Exercise* Prove Theorems *2* and *3* by using the Laplace transform to compute $\mathbf{x}(t;\mathbf{x}_0,t_0)$. (*Hint:* Use the basic property of the minimal polynomial given in *D.2.6*.)

Linear periodic systems

The study of the stability of linear periodic systems is important not only because such systems occur frequently in practice, say in parametric amplifiers, but also because the question of stability of periodic solutions of nonlinear systems reduces to that of linear periodic systems. More precisely, the relation is expressed by two fundamental theorems derived from the theory of nonlinear differential systems.[1] For the

[1] *Ibid.*

proofs of these theorems the reader is referred to the book indicated in the footnote.

5 **Theorem** Let the nonlinear system be $\dot{\mathbf{x}} = \mathbf{f}(\mathbf{x},t)$, where $\mathbf{f}$ is periodic in t. Suppose $\mathbf{s}(t)$ is a periodic solution of the nonlinear system which has the same period as $\mathbf{f}$. Then the solution $\mathbf{s}(t)$ is asymptotically stable as $t \to \infty$[1] if the characteristic exponents associated with the linear periodically varying equation

$$\dot{\mathbf{z}} = \mathbf{f}_x(\mathbf{s}(t),t)\mathbf{z}$$

have negative real parts. [$\mathbf{f}_x(\mathbf{s},t)$ is the Jacobian matrix of $\mathbf{f}$ evaluated at $(\mathbf{s},t)$, that is, the matrix whose (i,j) element is $\dfrac{\partial f_i}{\partial x_j}(\mathbf{s}(t),t)$.] $\triangleleft$

The linear equation above is called the equation of the first variation with respect to the solution $\mathbf{s}(t)$.

When the right-hand side, $\mathbf{f}(\mathbf{x},t)$, does not depend explicitly on t, a difficulty arises from the fact that the system by itself does not have a preferred origin of time, so that if $\mathbf{s}(t)$ is a periodic solution of $\dot{\mathbf{x}} = \mathbf{f}(\mathbf{x})$ so is $\mathbf{s}(t + c)$, where c is an arbitrary constant. Under these circumstances Theorem *5* becomes[2]

6 **Theorem** Let $(n - 1)$ characteristic exponents of $\dot{\mathbf{z}} = \mathbf{f}_x(\mathbf{s}(t))\mathbf{z}$ have negative real parts. Let $\mathbf{y}(t)$ be a solution of $\dot{\mathbf{x}} = \mathbf{f}(\mathbf{x})$. Then there exists an $\varepsilon > 0$ such that whenever, for some t_1, t_2, $\|\mathbf{y}(t_1) - \mathbf{s}(t_2)\| < \varepsilon$, there also exists a constant ϕ such that, as $t \to \infty$, $\|\mathbf{y}(t) - \mathbf{s}(t + \phi)\| \to 0$.

Roughly speaking, whenever the system starts from a state sufficiently close to the periodic orbit, the resulting motion approaches that orbit as $t \to \infty$. In Theorems *5* and *6*, the stability of a periodic solution depends on the stability properties of a linear periodically varying system.

The specific results concerning linear periodic systems follow directly from the theory of linear periodic systems developed in Chap. *6*, Sec. *7*. The proofs of the results are left as an exercise for the reader.

7 **Assertion** The periodic system described by the state equation $\dot{\mathbf{x}} = \mathbf{A}(t)\mathbf{x}$, where $\mathbf{A}(t)$ is periodic with period T, is stable i.s.L. $\Leftrightarrow$ {(I) the real parts of the characteristic exponents of $\mathbf{A}(t)$ are nonpositive (≤ 0) and (II) those characteristic exponents that are purely imaginary are simple zeros of the minimal polynomial of $\mathbf{B}$}. [Note that $\mathbf{B}$ is defined in terms of $\mathbf{A}(t)$ by *6.7.3*.]

[1] That is, any solution which starts, at t_0, close to $\mathbf{s}(t_0)$ will eventually become arbitrarily close to the periodic motion $\mathbf{s}(t)$.

[2] Coddington and Levinson, *op. cit.*

8 **Assertion** The periodic system described by the state transition equation $\dot{\mathbf{x}} = \mathbf{A}(t)\mathbf{x}$ is *asymptotically stable* $\Leftrightarrow$ all the characteristic exponents have negative (<0) real parts.

9 **Assertion** For both time-invariant linear systems and periodically varying linear systems described by *7.2.1* asymptotic stability implies that $\|\mathbf{x}(t;\mathbf{x}_0,0)\| \to 0$ *exponentially;* more precisely, there is a constant C and a number $\eta > 0$ such that

$$\|\mathbf{x}(t;\mathbf{x}_0,0)\| \leq Ce^{-\eta t} \qquad \text{for all } t \geq 0$$

10 *Comment* This is not true for general time-varying systems; for example, the first-order system $\dot{x} = -x/2t$, $t \geq 1$, has a solution $s(t) = t^{-\frac{1}{2}}$. Therefore, the system is asymptotically stable but its solutions do not go to zero exponentially. In fact, the solution s goes to zero so slowly that $\int_1^\infty |s(t)|\, dt = \infty$.

Systems characterized by $Ly = u$

Let $\mathfrak{A}$ be a system characterized by $L(p,t)y = u$, where $L(p,t)$ is an nth-order linear differential operator, and let

$$\mathbf{x}(t) = (y(t),y^{(1)}(t), \ldots ,y^{(n-1)}(t))$$

be its state vector at time t, with the corresponding state equations having the form *6.2.56*. From the general results which we established in the preceding discussion it is a simple matter to deduce a number of stability properties of the free motion of such systems. In what follows we shall merely state these properties in the form of assertions and leave the proofs as exercises for the reader.

11 **Assertion** The system characterized by $L(p,t) = u$ is stable i.s.L. (or equivalently, zero-input stable) $\Leftrightarrow$ for a set of basis functions $\phi_i(t)$ of the operator L there is a number M such that $|\phi_i^{(k)}(t)| \leq M$ for $i = 1, 2, \ldots, n$, for $k = 0, 1, \ldots, n-1$, and for all $t \geq t_0$.

12 **Assertion** The system described by $L(p,t)y = 0$ is *asymptotically stable* $\Leftrightarrow$ {for a set of basis functions $\phi_i(t)$ of the operator $L(p,t)$ (I) there is a number M such that $|\phi_i^{(k)}(t)| \leq M$ for $i = 1, 2, \ldots, n$, for $k = 0, 1, \ldots, n-1$, and for all $t \geq t_0$, and (II) $\lim_{t\to\infty} \phi_i^{(k)}(t) = 0$ for $i = 1, 2, \ldots, n$ and $k = 0, 1, \ldots, n-1$}.

13 **Assertion** The time-invariant system described by $L(p)y = 0$ is *stable* i.s.L. $\Leftrightarrow$ {(I) the zeros of the polynomial $L(s)$ have nonpositive real parts and (II) those zeros that lie on the imaginary axis are simple}.

14 **Assertion** The time-invariant system described by $Ly = 0$ is *asymptotically stable* $\Leftrightarrow$ all the zeros of the polynomial $L(s)$ have negative real parts. $\triangleleft$

In order to use Assertion *14*, it is not necessary to calculate the zeros of the polynomial $L(s)$; there are well-known necessary and sufficient conditions for the zeros of a polynomial to have negative real parts; these conditions are given in *9.4.22*.

15 **Assertion** The time-invariant system described by

$$\sum_{j=1}^{n} L_{ij}(p)x_j(t) = 0 \qquad i = 1, 2, \ldots, n$$

is *asymptotically stable* $\Leftrightarrow$ {all the zeros of $\Delta_0(s)$ have negative real parts, where Δ_0 is the quotient of Δ by g_0, which is the greatest common divisor of all the elements of the adjoint matrix $\mathbf{\Gamma}(s)$}.

Proof Follows directly from *5.7.8*.

5 *Some sufficient conditions for stability*

In this section we consider only systems of the form

1 $$\dot{\mathbf{x}} = \mathbf{A}(t)\mathbf{x}$$

where $\mathbf{A}(t)$ is continuous in t.

Let us first consider Wazewski's inequalities,[1] which bound the norm of free motions. More precisely we have the

2 **Theorem** Consider the system *1* and let $\mathbf{H}$ be the hermitian matrix defined by

3 $$\mathbf{H}(t) = \tfrac{1}{2}[\mathbf{A}(t) + \mathbf{A}^*(t)]$$

Let $\lambda(t)$ and $\Lambda(t)$ be, for each t, the smallest and largest eigenvalues of $\mathbf{H}(t)$. Then

4 $$\|\mathbf{x}_0\| \exp\left[\int_{t_0}^{t} \lambda(t')\, dt'\right] \leq \|\mathbf{x}(t;\mathbf{x}_0,t_0)\| \leq \|\mathbf{x}_0\| \exp\left[\int_{t_0}^{t} \Lambda(t')\, dt'\right]$$

where the norm is defined by $\|\mathbf{y}\|^2 = \langle\mathbf{y},\mathbf{y}\rangle$.

Proof Let us outline the proof. Consider $V(t) = \langle\mathbf{x}(t;\mathbf{x}_0,t_0), \mathbf{x}(t;\mathbf{x}_0,t_0)\rangle$. Then, by the definition of $\mathbf{H}$

$$\dot{V} = V\frac{2\langle\mathbf{x}(t),\mathbf{H}(t)\mathbf{x}(t)\rangle}{\langle\mathbf{x}(t),\mathbf{x}(t)\rangle}$$

[1] T. Wazewski, Sur la limitation des intégrales des systèmes d'equations différentielles lineáres ordinaires, *Studia Math.*, vol. 10, pp. 48–59, 1948.

where we have made an obvious simplification in the notation. From well-known properties of hermitian matrices (*C.19.15*),

$$\lambda(t)\langle \mathbf{y},\mathbf{y}\rangle \le \langle \mathbf{y},\mathbf{H}(t)\mathbf{y}\rangle \le \Lambda(t)\langle \mathbf{y},\mathbf{y}\rangle \qquad \text{for all } \mathbf{y}\text{'s}$$

Hence

$$2\lambda(t) \le \frac{d}{dt}(\log V) \le 2\Lambda(t)$$

Finally, *4* follows by integrating, taking the exponential of the integrals, and observing that $V = \|\mathbf{x}(t)\|^2$.

5 **Corollary** Using the notation of *2*, the system is stable i.s.L. if, for all t_0,

$$\limsup_{t\to\infty} \int_{t_0}^{t} \Lambda(t')\,dt' < \infty$$

6 **Corollary** All solutions of the system *1* are unstable if, for all t_0,

$$\limsup_{t\to\infty} \int_{t_0}^{t} \lambda(t')\,dt' = \infty \quad \triangleleft$$

There is a sharper result applicable only to systems for which $\mathbf{A}(t)$ is *normal.* $\mathbf{A}(t)$ is said to be normal if $\mathbf{A}^*(t)\mathbf{A}(t) = \mathbf{A}(t)\mathbf{A}^*(t)$ for all t. Equivalently, for each t, $\mathbf{A}(t)$ is unitarily similar to a diagonal matrix (see *C.19.1* and *C.19.11*). First let us introduce a

7 **Definition** For each $\mathbf{x}_i(t)$ which is a solution of *1*, we define a generalized characteristic exponent g_i of $\mathbf{A}(t)$:

$$g_i = \limsup_{t\to\infty} t^{-1} \log \|\mathbf{x}_i(t)\|$$

For the remainder of this section we shall use the norm defined by the scalar product $\|\mathbf{x}\|^2 = \langle \mathbf{x},\mathbf{x}\rangle$.

8 **Theorem**[1] Let $\mathbf{A}(t)$ be normal, continuous, and bounded for $t \ge t_0$. Let $R(t)$ and $r(t)$ be the maximum and the minimum of the real part of the eigenvalues of $\mathbf{A}(t)$. Then

9 $$\limsup_{t\to\infty} t^{-1} \int_{t_0}^{t} r(t')\,dt' \le g_i \le \limsup_{t\to\infty} t^{-1} \int_{t_0}^{t} R(t')\,dt'$$

for all generalized characteristic exponents of the system.

Proof Let $V(t) = \langle \mathbf{x}(t),\mathbf{x}(t)\rangle$, where $\mathbf{x}(t)$ is any solution. Then by *1* and using the definition of the adjoint (*C.14.1*)

$$\frac{\dot V(t)}{V(t)} = \frac{\langle \mathbf{Ax},\mathbf{x}\rangle + \langle \mathbf{x},\mathbf{Ax}\rangle}{\langle \mathbf{x},\mathbf{x}\rangle} = \frac{\langle \mathbf{Ax},\mathbf{x}\rangle + \langle \mathbf{A}^*\mathbf{x},\mathbf{x}\rangle}{\langle \mathbf{x},\mathbf{x}\rangle} \triangleq \tfrac{1}{2}\rho(t)$$

[1] L. Markus, Continuous Matrices and Stability of Differential Systems, *Math. Z.*, vol. 62, pp. 310–319, 1955.

Since the matrix $\mathbf{A}$ is normal, by *C.19.14*, $r(t) \leq \rho(t) \leq R(t)$; hence

$$\int_{t_0}^{t} r(t')\,dt' \leq \tfrac{1}{2} \log \frac{V(t)}{V(t_0)} \leq \int_{t_0}^{t} R(t')\,dt$$

Now, the generalized characteristic exponent of the solution $\mathbf{x}(t)$ is

$$g = \limsup_{t\to\infty} t^{-1} \log \|\mathbf{x}(t)\| = \tfrac{1}{2} \limsup_{t\to\infty} t^{-1} \log \frac{V(t)}{V(t_0)}$$

and *9* follows.

10 *Exercise* Use Theorem *8* to derive some sufficient conditions for stability (asymptotic stability) of the system *1* when $\mathbf{A}(t)$ is normal for all t. $\triangleleft$

Finally, let us present a sufficient condition for stability which may be regarded either as an extension of Wazewski's theorem or an application of the Lyapunov second method[1] to linear systems.

11 **Theorem** Let $\mathbf{Q}$ be any constant self-adjoint positive definite matrix. Let μ be a positive constant (say, its smallest eigenvalue, *C.19.15*) such that

12 $$\langle \mathbf{z},\mathbf{Qz}\rangle \geq \mu\langle \mathbf{z},\mathbf{z}\rangle \qquad \forall \mathbf{z}$$

and let $m(t)$ be a continuous function of t such that

13 $$\langle \mathbf{z},(\mathbf{A}^*(t)\mathbf{Q} + \mathbf{QA}(t))\mathbf{z}\rangle \leq m(t)\langle \mathbf{z},\mathbf{z}\rangle \qquad \forall \mathbf{z},\ \forall t \geq t_0$$

If there is a constant M such that

14 $$\int_{t_0}^{t} m(t')\,dt' \leq M < \infty \qquad \forall t \geq t_0$$

and if

15 $$\int_{t_0}^{t} m(t')\,dt' \to -\infty \qquad \text{as } t \to \infty$$

then the system *1* is *asymptotically stable*.

Proof Let $\mathbf{x}(t)$ be any solution of *1*. Let $\phi(t) = \langle \mathbf{x}(t),\mathbf{Qx}(t)\rangle$; then by *1* and the definition of the adjoint

$$\dot{\phi}(t) = \langle \mathbf{x},(\mathbf{A}^*\mathbf{Q} + \mathbf{QA})\mathbf{x}\rangle$$

By *13* and *12*

$$\dot{\phi}(t) \leq m(t)\langle \mathbf{x},\mathbf{x}\rangle \leq \frac{m(t)}{\mu}\langle \mathbf{x},\mathbf{Qx}\rangle$$

In other words

$$\dot{\phi}(t) \leq \frac{m(t)}{\mu}\,\phi(t)$$

[1] J. La Salle and S. Lefschetz, "Stability by Lyapunov's Direct Method with Applications," Academic Press, Inc., New York, 1961. See also R. E. Kalman and J. Bertram, Control System Design via the Second Method of Lyapunov, *Trans. A.S.M.E., Ser. D*, vol. 82, no. 2, pp. 371–400, 1960.

and

$$\phi(t) \leq \phi(t_0) \exp \left[\int_{t_0}^{t} \frac{m(t')}{\mu} \, dt' \right] \qquad \forall t \geq t_0$$

This inequality together with condition *14* implies that $\phi(t)$ is bounded on $[t_0, \infty)$ by $\phi(t_0) \exp (M/\mu)$. Finally, with *15*, it implies that $\phi(t) \to 0$ as $t \to \infty$. These two facts and the positive definiteness of $\mathbf{Q}$ imply that $\|\mathbf{x}(t)\|$ is bounded on $[t_0, \infty)$ and $\|\mathbf{x}(t)\| \to 0$ as $t \to \infty$. Since $\mathbf{x}(t)$ was an arbitrary solution of *1*, these facts hold for all solutions of *1*; hence, *1* is asymptotically stable

6 *Reducible systems*

In Chap. *5*, Sec. *4*, we wrote the solution of the system $\dot{\mathbf{x}} = \mathbf{A}\mathbf{x}$ ($\mathbf{A}$ is a constant matrix with distinct eigenvalues) as a linear combination of the eigenvectors of $\mathbf{A}$ and obtained a considerable insight into the dynamics of the system. The new basis vectors $\mathbf{q}_i$ were not time-varying: their lengths and directions were fixed with respect to the original basis since they were eigenvectors of the constant matrix $\mathbf{A}$. Suppose we wish to extend this idea by letting the new basis vectors $\mathbf{q}_i$ be functions of time. In other words, we write $\mathbf{x}(t) = \sum_{i=1}^{n} \eta_i(t)\mathbf{q}_i(t)$, where the $\mathbf{q}_i(t)$ are known vector functions of time. Equivalently, if $\mathbf{y} = (\eta_1,\eta_2, \ldots ,\eta_n)$, the above substitution may be written as

1 $$\mathbf{x}(t) = \mathbf{Q}(t)\mathbf{y}(t)$$

where $\mathbf{Q}(t)$ is the matrix whose *i*th column is $\mathbf{q}_i(t)$. In principle, once $\mathbf{Q}(t)$ is known, the stability of a solution $\mathbf{x}(t)$ can be inferred from the behavior of $\mathbf{y}(t)$. However, if no special conditions are imposed on $\mathbf{Q}(t)$, some difficulties may occur. For example, if, as $t \to \infty$, the length of one or more of the $\mathbf{q}_i(t)$ grows without bound, then even though $\mathbf{y}(t) \to \mathbf{0}$ it may happen that $\mathbf{x}(t)$ does not become arbitrarily small. Also if, say, as $t \to \infty$ the n vectors $\mathbf{q}_i(t)$ become coplanar (i.e., in the limit they all belong to the same hyperplane or belong to some subspace of $\mathcal{C}^n$ of dimension $< n - 1$), then it may happen that even though $\mathbf{x}(t) \to \mathbf{0}$, $\mathbf{y}(t)$ remains finite or even grows without bound. These considerations indicate that the transformation matrix $\mathbf{Q}(t)$ should be suitably restricted. For this purpose we introduce the

2 **Definition** The matrix $\mathbf{Q}(t)$ is said to represent a *Lyapunov transformation* (I) if $\mathbf{Q}(t)$ and $\dot{\mathbf{Q}}(t)$ are continuous and bounded on $[t_0, \infty)$ and

(II) if for some positive constant M

3 $$0 < M < |\det \mathbf{Q}(t)| \qquad \forall t \geq t_0$$

4 *Comment* It is easy to see that these conditions are equivalent to the following: (I) $\mathbf{Q}$ and $\dot{\mathbf{Q}}$ are continuous on $[t_0, \infty)$, (II) $\mathbf{Q}$ is nonsingular for all $t \geq t_0$, and (III) $\|\mathbf{Q}(t)\|$ and $\|\mathbf{Q}^{-1}(t)\|$ are bounded for all $t \geq t_0$.

5 **Assertion** The Lyapunov transformations constitute a group.
Proof First, if $\mathbf{Q}$ is a Lyapunov transformation, so is $\mathbf{Q}^{-1}(t)$. From *2* it is immediately apparent that the product of two such transformations is also a Lyapunov transformation.

6 *Exercise* Let $\mathbf{Q}(t)$ be an orthogonal transformation such that for all $t \geq t_0$ both $\mathbf{Q}$ and $\dot{\mathbf{Q}}$ are continuous. Show that it is a Lyapunov transformation.

7 *Exercise* Let $\mathbf{M}$ be a constant matrix. Let all the zeros of its minimal polynomial (*D.2.1*) be simple and purely imaginary. Show that $\exp(\mathbf{M}t)$ is a Lyapunov transformation.

Consider the system

8 $$\dot{\mathbf{x}}(t) = \mathbf{A}(t)\mathbf{x}(t)$$

where $\mathbf{A}(t)$ is continuous in t. Let $\mathbf{Q}(t)$ be a Lyapunov transformation and introduce the transformation *1*; then, by substituting in *8*,

$$\dot{\mathbf{Q}}\mathbf{y} + \mathbf{Q}\dot{\mathbf{y}} = \mathbf{A}\mathbf{Q}\mathbf{y}$$

and, since $\mathbf{Q}(t)$ is nonsingular,

$$\dot{\mathbf{y}} = \mathbf{Q}^{-1}(\mathbf{A}\mathbf{Q} - \dot{\mathbf{Q}})\mathbf{y}$$

If $\mathbf{Q}^{-1}(\mathbf{A}\mathbf{Q} - \dot{\mathbf{Q}}) = \mathbf{C}$ and if $\mathbf{C}$ is a constant matrix, then we say that the system *8* is *reducible.*

9 *Comment* Geometrically, with respect to the moving frame of reference defined by the column vectors of $\mathbf{Q}(t)$, any solution of *8* obeys the differential equation

10 $$\dot{\mathbf{y}} = \mathbf{C}\mathbf{y}$$

which has *constant* coefficients. Sometimes, it is said that *8* and *10* are *kinematically equivalent.*

11 *Comment* If $\mathbf{C} = \mathbf{0}$, the system is said to be *reducible to zero:* with respect to the moving frame of reference any of its solutions have constant components.

12 *Comment* Not all systems such as *8* are reducible. It is interesting, however, that from *6.7.2* it can be easily shown that

13 **Assertion** Every linear system of the form *8* which is periodically varying is reducible. ◁

A very important fact concerning reducible systems is that stated in the

14 **Theorem** If the system *8* is reducible to the system *10,* then the system *10* is stable (asymptotically stable, unstable) if and only if the system *8* is stable (asymptotically stable, unstable, respectively).
Proof Using Definition *2*, the proof is an easy exercise in norm comparison.

15 **Theorem** The system *8* is reducible to zero if and only if there is a constant M such that its state transition matrix satisfies

16 $$\|\mathbf{\Phi}(t,t_0)\| < M < \infty \qquad \|\mathbf{\Phi}(t,t_0)^{-1}\| < M < \infty \qquad \forall t_0,\ \forall t \geq t_0$$

Proof $\Rightarrow$ Let $\mathbf{Q}(t)$ be a Lyapunov transformation which reduces *8* to zero. Hence, $\dot{\mathbf{Q}}(t) = \mathbf{A}(t)\mathbf{Q}(t)$, and $\mathbf{Q}(t)$ is nonsingular. Hence by *6.2.15* there is a nonsingular constant matrix $\mathbf{K}$ such that $\mathbf{Q}(t) = \mathbf{\Phi}(t,t_0)\mathbf{K}$. Hence

$$\mathbf{\Phi}(t,t_0) = \mathbf{Q}(t)\mathbf{K}^{-1} \qquad \text{and} \qquad \mathbf{\Phi}(t,t_0)^{-1} = \mathbf{K}\mathbf{Q}^{-1}(t)$$

Therefore, by *C.16.13*, we have

$$\|\mathbf{\Phi}(t,t_0)\| \leq \|\mathbf{Q}(t)\|\|\mathbf{K}^{-1}\|$$

and

$$\|\mathbf{\Phi}(t,t_0)^{-1}\| \leq \|\mathbf{K}\|\|\mathbf{Q}(t)^{-1}\|$$

The inequalities *16* follow from the above inequalities and Comment *4*.
$\Leftarrow$ The state transition matrix $\mathbf{\Phi}(t,t_0)$ is continuous in t and

$$\dot{\mathbf{\Phi}}(t,t_0) = \mathbf{A}(t)\mathbf{\Phi}(t,t_0)$$

implies that $\dot{\mathbf{\Phi}}(t,t_0)$ is continuous. By *16*, the elements of both the matrix $\mathbf{\Phi}(t,t_0)$ and its inverse are bounded for $t \geq t_0$; it follows then by Cramer's rule that det $\mathbf{\Phi}(t,t_0)$ is bounded away from zero on $[t_0, \infty)$. By Definition *2*, $\mathbf{\Phi}(t,t_0)$ is a Lyapunov transformation. Finally, we obviously have

$$\mathbf{\Phi}(t,t_0)^{-1}(\dot{\mathbf{\Phi}}(t,t_0) - \mathbf{A}(t)\mathbf{\Phi}(t,t_0)) = \mathbf{0}$$

and hence *8* is reducible to zero.

17 *Exercise* Show that the following four conditions on the system *8* are equivalent:

(I) System *8* is reducible to zero.
(II) $\|\mathbf{\Phi}(t,t_0)\| < M < \infty$ for some M and $\forall t \geq 0$, $\forall t_0 \geq 0$.
(III) System *8* and its adjoint are stable.
(IV) $\|\mathbf{\Phi}(t,t_0)\| < M < \infty$, $\|\mathbf{\Phi}(t,t_0)^{-1}\| < M < \infty$ for some M and $\forall t \geq t_0$.

7 *Stability defined from the input-output point of view*

Definitions *7.2.2* and *7.2.3* are particularly well suited to the study of systems described by differential equations. However, they involve only the zero-input response (free motion) of these systems. In many applications, however, one is more interested in the input-output relationship than in the zero-input response of the system. Let us describe the input-output point of view. First consider the system described by

1 $$\dot{\mathbf{x}}(t) = \mathbf{A}(t)\mathbf{x}(t) + \mathbf{B}(t)\mathbf{u}(t)$$

where $\mathbf{A}(t)$ and $\mathbf{B}(t)$ are $n \times n$ and $n \times r$ matrices whose elements are known, bounded, continuous functions of time. The input is the r-rowed vector $\mathbf{u}$. For simplicity let us assume that the output is the state vector $\mathbf{x}$ rather than some linear function of $\mathbf{x}$ and $\mathbf{u}$.

The concept of stability we are about to define is usually referred to by the expression "any bounded input produces a bounded output." In order to distinguish this concept from the stability i.s.L. of linear differential systems defined in *7.2.2*, we shall refer to the new concept as stability b.i.b.o. It is defined as follows:

2 **Definition** The differential system *1* whose output is $\mathbf{x}$ and whose input is $\mathbf{u}$ is said to be *stable b.i.b.o.* if for all t_0, for all initial states $\mathbf{x}_0$, and for all bounded inputs $\mathbf{u}_{[t_0,\infty)}$, the output $\mathbf{x}(t;\mathbf{x}_0,t_0;\mathbf{u}_{[t_0,\infty)})$ is bounded on $[t_0, \infty)$. ◁

More precisely, the concept of stability b.i.b.o. can be formulated as follows: Let $\mathcal{B}$ be the set of all bounded inputs $\mathbf{u}_{[t_0,\infty)}$, that is,

$$\mathcal{B} = \{\mathbf{u}_{[t_0,\infty)} | \text{ for some } M < \infty, \ \|\mathbf{u}(t)\| < M, \text{ for all } t \geq t_0\}$$

The system *1* is said to be stable b.i.b.o. if $\forall t_0$, $\forall \mathbf{x}_0 \in \mathcal{C}^n$, and $\forall \mathbf{u}_{[t_0,\infty)} \in \mathcal{B}$ there exists a finite number K independent of t_0, such that

$$\|\mathbf{x}(t;\mathbf{x}_0,t_0;\mathbf{u}_{[t_0,\infty)})\| < K \qquad \forall t \geq t_0$$

The bound K may depend on $\mathbf{x}_0$, on the bound M of the inputs, and on the characteristics of the system.

The stability b.i.b.o. is characterized by the following

3 **Theorem** Consider the differential system described by *1*: let $\mathbf{u}$ be its input and $\mathbf{x}$ be its output. Let $\mathbf{A}(t)$ and $\mathbf{B}(t)$ be continuous and bounded on any interval of the form $[t_0, \infty)$. This system is stable b.i.b.o. if and only if (I) there exists a number M_1 such that

4 $$\|\mathbf{\Phi}(t,t_0)\| < M_1 < \infty \qquad \forall t_0, \ \forall t \geq t_0$$

and (II) there exists a number M_2 such that

5 $$\int_{t_0}^{t} \|\mathbf{\Phi}(t,t')\mathbf{B}(t')\|_1 \, dt' < M_2 < \infty \qquad \forall t_0, \forall t \geq t_0$$

where, in the integrand of *5*, the subscript 1 indicates that the l_1 norm must be used. (The l_1 norm of a vector in $\mathcal{C}^n$ is $\|\mathbf{x}\|_1 = \sum_{i=1}^{n} |x_i|$; see *C.16.7*, *C.16.8 et seq.*)

6 *Comment* Instead of defining stability b.i.b.o. for all $\mathbf{x}_0$ (as in Definition *2*) we could have prescribed that $\mathbf{x}_0 = \mathbf{0}$. System *1* would then be called *zero-state stable b.i.b.o.* Theorem *3* would then have the following interpretation: System *1* is stable b.i.b.o. (in the sense of Definition *2* above) if and only if it is zero-state stable b.i.b.o. and uniformly zero-input stable i.s.L.

7 *Comment* Since in $\mathcal{C}^n$ all norms are equivalent, condition *4* holds whichever norm is used. This is not the case, however, for *5*, in which the l_1 norm must be used.

8 *Comment* Equation *4* by itself guarantees that, when $\mathbf{u} = \mathbf{0}$ for all t, the system is stable i.s.L. (see *7.3.2*). The additional condition *5* is required in order to force the matrix product $\mathbf{\Phi}(t,t')\mathbf{B}(t')$ to decrease sufficiently fast that the integrated effect of any bounded input remains bounded.

Proof $\Leftarrow$ The response of *1* is given by (*6.2.21*)

9 $$\mathbf{x}(t;\mathbf{x}_0,t_0;\mathbf{u}_{[t_0,t]}) = \mathbf{\Phi}(t,t_0)\mathbf{x}_0 + \int_{t_0}^{t} \mathbf{\Phi}(t,t')\mathbf{B}(t')\mathbf{u}(t') \, dt'$$

By simplifying the notation of the left-hand side in an obvious manner and using *C.16.12* and *C.16.13*, we obtain

10 $$\|\mathbf{x}(t)\| \leq \|\mathbf{\Phi}(t,t_0)\| \; \|\mathbf{x}_0\| + \int_{t_0}^{t} \|\mathbf{\Phi}(t,t')\mathbf{B}(t')\| \; \|\mathbf{u}(t')\| \, dt'$$

Since $\mathbf{u}_{[t_0,\infty)}$ is bounded, for some constant M_3, $\|\mathbf{u}(t)\| < M_3 < \infty$, $\forall t \geq t_0$. By *4*, *5*, and *10* we get successively

$$\|\mathbf{x}(t)\| < M_1\|\mathbf{x}_0\| + M_3 \int_{t_0}^{t} \|\mathbf{\Phi}(t,t')\mathbf{B}(t')\| \, dt'$$

$$\|\mathbf{x}(t)\| < M_1\|\mathbf{x}_0\| + M_2M_3 \qquad \forall t \geq t_0$$

Hence *4* and *5* imply that the system is stable b.i.b.o.

$\Rightarrow$ First consider *9* with $\mathbf{u} = \mathbf{0}$. Clearly, for $\mathbf{x}$ to be bounded for all t and for all possible $\mathbf{x}_0$, *4* must hold; for otherwise from the definition of the norm of a linear transformation (*C.16.9*) there is an appropriate choice of $\mathbf{x}_0$ which would make $\mathbf{x}(t;\mathbf{x}_0,t_0;\mathbf{0})$ become arbitrarily large (see the proof of *7.3.1*). Thus stability b.i.b.o. implies *4*. In order to establish *5*, we consider the case $\mathbf{x}_0 = \mathbf{0}$; in other words, the first term on the right-hand side of *9* is zero in the proof that follows. Let us pick the l_1 norm: $\|\mathbf{x}\|_1 = \sum_{i=1}^{n} |x_i|$. The corresponding norm of a matrix **A** is then $\|\mathbf{A}\|_1 = \max_j \left(\sum_{i=1}^{n} |a_{ij}|\right)$, (see *C.16.17*). By assumption, $\mathbf{B}(t')$ is bounded for all t'. *4*, which we have just established, states that $\mathbf{\Phi}(t,t')$ is bounded for all $t \geq t'$. Therefore, the only way *5* may be violated is for the integral to become arbitrarily large as $t \to \infty$. For the purpose of a proof by contradiction, suppose that this is so: thus for any number N, however large, there is a T (which depends on N) such that

11 $$\int_{t_0}^{T} \|\mathbf{\Phi}(T,t')\mathbf{B}(t')\|_1 \, dt' > N$$

Let $\mathbf{\Phi}(T,t)\mathbf{B}(t) = \mathbf{\Psi}(T,t)$. *11* implies that for any N there is a T such that

$$\int_{t_0}^{T} \max_j \left(\sum_{i=1}^{n} |\psi_{ij}(T,t')|\right) dt' > N$$

This in turn implies that at least one component of $\mathbf{\Psi}$, say, the (i,j) component, has the property that $\int_{t_0}^{T} |\psi_{ij}(T,t')| \, dt'$ becomes arbitrarily large as $T \to \infty$. This is obvious because if it were not the case, we would have

$$\sup_{T \to \infty} \int_{t_0}^{T} |\psi_{kl}(T,t')| \, dt' < M < \infty \qquad \forall k,\, l, \text{ for some } M$$

and since $\mathbf{\Psi}$ has only nr components, this would contradict *11*. Therefore *11* implies that there is at least one component ψ_{ij} of $\mathbf{\Psi}$ such that given any number K, however large, there is a T' such that

$$\int_{t_0}^{T'} |\psi_{ij}(T',t)| \, dt > K$$

Pick the following bounded input: $u_l(t) = 0$, $\forall t$ and $\forall l \neq j$, and $u_j(t) = \operatorname{sgn} \psi_{ij}(T',t)$. Clearly from *9* we get

$$\|\mathbf{x}(T')\|_1 \geq |x_i(T')| = \int_{t_0}^{T'} |\psi_{ij}(T',t)| \, dt > K$$

This is a recipe for constructing a bounded input which will produce an output $\mathbf{x}(T')$ whose norm is larger than any preassigned number. In other words, the system is not stable b.i.b.o. This is a contradiction; therefore, stability b.i.b.o. implies *5*. ◁

12 *Comment* Throughout this section we have restricted ourselves to a differential system whose output is its state. In many practical instances, this is not so; usually, the output is a linear function of the state and the input. An analysis that would cover this general case

would be too involved. With the theory just developed, the reader will have no difficulty in using the specific features of the system under consideration to develop the necessary and sufficient conditions for the stability b.i.b.o. of that system.

13 *Exercise* Consider a linear time-invariant differential system defined by *1*. Suppose that $\mathbf{x}$ is the output of the system. Show that if such a system is asymptotically stable, then it is stable b.i.b.o. Show by an example that the converse is not true.

14 *Exercise* Give an example of a time-varying system which is asymptotically stable and which is not stable b.i.b.o. [*Hint:* Consider the scalar system $\dot{x} = -(1/2t)x + u(t)$, $t \geq 1$. $\Phi(t,t_0) = \sqrt{t_0/t}$.]

Theorem *3* has given a characterization of the stability b.i.b.o. If we put a few additional restrictions on $\mathbf{B}(t)$ of *1*, namely, that $\mathbf{B}(t)$ is a bounded $n \times n$ matrix whose inverse is bounded for all t, we can prove the rather surprising fact that the norm of the state transition matrix, $\|\mathbf{\Phi}(t,t_0)\|$, must decrease at least as fast as an exponential in $(t - t_0)$ in order that the system *1* be stable b.i.b.o., and conversely. We shall use a method of proof due to Kalman. More precisely, this fact is formulated as a

15 **Theorem** Consider the system *1*, where the input $\mathbf{u}$ and the output $\mathbf{x}$ are both n-vectors. Let the $n \times n$ matrices $\mathbf{A}(t)$ and $\mathbf{B}(t)$ be continuous and bounded for all t; that is,

16 $$\|\mathbf{B}(t)\|_1 \leq M_1 < \infty \qquad \forall t$$

Assume also that $\mathbf{B}(t)$ is nonsingular and that its inverse is bounded by M_2; that is,

17 $$\|\mathbf{B}^{-1}(t)\|_1 \leq M_2 < \infty \qquad \forall t$$

Then, system *1* is stable b.i.b.o. if and only if there are positive constants M_3 and M_4 such that

18 $$\|\mathbf{\Phi}(t,t_0)\|_1 \leq M_3 e^{-M_4(t-t_0)} \qquad \forall t_0,\ \forall t \geq t_0$$

Proof $\Leftarrow$ The response of the system to $\mathbf{u}_{[t_0,\infty)}$ starting from the state $\mathbf{x}_0$ at t_0 is given by *9*. As above, *9* implies *10*. If we call M the bound on the input $\mathbf{u}$, then by *16*, *18*, and the properties of the norm (see *C.16.10* and *C.16.13*), we get

$$\|\mathbf{x}(t;\mathbf{x}_0,t_0;\mathbf{u}_{[t_0\infty)})\|_1 \leq M_3\|\mathbf{x}_0\|_1 + \int_{t_0}^{t} M_3 e^{-M_4(t'-t_0)} M_1 M \, dt'$$

In order to get an upper bound on the right-hand side, let us replace the upper limit of integration by ∞; then an elementary integration gives

$$\|\mathbf{x}(t;\mathbf{x}_0,t_0;\mathbf{u}_{[t_0,\infty)})\|_1 \leq M_3\|\mathbf{x}_0\| + \frac{M_1 M_3 M}{M_4} \qquad \forall t \geq t_0$$

The right-hand side is a constant independent of t_0 which plays the role of the constant K which was used in the definition of stability b.i.b.o. (see *2*). Therefore, *18* implies stability b.i.b.o.

$\Rightarrow$ The second part of the proof consists of two steps: First we use the assumed stability b.i.b.o. and the assumed properties of $\mathbf{B}(t)$ to prove inequality *22* below; next, using techniques due to Kalman, we show that *19*, which is a consequence of the stability b.i.b.o., and *22* together with the group property of the state transition matrix (see *6.2.16*) imply *18*.

By assumption the system is stable b.i.b.o. Therefore, by Theorem *3*, there is a constant M_5 such that

19 $$\|\mathbf{\Phi}(t,t_0)\|_1 \leq M_5 < \infty \qquad \forall t_0,\ \forall t \geq t_0$$

Now, for any pair t, t_0 with $t \geq t_0$, let us consider the zero-state response of *1*. By Theorem *3*, the stability b.i.b.o. of *1* implies that for some constant M_6,

20 $$\int_{t_0}^{t} \|\mathbf{\Phi}(t,t')\mathbf{B}(t')\mathbf{u}(t')\|_1\, dt' \leq M_6 < \infty \qquad \forall t_0,\ \forall t \geq t_0$$

For all t', $\mathbf{B}(t')$ is an $n \times n$ nonsingular matrix which, by *17*, has a bounded inverse. Therefore, for any integer j, we can find a control $\mathbf{u}(t')$ such that $\|\mathbf{u}(t')\|_1 = M$ and such that the vector $\mathbf{B}(t')\mathbf{u}(t')$ has all its components equal to zero except the jth component. Call this jth component $b_j(t')$. Furthermore, by *17*, we have

$$|b_j(t')| \geq \|\mathbf{u}\|_1\, \|\mathbf{B}^{-1}\|_1^{-1} \geq MM_2^{-1}$$

Now, for that $\mathbf{u}$,

21 $$\|\mathbf{\Phi}(t,t')\mathbf{B}(t')\mathbf{u}(t')\|_1 = \sum_k |\phi_{kj}(t,t')b_j(t')| \geq |\phi_{kj}(t,t')|MM_2^{-1}$$

Clearly, this inequality holds for all $k,j = 1, 2, \ldots, n$. Since $\|\mathbf{\Phi}(t,t_0)\|_1 = \max_j \sum_k |\phi_{kj}(t,t_0)|$ (see *C.16.17*), we obtain from *20* and *21*

22 $$\int_{t_0}^{t} \|\mathbf{\Phi}(t,t')\|_1\, dt' \leq M_7 < \infty \qquad \forall t_0,\ \forall t \geq t_0$$

where M_7 can be taken to be nM_2M_6/M.

Now from *19* and *22* we have

$$\begin{aligned}\infty > M_5M_7 &\geq \int_{t_0}^{t} \|\mathbf{\Phi}(t,t')\|_1\, \|\mathbf{\Phi}(t',t_0)\|_1\, dt' \\ &\geq \int_{t_0}^{t} \|\mathbf{\Phi}(t,t')\mathbf{\Phi}(t',t_0)\|_1\, dt' \geq \int_{t_0}^{t} \|\Phi(t,t_0)\|_1\, dt'\end{aligned}$$

where we have used the properties of the norm and the group property of the state transition matrix. Thus, finally,

$$\|\mathbf{\Phi}(t,t_0)\|_1 \leq \frac{M_5 M_7}{t - t_0} \qquad \forall t_0, \forall t \geq t_0$$

Let us now define the time T by the condition

$$\frac{M_5 M_7}{T} = \frac{1}{2}$$

Consequently,

23 $$\|\mathbf{\Phi}(t_0 + T, t_0)\|_1 \leq \tfrac{1}{2} \qquad \forall t_0$$

By the group property of the state transition matrix, the properties of the norm, and *23*, we have

$$\|\mathbf{\Phi}(t_0 + kT, t_0)\|_1 = \|\mathbf{\Phi}(t_0 + kT, t_0 + (k-1)T) \cdots \mathbf{\Phi}(t_0 + T, t_0)\|_1$$
$$\leq 2^{-k} \qquad \forall \text{ integers } k > 0, \forall t_0$$

Consider an arbitrary $t \geq t_0$; let k be the largest integer in $(t - t_0)/T$; define τ by $t = t_0 + kT + \tau$. (By the definition of k, $0 \leq \tau < T$.) Using successively the group property of the state transition matrix, the properties of the norm *19*, and the above inequality we get

24 $$\begin{aligned} \|\mathbf{\Phi}(t,t_0)\|_1 &= \|\mathbf{\Phi}(t_0 + kT + \tau, \|t_0 + kT)\mathbf{\Phi}(t_0 + kT, \|t_0)\|_1 \\ &\leq \|\mathbf{\Phi}(t_0 + kT + \tau, \|t_0 + kT)\|_1 \quad \|\mathbf{\Phi}(t_0 + kT, \|t_0)\|_1 \\ &\leq \frac{M_5}{2^k} \end{aligned}$$

where k is the largest integer in $(t - t_0)/T$.

This inequality has the following interpretation which is valid for all t_0: the scalar $\|\mathbf{\Phi}(t,t_0)\|_1$ (considered as a function of t) is bounded by M_5 over $[t_0, t_0 + T]$; by *24*, the same scalar is bounded by $M_5/2$ over $[t_0 + T, t_0 + 2T]$; more generally, for any positive integer k, that scalar is bounded by $M_5/2^k$ over $[t_0 + (k-1)T, t_0 + kT]$. Therefore if we define the positive number M_9 by $e^{-M_9 T} = \frac{1}{2}$ we have

$$\|\mathbf{\Phi}(t,t_0)\|_1 \leq M_5 e^{-M_9(t - t_0 - T)} \qquad \forall t_0, \forall t \geq t_0$$

This last inequality is of the same form as *18*. ◁

Let us now establish a connection between the concepts of stability based on the properties of the zero-input response (free motion) and those based on the input-output relationship. For this purpose we shall need a stability concept slightly more restrictive than those specified by *7.2.2* and *7.2.3*.

25 **Definition** The linear system $\dot{\mathbf{x}} = \mathbf{A}(t)\mathbf{x}$ is said to be *uniformly asymptotically stable* if (I) the system is uniformly stable i.s.L. and (II) for any fixed R, however large, $\|\mathbf{x}_0\| < R$ implies that $\mathbf{x}(t;\mathbf{x}_0,t_0) \to \mathbf{0}$ as $t \to \infty$, uniformly in t_0. ◁

More precisely, the conditions are: (I) for any $\varepsilon > 0$, there is a $\delta > 0$, independent of t_0, such that $\|\mathbf{x}_0\| \leq \delta \Rightarrow \|\mathbf{x}(t;\mathbf{x}_0,t_0)\| < \varepsilon$ $\forall t \geq t_0$, $\forall t_0$; and (II) for any $R > 0$ and any $\eta > 0$, there is a T, independent of t_0 (but which may depend on R and η), such that

$$\|\mathbf{x}_0\| \leq R \Rightarrow \|\mathbf{x}(t;\mathbf{x}_0,t_0)\| < \eta \qquad \forall t > t_0 + T, \forall t_0$$

26 *Comment* Since the system is linear, the uniform stability implies that any free motion is uniformly bounded. If we were to define the uniform asymptotic stability of the zero state for a nonlinear system, we would have to add the requirement that any free motion be uniformly bounded because, in the case of nonlinear systems, uniform stability of the zero state has only purely local implications (see Remark *7.2.6*).

27 *Comment* Let us exhibit an implication of the uniform asymptotic stability defined in *25*. Let us use l_1 norms and pick $R = 1$ and $\eta = \frac{1}{2}$. Since $\mathbf{x}(t;\mathbf{x}_0,t_0) = \mathbf{\Phi}(t,t_0)\mathbf{x}_0$, it follows from Definition *25* and from the definition of the norm of an L.T. that there exists a T', independent of t_0, such that

28 $$\|\mathbf{\Phi}(t_0 + T', t_0)\|_1 \leq \tfrac{1}{2} \qquad \forall t_0$$

As a first step, let us establish a preliminary

29 **Assertion** The linear system $\dot{\mathbf{x}} = \mathbf{A}(t)\mathbf{x}$ is uniformly asymptotically stable if and only if there exist two positive constants K_1 and K_2 such that

30 $$\|\mathbf{\Phi}(t,t_0)\|_1 \leq K_1 e^{-K_2(t-t_0)} \qquad \forall t \geq t_0, \forall t_0$$

Proof $\Rightarrow$ Uniform asymptotic stability implies uniform stability; hence, if we let $K_1 \triangleq \delta/\varepsilon$ and if, as in Comment *27*, we use l_1 norms, we get

$$\|\mathbf{\Phi}(t,t_0)\|_1 \leq K_1 \qquad \forall t \geq t_0, \forall t_0$$

Furthermore, uniform asymptotic stability implies *28*; hence by the last steps of the proof of Theorem *15*, *30* follows.

$\Leftarrow$ Follows immediately from *30* and $\mathbf{x}(t;\mathbf{x}_0,t_0) = \mathbf{\Phi}(t,t_0)\mathbf{x}_0$. ◁

If now we combine the equivalences established by Theorem *15* and by Assertion *29*, we obtain the

31 **Theorem** Consider the linear system *1*, where the input $\mathbf{u}$ and the output $\mathbf{x}$ are both n-vectors. Let the matrices $\mathbf{A}(t)$ and $\mathbf{B}(t)$ be continuous and bounded for all t. Let us assume that *16* and *17* hold. Then, the linear system *1* is stable b.i.b.o. if and only if it is uniformly asymptotically stable.

REFERENCES AND SUGGESTED READING

1 Bellman, R.: "Stability Theory of Differential Equations," McGraw-Hill Book Company, Inc., New York, 1953.

2 Cesari, L.: "Asymptotic Behavior and Stability Problems in Ordinary Differential Equations," Springer Verlag OHG, Berlin, 1959.

3 Hahn, W.: "Theory and Application of the Direct Method of Lyapunov," Springer Verlag OHG, Berlin, 1959.

4 Kalman, R. E., and J. E. Bertram: Control System Analysis and Design via the Second Method of Lyapunov, *Trans. A.S.M.E., J. Basic Engrg.*, vol. 82, series D, 2, pp. 371–400, 1960.

5 LaSalle, J., and S. Lefschetz: "Stability by Lyapunov's Direct Method with Applications," Academic Press, Inc., New York, 1961.

6 Lefschetz, S.: "Differential Equations: Geometric Theory," Interscience Publishers, Inc., New York, 1957.

7 Sansone, G., and R. Conti: "Equazioni Differenziali Nonlineari," Edizioni Cremonese, Rome, 1956.

8 Bridgland, T. F., Jr.: Stability of Linear Transmission Systems, *Soc. Indust. Appl. Math. Rev.*, vol. 5, no. 1, pp. 7–32, 1963.

Impulse response of nondifferential linear systems

8

1 *Introduction*

In the preceding three chapters we have studied in detail the properties of both the zero-input and the zero-state response of linear, not necessarily time-invariant, differential systems. As was stated in Chap. 3 (*3.6.5*), the zero-state response of any nondifferential[1] nonanticipative linear system admits of the representation $\int_{t_0}^{t} h(t,\xi)u(\xi)\, d\xi$, where the impulse response $h(t,\xi)$ denotes the zero-state response of the system at time t to a unit impulse $\delta(t - \xi)$ applied at time ξ. In the case of an anticipative system (*1.8.13*), $h(t,\xi)$ does not vanish identically for $t < \xi$, as it does in the case of a nonanticipative system, and hence the expression for the zero-state response to $u \triangleq u_{(t_0,t]}$ must in general be written as $\int_{-\infty}^{+\infty} h(t,\xi)u(\xi)\, d\xi$.

Although the impulse response describes only the zero-state response of a system and hence can be used only to define the system to within zero-state equivalence, it is of considerable practical importance for a number of reasons. In the first place, in the case of nondifferential systems, the state space is, usually, infinite-dimensional and as a consequence it is usually much more difficult to characterize the system zero-input response than the zero-state response. [Among familiar examples of such systems are the ideal low-pass filter (see Chap. *9*, Sec. *5*), circuits containing transmission lines, ideal delay lines and wave guides, and control systems with transportation lags. In this connection it should be recalled that any nondifferential system whose impulse response is a reasonably well-behaved function of t and ξ can be approximated arbitrarily closely—in the sense of zero-state equivalence—by a differential system of sufficiently high order.

[1] The term "nondifferential" is used here in its wide sense to describe a system which is *not necessarily* differential, rather than one which is *not* differential. See *3.8.26* for the definition of a differential system.

See *9.16.2* for a more detailed discussion of this type of approximation in the case of time-invariant systems.] In the second place, there are many practical situations where the only data available about a system are measurements of its transfer function or its impulse response. (Knowing the impulse response, it is a routine matter to compute the transfer function, and vice versa, with the aid of a digital computer.) Frequently the impulse response is the only datum we are interested in because the rapid decay with time of the zero-input response makes its effect quite negligible in the analysis of many problems.

This is the motivation for focusing our attention in this chapter on those properties of nondifferential linear systems which involve only their impulse response. For simplicity, we shall restrict our attention to single-input single-output systems, since it is an easy matter to extend most of the results obtained under this assumption to multiple-input multiple-output systems.

In the following section, we consider the impulse response of the tandem connection of two time-varying systems $\mathcal{A}$ and $\mathcal{B}$ and show that, in general, $\mathcal{AB}$ is not zero-state equivalent to $\mathcal{BA}$. In Sec. *3*, we introduce a general definition of the adjoint of systems defined by their impulse response and show that it reduces to the conventional definition in the case of differential systems. In Sec. *4*, the problem of stability is met: Since the impulse response characterizes the system only as far as its zero-state response is concerned and since we do not have a state description of the system, we can define a stability only in terms of the zero-state response of the system to the class of all bounded inputs. Finally, an example shows that there is no simple relationship between this concept of stability and the concepts based on the state concept.

2 *Systems in tandem*

Consider two linear systems $\mathcal{A}$ and $\mathcal{B}$. Suppose that the only data available concerning the systems $\mathcal{A}$ and $\mathcal{B}$ are their respective impulse responses h_A and h_B. As in *1.10.23*, we denote by $\mathcal{BA}$ the tandem connection of $\mathcal{A}$ and $\mathcal{B}$, with $\mathcal{A}$ preceding $\mathcal{B}$; thus $\mathcal{BA}$ is the overall system obtained by connecting the output of $\mathcal{A}$ to the input of $\mathcal{B}$ (see Fig. *8.2.1*). Using the notation of the figure, the zero-state

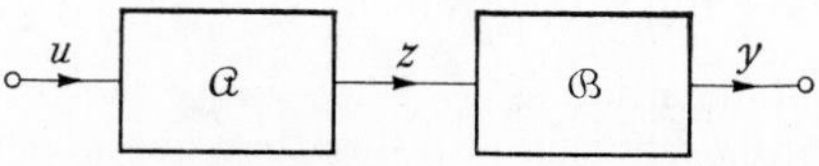

Fig. 8.2.1 The system $\mathcal{BA}$, the tandem connection of $\mathcal{A}$ preceding $\mathcal{B}$.

response of these systems is given by

1 $$z(t) = \int_{-\infty}^{+\infty} h_A(t,\xi)u(\xi)\,d\xi$$

2 $$y(t) = \int_{-\infty}^{+\infty} h_B(t,\eta)z(\eta)\,d\eta$$

Let us eliminate z between *1* and *2* and interchange the order of integration;[1] we thereby obtain

3 $$y(t) = \int_{-\infty}^{+\infty} \left[\int_{-\infty}^{+\infty} h_B(t,\eta)h_A(\eta,\xi)\,d\eta\right] \mu(\xi)\,d\xi$$

The bracketed term, which is a function of t and ξ, is the weighting function which relates the zero-state response of $\mathcal{B}\mathcal{A}$ to its input u; it is therefore the impulse response of $\mathcal{B}\mathcal{A}$. We can therefore state the

4 **Assertion** The tandem connection $\mathcal{B}\mathcal{A}$ (where $\mathcal{A}$ precedes $\mathcal{B}$) has an impulse response given by

5 $$h_{BA}(t,\xi) = \int_{-\infty}^{+\infty} h_B(t,\eta)h_A(\eta,\xi)\,d\eta$$

In the time-invariant case, *5* reduces to a convolution

$$h_{BA}(t-\xi) = \int_{-\infty}^{+\infty} h_B(t-\eta)h_A(\eta-\xi)\,d\eta$$

as can easily be seen by putting $t - \xi = \tau$ and $\eta - \xi \to \xi$; thus $h_{BA} = h_B * h_A$, where the $*$ denotes the operation of convolution (see *B.3.8*). From this relation (or also from its Laplace transform $H_{BA} = H_B H_A$) we immediately have $h_{BA} = h_{AB}$. Hence we state the

6 **Corollary** If $\mathcal{A}$ and $\mathcal{B}$ are time-invariant, the tandem connections $\mathcal{B}\mathcal{A}$ and $\mathcal{A}\mathcal{B}$ are zero-state equivalent:

$$\mathcal{A}\mathcal{B} \doteq \mathcal{B}\mathcal{A}$$

7 **Remark** For the time-varying case, $\mathcal{A}\mathcal{B}$ is not zero-state equivalent to $\mathcal{B}\mathcal{A}$. Consider the following example. Let

$\mathcal{A}$: $u \to z$ $\qquad z(t) = p\,u(t)$

$\mathcal{B}$: $v \to y$ $\qquad y = tv$

where the notation $u \to z$ indicates that u is the input and that z is the zero-state response due to u. Because we restrict ourselves to zero-state response, $\mathcal{A}$ defines a function which maps every u of the input function space into one and only one zero-state response z. Similarly, $\mathcal{B}$ maps the input v into the output y.

[1] The interchange of the order of integrations is not always permissible. Conditions under which the order of integration may be changed can be found in T. M. Apostol, "Mathematical Analysis," p. 448, Addison-Wesley Publishing Company, Inc., Reading, Mass., 1957.

The system $\mathcal{BA}$ (where $\mathcal{A}$ precedes $\mathcal{B}$) is characterized by

$$y_{BA} = t\,p\,u$$

whereas the system $\mathcal{AB}$ is characterized by

$$y_{AB} = p\,(tu) = u + t\,p\,u$$

8 *Exercise* Let $\mathcal{A}$ be time-varying and

$$h_A(t,\xi) = 1(t - \xi)(2 + \cos t) \exp\,[-(t - \xi)]$$

Let $\mathcal{B}$ be time-invariant and $h_B(t,\xi) = 1(t - \xi) - 1(t - \xi - 2)$. Show that $\mathcal{AB}$ and $\mathcal{BA}$ are not zero-state equivalent.

3 *Adjoint systems*

In this section we wish to develop the concept of the adjoint system of a linear system. This is an extension of the concept of the adjoint of a system of differential equations, which was introduced in *6.2.27* and *6.2.53*. The first step, however, is to introduce the idea of the zero-state inverse by the definition (compare with *2.10.6*):

1 **Definition** The system $\mathcal{A}^{-1}$ is said to be the *zero-state inverse* of the linear system $\mathcal{A}$ if, for all ξ, the zero-state response of $\mathcal{A}^{-1}\mathcal{A}$ and that of $\mathcal{A}\mathcal{A}^{-1}$ to a unit impulse applied at ξ are $\delta(t - \xi)$.

2 *Comment* Intuitively, we think of $\mathcal{A}^{-1}$ as canceling out the effect of $\mathcal{A}$: the system $\mathcal{A}$ spreads out the unit impulse along the time axis and $\mathcal{A}^{-1}$ reconcentrates the resulting output into a delta function. In practice, the concept of zero-state inverse is applied within an approximation for the following reason: The impulse response $h_A(t,\xi)$ of a nonanticipative system $\mathcal{A}$ usually differs from zero for $t > \xi$, that is, after the application of the impulse; thus the definition of the zero-state inverse requires $\mathcal{A}^{-1}$ to respond at time ξ to inputs which will be applied to $\mathcal{A}^{-1}$ at times later than ξ. In other words, if $\mathcal{A}$ is nonanticipative and if $h_A(t,\xi) \neq 0$ for some $t > \xi$, then $\mathcal{A}^{-1}$ will, in general, be anticipative and hence not physically realizable.[1] In practice, one builds systems that are approximately zero-state inverses of one another in the sense that the output of the tandem connection is a delayed delta function. For example, in amplitude-modulation communication systems any equalization network is, in this sense, the

[1] $\mathcal{A}^{-1}$ need not always be anticipative. For example, let $\mathcal{A}$ have $1/(s + 1)$ as a transfer function; then its zero-state inverse has $s + 1$ as a transfer function and $\delta^{(1)} + \delta$ as an impulse response. On the other hand, if $\mathcal{A}$ is an *RLC* circuit which contains delay lines, $\mathcal{A}^{-1}$ will then necessarily be anticipative, except, of course, for some trivial cases.

approximate zero-state inverse of that part of the system which requires equalization. Similarly, in a chirp radar system, the transmitter spreads out the radar pulse in time and the receiver is designed to reconcentrate it into a sharp pulse, ideally, a delta function.

3 **Remark** Definition *1* requires justification in that it is not a priori obvious (see *2.10.20*) that the same system $\mathcal{A}^{-1}$ may be connected either before $\mathcal{A}$ or after $\mathcal{A}$ and that the two resulting tandem connections are zero-state equivalent. Suppose that we have two linear systems $\mathcal{A}_R^{-1}$, $\mathcal{A}_L^{-1}$ such that $\mathcal{A}\mathcal{A}_R^{-1}$ ($\mathcal{A}_R^{-1}$ preceding $\mathcal{A}$) and $\mathcal{A}_L^{-1}\mathcal{A}$ ($\mathcal{A}$ preceding $\mathcal{A}_L^{-1}$) are zero-state equivalent to the identity operator. Consider then the tandem connections $\mathcal{A}_L^{-1}\mathcal{A}\mathcal{A}_R^{-1}$ (that is, $\mathcal{A}_R^{-1}$ precedes $\mathcal{A}$, which itself precedes $\mathcal{A}_L^{-1}$). Combine $\mathcal{A}$ and $\mathcal{A}_R^{-1}$; by definition this tandem connection is zero-state equivalent to the identity operator; hence $\mathcal{A}_L^{-1}\mathcal{A}\mathcal{A}_R^{-1}$ is zero-state equivalent to $\mathcal{A}_L^{-1}$. Similarly, by combining $\mathcal{A}_L^{-1}$ and $\mathcal{A}$ we can show that $\mathcal{A}_L^{-1}\mathcal{A}\mathcal{A}_R^{-1}$ is zero-state equivalent to $\mathcal{A}_R^{-1}$. Consequently, $\mathcal{A}_L^{-1}$ and $\mathcal{A}_R^{-1}$ are zero-state equivalent to one another. Another way of expressing this fact is to say that any left inverse of $\mathcal{A}$ (such as $\mathcal{A}_L^{-1}$) is necessarily zero-state equivalent to any right inverse of $\mathcal{A}$ (such as $\mathcal{A}_R^{-1}$).

4 *Exercise* Let $h(t,\xi)$ and $g(t,\xi)$ be respectively the impulse responses of a linear system $\mathcal{A}$ and its zero-state inverse $\mathcal{A}^{-1}$. Show that

$$\int_{-\infty}^{+\infty} g(t,\eta)h(\eta,\xi)\,d\eta = \delta(t-\xi) \qquad \forall t, \forall \xi$$

where the integral must be interpreted formally (see Appendix *A*). ◁

We now turn to the general definition of adjoint systems. In *6.2.27* we defined the adjoint of a set of differential equations. Using that definition, one could define the adjoint of a system. Such a definition would necessarily be restricted to differential systems. We shall introduce a definition of adjoint systems that is applicable to a much broader class of systems, namely, those characterized by their impulse response. We shall show that this more general definition reduces to the previous one for differential systems.

5 **Definition** Let the linear system $\mathcal{A}$ have a real-valued impulse response $h(t,\xi)$. The linear system $\mathcal{A}^{(a)}$ is said to be the *adjoint* of $\mathcal{A}$ if its impulse response $h^{(a)}(t,\xi)$ satisfies the relation

6
$$h^{(a)}(t,\xi) = h(\xi,t) \qquad \forall t, \forall \xi$$

where $h^{(a)}(t,\xi)$ is the response of $\mathcal{A}^a$ at time t to a unit impulse applied at time ξ. Thus *6* implies that $\mathcal{A}^{(a)}$ has a response at time t to a unit impulse applied at ξ equal to the response of $\mathcal{A}$ at time ξ to a unit impulse applied at time t. This definition implies that if $\mathcal{A}$ is nonanticipative [that is, $h(t,\xi) = 0$ for all $t < \xi$], then $\mathcal{A}^a$ is purely anticipative [that is, $h^{(a)}(t,\xi) = 0$ for all $t > \xi$.]

7 **Theorem** For any linear system, the zero-state inverse of its adjoint is zero-state equivalent to the adjoint of its zero-state inverse. Symbolically,

$$(\mathcal{A}^{(a)})^{-1} \doteq (\mathcal{A}^{-1})^{(a)}$$

Proof Let $h(t,\xi)$ and $g(t,\xi)$ be respectively the impulse response of $\mathcal{A}$ and that of $\mathcal{A}^{-1}$. Let us use the superscript (a) to denote the impulse responses of the adjoints. From the definition of inverse systems and *4* we have

$$\int_{-\infty}^{+\infty} h(\eta,\xi)g(t,\eta)\,d\eta = \delta(t-\xi) \qquad \forall t, \forall \xi$$

Using the defining relation *6* between $h^{(a)}$, $g^{(a)}$ and h, g, we get

$$\int_{-\infty}^{+\infty} h^{(a)}(\xi,\eta)g^{(a)}(\eta,t)\,d\eta = \delta(t-\xi) \qquad \forall t, \forall \xi$$

Interchanging t and ξ and observing that the delta function is unchanged, we get

$$\int_{-\infty}^{+\infty} h^{(a)}(t,\eta)g^{(a)}(\eta,\xi)\,d\eta = \delta(t-\xi) \qquad \forall t, \forall \xi$$

From *4*, this relation expresses the fact that $(\mathcal{A}^{-1})^{(a)}$ is the zero-state inverse of $\mathcal{A}^{(a)}$. ◁

As a first step in establishing the equivalence of the definitions of adjoint systems, consider a system $\mathcal{A}$ with input u and output y. Let its equation be

8 $\mathcal{A}: \; u \to y \qquad\qquad L(p,t)u = y$

with

9 $$L(p,t) \triangleq \sum_{k=0}^{n} a_{n-k}(t)\,p^k$$

where $a_{n-k} \in C^k$, for $k = 0, 1, \ldots, n$. The impulse response of $\mathcal{A}$ is obviously

$$h(t,\xi) = \sum_{k=0}^{n} a_{n-k}(t)\delta^{(k)}(t-\xi)$$

where $\delta^{(k)}$ is the kth derivative of δ (see *A.2.5* and *A.5.4*). By Definition *5* the impulse response of the adjoint system $\mathcal{A}^{(a)}$ is given by

$$h^{(a)}(t,\xi) = \sum_{k=0}^{n} a_{n-k}(\xi)\delta^{(k)}(\xi - t)$$

Let z be the zero-state response of $\mathcal{A}^{(a)}$ to an input r; then

$$\begin{aligned} z(t) &= \int_{-\infty}^{+\infty} h^{(a)}(t,\xi)r(\xi)\,d\xi \\ &= \sum_{k=0}^{n} \int_{-\infty}^{+\infty} \delta^{(k)}(\xi - t)a_{n-k}(\xi)r(\xi)\,d\xi \\ &= \sum_{k=0}^{n} (-1)^k p^k\,(a_{n-k}(t)r(t)) \end{aligned}$$

where we used *A.2.11*. Thus, the output z of $\mathcal{A}^{(a)}$ may be obtained by operating on the input r by the differential operator L^*:

10 $\mathcal{A}^{(a)}\colon\ r \to z \qquad L^*(p,t)r = z$

where

11 $$L^*(p,t)r = \sum_{k=0}^{n} (-1)^k p^k\,(a_{n-k}(t)r)$$

Observe that the differential operator L^* is the adjoint of the differential operator L (see *6.2.53*).

Consider now the systems $\mathcal{A}^{-1}$ and $(\mathcal{A}^{(a)})^{-1}$, where $\mathcal{A}$ is defined by *8*. Let y be the input of $\mathcal{A}^{-1}$ and u its output. Then $\mathcal{A}^{-1}$ is characterized by (see Chap. *4*, Secs. *3* and *4*)

12 $\mathcal{A}^{-1}\colon\ y \to u \qquad L(p,t)u = y$

This result applied to the adjoint system $\mathcal{A}^{(a)}$ gives the following characterization for its inverse:

13 $(\mathcal{A}^{(a)})^{-1}\colon\ y \to v \qquad L^*(p,t)v = y$

Thus by Theorem *7*, the adjoint of the system *12* is the system *13*, where $L(p,t)$ and $L^*(p,t)$ are respectively given by *9* and *11*.

It is important to observe that in the system interpretation of the systems *12* and *13*, the system *12* in nonanticipative, whereas the system *13* is purely anticipative.

Finally, observing that this result coincides with that of *6.2.53*, we conclude with the

14 **Assertion** The general definition *5* of an adjoint system reduces to the usual one of *6.2.53* when applied to systems described by

$\mathcal{A}\colon\ u \to y \qquad L(p,t)y = u$

4 *Zero-state stability*

In Chap. *7*, which was devoted to a detailed study of the stability of differential systems, three concepts of stability were introduced. Stability in the sense of Lyapunov and asymptotic stability are concepts which put restrictions on the motion of the *state* when the input is identically zero. The third concept, that of stability b.i.b.o., puts restrictions on the motion of the *state*, but the initial state is arbitrary and the input is only required to be bounded. The systems that we are considering in this chapter are specified only by their impulse response, so that we can only define a concept of stability which imposes restrictions on the *zero-state response* of the system. We shall require that the zero-state response remain bounded for all possible bounded inputs. For that reason we shall use the abbreviation b.i.b.o. We introduce the

1 **Definition** A linear system is said to be *zero-state stable* (*b.i.b.o.*) if its zero-state response to any bounded input u is bounded. ◁

To formulate this definition more precisely, let $A(t;\mathbf{\theta};u)$ be the zero-state response, at time t, of the system $\mathcal{A}$ to the input u. We do not write $u_{[t_0,\infty)}$, because we do not want to assume that the input was applied at some finite time t_0. With this notation the definition becomes

2 **Definition** $\mathcal{A}$ is said to be zero-state stable (b.i.b.o.) if and only if, for any input u such that $|u(t)| \leq M$, $\forall t \in (-\infty, \infty)$ and for some finite M, there is another constant M_0 (which depends on M) such that

3 $$|A(t;\mathbf{\theta};u)| \leq M_0 < \infty \qquad \forall t \in (-\infty, \infty)$$

4 *Comment* Whereas all the definitions of stability given in Chap. *7* apply only to differential systems which are nonanticipative, the present definition applies to anticipative systems just as well as to purely nonanticipative systems (see *1.8.13*).

5 *Exercise* Suppose the system is time-invariant and is defined by $h(t) = 1(t+1) - 1(t-1)$. Show that Definition *1* implies that it is zero-state stable b.i.b.o. In fact, show that M_0 can be taken to be $2M$.

6 *Exercise* Suppose again that the system is time-invariant and that $h(t) = 1(t) \cos \omega_0 t$. Show that it is not zero-state stable b.i.b.o. [*Hint:* Consider the input $1(t) \cos \omega_0 t$.]

Zero-state stable systems are characterized by the

7 **Theorem** Let $h(t,\xi)$ be the impulse response of the system $\mathcal{A}$. Then, $\mathcal{A}$ is zero-state stable b.i.b.o. if and only if there is a finite constant N such that

8 $$\int_{-\infty}^{+\infty} |h(t,\xi)|\, d\xi \leq N \qquad \forall t \in (-\infty,\infty)$$

Proof $\Leftarrow$ Consider an arbitrary bounded input u such that $|u(t)| < M$ for all $t \in (-\infty,\infty)$. The zero-state response of $\mathcal{A}$ to u is given by (see *3.6.3*)

9 $$A(t;\boldsymbol{\theta};u) = \int_{-\infty}^{+\infty} h(t,\xi)u(\xi)\, d\xi$$

We then obtain successively

$$|A(t;\boldsymbol{\theta};u)| \leq \int_{-\infty}^{+\infty} |h(t,\xi)u(\xi)|\, d\xi$$
$$< M \int_{-\infty}^{+\infty} |h(t,\xi)|\, d\xi$$

and, by *8*,

$$|A(t;\boldsymbol{\theta};u)| < MN \qquad \text{for all } t \in (-\infty,\infty)$$

Thus any bounded input u produces a zero-state response which is bounded for all t; hence $\mathcal{A}$ is zero-state stable b.i.b.o.

$\Rightarrow$ Let us start by an observation: the integral *8* defines a real-valued function f of t on $(-\infty,\infty)$. Now $\sup_{-\infty<t<\infty} |f(t)|$ is either finite or infinite.[1] If it is finite, we can take the supremum as the value for the constant N in *8*. The supremum is infinite if and only if the inequality *8* cannot hold for any finite N.

Thus for the purpose of a proof by contradiction, we assume that the system is zero-state stable b.i.b.o. and that *8* cannot hold for any finite N. In other words, we assume that

$$\sup_{-\infty<t<\infty} |f(t)| = \sup_{-\infty<t<\infty} \int_{-\infty}^{+\infty} |h(t,\tau)|\, d\tau = \infty$$

By definition of the supremum, it follows that given any positive M, however large, we can find a t_M in $(-\infty,\infty)$ such that

$$f(t_M) = \int_{-\infty}^{\infty} |h(t_M,\tau)|\, d\tau > M$$

To these numbers M and t_M, we associate a bounded input x_M defined by

$$x_M(\tau) = \operatorname{sgn} h(t_M,\tau) \qquad \forall \tau \in (-\infty,\infty)$$

[1] The supremum (abbreviated sup) of $|f(t)|$ on $(-\infty,\infty)$ is an upper bound b such that $b \geq |f(t)|$ for all t in $(-\infty,\infty)$ and such that no smaller number has the same property. Until recently, the supremum was called the least upper bound (abbreviated l.u.b.).

Then, by *8*, the output due to this input has the property that

$$y(t_M) > M$$

Therefore, we have shown that if the inequality *8* is not satisfied by any finite N, then, given any positive M, however large, we can construct a bounded input which will produce at a certain finite time t_M an output $y(t_M)$ which is larger than the given M. This clearly contradicts the assumption of stability b.i.b.o., which requires that any bounded input produce a bounded zero-state response.

10 *Example* Consider an infinite RC cable. Its input is a current source and its output is the voltage across the input terminals. It is well known that $h(t) = \sqrt{\frac{R}{\pi C t}}\, 1(t)$. Therefore, even though this system consists of a linear time-invariant dissipative network, it is not stable b.i.b.o., since the response to a unit step of current is a monotonically increasing voltage which tends to infinity as time increases indefinitely.

In some cases the concept of stability b.i.b.o. can easily be related to the concepts of stability introduced in Chap. *7*. For example, we have the

11 **Assertion** Let $\mathcal{A}$ be a linear time-invariant system characterized by the differential equation $L(p)y = u$. Then the following statements are equivalent:

(I) $\mathcal{A}$ is asymptotically stable (see *7.2.3*).
(II) The zeros of the polynomial $L(s)$ have negative (<0) real parts.
(III) The system $\mathcal{A}$ is zero-state stable b.i.b.o. (see *2*).

Proof Exercise for the reader.

12 *Comment* In the time-invariant case, the system

$$\dot{\mathbf{x}} = \mathbf{Ax} + \mathbf{Bu} \qquad \mathbf{y} = \mathbf{Cx} + \mathbf{Du}$$

may be zero-state stable b.i.b.o. but not stable i.s.L. This fact becomes obvious if the system has an unstable mode and either the input is not coupled to that mode or that mode is not coupled to the output. A further discussion of these points will be given in Chap. *11*, because it requires a thorough definition of the notions of controllability (see *11.3.3*) and observability (see *11.4.1*). ◁

For the case of periodically varying systems we have the

13 **Assertion** Let $\mathcal{P}$ be a periodically varying system described by the differential equation $\dot{\mathbf{x}} = \mathbf{A}(t)\mathbf{x}(t) + \mathbf{u}(t)$, where $\mathbf{A}(t)$ is an $n \times n$ matrix continuous and periodic in t and where the input $\mathbf{u}(t)$ is an n-vector. Then the following statements are equivalent:

(I) The system $\mathcal{P}$ is asymptotically stable (see *7.2.3* and *7.4.8*).

(II) The characteristic exponents of the system have negative (<0) real parts (see *6.7.8*).

(III) The system $\mathcal{P}$ is zero-state stable b.i.b.o.

14 *Comment* For time-invariant systems, zero-state stability b.i.b.o. does not imply that the impulse response is bounded. Consider, for example, $h(t) = (1 - t)^{-1/2}$ for $0 \leq t < 1$ and $h(t) = 0$ for all other t. By *7*, such a system is zero-state stable b.i.b.o., but its impulse response is arbitrarily large as t approaches 1 from the left.

15 *Comment* In general for linear time-varying differential systems there is no simple relationship between zero-state stability b.i.b.o. and the concepts of stability, defined in Chap. *7*, which are based on the motion of the state.[1] The time-varying character of the system introduces an additional possibility which is over and above the problems of controllability and observability. Roughly the additional difficulty is the following. Suppose we have

$$\dot{\mathbf{x}} = \mathbf{A}(t)\mathbf{x} + \mathbf{B}(t)\mathbf{u}(t)$$
$$\mathbf{y}(t) = \mathbf{C}(t)\mathbf{x}(t)$$

where $\mathbf{A}(t)$,$\mathbf{B}(t)$ are bounded and continuous. Suppose the system is not stable i.s.L. and furthermore that, for some $\mathbf{x}_0$, $\|\mathbf{x}(t;\mathbf{x}_0,t_0;\mathbf{0})\| \to \infty$ as $t \to \infty$. Still, the system might be stable b.i.b.o. (see Chap. *7*, Sec. *7*) provided the matrix $\mathbf{C}(t)$ has a norm that decreases so rapidly that even though $\|\mathbf{x}(t;\mathbf{x}_0,t_0;\mathbf{0})\| \to \infty$, $\|\mathbf{C}(t)\mathbf{x}(t;\mathbf{x}_0,t_0,\mathbf{u})\|$ remains bounded for all $t \in [t_0, \infty)$ and for all bounded inputs $\mathbf{u}$. In such circumstances the system would obviously be also zero-state stable b.i.b.o. This idea is illustrated by the following

16 *Example* Consider the single-input single-output time-varying system $\mathcal{S}$ shown in *Fig. 8.4.1*. Calling x_0 the integrator output at time t_0, we

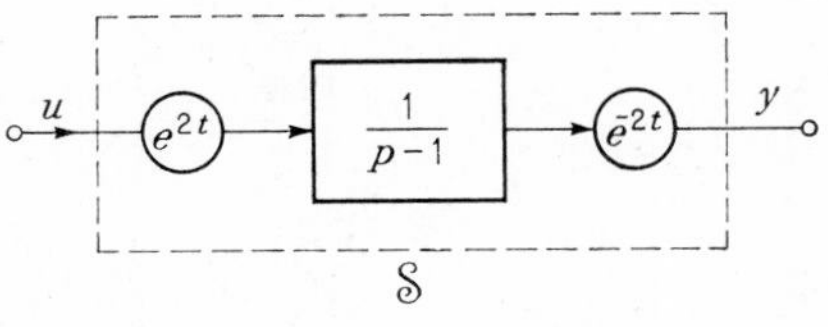

Fig. 8.4.1 System $\mathcal{S}$ considered in Example *8.4.16*.

obviously have

$$\begin{aligned} y(t;x_0,t_0;u_{(t_0,t]}) &= e^{-2t}e^{(t-t_0)}x_0 + e^{-2t}\int_{t_0}^{t} e^{\xi}e^{2(t-\xi)}u(t-\xi)\,d\xi \\ &= e^{-(t-t_0)}(e^{-2t_0}x_0) + \int_{t_0}^{t} e^{-\xi}u(t-\xi)\,d\xi \end{aligned}$$

[1] R. E. Kalman, On the Stability of Time-varying Systems, *I.R.E. Trans. Circuit Theory*, CT-9, no. 4, pp. 420–422, 1962.

The input-output relation of the system $\mathcal{S}$ is then seen to be identical to that of the time-invariant system $\mathcal{S}'$ shown in Fig. *8.4.2*, provided, of course, that the output at time t_0 of the integrator of the system $\mathcal{S}'$ is labeled $e^{-2t_0}x_0$. In other words, $\mathcal{S}$ and $\mathcal{S}'$ are equivalent systems. $\mathcal{S}'$ is stable i.s.L., asymptotically stable, stable b.i.b.o., and zero-state

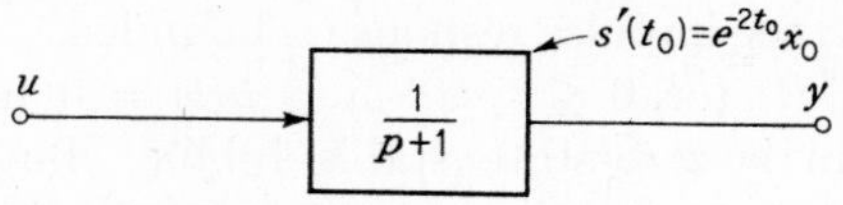

Fig. 8.4.2 The system $\mathcal{S}'$ shown here is equivalent to $\mathcal{S}$ shown in Fig. *8.4.1*.

stable b.i.b.o. On the other hand, $\mathcal{S}'$ is not even stable i.s.L. since

$$x(t;x_0,t_0;0) = e^{(t-t_0)}x_0$$

This concludes our consideration of systems specified by their impulse responses. In the next chapter we investigate in detail the properties of time-invariant systems from the transfer-function point of view.

REFERENCES AND SUGGESTED READING

1 Darlington, S.: Nonstationary Smoothing and Prediction Using Network Theory Concepts, *I.R.E. Trans. Circuit Theory*, vol. CT-6, pp. 1–13, 1959.

2 Laning, J. H., Jr., and R. H. Battin: "Random Processes in Automatic Control," McGraw-Hill Book Company, Inc., New York, 1956.

Transfer functions and their properties

9

1 *Introduction*

In the preceding chapters we have studied in detail the properties of the input-output relationships of linear systems. We now turn our attention to a very important tool in the analysis and design of linear systems: the transfer function. Since the transfer function is used most often in applications involving time-invariant linear systems, this chapter is devoted exclusively to time-invariant systems. From a purely mathematical point of view, the transfer function might be thought to be important because of its use in analyzing time-invariant differential systems and in solving integral equations of the form $y(t) = \int_0^\infty h(t - \xi)u(\xi)\, d\xi$. This point of view is valid as far as it goes, but it hides the main fact: the basic reason for the overwhelming importance of transfer functions is the fundamental theorem of the sinusoidal steady state (*9.4.17*), which states that any strictly stable transfer function can be determined by sinusoidal steady-state measurements. The practical importance of this fact arises from the availability of stable and accurate sinusoidal oscillators and of precise and convenient sinusoidal steady-state measurement equipment and techniques. In practice, it means that extremely complicated systems can be characterized by a number of simple measurements; indeed, in many practical instances, it would be extremely difficult and expensive to write the differential equations of the system under consideration. Consider, for example, a long-distance communications system with its dozens of amplifiers, filters, equalizers, modulators, etc. On the other hand, automatic measurement systems that determine in a few seconds the gain and phase [that is, $|H(j\omega)|$ and $\measuredangle H(j\omega)$] of such systems over a band of frequencies have been built. These facts of life explain why over the last decades engineers have developed so many analysis and synthesis techniques based on the concept of transfer function.

The purpose of this chapter is to present a number of basic properties of the transfer function that are useful for the intelligent application of the design techniques mentioned above. After a brief discussion of the realization of a system whose matrix transfer function is given, we consider the constraints imposed on transfer functions by certain physical characteristics of linear systems: stability, nonanticipative character, relation between the real and imaginary parts, uncertainty principle, dispersion of the impulse response. Next, we present a number of analysis techniques based on transfer functions: paired echoes, asymptotic relations between an impulse response and its transfer function, and the steady-state response to a periodic input. The third objective is to present methods for dealing with the stability problem for both single- and multiple-feedback-loop systems using exclusively data based on sinusoidal steady-state measurements. In order to deal with multiple-loop systems, we shall have to derive Mason's formula for the gain of a flow graph.

2 *Definition and basic relations*

In Chap. *3*, Sec. *6*, the notions of impulse response and transfer function have been defined to characterize the zero-state response of linear systems. In this chapter, we restrict ourselves to time-invariant systems; therefore (see *3.6.9*), the impulse response $h(\cdot)$ is the zero-state response of the system to $\delta(t)$, that is, to a unit impulse applied at $t = 0$. In this chapter we do not restrict ourselves to nonanticipative systems, and therefore it may happen that $h(t) \neq 0$ for some $t < 0$. For this reason, we introduce the following

1 **Definition** Let the system $\mathcal{A}$ be linear and time-invariant and let $h(\cdot)$ be its impulse response (*3.6.5*). Assume that h is Laplace transformable (unilateral transform if $\mathcal{A}$ is nonanticipative and bilateral if not). The relation

2 $$H(s) \triangleq \int_{-\infty}^{+\infty} e^{-st}h(t)\,dt$$

defines the *transfer function* H of $\mathcal{A}$.

3 *Comment* The transfer function H is defined only in the domain of convergence of the integral in *2*; in many practical instances it is possible to continue analytically the domain of definition of H to include the whole plane except the singular points of H. This extension is not always possible.

Alternatively, if (I) $\mathcal{A}$ has a ground state which coincides with its zero state [this implies that $\mathcal{A}$ is asymptotically stable (see *2.8.7* and *7.2.3*)] and (II) $\mathcal{A}$ is nonanticipative (*1.8.13*), then $H(s)$ can be expressed as follows:

$$H(s) \triangleq \frac{\text{steady-state response of } \mathcal{A} \text{ to } e^{st}}{e^{st}}$$

This relation is an immediate consequence of the definition of the steady-state response of $\mathcal{A}$. Thus by *2.8.20*

$$\begin{aligned}\text{Steady-state response of } \mathcal{A} \text{ to } e^{st} &= \lim_{t_0 \to -\infty} \int_{t_0}^{t} h(t-\xi)e^{-s\xi}\,d\xi \\ &= \lim_{\lambda\to\infty} e^{st} \int_0^{\lambda} h(\tau)e^{-s\tau}\,d\tau \\ &= e^{st}H(s)\end{aligned}$$

Note that the definition of $H(s)$ in terms of the steady-state response of $\mathcal{A}$ to e^{st} is not as general as *2*.

Finally, in the case of multiple-input multiple-output systems, the transfer function becomes a *matrix transfer function* $\mathbf{H}(s)$; its (i,j) element is the Laplace transform of $h_{ij}(t)$, the ith-output zero-state response due to a unit impulse applied at the jth input at time $t = 0$. ◁

If the transfer function $H(s)$ is given, then the impulse response can be calculated by the inversion integral, which reads

$$\frac{h(t+0) + h(t-0)}{2} = \frac{1}{2\pi j}\int_{c-j\infty}^{c+j\infty} H(s)e^{st}\,ds$$

where c is a real number which lies in the strip (or half-plane) of convergence of *2*. For more details the reader is referred to Appendix *B*. The property that makes the transfer function so useful in practice is contained in the

4 **Assertion** Let $\mathcal{A}$ be linear time-invariant and let it have $H(s)$ as a transfer function. If y is the zero-state response to the input u, then

5 $$Y(s) = H(s)U(s)$$

where Y and U are the Laplace transforms of y and u. [These transforms are bilateral if either $u(t) \neq 0$ or $h(t) \neq 0$ for some $t < 0$.]

Proof See *3.6.23*.

6 **Remark** It is of fundamental importance to constantly keep in mind that the transfer function of the system $\mathcal{A}$ *characterizes only its zero-state response.* In general, the transfer function gives only incomplete information regarding its zero-input response. For further elaboration of this fact, refer to Chap. *11*, Sec. *5*.

7 *Comment* The relationship between $H(s)$ and $h(t)$, which is expressed by *2* and *3*, deserves some comment in view of the importance of approximations in engineering problems. Suppose that the defining integrals of transfer functions $H(s)$ and $H_1(s)$ converge for Re $s = 0$. Roughly speaking, the point we wish to make is that if two transfer functions $H_1(j\omega)$ and $H(j\omega)$ are approximately equal for all ω's, it does not follow that their impulse responses $h_1(t)$ and $h(t)$ are approximately equal for all t.

To exhibit this fact, let $H_1(j\omega) = H(j\omega) + \varepsilon(j\omega)$, where

$$\varepsilon(j\omega) = \begin{cases} \eta\left(1 - \dfrac{|\omega|}{\Omega}\right) e^{-j\omega t_0} & |\omega| \leq \Omega \\ 0 & |\omega| > \Omega \end{cases}$$

and the constant $\eta \ll 1$ and $t_0 > 0$. Clearly, $|\varepsilon(j\omega)| \ll 1$ for all $\omega \in (-\infty, \infty)$. A simple calculation shows that

$$h_1(t_0) - h(t_0) = \frac{\eta\Omega}{2\pi}$$

Therefore, by choosing Ω sufficiently large and keeping η very small and fixed, we can make this difference as large as we wish. Thus, although the "peak" difference between $H_1(j\omega)$ and $H(j\omega)$ remains constant and equal to the small number η, the "peak" difference between h_1 and h can be made arbitrarily large.

In general, however, we can write

$$|h_1(t) - h(t)| \leq \frac{1}{2\pi} \int_{-\infty}^{+\infty} |H_1(j\omega) - H(j\omega)| \, |e^{j\omega t}| \, d\omega$$

and

8 $$|h_1(t) - h(t)| \leq \frac{1}{2\pi} \int_{-\infty}^{+\infty} |H_1(j\omega) - H(j\omega)| \, d\omega \qquad \forall t \in (-\infty, \infty)$$

Thus if we measure the "distance" between H_1 and H by the integral $\int_{-\infty}^{+\infty} |H_1(j\omega) - H(j\omega)| \, d\omega$, then *8* gives an upper bound on $|h_1(t) - h(t)|$ over $(-\infty, \infty)$.

3 *Realization of a matrix transfer function*

In Chap. *4*, Sec. *9*, we considered the problem of representing a system specified by a rational transfer function as an interconnection of scalors, adders, and integrators. We now consider the corresponding problem: given a multiple-input multiple-output linear time-invariant system specified by its matrix transfer function $\mathbf{H}(s)$, find a realization of this system as an interconnection of scalors, adders, and differentiators.

We shall assume that all the elements of $\mathbf{H}(s)$ are rational functions of s. For simplicity, we shall further assume that all the elements of $\mathbf{H}(s)$ have simple poles: the extension of the method to the case where multiple poles are present does not require any additional devices. Its description in general terms would require cumbersome notation, however.

1 **Remark** For simplicity, we shall say the input $\mathbf{u}(s)$ when we mean the input whose Laplace transform is $\mathbf{u}(s)$, and we shall similarly express the output.

Special case Suppose $\mathbf{H}(s)$ is of the form $\mathbf{R}/(s-\lambda)$, where $\mathbf{R}$ is an $n \times n$ constant matrix which can be represented by a single dyad $\boldsymbol{\sigma}\rangle\langle\boldsymbol{\rho}$ (see *5.4.15*). By definition, the result of the dyad $\boldsymbol{\sigma}\rangle\langle\boldsymbol{\rho}$ operating on any vector $\mathbf{u}$ is the vector $\boldsymbol{\sigma}$ times the scalar $\langle\boldsymbol{\rho},\mathbf{u}\rangle$. The dyad $\boldsymbol{\sigma}\rangle\langle\boldsymbol{\rho}$ may also be thought of as the product of the column vector $\boldsymbol{\sigma}$ and the row vector $\boldsymbol{\rho}^*$, whose elements are the complex conjugates of those of $\boldsymbol{\rho}$. Thus, if we consider an input described by the vector $\mathbf{u}(s)$, the output

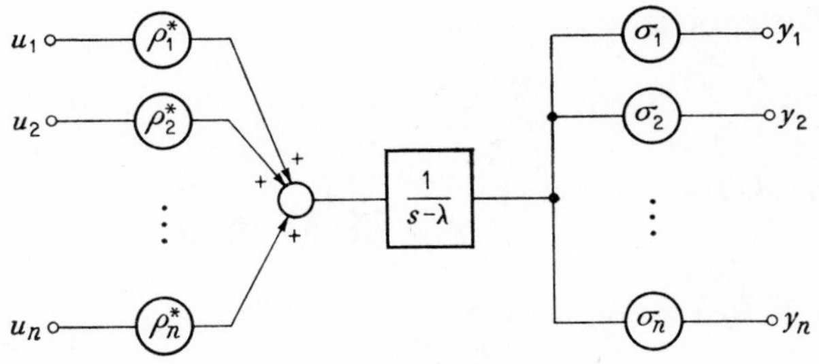

Fig. 9.3.1 Realization of the system represented by $\boldsymbol{\sigma}\rangle\langle\boldsymbol{\rho}/(s-\lambda)$.

will be the vector $\boldsymbol{\sigma}\langle\boldsymbol{\rho},\mathbf{u}(s)\rangle/(s-\lambda)$. This leads to the simple realization shown in Fig. *9.3.1* and the

2 **Assertion** If the transfer function $\mathbf{H}(s)$ is of the form $\mathbf{R}/(s-\lambda)$, where the constant matrix $\mathbf{R}$ is representable by a single dyad $\boldsymbol{\sigma}\rangle\langle\boldsymbol{\rho}$, then the system has a realization which requires only one integrator (see Fig. *9.3.1*).

3 *Exercise* Let $\mathbf{H}(s) = \mathbf{R}/d(s)$, where the constant matrix $\mathbf{R} = \boldsymbol{\sigma}\rangle\langle\boldsymbol{\rho}$ and $d(s)$ is a polynomial. Show that the realization of the system requires only that of the single-input single-output system whose transfer function is $1/d(s)$.

4 *Comment* The system shown in Fig. *9.3.1* exhibits very clearly the fact that for any real scalar k, $k\boldsymbol{\sigma}\rangle\langle k^{-1}\boldsymbol{\rho} = \boldsymbol{\sigma}\rangle\langle\boldsymbol{\rho}$. ◁

In order to proceed to the general case, we must first establish a lemma which gives the representation of any constant matrix $\mathbf{R}$ as a sum of dyads. Obviously if $\mathbf{R}$ is represented by a single dyad $\boldsymbol{\sigma}\rangle\langle\boldsymbol{\rho}$, the range of **R**, $\mathcal{R}(\mathbf{R})$, is spanned by the vector $\boldsymbol{\sigma}$ and hence is one-dimensional. If $\mathcal{R}(\mathbf{R})$ is of dimension c (that is, the matrix **R** has rank c) and is spanned by $\boldsymbol{\sigma}_1, \boldsymbol{\sigma}_2, \ldots, \boldsymbol{\sigma}_c$, then **R** has a dyadic representation of the form $\sum_{i=1}^{c} \boldsymbol{\sigma}_i\rangle\langle\boldsymbol{\rho}_i$. Now the range of **R** is spanned by the column vectors of the matrix **R**; therefore we may choose for the set $\{\boldsymbol{\sigma}_i\}_1^c$ a maximal set of linearly independent column vectors of **R**, that is, any set of linearly independent column vectors which spans $\mathcal{R}(\mathbf{R})$. This point of view naturally leads to the

5 **Lemma** Let **R** be an $n \times n$ matrix whose elements are complex numbers. Let $\tilde{\mathbf{R}}$ be any $n \times c$ matrix whose columns are a maximal set of linearly independent columns of **R**. Let the $c \times n$ matrix **S** be defined by

6
$$\mathbf{R} = \tilde{\mathbf{R}}\mathbf{S}$$

Let, for $i = 1, 2, \ldots, n$, $\boldsymbol{\sigma}_i$ be the ith column of $\tilde{\mathbf{R}}$ and $\boldsymbol{\rho}_i$ be the complex conjugate ith row of **S**; then

7
$$\mathbf{R} = \sum_{i=1}^{c} \boldsymbol{\sigma}_i\rangle\langle\boldsymbol{\rho}_i$$

Furthermore

8
$$\mathbf{S} = (\tilde{\mathbf{R}}^*\tilde{\mathbf{R}})^{-1}\tilde{\mathbf{R}}^*\mathbf{R}$$

where $\mathbf{R}^*$ is the conjugate transpose of **R**.

9 *Comment* The elements of **S** defined in *6* may be interpreted as follows: the c elements of the kth column of **S** are the weighting coefficients defining the linear combination of the $\boldsymbol{\sigma}_i$'s required to form the kth column of **R**. This **S** is defined uniquely by *6*.

10 *Comment* It is not necessary to use columns of **R** for the basis vectors $\boldsymbol{\sigma}_i$ since any basis of $\mathcal{R}(\mathbf{R})$ will do. Special choices of basis vectors may simplify greatly the inversion required by *8*.

Proof Let **x** be an arbitrary vector; then by *6*, $\mathbf{Rx} = \tilde{\mathbf{R}}\mathbf{Sx} = \tilde{\mathbf{R}}(\mathbf{Sx})$. Now **Sx** is a column vector whose components are $\langle\boldsymbol{\rho}_i,\mathbf{x}\rangle$. Note that we use a complex scalar product (see *C.5.4*). Multiplying **Sx** by $\tilde{\mathbf{R}}$ on the left, we get $\Sigma\langle\boldsymbol{\rho}_i,\mathbf{x}\rangle\boldsymbol{\sigma}_i$. Since this holds for all **x**, *7* follows.

From *6* we have

11
$$\tilde{\mathbf{R}}^*\mathbf{R} = (\tilde{\mathbf{R}}^*\tilde{\mathbf{R}})\mathbf{S}$$

Since the column vectors of $\tilde{\mathbf{R}}$ are linearly independent, with $\mathbf{z} \in \mathbb{C}^c$ we have $\mathbf{z} \neq 0 \Rightarrow \tilde{\mathbf{R}}\mathbf{z} \neq 0 \Rightarrow 0 < \langle\tilde{\mathbf{R}}\mathbf{z},\tilde{\mathbf{R}}\mathbf{z}\rangle = \langle\mathbf{z},\tilde{\mathbf{R}}^*\tilde{\mathbf{R}}\mathbf{z}\rangle$; that is, the hermitian matrix $\tilde{\mathbf{R}}^*\tilde{\mathbf{R}}$ is positive definite; hence it is nonsingular (see *C.19.19*). Multiplying *11* on the left by $(\tilde{\mathbf{R}}^*\tilde{\mathbf{R}})^{-1}$, we get *8*. ◁

We are now in a position to describe the main result of this section in a form of a

12 **Theorem** Let the system $\mathcal{A}$ be characterized by its transfer function matrix $\mathbf{H}(s)$. Suppose that all the elements of $\mathbf{H}(s)$ are rational functions and have simple poles. Let the partial-fraction expansion of $\mathbf{H}(s)$ be

13
$$\mathbf{H}(s) = \sum_{j=1}^{m} \frac{\mathbf{R}_j}{s - \lambda_j} + \mathbf{H}_0$$

where the residue matrices $\mathbf{R}_j$ and $\mathbf{H}_0$ are constant matrices. Let each residue matrix be expanded, as in Lemma *5*,

14
$$\mathbf{H}(s) = \sum_{j=1}^{m} \sum_{i=1}^{\alpha_j} \frac{\boldsymbol{\delta}_i^{(j)}\rangle \langle \boldsymbol{\varrho}_i^{(j)}}{s - \lambda_j} + \mathbf{H}_0$$

Then the system $\mathcal{A}$, represented by $\mathbf{H}(s)$, is zero-state equivalent to the system $\mathcal{B}$ described by the following state equation:

15
$$\begin{bmatrix} \dot{\mathbf{x}}_1 \\ \dot{\mathbf{x}}_2 \\ \cdots \\ \dot{\mathbf{x}}_m \end{bmatrix} = \begin{bmatrix} \lambda_1\mathbf{I}_1 & \mathbf{0} & \cdots & \mathbf{0} \\ \mathbf{0} & \lambda_2\mathbf{I}_2 & \cdots & \cdots \\ \cdots & \cdots & \cdots & \cdots \\ \mathbf{0} & \cdots & \cdots & \lambda_m\mathbf{I}_m \end{bmatrix} \begin{bmatrix} \mathbf{x}_1 \\ \mathbf{x}_2 \\ \cdots \\ \mathbf{x}_m \end{bmatrix} + \begin{bmatrix} \mathbf{S}_1 \\ \mathbf{S}_2 \\ \cdots \\ \mathbf{S}_m \end{bmatrix} \mathbf{u}$$

16
$$\mathbf{y} = [\tilde{\mathbf{R}}_1 \quad \tilde{\mathbf{R}}_2 \quad \cdots \quad \tilde{\mathbf{R}}_m] \begin{bmatrix} \mathbf{x}_1 \\ \cdots \\ \mathbf{x}_m \end{bmatrix} + \mathbf{H}_0\mathbf{u}$$

where $\mathbf{I}_j$ is the unit matrix of order α_j and, as in Lemma *5*, $\mathbf{R}_j = \tilde{\mathbf{R}}_j\mathbf{S}_j$, $j = 1, 2, \ldots, m$. Furthermore, there is no system of order smaller than $n \triangleq \sum_{j=1}^{m} \alpha_j$ which is zero-state equivalent to $\mathcal{A}$.

Proof Let us establish the zero-state equivalence of $\mathcal{A}$ and $\mathcal{B}$. Since the $\mathbf{A}$ matrix of *15* is diagonal and since all matrices of *15* and *16* are partitioned in a conforming manner, the output $\mathbf{y}$ is easily written as the sum of the contribution of each block. Therefore, remembering that we consider only the zero-state response, we have successively

$$\mathbf{y}(t) = \sum_j \tilde{\mathbf{R}}_j \int_0^t e^{\lambda_j(t-\xi)}\mathbf{I}_j\mathbf{S}_j\mathbf{u}(\xi)\, d\xi + \mathbf{H}_0\mathbf{u}(t)$$

$$= \sum_j \tilde{\mathbf{R}}_j\mathbf{S}_j \int_0^t e^{\lambda_j(t-\xi)}\mathbf{u}(\xi)\, d\xi + \mathbf{H}_0\mathbf{u}(t)$$

$$\mathbf{y}(t) = \sum_j \mathbf{R}_j \int_0^t e^{\lambda_j(t-\xi)}\mathbf{u}(\xi)\, d\xi + \mathbf{H}_0\mathbf{u}(t)$$

Clearly this is exactly the expression that one would have obtained by starting from *13* and inverting the Laplace transforms by the convolution theorem. Therefore $\mathcal{A}$ and $\mathcal{B}$ are zero-state equivalent.

To show that $\mathcal{B}$ is of minimal order, let us show that the number of components of the state vector associated with λ_j cannot be less than α_j, the dimension of the range of $\mathbf{R}_j$. For all $\mathbf{u}(s)$ the contribution of the output associated with λ_j is $\mathbf{R}_j\mathbf{u}(s)/(s - \lambda_j)$. Now $\mathbf{R}_j$ has an α_j-dimensional range; therefore, the specification of the vector $\mathbf{R}_j\mathbf{u}(s)$ requires at least α_j scalars. [In the present case, where we use the vectors $\boldsymbol{\sigma}_1^{(j)}, \ldots, \boldsymbol{\sigma}_{\alpha_j}^{(j)}$ as a basis for $\mathcal{R}(\mathbf{R}_j)$, these scalars are $\langle \boldsymbol{\sigma}_i^{(j)}, \mathbf{u}(s)\rangle$, $i = 1, 2, \ldots, \alpha_j$.] Therefore, the dimension of the state vector cannot be less than $\sum_{j=1}^{m} \alpha_j = n$ and $\mathcal{B}$ is of minimal order. Equivalently $\mathcal{B}$ is in reduced form (*2.2.11*).

17 *Example* Let the transfer function matrix be a 2×2 matrix. By expanding it in partial fractions, we get

$$\mathbf{H}(s) = \begin{bmatrix} \dfrac{2s+3}{s^2+3s+2} & \dfrac{6s^2+25s+23}{s^3+6s^2+11s+6} \\ \dfrac{1}{s+1} & \dfrac{3s+5}{s^2+3s+2} \end{bmatrix}$$

$$= \begin{bmatrix} \dfrac{1}{s+1} + \dfrac{1}{s+2} & \dfrac{2}{s+1} + \dfrac{3}{s+2} + \dfrac{1}{s+3} \\ \dfrac{1}{s+1} & \dfrac{2}{s+1} + \dfrac{1}{s+2} \end{bmatrix}$$

Thus

$$\mathbf{R}_1 = \begin{bmatrix} 1 & 2 \\ 1 & 2 \end{bmatrix} = \begin{bmatrix} 1 \\ 1 \end{bmatrix} [1 \quad 2]$$

$$\mathbf{R}_2 = \begin{bmatrix} 1 & 3 \\ 0 & 1 \end{bmatrix} = \begin{bmatrix} 1 \\ 0 \end{bmatrix} [1 \quad 0] + \begin{bmatrix} 3 \\ 1 \end{bmatrix} [0 \quad 1]$$

$$\mathbf{R}_3 = \begin{bmatrix} 0 & 1 \\ 0 & 0 \end{bmatrix} = \begin{bmatrix} 1 \\ 0 \end{bmatrix} [0 \quad 1]$$

Here the dyadic expansion of the $\mathbf{R}_i$'s is obtained by inspection using Comment *9*. The state equations of $\mathcal{B}$ are then

18 $$\dot{\mathbf{x}} = \begin{bmatrix} -1 & 0 & 0 & 0 \\ 0 & -2 & 0 & 0 \\ 0 & 0 & -2 & 0 \\ 0 & 0 & 0 & -3 \end{bmatrix} \mathbf{x} + \begin{bmatrix} 1 & 2 \\ 1 & 0 \\ 0 & 1 \\ 0 & 1 \end{bmatrix} \mathbf{u}$$

19 $$\mathbf{y} = \begin{bmatrix} 1 & 1 & 3 & 1 \\ 1 & 0 & 1 & 0 \end{bmatrix} \mathbf{x}$$

The realization of $\mathcal{B}$ is immediately obtained on the basis of *2* and Fig. *9.3.1*. It is shown in Fig. *9.3.2*. The scalors on the left of the

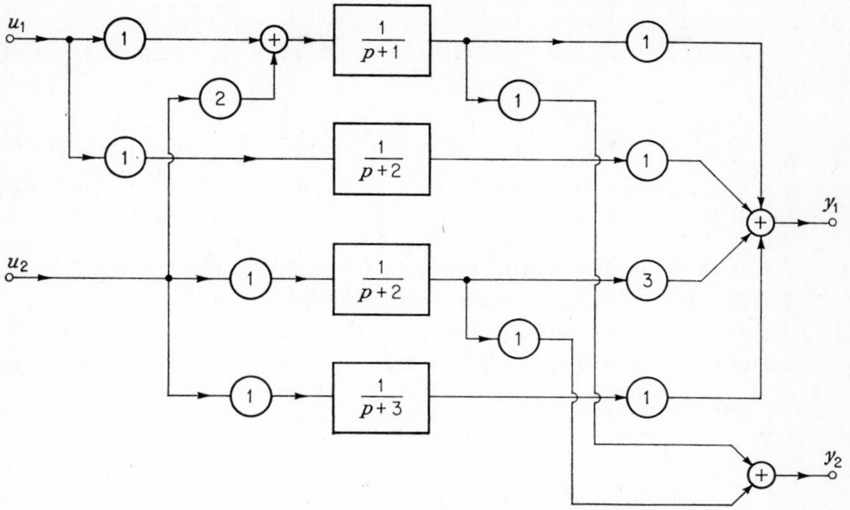

Fig. 9.3.2 Realization of the matrix transfer function of Example *9.3.17*.

integrators have multiplying factors which are the columns of the matrix multiplying **u** in *18*. Similarly, the scalors following the integrators have multiplying factors which are the rows of the matrix multiplying **x** in *19*. These two observations provide an easy check on the realization of $\mathcal{B}$.

4 *Stable transfer functions*

In Chap. *7*, we investigated the stability of differential systems, and in Chap. *8* we introduced the concept of zero-state stability for systems described by their impulse response. Here we consider exclusively time-invariant systems and we define stable and strictly stable transfer functions. The relationship between stable transfer functions and system stability is discussed below in Remark *15*.

Definition and characterization

1 **Definition** A transfer function $H(s)$ is said to be *stable* if (I) its impulse response $h(t)$ is bounded for all $t \in (-\infty, \infty)$ or if (II) h is the sum of such a bounded function and a countable linear combination of impulses such that the coefficients of the δ functions constitute an absolutely converging series.

2 *Example* For the circuit shown in Fig. *9.4.1*, $H(s) = 1/(s+1)$ and $h(t) = 1(t)e^{-t}$; hence, $H(s)$ is stable.

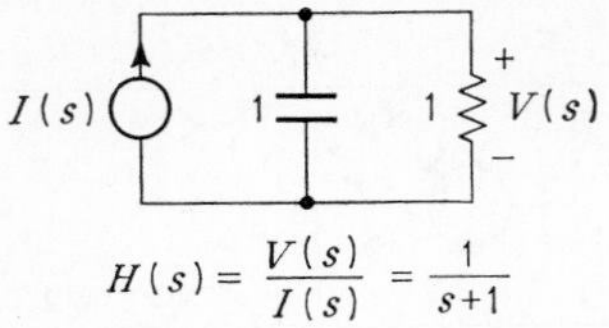

Fig. 9.4.1 Circuit whose transfer function is $H(s) = 1/(s+1)$.

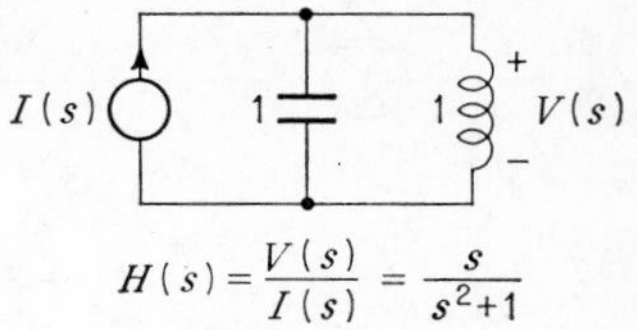

Fig. 9.4.2 Circuit whose transfer function is $H(s) = s/(s^2+1)$.

3 *Example* For the circuit shown in Fig. *9.4.2*, $H(s) = s/(s^2+1)$ and $h(t) = 1(t)\cos t$; again the transfer function is stable.

4 *Example* In the circuit shown in Fig. *9.4.3*, the transmission line is assumed to be lossless and to have a delay of 1 sec. The reflection

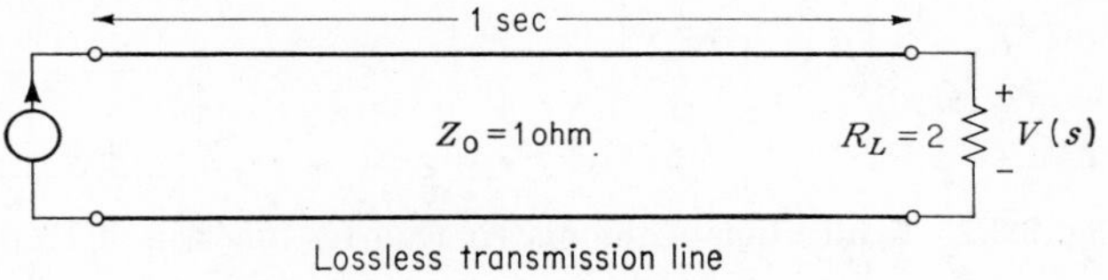

Fig. 9.4.3 Circuit whose impulse response is an infinite sum of impulses.

coefficient at the generator end is 1 and at the load end is $\frac{1}{3}$; therefore, the output voltage due to a unit impulse of current is

$$h(t) = \tfrac{4}{3}\Big[\delta(t-1) + \sum_{n=1}^{\infty} (\tfrac{1}{3})^n \delta(t-1-2n)\Big]$$

Again this particular transfer function is stable. Show that if the load resistance were -2 ohms, the transfer function would not be stable.

As an obvious consequence of the fact that, for any positive integer n,

5 $$\mathfrak{L}^{-1}\left(\frac{1}{(s-a)^n}\right) = 1(t)\,\frac{t^{n-1}}{(n-1)!}\,e^{at}$$

and of the partial-fraction expansion we have the

6 **Theorem** A rational transfer function is *stable* if and only if it has no poles inside the right half plane and its $j\omega$-axis poles (if any) are simple. [$H(s)$ is assumed to be nonanticipative.] ◁

From a practical point of view a more useful concept of stability is that of strict stability:

7 **Definition** A transfer function is said to be *strictly stable* if its zero-state response remains bounded for any bounded input. ◁

Therefore a linear time-invariant system that has a strictly stable transfer function is zero-state stable b.i.b.o. (*8.4.1*).

More precisely, a transfer function is said to be a strictly stable transfer function whenever any input x_i which satisfies $|x_i(t)| < M_i$, for all t and for some $M_i < \infty$, produces a zero-state response $x_0(t)$ which satisfies $|x_0(t)| < M_0$ for some finite M_0 and for all t. This bound M_0 depends on M_i and on the particular transfer function.

8 *Example* The transfer function $H(s) = 1/s$ is stable, since its impulse response $1(t)$ is uniformly bounded; but it is not strictly stable, since a bounded input $x_i(t) = 1(t)$ produces a zero-state response $x_0(t) = t1(t)$ which becomes arbitrarily large as $t \to \infty$.

9 *Example* There are system components that are not strictly stable in terms of certain variables; consider the conventional d-c motor which appears in every example of an electrical position servo. Its transfer function is $H(s) = \Theta(s)/I(s) = K/s(1 + Ts)$, where θ is the shaft position and i is the armature current. This transfer function is not strictly stable. Of course, the transfer function of the over-all position servo is obviously required to be strictly stable; hence, appropriate compensation and feedback networks are required.

10 *Example* The ideal low-pass filter, defined by

$$|H(j\omega)| = 1(\omega + 2\pi B) - 1(\omega - 2\pi B) \qquad \text{and} \qquad \measuredangle H(j\omega) = -j\omega t_0$$

has an impulse response $h(t) = 2B[\sin 2\pi B(t - t_0)]/2\pi B(t - t_0)$. Its transfer function is obviously stable, but a simple calculation will prove that it is not strictly stable. (See *12*.)

Again as a consequence of the partial-fraction expansion we have

11 **Theorem** A rational transfer function is strictly stable if and only if it has no poles inside the right half plane and no poles on the $j\omega$ axis.
Proof This follows immediately from the partial-fraction expansion of $H(s)$ and the convolution theorem. $\triangleleft$

A characterization of strictly stable transfer functions which applies to a much larger class of systems is the following

12 **Theorem** A transfer function $H(s)$ is strictly stable if and only if its impulse response $h(t)$ is such that

13 $$\int_{-\infty}^{+\infty} |h(t)|\, dt \triangleq A < \infty$$

that is, if and only if the area under the curve $|h(t)|$ is finite.
Proof $\Leftarrow$ Let us prove that if *13* holds, then $H(s)$ is strictly stable. Consider an arbitrary bounded input x_i; that is, there is a constant M_i such that

$$|x_i(t)| < M_i \qquad \forall t$$

The convolution theorem gives the zero-state response x_0 at time t due to the input x_i:

$$x_0(t) = \int_{-\infty}^{+\infty} x_i(t - \tau)h(\tau)\, d\tau$$

Hence

$$\begin{aligned} |x_0(t)| &= \left| \int_{-\infty}^{+\infty} x_i(t - \tau)h(\tau)\, d\tau \right| \\ &\leq \int_{-\infty}^{+\infty} |x_i(t - \tau)|\ |h(\tau)|\, d\tau \\ &< M_i \int_{-\infty}^{+\infty} |h(\tau)|\, d\tau \end{aligned}$$

Thus, in view of *13*, for all t,

$$|x_0(t)| < AM_i$$

That is, the output is uniformly bounded for all t.

$\Rightarrow$ It remains to prove that if $H(s)$ is strictly stable, then inequality *13* is satisfied. We shall establish this result by contradiction: we assume that *13* is not satisfied and then find a bounded input that will produce an output at time T which, for sufficiently large T, will be larger than any preassigned number.

Pick the input $\hat{x}_i$ defined as follows:

14 $$\hat{x}_i(t) = \begin{cases} \operatorname{sgn}[h(T - t)] & 0 \leq t \leq 2T \\ 0 & \text{elsewhere} \end{cases}$$

or equivalently, putting $T - t = \tau$,

$$\hat{x}_i(T - \tau) = \begin{cases} \operatorname{sgn}[h(\tau)] & -T \leq \tau \leq T \\ 0 & \text{elsewhere} \end{cases}$$

To this input $\hat{x}_i$ there corresponds an output $\hat{x}_0$ which at time T takes the value given by

$$\hat{x}_0(T) = \int_{-\infty}^{\infty} \hat{x}_i(T - \tau)h(\tau)\, d\tau = \int_{-T}^{T} h(\tau) \operatorname{sgn}[h(\tau)]\, d\tau$$

Thus,

$$\hat{x}_0(T) = \int_{-T}^{T} |h(\tau)|\, d\tau$$

The assumption that *13* does not hold means that given any positive number M, however large, we can find a value of T, say $T(M)$, such that

$$\int_{-T(M)}^{+T(M)} |h(\tau)|\, d\tau > M$$

The above two relations imply that if *13* is not satisfied, *14* gives a recipe for producing a bounded input such that the corresponding output becomes larger, in absolute value, then any preassigned M at time $T(M)$. In other words, if *13* does not hold, x_0 cannot be uniformly bounded for all bounded inputs. Hence if $H(s)$ is strictly stable, *13* must hold.

15 **Remark: transfer function stability versus other types of stability** Since the transfer function characterizes only the zero-state response of a system, one would expect that there are systems which have a strictly stable transfer function but which have a zero state that is unstable. Consider, for example, the system $\mathcal{S}$ shown in Fig. *9.4.4*. Its transfer function $H(s) = \frac{1}{2}$ and is strictly stable. The state is $\mathbf{x} = (x_1,x_2)$. It is obvious that any nonzero initial state such that $x_1(0) \neq x_2(0)$ will give rise to an exponentially increasing $\mathbf{x}(t;\mathbf{x}_0,0)$; in fact, it is easy to check that

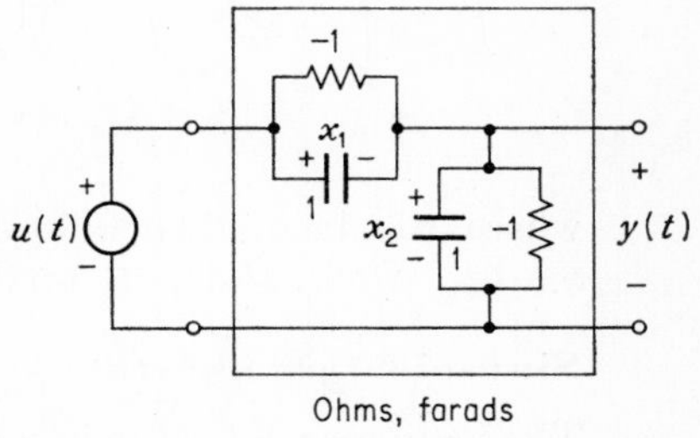

Fig. 9.4.4 Circuit whose transfer function is strictly stable but whose zero state is not asymptotically stable.

$$\mathbf{x}(t;\mathbf{x}_0,0) = \frac{e^t}{2}\begin{bmatrix} x_1(0) - x_2(0) \\ -x_1(0) + x_2(0) \end{bmatrix} \qquad \forall t > 0$$

Physically, an arbitrary small charge on either capacitor will produce an exponentially increasing output voltage. It should be stressed, however, that the voltage source, irrespective of its terminal voltage u, cannot excite the unstable mode of the system $\mathcal{S}$; thus in so far as $H(s)$ represents *only* the relation between the input u and the output y when the system is initially in the zero state, it is perfectly reasonable for the transfer function to be strictly stable. Needless to say, in engineering, our systems must have both an asymptotically stable zero state and a strictly stable transfer function.

The above example illustrates another point: the transfer function $H(s)$ becomes a constant independent of s if and only if the two RC parallel combinations have the same time constant (-1 sec in the present case); the slightest manufacturing deviation or change due to temperature or aging that makes the time constants different will cause $H(s)$ to be unstable. This shows the error that lies in the optimistic idea "let us cancel a right-half-plane pole (at $+1$ in the present case) by a zero at the same location." A further discussion of this subject using the concepts of controllability and observability is found in *11.5.10*.

A sufficient condition for strict stability is given by the following:

16 **Assertion** Let $H(s)$ be the transfer function. If $\int_{-\infty}^{+\infty} |H(j\omega)|^2\, d\omega < \infty$ and if $\int_{-\infty}^{+\infty} \left| \frac{d}{d\omega} H(j\omega) \right|^2 d\omega < \infty$, then $H(s)$ is strictly stable.

Proof By Parseval's theorem (*B.3.16*), the two assumptions imply that $\int_{-\infty}^{\infty} |h(t)|^2\, dt < \infty$, $\int_{-\infty}^{\infty} t^2 |h(t)|^2\, dt < \infty$. Now

$$\int_{-\infty}^{+\infty} |h(t)|\, dt = \int_{-\infty}^{+\infty} (1+t^2)^{1/2} |h(t)| (1+t^2)^{-1/2}\, dt$$
$$\leq \left[\int_{-\infty}^{\infty} (1+t^2) |h(t)|^2\, dt \right]^{1/2} \left(\int_{-\infty}^{\infty} \frac{dt}{1+t^2} \right)^{1/2} < \infty$$

where the inequality follows from Schwarz's inequality (*C.5.8* and *9.8.12*). $H(s)$ is strictly stable by Theorem *12*.

Sinusoidal steady state

The main reason for the importance of transfer functions in engineering is that they can be measured easily and accurately. The basis of the measurements is the following

17 **Theorem** Let $\mathcal{S}$ be a single-input single-output linear nonanticipative time-invariant system whose transfer function is $H(s)$. Let $H(s)$ be strictly stable. Then the zero-state response to the input $1(t) \exp(j\omega t)$ becomes arbitrarily close to $H(j\omega) \exp(j\omega t)$ as $t \to \infty$. More precisely, given $\varepsilon > 0$, there is a time $T(\varepsilon)$ such that

18 $$|y(t; \mathbf{0}, 0; 1(t) \exp(j\omega t)) - H(j\omega) \exp(j\omega t)| < \varepsilon \qquad \forall t > T(\varepsilon)$$

In practical application, $h(t)$ is real; hence, $H(j\omega)^* = H(-j\omega)$ and consequently we have the

19 **Corollary** Let the assumptions of Theorem *17* hold and let $h(t)$ be real for all t; then

$$\left. \begin{aligned} |y(t; \mathbf{0}, 0; 1(t) \cos \omega t) - |H(j\omega)| \cos [\omega t + \measuredangle H(j\omega)]| < \varepsilon \\ |y(t; \mathbf{0}, 0; 1(t) \sin \omega t) - |H(j\omega)| \sin [\omega t + \measuredangle H(j\omega)]| < \varepsilon \end{aligned} \right\} \forall t > T(\varepsilon)$$

The corollary follows immediately from $\exp(j\omega t) = \cos \omega t + j \sin \omega t$, the additivity property of the zero-state response (*3.4.1*) and *18*.

20 *Comment* $T(\varepsilon)$ sec after applying the excitation $1(t) \cos \omega t$, the amplitude of the response is within ε of that of the true steady state. Note that this $T(\varepsilon)$ is independent of the frequency of the excitation. Of course, if one knows more about the analytical properties of $H(s)$, one may obtain sharper estimates; see *9.13.11* for an example.

Proof of theorem Since $H(s)$ is strictly stable, $\int_0^\infty |h(t)|\, dt \triangleq A < \infty$ by *12*. Thus for any $\varepsilon > 0$, there is a $T(\varepsilon)$ such that $t > T(\varepsilon) \Rightarrow$

$\int_t^\infty |h(\xi)|\, d\xi < \varepsilon$. Consider now the zero-state response to $1(t) \exp(j\omega t)$; then

$$y(t; \mathbf{0}, 0; 1(t) \exp(j\omega t)) = \int_0^t h(\xi) \exp[j\omega(t - \xi)]\, d\xi$$
$$= [\exp(j\omega t)] \left[\int_0^\infty h(\xi)[\exp(-j\omega\xi)]\, d\xi - \int_t^\infty h(\xi)[\exp(-j\omega\xi)]\, d\xi \right]$$

Call $\eta_2(t)$ the second term in the outer brackets; then

21 $$y(t; \mathbf{0}, 0; 1(t) \exp(j\omega t)) - H(j\omega) \exp(j\omega t) = \eta_2(t) \exp(j\omega t)$$

Now

$$|\eta_2(t)| = \left| \int_t^\infty h(\xi)[\exp(-j\omega\xi)]\, d\xi \right| \leq \int_t^\infty |h(\xi)|\, d\xi$$

Thus

$$|\eta_2(t)| < \varepsilon \qquad \forall t < T(\varepsilon)$$

and, with this fact, *21* implies *18*.

Liénard and Chipart stability test

Theorem *11* states that a rational transfer function is strictly stable if and only if its denominator has all its roots inside the left half plane. It is important to be able to test a given transfer function for this condition. We shall now describe the Liénard and Chipart test, which is more efficient than the celebrated Hurwitz test.

Let the denominator of the given rational transfer function be

$$d(s) = a_0 s^n + a_1 s^{n-1} + \cdots + a_{n-1}s + a_n \qquad a_0 > 0$$

Let us define the Hurwitz determinants by the equality

$$\Delta_k = \begin{vmatrix} a_1 & a_3 & a_5 & \cdot & \cdot & \cdot & \cdot \\ a_0 & a_2 & a_4 & \cdot & \cdot & \cdot & \cdot \\ 0 & a_1 & a_3 & \cdot & \cdot & \cdot & \cdot \\ 0 & a_0 & a_2 & a_4 & \cdot & \cdot & \cdot \\ 0 & 0 & a_1 & a_3 & \cdot & \cdot & \cdot \\ 0 & 0 & a_0 & a_2 & \cdot & \cdot & \cdot \\ \cdot & \cdot & \cdot & \cdot & \cdot & \cdot & a_k \end{vmatrix} \qquad k = 1, 2, \ldots, n$$

where $a_k = 0$ for $k > n$. These determinants $\Delta_1, \Delta_2, \Delta_3, \ldots$ are called the *Hurwitz determinants.*

22 **Theorem**[1] The polynomial with real coefficients,

$$d(s) = a_0 s^n + a_1 s^{n-1} + \cdots + a_{n-1}s + a_n \qquad (a_0 > 0)$$

[1] The proof of this theorem is to be found in F. R. Gantmacher, "Theory of Matrices," vol. II, chap. XV, Chelsea Publishing Company, New York, 1959.

has all its roots with negative real parts if and only if any one of the following sets of conditions is satisfied:

(I) $a_n > 0, a_{n-2} > 0, \ldots; \Delta_1 > 0, \Delta_3 > 0, \ldots$
(II) $a_n > 0, a_{n-2} > 0, \ldots; \Delta_2 > 0, \Delta_4 > 0, \ldots$
(III) $a_n > 0, a_{n-1} > 0, a_{n-3} > 0, \ldots; \Delta_1 > 0, \Delta_3 > 0, \ldots$
(IV) $a_n > 0, a_{n-1} > 0, a_{n-3} > 0, \ldots; \Delta_2 > 0, \Delta_4 > 0 \ldots$

23 *Comment* Usually it is required that *all* the Hurwitz determinants be positive. However, this requirement is redundant because of the following fact: if $d(s)$ has all its coefficients positive and if the Hurwitz determinants of odd order are positive, then those of even order are also positive, and vice versa.

24 *Example* $a_0s^3 + a_1s^2 + a_2s + a_3 = 0 \qquad a_0 > 0$

If we take the second set of conditions, we get

$$a_1a_2 - a_0a_3 > 0 \qquad a_3 > 0, a_1 > 0$$

25 *Example* $a_0s^4 + a_1s^3 + a_2s^2 + a_3s + a_4 = 0 \qquad a_0 > 0$

If we take the first set of conditions, we get

$$a_4 > 0, a_2 > 0; a_1 > 0, a_1a_2a_3 - a_1^2a_4 - a_3^2a_0 > 0$$

Design considerations

In design problems it often occurs that we have to choose a parameter μ (say, the gain of some amplifier or some transducer) but the chosen μ must lead to a strictly stable transfer function. It is also usually the case that for some value of μ, say, μ_0, it is physically obvious or it is known that the transfer function is strictly stable. The problem is to devise an effective method for specifying the largest interval of the μ axis for which the transfer function is strictly stable. The answer is given by the

26 **Theorem** Given a system which has a rational transfer function whose coefficients are real and depend continuously on a parameter μ. Suppose that the denominator polynomial d has all its zeros with negative (<0) real parts when the parameter is equal to μ_0. Then, as μ moves away from μ_0, the first value of μ, say μ_1, at which a zero of d is on the $j\omega$ axis is such that $a_n(\mu_1) = 0$ or $\Delta_{n-1}(\mu_1) = 0$.

27 *Comment* In other words, we need only plot $a_n(\mu)$ and $\Delta_{n-1}(\mu)$ as a function of μ and detect the first time one of these curves touches the μ axis.

28 *Comment* The zeros of a polynomial are continuous functions of the coefficients; hence, in the present case, the zeros of d are continuous functions of μ. Thus the transfer function can become unstable only by some of its poles moving across the $j\omega$ axis. Therefore, Theorem 26

allows us to assert that *for all* $\mu \in [\mu_0,\mu_1)$, *the transfer function of the system is strictly stable.*

Proof *Case 1* As μ varies away from μ_0, a real zero may move to the right and into the right half plane. The value of μ for which it is on the $j\omega$ axis corresponds to the fact that d has a zero at the origin of coordinates; hence, $a_n(\mu_1) = 0$.

Case 2 As μ varies away from μ_0, a pair of complex conjugate zeros may move into the right half plane. The value of μ at which they are on the $j\omega$ axis is such that $\Delta_{n-1}(\mu_1) = 0$. For that value of μ, d has a pair of pure imaginary zeros, say, $\pm j\omega_0$, and consequently $\text{Re}\,[d(j\omega_0)] = 0$ and $\text{Im}\,[d(j\omega_0)] = 0$. In other words, two polynomials easily derived from d have a common zero. Therefore, their discriminant is zero.[1] A few simple manipulations show that this discriminant is $a_n\Delta_{n-1}(\mu_1)$.

5 *The Paley-Wiener criterion*

The Paley-Wiener criterion imposes a fundamental restriction on all physical transfer functions. In order to describe it, let us give a definition: A transfer function is *causal* if its impulse response is identical to zero for $t < 0$. Roughly speaking, the Paley-Wiener criterion states that a transfer function $H(j\omega)$ is *causal* if and only if the inequality

$$\int_{-\infty}^{+\infty} \frac{|\log |H(j\omega)||}{1+\omega^2}\, d\omega < \infty$$

is satisfied.

This requirement is not vacuous, as is shown by the following examples. (I) The ideal low-pass filter is defined by $H_L(j\omega) = e^{-j\omega\tau}$ for $|\omega| < 2\pi W$ and zero elsewhere; τ is the constant time delay. $H_L(j\omega)$ cannot be causal because $\log |H_L(j\omega)|$ is infinite in the intervals (W, ∞) and $(-\infty, -W)$. (II) No causal transfer function may be identical to zero in any interval (ω_0,ω_1) of positive length. It may, however, have a countable number of zeros on the $j\omega$ axis, as is shown by the example of Fig. *9.5.1*. At each resonance of the transmission line (and there is an infinite, but countable, number of resonances!) there is a zero of transmission. (III) The

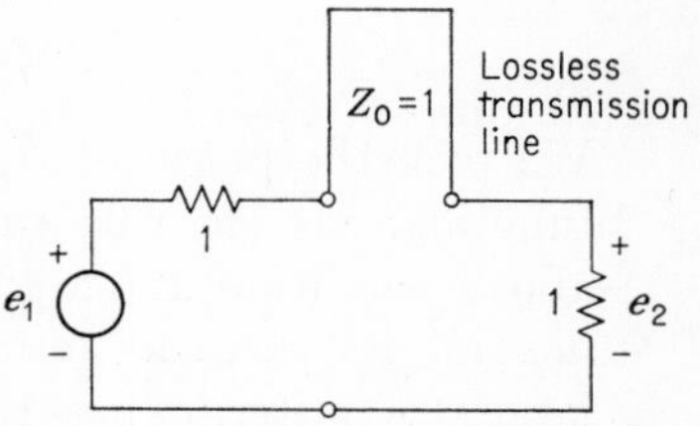

Fig. 9.5.1 Circuit whose transfer function has a countable number of zeros on the $j\omega$ axis.

[1] See, for example, M. Bocher, "Introduction to Higher Algebra," The MacMillan Company, New York, 1921.

Gaussian filter is defined by

$$H_G(j\omega) = (2\pi)^{-1/2} \exp\left(-j\omega\tau - \frac{\omega^2}{2}\right)$$

with τ as the constant time delay. It cannot be causal because $|\log |H_G(j)|| \sim \frac{\omega^2}{2}$ for large ω and the inequality above is not satisfied.

It is important to understand exactly what the Paley-Wiener criterion means in order not to draw false conclusions. An example in point is the Gaussian filter $H_G(j\omega)$. The criterion states that a system whose transfer function is *exactly* $H_G(j\omega)$, for all ω's, cannot be causal. It does not state that satisfactory approximations of $H_G(j\omega)$ will not be causal. For example, take $\tau = 0$ for simplicity and let

$$H_1(j\omega) = \begin{cases} \exp\left(-\frac{\omega^2}{2}\right) & \text{for } |\omega| \le 4 \\ \left(\frac{4}{\omega}\right)^4 e^{-8} & \text{for } |\omega| > 4 \end{cases}$$

It satisfies the Paley-Wiener criterion. From a practical point of view, since e^{-8} is a small number, $|H_1(j\omega)|$ will usually be sufficiently Gaussian to satisfy ordinary engineering requirements.

Let us consider the ideal low-pass filter $H_L(j\omega)$ defined in the introduction. From the criterion we expect that its impulse response $h_L(t)$ will differ from zero for some $t < 0$; in fact,

$$h_L(t) = 2W \frac{\sin 2\pi W(t - t_0)}{2\pi W(t - t_0)}$$

for all t. Consider now a sequence of filters approximating the ideal low-pass filter such that (for simplicity we put $2\pi W = 1$ in the following)

$$|H_n(j\omega)|^2 = \frac{1}{1 + \omega^{2n}}$$

We pick the phase of $H_n(j\omega)$ so that it is a minimum phase transfer function, i.e., in this case the transfer function which satisfies the above condition and which has all its poles inside the left half plane has all its zeros at infinity. Clearly, for every integer n, however large, the criterion is satisfied and the corresponding impulse response $h_n(t) = 0$ for $t < 0$. Furthermore,

$$\lim_{n \to \infty} |H_n(j\omega)| = |H_L(j\omega)|$$

for all ω's. Thus comes the question: why do we have $h_n(t) = 0$ for all $t < 0$ and all n on the one hand and $h_L(t) \neq 0$ for negative values of t arbitrarily far away from $t = 0$ on the other? The answer lies in the fact that as $n \to \infty$, $|H_n(j\omega)| \to |H_L(j\omega)|$ but that $\measuredangle H_n(j\omega)$ does not tend to $\measuredangle H_L(j\omega)$. In fact, for each fixed ω, $\measuredangle H_n(j\omega) \to \infty$. This follows from the potential analogy[1] point of view: $\measuredangle H_n(j\omega)$ is zero at the origin and $-d/d\omega \measuredangle H_n(j\omega)$ is proportional to the E-field component normal to the $j\omega$ axis provided every pole of $H_n(s)$ is replaced by a line charge of 1 coulomb/m. Now the n poles of $H_n(s)$ are symmetrically distributed on the left half of the unit circle centered on the origin of the s plane. Clearly, the total charge on the left half of the unit circle is n coulombs/m and, as $n \to \infty$, it becomes infinite. Thus at every point of the $j\omega$ axis in $[-j, +j]$, $-d/d\omega \measuredangle H_n(j\omega)$ becomes infinite. In other words, as $n \to \infty$, the group delay (see Sec. *11*) through the filter grows without bound. All this amounts to the observation that given an amplitude $|H(j\omega)|$ that does not satisfy the Paley-Wiener criterion it is impossible to associate with it a finite phase $\phi(\omega)$ such that $|H(j\omega)|e^{-j\phi(\omega)}$ is a causal transfer function.

A precise statement of the Paley-Wiener criterion is as follows:

1 **Theorem** Let $h(t) = 0$ for $t < 0$. Define $H(j\omega)$ by

2 $$\int_0^\infty h(t)e^{-j\omega t}\,dt \triangleq H(j\omega)$$

If $|H(j\omega)| \triangleq A(\omega)$ satisfies

3 $$\int_{-\infty}^{+\infty} A(\omega)^2\,d\omega < \infty$$

and if $H(s)$ is analytic for $\sigma = 0$, then

4 $$\int_{-\infty}^{+\infty} \frac{|\log A(\omega)|}{1+\omega^2}\,d\omega < \infty$$

Conversely, if conditions *3* and *4* hold, then a phase $\phi(\omega)$ can be found such that $H(j\omega) = A(\omega)e^{j\phi(\omega)}$ is a causal transfer function [i.e., the impulse response of $H(j\omega)$ vanishes identically for $t < 0$].

5 *Comment* The assumption that $H(s)$ is analytic for $\sigma = 0$ is not necessary; it is introduced here to facilitate the proof by allowing us to drop some delicate passages to the limit of integrals ranging over an infinite domain. ◁

In order to facilitate the proof of the criterion, we introduce three preliminary results.

6 **Lemma** For ω and σ real and for $\sigma > 0$,

$$\frac{1}{\pi}\int_{-\infty}^{+\infty} \frac{\sigma}{\sigma^2 + (\omega - \omega')^2}\,d\omega' = 1$$

Proof This result is easily established by Cauchy's integral formula and is left as an exercise for the reader. ◁

[1] S. Seshu and N. Balabanian, "Linear Network Analysis," John Wiley & Sons, Inc., New York, 1959.

The next preliminary result required is *Jensen's formula.* Let us first recall a classical fact concerning harmonic functions. If $\psi(z)$ is analytic in the disk $|z| \leq R$ and if $\psi(z)$ has no zeros in that disk, $\log |\psi(z)|$ is harmonic in the disk. Integrating $[\log \psi(z)]/z$ over the circle of radius R we get, after taking real parts,

7 $$\log |\psi(0)| = \frac{1}{2\pi} \int_0^{2\pi} \log |\psi(Re^{i\theta})| \, d\theta$$

Let us observe that $\log |\psi(z)|$, being the real part of an analytic function, is a harmonic function. The above equality is often referred to as the *mean-value property of harmonic functions.* Assuming that these facts are known, we wish to prove the

8 **Lemma** If $f(z)$ is analytic in $|z| \leq R$, if $f(z)$ has zeros $a_1, a_2, \ldots, a_n$ in $|z| < R$ (multiple zeros being repeated), and if $f(0) \neq 0$, then

9 $$\log |f(0)| = \frac{1}{2\pi} \int_0^{2\pi} \log |f(Re^{i\theta})| \, d\theta - \sum_{i=1}^{n} \log \left(\frac{R}{|a_i|} \right)$$

Proof The function

$$F(z) = f(z) \prod_{i=1}^{n} \frac{R^2 - a_i^* z}{R(z - a_i)}$$

has the property that $|F(z)| = |f(z)|$ on $|z| = R$ and $F(z) \neq 0$ for $|z| \leq R$. Hence, from 7,

$$\log |F(0)| = \frac{1}{2\pi} \int_0^{2\pi} \log |f(Re^{i\theta})| \, d\theta$$

and, using the first equation in the second, we get

$$\frac{1}{2\pi} \int_0^{2\pi} \log |f(Re^{i\theta})| \, d\theta = \log |f(0)| + \sum_{i=1}^{n} \log \left(\frac{R}{a_i} \right) \qquad \text{Q.E.D.}$$

Note If $f(0) = 0$, let $f(z) = b_n z^n + \cdots$ be its Taylor expansion about $z = 0$. Then apply the formula to $f(z)/b_n z^n$. The left-hand side of 9 then becomes

10 $$\log |b_n| + n \log R \quad \triangleleft$$

The next result we need makes use of the notion of convexity. By definition, e^z is a *convex* function because, for any two x, y

$$\exp [\alpha x + (1 - \alpha) y] \leq \alpha e^x + (1 - \alpha) e^y \qquad \text{for every } \alpha \in [0,1]$$

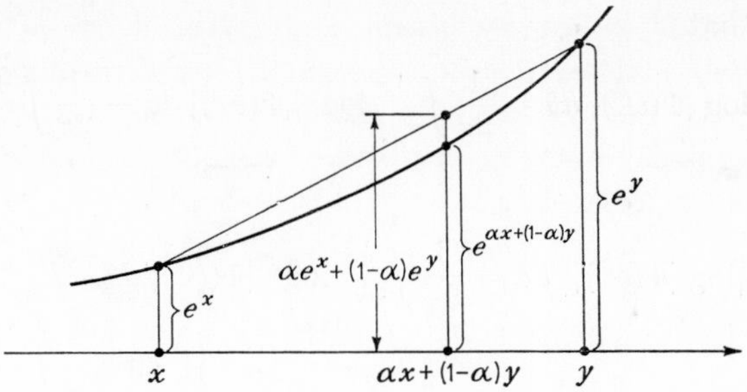

Fig. 9.5.2 Illustration exhibiting the convexity of the exponential function.

This inequality is illustrated in Fig. *9.5.2*. By induction it can be shown that if $w_1, w_2, \ldots, w_N$ are positive weights such that $\sum_1^N w_i = 1$, then

$$\exp\left(\sum_1^N w_i x_i\right) \leq \sum_{i=1}^N w_i e^{x_i}$$

and going over to the limit we get

11 **Lemma** If the weighting function $w(\omega')$ is such that $w(\omega') \geq 0$ for all ω' and $\int_{-\infty}^{+\infty} w(\omega')\,d\omega' = 1$, then

12 $$\exp\left[\int_{-\infty}^{+\infty} w(\omega')x(\omega')\,d\omega'\right] \leq \int_{-\infty}^{+\infty} w(\omega')\,\{\exp\,[x(\omega')]\}\,d\omega'$$

Proof of Theorem 1 $\Rightarrow$ By assumption, $H(s)$ is analytic for $\sigma = 0$. By *2*, $H(s)$ is analytic for all $\sigma \geq 0$. Map the right half s plane into the unit circle of the z plane by the transformation $z = (1 - s)/(1 + s)$; $H(s)$ becomes $\Phi(z) = \Phi(re^{j\theta})$. A simple computation gives [observe that $e^{j\theta} = (1 - j\omega)/(1 + j\omega)$; hence $\theta/2 = -\tan^{-1}\omega$]

13 $$\int_{-\pi}^{+\pi} |\Phi(e^{i\theta})|^2\,d\theta = 2\int_{-\infty}^{+\infty} \frac{|H(j\omega)|^2}{1+\omega^2}\,d\omega < \infty$$

where the inequality follows from assumption *3*.

It remains to establish *4*; observe that twice the L.H.S. of *4* is equal to $\int_{-\pi}^{+\pi} \log|\Phi(e^{j\theta})|\,d\theta$. Thus we must show that this integral is finite. For this purpose define over the interval $(-\pi,+\pi)$ the functions

$$\log^+ |\Phi(e^{j\theta})| = \max\,(0, \log|\Phi(e^{j\theta})|)$$

and

$$\log^- |\Phi(e^{j\theta})| = -\min\,(0, \log|\Phi(e^{j\theta})|)$$

Observe that, for all θ's, $\log^- |\Phi(e^{j\theta})| \geq 0$. From these definitions it follows that

$$\frac{1}{2\pi}\int_{-\pi}^{+\pi} \log |\Phi(e^{j\theta})|\, d\theta = \frac{1}{2\pi}\int_{-\pi}^{+\pi} \log^+ |\Phi(e^{j\theta})|\, d\theta - \frac{1}{2\pi}\int_{-\pi}^{+\pi} \log^- |\Phi(e^{j\theta})|\, d\theta$$

and

$$\frac{1}{2\pi}\int_{-\pi}^{+\pi} \big|\log |\Phi(e^{j\theta})|\big|\, d\theta = \frac{1}{2\pi}\int_{-\pi}^{+\pi} \log^+ |\Phi(e^{j\theta})|\, d\theta + \frac{1}{2\pi}\int_{-\pi}^{+\pi} \log^- |\Phi(e^{j\theta})|\, d\theta$$

From the fact that, for all real $x \geq 1$, $\log x < x^2$, it follows that

$$\frac{1}{2\pi}\int_{-\pi}^{+\pi} \log^+ |\Phi(e^{j\theta})|\, d\theta \leq \frac{1}{2\pi}\int_{-\pi}^{+\pi} |\Phi(e^{j\theta})|^2\, d\theta < \infty$$

Now $\Phi(z)$ is analytic in the unit circle, and hence $\log \Phi(e^{i\theta})$ is harmonic. Therefore, we may apply Jensen's formula *9*. Let us use the two inequalities above in the following computation:[1]

$$\frac{1}{2\pi}\int_{-\pi}^{+\pi} \big|[\log |\Phi(e^{j\theta})|]\big|\, d\theta = \frac{1}{2\pi}\int_{-\pi}^{+\pi} \log^+ |\Phi(e^{j\theta})|\, d\theta + \frac{1}{2\pi}\int_{-\pi}^{+\pi} \log^- |\Phi(e^{j\theta})|\, d\theta$$

14 $$= 2\frac{1}{2\pi}\int_{-\pi}^{+\pi} \log^+ |\Phi(e^{j\theta})|\, d\theta - \frac{1}{2\pi}\int_{-\pi}^{+\pi} \log |\Phi(e^{j\theta})|\, d\theta$$

$$\leq \frac{1}{\pi}\int_{-\pi}^{+\pi} |\Phi(e^{j\theta})|^2\, d\theta - \log |\Phi(0)|$$

Therefore by *13*

$$\int_{-\pi}^{+\pi} \big|[\log |\Phi(e^{j\theta})|]\big|\, d\theta < \infty$$

and, finally,

$$\int_{-\infty}^{+\infty} \frac{\big|[\log |H(j\omega)|]\big|}{1+\omega^2}\, d\omega < \infty$$

This concludes the proof of the direct statement.

$\Leftarrow$ Let $s = \sigma + j\omega$. For $\sigma > 0$, define

15 $$\alpha(\sigma + j\omega) = \int_{-\infty}^{+\infty} \log A(\omega') \cdot \frac{1}{\pi}\frac{+\sigma}{\sigma^2 + (\omega - \omega')^2}\, d\omega'$$

This integral converges because inequality *4* is satisfied; hence, $\alpha(\sigma + j\omega)$ is a real finite harmonic function for all $\sigma > 0$. For $\sigma \to 0$, $\alpha(\sigma + j\omega) \to \log A(\omega)$ because the weighting function in *15* becomes $\delta(\omega - \omega')$. Thus $\alpha(j\omega)$ is the gain in nepers corresponding to $A(\omega)$. The next step is to construct the phase associated with $\alpha(j\omega)$. Let $\beta(\sigma + j\omega)$ be the harmonic function conjugate to $\alpha(\sigma + j\omega)$ in the

[1] The computation assumes that $\Phi(0) \neq 0$. If this is not the case, consider the Taylor expansion $\Phi(z) = b_n z^n + \cdots$. By *10*, the term $\log |\Phi(0)|$ in the right-hand side of *14* is replaced by $\log |b_n|$.

domain $\sigma > 0$. It is well known that $\beta(\sigma + j\omega)$ is determined only within an additive constant.[1] Since $\beta(j\omega)$ will be the phase associated with $\alpha(j\omega)$, take $\beta(0) = 0$. Therefore, for every point (σ,ω) such that $\sigma > 0$,

$$\beta(\sigma + j\omega) = \int_0^{\sigma+j\omega} \left(-\frac{\delta\alpha}{\delta\omega}\, d\sigma + \frac{\delta\alpha}{\delta\sigma}\, d\omega \right)$$

where the path of integration from 0 to $\sigma + j\omega$ must lie completely in the right half plane. The integral above is independent of the path because $\alpha(\sigma + j\omega)$ is harmonic.[1]

The functions $\theta(s) = \alpha(\sigma + j\omega) + j\beta(\sigma + j\omega)$ and $e^{\theta(s)}$ are analytic for all $\sigma > 0$. Observe that

$$\lim_{\sigma\to 0} e^{\alpha(\sigma+j\omega)} = A(\omega)$$

Since the exponential function e^z is a convex function of the real variable z, and since the weighting function

$$w(\omega') = \frac{1}{\pi} \frac{\sigma}{\sigma^2 + (\omega - \omega')^2}$$

is positive and $\int_{-\infty}^{+\infty} w(\omega')\, d\omega' = 1$, then by Lemma *11* it follows that

$$e^{\alpha(s)} \le \frac{1}{\pi} \int_{-\infty}^{+\infty} \frac{A(\omega')\sigma}{(\omega - \omega')^2 + \sigma^2}\, d\omega' \qquad \text{for all } \sigma > 0$$

and, with the Schwarz inequality,

$$\int_{-\infty}^{+\infty} e^{2\alpha(\sigma+i\omega)}\, d\omega$$

$$\le \frac{1}{\pi^2} \int_{-\infty}^{+\infty} d\omega \int_{-\infty}^{+\infty} \frac{A^2(\omega')\sigma}{(\omega - \omega')^2 + \sigma^2}\, d\omega' \int_{-\infty}^{+\infty} \frac{\sigma\, d\omega''}{(\omega - \omega'')^2 + \sigma^2}$$

The last integral is equal to π by Lemma *6*. Reordering the right-hand side, it becomes successively

$$\frac{1}{\pi} \int_{-\infty}^{+\infty} d\omega \int_{-\infty}^{+\infty} \frac{A^2(\omega')\sigma}{(\omega - \omega')^2 + \sigma^2}\, d\omega'$$

$$= \frac{1}{\pi} \int_{-\infty}^{+\infty} A^2(\omega')\, d\omega' \int_{-\infty}^{+\infty} \frac{\sigma\, d\omega}{(\omega - \omega')^2 + \sigma^2}$$

$$= \int_{-\infty}^{+\infty} A^2(\omega')\, d\omega'$$

Hence, for all $\sigma > 0$,

$$\int_{-\infty}^{+\infty} e^{2\alpha(\sigma+j\omega)}\, d\omega \le \int_{-\infty}^{+\infty} A^2(\omega')\, d\omega' < \infty$$

where the last inequality follows by assumption *3*.

[1] W. Kaplan, "Advanced Calculus," sec. 9.22, Addison-Wesley Publishing Company, Reading, Mass., 1952.

Since $|e^{\theta(s)}|^2 = e^{2\alpha(\sigma+j\omega)}$, the above inequality implies that $e^{\theta(s)}$ is integrable square along any parallel to the $j\omega$ axis for all $\sigma > 0$. Furthermore, it is analytic in the right half plane. Therefore,[1] there exists a function of time $h(t)$ (the corresponding impulse response) vanishing for $t < 0$ such that

$$e^{\theta(s)} = \lim_{\Omega\to\infty} \int_{-\Omega}^{+\Omega} h(t)e^{-(\sigma+j\omega)t}\, dt$$

We have, then, shown that if *3* and *4* hold, we can associate with $A(\omega)$ a phase $\beta(\omega)$ such that the transfer function $A(\omega)e^{j\beta(\omega)}$ has an impulse response which vanishes for all $t < 0$. Q.E.D.

6 *Relation between the real and imaginary parts of $T(s)$*

The purpose of this section is to establish a number of important relationships between the real part and the imaginary part of the values taken on the $j\omega$ axis by transfer functions and related functions. Bode's book (Ref. *1*) is the most complete reference on this subject. The proofs that follow are based on Cauchy's residue theorem and are due to Bode. In this section we make the following assumptions:

1 **Assumption** $T(s)$ is analytic for Re $s > 0$.

2 **Assumption** $[T(s)]^* = T(s^*)$ for Re $s \geq 0$. In particular, if we let $T(j\omega) = R(j\omega) + jI(j\omega)$, then $R(j\omega) = R(-j\omega)$ and $I(j\omega) = -I(-j\omega)$ for all real ω.

3 **Assumption** $T(s)$ may have a finite number of singularities on the $j\omega$ axis provided that at each such singularity, say $j\omega_0$, $(s - j\omega_0)T(s) \to 0$ as $s - j\omega_0 \to 0$.

4 **Assumption** As $|s| \to \infty$, $\dfrac{T(s)}{s} \to 0$ uniformly in $|\measuredangle s| \leq \dfrac{\pi}{2}$.

5 *Comment* If $T(s)$ is a strictly stable rational transfer function and if $T(j\omega) \to 0$ as $|\omega| \to \infty$, Assumptions *1* to *4* are satisfied; the results that follow will therefore be applicable to the usual finite lumped linear systems. These assumptions, however, cover a broader class of functions. Consider

$$H(j\omega) = \frac{1}{\sqrt{1 - \omega^2 + j\omega}}$$

Clearly, $|H(j\omega)| = 1$ for $-1 \leq \omega \leq 1$ and $|H(j\omega)|$ monotonically decreases to zero as $\omega \to \infty$; hence, H is the transfer function of a low-pass filter. Let $T(j\omega) = \log H(j\omega)$: $T(j\omega)$ satisfies the above assumptions and $R(j\omega)$ and $I(j\omega)$ are respectively the gain (in nepers) and the phase (in radians) of that low-pass filter.

[1] Ref. 6, p. 8; or Ref. 7, p. 214.

6 **Theorem** If $T(s)$ fulfills Assumptions *1* to *4* and if s_1 is inside the right half plane ($\text{Re}\, s_1 > 0$), then

7 $$T(s_1) = \frac{2s_1}{\pi} \int_0^\infty \frac{R(j\omega)}{\omega^2 + s_1^2} d\omega$$

In other words, the knowledge of the real part of $T(s)$ along the $j\omega$ axis determines completely $T(s)$ inside the right half plane. This fact has been used for solving some time-domain approximation problems and for designing equalizers.

Proof The proof is a direct application of Cauchy's residue theorem. We shall take as contour the $j\omega$ axis from $+jR$ to $-jR$ and the right-half-plane semicircle of radius R, as shown in Fig. *9.6.1*. The integrand is chosen to be

$$\theta(s) = \frac{T(s)}{s - s_1} - \frac{T(s)}{s + s_1} = \frac{2s_1}{s^2 - s_1^2} T(s)$$

Assume first that $T(s)$ has no $j\omega$-axis singularities. Then $\theta(s)$ is analytic everywhere on the contour and inside it except for a pole at $s = s_1$, where its residue is $T(s_1)$; hence

$$T(s_1) = \frac{1}{2\pi j} \oint_C \frac{2s_1 T(s)}{s^2 - s_1^2} ds$$

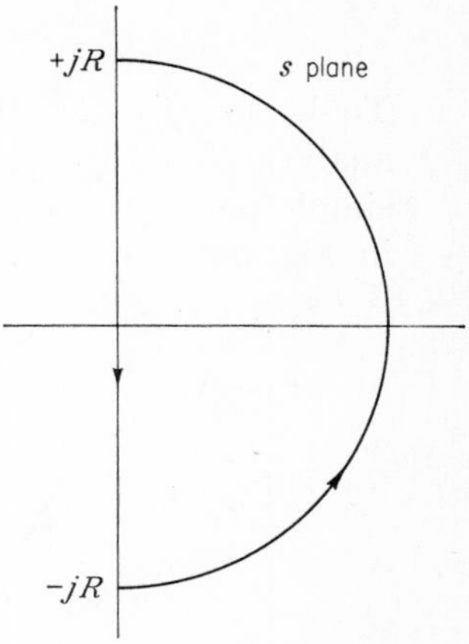

Fig. 9.6.1 Path of integration used in proving Theorem *9.6.6*.

The integral along the right-half-plane semicircle of radius R will go to zero as $R \to \infty$ because, as $|s| \to \infty$, $s\theta(s) \sim 2s_1 T(s)/s \to 0$ uniformly in $|\measuredangle s| \le \pi/2$. Thus

$$T(s_1) = \frac{-1}{2\pi j} \int_{-\infty}^{+\infty} \frac{2s_1[R(j\omega) + jI(j\omega)]}{-(\omega^2 + s_1^2)} j\, d\omega$$

or

$$T(s_1) = \frac{s_1}{\pi} \int_{-\infty}^{+\infty} \frac{R(j\omega) + jI(j\omega)}{\omega^2 + s_1^2} d\omega$$

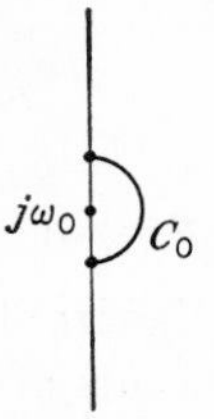

Fig. 9.6.2 Indentation used to bypass the singular point $j\omega_0$.

7 follows directly from the last equation by the symmetry properties mentioned in *2*.

If $T(s)$ has a singularity at $j\omega_0$, the contour C is modified by an indentation consisting of a semicircle C_0 of radius ρ centered on $j\omega_0$ (see Fig. *9.6.2*). The integral along C_0 vanishes, as $\rho \to 0$, because the length of the path of integration is $\pi\rho$ and, by *3*,

$$\lim_{\rho \to 0} \left[\rho \sup_{s \in C_0} \frac{T(s)}{s^2 - s_1^2} \right] = 0$$

Thus the $j\omega$ singularities will not contribute to the contour integral. This completes the proof of *7*.

8 **Theorem** If $T(s)$ satisfies Assumptions *1* to *4*, then, for any point $j\omega_1$ of the $j\omega$ axis,

9
$$I(j\omega_1) = \frac{2\omega_1}{\pi}\int_0^{\infty} \frac{R(j\omega) - R(j\omega_1)}{\omega^2 - \omega_1^2}\, d\omega$$

Proof Here we consider the following integrand:

$$\theta(s) = \frac{T(s) - R(j\omega_1)}{s - j\omega_1} - \frac{T(s) - R(j\omega_1)}{s + j\omega_1} = \frac{2j\omega_1[T(s) - R(j\omega_1)]}{s^2 + \omega_1^2}$$

To begin with, let $T(s)$ be analytic along the $j\omega$ axis; then $\theta(s)$ is analytic inside the right half plane and on the $j\omega$ axis except for two simple poles at $\pm j\omega_1$. Let us integrate $\theta(s)$ on the contour C shown in Fig. *9.6.3*: note the indentations C_1 and C_2 of the contour at the poles $j\omega_1$ and $-j\omega_1$. From Cauchy's integral theorem

$$\oint_C \theta(s)\, ds = 0$$

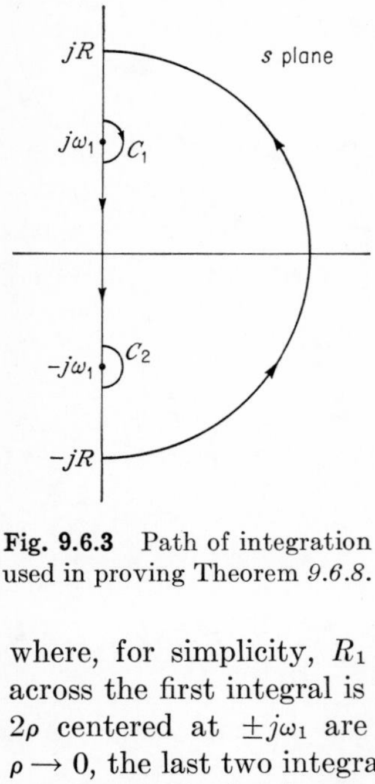

Fig. 9.6.3 Path of integration used in proving Theorem *9.6.8*.

Since for $|s| \to \infty$, $s\theta(s) \sim T(s)/s \to 0$ uniformly in $|\measuredangle s| \leq \pi/2$, the contribution of the right semicircle of radius R vanishes as $R \to \infty$. Therefore, in the limit of $R \to \infty$,

$$⨍_{-\infty}^{+\infty} \frac{2\omega_1[T(j\omega) - R_1]}{\omega^2 - \omega_1^2}\, d\omega + \int_{C_1} \frac{T(s) - R_1}{s - j\omega_1}\, ds - \int_{C_2} \frac{T(s) - R_1}{s + j\omega_1}\, ds - \int_{C_1} \frac{T(s) - R_1}{s + j\omega_1}\, ds + \int_{C_2} \frac{T(s) - R_1}{s - j\omega_1}\, ds = 0$$

where, for simplicity, R_1 is written for $R(j\omega_1)$. The horizontal bar across the first integral is used to indicate that the intervals of length 2ρ centered at $\pm j\omega_1$ are not included in the integration. Now as $\rho \to 0$, the last two integrals vanish, since their integrands are analytic in the neighborhoods of $-j\omega_1$ and $+j\omega_1$, respectively. Consider now the second integral: its integrand has a pole at the center of the semicircle C_1 and has the Laurent series expansion about $s = j\omega_1$,

$$\frac{T(s) - R_1}{s - j\omega_1} = \frac{jI(j\omega_1)}{s - j\omega_1} + \frac{d}{ds}[R(s) - R_1 + jI(s)]\Big|_{s=j\omega_1} + \frac{s - j\omega_1}{2!}\frac{d^2}{ds^2}[R(s) - R_1 + jI(s)]\Big|_{s=j\omega_1} + \cdots$$

Clearly, as $\rho \to 0$, only the first term contributes to the integral and

$$\int_{C_1} \frac{T(s) - R_1}{s - j\omega_1} ds \to jI(j\omega_1) \int_{C_1} \frac{ds}{s - j\omega_1} = -\pi I(j\omega_1)$$

The third integral gives the same answer. Therefore, as $\rho \to 0$, we get

$$2\pi I(j\omega_1) = \int_{-\infty}^{+\infty} \frac{2\omega_1[R(j\omega) - R(j\omega_1)]}{\omega^2 - \omega_1^2} d\omega + 2j\omega_1 \int_{-\infty}^{+\infty} \frac{I(j\omega)}{\omega^2 - \omega_1^2} d\omega$$

The last integral is zero, since $I(j\omega)$ is an odd function of ω by *2*. Since $R(j\omega)$ is an even function of ω, the first integrand remains finite at $\omega = \pm\omega_1$ and is an even function of ω; therefore, the integration need only be carried from 0 to ∞, and *9* follows.

If $T(s)$ has singularities on the $j\omega$ axis, the contour has to be appropriately indented and it can be shown, as in the preceding case, that the integrals along these indentations do not contribute to the integral. Q.E.D.

The next question that comes to mind is the following: Since $R(j\omega)$ determines the imaginary part, does the imaginary part determine the real part? Consider the example of $T(s)$ equal to an arbitrary real constant for all s. $I(j\omega)$ is identically zero, but $R(j\omega)$ is a nonzero constant. The answer to the question is, therefore, negative. The precise result is the following

10 **Theorem** If $T(s)$ satisfies Assumptions *1* to *3*, and if $T(s)$ is analytic at infinity with the Taylor expansion

$$T(s) = R_\infty + \frac{I_\infty}{s} + \frac{R_2}{s^2} + \cdots$$

then, for any point $j\omega_1$ of the $j\omega$ axis

11 $$R(j\omega_1) = R_\infty - \frac{2}{\pi} \int_0^\infty \frac{\omega I(j\omega) - \omega_1 I(j\omega_1)}{\omega^2 - \omega_1^2} d\omega$$

Proof Exercise for the reader. [*Hint:* Use the integrand

$$\theta(s) = \frac{T(s) - jI(j\omega_1)}{s - j\omega_1} + \frac{T(s) + jI(j\omega_1)}{s + j\omega_1}$$

It is the integration along the right half semicircle of radius R which contributes the term R_∞ in *11*.]

12 *Comment* In each of the above three formulas *7*, *9*, and *11*, the left-hand side is a *functional* of $R(\cdot)$, $R(\cdot) - R(j\omega_1)$, $I(\cdot) - j\omega_1 I(j\omega_1)$, respectively. [The dot $(\cdot)$ is used to indicate the variable $j\omega$ which runs from $-j\infty$ to $j\infty$.] For example, in *9*, $I(j\omega_1)$ depends on the values that $R(\cdot)$ takes over the whole $j\omega$ axis. The weighting function $2\omega_1/\omega^2 - \omega_1^2$ does give more emphasis to the values in the neighborhood of ω_1. However, it is instructive to consider a case where the value of $I(j\omega_1)$ is determined by the values of $R(j\omega)$ taken several decades away from ω_1. For example, consider a strictly stable amplifier with $H(s)$ as a transfer function. Take $T(s) = \log_e H(s)$; hence, $R(j\omega) = \log_e |H(j\omega)|$ and $I(j\omega) = \measuredangle H(j\omega)$. Let the gain $R(j\omega)$ be zero nepers for $\omega < \omega_0$ and be $-N$ nepers for $\omega > \omega_0$. Consider a frequency $\omega_1 \ll \omega_0$, say $10^{-3} \times \omega_0$. Then, since $\omega \gg \omega_1$ whenever $R(j\omega) \neq 0$, we obtain from *9*

$$I(j\omega_1) \simeq \frac{2\omega_1}{\pi} \int_0^\infty \frac{-N}{\omega^2}\, d\omega = \frac{-2N\omega_1}{\pi\omega_0} \qquad \text{rad}$$

Thus for any $\omega_1 \ll \omega_0$, the phase shift is linear with frequency but the slope of the phase curve depends on the amplifier gain many decades above the frequency ω_1.

13 *Comment* The three relations just established, *9* and *11* especially, are of great practical importance in the design of communication systems. For example, with $T(s)$ = log of a transfer function, it is often required to design a network that has a given gain $R(j\omega)$ and whose phase shift has a derivative almost constant through a certain frequency band: $dI(j\omega)/d\omega \simeq$ constant, i.e., the delay through the network is constant (*9.11.2*). The network is designed in two steps (see Fig. *9.6.4*): First a filter that provides the specified gain $R_F(j\omega) = R(j\omega)$

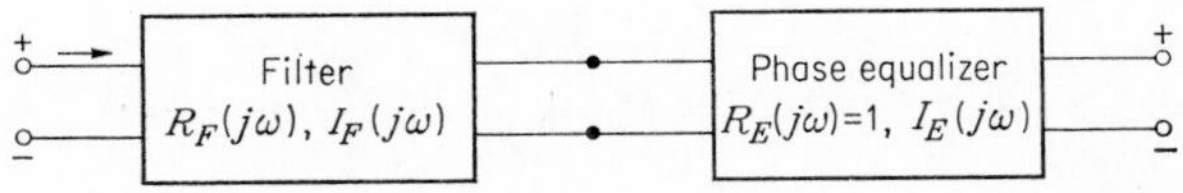

Fig. 9.6.4 Tandem connection of a filter and phase equalizer.

and the phase $I_F(j\omega)$ associated with $R(j\omega)$ as computed by *9* is designed. Next a phase equalizer whose gain $R_E(j\omega)$ is unity at all frequencies and whose phase $I_E(j\omega)$ when added to $I_F(j\omega)$ gives the required phase $I(j\omega)$ is designed. Formula *9* allows the designer to compute $I_F(j\omega)$ before the filter is built and therefore allows the design and testing of both filter and equalizer to proceed simultaneously. Another well-known example is the problem of shaping the loop gain of a single-loop-feedback amplifier. Bode's book is the best reference on this subject. Recently the extension to conditionally stable amplifiers has been carried out.[1] In physics, these relations are known as the

[1] J. Oizumi, M. Kimura, Design of Conditionally Stable Feedback System, *I.R.E. Trans. Circuit Theory*, vol. CT-4, no. 3, 1957.

Kramers-Kronig[1] relations or the dispersion relations; they relate, for example, the real and imaginary parts of the magnetic susceptibility χ and those of the dielectric constant ε. In nuclear theory these dispersion relations have recently received a great deal of attention.[2]

14 *Comment* In practice, it is convenient to plot curves on a log frequency scale. For this reason, a change of variable $u = \log(\omega/\omega_2)$, where ω_2 is a normalizing frequency, is introduced. The result is

$$I(j\omega_1) = \frac{1}{\pi}\int_0^\infty \frac{R(j\omega) - R(j\omega_1)}{\sinh u}\,du$$

or

$$I(j\omega_1) = \frac{1}{\pi}\int_{-\infty}^\infty \frac{dR}{du}\log\left|\coth\frac{u}{2}\right|du$$

This integral is of interest because it shows that $I(j\omega_1)$ is a weighted average of the slope of R when plotted on the log frequency scale $u = \log(\omega/\omega_1)$. A plot of the weighting function $\log\left|\coth\frac{u}{2}\right|$ is shown in Fig. *9.6.5*.

[1] See, for example, C. Kittel, "Elementary Statistical Physics," John Wiley & Sons, Inc., New York, 1958.

[2] A. Bohr, in W. E. Brittin (ed.), "Lectures in Theoretical Physics," vol. III, Interscience Publishers, Inc., New York, 1961.

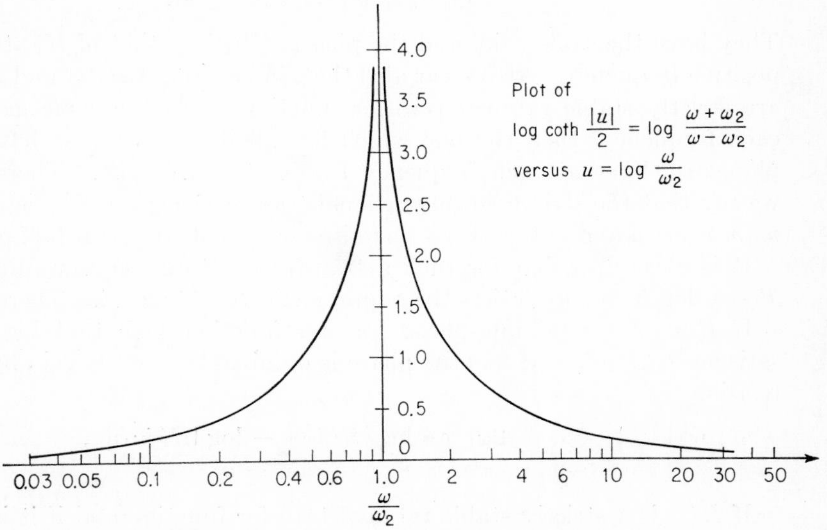

Fig. 9.6.5 Plot of $\log\coth\frac{|u|}{2} = \log\frac{\omega + \omega_2}{\omega - \omega_2}$ versus $u = \log\frac{\omega}{\omega_2}$.

7 *Minimum-phase transfer functions*

Consider the two rational transfer functions $H_1(s)$ and $H_2(s)$ that have the pole and zero configurations shown in Fig. *9.7.1*. They have identical pole locations, but the zeros of $H_2(s)$ are the mirror images of those of $H_1(s)$ with respect to the $j\omega$ axis.

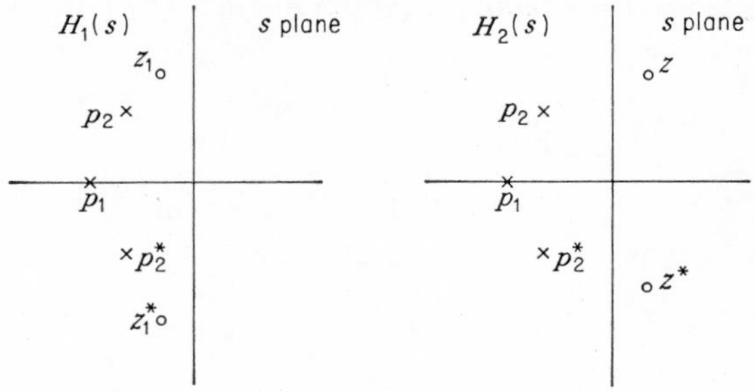

Fig. 9.7.1 Pole and zero locations of $H_1(s)$ and $H_2(s)$.

Assume that $H_1(s)$ and $H_2(s)$ have the same constant factor; then from the potential analogy it is obvious that, for all ω's,

$$|H_1(j\omega)| = |H_2(j\omega)|$$

and for $\omega > 0$

$$\measuredangle H_1(j\omega) > \measuredangle H_2(j\omega)$$

They have the same gain, and the phase of H_2 lags that of H_1 at each positive frequency. It is clear also that, in general, if $H_1(s)$ and $H_2(s)$ are strictly stable rational transfer functions with the same gain at each frequency, then the one which has all its zeros in the left half plane will have at each frequency the least phase shift. Therefore, we say that the strictly stable rational transfer function $H(s)$ is *minimum phase* if and only if it has no finite zeros inside the right half plane.

It is clear also that for such a transfer function the new function $T(s) = \log H(s)$ may satisfy the requirements *9.6.1* to *9.6.4*. Therefore:

1 If $H(s)$ is a minimum-phase transfer function such that $\log H(s)$ satisfies *9.6.1* to *9.6.4*, then its phase is obtainable from its gain by the relation

$$\measuredangle H(j\omega_1) = \frac{2\omega_1}{\pi} \int_0^\infty \frac{\log |H(j\omega)| - \log |H(j\omega_1)|}{\omega^2 - \omega_1^2} \, d\omega$$

If $H(s)$ is a strictly stable rational transfer function and if it is not minimum phase, can its phase be computed by the contour integration technique used in the proof of *9.6.8*? The answer is yes, provided certain modifications are introduced: $T(s) = \log H(s)$ will have a branch point at each right-half-plane zero. For the case of Fig. *9.7.1*, the appropriate contour is shown in Fig. *9.7.2*: in order to remain on the same sheet of the Riemann surface of the integrand

$$\frac{2j\omega_1[\log H_2(s) - \log H_2(j\omega_1)]}{s^2 + \omega_1^2}$$

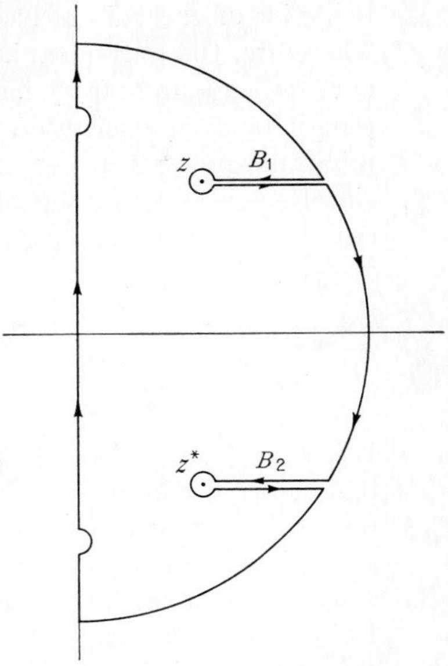

Fig. 9.7.2 Appropriate contour to compute the phase of H_2 from its gain along the $j\omega$ axis.

the branch cuts B_1 and B_2 had to be introduced. With respect to these branch-cut integrations it is straightforward to establish that (I) the numerator bracket of the integrand takes on the lower (outgoing) integration path of each cut a value larger by $2\pi j$ than the value it takes on the upper (incoming) integration path; (II) the integration around the almost complete circles centered on the zeros of $H_2(s)$ contribute nothing in the limit; and (III) a few standard manipulations lead to the answer

$$\measuredangle H_2(j\omega_1) = \frac{2\omega_1}{\pi}\int_0^\infty \frac{\log H(j\omega) - \log H(j\omega_1)}{\omega^2 - \omega_1^2}\,d\omega - 2\sum_i \tan^{-1}\frac{\sigma_{z_i}}{\omega_1 - \omega_{z_i}} - 2\sum_i \tan^{-1}\frac{\sigma_{z_i}}{\omega_1 + \omega_{z_i}}$$

where σ_{z_i} and ω_{z_i} are the real and imaginary parts of the first-quadrant zeros z_i of $H(s)$.

For the case where $H(s)$ is not rational, we adopt the following

2 **Definition** If $H(s)$ satisfies Assumptions *9.6.1* to *9.6.4* and if it satisfies the Paley-Wiener criterion, then it is said to be minimum phase if and only if its phase is given by

$$\measuredangle H(j\omega_1) = \frac{2\omega_1}{\pi}\int_0^\infty \frac{\log H(j\omega) - \log H(j\omega_1)}{\omega^2 - \omega_1^2}\,d\omega$$

3 *Comment* In evaluating experimental data it is strictly impossible to determine whether or not measured gain and phase curves are those of a minimum-phase transfer function. The reason is that no experimental data extend over all frequencies from 0 to ∞, and we have seen in *9.6.12* that the phase at some fixed frequency may depend significantly on the behavior of the gain at frequencies arbitrarily large compared with ω_1. Therefore, the only meaningful question is this: given gain and phase curves over a finite frequency band, and given an assumed gain over the remaining frequencies, do these gain and phase curves belong to a minimum-phase transfer function? This question can be answered simply by calculating the minimum phase associated with the given gain curve and comparing it with the given phase curve.

8 *Uncertainty principle*

It is a fact of experience that as the width of a pulse becomes smaller its bandwidth becomes larger in such a manner that the product of the two remains roughly constant. It is possible to give an exact and very general statement of this fact. It will turn out that the resulting inequality is exactly the same as that occurring in the statement of Heisenberg's uncertainty principle in quantum mechanics. The reason why this inequality occurs both in a time-frequency discussion and in a position-momentum discussion follows from the fact that in quantum mechanics the momentum is associated with the ϕ function that is the Fourier transform of the ψ function, which is related to the position.

We consider a real signal $h(t)$ and its Fourier transform

$$H(j\omega) = \int_{-\infty}^{+\infty} h(t)e^{-j\omega t}\,dt$$

We assume that the following inequalities are satisfied:

1 $$\|h\|^2 \triangleq \int_{-\infty}^{+\infty} h^2(t)\,dt < \infty$$

2 $$\bar{t} \triangleq \frac{\int_{-\infty}^{+\infty} th^2(t)\,dt}{\|h\|^2} < \infty$$

3 $$(\Delta t)^2 \triangleq \frac{1}{\|h\|^2}\int_{-\infty}^{+\infty} (t-\bar{t})^2h^2(t)\,dt < \infty$$

If we think of $h(t)$ as a voltage across a 1-ohm load, $h^2(t)$ is the instantaneous power dissipated in that load. Therefore, $\|h\|^2$ represents the total energy dissipated in the load. Following Gabor, we shall call $\bar{t}$ the "epoch" of the signal: $\bar{t}$ is the center of gravity of the area under the curve $h^2(t)$. And $(\Delta t)^2$ is called the *dispersion* in time of the signal: it is a measure of how much the signal is spread about $\bar{t}$. More technically, Δt is the radius of gyration of the area under $h^2(t)$ about an axis going through $\bar{t}$. From another point of view, since the step response is the integral of the impulse response, Δt is a measure of the rise time of a linear system whose transfer function is $H(s)$. Similarly, we can define

4 $$\|H\|^2 = \int_{-\infty}^{+\infty} H(j\omega)H^*(j\omega)\, d\omega$$

5 $$\bar{\omega} \triangleq \frac{1}{\|H\|^2} \int_{-\infty}^{+\infty} \omega H(j\omega)H^*(j\omega)\, d\omega$$

6 $$(\Delta\omega)^2 = \frac{1}{\|H\|^2} \int_{-\infty}^{+\infty} \omega^2 H(j\omega)H^*(j\omega)\, d\omega$$

We assume that $\bar{\omega}$ and $(\Delta\omega)^2$ are finite. From Parseval's theorem,

$$\|h\|^2 = \frac{1}{2\pi} \|H\|^2$$

Since h is real, $H(-j\omega) = H(j\omega)^*$ for all real ω; hence $\bar{\omega} = 0$. Again $\Delta\omega$ is a measure of the bandwidth of the signal. The precise relationship between this bandwidth $\Delta\omega$ and the width Δt is the uncertainty principle, which may be expressed as the

7 **Theorem** If the signal $h(t)$ is such that the integrals *1* to *6* are finite, then

8 $$\Delta t \cdot \Delta\omega \geq \tfrac{1}{4}$$

Proof Define

$$H_1(j\omega) = H(j\omega)e^{+j\omega\bar{t}}$$

Then

$$|H_1(j\omega)|^2 = |H(j\omega)|^2 \qquad \text{and} \qquad \|h\|^2 = \|h_1\|^2$$

and since the Fourier transform is a special case of the bilateral Laplace transform (*B.2.12 et seq.*)

$$\mathcal{L}_{\mathrm{II}}^{-1}[H_1(s)] = h_1(t) = h(t + \bar{t})$$

From *3*

$$(\Delta t)^2 = \frac{1}{\|h\|^2} \int \tau^2 h_1^2(\tau)\, d\tau$$

Differentiating $H_1(j\omega) = \mathcal{L}_{\mathrm{II}}[h_1(t)]$, we get

$$j\,\frac{d}{d\omega} H_1(j\omega) = \int t h_1(t) e^{-j\omega t}\, dt$$

which means that the transform of $th_1(t)$ is $j\,\dfrac{d}{d\omega} H_1(j\omega)$. Parseval's theorem gives

$$\int t^2 h_1^2(t)\, dt = \frac{1}{2\pi} \int \frac{dH_1}{d\omega}\frac{dH_1^*}{d\omega}\, d\omega$$

and hence

9 $$(\Delta t)^2 = \frac{1}{\|H_1\|^2} \int \frac{dH_1}{d\omega}\frac{dH_1^*}{d\omega}\, d\omega$$

Consider the product of *6* and *9*. Since the product will not be affected if H_1 is multiplied by a constant, we may assume, without any loss of generality, that $\|H_1\|^2 = 1$. The result is

10
$$(\Delta\omega\,\Delta t)^2 = \int \omega^2 H_1 H_1^*\,d\omega \int \frac{dH_1}{d\omega}\frac{dH_1^*}{d\omega}\,d\omega$$

Now recall that the Schwarz inequality applied to complex functions states that

$$\int \psi_1\psi_1^*\,d\omega \int \psi_2\psi_2^*\,d\omega \geq \tfrac{1}{4}\left[\int (\psi_1\psi_2^* + \psi_2\psi_1^*)\,d\omega\right]^2$$

With $\psi_1 = \omega H_1$ and $\psi_2 = dH_1/d\omega$ the left-hand side of the above inequality is identical with the right-hand side of *10*; therefore

11
$$(\Delta t\,\Delta\omega)^2 \geq \tfrac{1}{4}N^2$$

where

$$N = \int \left(\omega H_1 \frac{dH_1^*}{d\omega} + \frac{dH_1}{d\omega}\,\omega H_1^*\right) d\omega$$

Upon integrating the first term by parts and observing that

$$\omega|H_1(j\omega)|^2 \to 0$$

as $\omega \to \pm\infty$, we get

$$N = -\int H_1(j\omega)H_1^*(j\omega)\,d\omega = -1$$

in view of the normalization assumption. Substituting this into *11* establishes the inequality *8*.

12 *Exercise* Prove Schwarz's inequality for complex functions. (*Hint:* Define the scalar product $\langle\psi_1,\psi_2\rangle \equiv \int \psi_1^*\psi_2\,d\omega$. Now, for all real λ, $\langle\psi_1 + \lambda\psi_2, \psi_1 + \lambda\psi_2\rangle = \langle\psi_1,\psi_1\rangle + \lambda^2\langle\psi_2,\psi_2\rangle + \lambda[\langle\psi_1,\psi_2\rangle + \langle\psi_2,\psi_1\rangle] \geq 0$, from which the desired inequality follows.)

9 *The dispersion of the unit-impulse response*

If the transfer function of a linear system has a constant gain $H(j\omega) = A$ and a phase linear with frequency $\phi(\omega) = -\omega\tau$ (that is, constant group delay τ), the impulse response is given by $A\,\delta(t - \tau)$. We know also that any system with only one of these types of ideal behavior no longer has an impulse response consisting of a single impulse; that is, if either or both of these properties are not fulfilled, the impulse response has a dispersion $(\Delta t)^2 > 0$. This intuitive idea can be given a precise expression by the following result.

1 **Theorem** If assumptions *9.8.1* to *9.8.3* hold and if we let

$$H(j\omega) = A(\omega)e^{j\phi(\omega)}$$

and $\phi(\omega) = -\omega\bar{t} + \Delta\phi(\omega)$, then

2 $$(\Delta t)^2 = \frac{1}{\|A\|^2}\int_{-\infty}^{+\infty} A^2(\omega)\left[\left(\frac{d}{d\omega}\log A\right)^2 + \left(\frac{d\Delta\phi}{d\omega}\right)^2\right] d\omega$$

where

$$\|A\|^2 = \int_{-\infty}^{+\infty} A^2(\omega)\, d\omega$$

3 *Comment* The energy density along the ω axis, $A^2(\omega)$, is a common weighting factor in the numerator. In addition, two terms contribute to $(\Delta t)^2$, one involving $(d \log A/d\omega)^2$, which is a measure of the *gain distortion* (the deviation of the gain from a constant), and the second involving $(d\Delta\phi/d\omega)^2$, which is a measure of the *group delay distortion.* Finally, this theorem implies the

4 **Assertion** Of all systems that have the same gain curve (i.e., the same $|H(j\omega)|$), the linear phase system has the least dispersion $(\Delta t)^2$.

Proof As a first step in the derivation, let us introduce $h_1(t)$ and $H_1(j\omega)$ as in *9.8.7*. With our present notations,

$$H_1(j\omega) = A(\omega)e^{j\Delta\phi(\omega)}$$

Furthermore, $h_1(t)$ has the same dispersion as $h(t)$, since it results from $h(t)$ by a translation in time of $\bar{t}$ sec. Observing that

$$\mathfrak{L}[th_1(t)] = j\frac{d}{d\omega}H_1(j\omega)$$

we have, by Parseval's theorem,

5 $$(\Delta t)^2 = \frac{1}{\|H_1\|^2}\int_{-\infty}^{+\infty} \frac{d}{d\omega}H_1(j\omega)\cdot\frac{d}{d\omega}H_1^*(j\omega)\, d\omega$$

Since $\dfrac{d}{d\omega}H_1(j\omega) = A\left(\dfrac{1}{A}\dfrac{dA}{d\omega}e^{j\Delta\phi} + j\dfrac{d\Delta\phi}{d\omega}e^{j\Delta\phi}\right)$, we have

6 $$\frac{d}{d\omega}H_1(j\omega)\frac{d}{d\omega}H_1(j\omega)^* = A^2(\omega)\left[\left(\frac{d}{d\omega}\log A\right)^2 + \left(\frac{d\,\Delta\phi}{d\omega}\right)^2\right]$$

Finally,

7 $$\|H_1\|^2 = \int_{-\infty}^{+\infty}|H_1(j\omega)|^2\, d\omega = \int_{-\infty}^{+\infty}A^2(\omega)\, d\omega$$

and *2* follows from *5* to *7*.

10 *Moments*

Consider a linear time-invariant system $\mathcal{S}$ whose impulse response h is such that the integral $\int_{-\infty}^{+\infty} t^k h(t)\,dt$ exists for all integers $k \geq 0$. The value of the integral is called the *kth moment of h,* and we shall label it M_k; thus

1 $$M_k = \int_{-\infty}^{+\infty} t^k h(t)\,dt \qquad k = 0, 1, 2, \ldots$$

We shall now exhibit a relation between M_k and the system transfer function H. By definition

$$H(s) = \int_{-\infty}^{+\infty} h(t) e^{-st}\,dt$$

Let us proceed formally and differentiate k times under the integral sign. Thus, for s such that $\alpha < \operatorname{Re} s < \beta$, where α and β are the abscissae of absolute convergence of h (see *B.2.13*),

$$H^{(k)}(s) = \int_{-\infty}^{+\infty} (-t)^k h(t) e^{-st}\,dt$$

and, provided $\alpha < 0 < \beta$,

2 $$M_k = (-1)^k H^{(k)}(0) = \int_{-\infty}^{+\infty} t^k h(t)\,dt$$

From the Taylor series expansion of H about $s = 0$,

$$H(s) = \sum_{k=0}^{\infty} H^{(k)}(0) \frac{s^k}{k!}$$

and by *2*, we have

3 $$H(s) = \sum_{k=0}^{k} (-1)^k \frac{M_k}{k!} s^k$$

since $H(s)$ is analytic inside its strip of convergence. Therefore, the moments of h prescribe the behavior of H in the neighborhood of the origin. In those cases where, for example, H may be continued analytically in the whole plane, the knowledge of all the moments specifies H uniquely and, consequently, the function h itself. In general, however, the moments do not specify h uniquely.

4 *Exercise* Assume H to be analytic in a neighborhood of the origin. Let its Taylor expansion be written as *3* above. Is M_k the kth moment of h? [*Hint:* Consider the case $h(t) = 1(t)e^t$.]

The moments are of importance in engineering because the knowledge of, say, the first N moments of h describes h to a certain extent. For example, we may state the following

5 **Theorem** Let $\mathcal{S}_1$ ($\mathcal{S}_2$, respectively) be a linear time-invariant system with impulse response h_1 (h_2, respectively) and transfer function H_1 (H_2, respectively). Assume that the first N moments are equal. Then, for all t, the zero-state responses of $\mathcal{S}_1$ and $\mathcal{S}_2$ are equal provided their common input is a polynomial in t of degree smaller than or equal to N.

6 *Comment* We could say that the equalities

7 $$\int_{-\infty}^{+\infty} t^k h_1(t)\, dt = \int_{-\infty}^{+\infty} t^k h_2(t)\, dt = M_k \qquad k = 1, 2, \ldots, N$$

imply that the systems $\mathcal{S}_1$ and $\mathcal{S}_2$ are *zero-state equivalent* (*2.9.1*) over the class of polynomial inputs of degree $\leq N$.

Proof Let $\sum_{k=0}^{N} c_k t^k$ be the common input; then the outputs y_1 and y_2 are given by

$$\begin{aligned} y_i(t) &= \int_{-\infty}^{+\infty} \sum_{0}^{N} c_k (t - \tau)^k h_i(\tau)\, d\tau \qquad i = 1, 2 \\ &= \sum_{k=0}^{N} c_k \sum_{\alpha=0}^{k} \binom{k}{\alpha} (-1)^\alpha t^{k-\alpha} \int_{-\infty}^{+\infty} \tau^\alpha h_i(\tau)\, d\tau \end{aligned}$$

and using *7*,

$$y_i(t) = \sum_{k=0}^{T} c_k \sum_{k=0}^{k} \binom{\alpha}{k} (-1)^\alpha t^{k-\alpha} M_\alpha$$

The right-hand side is independent of i; thus the outputs y_1 and y_2 are identical for all t.

11 *Group delay*

The group delay—a concept closely related to the group velocity of the physicist—is a very basic concept which is very frequently used when requirements are set up for communication systems. In order to introduce the concept, let us consider the following situation. We are given a strictly stable linear system: it may be an amplifier, a filter, or a whole communication system. Let us excite it by a unit impulse $\delta(t)$; in other words, the input signal contains all frequencies with equal amplitude and with the same phase. The output is by definition the unit-impulse response $h(t)$. According to the Fourier integral theorem

1 $$h(t) = \frac{1}{2\pi} \int_{-\infty}^{+\infty} H(j\omega)e^{j\omega t}\, d\omega$$

That is, $h(t)$ is a superposition of sine waves of all frequencies. Let us ask the following question: If we consider only the contributions to $h(t)$ of the frequencies in the interval $(\omega_0 - \Delta, \omega_0 + \Delta)$, where Δ is very small and $\Delta \ll \omega_0$, is it possible to ascribe to this "group" of frequencies a time at which they appear at the output? The answer will turn out to be that it is possible to do so in a certain approximate sense, and the time required for the "group" of frequencies centered at ω_0 to emerge from the system is called the *group delay at* ω_0.

We shall now proceed with some analysis to answer the question fully. Let us exhibit in *1* the amplitude $A(\omega)$ and the phase $\phi(\omega)$ of the transfer function:

$$h(t) = \frac{1}{2\pi} \int_{-\infty}^{+\infty} A(\omega)e^{j[\omega t + \phi(\omega)]}\, d\omega$$

Let us now divide the frequency axis in equal segments of length Δ. Then

$$h(t) = \frac{1}{2\pi} \sum_{n=-\infty}^{+\infty} \int_{n\Delta}^{(n+1)\Delta} A(\omega)\, \{\exp j[\omega t + \phi(\omega)]\}\, d\omega$$

Suppose Δ is taken sufficiently small so that for all segments $(n\Delta, (n+1)\Delta)$ the amplitude $A(\omega)$ is almost constant. Also let $\omega_{0n} = (n + \frac{1}{2})\Delta$. Thus

$$h(t) \simeq \frac{1}{2\pi} \sum_{-\infty}^{+\infty} A(\omega_{0n}) \int_{n\Delta}^{(n+1)\Delta} \{\exp j[\omega t + \phi(\omega)]\}\, d\omega$$

Let us further require that Δ be sufficiently small that over each interval $(n\Delta, (n+1)\Delta)$ we may, with negligible error, replace $\phi(\omega)$ by

$$\phi(\omega_{0n}) + (\omega - \omega_{0n}) \left.\frac{d\phi}{d\omega}\right|_{\omega_{0n}}$$

Introducing this approximation, we get

$$h(t) \simeq \frac{1}{2\pi} \sum_{-\infty}^{+\infty} A(\omega_{0n})e^{j[\omega_{0n}t - \phi(\omega_{0n})]} \int_{\omega_{0n}-\Delta/2}^{\omega_{0n}+\Delta/2} \{\exp j[(\omega - \omega_{0n})(t + \phi_n')]\}\, d\omega$$

where we wrote ϕ_n' for $\left.\frac{d\phi}{d\omega}\right|_{\omega_{0n}}$. Carrying out the integration, we get

$$h(t) \simeq \frac{\Delta}{2\pi} \sum_{-\infty}^{+\infty} A(\omega_{0n}) \frac{\sin (\Delta/2)(t + \phi_n')}{(\Delta/2)(t + \phi_n')} e^{j[\omega_{0n}t - \phi(\omega_{0n})]}$$

If we collect together the terms corresponding to ω_{0n} and $-\omega_{0n}$, then, taking into account the evenness of $A(\omega)$ and $d\phi/d\omega$, we get

$$h(t) \simeq \frac{\Delta}{\pi} \sum_{n=1}^{\infty} A(\omega_{0n}) \frac{\sin (\Delta/2)(t + \phi_n')}{(\Delta/2)(t + \phi_n)} \cos [\omega_{0n}t - \phi(\omega_{0n})]$$

Each term of the sum can be interpreted as an amplitude-modulated cosine wave: $\cos [\omega_{0n}t - \phi(\omega_{0n})]$ is the carrier and the instantaneous amplitude is

$$\frac{\Delta}{\pi} A(\omega_{0n}) \frac{\sin (\Delta/2)(t + \phi_n')}{(\Delta/2)(t + \phi_n')}$$

The contribution of a single term is plotted in Fig. *9.11.1*. The shape of the curve suggests the following statement: the group of frequencies

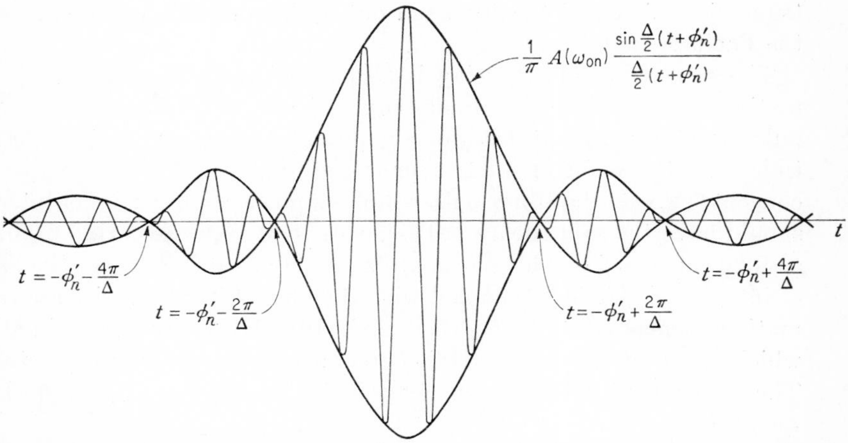

Fig. 9.11.1 Amplitude-modulated wave representing the contribution of the interval $(\omega_{0n} - \Delta/2, \omega_{0n} + \Delta/2)$.

centered around ω_{0n} are delayed by $-\left.\frac{d\phi}{d\omega}\right|_{\omega_{0n}}$ in the sense that their contribution to $h(t)$ is maximum at that instant.[1] For this reason, and in this sense, we say that

2 **Definition** $-\left.\frac{d\phi}{d\omega}\right|_{\omega_0}$ is the group delay of $H(j\omega) = A(\omega)e^{j\phi(\omega)}$ at the frequency ω_0.

Radio engineers talk about the *group velocity* for the excellent reason that they are interested in propagation through various media. If the

[1] To be accurate, we should take into account the phase of the carrier and say that the maximum occurs in the small interval $\left[-\frac{d\phi}{d\omega} - \frac{\pi}{2\omega_{0n}}, -\frac{d\phi}{d\omega} + \frac{\pi}{2\omega_{0n}}\right]$.

unit impulse of the preceding analysis is applied at $x = 0$ and $t = 0$ and the resulting phenomenon is observed at x_0, the appropriate transfer function is

$$A(\omega)e^{j[\omega t - \beta(\omega)x_0]}$$

Therefore, the phase shift $\phi(\omega)$ is now $-\beta(\omega)x_0$. The group delay is therefore $(d\beta/d\omega)x_0$, and the *group velocity* is $(d\beta/d\omega)^{-1} = d\omega/d\beta$.

The concept of group velocity is of great importance because in homogeneous media the group velocity is the velocity at which energy propagates. This concept appears in quantum mechanics and in the propagation of electromagnetic waves in wave guides, velocity waves in electron streams, and electromagnetic waves in ionized media (in fact, the group velocity explains the whistlers). In the case of gravity waves in deep water, the concept explains the great velocity of the tsunamis which periodically wash out a city or two on the shores of the Pacific.

The concept of group delay is also useful in the network approximation problem. For example, suppose we have to design a linear pulse amplifier. What criterion should one introduce: constant amplitude over the band of interest or something else? The group delay concept suggests that for a pulse amplifier all the frequencies of interest should have the same delay. This leads to an approximation problem as follows: $H(j\omega)$ should be such that $d\phi/d\omega$ is constant over the band of interest. This idea, coupled with the idea of Taylor series approximation, leads naturally to the maximally flat delay approximation which has recently been used with great success in many pulse systems. The concept of group delay is basic to the invention of the chirp radar.[1]

3 *Exercise* Can there exist a physical transfer function that has negative delay at some frequencies? (*Hint:* Use the potential analogy to construct a strictly stable rational transfer function that has negative group delay at some frequencies.) Compare the rate of change of $A(\omega)$ with that of $\phi(\omega)$ in the frequency interval where the delay is negative.

4 *Exercise* Physicists define the phase velocity v_p as $v_p = \lambda\nu = \omega/\beta$, where λ is the wavelength and ν the frequency. The group velocity v_g is $(d\beta/d\omega)^{-1}$. Show that

$$v_g = v_p - \lambda \frac{dv_p}{d\lambda} = v_p + \frac{1}{\lambda}\frac{dv_p}{d(1/\lambda)}$$

(*Hint:* $\beta = 2\pi/\lambda$. These relations are useful; for the phase velocity v_p is often plotted against the wavelength λ or the wave number $1/\lambda$.)

[1] J. R. Klauder, A. C. Price, S. Darlington, and W. J. Albersheim, The Theory and Design of Chirp Radars, *Bell System Tech. J.*, vol. 39, no. 4, pp. 745–808, 1960.

12 *Paired echoes*

Paired-echo theory

We wish to include a brief discussion of the theory of paired echoes for two reasons: first, it illuminates certain aspects of the relationship between a time function and its Fourier transform; second, it is the basis of the time-domain equalizer and the transversal filter which have found use in communication systems and in servomechanisms.

We shall be concerned with the following questions. Given a time function $h(t)$ with $H(j\omega)$ as its transform, what happens to the time function (I) if $|H(j\omega)|$ is changed but $\measuredangle H(j\omega)$ is left unchanged and (II) if $|H(j\omega)|$ is left unchanged but $\measuredangle H(j\omega)$ is changed? We can also think of $H(j\omega)$ as a transfer function and $h(t)$ as the corresponding impulse response. With this interpretation we ask what happens to the impulse response when we modify the gain $|H(j\omega)|$ of the system and leave the phase $\measuredangle H(j\omega)$ alone or vice versa. Let $H_1(j\omega)$ be the modified transforms.

Case 1 $H_1(j\omega) = H(j\omega)\,(1 + 2a\cos\omega\tau)$. Of course a must be real in order that $H_1(0)$ be real, and we assume $0 < |a| < \frac{1}{2}$. To be specific, we shall assume $a > 0$. Clearly

$$|H_1(j\omega)| = |H(j\omega)|\,(1 + 2a\cos\omega\tau) \qquad \text{and} \qquad \measuredangle H_1(j\omega) = \measuredangle H(j\omega)$$

Using the fact that

$$1 + 2a\cos\omega\tau = ae^{-j\omega\tau} + 1 + ae^{+j\omega\tau}$$

we get

1 $$\mathcal{L}_{\mathrm{II}}^{-1}[H_1(j\omega)] = ah(t-\tau) + h(t) + ah(t+\tau)$$

The new impulse response is equal to the original one plus two echoes: $ah(t-\tau)$ is the original impulse response multiplied by $a < \frac{1}{2}$ lagging $h(t)$ by τ sec. Similarly, $ah(t+\tau)$ leads it by τ sec. The pattern is illustrated by Fig. *9.12.1*.

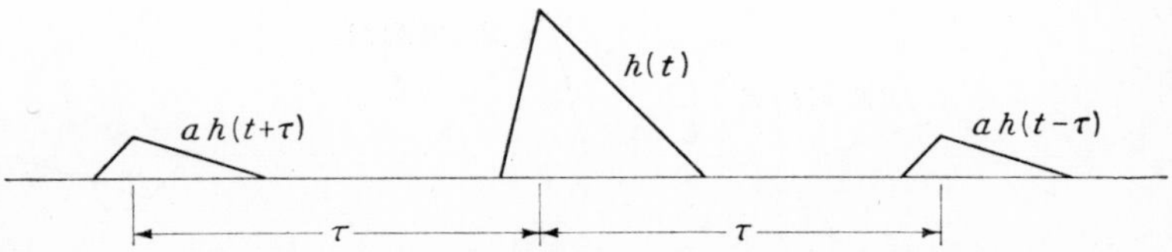

Fig. 9.12.1 Paired echoes created by a cosinusoidal perturbation of the gain.

Case 2 $H_1(j\omega) = H(j\omega) \exp(j\beta \sin \omega\tau)$, β real and constant. In this case,

$$|H_1(j\omega)| = |H(j\omega)|$$

and

$$\measuredangle H_1(j\omega) = \measuredangle H(j\omega) + \beta \sin \omega\tau$$

Therefore, β measures, in radians, the peak phase deviation from the original phase curve. Now consider the following Fourier series expansion:

$$\exp(j\beta \sin \theta) = \sum_{-\infty}^{+\infty} J_n(\beta) e^{jn\theta}$$

where $J_n(\cdot)$ is the nth Bessel function of the first kind. Hence

$$H_1(j\omega) = H(j\omega) \sum_{-\infty}^{+\infty} J_n(\beta) e^{jn\omega\tau}$$

Using an obvious notation, we get

2 $$h_1(t) = \sum_{n=-\infty}^{+\infty} J_n(\beta) h(t + n\tau)$$

Note that, for all integers n,

3 $$J_{-n}(\beta) = (-1)^n J_n(\beta)$$

In contrast with the preceding case, we have here an infinite number of echoes and the echoes have positive and negative weighting factors. Practically, however, for $\beta < \frac{1}{2}$ rad, a very good approximation is obtained by a few terms. This follows from the following expansion:

4 $$J_n(\beta) = \left(\frac{\beta}{2}\right)^n \sum_{l=0}^{\infty} \frac{(j\beta/2)^{2l}}{l!(n+l)!}$$

$$= \frac{1}{n!}\left(\frac{\beta}{2}\right)^n - \frac{1}{(n+1)!}\left(\frac{\beta}{2}\right)^{n+2} + \frac{1}{2!(n+2)!}\left(\frac{\beta}{2}\right)^{n+4} - \cdots$$

For example, if the peak phase deviation is 15°, $\beta \simeq 0.3$, $J_2(\beta) < 0.011$, and all terms beyond $|n| = 1$ are negligible. Hence

$$h_1(t) \simeq -J_1(\beta)h(t - \tau) + J_0(\beta)h(t) + J_1(\beta)h(t + \tau)$$

Again there are two "echoes," but their signs are reversed in the present case. In addition, the central term is multiplied by $J_0(\beta)$. This is illustrated in Fig. *9.12.2*.

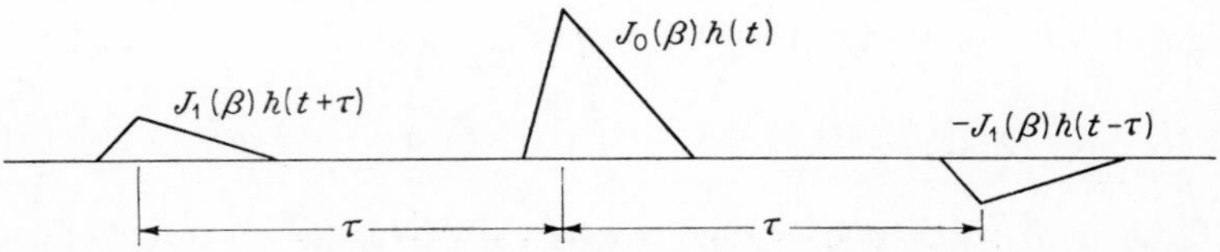

Fig. 9.12.2 Paired echoes created by a sinusoidal perturbation of the phase.

The transversal filter

In order to illustrate the concept, we shall briefly discuss the basic idea behind the transversal filter and the time-domain equalizer. The principal idea is to use a lossless delay line with $N + 1$ equally spaced taps. The delay between any two successive taps is τ sec. We assume that the delay line is matched at its end and that the energy derived from the main signal at each tap is a negligible portion of it. At each tap the signal is multiplied by a constant c_k, and if necessary its sign is changed by a phase inverter. The results of each multiplication are added together to form the output. Clearly, the transfer function is (except for a multiplicative constant independent of frequency which represents the "flat" attenuation through the system)

5
$$H(j\omega) = e^{-jN\omega\tau} \sum_{-N}^{+N} c_k e^{-jk\omega\tau} \qquad \text{with } c_0 = 1$$
$$= e^{-jN\omega\tau} \left(1 + \sum_{1}^{N} a_k \cos k\omega\tau + \sum_{1}^{N} b_k \sin k\omega\tau\right)$$

where we put

6
$$a_k = c_k + c_{-k} \qquad b_k = c_k - c_{-k} \qquad k = 1, 2, \ldots$$

The system is illustrated in Fig. *9.12.3*. If we set all the $b_k = 0$, we

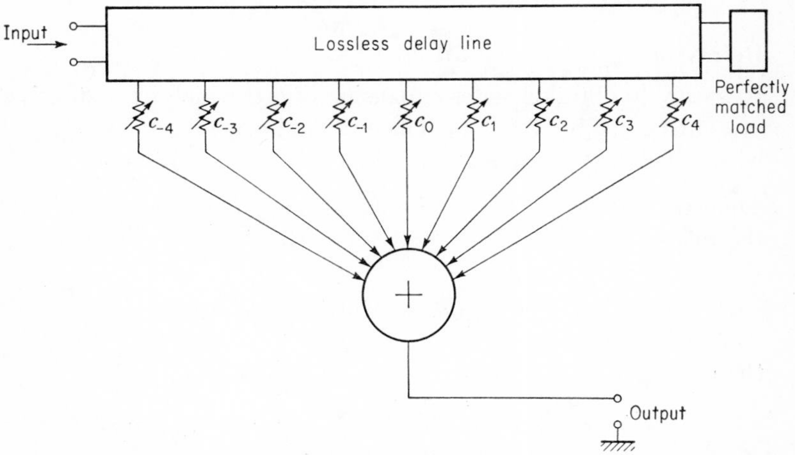

Fig. 9.12.3 A transversal filter.

get a transversal filter with a transfer function

$$H(j\omega) = e^{-jN\omega\tau} \left(1 + \sum_{1}^{N} a_k \cos k\omega\tau\right)$$

This is a *linear phase filter* whose gain is given by an N-term cosine Fourier series. The gain is adjustable.

In the time-domain equalizer case, let us assume $\varepsilon = \sum_1^N |c_k| \ll 1$.

Then

$$H(j\omega) \simeq e^{-jN\omega\tau}\left(1 + \sum_1^N a_k \cos k\omega\tau + j\sum_1^N b_k \sin k\omega\tau\right)$$

$$\simeq \left(1 + \sum_1^N a_k \cos k\omega\tau\right) \exp\left[-j\left(N\omega\tau - \sum_1^N b_k \sin k\omega\tau\right)\right] + 0(\varepsilon^2)$$

Therefore, provided the c_k's are kept sufficiently small, the equalizer provides an N-term cosine series for its gain and an N-term sine series for its phase. In addition, the adjustment of the gain can be made independently from that of the phase by *6*.

The reader should keep in mind that this elegant and simple behavior results from our assumptions: (I) a perfect delay line, (II) a perfect match at the end of the delay line, and (III) negligible loading by the taps. In practice, the delay line will be imperfectly uniform, lossy, and imperfectly matched.

13 *Asymptotic relations between $H(s)$ and $h(t)$*

Behavior of $h(t)$ for small t

It is easy to obtain a series expansion of $h(t)$ which has extensive use in evaluating $h(t)$ for small t. The advantage of this expansion is the ease with which a few terms of the series can be computed.

1 **Theorem** If $H(s)$ has a Taylor expansion about the point at infinity of the form

2 $$H(s) = \sum_{k=1}^{\infty} \frac{a_k}{s^k} \qquad \text{for } |s| > R > 0$$

then

3 $$h(t) = 1(t) \sum_{k=1}^{\infty} \frac{a_k}{(k-1)!}\, t^{k-1} \qquad \text{for all } t$$

where $\mathcal{L}\{h(t)\} = H(s)$.

4 *Comment* If $H(s)$ is rational, then $H(s)$ is analytic for $|s| > R_0$, where R_0 is the distance between the origin and the farthest pole of $H(s)$ and the Taylor series expansion of $H(s)$ about the point at infinity converges for all s such that $|s| > R_0$.

Proof First observe that, for the inversion integral, a suitable abscissa for the integration path is any $c > R$. With such a choice of c, we may replace $H(s)$ by its series expansion *2*, since the series expansion is valid along the whole path of integration. Furthermore, since inside its circle of convergence (which is $|s| > R$, in the present case) a power series converges uniformly, the summation and integration may be interchanged. Thus, successively

$$h(t) = \frac{1}{2\pi j}\int_{c-j\infty}^{c+j\infty}\left(\sum_{k=1}^{\infty}\frac{a_k}{s^k}\right)e^{st}\,ds = \sum_{k=1}^{\infty}\frac{a_k}{2\pi j}\int_{c-j\infty}^{c+j\infty}\frac{e^{st}}{s^k}\,ds$$

and
$$h(t) = 1(t)\sum_{k=1}^{\infty}\frac{a_k}{(k-1)!}\,t^{k-1} \qquad \text{for all } t$$

5 *Comment* This result is very useful in practical applications for the following reasons: (I) In order to obtain the expansion in powers of $1/s$ of a rational transfer function, simply divide the denominator into the numerator. For example, let $H(s) = (s+1)/(s^2+s+1)$:

$$
\begin{array}{r|l}
 & \frac{1}{s} - \frac{1}{s^3} + \frac{1}{s^4} + \cdots \\ \hline
s^2+s+1 & s+1 \\
 & s+1+\frac{1}{s} \\ \hline
 & -\frac{1}{s} \\
 & -\frac{1}{s} - \frac{1}{s^2} - \frac{1}{s^3} \\ \hline
 & \frac{1}{s^2}+\frac{1}{s^3} \\
 & \frac{1}{s^2}+\frac{1}{s^3}+\frac{1}{s^4} \\ \hline
 & -\frac{1}{s^4}
\end{array}
$$

Hence $h(t) = 1(t)\left(1 - \frac{t^2}{2!} + \frac{t^3}{3!} + \cdots\right)$. (II) The power series in time is usually the fastest and most accurate way of obtaining the $h(t)$ for small t. (III) It is a useful check on numerical work when $h(t)$ is obtained by the partial-fraction-expansion method or by residues. ◁

The following result, which generalizes the preceding one, is often useful:

6 **Theorem** If, for $|s| > R$,

$$H(s) = \sum_{k=0}^{\infty}\frac{a_k}{s^{\alpha_k}} \qquad 0 < \alpha_0 < \alpha_1 < \cdots \to \infty$$

is an absolutely convergent series, then

$$h(t) = 1(t) \sum_{k=0}^{\infty} a_k \frac{t^{\alpha_k - 1}}{\Gamma(\alpha_k)} \qquad t \neq 0$$

where $\mathcal{L}\{h(t)\} = H(s)$ and the series converges absolutely.

Proof The derivation is identical to the preceding one.[1]

7 *Example* Let $H(s) = 1/s\sqrt{1+s}$. Using standard series expansions, we get successively, for $|s| > 1$,

$$H(s) = \frac{1}{s^{3/2}}\left(1 + \frac{1}{s}\right)^{-1/2} = \frac{1}{s^{3/2}} - \frac{1}{2s^{5/2}} + \frac{1 \times 3}{2 \times 4}\frac{1}{s^{7/2}} - \cdots$$

Hence, since $\Gamma(\frac{1}{2}) = \sqrt{\pi}$ and $\Gamma(z+1) = z\Gamma(z)$,

$$h(t) = 1(t)\left(\frac{2t^{1/2}}{\sqrt{\pi}} - \frac{2t^{3/2}}{3\sqrt{\pi}} + \frac{t^{5/2}}{5\sqrt{\pi}} - \cdots\right)$$

Asymptotic behavior for $t \to \infty$

To estimate the behavior of $h(t)$ for large t on the basis of $H(s)$ is very important in many applications, stability problems in particular. We shall give two results. The first one is well known and applies to rational $H(s)$; the second one is useful when $H(s)$ has more general singularities.

8 **Theorem** Assume that (I) $H(s)$ is a rational function of s that vanishes for $|s| \to \infty$ and is analytic for $\operatorname{Re} s > \alpha$, (II) $s_1, s_2, \ldots, s_n$ are the only poles of $H(s)$ in the strip $\alpha - \delta \leq \operatorname{Re} s \leq \alpha$, where $\delta > 0$, and (III) at each of these poles, the principal part of the Laurent series expansion of $H(s)$ is

$$\frac{b_1^{(k)}}{s - s_k} + \frac{b_2^{(k)}}{(s - s_k)^2} + \cdots + \frac{b_{l_k}^{(k)}}{(s - s_k)^{l_k}} \qquad k = 1, 2, \ldots, n$$

Then, as $t \to \infty$,

9 $$h(t) = 1(t)\left[\sum_{k=1}^{n}\left(b_1^{(k)} + b_2^{(k)}t + \cdots + \frac{b_{l_k}^{(k)}}{(k-1)!}t^{k-1}\right)e^{s_k t} + 0(e^{(\alpha-\delta)t})\right]$$

Proof The proof is very simple; so we shall only outline its steps: (I) consider the complete partial-fraction expansion of $H(s)$; (II) take its inverse transform; and (III) observe that, for any real ξ and η such that $\xi < \eta$, $e^{\xi t} + e^{\eta t} \sim e^{\eta t}$ as $t \to \infty$, from which *9* follows.

10 **Corollary** Let $H(s)$ be a rational transfer function. $H(s)$ is strictly stable if and only if all its poles are inside the left half plane, i.e., have negative (<0) real parts.

[1] G. Doetsch, "Handbuch der Laplace Transformation," vol. II, p. 175.

We shall now state, without proof, a result which is often useful when $H(s)$ is not rational. Doetsch (II, page 159) has the most complete discussion of this and many other asymptotic results.

11 **Theorem** Assume that (I) $H(s)$ is singular at s_0; (II) the path of the inversion integral can be deformed into the path C shown in Fig. *9.13.1*, where $\pi/2 < \phi < \pi$; (III) $H(s)$ is analytic on C; and (IV) the following asymptotic expansion is valid uniformly in the angle $|\measuredangle(s - s_0)| \le \phi$:

$$H(s) \sim \sum_{\nu=0}^{\infty} c_\nu (s - s_0)^{\gamma_\nu}$$

where $\operatorname{Re}\gamma_0 < \operatorname{Re}\gamma_1 < \operatorname{Re}\gamma_2 < \cdots$. Then, as $t \to \infty$,

$$h(t) \sim 1(t) e^{s_0 t} \sum_{\nu=0}^{\infty} \frac{c_\nu}{\Gamma(-\gamma_\nu)} t^{-1-\gamma_\nu}$$

where $\dfrac{1}{\Gamma(-\gamma_\nu)} = 0$ if γ_ν is a positive integer.

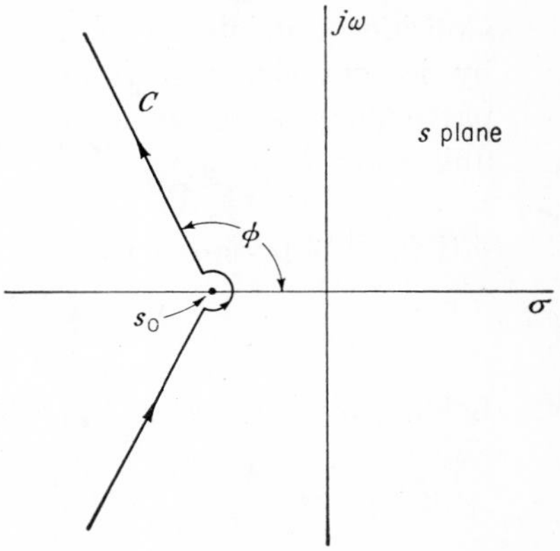

Fig. 9.13.1 Path C referred to in the statement of Theorem *9.13.11*.

12 *Example* $H(s) = \dfrac{1}{(s+2)\sqrt{s+1}}$. Since $H(s) \to 0$ as $|s| \to \infty$, uniformly in the angle $\measuredangle s$, by Jordan's lemma, the contour may be deformed as shown in Fig. *9.13.1*. Now

$$H(s) = \frac{1}{1 + s + 1}\frac{1}{\sqrt{s+1}} = \frac{1}{(s+1)^{1/2}} - (s+1)^{1/2} + (s+1)^{3/2} - \cdots$$

Hence

$$h(t) = 1(t)e^{-t}\left(-\frac{t^{-3/2}}{2\sqrt{\pi}} - \frac{t^{-5/2}}{\sqrt{\pi}} + \cdots\right)$$

13 *Comment* A word of warning should be inserted at this point: From the above it might appear that the only feature of $H(s)$ that counts as far as the behavior of $h(t)$ for $t \to \infty$ is concerned is the nature of the singularity that lies the farthest to the right in the s plane. This is not so; for such a statement to be true, $H(s)$ must behave appropriately at infinity. Observe that each of the last two theorems does impose conditions on the behavior of $H(s)$ as $|s| \to \infty$. A well-known example, due to Widder, is the following: $h(t) = 1(t)e^t \sin e^t$; that is, a signal whose amplitude and frequency increase exponentially with time. It can be shown, however, that $H(s) \triangleq \mathcal{L}\{e^t \sin e^t\}$ has no singularities

in the finite plane. It is, of course, singular at infinity, as required by Liouville's theorem; in fact, it is an essential singularity.

14 *Steady-state response to a periodic input*

Consider a strictly stable, causal, time-invariant system characterized by its transfer function $H(s)$. Let $H(s)$ be strictly stable and, in particular, be analytic for $\text{Re}\, s \geq \sigma_2$, where $\sigma_2 < 0$. Let $H(s)$ be uniformly bounded as $|s| \to \infty$ and $\measuredangle s \in [\pi/2, 3\pi/2]$. At $t = 0$ the system is in the zero state and a periodic input $v(t)$ is applied: $v(t)$ satisfies the periodicity condition

1 $$v(t + T) = v(t) \qquad \text{for all } t \geq 0$$

Let us assume that $v(t)$ is Riemann integrable over the interval $[0,T]$. Since $H(s)$ is strictly stable, the response will eventually become periodic. We wish to evaluate this steady-state response. Let

2 $$v_0(t) = \begin{cases} v(t) & 0 \leq t < T \\ 0 & \text{elsewhere} \end{cases}$$

Consequently, $V_0(s)$ is an entire function of s: its singularities lie at infinity. It is well known that

$$V(s) \triangleq \int_0^\infty v(t)e^{-st}\,dt = \frac{V_0(s)}{1 - e^{-sT}}$$

Let us evaluate the response y of the system to the input $v(t)$ in the interval $(0,T)$. Since the system is causal, we have

3 $$y(t) = \mathcal{L}^{-1}\left\{H(s)\frac{V_0(s)}{1 - e^{-sT}}\right\} = \mathcal{L}^{-1}\{H(s)V_0(s)\} \qquad \text{for } 0 < t < T$$

Note that the second equality in *3* holds only because t is restricted to belonging to $(0,T)$. Furthermore, since $H(s)$ is analytic for $\text{Re}\, s \geq \sigma_2$, and since $V_0(s)$ is an entire function,

4 $$y(t) = \frac{1}{2\pi j}\int_{\sigma_0 - j\infty}^{\sigma_0 + j\infty} H(s)V_0(s)e^{st}\,ds \qquad 0 < t < T,\ \sigma_0 \geq \sigma_2$$

Since $\sigma_2 < 0$ and since $1/(1 - e^{-sT})$ has simple poles located at $s = j2\pi n/T$, $n = \ldots, -1, 0, 1, \ldots$, the first inversion integral in *3* may be carried over any vertical path inside the right half plane:

$$y(t) = \frac{1}{2\pi j}\int_{\sigma_1 - j\infty}^{\sigma_1 + j\infty} \frac{H(s)V_0(s)}{1 - e^{-sT}}\,e^{st}\,ds \qquad \sigma_1 > 0$$

Let $\omega_n = (2n + 1)\pi/T$, $n = \ldots, -1, 0, 1, \ldots$. The above equation may be rewritten as

$$y(t) = \frac{1}{2\pi j} \lim_{n \to \infty} \int_{\sigma_1 - j\omega_n}^{\sigma_1 + j\omega_n} \frac{H(s)V_0(s)e^{st}}{1 - e^{-sT}}\, ds$$

$$= \frac{1}{2\pi j} \lim_{n \to \infty} \left(\int_{\sigma_1 - j\omega_n}^{\sigma_1 + j\omega_n} - \int_{\sigma_2 - j\omega_n}^{\sigma_2 + j\omega_n} + \int_{\sigma_2 - j\omega_n}^{\sigma_2 + j\omega_n} \right)$$

where σ_2 has been defined previously.

The integration paths are illustrated in Fig. *9.14.1*. The first two integrals may be combined to form a closed integration path by adding the paths joining $\sigma_2 - j\omega_n$ to $\sigma_1 - j\omega_n$ and $\sigma_1 + j\omega_n$ to $\sigma_2 + j\omega_n$. The integration along these paths tends to zero as $n \to \infty$ because (I) $e^{st}/(1 - e^{-sT})$ is uniformly bounded along the path, (II) $V_0(s) \to 0$ along the path by the Riemann-Lebesgue lemma, and (III) $H(s)$ is uniformly bounded on the path, by assumption. Let C_n denote the counterclockwise closed path described above; then

$$y(t) = \frac{1}{2\pi j} \int_{\sigma_2 - j\infty}^{\sigma_2 + j\infty} \frac{H(s)V_0(s)}{1 - e^{-sT}} e^{st}\, ds + \frac{1}{2\pi j} \lim_{n \to \infty} \oint_{C_n} \frac{H(s)V_0(s)}{1 - e^{-sT}} e^{sT}\, ds$$

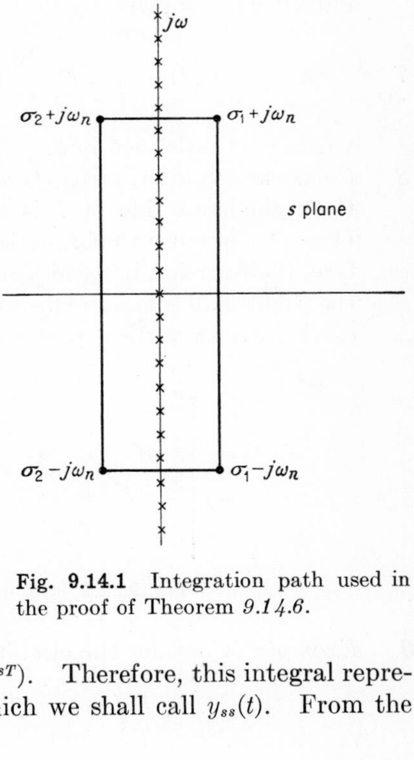

Fig. 9.14.1 Integration path used in the proof of Theorem *9.14.6*.

Since $\sigma_2 < 0$, the contour integration will contribute a Fourier series since the only singularities inside C_n are the simple poles of $1/(1 - e^{-sT})$. Therefore, this integral represents the periodic steady state, which we shall call $y_{ss}(t)$. From the equation above and *4* we have

5 $$y_{ss}(t) = \frac{1}{2\pi j} \int_{\sigma_0 - j\infty}^{\sigma_0 + j\infty} H(s)V_0(s)e^{st}\, ds - \frac{1}{2\pi j} \int_{\sigma_2 - j\infty}^{\sigma_2 + j\infty} \frac{H(s)V_0(s)e^{st}}{1 - e^{-sT}}\, ds \qquad \text{for } 0 < t < T$$

where σ_0 is arbitrary except that $\sigma_0 \geq \sigma_2$. If σ_0 is taken equal to σ_2, this last equation can be rewritten by observing that

$$1 - \frac{1}{1 - e^{-sT}} = \frac{e^{-sT}}{e^{-sT} - 1} = \frac{1}{1 - e^{sT}}$$

Hence,

$$y_{ss}(t) = \frac{1}{2\pi j} \int_{\sigma_2 - j\infty}^{\sigma_2 + j\infty} \frac{H(s)V_0(s)e^{st}}{1 - e^{sT}}\, ds \qquad \text{for } 0 < t < T$$

We may state the result in the form of a

6 **Theorem** Given a linear, time-invariant, nonanticipative, system defined by its strictly stable transfer function $H(s)$, let the input $v(t)$ be periodic with period t. Then if $v(t)$ is Riemann integrable over $(0,T)$, if $H(s)$ is analytic for Re $s \geq \sigma_2$, where $\sigma_2 < 0$, and if $H(s)$ is uniformly bounded as $|s| \to \infty$ for $\measuredangle s \in [\pi/2, 3\pi/2]$, then the periodic steady-state output $y_{ss}(t)$ is given by

7 $$y_{ss}(t) = \frac{1}{2\pi j} \int_{\sigma_2 - j\infty}^{\sigma_2 + j\infty} \frac{H(s)V_0(s)}{1 - e^{sT}}\, e^{st}\, ds \qquad 0 < t < T$$

where $v_0(t)$ is defined in *2*.

8 *Comment* *7* describes $y_{ss}(t)$ *only* on the interval $(0,T)$. Furthermore, the right-hand side of *7* is *not* the inversion integral of $H(s)V_0(s)/(1 - e^{sT})$ because that function has singularities on the $j\omega$ axis; therefore, its inversion integral should be carried over a vertical path inside the right half plane. Observe that $\sigma_2 < 0$; so the integration *7* is carried over a vertical path inside the left half plane.

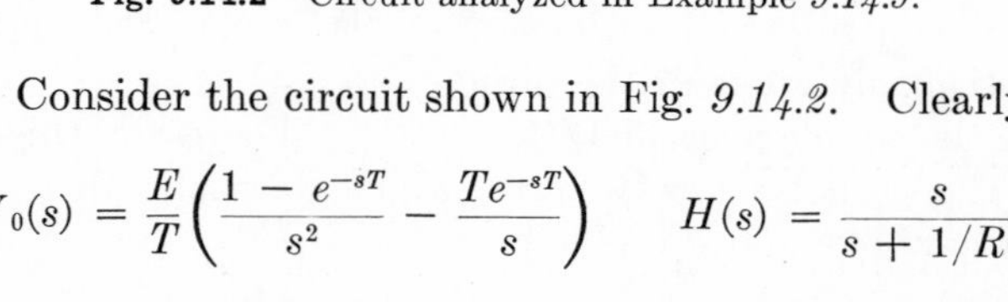

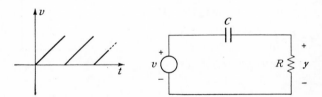

Fig. 9.14.2 Circuit analyzed in Example *9.14.9*.

9 *Example* Consider the circuit shown in Fig. *9.14.2*. Clearly,

$$V_0(s) = \frac{E}{T}\left(\frac{1 - e^{-sT}}{s^2} - \frac{Te^{-sT}}{s}\right) \qquad H(s) = \frac{s}{s + 1/RC}$$

Let us calculate the steady-state output by *5*. Consider the first integral:

$$H(s)V_0(s) = \underbrace{\frac{E}{T}\frac{1}{s(s + 1/RC)}}_{\text{one}} - \underbrace{\frac{E}{T}\frac{e^{-sT}}{s(s + 1/RC)}}_{\text{two}} - \underbrace{E\frac{e^{-sT}}{s + 1/RC}}_{\text{three}}$$

Let us take $\sigma_0 = \sigma_2$; then $-1/RC < \sigma_0 < 0$. Consider term one: by Jordan's lemma (see *B.3.36*) we may close the integration path by a left-half-plane semicircle, and since the only enclosed pole is $s = -1/RC$, one gives $-(ERC/T)\exp[-(t/RC)]$. Terms two and three are such that Jordan's lemma requires that the integration path be closed *on the right,* because we consider values of t in $(0,T)$. The only enclosed pole is $s = 0$; hence, two and three give ERC/T and 0, respectively. Note the change of sign due to the fact that the integration is clockwise. Thus the first integral of *5* contributes

$$-\frac{ERC}{T}e^{-t/RC} + \frac{ERC}{T}$$

Now consider the second integral. Its integrand with sign reversed is

$$-\underbrace{\frac{E}{T}\frac{1}{s(s+1/RC)}}_{\text{four}} + \underbrace{\frac{E}{s+1/RC}\frac{e^{-sT}}{1-e^{-sT}}}_{\text{five}}$$

Jordan's lemma allows us to close the integration of four and five to the left. In both cases the only pole enclosed is at $-1/RC$. Hence the second integral contributes

$$\frac{ERC}{T}e^{-t/RC} - E\frac{e^{-t/RC}}{1-e^{-T/RC}}$$

The result is

$$y_{ss}(t) = \frac{ERC}{T} - E\frac{e^{-t/RC}}{1-e^{-T/RC}} \qquad 0 < t < T$$

15 *Signal-flow graphs*

In this section we define the signal-flow graph and prove the Mason formula for the gain of a signal-flow graph.

Definition of a linear signal-flow graph

The purpose of this section is to present precisely and completely some basic facts about linear signal-flow graphs. The reader is assumed to have a certain amount of familiarity with signal-flow graphs and their usual engineering applications. Instead of going through a long detailed example, let us assume that the reader has his pet example in mind and let us observe the following: (I) A signal-flow graph gives a graphical representation of the causal relationships between the variables chosen for the analysis of the system. It is the causal aspect of these relationships which makes the use of signal-flow graphs so intuitively appealing: the signal-flow graph gives a very satisfying graphical representation of these relationships. (II) For any given system, there are many ways of choosing variables and of writing equations. With each set of equations is associated a signal-flow graph, and thus a given system may be represented by many different signal-flow graphs. (III) It is of interest to note that the diagram of an analog-computer setup can with slight modification become a signal-flow graph. In fact the signal-flow graphs thus obtained are rather special, since their branches are restricted to have gains equal to $-1/s$ or -1 or a (where $0 \leq a \leq 1$), the corresponding analog-computer elements being, respectively, integrators, summing amplifiers, and potentiometers (scalors).

A (linear) signal-flow graph is a graphical means for representing linear equations. For convenience we write them in the form

1
$$\begin{aligned} (1-g_{11})x_1 - g_{12}x_2 - \cdots - g_{1n}x_n &= f_1 \\ -g_{21}x_1 + (1-g_{22})x_2 - \cdots - g_{2n}x_n &= f_2 \\ \cdots\cdots\cdots\cdots\cdots\cdots\cdots\cdots & \\ -g_{n1}x_1 - g_{n2}x_2 - \cdots + (1-g_{nn})x_n &= f_n \end{aligned}$$

The dependent variables x_i and the independent variables f_i (usually called inputs) are either functions of time or Laplace transforms of functions of time. The matrix elements g_{ij} are correspondingly either integrodifferential operators or transfer functions, i.e., functions of the complex frequency variable s. Thus, these equations may, for example, represent the familiar circuit equations resulting from Kirchhoff laws.

Let us rewrite the equations as follows:

2
$$x_i = \sum_{j=1}^{n} g_{ij}x_j + f_i \qquad i = 1, 2, \ldots, n$$

The relationship between this system of equations and the signal-flow graph is best explained by describing how one associates a signal-flow graph with the system of equations.

3 **Procedure: from the equations to the signal-flow graph** Carry out the following steps: (I) With each dependent variable x_i is associated one node. For convenience, the node associated with x_i is called the ith node. (II) With each input variable f_i is associated a node, a source node. (III) For all i,j if $g_{ij} \neq 0$, there is a directed branch that originates at node j and terminates at node i; this branch is assigned a gain g_{ij}. If $g_{ij} = 0$, no branch is introduced. (IV) A branch of unity gain joins the node associated with f_i to the ith node, $i = 1, 2, \ldots, n$.

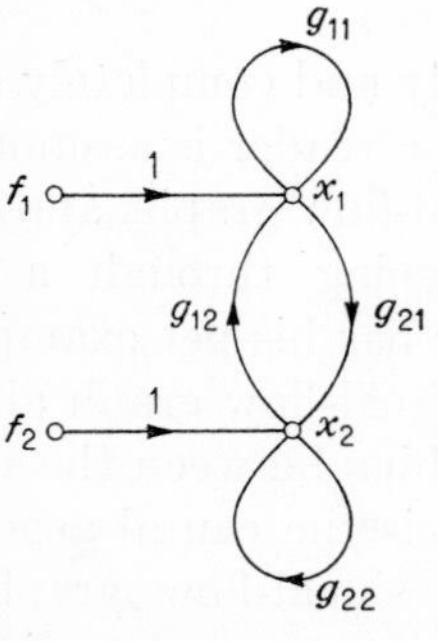

Fig. 9.15.1 Example of a signal-flow graph with two nodes.

The signal-flow graph associated with the system *1* for the case $n = 2$ is illustrated in Fig. *9.15.1*.

4 **Definition** A node on which no branch terminates is said to be a *source node*.

5 **Procedure: from the signal-flow graph to the equations** There is one equation associated with each node that is not a source node. The equation associated with the ith node is obtained by (I) considering all branches terminating on the ith node, (II) forming the product of the gain of each such branch with the node variable from which this branch originates, and (III) equating the sum of all these products to x_i. Thus we are led to the following

6 **Definition** A *signal-flow graph* is a weighted oriented graph which stands in a one-one correspondence (described by *3* and *5*) with a set of linear equations. ◁

Any system of linear algebraic equations such as *1* can be solved by systematic algebraic techniques, e.g., by the Gauss elimination method. However, in engineering it usually happens that the matrix **M** of the system *1* contains a large number of zero elements: it is this circumstance that makes the signal-flow-graph approach desirable and effective. Inspection of the signal-flow graph suggests the order in which the elimination should be carried out. The key operation is the node elimination, which will be discussed in the next subsection. It is also possible to solve directly for some x_k without successively eliminating all other nodes: this will be described in the subsection entitled The Gain of a Signal-flow Graph.

The node elimination

The node elimination technique consists in obtaining from the signal-flow graph G an equivalent signal-flow graph G' that has only $n - 1$ nodes. The equivalence means that the relationships between the $n - 1$ remaining variables expressed by G' are identical to those implied by G. By successively applying this operation to all the nodes except the kth node, we end up with the graph where each gain G_i is expressed in terms of the elements of the matrix **M**, as in Fig. *9.15.2*.

The quantities G_i play a prominent role in signal-flow-graph theory. Refer to Fig. *9.15.2*, where G_i is the value of the output x_k when all inputs are set to zero except the ith input, which is set equal to unity. G_i is called the transmission from the ith input node to the kth node. Thus the

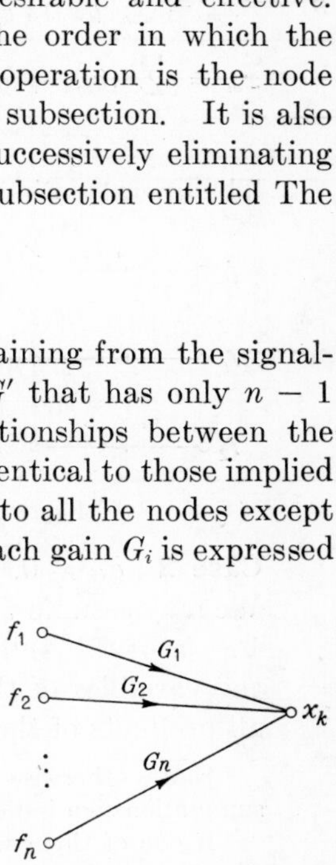

Fig. 9.15.2 Signal-flow graph resulting from the elimination of all nodes but node x_k.

7 **Definition** The graph transmission from node i to node j is the value of x_j when

a unit input is applied to node i and all other inputs are set equal to zero.

8 *Comment* Suppose there is a branch g_{ji} joining node i to node j; then we should stress the difference between the gain of the branch joining node i to node j and the graph transmission from node i to node j. It is obvious that the former is simply g_{ji}, whereas the latter usually depends on the gain of all the branches of the graph. The graph transmission is a property of the whole system. ◁

Let us describe the node elimination method by eliminating the ith node. For convenience define a *self-loop* as a single branch originating from and terminating at the same node.

Case 1 $g_{ii} = 0$, **that is, the** i**th node has no self-loop** The ith equation of *1* reads[1]

$$x_i = \sum_{j \neq i}{}' g_{ij} x_j + f_i$$

Substitution into any of the other equations gives

9
$$x_m = \sum_{\alpha \neq i}{}' g_{m\alpha} x_\alpha + g_{mi} x_i + f_m = \sum_{\alpha \neq i}{}' g_{m\alpha} x_\alpha + g_{mi} \sum_{\alpha \neq i} g_{i\alpha} x_\alpha + g_{mi} f_i + f_m$$

$$x_m = \sum_{\alpha \neq i} (g_{m\alpha} + g_{mi} g_{i\alpha}) x_\alpha + g_{mi} f_i + f_m$$

$$m = 1, \ldots, i-1, i+1, \ldots, n$$

The operation is illustrated by Fig. *9.15.3*.

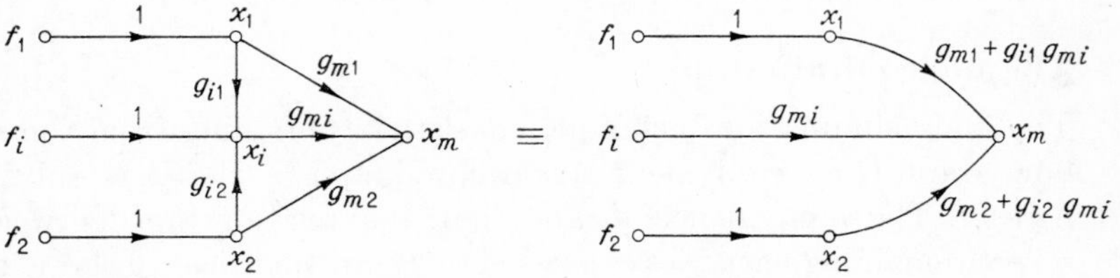

Fig. 9.15.3 Elimination of the ith node when $g_{ii} = 0$.

Case 2 $g_{ii} \neq 0$, **that is, the node to be eliminated has one self-loop** We may assume without restricting the generality of the discussion that $1 - g_{ii} \neq 0$. Indeed, if it were not possible to order the equations and the variables of the system *1* so that all diagonal elements $\neq 0$, then all products of the determinant expansion of **M** would be zero.[2] Since

[1] Unless otherwise indicated, the summation runs from 1 to n. The prime on the summation sign indicates that one value of the summation index is omitted.

[2] If one of them were not zero, each one of its factors would differ from zero. Consider one such nonzero product π. If we so reorder the columns that the element of π which is in the kth row of **M** ends up in the kth column, $k = 1, 2, \ldots, n$, we obtain a new determinant all of whose diagonal elements are different from zero. Thus such an ordering is impossible if and only if all products of the determinant expansion of **M** are zero. That is, det $\mathbf{M} \equiv 0$; hence *1* does not specify the x_i uniquely.

$1 - g_{ii} \neq 0$, substitution in the mth equation gives

10 $$x_m = \sum_{\alpha \neq i}{}' \left(g_{m\alpha} + \frac{g_{mi}g_{i\alpha}}{1 - g_{ii}} \right) x_\alpha + \frac{g_{mi}}{1 - g_{ii}} f_i + f_m$$

$$m = 1, 2, \ldots, i - 1, i + 1, \ldots, n$$

The operation is illustrated by Fig. *9.15.4*. ◁

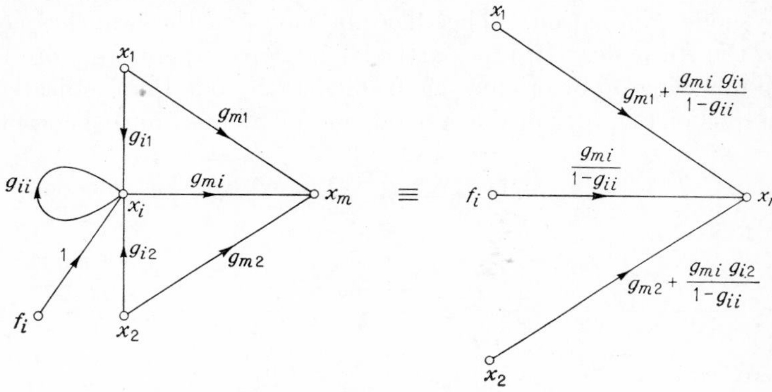

Fig. 9.15.4 Elimination of the ith node when $g_{ii} \neq 0$.

Since Case 1 is a special case of Case 2, we need formulate only one general statement.

11 **Node elimination rule** (refer to Fig. *9.15.5*) Suppose we wish to eliminate node i. With the exception of the possible self-loop of gain

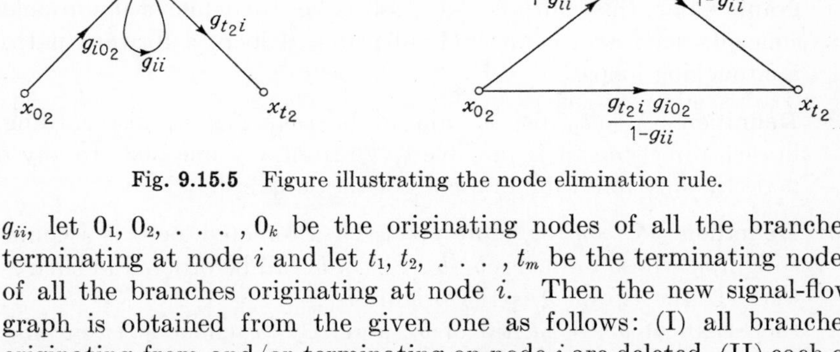

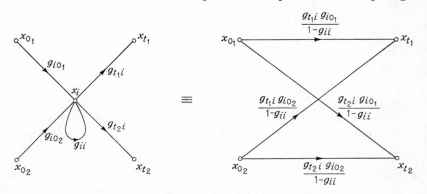

Fig. 9.15.5 Figure illustrating the node elimination rule.

g_{ii}, let $0_1, 0_2, \ldots, 0_k$ be the originating nodes of all the branches terminating at node i and let $t_1, t_2, \ldots, t_m$ be the terminating nodes of all the branches originating at node i. Then the new signal-flow graph is obtained from the given one as follows: (I) all branches originating from and/or terminating on node i are deleted, (II) each of the nodes $0_1, 0_2, \ldots, 0_k$ is connected to each one of the nodes

$t_1, t_2, \ldots, t_m$ by a new branch, and (III) the new branch connecting 0_α to t_β has a gain

$$\frac{g_{i0_\alpha}g_{t_\beta i}}{1 - g_{ii}} \qquad \alpha = 1, 2, \ldots, k; \beta = 1, 2, \ldots, m \quad \triangleleft$$

The diagrams of Fig. *9.15.6* show portions of a signal-flow graph the ith node of which is to be eliminated and the resulting graphs obtained by node elimination. The diagram shows *all* the branches connected to the ith node. If, in a particular instance, there are more branches terminating on or originating from the ith node than indicated on the graphs of Fig. *9.15.6*, the general rule just stated must be applied.

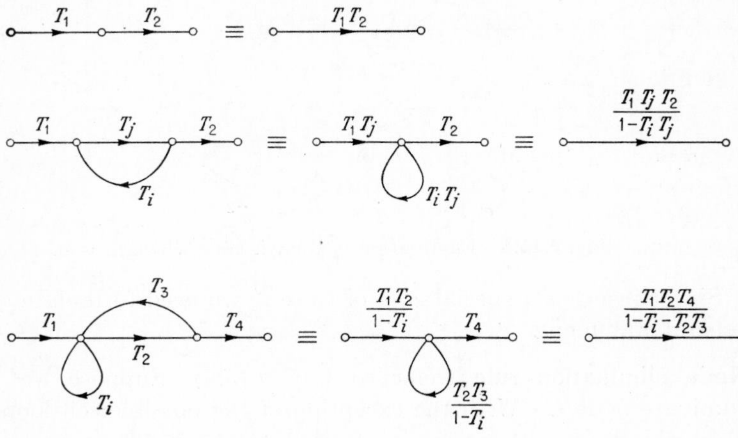

Fig. 9.15.6 Examples of node elimination in simple cases.

The gain of a signal-flow graph

Let us restrict ourselves to a single input f_1 and let us select an arbitrary variable, say, x_k, as output. We shall derive directly from the definition of a determinant the general expression for the gain of that signal-flow graph. For this purpose we first have to define a few topological concepts such as a connected subgraph, a loop, a forward path, and nontouching loops.

12 **Definition** A *subgraph* is said to be *connected* if, disregarding the branch directions, it is possible to go from any one node to any other node by only following branches of the subgraph.

13 **Definition** A *loop* (or, more precisely, a directed loop) is a connected subgraph whose branches $b_1, b_2, \ldots, b_l$ can be ordered in such a way that (I) the tip of b_k is the origin of b_{k+1}, $k = 1, 2, \ldots, l - 1$; (II) the origin of b_1 is the tip of b_l; and (III) each node is encountered only once when the loop is traversed in the positive direction.

14 *Example* Figure *9.15.7a* is a loop; Fig. *9.15.7b* is not a loop because it violates (III); Fig. *9.15.7c* is not a loop because it violates (I).

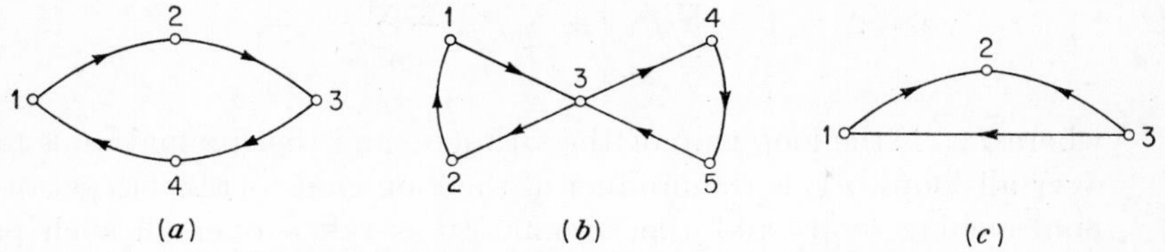

Fig. 9.15.7 Illustrations clarifying the concept of a loop.

15 **Definition** The *loop gain* of a loop is the product of the gains of the branches constituting that loop.

16 **Definition** A collection of loops is said to be *nontouching* if no two of the loops have either a branch or a node in common.

17 **Definition** A *directed path* from node α to node β is a connected subgraph such that (I) none of its branches terminates at node α and only one branch originates from it, (II) none of its branches originates from node β and only one branch terminates on it, and (III) all other branches connect at nodes in such a way that each node has only one incoming branch and one outgoing branch in the subgraph.

18 **Definition** A directed path from the input node f_1 to the output node k is called a *forward path.*

19 *Example* In Fig. *9.15.8a* is shown a directed path; however, *9.15.8b* violates (III), and *9.15.8c* violates (I) and (II).

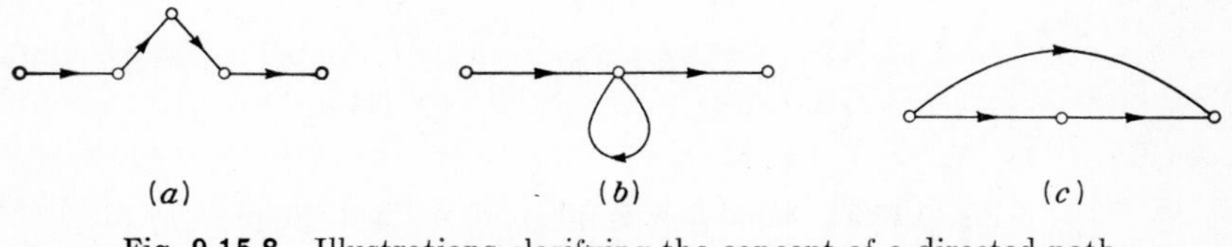

Fig. 9.15.8 Illustrations clarifying the concept of a directed path.

Now we are ready to state the main result in the form of a

20 **Theorem** The graph transmission G from input to output of a single-input signal-flow graph is given by Mason's formula

21 $$G = \frac{\Sigma G_k \Delta_k}{\Delta}$$

where the summation is taken over all forward paths from input to output, G_k is the gain of the kth forward path (i.e., the product of the gains of all branches constituting that forward path), and Δ is the determinant of the graph, given by

22 $$\Delta = 1 - \sum_m P_{m1} + \sum_k P_{k2} - \sum_l P_{l3} + \cdots$$

where P_{m1} is the loop gain of the mth loop and the summation is taken over all loops, P_{k2} is the product of the loop gains of the kth set of two nontouching loops and the summation is taken over all such pairs, P_{l3} is the product of the loop gains of the lth set of three nontouching loops and the summation is taken over all such triples, etc. Δ_k is the determinant of the graph obtained from the original graph by deleting all branches of the kth forward path and all branches having a node in common with it.

23 *Example* Consider the graph shown in Fig. *9.15.9*. It has four loops whose respective gains are g_{22}, g_{33}, $g_{41}g_{34}g_{13}$, $g_{21}g_{42}g_{34}g_{13}$. Consequently

$$\Delta = 1 - g_{22} - g_{33} - g_{41}g_{34}g_{13} - g_{21}g_{42}g_{34}g_{13} + g_{22}g_{33}$$

because g_{22} and g_{33} are the only nontouching loops.

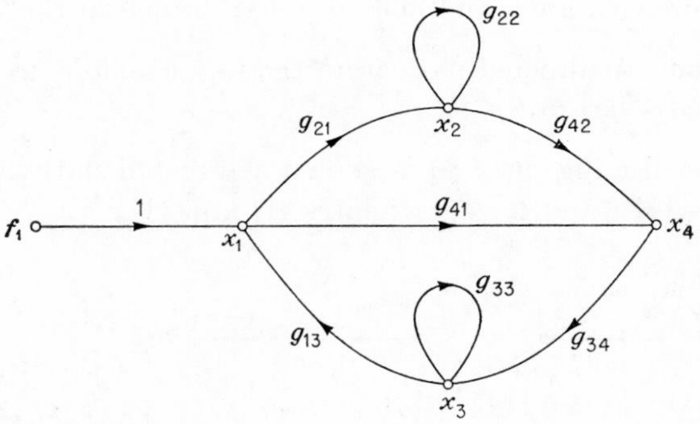

Fig. 9.15.9 Signal-flow graph analyzed in Example *9.15.23*.

There are two forward paths, and

$$G_1 = g_{41} \qquad \Delta_1 = 1 - g_{22} - g_{33} + g_{22}g_{33}$$
$$G_2 = g_{21}g_{42} \qquad \Delta_2 = 1 - g_{33}$$

Hence

$$G = \frac{g_{41}(1 - g_{22} - g_{33} + g_{22}g_{33}) + g_{21}g_{42}(1 - g_{33})}{1 - g_{22} - g_{33} - g_{41}g_{34}g_{13} - g_{21}g_{42}g_{34}g_{13} + g_{22}g_{33}}$$

Proof The proof is based on elementary properties of determinants.

First, recall that the determinant of a matrix **M** is

$$\det \mathbf{M} = \sum_P \operatorname{sgn}(P) m_{i_1 1} m_{i_2 2} m_{i_3 3} \cdots m_{i_n n}$$

where $\sum_P$ denotes that the summation is taken over all the $n!$ permutations $i_1, i_2, \ldots, i_n$ of $1, 2, \ldots, n$ and $\operatorname{sgn}(P)$ is $+1$ or -1 depending on whether the permutation $i_1, i_2, \ldots, i_n$ is even or odd. Second, the permutation of two symbols of a permutation changes the sign of the permutation. Finally, if any two rows or columns of **M** are interchanged, the determinant of the resulting matrix is $-\det \mathbf{M}$.

Since f_1 is the only input, Eqs. *1* have zeros in their right-hand sides except the first one, which has f_1 as the right-hand side. The

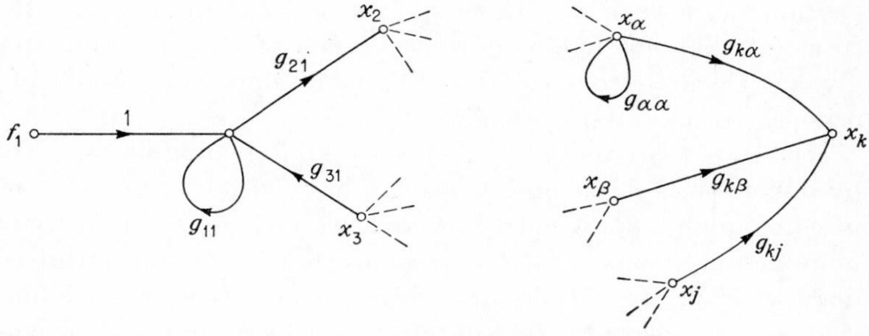

Fig. 9.15.10 Single-input signal-flow graph considered in the proof of Theorem *9.15.20*.

corresponding graph is shown in Fig. *9.15.10*. The output x_k of the graph is given by Cramer's rule:

24
$$x_k = \frac{N_{1k}}{\Delta}$$

where $\Delta = \det \mathbf{M}$ and N_{1k} is the determinant of the matrix obtained from **M** by replacing its kth column by a column vector whose first element is f_1 and all others are zero.

Evaluation of Δ

Let us expand Δ according to the definition of the determinant. Collecting terms, we get $\Delta = 1 + \sum_\alpha \Pi_\alpha$, where each Π_α is a product of branch gains. Consider a particular such product, say Π_β. Let us turn our attention to the topology of G_β, the subgraph formed by the branches whose gains appear in Π_β.

To start with, let us make three observations on the subgraph G_β and the gain product π_β.

(I) In G_β not more than one branch either originates from any given node or terminates at any given node. In other words, in G_β, the occurrences shown in Fig. *9.15.11* are excluded by this statement.

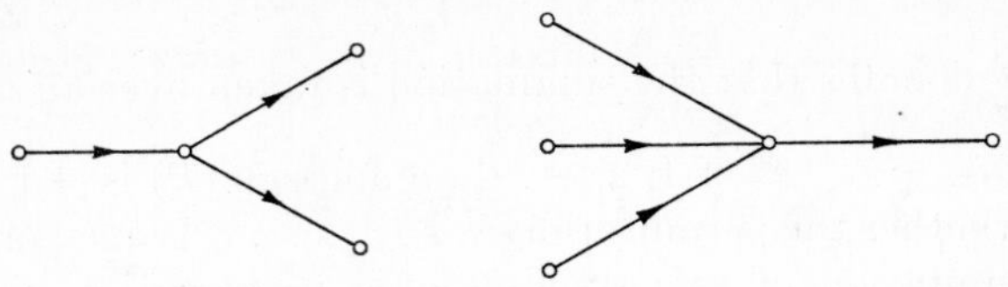

Fig. 9.15.11 Subgraphs that cannot occur in G_β.

This result follows directly from the definition of a determinant. Π_β is a product of branch gains with two properties: (*a*) it does not contain more than one element from each row of Δ and (*b*) it does not contain more than one element from each column of Δ. It follows from (*a*) that not more than one branch of G_β can terminate at any given node and from (*b*) that not more than one branch of G_β can originate from any given node.

(II) Π_β is a product of loop gains of nontouching loops. Note that, by definition, nontouching loops can have *neither* a branch *nor* a node in common. If G_β is not connected, we must show that it consists of nontouching loops. That the loops must be nontouching follows directly from (I). Therefore, if G_β is not connected, we must show that each connected subgraph of G_β is a loop; and if G_β is connected, we need only show that it is a loop. We establish this property by contradiction. Suppose that G_β consists of a directed path between some pair of nodes and some other nontouching configurations. Suppose, for simplicity, that the forward path is made of g_{21} and g_{32}, that is, originates from node 1 and terminates at node 3. Hence no branch of G_β terminates at 1 and no branch of G_β originates from 3. Hence the product cannot contain factors like g_{1k}, $k = 1, 2, \ldots, n$, and g_{k3}, $k = 1, 2, \ldots, n$; that is, no elements of row 1 and column 3 appear in G_β. The definition of a determinant implies, therefore, that Π_β includes the 1's which are part of the elements which are in the (1,1) and (3,3) location in the matrix **M**. This implies a contradiction, because Π_β already includes g_{21} and g_{32} elements of column 1 and row 3 and hence cannot include, in addition, elements at locations (1,1) and (3,3). Therefore, if G_β is not connected, it consists of nontouching loops. If G_β is connected, it consists, obviously, of a single loop.

(III) The gain product in Π_β is assigned a negative sign if G_β consists of an odd number of loops and a positive sign if the number of loops is even. Recall that if, in a matrix, any two rows *and* any two columns are interchanged, the value of the determinant is unaffected. Observe the following: Suppose we are given two identical graphs G and G'. Suppose their nodes are identically numbered except that the nodes

i and j of G are labeled j and i, respectively, in G'. The matrix of the signal-flow graph G' can be obtained from that of G by interchanging rows i and j as well as columns i and j. Hence, the determinants are identical. Therefore, in evaluating the determinant of a signal-flow graph, we may arbitrarily number the nodes without affecting the determinant.

Suppose G_β consists of *two* nontouching loops. Let the nodes of each loop be numbered $1, 2, \ldots, l_1; l_1 + 1, \ldots, l_2$, respectively. The gain products associated with the loops are

$$g_{21}g_{32}g_{43} \cdots g_{l_1,l_1-1}g_{1l_1}g_{l_1+2,l_1+1} \cdots g_{l_2,l_2-1}g_{l_1+1,l_2}$$

This product will be assigned a sign according to the parity of the permutation P:

$$(2, 3, 4, \ldots, l_1, 1; l_1 + 2, l_1 + 3, \ldots, l_2, l_1 + 1)$$

Since the l_1th element, 1, can be brought to the position 1 by $l_1 - 1$ interchanges of adjacent symbols and since the $(l_1 + l_2)$nd element, $l_1 + 1$, can be brought to the $(l_1 + 1)$st position by $l_2 - 1$ interchanges of consecutive symbols, the sign of the permutation is

$$\text{sgn } P = (-1)^{l_1-1}(-1)^{l_2-1}$$

Since, as elements of the system matrix, each of the g_{ik}'s has a minus sign, (see Eqs. *1*), the sign of the product Π_β is

$$(-1)^{l_1}(-1)^{l_2} \text{ sgn } P = (-1)^2$$

If G_β had consisted of λ loops, the reasoning above would have led to $(-1)^\lambda$. Therefore, any term of the expansion of Δ is either 1 or a product Π_α of loop gains of nontouching loops times $(-1)^{\lambda_\alpha}$, where λ_α is the number of loops corresponding to the product Π_α.

Conversely, any product of loop gains of nontouching loops of the graph G, with the appropriate sign, will appear as a term of the expansion of Δ. This follows directly from considerations almost identical with those outlined above.

Thus Eq. *22* is justified.

Evaluation of N_{1k}

Consider the matrix $\mathbf{M}'$ whose determinant appears as the numerator of *24*. Let $G_{M'}$ be the graph corresponding to the matrix $\mathbf{M}'$. $G_{M'}$ can be obtained from G by (I) deleting all branches that originate from the output node k and (II) inserting a branch of gain f_1 originating at k and terminating at 1. Since f_1 is the only nonzero element in the kth column of $\mathbf{M}'$, every nonzero product of the expansion of det $\mathbf{M}'$ includes the factor f_1. Since each such product corresponds to a set of nontouching loops, when f_1 is factored out, the remaining branch gains correspond to a set of directed loops and one *forward path* originating at the input node 1 and terminating at the output node k.

Let us consider a particular product Π'. Let the forward path of Π' contain $\lambda - 1$ branches and let its nodes be numbered $1, 2, \ldots, \lambda$, where 1 corresponds to the input node and λ to the output node. Such a renumbering does not affect the value of det $\mathbf{M}'$. The gain of the forward path is $g_{21}g_{32}g_{43} \cdots g_{\lambda,\lambda-1}$. Let us write the matrix $\mathbf{M}'$, after the reordering, putting the branch gains of the forward path in evidence.

$$\left[\begin{array}{cccccc|c}
\cdot & \cdot & \cdot & & & f_1 & \\
-g_{21} & & & & & \cdot & \\
 & -g_{32} & & & & \cdot & \\
 & & -g_{43} & & & \cdot & \\
 & & & \cdot & & \cdot & \\
 & & & & \cdot & \cdot & \\
 & & & & -g_{\lambda,\lambda-1} & \cdot & \\
\hline
 & & & & & & \\
 & & & & & & \mathbf{M}'_\lambda \\
 & & & & & &
\end{array}\right]$$

From the form of the matrix it is clear that the loop gain products appearing in Π' must come from the expansion of det $\mathbf{M}'_\lambda$. Consequently, if we consider in the expansion of det $\mathbf{M}'$ all the terms that have the product $f_1 g_{21} g_{32} \cdots g_{\lambda,\lambda-1}$ as a common factor, we get

$$(-1)^{\lambda-1} f_1(-g_{21})(-g_{32})(-g_{43}) \cdots (-g_{\lambda,\lambda-1}) \det \mathbf{M}_\lambda$$

where $(-1)^{\lambda-1}$ comes from the fact that f_1 belongs to the row 1 and column λ of $\mathbf{M}'$. This product is thus

$$\underbrace{f_1 g_{21} g_{32} \cdots g_{\lambda,\lambda-1}}_{\text{forward path gain}} \det \mathbf{M}'_\lambda$$

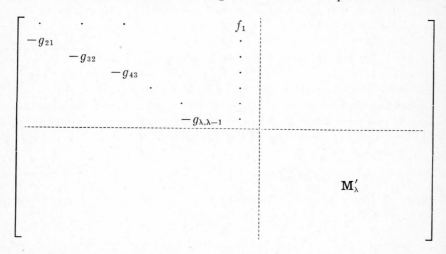

From a topological point of view, det $\mathbf{M}'_\lambda$ is the determinant associated with the signal-flow graph G_λ obtained from G by deleting all the nodes of the forward path and all the branches connected to this forward path. Therefore, any product Π' of the expansion of det $\mathbf{M}'$ is a term in an expression of the form $G_k\Delta_k$. Conversely, it is easy to establish that any expression of the form $G_k\Delta_k$ includes all terms of the expansion of det $\mathbf{M}'$ with the correct sign. Therefore, the formula det $\mathbf{M}' = \sum_k G_k\Delta_k$ is established.

25 *Exercise* Use Mason's formula (*21*) to compute the transfers function of the systems shown on Figs. *4.9.1* to *4.9.10* and Fig. *4.9.12*.

16 *Nyquist criterion*

In this section we shall consider exclusively linear time-invariant systems whose signal-flow graph is of the form shown in Fig. *9.16.1*. For obvious reasons such systems are called single-loop-feedback systems. Our purpose will be to characterize their stability in terms of the properties of the transfer functions F and H. Throughout this section we shall make the following

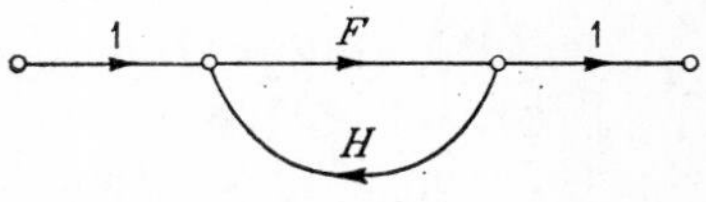

Fig. 9.16.1 Signal-flow-graph representation of a single-loop-feedback system; its transfer function is given by $G = F/(1 - FH)$.

1 **Assumption** The transfer functions F and H are rational functions of the complex frequency variable s.

2 *Comment* Of course, this assumption considerably simplifies the developments that follow. From an engineering point of view, it is certainly not a restriction to assume that the impulse response h of any transfer function that occurs in practice goes to zero at $t = \infty$ and belongs to $L^2(0, \infty)$; more precisely, that $\int_0^\infty |h(t)|^2\, dt < \infty$.[1] We assert that any such $h(t)$ can be approximated by an appropriately chosen linear combination of exponentials $\{e^{-(n+\frac{1}{2})t}\}_0^\infty$ and, therefore, the transfer function $H(s)$ can be approximated by an appropriately chosen linear combination of terms of the form $1/[s + (n + \frac{1}{2})]$. To be more explicit, let us show how this assertion follows from the Weierstrass approximation theorem. From the impulse response h, define a function f whose argument varies over (0,1), as follows:

$$h(t) = f(e^{-t})e^{-t/2}$$

[1] In many control applications, the transfer function has a pole at $s = 0$; in such a case, the impulse response can be written as a sum of two terms,

$$h(t) = a_0 1(t) + h_1(t)$$

where a_0 is the residue of $H(s)$ at $s = 0$. The function $h_1(t)$ satisfies the conditions above.

It is easy to check that the transformation $\xi = e^{-t}$ gives

$$\int_0^\infty |h(t)|^2\,dt = \int_0^1 |f(\xi)|^2\,d\xi$$

implying that $f \in L^2(0,1)$. Now, by the Weierstrass approximation theorem, f can be approximated (arbitrarily closely in the L^2 sense) by a polynomial $\sum_{n=0}^{N} \alpha_n x^n$, provided N is taken sufficiently large. Therefore, for N sufficiently large we can find a sequence of coefficients $\{\alpha_n\}$ such that $\int_0^\infty |h(t) - \sum_0^N \alpha_n[\exp -(n+\frac{1}{2})t]|^2\,dt$ is as small as we wish.

3 *Exercise* Show that if h is continuous on $[0,\infty)$ and goes to zero as $t \to \infty$, it can be approximated uniformly arbitrarily closely by a suitable linear combination of $\exp[-(n-\frac{1}{2})t]$, $n = 1, 2, \ldots$. (*Hint:* Use the following form of the Weierstrass approximation theorem: if f is continuous on $[0,1]$, then, for any $\varepsilon > 0$, there is a polynomial p such that

$$|f(x) - p(x)| < \varepsilon \qquad \forall x \in [0,1])$$

The first step in the analysis is to relate the strict stability of the gain of the single-loop-feedback system shown in Fig. *9.16.1* to the behavior of its loop gain FH. This is done by the following

4 **Theorem** Consider the single-loop-feedback system shown in Fig. *9.16.1*. If F and H are rational functions of s and if in the product FH the only cancellations that occur involve poles and zeros inside the left half plane, then the transfer function $G(s) = F/(1 - FH)$ is strictly stable if and only if $1 - FH$ has no zeros either on the $j\omega$ axis or in the right half plane.

5 *Comment* This theorem is intuitively reasonable: if F has a pole p_1 such that $\mathrm{Re}\, p_1 > 0$, a little analysis of the formula for G shows that G is well behaved in a small neighborhood of p_1 and $G(p_1) = -1/H(p_1)$. Similarly, if H has a pole at p_1, G is well behaved in a small neighborhood of p_1 and $G(p_1) = 0$.

Proof $\Rightarrow$ Use contradiction. Suppose that for some z_1 in the closed right half plane ($\mathrm{Re}\, z_1 \geq 0$), $1 - F(z_1)H(z_1) = 0$. By the second assumption, the last equality implies $F(z_1) \neq 0$; hence, G has a pole at z_1 and G is not strictly stable. This contradicts the hypothesis; therefore, $1 - FH$ cannot have a zero in the closed right half plane.

$\Leftarrow$ The only way G could have a pole p_0 in the closed right half plane (i.e., $\mathrm{Re}\, p_0 \geq 0$) is that either $1 - FH = 0$ at p_0 with $F(p_0) \neq 0$

or that F has a pole of order m at p_0 but $1 - FH$ has a pole of order $<m$. The first possibility is ruled out by the assumption of this sufficiency proof. The second possibility requires that there be a cancellation of factors of the form $(s - p_0)$ in the product FH. Since $\text{Re } p_0 \geq 0$, this is ruled out by the second assumption of the theorem. Hence G is strictly stable.

6 *Comment* The theorem makes no assumptions relative to the stability of either F or H. Furthermore, no practical system would ever violate the second assumption, namely, that there would be a right-half-plane pole canceled by a right-half-plane zero in the product FH. The reasons for this are well known and discussed in *11.5.10*. ◁

The most useful tool for the study of the loop gain FH is the

7 **Principle of the argument** Let C be a simple closed curve in the s plane. Let f be a rational function of s which has neither zeros nor poles on C. Let f map the curve C into the curve Γ of the f plane (see Fig. *9.16.2*). Then as the point s runs through the contour C in the

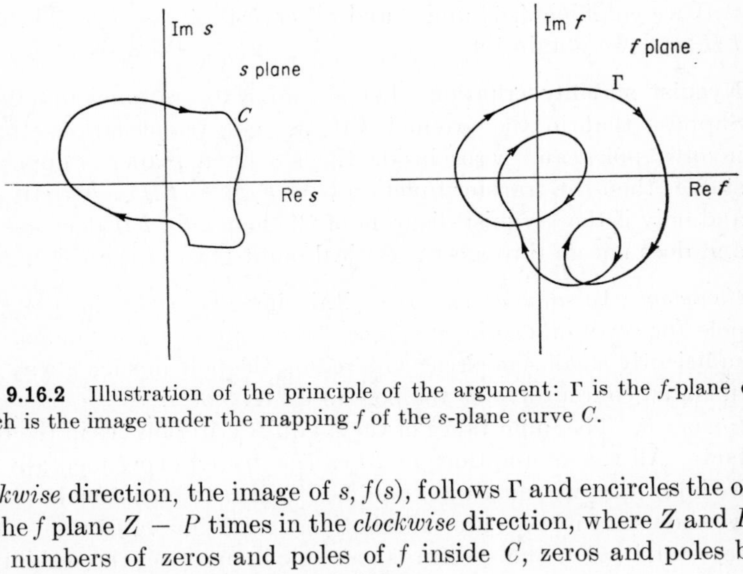

Fig. 9.16.2 Illustration of the principle of the argument: Γ is the f-plane curve which is the image under the mapping f of the s-plane curve C.

clockwise direction, the image of s, $f(s)$, follows Γ and encircles the origin of the f plane $Z - P$ times in the *clockwise* direction, where Z and P are the numbers of zeros and poles of f inside C, zeros and poles being counted with their proper multiplicities.

We shall not prove this result since it is classical.[1]

8 *Comment* For the purpose of investigating the stability of a transfer function, one uses the contour C_R, which consists of the j axis and the right-hand semicircle of infinite radius. Therefore, by *4*, any zero of $1 - FH$ inside C_R will make the transfer function G unstable.

[1] E. Hille, "Analytic Function Theory," Ginn and Co., Boston, 1959.

9 **Definition** The mapping of the contour C_R by a transfer function T is called the *Nyquist diagram* of T.

A Nyquist diagram of a simple low-pass amplifier is shown in Fig. *9.16.3*.

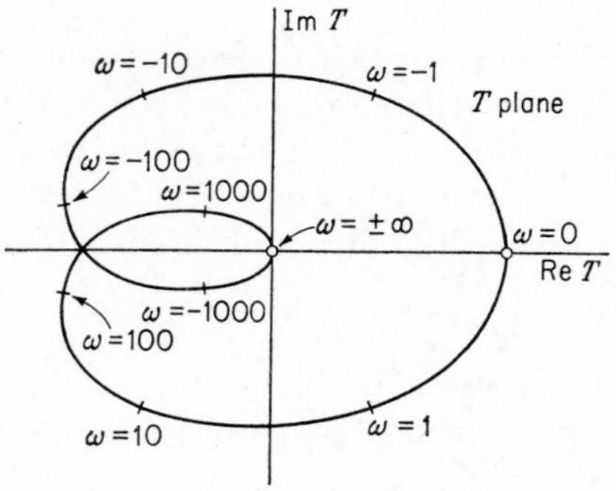

Fig. 9.16.3 Example of a Nyquist diagram (not to scale).

If we combine *4*, *7*, and *8* and observe that $1 - FH = 0$ whenever $FH = 1$, we obtain the

10 **Nyquist stability criterion** Let F and H be rational functions of s. Suppose that in the product FH the only cancellations that occur involve poles and zeros inside the left-hand plane. Suppose FH is stable: then the transfer function $G = F/(1 - FH)$ is strictly stable if and only if the Nyquist diagram of the loop gain FH does not encircle and does not go through the critical point (1,0) of the FH plane.

11 *Comment* In some cases a technical difficulty occurs in that FH has a pole (or zero) on C_R; in such a case the contour C_R is "indented" by a sufficiently small semicircle centered on the pole in such a way that the indented contour avoids the pole (see Fig. *9.6.2*).

12 *Comment* The importance of the Nyquist criterion lies in the following fact. All the assumptions of *10* can be tested experimentally: from *2* we know that we can always assume F and H to be rational. In *11.5.10* we show that if there are cancellations in FH involving right-half-plane zeros and poles, the system is unstable in practice; the stability of FH can be decided by observing the open-loop behavior of the system; and finally, the Nyquist diagram is obtained by plotting the result of sinusoidal steady-state measurements of the open-loop gain. In practice, there are simplifications: (I) $F(s)H(s) \to 0$ as $|s| \to \infty$; hence the right-half-plane semicircle of C_R maps into the origin of the FH plane, and (II) since $F(-j\omega)H(-j\omega) = [F(j\omega)H(j\omega)]^*$, the mapping of the negative part of the $j\omega$ axis is the mirror image of that of the positive part.

17 *Stability of multiple-loop systems*

Consider an example of a linear time-invariant multiple-feedback-loop system; in particular, consider the system shown in Fig. *9.17.1*. The

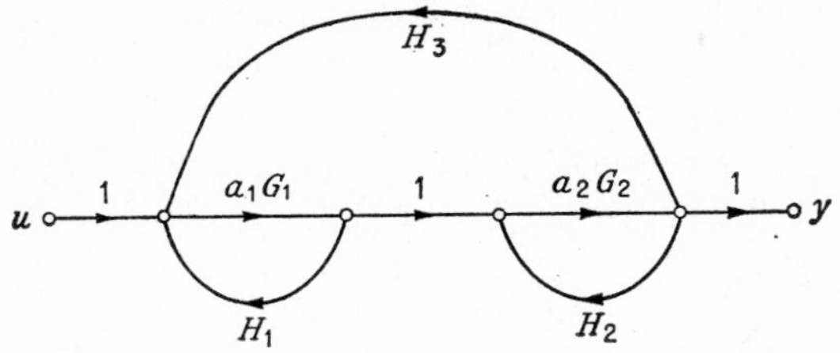

Fig. 9.17.1 Example of a multiple-feedback-loop system.

gain of the two forward branches is a_1G_1 and a_2G_2, where a_1 and a_2 are real numbers in [0,1] and G_1 and G_2 are functions of the complex variable s. The gain of the system from the input u to the output y is, according to Mason's formula *9.15.21*,

1 $$\frac{a_1a_2G_1G_2}{1 - a_1G_1H_1 - a_2G_2H_2 - a_1a_2G_1G_2H_3 + a_1a_2G_1G_2H_1H_2}$$

Suppose that while G_1, G_2, H_1, H_2, and H_3 are fixed functions of s, the parameters a_1 and a_2 are allowed to take any value in the square defined by $0 \le a_1 \le 1$, $0 \le a_2 \le 1$. The problem is to establish necessary and sufficient conditions for stability of the system irrespective of the values of a_1 and a_2 provided $0 \le a_1 \le 1$, $0 \le a_2 \le 1$.

The problem is important in many areas of engineering, in particular, in communications. It is often proposed to duplicate equipment to make the system immune to the failure or degradation of tubes, transistors, or other delicate devices. These questions have been considered in connection with active satellite repeaters, submarine cable repeaters, and, in general, any equipment whose maintenance is either impossible or prohibitively expensive. In repeaters it is proposed to duplicate the forward amplifiers in such a way that the failure or degradation of any one of them leaves the repeater performance within its specifications; this implies that the repeater is stable for all values of α_0 of the transistors lying between 0 and their nominal values.

Throughout the development of this section[1] we shall make the following

[1] The general method used in the following is originally due to L. Curtis of the Bell Telephone Laboratories. See also F. H. Blecher, Design Principles for Multiple Loop Transistor Feedback Amplifiers, *Proc. NEC,* vol. 13, pp. 19–34, 1957.

2 **Assumption** The system under consideration is a single-input single-output linear time-invariant system represented by a linear signal-flow graph.

3 **Assumption** All branches of the signal-flow graph are strictly stable.

4 **Assumption** There is a subset of l branches such that each branch of the subset has a transfer function proportional to one (real) parameter; the gain of the ith branch of the subset is proportional to a_i. These l parameters define a vector $\mathbf{a} = (a_1, a_2, \ldots, a_l)$. Since the components of $\mathbf{a}$ are subject to the inequalities $0 \leq a_i \leq 1$, the vector $\mathbf{a}$ is restricted to the cube

5 $$\mathcal{A} = \{\mathbf{a} | 0 \leq a_i \leq 1, i = 1, 2, \ldots, n\}$$

6 **Assumption** The gain of the system is strictly stable when $\mathbf{a} = \mathbf{0}$.

7 **Assumption** The zeros of the determinant $\Delta(s,\mathbf{a})$ of the signal-flow graph are continuous functions of $\mathbf{a}$.

8 *Comment* When all branch gains have their nominal values, $a_i = 1$ for $i = 1, 2, \ldots, l$. When aging, deterioration, or even failure occurs, some or all a_i decrease and may even become 0. Assumption *6* amounts to assuming that the gain of the system is strictly stable when all the elements of the subset have zero gain.

9 *Comment* Assumption *7* is always satisfied in practice: the implicit-function theorem[1] implies that *7* holds whenever each branch gain is the ratio of entire functions of s. In particular, if the system consists of lumped elements, each branch gain is a ratio of two polynomials. If in addition the system includes ideal transmission lines or transportation lags, the branch gains are ratios of polynomials in s, $e^{-T_1 s}$, $e^{-T_2 s}$, . . . , where T_1, T_2 are constants, and again *7* is satisfied.

The problem is to obtain necessary and sufficient conditions for the strict stability of the gain of the whole system. For this purpose we turn to the analysis of the problem. From Mason's formula (*9.15.21*) the gain of the system is of the form

$$G = \frac{\Sigma G_k \Delta_k}{\Delta(s,\mathbf{a})}$$

For each forward path, G_k and Δ_k are respectively a product and 1 minus an algebraic sum of products of branch gains; hence by *3*, the numera-

[1] T. M. Apostol, "Mathematical Analysis," p. 147, Addison-Wesley Publishing Company, Inc. Reading, Mass., 1957.

tor is analytic in the closed right half plane. Similarly, for all $\mathbf{a}$ in $\mathcal{A}$, $\Delta(s,\mathbf{a})$ is analytic in the closed right half plane. Thus,

10 **Assertion** The gain of the system is strictly stable for all $\mathbf{a} \in \mathcal{A}$ if and only if $\Delta(s,\mathbf{a})$ has no zeros in the closed right half plane for all $\mathbf{a} \in \mathcal{A}$. ◁

So the stability of the gain G depends on whether or not $\Delta(s,\mathbf{a})$ has right-half-plane zeros. Now, as in the Nyquist criterion case, we need only investigate the $j\omega$-axis behavior of $\Delta(s,\mathbf{a})$ in order to test for stability. More precisely, we have the

11 **Assertion** Let the system satisfy the assumptions *3* to *7*. If the gain of the system is unstable for some $\mathbf{a}_0 \in \mathcal{A}$, then there is a number $\lambda_0 \in (0,1]$ such that $\Delta(s,\lambda_0\mathbf{a}_0)$ has at least one $j\omega$-axis zero.

Proof Since the gain of the system is unstable at $\mathbf{a}_0$, *10* requires that at least one root of $\Delta(s,\mathbf{a}_0)$, say $s_1 = \sigma_1 + j\omega_1$, have a nonnegative real part σ_1. Note that σ_1 will vary with $\mathbf{a}$: $\sigma_1 = f(\mathbf{a})$, $f(\mathbf{a}_0) \geq 0$. Now introduce the function of the real variable λ defined by $\phi(\lambda) = f(\lambda\mathbf{a}_0)$. By *7*, $\phi(\lambda)$ is a continuous function of λ and $\phi(1) \geq 0$ but, by *6*, $\phi(0) < 0$. Therefore, there is a $\lambda_0 \in (0,1]$ such that $\phi(\lambda_0) = 0$; hence, at $\mathbf{a} = \lambda_0\mathbf{a}_0$, s_1 is on the $j\omega$ axis and $\Delta(s,\lambda_0\mathbf{a}_0)$ has a $j\omega$-axis zero.

12 **Corollary** The system is strictly stable if and only if $\Delta(s,\mathbf{a})$ has no $j\omega$-axis zeros for all $\mathbf{a} \in \mathcal{A}$. ◁

For convenience, let $\mathcal{R}^1$ be the set of all real numbers and define $T(s,\mathbf{a})$ by $\Delta(s,\mathbf{a}) = 1 - T(s,\mathbf{a})$. From Mason's formula (*9.15.21*), T is a linear combination of loop-gain products; hence, because of *4*, for any $\mathbf{a}$ and ω, the complex number $T(j\omega,\mathbf{a})$ can be determined experimentally by sinusoidal steady-state measurement of all the loop gains. In other words, the situation is analogous to the Nyquist case. Finally, if we observe that $\Delta(s,\mathbf{a}) = 0 \Leftrightarrow T(s,\mathbf{a}) = 1$, we may summarize the developments above by the

13 **Theorem** Let the system satisfy Assumptions *3* to *7*. The gain of the system is strictly stable for all $\mathbf{a} \in \mathcal{A}$ if and only if, for all $\omega \in \mathcal{R}^1$, the mapping of the cube $\mathcal{A}$ on the complex T plane by the function $T(j\omega,\cdot)$ does not include the point $1 + j0$. ◁

The problem now is to find an effective method of carrying out the mapping of $\mathcal{A}$ on the T plane for each $\omega \in \mathcal{R}^1$. Therefore, let us investigate some properties of the mapping.

Let the vector $\mathbf{a} \in \mathcal{A}$ and think of $\mathbf{a}$ as the point $(a_1,a_2, \ldots ,a_n)$ in $\mathcal{A}$. Since the cube $\mathcal{A}$ is convex, if a line is drawn through $\mathbf{a}$ parallel to the ith axis of coordinates, it will intersect the boundary of $\mathcal{A}$ at two points $\mathbf{a}'$ and $\mathbf{a}''$. Let $\mathbf{a}'$ (respectively, $\mathbf{a}''$) be the boundary point on the hyperplane $a_i = 0$ (respectively, $a_i = 1$). Observe that $\mathbf{a}$ belongs to the closed segment joining a′ to a″ (see Fig. *9.17.2*). Let $\mathbf{e}_i$ be the unit vector along the ith axis of coordinates; then

$$\mathbf{a} = \mathbf{a}' + a_i\mathbf{e}_i$$
$$\mathbf{a}'' = \mathbf{a}' + \mathbf{e}_i$$

Since each loop gain depends linearly on each of the branch gains of that loop, T is a multilinear function of the a_k's. More precisely, in

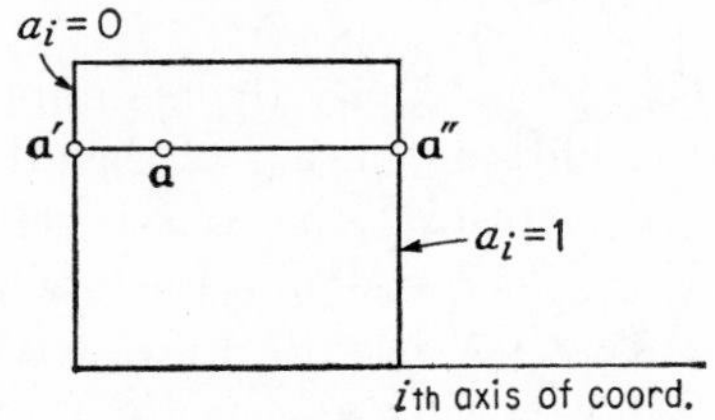

Fig. 9.17.2 Cross section of the n-dimensional cube $\mathcal{Q}$ showing the segment a′a″.

the expression of T we can put any one of them in evidence, say, a_i, and write the complex number $T(j\omega,\mathbf{a})$ as $T(j\omega,\mathbf{a}) = A + a_iB$, where A and B depend on s, $a_1, a_2, \ldots, a_{i-1}, a_{i+1}, \ldots, a_n$. Observing that the ith components of a′ and a″ are 0 and 1, respectively, we have

$$T(j\omega,\mathbf{a}') = A \qquad T(j\omega,\mathbf{a}'') = A + B$$

Hence

$$T(j\omega,\mathbf{a}) = (1 - a_i)T(j\omega,\mathbf{a}') + a_iT(j\omega,\mathbf{a}'')$$

or

14 $$T(j\omega, \mathbf{a}' + a_i\mathbf{e}_i) = (1 - a_i)T(j\omega,\mathbf{a}') + a_iT(j\omega, \mathbf{a}' + \mathbf{e}_i)$$

Thus, in terms of mappings on the T plane, the point $T(j\omega, \mathbf{a}' + a_i\mathbf{e}_i)$, where $0 \leq a_i \leq 1$, lies on the segment joining $T(j\omega,\mathbf{a}')$ to $T(j\omega, \mathbf{a}' + \mathbf{e}_i)$. This is the fundamental property for the mapping of $\mathcal{Q}$ into the complex T plane. Its geometric meaning can be stated as follows:

15 **Assertion** Any line segment of the cube $\mathcal{Q}$ parallel to an axis of coordinates maps into a line segment on the T plane. The end points of the T-plane segment are the images of the end points of the segment in $\mathcal{Q}$. ◁

Before deriving the general theorem, let us consider a simple example. Let $l = 2$; hence, the cube $\mathcal{Q}$ reduces to a square with four vertices that are designated as $\mathbf{0},\boldsymbol{\alpha},\boldsymbol{\beta},\boldsymbol{\gamma}$, as shown in Fig. *9.17.3*. We consider a fixed ω and wish to investigate the mapping of $\mathcal{Q}$ on the complex T plane for that value of ω. Suppose for simplicity that $T(j\omega,\mathbf{0}) = 0$. In Fig. *9.17.4*, the images of the vertices are shown and are labeled with a primes in order to distinguish them from the vertices of $\mathcal{A}$. From *15* the mapping has the following properties:

16 $$\begin{aligned} &\text{Segment } [\mathbf{0},\boldsymbol{\alpha}] \to \text{segment } [\mathbf{0},\boldsymbol{\alpha}'] \\ &\text{Segment } [\boldsymbol{\alpha},\boldsymbol{\gamma}] \to \text{segment } [\boldsymbol{\alpha}',\boldsymbol{\gamma}'] \\ &\text{Segment } [\mathbf{0},\boldsymbol{\beta}] \to \text{segment } [\mathbf{0},\boldsymbol{\beta}'] \\ &\text{Segment } [\boldsymbol{\beta},\boldsymbol{\gamma}] \to \text{segment } [\boldsymbol{\beta}',\boldsymbol{\gamma}'] \end{aligned}$$

Consider now a segment parallel to the a_2 axis and of abscissa λ, $0 < \lambda < 1$. This segment is shown in Fig. *9.17.3*, and its vertices are labeled $\boldsymbol{\delta},\boldsymbol{\eta}$. Again, this segment maps onto the segment $[\boldsymbol{\delta}',\boldsymbol{\eta}']$ in Fig. *9.17.4*. It is clear that, as λ goes from 0 to 1, $[\boldsymbol{\delta},\boldsymbol{\eta}]$ sweeps through

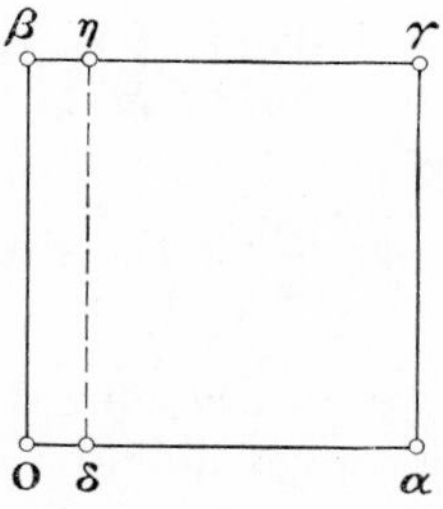

Fig. 9.17.3 Special case $l = 2$. The cube $\mathcal{A}$ reduces to a square.

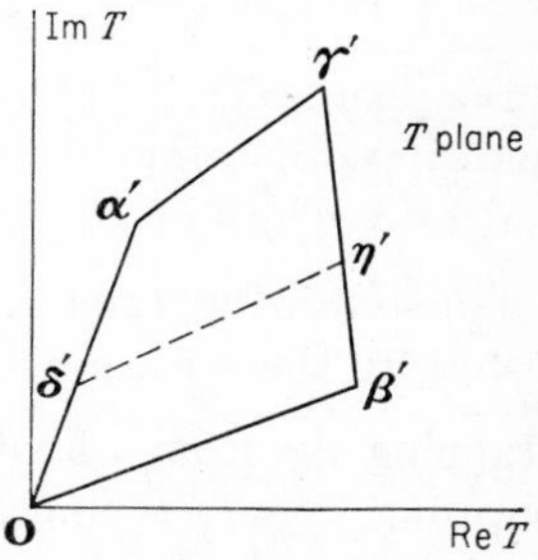

Fig. 9.17.4 T-plane image, for some fixed ω, of the square $\mathcal{A}$ of Fig. *9.17.3*.

the whole square $\mathcal{A}$ and $[\boldsymbol{\delta}',\boldsymbol{\eta}']$ sweeps through the whole quadrilateral $\mathbf{0}\boldsymbol{\alpha}'\boldsymbol{\gamma}'\boldsymbol{\beta}'$. Therefore, for that particular ω, the mapping of $\mathcal{A}$ requires only the plotting of the images of the vertices of $\mathcal{A}$. It is a fact that these happy circumstances will not always occur. Suppose the mapping of the vertices of $\mathcal{A}$ had been of the form shown in Fig. *9.17.5*. The statements *15* and *16* still hold: for small λ, the segment $[\boldsymbol{\delta}',\boldsymbol{\eta}']$ lies inside the quadrilateral $\mathbf{0}\boldsymbol{\alpha}'\boldsymbol{\gamma}'\boldsymbol{\beta}'$. However, for a larger λ, it maps onto

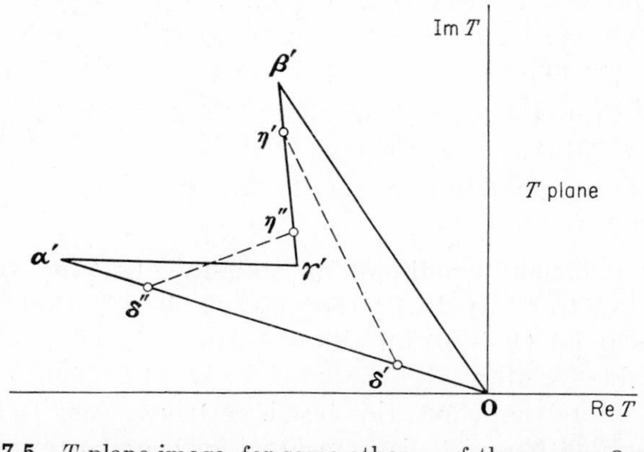

Fig. 9.17.5 T-plane image, for some other ω, of the square $\mathcal{A}$ of Fig. *9.17.3*.

$[\boldsymbol{\delta}'',\mathbf{n}'']$, some points of which are outside the quadrilateral! It is also easy to see that for all λ's it will be inside the triangle $\mathbf{0}\boldsymbol{\alpha}'\boldsymbol{\beta}'$.

In order to proceed to the general case, we must introduce some new terms.

17 **Definition** For any $\omega \in \mathcal{R}^1$, let $V(\omega)$ be the images, on the T plane, of the 2^l vertices of $\mathcal{A}$. $V(\omega)$ is therefore a set of at most 2^l points, since the images of the vertices are not necessarily distinct.

18 **Definition** Let $X = \{\mathbf{x}_1,\mathbf{x}_2, \ldots ,\mathbf{x}_N\}$ be a finite set of points in the space $\mathcal{R}^N$. The *convex hull* of X, denoted by $[X]$, is the set

$$[X] = \left\{\mathbf{x}|\mathbf{x} = \sum_{i=1}^{N} \lambda_i\mathbf{x}_i ; \lambda_i \geq 0 \text{ and } \sum_{i=1}^{N} \lambda_i = 1\right\}$$

For example, in Fig. *9.17.4*, the convex hull of $\{\mathbf{0},\boldsymbol{\alpha}',\boldsymbol{\beta}',\boldsymbol{\gamma}'\}$ is the quadrilateral defined by $\mathbf{0}$, $\boldsymbol{\alpha}'$, $\boldsymbol{\beta}'$, $\boldsymbol{\gamma}'$. On the other hand, in Fig. *9.17.5*, the convex hull of $\{\mathbf{0},\boldsymbol{\alpha}',\boldsymbol{\beta}',\boldsymbol{\gamma}'\}$ is the triangle defined by $\mathbf{0},\boldsymbol{\alpha}',\boldsymbol{\beta}'$. ◁

The following theorem states for the general case the situation suggested by these examples.

19 **Mapping theorem** For all $\omega \in \mathcal{R}^1$, the image of the cube $\mathcal{A}$ under the mapping $T(j\omega,\cdot)$ is contained in $[V(\omega)]$, the convex hull of $V(\omega)$ defined in *17*.

Proof The derivation is purely computational and is based on *14*. For simplicity we consider the case $l = 2$. From *14*, for all $\mathbf{a} = (a_1,a_2)$ in $\mathcal{A}$ we have

$$\begin{aligned} T(j\omega,\mathbf{a}) &= T(j\omega, a_1\mathbf{e}_1 + a_2\mathbf{e}_2) \\ &= (1 - a_2)T(j\omega,a_1\mathbf{e}_1) + a_2T(j\omega, a_1\mathbf{e}_1 + \mathbf{e}_2) \\ &= (1 - a_1)(1 - a_2)T(j\omega,\mathbf{0}) + a_1(1 - a_2)T(j\omega,\mathbf{e}_1) \\ &\qquad + (1 - a_1)a_2T(j\omega,\mathbf{e}_2) + a_1a_2T(j\omega, \mathbf{e}_1 + \mathbf{e}_2) \end{aligned}$$

This proves that, for all $\mathbf{a} \in \mathcal{A}$, the point $T(j\omega,\mathbf{a})$ belongs to the convex hull of the set $\{T(j\omega,\mathbf{0}),T(j\omega,\mathbf{e}_1),T(j\omega,\mathbf{e}_2),T(j\omega, \mathbf{e}_1 + \mathbf{e}_2)\}$, because each of the weighting factors is nonnegative and the sum of the weighting factors is equal to 1.

20 *Comment* From the example of Fig. *9.17.5* we know that there may be points in $[V(\omega)]$ that do not belong to the image of $\mathcal{A}$. We may finally state a sufficient condition for the stability of the system which follows directly from *13* and *19*.

21 **Theorem: sufficient condition for stability** Let the system satisfy assumptions *3* to *7*. If $[V(\omega)]$, the convex hull of $V(\omega)$, does not include the critical point $(1 + j0)$ for all $\omega \in \mathcal{R}^1$, then the gain of the system is strictly stable for all $\mathbf{a} \in \mathcal{A}$.

22 *Comment* Note that, first, this test is relatively easy to apply since it involves only 2^l Nyquist diagrams, one for each vertex of the cube $\mathcal{A}$, whereas the brute-force approach would require one Nyquist diagram

for each point of $\mathcal{A}$. Second, *21* together with *13* is a quite powerful tool. Indeed, if for some ω, $[V(\omega)]$ includes the point $1 + j0$, *13* suggests that the shape of the mapping of $\mathcal{A}$ for that ω be sketched out in order to find out whether or not the system is actually unstable. Consider, for example, the case illustrated in Fig. *9.17.6*. The cube $\mathcal{A}$ is shown with its vertices **1,2,3,4,5,6,7,8.** On the T plane shown in Fig. *9.17.6* the points **1′,2′**, . . . ,**8′** are the mappings of the vertices

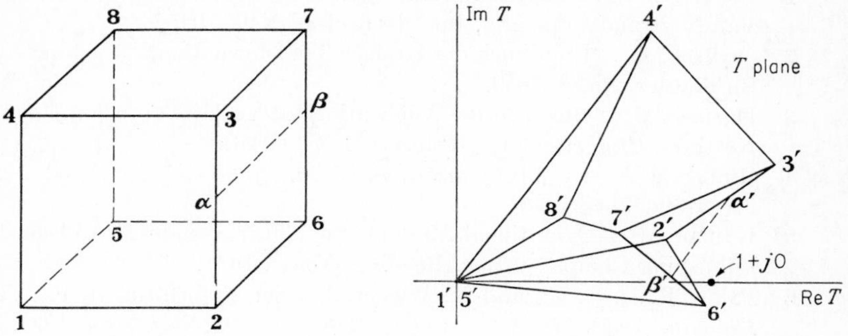

Fig. 9.17.6 Cube $\mathcal{A}$ and its T-plane image for some fixed ω.

of $\mathcal{A}$ for a particular ω, say, ω_0. It is clear that the critical point $(1 + j0)$ is inside $[V(\omega_0)]$. However, the critical point does not belong to the mapping of $\mathcal{A}$ at ω_0; all the faces of $\mathcal{A}$ map inside the polygon **1′,6′,2′,3′,4′** except the face **2,3,7,6.** The figure shows the mapping of the four edges of that face. Now consider parallels to the edge **3,7** such as the segment $\boldsymbol{\alpha\beta}$, which maps onto the segment $\boldsymbol{\alpha'\beta'}$. As $\boldsymbol{\alpha}$ moves along the edge **2,3**, the segment $\boldsymbol{\alpha'\beta'}$ slides in the T plane with $\boldsymbol{\alpha'}$ constrained to be on **2′3′** and $\boldsymbol{\beta'}$ constrained to remain on **6′7′**. The boundary of the mapping of the face **2,3,7,6** is the envelope generated by the motion of $\boldsymbol{\alpha'\beta'}$. It can be shown that it is an *arc of a parabola* and two straight-line segments. In practice, however, one need only trace a few positions of the segment $\boldsymbol{\alpha'\beta'}$ to decide whether or not the critical point is included in the mapping of $\mathcal{A}$.

23 *Exercise* Suppose that the vertices **2,3,6,7** of $\mathcal{A}$ map into the points $\mathbf{x}_2$, $\mathbf{x}_3$, $\mathbf{x}_6$, and $\mathbf{x}_7$ in the T plane shown in Fig. *9.17.7*. Segment $\boldsymbol{\alpha'\beta'}$ is

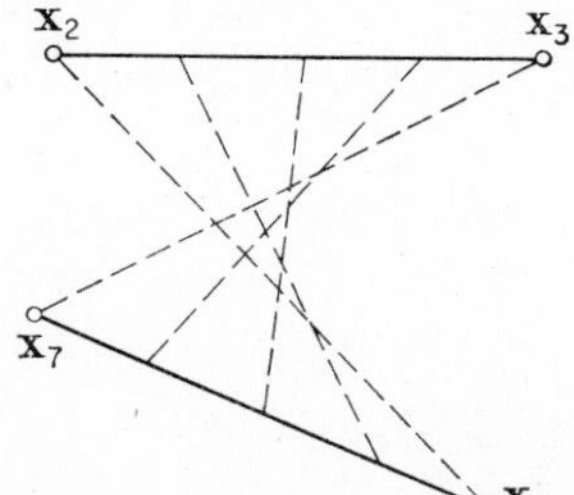

Fig. 9.17.7 Figure showing the segments $\mathbf{x}_2\mathbf{x}_3$ and $\mathbf{x}_6\mathbf{x}_7$ of Exercise *9.17.23*.

the segment joining $\boldsymbol{\alpha}' = \mathbf{x}_2 + \lambda\mathbf{x}_{23}$ and $\boldsymbol{\beta}' = \mathbf{x}_{6'} + \lambda\mathbf{x}_{67}$, where $\mathbf{x}_{23} = \mathbf{x}_3 - \mathbf{x}_2$, $\mathbf{x}_{67} = \mathbf{x}_7 - \mathbf{x}_6$, and $\lambda \in [0,1]$. Show that the envelope of that segment as λ traverses the interval [0,1] is an arc of a parabola and two straight lines.

REFERENCES AND SUGGESTED READING

1 Bode, H. W.: "Network Analysis and Feedback Amplifier Design," D. Van Nostrand Company, Inc., Princeton, N.J., 1945.

2 Doetsch, G.: "Handbuch der Laplace Transformation," 3 volumes, Verlag Birkhäuser, Basel, 1950.

3 Doetsch, G.: "Guide to the Applications of Laplace Transforms," D. Van Nostrand Company, Inc., Princeton, N.J., 1961.

4 Guillemin, E. A.: "Mathematics of Circuit Analysis," John Wiley & Sons, Inc., New York, 1949.

5 Kaplan, W.: "Operational Methods for Linear Systems," Addison-Wesley Publishing Company, Inc., Reading, Mass., 1962.

6 Paley, R. E. A. C., and N. Wiener: Fourier Transforms in the Complex Domain, *Amer. Math. Soc. Colloq. Publ.*, vol. 19, New York, 1934.

7 Papoulis, A.: "The Fourier Integral and Its Applications," McGraw-Hill Book Company, Inc., New York, 1962.

8 Seshu, S., and N. Balabanian: "Linear Network Analysis," John Wiley & Sons, Inc., New York, 1959.

9 Van der Pol, B., and H. Bremmer: "Operational Calculus Based on the Two Sided Laplace Integral," Cambridge University Press, New York, 1950.

10 Widder, D. V.: "The Laplace Transform," Princeton University Press, Princeton, N.J., 1941.

Discrete-time systems **10**

1 *Introduction*

So far we have considered exclusively systems in which the variables (input, output, state, etc.) can be observed at all instants of time. This is not always possible. Digital computers, for example, take in and print out data representing the values of variables at discrete instants of time. These discrete instants are taken sufficiently close that a simple interpolation would yield a satisfactory approximation for all intermediate values of time. In some other circumstances the system itself is not digital but observations can be made only periodically. A pulse radar, for example, obtains data from the target only at equally spaced instants of time. Another example comes from chemical engineering: it sometimes happens that an expensive analyzer is shared by several identical processes so that the output product of each process is analyzed only periodically.

Thus in general, when one or more variables can be observed only periodically and when the period of observation is sufficiently small that all variables can be reconstructed sufficiently accurately from their samples, it is an obvious simplification to write the equations of the system in terms of the sampled values of all the variables. In other words, we model the system by a *discrete-time system* (see *3.8.42*). This simplifies the analysis considerably, and, furthermore, it is precisely that which is done in numerical computation. We shall therefore restrict ourselves to *periodic sampling*, i.e., to cases where the samples are taken at equally spaced instants of time. We shall, furthermore, consider only *time-invariant* systems. This will be sufficient for our main purpose, which is to show the considerable extent to which the analysis of discrete systems follows that of continuous systems. The analysis and design of discrete control systems is a vast subject. Several books, listed in the references, have been written on the subject in the last few years, and the reader is referred to them if he wishes to pursue the subject beyond our brief treatment.

2 *Systems represented by their state equations*

Representation of discrete systems obtained by sampling a differential system

Suppose we are given a differential system $\mathcal{S}$ represented by its state equations

1 $$\dot{\mathbf{x}} = \mathbf{A}\mathbf{x} + \mathbf{B}\mathbf{u}$$

2 $$\mathbf{y} = \mathbf{C}\mathbf{x} + \mathbf{D}\mathbf{u}$$

where **A**, **B**, **C**, and **D** are, respectively, $(n \times n)$, $(n \times r)$, $(p \times n)$, and $(p \times r)$ constant matrices. Suppose that the components of the input vector are sampled periodically and are constrained to be constant over each interval $(kT, (k + 1)T)$, where $k = \ldots, -1, 0, 1, \ldots$. In Fig. *10.2.1*, this constraint is represented by the insertion of the sample-

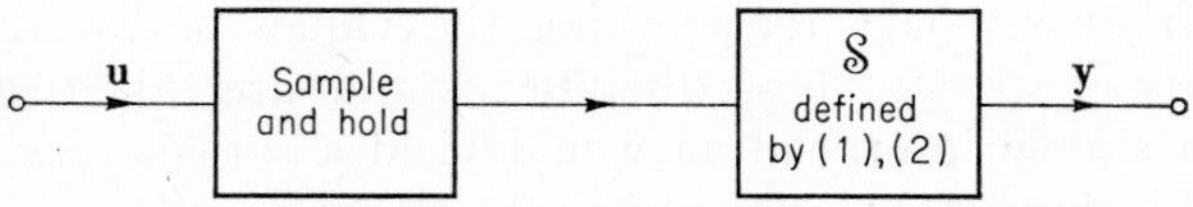

Fig. 10.2.1 The input u is sampled and held constant over the intervals $(kT, (k + 1)T)$ by the sample-and-hold box before being applied to the system $\mathcal{S}$.

and-hold box between the input **u** and the system $\mathcal{S}$. By definition of the sample-and-hold box, if $\alpha(t)$ is its input, then its output is the piecewise constant function α_0 specified by

$$\alpha_0(t) = \alpha(kT) \qquad kT < t \leq (k + 1)T, \text{ for all integers } k$$

We shall say that the input is sampled every T sec, and we shall refer to T as the *sampling period*. Thus the input is completely specified by the sequence of vectors $\{\mathbf{u}_k\}$, where $\mathbf{u}_k = \mathbf{u}(kT+)$. As stated earlier, in most applications the sampling period T is chosen sufficiently small that the interpolation of the sequences $\{\mathbf{x}_k\}$ and $\{\mathbf{y}_k\}$, where $\mathbf{x}_k = \mathbf{x}(kT+)$, $\mathbf{y}_k = \mathbf{y}(kT+)$, determines the functions $\mathbf{x}(t)$ and $\mathbf{y}(t)$ with sufficient accuracy for all t. For this reason, it is reasonable to seek the relations between the sequences $\{\mathbf{x}_k\}$ and $\{\mathbf{y}_k\}$ and the input sequence $\{\mathbf{u}_k\}$. It is most convenient to express these relations as recurrence relations giving $\mathbf{x}_{k+1}$ and $\mathbf{y}_{k+1}$ in terms of $\mathbf{x}_k$ and $\mathbf{u}_k$. Using *5.2.19* and defining

3 $$\mathbf{F} = \exp \mathbf{A}T$$

4 $$\mathbf{G} = \left(\int_0^T [\exp(\mathbf{A}\tau)]\, d\tau\right) \mathbf{B}$$

we immediately obtain

5 $$\mathbf{x}_{k+1} = \mathbf{F}\mathbf{x}_k + \mathbf{G}\mathbf{u}_k$$

6 $$\mathbf{y}_{k+1} = \mathbf{C}\mathbf{x}_{k+1} + \mathbf{D}\mathbf{u}_{k+1}$$

We can consider *5* and *6* as the state equations of a discrete-time system whose input, state, and output are respectively specified by the vector-valued sequences $\{\mathbf{u}_k\}$, $\{\mathbf{x}_k\}$, and $\{\mathbf{y}_k\}$. We shall refer to this system as the *discrete-time system 5* and *6*. Since **A**, **B**, **C**, and **D** are constant matrices, it is easy to verify that this system is linear and time-invariant (see *3.4.25* and *3.2.36*).

If we iterate *5*, then we can express $\mathbf{x}_k$ in terms of the initial state $\mathbf{x}_0$ and the sequence $\{\mathbf{u}_i\}_0^{k-1}$:

7 $$\mathbf{x}_k = \mathbf{F}^k\mathbf{x}_0 + \sum_{i=0}^{k-1} \mathbf{F}^i\mathbf{G}\mathbf{u}_{k-i-1} \qquad k = 0, 1, \ldots$$

The R.H.S. of *7* may also be written $\mathbf{x}(kT;\mathbf{x}_0,0;\{\mathbf{u}_i\}_0^{k-1})$ to emphasize that it is the state at time kT resulting from the initial state $\mathbf{x}_0$ at time 0 and the input defined by the sequence $\{\mathbf{u}_i\}_0^{k-1}$.

8 **Summary** Let the (continuous-time) system $\mathcal{S}$ be defined by its state equations *1* and *2*, where **A**, **B**, **C**, and **D** are constant matrices. Let the input be piecewise constant over the intervals $(kT,(k+1)T)$, $k = \ldots, -1, 0, 1, \ldots$; then the sampled values of the state vector, input, and output vector are related by *5* and *6*. $\mathbf{x}(kT;\mathbf{x}_0,0;\{\mathbf{u}_0\}_0^{k-1})$ is given by *7*.

9 *Exercise* Show that whatever **A** and $T > 0$ may be, **F** is always a nonsingular matrix.

10 *Example* For simplicity consider the single-input single-output differential system defined by

$$\begin{bmatrix} \dot{x}_1 \\ \dot{x}_2 \end{bmatrix} = \begin{bmatrix} -1 & 3 \\ 0 & -2 \end{bmatrix} \begin{bmatrix} x_1 \\ x_2 \end{bmatrix} + \begin{bmatrix} 0 \\ 1 \end{bmatrix} u$$

$$y = [1 \quad 1] \begin{bmatrix} x_1 \\ x_2 \end{bmatrix}$$

To obtain **F**, compute exp $(\mathbf{A}T)$ by the interpolation method of Appendix *D*, Sec. *8*; by integrating the result, **G** is easily obtained by *4*. The result is

$$\mathbf{x}_{k+1} = \begin{bmatrix} e^{-T} & 3(e^{-T} - e^{-2T}) \\ 0 & e^{-2T} \end{bmatrix} \mathbf{x}_k + \tfrac{1}{2} \begin{bmatrix} 3 - 6e^{-T} + 3e^{-2T} \\ 1 - e^{-2T} \end{bmatrix} u_k$$

$$y_{k+1} = [1 \quad 1]\mathbf{x}_{k+1}$$

Stability considerations

Consider now the discrete system *5* and *6* with its input, its state, and its output respectively specified by the sequences $\{\mathbf{u}_k\}$, $\{\mathbf{x}_k\}$, $\{\mathbf{y}_k\}$. In other words, we disregard the values of $\mathbf{x}(t)$ and $\mathbf{y}(t)$ for all t that are outside the set $\{kT\}$, where $k = \ldots, -1, 0, 1, \ldots$.

Let us first consider the idea of *asymptotic stability*. It will be recalled that asymptotic stability concerns itself with the state and not the output and that it imposes requirements only on the motion of the state in state space under zero-input conditions, in other words, under free motion (see *7.2.3*). By analogy with *7.2.4* we introduce the

11 **Definition** A linear time-invariant discrete system described by *5* is said to be *asymptotically stable* (in the large) if

(I) For any $M > 0$, there is a $\delta > 0$ such that

$$\|\mathbf{x}_0\| < \delta \Rightarrow \|\mathbf{x}(kT;\mathbf{x}_0,0;\mathbf{0})\| < M \qquad \text{for } k = 0, 1, 2, \ldots$$

(II) For all initial states $\mathbf{x}_0$, $\lim_{k\to\infty} \mathbf{x}(kT;\mathbf{x}_0,0;\mathbf{0}) = \mathbf{0}$. ◁

In other words, as in the continuous case, asymptotic stability implies that during any zero-input response (free motion) the state remains bounded and eventually tends to the zero state as $kT \to \infty$. As shown previously (*7.2.6*), the asymptotic stability of the zero state implies that the discrete system is asymptotically stable in the large.

12 **Theorem** The following three statements are equivalent:

(I) The linear time-invariant sampled system *5* is asymptotically stable (in the large).

(II) $\|\mathbf{F}^n\| \to 0$ as $n \to \infty$.

(III) All the eigenvalues of $\mathbf{F}$ are in the open disk $|\lambda| < 1$.

Proof Exercise for the reader. For the case where $\mathbf{F}$ has distinct eigenvalues use *C.18.18*; for the general case use *D.6.17*.

13 *Comment* If $\lambda_1, \lambda_2, \ldots, \lambda_\sigma$ are the eigenvalues of $\mathbf{A}$, then $e^{\lambda_1 T}, \ldots, e^{\lambda_\sigma T}$ are the eigenvalues of $\mathbf{F}$ (defined by *3*). This follows from the definition of a function of a matrix (see *D.4.1*). Therefore, the following three statements are equivalent:

(I) All eigenvalues of $\mathbf{F}$ are in the open disk $|\lambda| < 1$.

(II) All eigenvalues of $\mathbf{A}$ are inside the left half plane.

(III) The (continuous-time) system 1 is asymptotically stable (in the large).

In particular, the asymptotic stability of the sampled system *5* is equivalent to the asymptotic stability of the continuous system *1* from which it is obtained. Note that this equivalence holds for all possible sampling periods $T > 0$.

14 **Theorem** Let the discrete system be described by *5* and let the state $\mathbf{x}$ itself be the output. Then, if all the eigenvalues of $\mathbf{F}$ are in the open disk $|\lambda| < 1$ then, for all initial states, any bounded input $\{\mathbf{u}_i\}_0^\infty$ produces a bounded state vector.

Proof The input sequence is bounded; hence there is a finite number M such that $\|\mathbf{u}_i\| < M$ for $i = 0, 1, \ldots$. Then, by *7*, *C.16.4*, and *C.16.12* we obtain successively

15 $$\|\mathbf{x}_k\| \leq \|\mathbf{F}^k\mathbf{x}_0\| + \sum_{i=0}^{k-1} \|\mathbf{F}^i\mathbf{G}\mathbf{u}_{k-i-1}\| \leq \|\mathbf{F}^k\| \cdot \|\mathbf{x}_0\| + M\|\mathbf{G}\| \sum_{i=0}^{k-1} \|\mathbf{F}^i\|$$

Since the eigenvalues of $\mathbf{F}$ are in the open disk $|\lambda| < 1$, for some constant C we have

16 $$\|\mathbf{F}^i\| < C\rho^i \qquad i = 0, 1, 2, \ldots$$

where ρ is a real positive number smaller than 1 but larger than the absolute value of all the eigenvalues of $\mathbf{F}$. Therefore, *16* implies that

$$\|\mathbf{F}^k\| < C \qquad k = 0, 1, 2, \ldots$$

$$\sum_{i=0}^{\infty} \|\mathbf{F}^i\| < C(1 - \rho)^{-1}$$

Here, the first term of *15* is bounded, for all k, by $C\|\mathbf{x}_0\|$ and the second is bounded by $M\|\mathbf{G}\|C(1 - \rho)^{-1}$.

17 *Exercise* Show that if only the zero-state response of *5* were required to remain bounded for all bounded inputs, $\mathbf{F}$ might in some cases have eigenvalues larger than 1 in absolute value. [*Hint:* Let $\mathbf{F}$ have distinct eigenvalues $\lambda_1, \lambda_2, \ldots, \lambda_n$. Let λ_1 be the only eigenvalue outside the disk $|\lambda| < 1$ and let $|\lambda_1| > 1$. Pick $\mathbf{G}$ such that the range of $\mathbf{G}$, $\mathcal{R}(\mathbf{G})$, is spanned by the eigenvectors of $\lambda_2, \lambda_3, \ldots, \lambda_n$.]

3 *Transform theory of discrete systems*

In this section we shall consider discrete systems obtained by periodic-sampling continuous-time systems which are defined by their impulse response. Again we shall assume that the continuous-time systems are time-invariant. From Chap. *9* we would expect that the analysis can be considerably simplified by the introduction of a suitable transformation which, with respect to discrete systems, would play the role that the Laplace transform plays for continuous-time systems. The appropriate transform for the present case turns out to be the z transform. As a first step let us set up the model that we shall use throughout the section.

Impulse modulators and sampling

For simplicity, we consider a single-input single-output linear time-invariant system $\mathcal{S}$ represented by its impulse response h. We shall assume that the system is nonanticipative; therefore, $h(t) = 0$ for $t < 0$. The sampling will affect this continuous-time system $\mathcal{S}$ in the following manner (refer to Fig. *10.3.1*). Before being applied to the continuous-time system $\mathcal{S}$, the input u is periodically sampled with period T. Its value at the kth sampling instant, $u(kT)$, is used to amplitude-modulate a pulse generator whose output pulse is of height $u(kT)/\Delta$ and of width Δ. More precisely, the output pulse is given by

$$\Delta^{-1}[1(t - kT) - 1(t - kT - \Delta)]u(kT)$$

The zero-state response of the system $\mathcal{S}$ to this pulse can be shown to tend to $u(kT)h(t - kT)$ as $\Delta \to 0$; that is, in the limit of $\Delta \to 0$, the zero-state response of $\mathcal{S}$ is equal to its zero-state response to $u(kT)\delta(t - kT)$. This leads to the following idealization: Let us replace the pulse generator of Fig. *10.3.1* by an *impulse modulator*. By definition, an

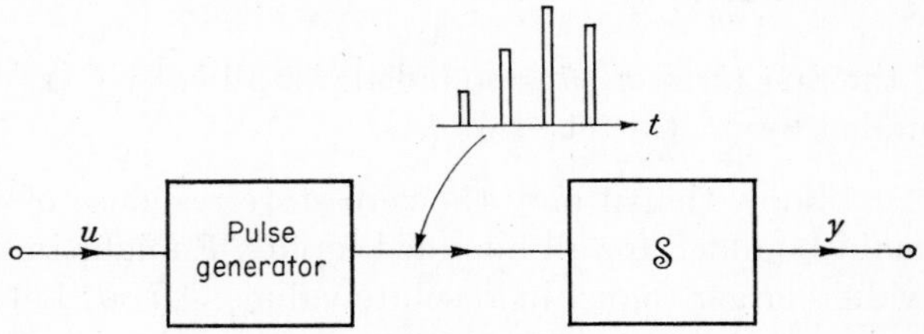

Fig. 10.3.1 The input u modulates the amplitude of the pulses produced by the pulse generator.

impulse modulator is characterized by its sampling period T; and if u is its input, its output is the sequence of impulses $\sum_{k=-\infty}^{\infty} u(kT)\delta(t - kT)$. This model is illustrated by Fig. *10.3.2*. The input u is fed into the

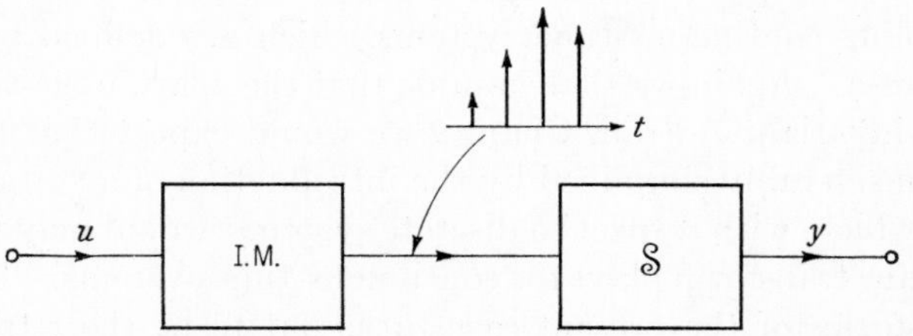

Fig. 10.3.2 The system of Fig. *10.3.1* can be idealized by the one shown here where the pulse generator is replaced by an impulse modulator.

impulse modulator (abbreviated as I.M.) whose output is the sequence of impulses just described. This sequence of impulses is the input of the continuous-time system $\mathcal{S}$; therefore, its zero-state output is given by

1 $$y(t) = \sum_{m=-\infty}^{+\infty} u(mT)h(t - mT) \qquad \forall t$$

Note that the output of $\mathcal{S}$ is defined for all t. If we restrict our attention to the sequence of values taken by y at the instants kT, then we obtain the relation

2 $$y_k = \sum_{m=-\infty}^{+\infty} u_m h_{k-m} \qquad k = \ldots, -1, 0, 1, \ldots$$

where $y_k = y(kT)$, $u_m = u(mT)$, $h_k = h(kT)$. Equation *2* is a linear relation between the *input sequence* $\{u_m\}$ and the (zero-state) *output sequence* $\{y_k\}$. In view of the close analogy between *2* and the convolution integral of continuous-time systems (*3.6.35*), the sequence $\{h_k\}$ is called the *weighting sequence.* In particular, if the input is applied at $t = 0$ and if the system is nonanticipative, the zero-state output sequence is given by

3 $$y_k = \sum_{m=0}^{\infty} u_m h_{k-m} \qquad k = 0, 1, \ldots$$

Because we restrict our attention to the sequence of values $y(kT)$ of the continuous-time output and because the impulse-modulator output depends only on the sequence of values, $u(kT)$, of the input, we think of the system shown in Fig. *10.3.2* as a *discrete system* whose input is completely characterized by the sequence $\{u_k\}$ and whose output is the sequence $\{y_k\}$. It is important to note that, in order to adopt this point of view, there is no need for an actual sampler to sample the output of $\mathcal{S}$. However, when systems are interconnected together, it will make a great difference whether there actually is or is not a sampler or impulse modulator at the output of $\mathcal{S}$ (see Remark *16*, below). For the remainder of this section, we shall consider the system of Fig. *10.3.2* as a linear discrete system transforming the input sequence $\{u_m\}$ into the output sequence $\{y_k\}$ by Eq. *3*.

4 *Comment* We have so far considered, and shall consider later in this section, only single-input single-output systems; the analysis that follows is also applicable to multiple-input and multiple-output systems. The extension is easy: it requires no new concepts but an elaborate notation.

z transform

In order to study the properties and relations between the input and output sequences of the system of Fig. *10.3.2*, we shall use the z transform. The definition and the principal theorems of the z transform are given in Appendix B, Sec. *4*. Let us, however, recall the

5 **Definition** The z transform of the function $u_{[0,\infty)}$ is the function $\tilde{U}$ of the complex variable z defined by

6 $$\tilde{U}(z) = \mathcal{Z}(u) = \sum_{n=0}^{\infty} u(nT)z^{-n}$$

where T is the sampling period of the impulse modulator.

7 **Remark** If u has a discontinuity at any of the sampling points, the defining relation *6* is ambiguous. We shall, therefore, restrict ourselves to the most important case that occurs in practice: we require all the functions of time which will be sampled to belong to the class A; that is, they are zero for $t < 0$, and if they are discontinuous at some sampling instant, then $u(nT-)$ and $u(nT+)$ must exist. In *6* we shall always take

8 $$u(nT) = u(nT+) \qquad n = 0, 1, \ldots$$

9 *Exercise* Establish the following z transforms. (*Hint:* Use *6* and sum the geometric series.)

Time function	*z transform*
$1(t)$	$1/(1 - z^{-1})$
e^{-at}	$1/(1 - z^{-1}e^{-aT})$
$e^{-\alpha t} \sin \omega t$	$ze^{-\alpha T} \sin \omega T(z^2 - 2e^{-\alpha T}z \cos \omega T + e^{-2\alpha T})^{-1}$

10 *Comment* $\tilde{U}(z)$ is defined by the power series in z^{-1} given in *6*. This power series converges for all z outside the circle $|z| = R_u$, where $R_u = \limsup_{n\to\infty} \sqrt[n]{|u(nT)|}$. (See Ref. *5*, page 141, and Ref. *6*, page 118.) Some functions of class A have a radius of convergence R_u that is infinite; for example, $u(t) = 1(t) \exp(t^4)$. We shall henceforth assume that each function of class A that we consider has a finite radius of convergence.

11 *Comment* If u is the input of the impulse modulator, its output is $\bar{u} = \sum_{k=0}^{\infty} u(kT)\delta(t - kT)$. This series of impulses has a Laplace transform $\bar{U}(s) = \sum_{k=0}^{\infty} u(kT)e^{-skT}$. Comparing *6* with this relation leads to the observation that $\tilde{U}(z)\Big|_{z=e^{sT}} = \bar{U}(s)$. In this sense, we might say

that the z plane, the complex plane over which $\tilde{U}$ is defined, is related to the s plane (of the Laplace transform of $\bar{u}$) by $z = e^{sT}$. The important fact to remember is that $\bar{U}(s)$ is *not* the Laplace transform of u; therefore, $\tilde{U}(z)$ is *not* obtained by taking the Laplace transform of u and then replacing s by $(1/T) \log z$. (See *19* and *22* below.)

12 **Theorem** Consider the system shown in Fig. *10.3.2*. Let $\tilde{H}(z)$ be the z transform of the impulse response h. Let y be the zero-state response due to the input u applied at $t = 0$. Then,

13 $$\tilde{Y}(z) = \tilde{H}(z)\tilde{U}(z) \qquad \text{for } |z| > \max (R_u, R_h)$$

14 *Comment* *13* is completely analogous to *3.6.23*, which relates the zero-state response, the impulse response, and the input of a continuous-time system. For this reason $\tilde{H}(z)$ is referred to as the *sampled transfer function* or the *z-transfer function.* It should be stressed that, in contradistinction to *3.6.23*, *13* does not define the zero-state response of the system shown in Fig. *10.3.2* for all t; it gives only the sequence $\{y_k\}$ of the output values at the sampling instants. If one wanted to obtain the output y for all t, then the usual Laplace transform technique (taking into account the presence of the impulse modulator) could be used. The same information can be obtained by the so-called modified z transform. A description of this technique is to be found in the books listed in the references.

Proof From Definition *5* we have

$$\tilde{H}(z)\tilde{U}(z) = \left(\sum_{\alpha=0}^{\infty} u_\alpha z^{-\alpha}\right)\left(\sum_{\beta=0}^{\infty} h_\beta z^{-\beta}\right) \qquad |z| > \max (R_h, R_u)$$
$$= \sum_{l=0}^{\infty}\left(\sum_{\alpha=0}^{l} u_\alpha h_{l-\alpha}\right) z^{-l}$$

and, with *3*,

$$\tilde{H}(z)\tilde{U}(z) = \sum_{l=0}^{\infty} y_l z^{-l} = \tilde{Y}(z) \qquad |z| > \max (R_h, R_u)$$

15 *Example* Consider the discrete system shown in Fig. *10.3.3*. Let us find the "sampled output" (i.e., the sequence $\{y(kT)\}$) caused by a unit step input. The system is known to be in the zero state at $t = 0$.

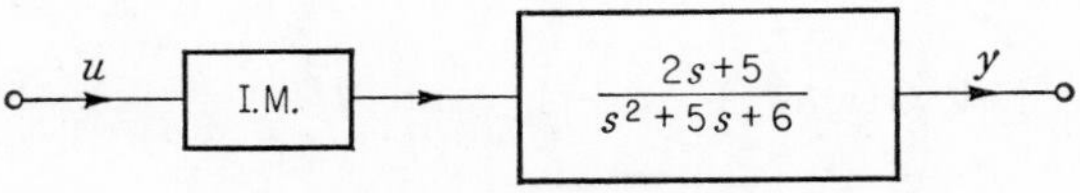

Fig. 10.3.3 System studied in Example *10.3.15*.

First, from $H(s)$ we obtain $h(t) = 1(t)(e^{-2t} + e^{-3t})$. Therefore,

$$\tilde{H}(z) = \sum_{k=0}^{\infty} (e^{-2kT} + e^{-3kT})z^{-k} = \frac{1}{1 - z^{-1}e^{-2T}} + \frac{1}{1 - z^{-1}e^{-3T}}$$

Since $\tilde{U}(z) = 1/(1 - z^{-1})$, the zero-state output sequence has a z transform given by

$$\begin{aligned}\tilde{Y}(z) &= \tilde{H}(z)\tilde{U}(z)\\ &= \frac{1}{1 - z^{-1}}\left(\frac{1}{1 - e^{-2T}} + \frac{1}{1 - e^{-3T}}\right) - \frac{1}{1 - z^{-1}e^{-2T}}\frac{1}{e^{2T} - 1}\\ &\qquad - \frac{1}{1 - z^{-1}e^{-3T}}\frac{1}{e^{3T} - 1}\end{aligned}$$

which has been obtained by partial-fraction expansion. The magnitude of the nth sample is (see Exercise *9*)

$$y_n = y(nT+) = \frac{1}{1 - e^{-2T}} + \frac{1}{1 - e^{-3T}} - \frac{e^{-n2T}}{e^{2T} - 1} - \frac{e^{-n3T}}{e^{3T} - 1}$$

The reader should sketch out the output y and observe that y is discontinuous at $t = nT$, $n = 0, 1, 2, \ldots$. This illustrates once more the importance of Remark *7* in the interpretation of the relationship between $\tilde{Y}(z)$ and $y_{[0,\infty)}$.

16 **Remark** When one interconnects several subsystems, it is very important to observe the position of the impulse modulators carefully before applying *13*. Consider the systems shown in Figs. *10.3.4* and

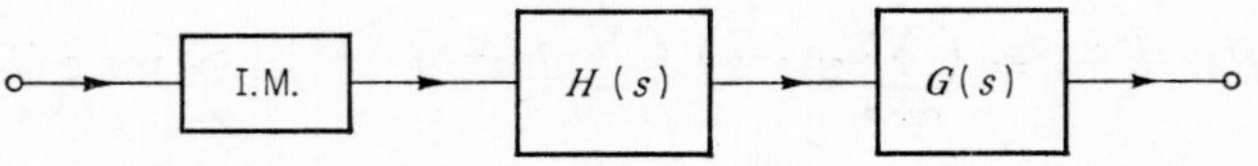

Fig. 10.3.4 The system G is directly connected to H.

10.3.5. (In both cases the impulse modulators are synchronized and have the same period.) Their respective z-transfer functions are $(\widetilde{GH})(z)$ and $\tilde{G}(z)\tilde{H}(z)$; these are different functions of z.

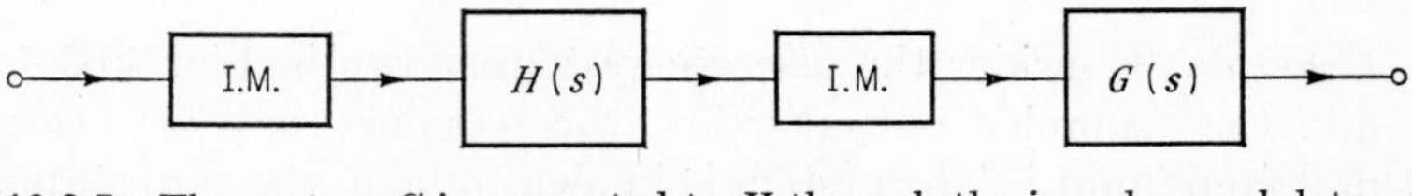

Fig. 10.3.5 The system G is connected to H through the impulse modulator. The two impulse modulators are synchronized and have the same period.

17 *Exercise* Let $G(s) = 1/(s + 1)$ and $H(s) = 1/(s + 2)$. Show that

$$(\widetilde{GH})(z) = \frac{e^{-T} - e^{-2T}}{(z - e^{-T})(z - e^{-2T})} \qquad \tilde{G}(z)\tilde{H}(z) = \frac{z^2}{(z - e^{-T})(z - e^{-2T})}$$

Sketch out the time functions at the input and output of the G and H boxes of Figs. *10.3.4* and *10.3.5*.

In Comment *11* we pointed out that the relation between $H(s)$ and $\tilde{H}(z)$ (respectively the Laplace transform of the function h and the z transform of the function h) is *not* merely a matter of substituting for s by some expression in z. In the case of rational functions, the relation between $H(s)$ and $\tilde{H}(z)$ is easily obtained through their partial-fraction expansions.

18 **Theorem** If $H(s)$ is a rational function of s, then $\tilde{H}(z)$ is also a rational function of z.

Proof If $H(s)$ is rational, $h(t)$ is a finite sum of terms of the form e^{-at}, $t^k e^{-at}$, where a may be complex and where k is an integer. Consider the contribution of the term e^{-at} in the defining relation *6*; then

$$\sum_{n=0}^{\infty} e^{-anT} z^{-n} = \sum_{n=0}^{\infty} (ze^{aT})^{-n} = \frac{1}{1-(ze^{aT})^{-1}} = \frac{z}{z-e^{-aT}} \qquad |z| > e^{-aT}$$

In other words, a simple pole of H at $s = -a$ contributes a simple pole of $\tilde{H}$ at $z = e^{-aT}$.

The term $t^k e^{-at}$ will occur in $h(t)$ when $H(s)$ has a pole of order $k+1$ at $s = -a$. Since

$$t^k e^{-at} = (-1)^k \frac{\partial^k}{\partial a^k} (e^{-at})$$

we have

$$\mathrm{Z}(t^k e^{-at}) \triangleq \sum_{n=0}^{\infty} (nT)^k e^{-anT} z^{-n} = (-1)^k \frac{\partial^k}{\partial a^k} \mathrm{Z}(e^{-at}) = (-1)^k \frac{\partial^k}{\partial a^k}\left(\frac{z}{z-e^{-aT}}\right)$$

It is clear that the right-hand side will be a rational function of z with a pole of order $k+1$ at $z = e^{-aT}$. Hence a pole of order $k+1$ of $H(s)$ at $s = a$ contributes a pole of order $k+1$ at $z = e^{-aT}$ in $\tilde{H}(z)$.

19 *Comment* The above proof shows that, given the partial-fraction expansion of $H(s)$, the expansion of $\tilde{H}(z)$ is immediately obtained by observing the following correspondences:

$$\frac{1}{s+a} \qquad \frac{z}{z-e^{-aT}}$$

$$\frac{1}{(s+a)^{k+1}} \qquad \frac{(-1)^k}{k!}\frac{\partial^k}{\partial a^k}\left(\frac{z}{z-e^{-aT}}\right)$$

20 **Corollary** If $H(s)$ has all its poles inside the left half plane, then $\tilde{H}(z)$ has all its poles in the open disk $|z| < 1$.

21 *Exercise* Give an example to show that the converse is false. [*Hint:* Consider $h(t) = e^t \sin 2\pi t$ and choose T appropriately.]

There is a useful relation between $H(s)$ and $\tilde{H}(z)$ which allows the direct determination of $\tilde{H}(z)$ when $H(s)$ is not rational. Let us express it in the form of a

22 **Theorem** Let f be a function belonging to class A (see Remark 7) and be continuous at all points $t = kT$, $k = 1, 2, \ldots$. Let f have a Laplace transform F and let σ_f be its abscissa of convergence (see *B.2.6*). Let $\tilde{F}$ be the z transform of f. Then

23 $$\tilde{F}(e^{sT}) = \tfrac{1}{2}f(0+) + \frac{1}{2\pi j}\int_{c-j\omega}^{c+j\omega} \frac{F(p)}{1 - \exp[-T(s-p)]}\,dp \qquad \sigma_f < c < \operatorname{Re} s$$

24 *Comment* In the literature of z transforms many authors assume, often implicitly, that $F(s) \to 0$ at least as fast as $1/s^2$ as $s \to \infty$. Then f is continuous at 0 and the term $(\frac{1}{2})f(0+)$ does not appear in *23* since $f(0+) = 0$.

Proof By definition *6*, putting $z = e^{sT}$,

$$\tilde{F}(e^{sT}) = \sum_{n=0}^{\infty} f(nT)e^{-nsT}$$

The right-hand side of the above relation can be recognized to be the L transform of $f(t+)\left(\sum_{n=0}^{\infty} \delta(t - nT)\right)$, where the argument of f is $t+$ and not t (see Remark 7). Since we shall evaluate $f(t)$ in terms of its $\mathfrak{L}$ transform $F(s)$ and since the Laplace transformation inversion integral gives $\frac{1}{2}[f(t-) + f(t+)]$ (see *B.3.35*), let us rewrite the expression above in the following manner:

$$\begin{aligned}\tilde{F}(e^{sT}) &= \tfrac{1}{2}f(0+) + \sum_{n=0}^{\infty} \tfrac{1}{2}[f(nT-) + f(nT+)]e^{-nsT} \\ &= \tfrac{1}{2}f(0+) + \mathfrak{L}\left\{\tfrac{1}{2}[f(t-) + f(t+)] \sum_{n=0}^{\infty} \delta(t - nT)\right\}\end{aligned}$$

Now

$$\mathfrak{L}\left[\sum_{n=0}^{\infty} \delta(t - nT)\right] = \frac{1}{1 - e^{-sT}} \qquad \operatorname{Re} s > 0$$

and *23* follows by the complex convolution theorem (see *B.3.13*).

Relation to difference equations

In preceding chapters (*3.6.12* and *4.5.31*), we have seen that a system described by a differential equation with constant coefficients of the form $L(p)y = M(p)u$ is zero-state equivalent to the system described by the transfer function $H(s) = L(s)/M(s)$. We would expect that a similar situation exists for sampled systems; in fact, we have the

25 **Theorem** Let the linear discrete system $\mathcal{S}$ be characterized by its z-transfer function $\tilde{H}(z) = P(z)/Q(z)$, where P and Q are polynomials. Let

$$P(z) = \sum_{k=0}^{n} p_k z^{-k} \qquad \text{and} \qquad Q(z) = \sum_{k=0}^{m} q_k z^{-k}$$

Then the zero-state output sequence $\{y_0, y_1, \ldots\}$ of $\mathcal{S}$ is related to the input sequence $\{u_0, u_1, \ldots\}$ by the difference equation

26
$$\sum_{k=0}^{n} q_k y_{l-k} = \sum_{k=0}^{m} p_k u_{l-k} \qquad l = 0, 1, 2, \ldots$$

with the convention that all symbols with negative indices are zero.

Proof Since $\{y_n\}$ is a zero-state output sequence, we have by *12* $\tilde{Y}(z) = \tilde{H}(z)\tilde{U}(z)$; hence, $Q(z)\tilde{Y}(z) = P(z)\tilde{U}(z)$. Let us now express $\tilde{Y}$ and $\tilde{U}$ by their defining power series; see *6*. Since the last relation holds for all z such that $|z| > \max(R_u, R_y)$, the coefficients of like powers of z are equal. Considering the coefficients of z^{-l}, we get

$$q_0 y_l + q_1 y_{l-1} + \cdots + q_n y_{l-n} = p_0 y_l + p_1 u_{l-1} + \cdots + p_m u_{l-m}$$

Since this relation holds for all nonnegative integers l, *26* follows. ◁

The difference equation *26* has a representation in terms of adders, scalors, and delayors. The diagram is given by Fig. *10.3.6*. Note that

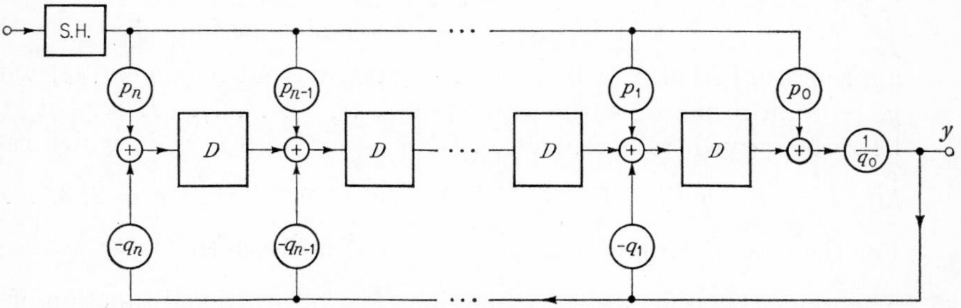

Fig. 10.3.6 Realization of the difference equation *10.3.26* by delayors, scalors, and a sample-and-hold box.

it is analogous to that given for differential systems. The only difference is that every integrator is now replaced by a delayor; furthermore in the discrete case there is a sample-and-hold circuit directly connected to the input. Compare Fig. *10.3.6* with Fig. *4.9.4*.

Stability considerations

The stability of a nonanticipative linear discrete system described by its z-transfer function $\tilde{H}(z)$ follows the same lines as that of the continuous system described by its transfer function $H(s)$ (Chap. *9*, Sec. *4*). Let us first introduce a

27 **Definition** Consider the system illustrated by Fig. *10.3.2*; its z-transfer function $\tilde{H}(z)$ is said to be *strictly stable* if any bounded input sequence produces a zero-state output sequence which is bounded. ◁

Strictly stable z-transfer functions and the usual transfer functions are characterized in a completely analogous manner. Indeed, we have the

28 **Theorem** The z-transfer function $\tilde{H}(z)$ of a nonanticipative discrete system is strictly stable if and only if its zero-state response sequence $\{h_n\}$ to the input 1, 0, . . . satisfies the condition

29 $$\sum_{n=0}^{\infty} |h_n| < \infty$$

30 *Comment* Condition *29* is the discrete form of condition *9.4.13* for the continuous case. Note, however, that, in general, *9.4.13* does not imply that $|h(t)| \to 0$ as $t \to \infty$, whereas *29* does imply that $|h_n| \to 0$ as $n \to \infty$.

31 *Comment* In *29*, the summation is carried from $n = 0$ to ∞ because the system is assumed nonanticipative. If the system were anticipative, we would have to sum from $-\infty$ to ∞ (compare with *9.4.13*).

Proof Exercise for the reader. (*Hint:* Use the proof of *9.4.12* as a guide.)

32 *Exercise* (For the reader interested in teratology!) Find a nonanticipative linear time-invariant system whose impulse response satisfies $\int_0^\infty |h(t)|\, dt < \infty$ and is such that, if sampled periodically with the appropriate period, it will have a zero-state output sequence $\{y_n\}$ with $y_n \to \infty$ in response to the input $\{1,0, \ldots ,0, \ldots\}$. *Hint:* Let $h(t)$ be zero everywhere except when $t \in (n - n^{-3}, n + n^{-3})$, in which case

$$h(t) = n \exp \{n^{-6}[t - (n - n^{-3})]^{-1}[t - (n + n^{-3})]^{-1}\} \qquad n = 2, 3, \ldots$$

For the case of rational transfer functions, we have the

33 **Theorem** Let the z-transfer function $\tilde{H}(z)$ be a rational function of z. Then $\tilde{H}(z)$ is strictly stable if and only if all the poles of $\tilde{H}$ are in the open disk $|z| < 1$.

Proof Exercise for the reader. (*Hint:* $\Rightarrow$ Use contradiction and invoke the inversion theorem *B.4.8*. $\Leftarrow$ Use the inversion theorem.)

34 *Caveat* If, as in Fig. *10.3.2*, the discrete system $\mathcal{S}$, with z-transfer function $\tilde{H}(z)$, is obtained by sampling the continuous system Σ whose transfer function is $H(s)$, then the strict stability of $\tilde{H}(z)$ does not imply that of $H(s)$. This follows from the observation that the strict stability of $\tilde{H}(z)$ imposes a boundedness requirement on the zero-state output sequence $\{y_k\}$; it does not require the output $y(t)$ to be bounded for all $t \in (0, \infty)$. Consider the following example: $h(t) = 1(t)[e^{-t} + e^t \sin (\pi t/T)]$. Clearly the transfer function $H(s)$ is unstable, since $h(t)$ increases exponentially with t (see *9.4.1*). However, if the sampling period is T, the sequence $\{h_n\}$ is $\{e^{-nT}, n = 0, 1, 2, \ldots\}$ and $\tilde{H}(z)$ is strictly stable. In Sec. *2*, where the systems were described by their state equations, asymptotic stability of the sampled system was equivalent to that of the continuous system from which the sampled system was obtained (see *10.2.12*). This again stresses the importance of the state concept and that the attempt to think of linear systems exclusively in terms of transfer functions leads to difficulties.

By Theorem *33* the problem of checking the strict stability of a rational z-transfer function $\tilde{H}(z)$ reduces to finding conditions under which its denominator polynomial has all its zeros in the open disk $|z| < 1$. The classical test for this condition is the celebrated Schur-Cohn criterion. Recently, however, Jury has simplified the test considerably. Let us now describe the *Jury stability test.*

35 **Theorem**[1] Let f be a polynomial with real coefficients.

36 $$f(z) = a_n z^n + a_{n-1} z^{n-1} + \cdots + a_1 z + a_0 \qquad a_n > 0$$

Define the triangular matrices

37 $$\mathbf{X}_k = \begin{bmatrix} a_0 & a_1 & \cdots & a_{k-1} \\ 0 & a_0 & a_1 & \cdots \\ \cdots & \cdots & \cdots & \cdots \\ 0 & \cdots & \cdots & a_1 \\ 0 & 0 & \cdots\ 0 & a_0 \end{bmatrix} \qquad \mathbf{Y}_k = \begin{bmatrix} a_{n-k+1} & \cdots & a_{n-1} & a_n \\ \cdots & \cdots & a_n & 0 \\ \cdots & \cdots & \cdots & \cdots \\ a_{n-1} & a_n & 0 & 0 \\ a_n & 0 & 0 & 0 \end{bmatrix}$$

$$k = 1, 2, \ldots, n$$

Define the numbers A_k and B_k by the relations

38 $$\begin{aligned} \det(\mathbf{X}_k + \mathbf{Y}_k) &= A_k + B_k \\ \det(\mathbf{X}_k - \mathbf{Y}_k) &= A_k - B_k \end{aligned} \qquad k = 1, 2, \ldots, n$$

Then the polynomial f has all its zeros in the open disk $|z| < 1$ if and only if

39

n even		*n odd*	
$f(1) > 0,$	$f(-1) > 0$	$f(1) > 0,$	$f(-1) < 0$
$\|A_1\| < B_1$			
$\|A_3\| < \|B_3\|,$	$B_3 < 0$	$\|A_2\| > \|B_2\|,$	$A_2 < 0$
$\|A_5\| < \|B_5\|,$	$B_5 > 0$	$\|A_4\| > \|B_4\|,$	$A_4 > 0$
$\|A_7\| < \|B_7\|,$	$B_7 < 0$	$\|A_6\| > \|B_6\|,$	$A_6 < 0$
$\vdots$	$\vdots$	$\vdots$	$\vdots$
$\|A_{n-1}\| < \|B_{n-1}\|,$	$B_{n-1} \begin{cases} <0 \text{ if } n = 4k \\ >0 \text{ otherwise} \end{cases}$	$\|A_{n-1}\| > \|B_{n-1}\|,$	$A_{n-1} \begin{cases} >0 \text{ if } n = 4k+1 \\ <0 \text{ otherwise} \end{cases}$

(k is an integer)

[1] E. I. Jury, A Simplified Stability Criterion for Linear Discrete Systems, *Proc. I.R.E.*, vol. 50, no. 6, pp. 1493–1500, and no. 9, p. 1973, 1962. See also *I.R.E. Trans. Automatic Control*, vol. AC-7, no. 4, pp. 51–55, 1962.

40 *Comment* A systematic way of obtaining A_k and B_k from their defining equations *34* is as follows: (I) put a ^ on all the elements of $\mathbf{Y}_k$; then expand det $(\mathbf{X}_k + \mathbf{Y}_k)$. The result is a polynomial in the a_i and $\hat{a}_i$. (II) A_k is the sum of all the monomial terms which include an *even* number of $\hat{a}_i$, and B_k is the sum of all those which include an *odd* number of $\hat{a}_i$.

41 *Example* For $n = 2$ the conditions are (by assumption $a_2 > 0$)

$$|a_0| < a_2 \qquad a_0 + a_1 + a_2 > 0 \qquad a_0 - a_1 + a_2 > 0$$

Observe that the last two inequalities allow us to replace the first one by $a_0 < a_2$.

For $n = 3$ the conditions are (by assumption $a_3 > 0$)

$$|a_0| < a_3 \qquad a_0^2 - a_3^2 < a_0a_2 - a_1a_3 \qquad \sum_0^3 a_i > 0 \qquad \sum_0^3 (-1)^i a_i < 0$$

42 *Comment* In the design of sampled systems one encounters the same problem as that solved by *9.4.22* and *9.4.24*. For the sampled systems with rational z-transfer functions whose denominator $f(z,\mu)$ depends on a parameter μ, the end point μ_1 of the stability interval is given[1] by either $f(1,\mu_1) = 0$, $f(-1,\mu_1) = 0$, or $A_{n-1}(\mu_1) - B_{n-1}(\mu_1) = 0$.

REFERENCES AND SUGGESTED READING

1 Bridgland, T. F., Jr.: A Linear Algebraic Formulation of the Theory of Sampled Data Control, *J. Soc. Indust. Appl. Math.*, vol. 7, no. 4, pp. 431–446, 1959.

2 Jury, E. I.: "Sampled Data Control Systems," John Wiley & Sons, Inc., New York, 1958.

3 Ragazzini, J. R., and G. F. Franklin: "Sampled-data Control Systems," McGraw-Hill Book Company, Inc., New York, 1958.

4 Tou, J. T.: "Digital and Sampled-data Control Systems," McGraw-Hill Book Company, Inc., New York, 1959.

5 Ahlfors, L. V.: "Complex Analysis," McGraw-Hill Book Company, Inc., New York, 1953.

6 Hille, E.: "Analytic Function Theory," vol. 1, Ginn and Company, Boston, 1959.

[1] *Ibid.*

Controllability and observability — 11

1 *Introduction*

In this chapter we shall apply the technical background provided by the preceding chapters to a study of an aspect of the behavior of linear systems which is of particular importance in control theory. For simplicity, we shall focus our attention on time-invariant systems.

It will be recalled (*3.6.1*) that the response of any linear system comprises two parts: the zero-input response and the zero-state response, with the latter characterized by the transfer function of the system. As we have seen in Chap. *5*, the zero-input response can be described in terms of modes of various types and may exhibit rather complex behavior. For example let the matrix **A** of the linear time-invariant system described by

1

$$\begin{aligned} \dot{\mathbf{x}} &= \mathbf{A}\mathbf{x} + \mathbf{B}\mathbf{u} \\ \mathbf{y} &= \mathbf{C}\mathbf{x} + \mathbf{D}\mathbf{u} \end{aligned}$$

have distinct eigenvalues. In this case, the simple concept of modes of oscillations is applicable (see *5.4.27*). We know from experience that some systems have modes that are uncoupled to the input or the output or both. Thus for this special case we see that we have a four-way classification of the modes: (I) coupled to both the input and the output, (II) coupled to the input but not the output, (III) coupled to the output but not to the input, and (IV) coupled to neither. Is this classification valid in general? We shall see that it is approximately valid, but in order to be able to develop the theory, we must first consider in detail the dual concepts of controllability and observability.[1]

[1] The theory of controllability and observability of linear systems is due largely to R. E. Kalman. (See Refs. *1*, *3*, and *4*). As pointed out in *11.3.11* and *11.4.3*, the concepts of controllability and observability are closely related to those of "strong connectedness" and "reduced system," which were introduced by E. F. Moore in the context of finite-state systems.

Once they are available, we shall develop the canonical decomposition of the state space. In terms of this canonical decomposition, the question raised above is easily answered.

2 *Exercise* This simple exercise is intended for the student who has had no experience in the ideas mentioned above. Consider the circuit shown in Fig. *11.1.1*. Write the state equations of the circuit in the

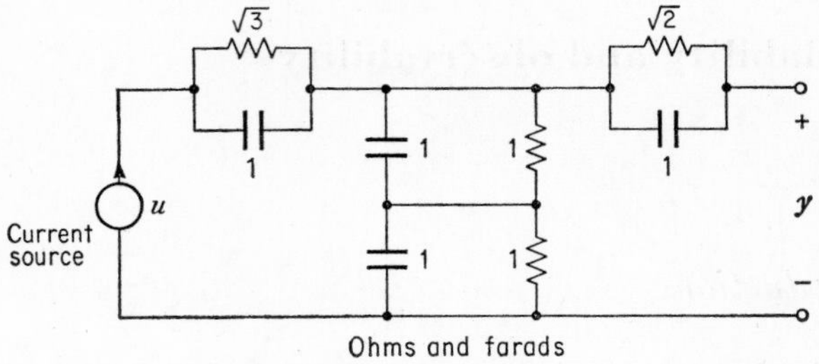

Fig. 11.1.1 Circuit to be analyzed in Exercise *11.1.2*.

form *1*. Analyze the circuit and exhibit the four-way classification of the modes.

2 *Impulse and doublet responses of a single-input system*

Consider a single-input linear time-invariant system described by its state equation

$$\dot{\mathbf{x}} = \mathbf{A}\mathbf{x} + \mathbf{b}u$$

where $\mathbf{A}$ and $\mathbf{b}$ are $(n \times n)$ and $(n \times 1)$ constant matrices. The output is the state vector $\mathbf{x}$ itself. The *unit-impulse response* of the system is, by definition, the zero-state response to a unit impulse applied at $t = 0$. By *6.2.21* we have

$$\mathbf{x}(t;\mathbf{0},0-;\delta(t)) = \int_{0-}^{t} \{\exp[\mathbf{A}(t-\tau)]\}\mathbf{b}\delta(\tau)\,d\tau \qquad t > 0$$

By the sifting property of δ (see *A.2.11*), this expression becomes

$$\exp[\mathbf{A}(t-\tau)]\Big|_{\tau=0}\mathbf{b} = [\exp(\mathbf{A}t)]\mathbf{b} \qquad t > 0$$

Since the impulse response is identically zero for $t < 0$, we finally write

1 $$\mathbf{x}(t;\mathbf{0},0-;\delta(t)) = [\exp(\mathbf{A}t)]\mathbf{b}1(t) \quad \forall t$$

Thus in state space the trajectory of the impulse response is not continuous at $t = 0$; it undergoes a "jump" $\mathbf{b}$ at $t = 0$.

Similarly, the *doublet response* is the zero-state response to a doublet applied at $t = 0$. It is given by

2 $$\mathbf{x}(t;\mathbf{0},0-;\delta^{(1)}(t)) = \mathbf{A}[\exp(\mathbf{A}t)]\mathbf{b}1(t) + \mathbf{b}\delta(t) \qquad \forall t$$

Let us justify *2* by three observations: (I) *2* indicates that, for $t < 0$, the response is identically zero as it should be. (II) For $t > 0$, *2* reduces to[1]

$$\mathbf{A}[\exp(\mathbf{A}t)]\mathbf{b} = [\exp(\mathbf{A}t)]\mathbf{A}\mathbf{b}$$

which is a solution of $\dot{\mathbf{x}} = \mathbf{A}\mathbf{x}$ as it should be for $t > 0$. (III) Finally, by inserting *2* in the system equation and performing the differentiation in the distribution sense, it is found that $\dot{\mathbf{x}} - \mathbf{A}\mathbf{x} = \mathbf{b}\delta^{(1)}(t)$.

The zero-state response to the kth derivative of δ is by definition $\mathbf{x}(t;\mathbf{0},0-;\delta^{(k)}(t))$ and, in fact,

3 $$\mathbf{x}(t;\mathbf{0},0-;\delta^{(k)}(t)) = \mathbf{A}^k[\exp(\mathbf{A}t)]\mathbf{b}1(t) + \sum_{i=1}^{k} \mathbf{A}^{(k-i)}\mathbf{b}\delta^{(i-1)}(t) \qquad \forall t$$

This can be verified in three steps, as above. Note that for $t > 0$

$$\mathbf{x}(t;\mathbf{0},0-;\delta^{(k)}(t)) = \mathbf{A}^k[\exp(\mathbf{A}t)]\mathbf{b} \qquad t > 0$$

If we compare *1* and *3*, we see that (see *A.5.20*)

$$\mathbf{x}(t;\mathbf{0},0-;\delta^{(k)}(t)) = \frac{d^k}{dt^k}\mathbf{x}(t;\mathbf{0},0-;\delta(t)) \qquad \forall t$$

provided the derivatives are taken in the distribution sense. Let us next prove a lemma which will be necessary for the following developments.

4 **Lemma** Let $\{\varphi_i\}$ be a set of N complex-valued continuous functions of t defined over $[0,T]$. Let $\mathbf{G}$ be the $N \times N$ matrix whose (i,j) element is $g_{ij} = (\varphi_i,\varphi_j) \triangleq \int_0^T \varphi_i^*(t)\varphi_j(t)\,dt$. Then the functions φ_i are linearly independent if and only if $\det \mathbf{G} \neq 0$.

5 *Comment* The continuous functions φ_i may be considered as vectors of an obviously defined linear vector space: $\det \mathbf{G}$ is called the *Gram determinant* of the vectors $\varphi_1, \varphi_2, \ldots, \varphi_N$.

6 *Comment* Since $g_{ij} = g_{ji}^*$ $(\forall i,j)$, $\mathbf{G}$ is a *hermitian matrix* (*C.14.8*). Furthermore, $\mathbf{G}$ is *nonnegative definite;* indeed, let $\boldsymbol{\alpha} = (\alpha_1, \ldots, \alpha_N)$ be an N-tuple of complex numbers: then with $\psi = \sum_{i=1}^{N} \alpha_i\varphi_i$

[1]From *5.2.3*, the matrices $\mathbf{A}$ and $\exp(\mathbf{A}t)$ commute.

7 $$\|\psi\|^2 = (\psi,\psi) = (\Sigma\alpha_i\varphi_i,\Sigma\alpha_j\varphi_j) = \Sigma\alpha_i^*\alpha_j(\varphi_i,\varphi_j) = \langle\boldsymbol{\alpha},\mathbf{G}\boldsymbol{\alpha}\rangle \geq 0$$

where $\langle\cdot,\cdot\rangle$ is the usual complex scalar product over $\mathcal{C}^N$ (see *C.5.4*).

Proof $\Rightarrow$ The φ_i are linearly independent. Therefore, for all $\boldsymbol{\alpha} \in \mathcal{C}^N$, ψ is not identically zero; hence $\|\psi\|^2 = \int_0^T |\psi(t)|^2\,dt > 0$ and

$$\langle\boldsymbol{\alpha},\mathbf{G}\boldsymbol{\alpha}\rangle > 0 \qquad \forall\boldsymbol{\alpha} \in \mathcal{C}^N$$

Consequently det $\mathbf{G} \neq 0$ (see *C.19.19*).

$\Leftarrow$ By hypothesis det $\mathbf{G} \neq 0$. For the purpose of a proof by contradiction, suppose the φ_i's were linearly dependent. Then for some $\boldsymbol{\alpha} \neq \mathbf{0}$, say, $\boldsymbol{\alpha}_0$, the corresponding ψ would be identical to zero over $[0,T]$. Hence, by *7*, $\langle\boldsymbol{\alpha}_0,\mathbf{G}\boldsymbol{\alpha}_0\rangle = 0$. Therefore, the smallest eigenvalue of $\mathbf{G}$ is zero (*C.19.15*) and consequently det $\mathbf{G} = 0$. This is a contradiction.

3 *Controllability*

Consider a multiple-input multiple-output linear time-invariant system $\mathcal{S}$ described by

1 $$\dot{\mathbf{x}} = \mathbf{A}\mathbf{x} + \mathbf{B}\mathbf{u}$$

2 $$\mathbf{y} = \mathbf{C}\mathbf{x} + \mathbf{D}\mathbf{u}$$

where $\mathbf{A}$, $\mathbf{B}$, $\mathbf{C}$, and $\mathbf{D}$ are, respectively, $(n \times n)$, $(n \times r)$, $(p \times n)$, $(p \times r)$ constant matrices. The n-vector $\mathbf{x}$ is the state of the system (*4.5.19*), the r-vector $\mathbf{u}$ is the input, and the p-vector $\mathbf{y}$ is the output of $\mathcal{S}$.

Speaking intuitively, we shall say that the system $\mathcal{S}$ is *controllable* if, knowing the matrices $\mathbf{A}$ and $\mathbf{B}$ and the state of $\mathcal{S}$ at t_0, $\mathbf{x}_0$, we can construct an input $\mathbf{u}_{[t_0,t_0+T]}$ which will bring the state of $\mathcal{S}$ to the zero state $\mathbf{0}$ at time $t_0 + T$. Since the system $\mathcal{S}$ is time-invariant, we may take $t_0 = 0$ without loss of generality (*3.2.36*). More formally, we have the

3 **Definition** The system $\mathcal{S}$ defined by *1* is said to be *controllable* if and only if the following is true for all $\mathbf{x}_0 \in \mathcal{C}^n$: given that the system is in state $\mathbf{x}_0$ at time 0, then for some *finite* $T > 0$, there is an input $\mathbf{u}_{[0,T]}$ such that

4 $$\mathbf{x}(T;\mathbf{x}_0,0;\mathbf{u}_{[0,T]}) = \mathbf{0} \quad \triangleleft$$

The controllability of the system $\mathcal{S}$ is characterized by the following

5 **Theorem** The system $\mathcal{S}$ described by *1* is *controllable* if and only if the column vectors of the matrix

6 $$\mathbf{Q} \triangleq [\mathbf{B},\mathbf{AB}, \ldots ,\mathbf{A}^{n-1}\mathbf{B}]$$

where $\mathbf{B}$, $\mathbf{AB}$, . . . , $\mathbf{A}^{n-1}\mathbf{B}$ denote the columns of $\mathbf{Q}$, span the state space $\mathcal{C}^n$ of $\mathcal{S}$.

7 *Comment* This condition can also be expressed as follows: The matrix $\mathbf{Q}$ has rank n; among the nr columns of $\mathbf{Q}$ there is a set of n linearly independent vectors which, therefore, constitute a basis for $\mathcal{C}^n$.

Proof $\Rightarrow$ The system is controllable by hypothesis; therefore, any state $\mathbf{x}_0$ can be transferred to the zero state in a finite time; thus,

8 $$\mathbf{0} = [\exp(\mathbf{A}T)\mathbf{x}_0] + \int_0^T \{\exp[\mathbf{A}(T-\tau)]\}\mathbf{Bu}(\tau)\,d\tau$$

Multiplying *8* by $\exp(-\mathbf{A}T)$ on the left and remembering that $\exp(-\mathbf{A}\tau) = \sum_{k=0}^{n-1} \mathbf{A}^k\alpha_k(-\tau)$ (*D.8.12*), we have

$$-\mathbf{x}_0 = \sum_{k=0}^{n-1} \mathbf{A}^k\mathbf{B}\int_0^T \alpha_k(-\tau)\mathbf{u}(\tau)\,d\tau$$

Thus any $\mathbf{x}_0$ that can be transferred to $\mathbf{0}$ in a finite time is a linear combination of the column vectors of $\mathbf{Q}$. Hence, controllability of $\mathcal{S}$ implies that the columns of $\mathbf{Q}$ span the state space $\mathcal{C}^n$.

$\Leftarrow$ In order to give a constructive proof and not bog down in notational difficulties, consider the case where $n = 3$ and $r = 2$. By assumption, $\mathcal{R}(\mathbf{Q}) = \mathcal{C}^n$. Suppose, for example, that $\mathcal{C}^n$ is spanned by $\mathbf{a}_1,\mathbf{a}_2$, and $\mathbf{a}_3$, where, say, $\mathbf{a}_1$ is the second column of $\mathbf{B}$, $\mathbf{a}_2$ is the first column of $\mathbf{AB}$, and $\mathbf{a}_3$ is the second column of $\mathbf{A}^2\mathbf{B}$. Consider a control $\mathbf{u}_{[0,T]} = \sum_{i=1}^{3} \gamma_i\mathbf{u}_i(t)$, where the constants γ_i will be chosen later, $\mathbf{u}_1(t) = (0,\delta(t))$, $\mathbf{u}_2(t) = (\delta^{(1)}(t),0)$, $\mathbf{u}_3(t) = (0,\delta^{(2)}(t))$, and T is an arbitrary finite positive number. If $\mathbf{u}_{[0,T]}$ drives $\mathbf{x}_0$ to $\mathbf{0}$, then

$$\mathbf{x}(T;\mathbf{0},0;\mathbf{u}_{[0,T]}) = \mathbf{0} = [\exp(\mathbf{A}T)]\mathbf{x}_0 + [\exp(\mathbf{A}T)]\sum_{i=1}^{3}\gamma_i\mathbf{a}_i$$

where we have used the definitions of the $\mathbf{a}_i$'s and *11.2.3*. Since the $\mathbf{a}_i$'s constitute a basis for $\mathcal{C}^n$, if we pick the γ_i's to be the components of $-\mathbf{x}_0$ with respect to that basis, then $\mathbf{u}_{[0,T]} = \Sigma\gamma_i\mathbf{u}_i(t)$ will transfer $\mathbf{x}_0$ at time 0 to $\mathbf{0}$ at time T.

9 *Exercise* Show that $\mathcal{S}$ is controllable if and only if any state $\mathbf{x}$ is reachable from the origin in a finite time.

10 *Exercise* Show that $\mathcal{S}$ is controllable if and only if any state $\mathbf{x}_1$ is reachable from any initial state $\mathbf{x}_0$.

11 *Comment* Note that this implies that, in the case of linear systems, the concept of a controllable system coincides with the concept of a "strongly connected" system, which was introduced by E. Moore (see *2.4.17*).

12 *Exercise* Show that the system $\mathcal{S}$ described by

$$(a_0p^n + \cdots + a_n)y = (b_0p^m + \cdots + b_m)u \qquad m \leq n$$

or, more compactly, $L(p)y = M(p)u$, is controllable if and only if $L(p)$ and $M(p)$ have no factors in common. [*Hint:* Note that if $L(p)$ and $M(p)$ have a factor in common, then $\mathcal{S}$ is zero-state equivalent to a system $\mathcal{S}'$ of lower order than n. If all the states in the state spaces of $\mathcal{S}$ and $\mathcal{S}'$ are reachable from the origin, then by *2.9.5* $\mathcal{S}$ and $\mathcal{S}'$ would be equivalent, which contradicts *4.2.12*.]

13 **Assertion** The subspace spanned by the column vectors of the matrix $\mathbf{Q}$ defined in *6* is an invariant subspace of $\mathbf{A}$ (see *C.13.1*).
Proof Exercise for the reader. (*Hint:* Use the Cayley-Hamilton theorem, *5.13.19*.)

It is useful to apply the concept of controllability to a particular state and introduce the

14 **Definition** A state $\mathbf{x}_1$ of the system $\mathcal{S}$ described by *1* is said to be *controllable* if and only if, for some finite T, there exists a control $\mathbf{u}_{[0,T]}$ such that

$$\mathbf{x}(T;\mathbf{x}_1,0;\mathbf{u}_{[0,T]}) = \mathbf{0}$$

15 **Corollary** A state of the system $\mathcal{S}$ is controllable if and only if it belongs to $\mathcal{R}(\mathbf{Q})$, the subspace spanned by the column vectors of $\mathbf{Q}$.
Proof Exercise for the reader.

The corollary states that $\mathcal{R}(\mathbf{Q})$ is the subspace of all controllable states. Let us exhibit the meaning of this fact in terms of special representations of $\mathcal{S}$. Let $\mathcal{R}(\mathbf{Q})$ be of dimension $\gamma < n$. Of course, $\mathcal{C}^n = \mathcal{R}(\mathbf{Q}) \oplus \mathcal{R}(\mathbf{Q})^\perp$. Let us pick a new basis for $\mathcal{C}^n$ as follows: the first γ basis vectors constitute a basis for $\mathcal{R}(\mathbf{Q})$ and the $(n - \gamma)$ remaining ones constitute a basis for $\mathcal{R}(\mathbf{Q})^\perp$. Let us use a prime to indicate the matrices representing $\mathbf{x}$, $\mathbf{A}$, $\mathbf{B}$, and $\mathbf{u}$ in the new basis. We shall show that we have

16 $$\mathbf{A}' = \begin{bmatrix} \mathbf{A}'_{11} & \mathbf{A}'_{12} \\ \mathbf{0} & \mathbf{A}'_{22} \end{bmatrix} \qquad \mathbf{B}' = \begin{bmatrix} \mathbf{B}'_1 \\ \mathbf{0} \end{bmatrix}$$

where $\mathbf{A}'_{11}$ is $\gamma \times \gamma$, $\mathbf{A}'_{12}$ is $\gamma \times (n - \gamma)$, and $\mathbf{A}'_{22}$ is $(n - \gamma) \times (n - \gamma)$.

$\mathbf{B}_1'$ is a $\gamma \times r$ matrix. Equation *1* can be partitioned into two vector equations if we write $\mathbf{x}' = \mathbf{x}_1' + \mathbf{x}_2'$, where $\mathbf{x}_1' \in \mathcal{R}(\mathbf{Q})$ and $\mathbf{x}_2' = \mathcal{R}(\mathbf{Q})^\perp$:

17
$$\begin{aligned}\dot{\mathbf{x}}_1' &= \mathbf{A}_{11}'\mathbf{x}_1' + \mathbf{A}_{12}'\mathbf{x}_2' + \mathbf{B}_1'\mathbf{u}' \\ \dot{\mathbf{x}}_2' &= \mathbf{A}_{22}'\mathbf{x}_2'\end{aligned}$$

The lower submatrix of $\mathbf{B}'$ in *16* is zero because the columns of $\mathbf{B}$ are necessarily in $\mathcal{R}(\mathbf{Q})$ by the definition *6* of $\mathbf{Q}$. The lower left-hand submatrix of $\mathbf{A}'$ in *16* is zero because, by *13*, $\mathcal{R}(\mathbf{Q})$ is an invariant subspace under $\mathbf{A}$, that is, $\mathbf{x}' \in \mathcal{R}(\mathbf{Q}) \Rightarrow \mathbf{A}'\mathbf{x}' \in \mathcal{R}(\mathbf{Q})$. Thus if $\mathbf{x}' = (\mathbf{x}_1',\mathbf{0})$, then for all possible $\mathbf{x}_1'$, $\mathbf{A}'\mathbf{x}' = (\mathbf{A}_{11}'\mathbf{x}_1',\mathbf{A}_{21}'\mathbf{x}_1') = (\mathbf{A}_{11}'\mathbf{x}_1',\mathbf{0})$, and therefore $\mathbf{A}_{21}' = \mathbf{0}$.

18 *Comment* Equation *17* shows that whenever $\gamma < n$, any state vector $\mathbf{x}'$ can be decomposed in a sum $\mathbf{x}_1' + \mathbf{x}_2'$, where $\mathbf{x}_2'$ is unaffected by the input $\mathbf{u}$, whatever it may be. Furthermore, $\mathbf{x}'$ is controllable if and only if it is of the form $\mathbf{x}_1' + \mathbf{0}$. This leads to the representation of Fig. *11.3.1*. It is of interest to note that both $\mathbf{x}'(t)$ and $\mathbf{x}_1'(t)$ depend

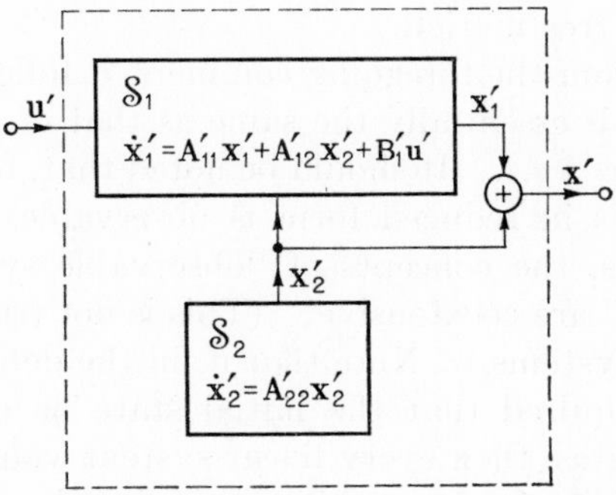

Fig. 11.3.1 Direct sum decomposition of the state space $\mathcal{C}^n$ in controllable states $\mathbf{x}_1'$ and uncontrollable states $\mathbf{x}_2'$.

(for $t > 0$) on $\mathbf{x}_2'(0)$. The transfer function of the system shown in Fig. *11.3.1* depends only on $\mathbf{A}_{11}'$ and $\mathbf{B}_1'$ because the transfer function depends only on the zero-state response and $\mathbf{x}_2'(0) = \mathbf{0} \Rightarrow \mathbf{x}_2'(t) = \mathbf{0}$ for all t.

4 *Observability*

The idea of observability is closely related to that of controllability. Controllability means that knowing the initial state and the matrices characterizing the system, we can find an input which brings this state to the zero state in a finite time. Observability means that the knowledge of the matrices characterizing the system and the zero-input response $\mathbf{y}_{[0,T]}$ over a finite interval is sufficient to determine uniquely the initial state of the system. More precisely, we have the

1 **Definition** The system $\mathcal{S}$ defined by *11.3.1* and *11.3.2* is said to be *observable* if and only if, for some $T > 0$ and for all initial states $\mathbf{x}(0)$, the knowledge of $\mathbf{A}$, $\mathbf{C}$, and the zero-input response $\mathbf{y}_{[0,T]}$ suffices to determine the initial state $\mathbf{x}(0)$.

2 *Comment* Since throughout this section we assume that the matrices $\mathbf{A}$, $\mathbf{B}$, $\mathbf{C}$, and $\mathbf{D}$ are known, we could just as well have said that the system is observable if the input $\mathbf{u}_{[0,T]}$ and the output $\mathbf{y}'_{[0,T]}$ resulting from $\mathbf{u}_{[0,T]}$ suffice to determine $\mathbf{x}(0)$. Indeed, the contribution to the output due to the observed input, namely,

$$\mathbf{C}\int_0^t \{\exp [\mathbf{A}(t-\tau)]\}\, \mathbf{B}\mathbf{u}(\tau)\, d\tau + \mathbf{D}\mathbf{u}(t)$$

may always be subtracted from the observed output $\mathbf{y}'_{[0,T]}$ to obtain the output under free motion.

3 *Comment* From the foregoing comment it follows that the concept of observability is essentially the same as that of initial state determinability (*1.8.12 et seq.*). It should be noted that, by Corollary *3.7.55*, any system that is in reduced form is observable. Thus, in the case of linear systems, the concepts of "observable system" and "system in reduced form" are coextensive. (This is not true, however, in the case of nonlinear systems.) Note that if, in the definition of observability, we merely required that the initial state be determinable to within equivalent states, then every linear system would be observable.

The property of observability can be characterized in a manner similar to that of controllability (see *11.3.5*). We have the

4 **Theorem** The system $\mathcal{S}$ described by *11.3.1* and *11.3.2* is *observable* if and only if the np columns of the matrix

$$\mathbf{P} \triangleq [\mathbf{C}^*,\mathbf{A}^*\mathbf{C}^*, \ldots ,\mathbf{A}^{*(n-1)}\mathbf{C}^*]$$

span the state space $\mathcal{C}^n$. (The superscript * indicates the conjugate transpose of the unstarred matrix.)

Proof The zero-input response is $\mathbf{y}(t) = \mathbf{C}[\exp (\mathbf{A}t)]\mathbf{x}_0$, and by *D.8.12*,

5
$$\mathbf{y}(t;\mathbf{x}_0,0;\mathbf{0}) = \sum_{k=0}^{m-1} \alpha_k(t)\mathbf{C}\mathbf{A}^k\mathbf{x}_0$$

where m is the degree of the minimal polynomial of $\mathbf{A}$.

$\Rightarrow$ Use contradiction. Suppose the columns of $\mathbf{P}$ do not span $\mathcal{C}^n$. Then there exists a nonzero vector $\boldsymbol{\eta} \in \mathcal{C}^n$ which is orthogonal to all the columns of $\mathbf{P}$. This orthogonality may be expressed by

$$\mathbf{0} = (\mathbf{A}^{*k}\mathbf{C}^*)^*\boldsymbol{\eta} = \mathbf{C}\mathbf{A}^k\boldsymbol{\eta} \qquad k = 0, 1, \ldots, n-1$$

where we have used $(\mathbf{AB})^* = \mathbf{B}^*\mathbf{A}^*$ (see *C.14.4*). From *5*,

$$\mathbf{y}(t;\boldsymbol{\eta},0;\mathbf{0}) = \mathbf{0}$$

for all t; thus, any initial state proportional to η produces a zero-input response which is identical to zero. In other words, there are nonzero initial states which cannot be determined by observing only the zero-input response. This contradicts the assumption that $\mathcal{S}$ is observable. Hence, the columns of $\mathbf{P}$ span $\mathcal{C}^n$.

$\Leftarrow$ Let $\mathbf{c}_j^*$ be the jth column of $\mathbf{C}^*$ (consequently $\mathbf{c}_j$ is the jth row of $\mathbf{C}$). Remembering that we use the complex scalar product, the jth component of $\mathbf{y}$ is

$$y_j(t) = \langle \mathbf{c}_j^*, [\exp(\mathbf{A}t)]\mathbf{x}_0 \rangle = \sum_{k=1}^{m-1} \alpha_k(t)\langle \mathbf{c}_j^*, \mathbf{A}^k\mathbf{x}_0 \rangle$$

or

6 $$y_j(t) = \sum_{k=0}^{m-1} \alpha_k(t)\langle \mathbf{A}^{*k}\mathbf{c}_j^*, \mathbf{x}_0 \rangle$$

where we have used the definition of the adjoint (*C.14.2*). Now, from *D.8.13*, the functions α_k are linearly independent over $[0,T]$. Taking the scalar product of *6* with α_i (as in Lemma *11.2.4*) we obtain the system of equations

$$(\alpha_i, y_j) = \sum_{k=0}^{m-1} (\alpha_i, \alpha_k)\langle \mathbf{A}^{*k}\mathbf{c}_j^*, \mathbf{x}_0 \rangle \qquad \begin{array}{l} i = 0, 1, \ldots, m-1 \\ j = 1, 2, \ldots, p \end{array}$$

For each j, this is a set of m equations in the m scalars $\langle \mathbf{A}^{*k}\mathbf{c}_j^*, \mathbf{x}_0 \rangle$,

$$k = 0, 1, \ldots, m-1$$

and the determinant of the system is different from zero by *11.2.4*. Solving these p systems yields the mp scalars $\langle \mathbf{A}^{*k}\mathbf{c}_j^*, \mathbf{x}_0 \rangle$. Now, by assumption, among the mp vectors $\mathbf{A}^{*k}\mathbf{c}_j^*$ there is a basis for $\mathcal{C}^n$; therefore, $\mathbf{x}_0$ is uniquely specified, since we know the scalar product of $\mathbf{x}_0$ with n basis vectors of $\mathcal{C}^n$ (*C.8.5*).

7 *Comment* The proof of Theorem *4* shows that if the system is observable in an interval $[0,T]$, then it is observable in any interval $[0,T_1]$, where $0 < T_1$.

8 *Comment* If $\mathcal{R}(\mathbf{P})$, the subspace spanned by the column vectors of $\mathbf{P}$, is a proper subset of $\mathcal{C}^n$, the proof of *4* shows that $\mathbf{y}_{[0,T]}$ is not sufficient to specify $\mathbf{x}_0$ uniquely. Now, *5* shows that the knowledge of $\mathbf{y}_{[0,T]}$ is equivalent to that of the mp scalar products $\langle \mathbf{A}^{*k}\mathbf{c}_j^*, \mathbf{x}_0 \rangle$. The mp vectors $\mathbf{A}^{*k}\mathbf{c}_j^*$ span $\mathcal{R}(\mathbf{P})$. Consider the orthogonal decomposition of the state space $\mathcal{C}^n = \mathcal{R}(\mathbf{P}) \oplus \mathcal{R}(\mathbf{P})^\perp$ and the corresponding decomposition of $\mathbf{x}_0$, $\mathbf{x}_0 = \mathbf{x}_1' + \mathbf{x}_2'$, where $\mathbf{x}_1' \in \mathcal{R}(\mathbf{P})$, $\mathbf{x}_2' \in \mathcal{R}(\mathbf{P})^\perp$. All the scalar products $\langle \mathbf{A}^{*k}\mathbf{c}_j^*, \mathbf{x}_0 \rangle$ determine $\mathbf{x}_1'$ uniquely but give no information whatsoever about $\mathbf{x}_2'$. In other words, we have the

9 **Assertion** When $\mathcal{R}(\mathbf{P})$ is a proper subset of $\mathcal{C}^n$, the output $\mathbf{y}_{[0,T]}$ determines only the orthogonal projection of $\mathbf{x}_0$ on $\mathcal{R}(\mathbf{P})$. ◁

If the initial state $\mathbf{x} \in \mathcal{R}(\mathbf{P})^\perp$, then the corresponding zero-input response $\mathbf{y}_{[0,T]}$ is identically zero; in that sense, $\mathbf{x}$ is said to be *unobservable*. Furthermore,

10 **Assertion** The set of all *unobservable* states of the system $\mathcal{S}$ is the subspace $\mathcal{R}(\mathbf{P})^\perp$.

It is of interest to note that $\mathcal{R}(\mathbf{P})$ is not necessarily invariant under $\mathbf{A}$ but that we have the

11 **Assertion** The subspace $\mathcal{R}(\mathbf{P})^\perp$ is invariant under $\mathbf{A}$.
Proof Exercise for the reader. [*Hint:* Use the definition of $\mathcal{R}(\mathbf{P})^\perp$ and the Cayley-Hamilton theorem.] ◁

The close relationship between the concept of controllability and that of observability is clearly exhibited by the

12 **Duality theorem of Kalman** Consider the system $\mathcal{S}$ defined by *11.3.1* and *11.3.2*: $\mathbf{x}$ is an n-vector, $\mathbf{u}$ an r-vector, and $\mathbf{y}$ a p-vector. Consider also the system Σ defined by

13 $$\dot{\boldsymbol{\xi}} = \mathbf{A}^*\boldsymbol{\xi} + \mathbf{C}^*\mathbf{v}$$

14 $$\boldsymbol{\eta} = \mathbf{B}^*\boldsymbol{\xi} + \mathbf{D}^*\mathbf{v}$$

where the state $\boldsymbol{\xi}$ is an n-vector, the input $\mathbf{v}$ is a p-vector, and the output $\boldsymbol{\eta}$ is an r-vector. The system $\mathcal{S}$ is controllable (observable) if and only if the system Σ is observable (controllable, respectively).
Proof Immediate consequence of Theorem *11.3.5* and *4*.

15 *Exercise* The purpose of this exercise is to relate the concept of observability and that of state equivalence (see *2.2.1*). Consider the differential system described by *11.3.1* and *11.3.2*. Show that if the system is observable, any two distinct points of its state space are not equivalent states. Prove the converse.

5 *Canonical decomposition of the state space of* $\mathcal{S}$

We have shown that intrinsically associated with the system $\mathcal{S}$, defined by (*11.3.1* and *11.3.2*), there are two invariant subspaces: $\mathcal{R}(\mathbf{Q})$, the subspace of all controllable states, and $\mathcal{R}(\mathbf{P})^{\perp}$, the subspace of all unobservable states. Our purpose is to use these subspaces to create a direct sum decomposition of the whole state space $\mathcal{C}^n$. Let $\mathcal{M}_1$ be the subspace defined by

1 $$\mathcal{M}_1 = \mathcal{R}(\mathbf{Q}) \cap \mathcal{R}(\mathbf{P})^{\perp}$$

$\mathcal{M}_1$ is also an invariant subspace under $\mathbf{A}$. It is uniquely defined by *1*. Define $\mathcal{M}_2$, $\mathcal{M}_3$, and $\mathcal{M}_4$ by the following relations:

2 $$\mathcal{R}(\mathbf{Q}) = \mathcal{M}_1 \oplus \mathcal{M}_2$$

3 $$\mathcal{R}(\mathbf{P})^{\perp} = \mathcal{M}_1 \oplus \mathcal{M}_3$$

4 $$\mathcal{C}^n = \mathcal{M}_1 \oplus \mathcal{M}_2 \oplus \mathcal{M}_3 \oplus \mathcal{M}_4$$

Clearly, $\mathcal{M}_1$ is the subspace of the states that are both controllable and unobservable. Any state in $\mathcal{M}_2$ is controllable, but only its projection on $\mathcal{R}(\mathbf{P})$ is observable. Any state in $\mathcal{M}_3$ is unobservable, but it is also not controllable. Any state in $\mathcal{M}_4$ is uncontrollable, and its projection on $\mathcal{R}(\mathbf{P})^{\perp}$ is unobservable.

It is important to note that the subspaces $\mathcal{M}_2$, $\mathcal{M}_3$, and $\mathcal{M}_4$ are not uniquely defined. However, as long as they satisfy the conditions *2* to *4* the above statements hold.

Let us now use the direct sum decomposition *4* to write the equations of the system. More precisely, we use a basis of $\mathcal{C}^n$ which is the union of bases for $\mathcal{M}_1$, $\mathcal{M}_2$, $\mathcal{M}_3$, $\mathcal{M}_4$. In this new basis, the state is $\boldsymbol{\xi}_1 + \boldsymbol{\xi}_2 + \boldsymbol{\xi}_3 + \boldsymbol{\xi}_4$, where $\boldsymbol{\xi}_i \in \mathcal{M}_i$. Equations *11.3.1* and *11.3.2* become in these new coordinates

5 $$\begin{bmatrix} \dot{\boldsymbol{\xi}}_1 \\ \dot{\boldsymbol{\xi}}_2 \\ \dot{\boldsymbol{\xi}}_3 \\ \dot{\boldsymbol{\xi}}_4 \end{bmatrix} = \begin{bmatrix} \bar{\mathbf{A}}_{11} & \bar{\mathbf{A}}_{12} & \bar{\mathbf{A}}_{13} & \bar{\mathbf{A}}_{14} \\ \mathbf{0} & \bar{\mathbf{A}}_{22} & \mathbf{0} & \bar{\mathbf{A}}_{24} \\ \mathbf{0} & \mathbf{0} & \bar{\mathbf{A}}_{33} & \bar{\mathbf{A}}_{34} \\ \mathbf{0} & \mathbf{0} & \mathbf{0} & \bar{\mathbf{A}}_{44} \end{bmatrix} \begin{bmatrix} \boldsymbol{\xi}_1 \\ \boldsymbol{\xi}_2 \\ \boldsymbol{\xi}_3 \\ \boldsymbol{\xi}_4 \end{bmatrix} + \begin{bmatrix} \bar{\mathbf{B}}_1 \\ \bar{\mathbf{B}}_2 \\ \mathbf{0} \\ \mathbf{0} \end{bmatrix} \mathbf{v}$$

6 $$\mathbf{n} = [\mathbf{0} \quad \bar{\mathbf{C}}_2 \quad \mathbf{0} \quad \bar{\mathbf{C}}_4] \begin{bmatrix} \boldsymbol{\xi}_1 \\ \boldsymbol{\xi}_2 \\ \boldsymbol{\xi}_3 \\ \boldsymbol{\xi}_4 \end{bmatrix} + \mathbf{D}\mathbf{v}$$

The pattern of the zero submatrices in *5* and *6* is justified as follows. $\mathcal{R}(\mathbf{Q}) = \mathcal{M}_1 \oplus \mathcal{M}_2$ is invariant under $\mathbf{A}$ (see *11.3.13*); therefore, the submatrices in the positions (3,1), (3,2), (4,1), and (4,2) are zero matrices in this basis (see *C.13.3*). $\mathcal{R}(\mathbf{P})^{\perp} = \mathcal{M}_1 \oplus \mathcal{M}_3$ is invariant under $\mathbf{A}$ (see *11.4.11*); hence the submatrices in the positions (2,1), (4,1), (2,3), and (4,3) are zero matrices. By *2* and *4*, all states in $\mathcal{M}_3 \oplus \mathcal{M}_4$ are outside $\mathcal{R}(\mathbf{Q})$ and hence are uncontrollable; consequently, the bottom two submatrices of $\mathbf{B}$ in *5* are zero matrices. From *11.4.10* and *11.4.11*, any initial state in the invariant subspace $\mathcal{R}(\mathbf{P})^{\perp} = \mathcal{M}_1 \oplus \mathcal{M}_3$ will produce a zero-input response which is identical to zero; hence, the first and third submatrices of $\mathbf{C}$ in *6* are zero.

The decomposition *5*, *6* leads to the block diagram shown in Fig. *11.5.1*. This decomposition, though not unique, can be said to be *canonical* because it is based on the intrinsic properties of the linear transformations $\mathbf{A}$, $\mathbf{B}$, $\mathbf{C}$.

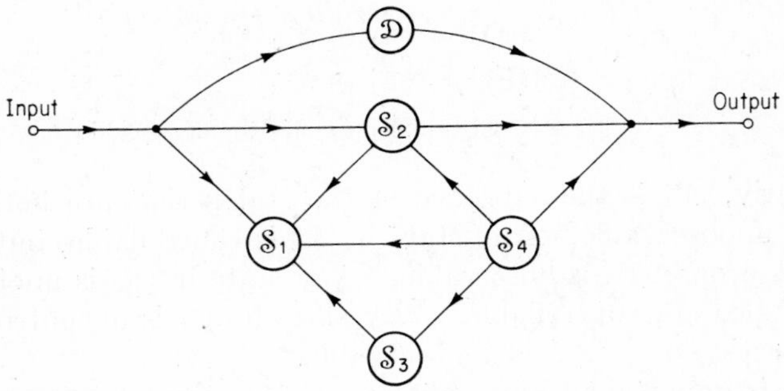

Fig. 11.5.1 Canonical decomposition of the state space $\mathcal{C}^n$ into the direct sum of four subspaces. With each subspace is associated a subsystem $\mathcal{S}_i$, $i = 1, 2, 3, 4$.

7 *Comment* Suppose we consider Eqs. *5* and *6* and try to construct an example of the system. Can the matrices $\bar{\mathbf{A}}_{ij}$, $\bar{\mathbf{B}}_i$, $\bar{\mathbf{C}}_j$ be chosen arbitrarily? The answer is no. The matrices $\bar{\mathbf{A}}_{ij}$, $\bar{\mathbf{B}}_i$ must be such that

$$\mathcal{R}(\mathbf{Q}) = \mathcal{M}_1 \oplus \mathcal{M}_2$$

and the matrices $\bar{\mathbf{A}}_{ij}$, $\bar{\mathbf{C}}_j$ must be such that $\mathcal{R}(\mathbf{P})^{\perp} = \mathcal{M}_1 \oplus \mathcal{M}_3$.

8 *Comment* The (matrix) transfer function of the system of Fig. *11.5.1* will characterize only the properties of $\mathcal{S}_2$ (that part of the system that is both observable and controllable) and D. $\mathcal{S}_1$ does not affect the transfer function because all states of $\mathcal{S}_1$ are unobservable. $\mathcal{S}_3$ and $\mathcal{S}_4$ do not affect the transfer function because all states of $\mathcal{S}_3$ and $\mathcal{S}_4$ are uncontrollable and because the transfer function is defined on the basis of the *zero-state response* of the system; indeed, when the system starts from the zero state, $\boldsymbol{\xi}_3 = \boldsymbol{\xi}_4 = \mathbf{0}$, for all t, irrespective of the input $\mathbf{u}$.

9 *Example* The purpose of this example is to illustrate the concepts of controllability and observability in a simple situation and also to show

how it can throw some light on certain puzzling situations. Consider the linear feedback system shown in Fig. *11.5.2*. It is a single-input

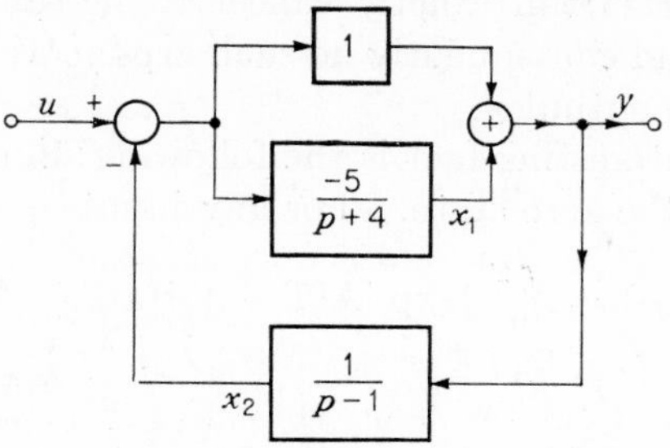

Fig. 11.5.2 Linear feedback system considered in Example *11.5.9*.

(u), single-output (y) system. Let us pick x_1 and x_2 as the components of the state vector. It is immediately found that

10 $$\begin{bmatrix}\dot{x}_1\\ \dot{x}_2\end{bmatrix} = \begin{bmatrix}-4 & 5\\ 1 & 0\end{bmatrix}\begin{bmatrix}x_1\\ x_2\end{bmatrix} + u\begin{bmatrix}-5\\ 1\end{bmatrix}$$

11 $$y = u + \langle \mathbf{c},\mathbf{x}\rangle$$

where $\mathbf{c} = (1,-1)$.

Referring to the figure, the transfer function of the two forward paths combined is easily seen to be $G(s) = (s-1)/(s+4)$. That of the feedback branch is $H(s) = 1/(s-1)$. Therefore, the transfer function of the system is

$$\frac{G}{1+GH} = \frac{(s-1)/(s+4)}{1+(s-1)^{-1}(s-1)/(s+4)} = \frac{s-1}{s+5}$$

12 Hence the transfer function of the system is strictly stable (see *9.4.7*).

From *10* we find that the eigenvalues and eigenvectors are[1] $\lambda_1 = 1$, $\mathbf{u}_1 = (1,1)$; $\lambda_2 = -5$, $\mathbf{u}_2 = (5,-1)$. The system has an eigenvalue with a positive real part ($\lambda_1 = 1$), and

13 Therefore the system *10* is unstable i.s.L (see *7.2.2* and *7.4.2*).

The apparent contradiction between *12* and *13* is easily resolved by noting that the output y depends on $\mathbf{x}$ through the scalar product $\langle \mathbf{c},\mathbf{x}\rangle$ and since $\langle \mathbf{c},\mathbf{u}_1\rangle = 0$,

14 The output y is uncoupled to the unstable mode of *10* and *11*.

Equivalently, the subspace of unobservable states, $\mathcal{R}(\mathbf{P})^{\perp}$, is spanned by $\mathbf{u}_1$.

It is of interest to follow around the loop the physical events: suppose there is some initially stored energy in the black box in the feedback

[1] For the eigenvectors, we picked a normalization which suited our numerical convenience.

branch; then x_2 will increase exponentially at the rate e^t, and x_1 will also include a term which increases as e^t. However, it is easy to check that these two terms will exactly cancel at the summing point in the forward path, and consequently no such exponentially increasing term will appear in the output y.

Another interesting fact is the following: Suppose that at $t = 0$ the system is in the zero state. For any input $u_{[0,T]}$, the resulting state is

$$\begin{aligned}\mathbf{x}(T;\mathbf{0},0;u_{[0,T]}) &= \int_0^T \{\exp[\mathbf{A}(T-\tau)]\}\mathbf{a}u(\tau)\,d\tau \\ &= \mathbf{a}\int_0^T \alpha_1(T-\tau)u(\tau)\,d\tau + \mathbf{Aa}\int_0^T \alpha_2(T-\tau)u(\tau)\,d\tau\end{aligned}$$

where we used the fact that $\exp(\mathbf{A}t) = \alpha_1(t)\mathbf{I} + \alpha_2(t)\mathbf{A}$ and we called $\mathbf{a}$ the forcing vector of *10*. In the present case, both $\mathbf{a}$ and $\mathbf{Aa}$ are easily verified to be proportional to $\mathbf{u}_2$; therefore, the only states reachable from the zero state are the states in the one-dimensional subspace spanned by $\mathbf{u}_2$. In other words,

15 The input is uncoupled to the unstable mode and therefore the unstable mode can be excited only if initially the system is not in the zero state.

The canonical structure of the system shown in Fig. *11.5.2* is given, for the particular choice of state vector, by Fig. *11.5.3*.

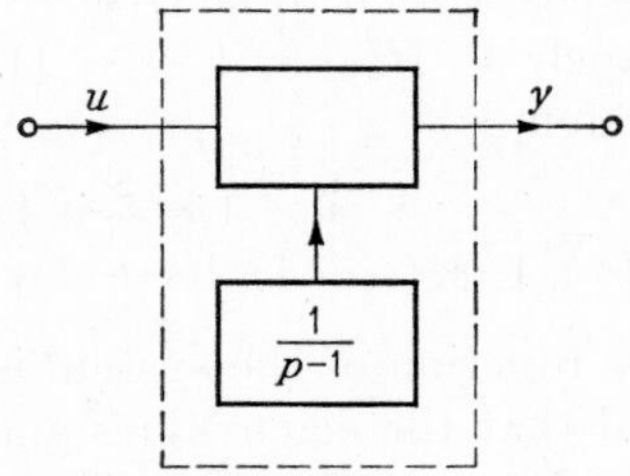

Fig. 11.5.3 Canonical decomposition of the system of Fig. *11.5.2*.

16 **Remark** Observe that if the two forward paths of the system of Fig. *11.5.3* are joined together, the resulting gain is $(s-1)/(s+4)$. Thus the right-half-plane zero of the forward path cancels the right-half-plane pole of the feedback path. The usual admonition given to beginners to the effect that they should never design a system such that a right-half-plane pole is canceled by a right-half-plane zero can now be justified in two ways: (I) The boundedness of y is based on the *exact* cancellation of rising exponentials at the summing node in the forward path; the cancellation will never be exact in practice because physical components cannot be specified with arbitrary precision and because of aging, temperature variations, etc., of the same components. (II) Even if the cancellation did occur exactly as on paper, any noise or other spurious input to the black box in the feedback loop would create two exponentially increasing outputs x_1 and x_2. This instability, excitable by any suitably placed noise source, demonstrates also the worthlessness of such cancellation schemes. ◁

Finally, it should be stressed that the particular canonical structure one obtains for the system of Fig. *11.5.2* depends on the choice of the state vector (see Exercise *18*).

17 *Exercise* Apply the theory of Secs. *2* and *3* to verify that the system of Fig. *11.5.2* is neither controllable nor observable.

18 *Exercise* Consider the system of Fig. *11.5.2*. Choose y and x_2 as state variables. Find the state equations and discuss the stability, observability, and controllability of the system. Give its canonical structure.

19 *Exercise* Call $\mathcal{A}$ the system shown in Fig. *11.5.1* and described by Eqs. *5* and *6*. Call $\mathcal{A}_{24}$ the system obtained from $\mathcal{A}$ by deleting the subsystems $\mathcal{S}_1$ and $\mathcal{S}_3$. Call $\mathcal{A}_2$ the system obtained by deleting from $\mathcal{A}$ the subsystems $\mathcal{S}_1$, $\mathcal{S}_3$, and $\mathcal{S}_4$. Show that (I) $\mathcal{A}_{24} \doteq \mathcal{A}_2 \doteq \mathcal{A}$, (II) $\mathcal{A}_2$ is not zero-input equivalent to $\mathcal{A}_{24}$, (III) $\mathcal{A}_2$ is not zero-input equivalent to $\mathcal{A}$, and (IV) $\mathcal{A}_{24}$ is zero-state and zero-input equivalent to $\mathcal{A}$. (*Hint:* See Definitions *2.9.1* and *2.9.2*.)

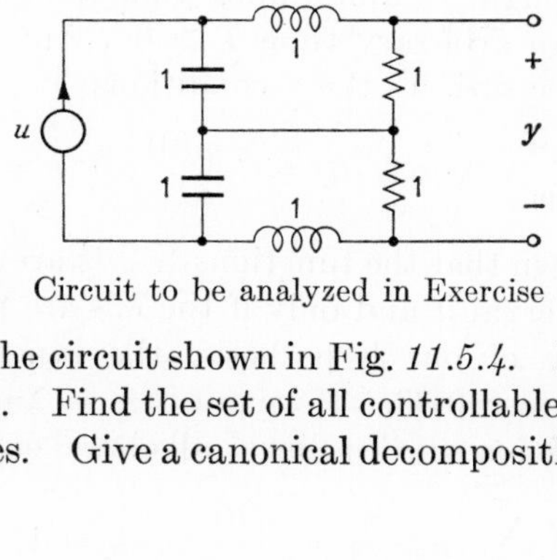

Fig. 11.5.4 Circuit to be analyzed in Exercise *11.5.20*.

20 *Exercise* Consider the circuit shown in Fig. *11.5.4*. It is a single-input single-output system. Find the set of all controllable states and the set of unobservable states. Give a canonical decomposition for the system.

6 *Alternate characterization of controllability*

Let us consider the interpretation of Theorem *11.3.5* in terms of the Jordan canonical form of the system. Using the Jordan form will allow us to actually compute the control required to bring any state to **0**. For simplicity we shall consider a single-input system described by

1 $$\dot{\mathbf{x}} = \mathbf{A}\mathbf{x} + \mathbf{b}u$$

where **A** is an $n \times n$ constant matrix and **b** is an n-vector. u is the scalar input.

2 *Exercise* Show that if the minimum polynomial of **A** is of degree $k \leq n - 1$, then the system *1* is not controllable. (*Hint:* Use *11.3.5* and note that since k is the degree of the minimal polynomial, $\mathbf{A}^k$ is a linear combination of $\mathbf{I}, \mathbf{A}, \ldots, \mathbf{A}^{k-1}$.)

Let us change variables: let $\mathbf{x} = \mathbf{Ty}$, where the transformation matrix $\mathbf{T}$ is such that $\mathbf{T}^{-1}\mathbf{AT} = \mathbf{J}$ and $\mathbf{J}$ is the Jordan canonical form of $\mathbf{A}$ (see *D.5.21*). With $\mathbf{e} = \mathbf{T}^{-1}\mathbf{b}$, *1* becomes

3 $$\dot{\mathbf{y}} = \mathbf{Jy} + \mathbf{e}u$$

The first characterization of controllability for the case where the eigenvalues of $\mathbf{A}$ are distinct is given by the

4 **Theorem** Let $\mathbf{A}$ have distinct eigenvalues; hence $\mathbf{J} = \text{diag}(\lambda_1, \ldots, \lambda_n)$. Then the system *1* is controllable if and only if all the components of $\mathbf{e} = \mathbf{T}^{-1}\mathbf{d}$ are different from zero.

5 *Comment* In terms of the mode interpretation of the dynamics of the system (Chap. *5*, Sec. *4*), the conditions are equivalent to the following: The (scalar) input must be coupled to all the modes of the system.

Proof $\Rightarrow$ The ith component of the vector equation *3* is $\dot{y}_i = \lambda_i y_i + e_i u$. Suppose that one component of $\mathbf{e}$, say, e_k, is zero. Then the kth component of $\mathbf{y}$ is $y_k(t) = y_k(0)e^{\lambda_k t}$, which differs from zero for all *finite t* once $y_k(0) \neq 0$. Therefore, if $e_k = 0$, any state $\mathbf{y}$ such that $y_k(0) \neq 0$ cannot be brought to $\mathbf{0}$ in a finite time.

$\Leftarrow$ Pick an arbitrary time $T > 0$. Any input $u_{[0,T]}$ which brings $\mathbf{y}$ to $\mathbf{0}$ in T sec satisfies the n conditions

6 $$\int_0^T e^{-\lambda_i \xi} u(\xi)\, d\xi = \frac{-y_i(0)}{e_i} \qquad i = 1, 2, \ldots, n$$

It is well known that the functions $\{e^{-\lambda_i \xi}\}$ are linearly independent over any finite interval if and only if the λ_i's are pairwise distinct. Therefore, in view of our hypothesis, the functions $\{e^{-\lambda_i \xi}\}$ are linearly independent over $[0,T]$. If we put $u(\xi) = \Sigma \eta_j \exp(-\lambda_j^* \xi)$, the n conditions *6* will give a set of n linear algebraic equations in n unknowns,

7 $$\sum_{j=1}^{n} (\varphi_i, \varphi_j)\eta_j = \frac{y_i(0)}{e_i} \qquad i = 1, 2, \ldots, n$$

where $\varphi_i(\xi) = \exp(-\lambda_i^* \xi)$. By Lemma *11.2.4*, the determinant of the system *7* is nonzero and the solution is unique. The solution of *7* specifies a control $u_{[0,T]}$ which will bring the state $\mathbf{y}(0)$ to $\mathbf{0}$ in T sec.

8 *Exercise* If to the control u just computed one would add any function v such that $(\varphi_i, v) = 0$ for all i, the control $u + v$ would still bring the state $\mathbf{y}(0)$ to zero in T sec. $\triangleleft$

Suppose now that the eigenvalues of $\mathbf{J}$ are not distinct: let the matrix $\mathbf{J}$ consist of α Jordan blocks of respective size $r_1, r_2, \ldots, r_\alpha$; let the corresponding eigenvalues be $\lambda_1, \lambda_2, \ldots, \lambda_\alpha$. Note that, in general, these λ's are not necessarily distinct, since the same eigenvalue may be associated with two or more Jordan blocks (*D.5.21*). For example, suppose $r_1 = 1$, $r_2 = 2$, $r_3 = 3$. The matrix is then

9
$$\begin{bmatrix} \lambda_1 & 0 & 0 & 0 & \cdot & 0 \\ 0 & \lambda_2 & 1 & \cdot & \cdot & \cdot \\ 0 & 0 & \lambda_2 & \cdot & \cdot & \cdot \\ \cdot & \cdot & \cdot & \lambda_3 & 1 & 0 \\ \cdot & \cdot & \cdot & 0 & \lambda_3 & 1 \\ 0 & \cdot & \cdot & 0 & 0 & \lambda_3 \end{bmatrix}$$

The block-diagram representation corresponding to this matrix with the notation of *2* is shown in Fig. *11.6.1*. The general characterization of controllability is contained in the

10 **Theorem** With the notation just described, the system *1* is controllable if and only if (I) the eigenvalues $\lambda_1, \ldots, \lambda_\alpha$ are pairwise distinct and

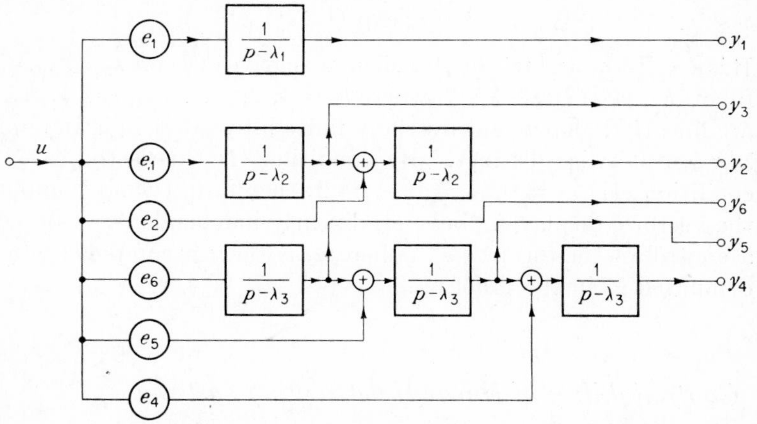

Fig. 11.6.1 Realization of the system whose matrix **A** is given by *11.6.9*.

(II) all the components of **e** that are in the last row of each Jordan block are different from zero.

Proof $\Rightarrow$ The system is assumed to be controllable. Condition (II) is easily shown to hold by the use of the same argument as that used in the proof of *4*. Suppose condition (I) were violated; say, $\lambda_i = \lambda_j$. Considering the components of the vector equation *3* corresponding to the last row of the ith and jth Jordan blocks, we get

$$\dot{y}_i = \lambda_i y_i + e_i u \qquad \dot{y}_j = \lambda_i y_j + e_j u$$

If we put $z = e_j y_i - e_i y_j$, we see that

$$\dot{z} = \lambda_i z$$

Therefore z is independent of the input and $z(t) = z(0) \exp(\lambda_i t) \neq 0$ for all finite t provided $z(0) \neq 0$. Therefore, it is obvious that there are noncontrollable states. This is a contradiction; hence condition (II) must hold.

⇐ Let us establish controllability by actually computing a control $u_{[0,T]}$ which brings any state $\mathbf{y}(0)$ to $\mathbf{0}$ in T sec. By *5.2.17*, any such control is characterized by

$$-\mathbf{y}(0) = \int_0^T [\exp(-\mathbf{J}\xi)]\, \mathbf{e}u(\xi)\, d\xi$$

Suppose, for simplicity, that $\mathbf{J}$ is given by *9*; then

$$\boldsymbol{\phi} \triangleq [\exp(-\mathbf{J}\xi)]\mathbf{e} = \begin{bmatrix} e_1 \exp(-\lambda_1\xi) \\ e_2 \exp(-\lambda_2\xi) - e_3\xi \exp(-\lambda_2\xi) \\ e_3 \exp(-\lambda_2\xi) \\ e_4 \exp(-\lambda_3\xi) - e_5\xi \exp(-\lambda_3\xi) \\ \qquad + e_6(\xi^2/2) \exp(-\lambda_3\xi) \\ e_5 \exp(-\lambda_3\xi) - e_6\xi \exp(-\lambda_3\xi) \\ e_6 \exp(-\lambda_3\xi) \end{bmatrix}$$

It is a well-known fact that for all nonnegative integers $r_1, r_2, \ldots, r_\alpha$, the functions $\{\xi^{k_i} \exp(-\lambda_i\xi)\}$, where $k_i = 1, 2, \ldots, r_i$, $i = 1, 2, \ldots, \alpha$, are linearly independent over any finite interval $[0,T]$ if and only if the λ_i's are pairwise distinct. By condition (I) this is the case, and by condition (II) $e_1 \neq 0$, $e_3 \neq 0$, $e_6 \neq 0$; therefore, the six components of the vector $\boldsymbol{\phi}$ displayed above are linearly independent. Consequently, a control of the form $\Sigma\eta_j\varphi_j^*$ (where φ_j is the jth componet of $\boldsymbol{\phi}$) can be computed as in the proof of *4*.

7 *Controllability of linear time-varying systems*

In order to check the controllability of a time-invariant system, one need only find the rank of a matrix with constant elements (*11.3.5*). In the time-varying case, Kalman et al. have shown that it is still possible to check the controllability by evaluating the rank of a matrix with constant elements.

We consider the system $\mathcal{S}$ defined by

1 $$\dot{\mathbf{x}} = \mathbf{A}(t)\mathbf{x} + \mathbf{B}(t)\mathbf{u}(t)$$

where $\mathbf{A}(t)$ and $\mathbf{B}(t)$ are $n \times n$ and $n \times r$ matrices of continuous elements. By analogy with the time-invariant case (*11.3.3*), we introduce the

2 **Definition** The system $\mathcal{S}$ defined by *1* is said to be *controllable at time* t_0 if and only if the following is true for all states $\mathbf{x}_0$ at time t_0: Given that the system is in state $\mathbf{x}_0$ at t_0, then, for some finite time t_1, there exists an input $\mathbf{u}_{[t_0,t_1]}$ such that

$$\mathbf{x}(t_1;\mathbf{x}_0,t_0;\mathbf{u}_{[t_0,t_1]}) = \mathbf{0}$$

3 *Comment* More informally, the system is controllable at t_0 if any possible state at t_0 can be brought to the zero state in a finite time.

4 *Comment* In the time-invariant case we could say "the system $\mathcal{S}$ is controllable." Here we have to say "controllable at time t_0" because the properties of the system vary with time so that it may happen that the system is controllable up to some time T and not controllable forever after. It is obvious, however, that the definition implies that if the system is *controllable at time* T, it is controllable at time t_0 for all $t_0 < T$. ◁

Let us state a result analogous to *11.3.10.*

5 **Assertion** The system $\mathcal{S}$ is controllable at time t_0 if and only if any state $\mathbf{x}_0$ at time t_0 can be transferred to any state $\mathbf{x}_1$ at time t_1 (where $t_1 < \infty$ and depends on $\mathbf{x}_0$, $\mathbf{x}_1$, and t_0).

Proof Exercise for the reader. [*Hint:* The state transition matrix $\mathbf{\Phi}(t_1,t_2)$ is nonsingular for all t_1,t_2.] ◁

Let us now turn to the test for controllability: define

6 $$\mathbf{W}(t_0,t) = \int_{t_0}^{t} \mathbf{\Phi}(t_0,t')\mathbf{B}(t')\mathbf{B}^*(t')\mathbf{\Phi}^*(t_0,t')\,dt'$$

where the superscript * denotes the conjugate transpose. $\mathbf{W}(t_0,t)$ is a hermitian matrix; in particular, if $\mathbf{A}(t)$ and $\mathbf{B}(t)$ are real, $\mathbf{W}$ is real and symmetrical.

7 **Theorem** The system $\mathcal{S}$ defined by *1* is *controllable at time* t_0 if and only if, for some finite t_1, the matrix $\mathbf{W}(t_0,t_1)$ defined by *6* is positive definite.

8 *Comment* For any fixed t_1, $\mathbf{W}(t_0,t_1)$ is a matrix whose elements are numbers; furthermore, since $\mathbf{W}$ is hermitian, it is easy to check its positive definiteness by diagonalizing it and requiring that all the resulting diagonal elements be positive (see *C.19.18*).

Proof For purposes of the proof let us pick t_1 to be the smallest t for which $\mathbf{W}$ has maximal rank.

$\Leftarrow$ The assumption is that $\mathbf{W}(t_0,t_1)$ is positive definite: consequently it is nonsingular. Consider the control $\mathbf{u}'_{[t_0,t_1]}$ defined by

$$\mathbf{u}'(t) = -\mathbf{B}^*(t)\mathbf{\Phi}^*(t_0,t)\mathbf{W}^{-1}(t_0,t_1)\mathbf{x}_0$$

Now since

$$\mathbf{x}(t_1;\mathbf{x}_0,t_0;\mathbf{u}'_{[t_0,t_1]}) = \mathbf{\Phi}(t_1,t_0)\mathbf{x}_0 + \int_{t_0}^{t_1} \mathbf{\Phi}(t_1,\tau)\mathbf{B}(\tau)\mathbf{u}'(\tau)\,d\tau$$

it is easy to check, using *6.2.16*, that $\mathbf{u}'_{[t_0,t_1]}$ transfers $(\mathbf{x}_0,t_0)$ to $(\mathbf{0},t_1)$.

$\Rightarrow$ The assumption is that $\mathcal{S}$ is controllable at t_0. First observe that *6* requires that $\mathbf{W}$ be nonnegative definite. Indeed, let $\boldsymbol{\xi}$ be any state. We have to show that the quadratic form $\langle\boldsymbol{\xi},\mathbf{W}\boldsymbol{\xi}\rangle \geq 0$ for all $\boldsymbol{\xi}$. From *6*, we obtain successively

$$\begin{aligned}\langle \boldsymbol{\xi}, \mathbf{W}\boldsymbol{\xi}\rangle &= \int_{t_0}^{t_1} \langle \boldsymbol{\xi}, \boldsymbol{\Phi}\mathbf{B}\mathbf{B}^*\boldsymbol{\Phi}^*\boldsymbol{\xi}\rangle\, dt \\ &= \int_{t_0}^{t_1} \langle \mathbf{B}^*\boldsymbol{\Phi}^*\boldsymbol{\xi}, \mathbf{B}^*\boldsymbol{\Phi}^*\boldsymbol{\xi}\rangle\, dt \\ &= \int_{t_0}^{t_1} \|\mathbf{B}^*\boldsymbol{\Phi}^*\boldsymbol{\xi}\|^2\, dt \geq 0 \qquad \forall \boldsymbol{\xi}\end{aligned}$$

It remains, therefore, to show that $\mathbf{W}$ is nonsingular. We shall prove this by contradiction in two steps. (I) Suppose $\mathbf{W}$ is singular; then there is a state $\mathbf{n} \neq \mathbf{0}$ such that $\langle \mathbf{n}, \mathbf{W}\mathbf{n}\rangle = 0$. Define, then, $\mathbf{u}''_{[t_0,t_1]}$ by $\mathbf{u}''(t) = -\mathbf{B}^*(t)\boldsymbol{\Phi}^*(t_0,t)\mathbf{n}$; $\mathbf{u}''(t)$ is continuous in t. Then

$$\begin{aligned}\int_{t_0}^{t_1} \|\mathbf{u}''(t)\|^2\, dt &= \int_{t_0}^{t_1} \langle \mathbf{B}^*\boldsymbol{\Phi}^*\mathbf{n}, \mathbf{B}^*\boldsymbol{\Phi}^*\mathbf{n}\rangle\, dt \\ &= \int_{t_0}^{t_1} \langle \mathbf{n}, \boldsymbol{\Phi}\mathbf{B}\mathbf{B}^*\boldsymbol{\Phi}^*\mathbf{n}\rangle\, dt \\ &= \left\langle \mathbf{n}, \int_{t_0}^{t_1} \boldsymbol{\Phi}\mathbf{B}\mathbf{B}^*\boldsymbol{\Phi}^*\, dt\, \mathbf{n}\right\rangle = \langle \mathbf{n}, \mathbf{W}\mathbf{n}\rangle = 0\end{aligned}$$

Thus $\mathbf{u}''(t) = \mathbf{0}$ for all t in $[t_0,t_1]$.

(II) The system is completely controllable; hence by *5* there is a control $\mathbf{u}^{(1)}_{[t_0,t_1]}$ which transfers the state $\mathbf{n} \neq \mathbf{0}$ at t_0 to $\mathbf{0}$ at t_1. That is, the control $\mathbf{u}^{(1)}_{[t_0,t_1]}$ satisfies the condition (see *6.2.21*)

9 $$\mathbf{n} = -\int_{t_0}^{t_1} \boldsymbol{\Phi}(t_0,t)\mathbf{B}(t)\mathbf{u}^{(1)}(t)\, dt$$

Now, the contradiction is obtained by the following calculations:

$$\begin{aligned}0 &= \int_{t_0}^{t_1} \langle \mathbf{u}''(t), \mathbf{u}^{(1)}(t)\rangle\, dt = -\int_{t_0}^{t_1} \langle \mathbf{B}^*(t)\boldsymbol{\Phi}^*(t_0,t)\mathbf{n}, \mathbf{u}^{(1)}\rangle\, dt \\ &= -\int_{t_0}^{t_1} \langle \mathbf{n}, \boldsymbol{\Phi}(t_0,t)\mathbf{B}(t)\mathbf{u}^{(1)}(t)\rangle\, dt \\ &= -\left\langle \mathbf{n}, \int_{t_0}^{t_1} \boldsymbol{\Phi}(t_0,t)\mathbf{B}(t)\mathbf{u}^{(1)}(t)\, dt\right\rangle\end{aligned}$$

Hence, by *9*, $0 = \langle \mathbf{n}, \mathbf{n}\rangle = \|\mathbf{n}\|^2$. This is a contradiction, since in (I) we had $\mathbf{n} \neq \mathbf{0}$ by assumption.

REFERENCES AND SUGGESTED READING

1 Kalman, R. E.: On the General Theory of Control Systems, *Proc. First Intl. Cong. Automatic Cont., Moscow, 1960,* vol. 1, pp. 481–493, 1961, Butterworth & Co. (Publishers), Ltd., London.

2 Bertram, J. E., and P. E. Sarachik: On Optimal Computer Control, *Proc. First Intl. Cong. Automatic Cont., Moscow, 1960,* vol. 1, pp. 419–423, 1961, Butterworth & Co. (Publishers), Ltd., London.

3 Kalman, R. E., Y. C. Ho, and K. S. Narendra: Controllability of Linear Dynamical Systems, in "Contributions to Differential Equations," vol. 1, Interscience Publishers, Inc., New York, 1962.

4 Kalman, R. E.: Canonical Structure of Linear Dynamical Systems, *Proc. Natl. Acad. Sci. U.S.A.,* vol. 48, no. 4, pp. 596–600, 1962

Delta functions and distributions

A

1 *Introduction*

Dirac delta functions, or simply *delta functions,* denote singular "functions" having the form of impulses. Strictly speaking, they are not functions in the accepted mathematical sense, and they cannot be treated with complete rigor within the framework of classical analysis.

Distributions, on the other hand, are "generalized functions" in a sense which will be defined in Sec. *4*. Thus, distributions subsume both ordinary functions[1] and delta functions as special cases. The theory of distributions, which is due to L. Schwartz, provides a framework within which the concept of a delta function and operations on delta functions can be given a precise meaning. Thus, familiarity with the theory of distributions is indispensable for one who is not satisfied with the conventional formalistic way of manipulating delta functions and their derivatives.

Since we make considerable use of delta functions and their properties in the main body of this text, a summary of the principal definitions and main properties of delta functions is given in Sec. *2*.[2] Later sections constitute a self-contained and compact exposition of the theory of distributions in which the properties deduced in a purely formal way in Sec. *2* are established in a rigorous fashion.

2 *Delta functions*

Intuitively, a delta function is an idealization of a very narrow pulse or impulse occurring at, say, $t = 0$, with a finite total area which, for

[1] Not every ordinary function is a distribution. Specifically, as will be indicated in *A.6.1*, a distribution is essentially a derivative (of some finite order) of a continuous function. (See also Example *A.4.3*.)

[2] A detailed exposition of the properties of delta functions and a historical account of the development of the concept of a delta function and related notions can be found in Ref. *1*.

convenience, is normalized to 1. Thus, formally, $\delta(t) = 0$ for all $t \neq 0$, $\delta(0) = \infty$, and $\int_{-\infty}^{\infty} \delta(t)\, dt = 1$. Furthermore, if $\delta(t)$ is a narrow pulse of area 1, then $g(t)\delta(t)$,[1] where g is any function which is "well behaved" in the neighborhood of $t = 0$, will be a narrow pulse of area $g(0)$. Thus, intuitively, $\delta(t)$ should have the property expressed in a formal way by the relation

1
$$\int_{-\infty}^{\infty} \delta(t) g(t)\, dt = g(0)$$

This suggests that $\delta(t)$ be defined as a "limit" of an approximating sequence of functions $f(t,\lambda)$ such that, for any "well-behaved" g,

$$\lim_{\lambda \to 0} \int_{-\infty}^{\infty} f(t,\lambda) g(t)\, dt = g(0)$$

There are many approximating sequences which have this property (see *A.4.6* and Ref. *1*). A simple one is the sequence of pulses of width λ and height $1/\lambda$ centered on $t = 0$, in which case $f(t,\lambda)$ is expressed by

$$f(t,\lambda) = \frac{1}{\lambda}\left[1\left(t + \frac{\lambda}{2}\right) - 1\left(t - \frac{\lambda}{2}\right)\right]$$

Now if $\delta(t) = \lim_{\lambda \to 0} f(t,\lambda)$, then formally

2
$$\delta(t) = \lim_{\lambda \to 0} \frac{1}{\lambda}\left[1\left(t + \frac{\lambda}{2}\right) - 1\left(t - \frac{\lambda}{2}\right)\right] = \frac{d}{dt} 1(t)$$

To say that $\delta(t)$ is the derivative of a unit step function does not constitute a satisfactory definition of a delta function in the context of differential calculus, since $\frac{d}{dt} 1(t)$ has no existence in the conventional sense of the derivative. Nonetheless, if a relation such as *2* is interpreted in the sense of Definition *6* given below, then *2* offers a convenient point of departure if not a rigorous definition of $\delta(t)$.

3 *Note* When the derivative of a time function, say, v, is expressed in terms of delta functions and is interpreted in the sense of Definition *6*, then dv/dt or, in symbolic form, $p\, v$ is said to be the derivative of v in the *distribution sense.* (A rigorous definition of this term is given in *A.5.4.*)

With these remarks as a background, the definition of $\delta(t)$ may be worded as follows:

[1] In this section we are not using our notation for time functions (*1.3.3*) in a consistent manner, for reasons explained in *1.3.3*. Thus, $g(t)\delta(t)$ should be interpreted as the time function $g(\cdot)\delta(\cdot)$ rather than as the value of this time function at time t.

4 **Definition** The zero-order delta function, or simply delta function, $\delta(t)$, is the derivative of $1(t)$ in the distribution sense; i.e.,

$$\delta(t) = \frac{d}{dt} 1(t)$$

More generally, $\delta^{(n)}(t)$, the delta function of order n, is the $(n + 1)$st derivative of $1(t)$ in the distribution sense or, recursively, the first derivative of $\delta^{(n-1)}(t)$. $\triangleleft$

Thus

5 $$\delta^{(n)}(t) = \frac{d^{n+1}}{dt^{n+1}} 1(t) = \frac{d}{dt} \delta^{(n-1)}(t) \qquad n = 1, 2, \ldots$$

Since pointwise equality of functions is not applicable to delta functions, we must define what is meant by the equality of expressions involving delta functions. This is done in the

6 **Definition** Let $\Delta_1(t)$ and $\Delta_2(t)$ be two expressions involving delta functions and ordinary time functions. Then $\Delta_1(t)$ and $\Delta_2(t)$ are identical (or equal), written as $\Delta_1(t) \equiv \Delta_2(t)$ or, more simply, $\Delta_1(t) = \Delta_2(t)$, if and only if

7 $$\int_{-\infty}^{\infty} \Delta_1(t) g(t)\, dt = \int_{-\infty}^{\infty} \Delta_2(t) g(t)\, dt$$

for all time functions g for which the integrals in question exist. (Compare with *A.5.1*.) In this sense, the equality $\delta(t) = \frac{d}{dt} 1(t)$ has the meaning

$$\int_{-\infty}^{\infty} \delta(t) g(t)\, dt = \int_{-\infty}^{\infty} g(t) d1(t) = g(0)$$

which agrees with *1*. $\triangleleft$

By treating $\delta(t)$ and its derivatives as if they were ordinary time functions, the following basic properties of delta functions can readily be deduced from Definition *4*.

8 **Property**

$$\delta(t - t_0) = \frac{d}{dt} 1(t - t_0) \qquad \forall t_0$$

$\delta(t - t_0)$ is usually referred to as a delta function which *occurs* at $t = t_0$.

9 **Property**

$$\delta^{(n)}(-t) = (-1)^n \delta^{(n)}(t)$$

[*Hint:* Express $\delta(t)$ as a sum of an even function and an odd function and then use *5* and the fact that the derivative of an odd function is even and, conversely, the derivative of an even function is odd.]

10 **Property** The key property of delta functions is the so-called *sifting property* expressed by

11 $$\int_{-\infty}^{\infty} \delta^{(n)}(t-\xi)g(\xi)\,d\xi = g^{(n)}(t) \qquad \text{for all finite } t$$

where g is any function which is n-fold differentiable in the usual sense. If g is not such a function, but its nth derivative is defined in the distribution sense, then *11* should be interpreted as an identity in the sense of Definition *6*. ◁

Property *10* can readily be established by repeated integration by parts. For example, on replacing the infinite limits in *11* by finite limits $-a$, a [which does not change the value of the integral so long as $|t| < a$, since $\delta^{(n)}(t-\xi)$ vanishes for $\xi \neq t$], we have for $\delta(t)$

$$\int_{-a}^{a} \delta(t-\xi)f(\xi)\,d\xi = -f(\xi)1(t-\xi)\Big]_{-a}^{a} + \int_{-a}^{a} 1(t-\xi)\dot{f}(\xi)\,d\xi \qquad -a < t < a$$

$$= f(t)$$

and similarly for higher-order delta functions.

A special instance of *11* is the relation

$$\int_{-\infty}^{\infty} \delta^{(n)}(t-\xi)\delta^{m}(\xi)\,d\xi = \delta^{(m+n)}(t)$$

12 **Remark** In the main body of the text, we frequently use the symbol p to denote the operator which, acting on g, yields the derivative of g in the distribution sense. Thus on the basis of *11* we can write

13 $$p^n u = \int_{-\infty}^{\infty} \delta^{(n)}(t-\xi)u(\xi)\,d\xi$$

14 **Property** (see Exercise *A.5.19*)

15 $$f(t)\delta^{(n)}(t) = \sum_{0}^{n} (-1)^k \binom{n}{k} f^{(k)}(0)\delta^{(n-k)}(t)$$

where the equality should be understood in the sense of Definition *6*. To demonstrate this property, it is sufficient to multiply both sides of *15* by $g(t)$ and verify that *6* holds.

16 **Property** (See also *A.7.14*.) Let $r(t)$ be a function with simple zeros at $t_1, t_2, \ldots$. Then

17 $$\delta(r(t)) = \sum_i \frac{1}{|\dot{r}(t_i)|}\delta(t-t_i)$$

18 $$\delta^{(1)}(r(t)) = \sum_i \frac{1}{\dot{r}(t)|\dot{r}(t_i)|}\delta^{(1)}(t-t_i)$$

Hint: Write

19 $$1(r(t)) = \sum_i \varepsilon_i 1(t - t_i)$$

where $\varepsilon_i = 1$ if $\dot{r}(t_i) > 0$ and $\varepsilon_i = -1$ if $\dot{r}(t_i) < 0$. Then, by *4*,

$$\delta(r(t)) = \frac{d}{d(r(t))} 1(r(t))$$

$$= \frac{1}{\dot{r}(t)} \frac{d}{dt} 1(r(t))$$

and the rest follows from *19* and *18*.

A special instance of *16* is the simple relation

$$\delta(at) = \frac{1}{|a|} \delta(t) \qquad \forall a$$

Thus concludes our brief discussion of those properties of delta functions which are relevant to the material in the main body of the text.

3 *Testing functions*

A distribution is a generalization of a function.[1] Distributions are very useful in engineering because many operations which have no meaning when applied to certain functions are quite meaningful when applied to distributions. For example, within the framework of distributions, any function encountered in applications (steps, rectangular pulses, etc.) may be differentiated as many times as we wish; any convergent series of functions may be differentiated term by term and the sum of the derivatives is the derivative of the sum, etc. In other words, distribution theory provides a framework in which the sometimes illegitimate (in the usual sense) operations that engineers like to perform become legitimate and meaningful; furthermore, the theory provides a sure way to carry them out and to interpret them.

Since a distribution is a generalization of the concept of function, let us review what is meant by a function. With any *function* is associated a set A of elements called the *domain* of the function and another set B called the *range;* the function associates with each element of the domain A one and only one element of the range. Thus a function is defined by all the ordered pairs $(x,f(x))$, where $x \in A$ and $f(x)$ is the unique element

[1] The reader should be warned that distributions (in the sense used here) have nothing to do with probability distributions and distribution functions encountered in probability. Distributions are sometimes called generalized functions or symbolic functions. None of these terminologies is above criticism; so we have used Schwartz's terminology.

of B associated with x by the function f. $f(x)$ is called the value of f at x. For example, let the values of f be given by $f(x) = 1 + x + x^2$, where A is the set of all real numbers and so is B. This formula specifies a rule for computing $f(x)$ for each $x \in A$; in other words, it specifies all ordered pairs $(x,f(x))$ for $x \in A$.

There are other ways of defining functions. Consider, for example, a periodic function ψ of period 2π which can be expanded in Fourier series. In principle, at least, it is equivalent to knowing all the ordered pairs $(t,\psi(t))$ for $t \in [-\pi,\pi]$ or all of its Fourier coefficients $\ldots, c_{-1}, c_0, c_1, \ldots$; these are given by

1 $$c_k = \frac{1}{2\pi} \int_{-\pi}^{\pi} \psi(t) [\exp(-jkt)] \, dt \qquad k = \ldots, -1, 0, 1, \ldots$$

The point is that *1* sets up a one-one correspondence between the functions ψ and the sequences $\{\ldots, c_{-1}, c_0, c_1, \ldots\}$. We may interpret *1* as defining a functional[1] associated with ψ, which assigns to each function $\rho_k = \exp(-jkt)$ the number c_k. Observe also that this functional is linear. The function ψ is completely defined by the values taken by the functional (associated with ψ) at the functions ρ_k, $k = \ldots, -1, 0, 1, \ldots$. This leads to the point of view that ψ could just as well be defined by all the ordered pairs (c_k,ρ_k). The usefulness of this point of view is that even though with each periodic function ψ (which has a Fourier series) is associated a unique set of ordered pairs (c_k,ρ_k), there are sets of ordered pairs to which there do not correspond periodic function. If $c_k = 1$ for all k, one has the set of ordered pairs associated with $2\pi \sum_{-\infty}^{+\infty} \delta(t - 2n\pi)$, which is not a function.

It is by generalizing this approach to the definition of functions that L. Schwartz has constructed the theory of distributions. The first step will be to specify which functions will play the role of the exponentials $\exp(-jkt)$. These will be the so-called testing functions. We shall define these first before giving the formal definition of a distribution. We shall next define operations on distributions, and, finally, we shall give applications.

For our purposes it is sufficient to consider distributions in one variable. The extension to several variables does not involve any new ideas. On this topic the reader should consult Ref. *2*.

2 **Definition** A *testing function* is a real-valued function of the real variable which may be differentiated an arbitrary number of times and which is identical to zero outside a finite interval.

We shall denote testing functions by φ and the variable by t. The closure of the set of all points at which $\varphi \neq 0$ is called the *support of* φ;

[1] A functional is a function whose range is the set of all real (or complex) numbers.

or equivalently, the support of φ consists of (I) the set of all points at which $\varphi(t) \neq 0$ and (II) the limit points of that set. In other words, if φ is a testing function, $\varphi^{(n)}(t)$ exists for all t and all n, and φ is identical to zero outside its support.

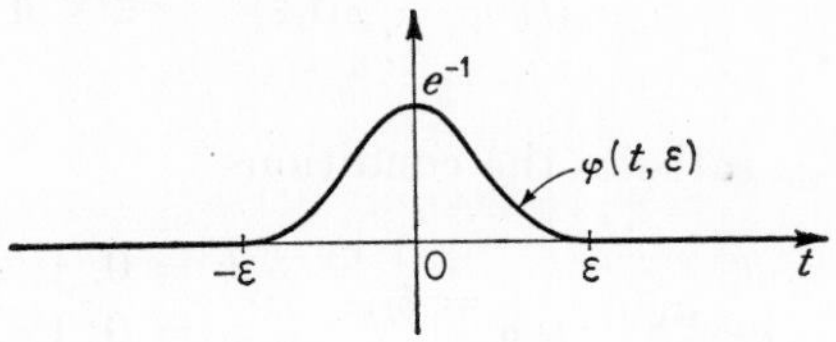

Fig. A.3.1 The testing function $\varphi(t,\varepsilon)$.

3 *Example* A well-known example of a testing function is illustrated in Fig. *A.3.1*. By definition

4
$$\varphi(t,\varepsilon) = \begin{cases} \exp\left(-\dfrac{\varepsilon^2}{\varepsilon^2 - t^2}\right) & |t| < \varepsilon \\ 0 & |t| \geq \varepsilon \end{cases}$$

The support of $\varphi(t,\varepsilon)$ is $[-\varepsilon,\varepsilon]$.

5 *Example* Given any continuous function, say, f, identically zero outside a finite interval and any testing function φ, the function ψ defined by

6
$$\psi(t) = \int_{-\infty}^{+\infty} f(\tau)\varphi(t-\tau)\,d\tau \qquad -\infty \leq t \leq \infty$$

is a testing function. The conditions on f imply that *6* is always the integral of a continuous function which differs from zero only on a finite interval; therefore, it is well defined for each t. Since φ can be differentiated arbitrarily often, it is easy to see that ψ has the same property. Finally, since both f and φ are zero outside some finite interval, so is ψ. Hence ψ is a testing function.

7 *Example* If f is any function that can be differentiated arbitrarily often (for example, a polynomial in t) and if φ is a testing function, then so is $f\varphi$.

8 *Example* The testing function $\rho(t,\varepsilon)$, shown in Fig. *A.3.2*, is defined by

9
$$\rho(t,\varepsilon) = k \int_{-1}^{+1} \varphi(t-\tau,\varepsilon)\,d\tau \qquad \varepsilon < 1$$

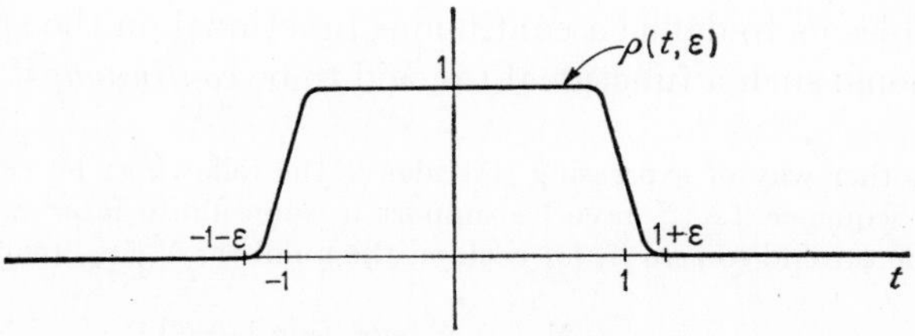

Fig. A.3.2 The testing function $\rho(t,\varepsilon)$.

where the constant k is so selected that $\rho(0,\varepsilon) = 1$. Note that $\rho(t,\varepsilon) = 1$ for all $t \in [-1 + \varepsilon, 1 - \varepsilon]$.

10 *Example*

11
$$\varphi_n(t) = \frac{t^n}{n!}\rho(t,\varepsilon) \qquad \varepsilon < 1$$

Observe that φ_n satisfies the conditions

12
$$\left.\frac{d^k}{dt^k}\varphi_n(t)\right|_{t=0} = \delta_{kn} \qquad \begin{array}{l} k = 0, 1, 2, \ldots \\ n = 0, 1, 2, \ldots \end{array}$$

where δ_{kn} is the Kronecker symbol. Furthermore,

13
$$\varphi_n(t) = \frac{t^n}{n!} \qquad \text{for } -1 + \varepsilon \leq t \leq 1 - \varepsilon$$

4 *Definition of distributions*

Let $\mathfrak{D}$ be the set of all testing functions. $\mathfrak{D}$ is a linear vector space because whenever $\varphi_1 \in \mathfrak{D}$ and $\varphi_2 \in \mathfrak{D}$, then $\varphi_1 + \varphi_2 \in \mathfrak{D}$ and $a\varphi_1 \in \mathfrak{D}$ for any number a (see *C.2.1*).

In a very rough way and following the analogy with the definition of the periodic function by its Fourier coefficients, a distribution will be defined as an object specified by all the values taken by a linear functional at all the testing functions $\varphi \in \mathfrak{D}$.

As a first step toward a more rigorous definition, let us define the notion of convergence in the space of testing function $\mathfrak{D}$. We say that a sequence of testing functions $\{\varphi_n\}_1^\infty$ converges to zero if (I) all φ_n's are identically zero outside some fixed interval independent of n and (II) each φ_n, as well as all its derivatives, tends uniformly to zero. Observe that the convergence to zero is required for derivatives of all orders and that the uniformity (in t) of the convergence is required only separately for each order.[1]

The reason for defining the convergence of testing functions is that it enables us to define a continuous functional on the space $\mathfrak{D}$ of testing functions: such a functional f is said to be *continuous* if the convergence

[1] Another way of expressing this idea is the following: let each testing function of the sequence $\{\varphi_j\}_0^\infty$ have its support in some finite interval K. We shall say that the φ_j tend to zero if, for each m, the numbers $N_m(\varphi_j)$ tend to zero as $j \to \infty$, where

$$N_m(\varphi) \triangleq \sup_{k \leq m} [\sup_{t \in K} |\varphi^{(k)}(t)|]$$

of any sequence of testing functions φ_n to φ implies the convergence of the numbers $f(\varphi_n) \to f(\varphi)$, where $f(\varphi_n)$ is the value taken by the functional f at φ_n.

Let $\mathfrak{D}_K$ be the subspace of $\mathfrak{D}$ containing all testing functions whose support is contained in the closed and bounded interval K.

1 **Definition** A *distribution* is a linear functional defined on the space $\mathfrak{D}$ of testing functions and such that, for all closed and bounded intervals K, the restriction of the functional to $\mathfrak{D}_K$ is continuous. We shall denote distributions by $T, F, S, \ldots$. Let us denote by $\langle T,\varphi\rangle$ the number which is the value that the distribution T takes at φ. Thus T is a linear mapping of $\mathfrak{D}$ into the set of all real (or complex) numbers. Linearity implies that

2 $$\begin{cases} \langle T, \varphi_1 + \varphi_2\rangle = \langle T,\varphi_1\rangle + \langle T,\varphi_2\rangle & \forall \varphi_1,\varphi_2 \in \mathfrak{D} \\ \langle T,a\varphi_1\rangle = a\langle T,\varphi_1\rangle & \forall \text{ numbers } a \end{cases}$$

The continuity of T and the restriction of the testing functions to $\mathfrak{D}_K$ implies that if the $\{\varphi_n\}_1^\infty$ have their supports in a fixed closed and bounded interval K and if the φ_j's as well as all their derivatives converge uniformly to zero, then the numbers $\langle T,\varphi_n\rangle \to 0$. We shall not pursue the requirements of continuity further.

3 *Example* Any real-valued function f integrable (in the Lebesgue sense) over any finite interval can be identified with a distribution; indeed, from the definition of the testing functions, the integral

$$\int_{-\infty}^{+\infty} f(t)\varphi(t)\,dt$$

is a continuous linear functional on the space $\mathfrak{D}$. Thus with any such function f we can associate a distribution F such that

$$\langle F,\varphi\rangle = \int_{-\infty}^{+\infty} f(t)\varphi(t)\,dt \qquad \forall \varphi \in \mathfrak{D}$$

4 *Example* Distributions include more general objects than functions. For example, the relations

5 $$\langle T,\varphi\rangle = \varphi(0) \qquad \forall \varphi \in \mathfrak{D}$$

define the distribution δ of Dirac (the unit impulse of electrical engineers) by its sifting property over the space of testing functions. The relations

$$\langle S,\varphi\rangle = \varphi''(0) \qquad \forall \varphi \in \mathfrak{D}$$

define a linear functional on $\mathfrak{D}$; hence, it defines a distribution S which we shall later identify with δ'', the second derivative of the distribution δ.

We shall see later that the class of distributions includes all the functions which are integrable over every finite interval as well as all their derivatives (to be taken in the distribution sense when they do not exist in the sense of the calculus).

6 *Comment* It is very important to appreciate the difference between a function of the real variable t and a distribution. Whereas a function f associates with every real number t one and only one value $f(t)$, it is usually not possible to associate a "value" to a distribution for each t. The following is an example where it is possible. Let T be a distribution such that $\langle T,\varphi\rangle = 0$ for all those φ which are zero outside $[-1,1]$. Then it is natural to say that $T = 0$ on $(-1,1)$. Similarly, the distribution R such that $\langle R,\varphi\rangle = 0$ for all φ's is the zero distribution.

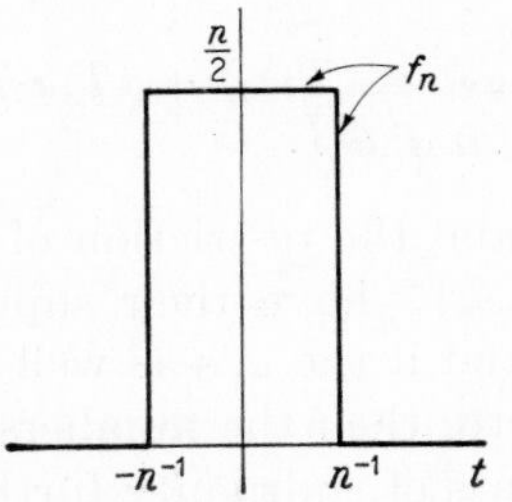

Fig. A.4.1 Example of a function that tends to δ and for which $\lim_{n\to\infty} f_n(0) = \infty$.

Consider the distribution δ. It is defined by its sifting property *5*. Now, many sequences of functions have this property; for example, consider the functions illustrated by Figs. *A.4.1* to *A.4.3* and defined by

$$f_n(t) = \begin{cases} \dfrac{n}{2} & |t| < n^{-1} \\ 0 & \text{elsewhere} \end{cases}$$

$$g_n(t) = \begin{cases} 2n^2 t & 0 \le t < \dfrac{1}{2n} \\ 2n^2(n^{-1} - t) & \dfrac{1}{2n} < t \le \dfrac{1}{n} \\ 0 & t > \dfrac{1}{n} \\ g_n(t) = g_n(-t) & \forall t \end{cases}$$

$$h_n(t) = \begin{cases} -\dfrac{n}{10} & |t| < \dfrac{1}{n} \\ \dfrac{3n}{5} & \dfrac{1}{n} < |t| < \dfrac{2}{n} \\ 0 & \text{elsewhere} \end{cases}$$

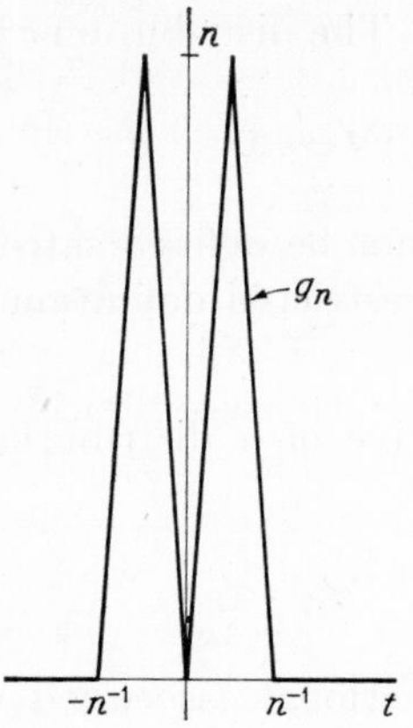

Fig. A.4.2 Example of a function that tends to δ and for which $\lim_{n\to\infty} g_n(0) = 0$.

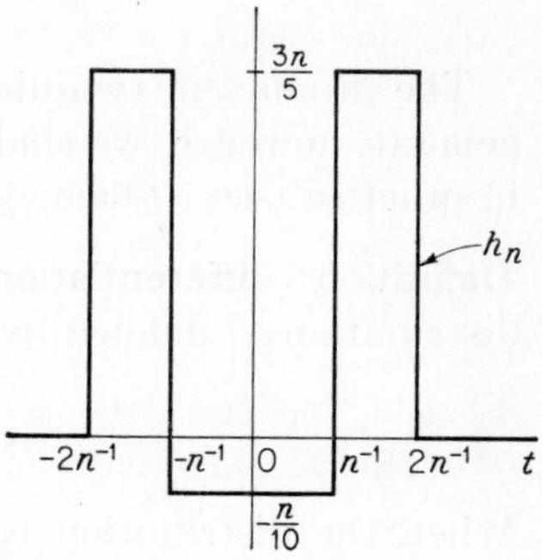

Fig. A.4.3 Example of a function that tends to δ and for which $\lim_{n\to\infty} h_n(0) = -\infty$

These three sequences of functions have the property that

$$\lim_{n\to\infty} \langle f_n,\varphi\rangle = \lim_{n\to\infty} \int_{-\infty}^{+\infty} f_n(t)\varphi(t)\,dt = \varphi(0) \qquad \forall \varphi \in \mathfrak{D}$$

$$\lim_{n\to\infty} f_n(t) = 0 \qquad \forall t \neq 0$$

and similar relations for g_n and h_n. Thus in the limit, these sequences behave like δ. It is of interest to note that for $t = 0$,

$$\lim f_n(0) = \infty \qquad \lim g_n(0) = 0 \qquad \lim h_n(0) = -\infty$$

These facts emphasize the point that although it is meaningful to state that the distribution δ is zero in any closed interval excluding the origin, it is impossible to assign a "value" to δ at $t = 0$.

5 *Operations on distributions*

Let S, T denote distributions: they are linear continuous functionals over $\mathfrak{D}$ and they are defined by all the numbers $\langle S,\varphi\rangle$, $\langle T,\varphi\rangle$ for all $\varphi \in \mathfrak{D}$.

1 **Definition: equality** Two distributions S, T are equal if

$$\langle T,\varphi\rangle = \langle S,\varphi\rangle \qquad \forall \varphi \in \mathfrak{D}$$

2 **Definition: addition** The distribution $S + T$ is that linear functional which with each $\varphi \in \mathfrak{D}$ associates the number

$$\langle S + T, \varphi\rangle \triangleq \langle S,\varphi\rangle + \langle T,\varphi\rangle$$

3 **Definition: multiplication by a scalar c** The distribution cT is defined by

$$\langle cT,\varphi\rangle \triangleq c\langle T,\varphi\rangle \qquad \forall \varphi \in \mathfrak{D}$$

The product of two distributions cannot be defined satisfactorily in general; however, we shall give later a restricted definition of interest in practice (see *10* below).

4 **Definition: differentiation** The derivative of a distribution S is the distribution S' defined by

$$\langle S',\varphi\rangle \triangleq -\langle S,\varphi'\rangle \qquad \forall \varphi \in \mathfrak{D}$$

When the distribution is the linear functional associated with a differentiable function $s(t)$, *4* is simply the rule of integration by parts,

$$\int_{-\infty}^{+\infty} s'(t)\varphi(t)\,dt = s(t)\varphi(t)\Big|_{-\infty}^{+\infty} - \int_{-\infty}^{+\infty} s(t)\varphi'(t)\,dt$$

where the integrated term is identically zero in view of the properties of the testing functions.

For derivatives of higher order we have

5
$$\langle S^{(k)},\varphi\rangle = (-1)^k\langle S,\varphi^{(k)}\rangle \qquad \forall \varphi \in \mathfrak{D}$$

Note that if $\varphi \in \mathfrak{D}$, then for any positive integer k, $\varphi^{(k)} \in \mathfrak{D}$; hence *4* and *5* have the very useful and important consequence:

6 **Theorem** Any distribution T may be differentiated as many times as we wish; that is, the derivative of any distribution always exists (in the distribution sense) and is a distribution.

7 *Example* Associated with the unit step $1(t)$ is the distribution T defined by

$$\langle T,\varphi\rangle = \int_0^\infty 1(t)\varphi(t)\,dt = \int_0^\infty \varphi(t)\,dt$$

Although $\frac{d}{dt}1(t)$ does not exist at $t = 0$ in the calculus sense, we may define T' by *4*:

$$\langle T',\varphi\rangle = -\int_0^\infty \varphi'(t)\,dt = -\varphi(t)\Big|_0^\infty = \varphi(0)$$

Therefore

8
$$\left[\frac{d}{dt}1(t)\right] = \delta(t)$$

That is, the derivative of $1(t)$ *in the distribution sense* is the Dirac delta function (see *A.4.5*).

The product of two distributions cannot be defined satisfactorily in general. Some restrictions are required; to present them we give the following

9 **Definition** An (ordinary) function f is said to *belong to* C^m if $f, f', \ldots, f^{(m)}$ are continuous functions of t. (*Note:* $f', \ldots, f^{(m)}$ are the first m derivatives of f in the calculus sense.)

10 **Definition** A *distribution* is said to be of *order* m if m is the least integer for which it is the $(m + 1)$st derivative (in the distribution sense) of a function integrable over any finite interval.

11 *Example* $\delta(t)$ is the derivative (in the distribution sense) of $1(t)$, and hence it is of order 0. $\delta'(t)$ is $\left[\dfrac{d^2}{dt^2}1(t)\right]$; hence it is of order 1.

In some cases, distributions of finite order have an interesting integral representation. First a definition: a distribution T is said to be of *finite support* and its support is said to be in $(-a,a)$ if the interval $(-a,a)$ is such that, for all testing functions φ whose support is outside $(-a,a)$, $\langle T,\varphi\rangle = 0$. The representation theorem is as follows (Ref. 5, vol. 2, p. 31): Let T be of finite support and let its support be in $(-a,a)$. Let T be of finite order m. Then $\langle T,\varphi\rangle$ is given in terms of the Stieltjes integral

$$\langle T,\varphi\rangle = \int_{-a}^{+a} \varphi^{(m)}(x)\, d\mu(x) \qquad \forall \varphi \in \mathfrak{D}$$

where μ is a function of bounded variation.

12 **Definition: product of a distribution by a function** If T is a distribution of order $\leq m$ and if $f \in C^m$, then the product of T by f is the distribution defined by

13 $$\langle fT,\varphi\rangle = \langle T,f\varphi\rangle \qquad \forall \varphi \in \mathfrak{D}$$

Since T is of order $\leq m$, no trouble will arise from the fact that the functional has to be evaluated at $f\varphi$ rather than φ even though $f\varphi$ is not a testing function. The reason is that T is of order $\leq m$ and $f\varphi \in C^m$.

14 *Example* Let T be the distribution δ (of order 0); hence, in order for the product fT to be meaningful, f need only be continuous:[1]

$$\langle f\delta,\varphi\rangle \triangleq \langle \delta,f\varphi\rangle = f(0)\varphi(0)$$

Hence, if f is continuous at 0, we have the distribution equality: $f\delta = f(0)\delta$.

[1] Compare this result with the usual definition of δ in physics texts: δ is a "function" such that $\delta(t) = 0$ for all $t \neq 0$ and $\int_{-\infty}^{+\infty} \delta(t)\psi(t)\, dt = \psi(0)$ for all functions ψ continuous at 0.

15 *Exercise* Show that $t\delta(t)$ is the zero distribution.

16 *Example* Let T be δ' (of order 1); hence, f must have a continuous first derivative. The product of δ' and f is defined by

$$\langle f\delta',\varphi\rangle \triangleq \langle \delta', f\varphi\rangle$$

and by the definition of the derivative (*4*)

17 $$\langle \delta', f\varphi\rangle = -\left\langle \delta, \frac{d}{dt}(f\varphi)\right\rangle = -f'(0)\varphi(0) - f(0)\varphi'(0)$$

where the last equality follows from the definition of the distribution δ. Referring to the definition of the product of a distribution by a scalar and to the definition of δ and δ', we recognize that the last right-hand side can be written as $-f'(0)\langle\delta,\varphi\rangle + f(0)\langle\delta',\varphi\rangle$. Hence if $f \in C^1$,

18 $$f(t)\delta'(t) = -f'(0)\delta(t) + f(0)\delta'(t)$$

which is an equality between distributions (to be interpreted by *1*).

19 *Exercise* Show that if $f \in C^{n+1}$ in some neighborhood of zero,

$$f(t)\delta^n(t) = \sum_{k=0}^{n} (-1)^k \binom{n}{k} f^{(k)}(0)\delta^{n-k}(t)$$

and that the nth derivative of $f\delta$ is $f(0)\delta^{(n)}$.

20 *Exercise* Let $f \in C^n$ over $(-\infty,\infty)$. Let $g(t) = f(t)1(t)$. Show that, in the sense of distributions,

$$g^{(1)}(t) = f^{(1)}(t)1(t) + f(0)\delta(t)$$
$$g^{(2)}(t) = f^{(2)}(t)1(t) + f'(0)\delta(t) + f(0)\delta'(t)$$
$$\vdots$$
$$g^{(k)}(t) = f^{(k)}(t)1(t) + \sum_{i=1}^{k} f^{(k-i)}(0)\delta^{(i-1)}(t) \qquad k \le n$$

6 *Further properties*

We state here without proof some properties of distributions which illustrate their nature and their convenience in applications.

1 **Theorem** Over any finite interval, a distribution T is the derivative of some finite order of some continuous function.[1] This property does

[1] L. Schwartz, "Théorie des distributions," vol. 1, p. 82, Hermann & Cie., Paris, 1957.

not extend to infinite intervals. Consider, for example,

$$\langle T,\varphi\rangle = \sum_{k=1}^{\infty} \varphi^{(k)}(k)$$

The notion of convergence of distributions is defined as follows:[1]

2 **Definition** The sequence of distributions $\{T_n\}_1^\infty$ is said to converge to the linear functional T if

$$\lim_{n\to\infty} \langle T_n,\varphi\rangle = \langle T,\varphi\rangle \qquad \forall \varphi \in \mathfrak{D}$$

It can be shown that the functional T is a distribution; this fact is not obvious because, in general, a limit of a sequence of continuous functionals is not a continuous functional.

3 **Theorem** Every distribution is the limit, in the sense of distributions, of a sequence of infinitely differentiable functions.

For example, $\delta(t) = \lim_{\sigma\to 0} (1/\sqrt{2\pi}\,\sigma) \exp(-t^2/2\sigma^2)$.

4 **Theorem** If $T_n \to T$, $R_n \to R$ (in the sense of distributions), and the numbers $a_n \to a$, then

$$T'_n \to T' \qquad R_n + T_n \to R + T \qquad a_n T_n \to aT$$

This implies, in particular, that every series of functions may be differentiated term by term any number of times; however, the sum must then be interpreted in the sense of distributions. For example, any Fourier series, such as $\sum_{-\infty}^{+\infty} c_n e^{jnt}$, where the c_n's behave for n large like a fixed finite power of n, converges in the sense of distributions because it is the finite-order derivative of a Fourier series that converges in the usual sense.

7 *Applications*

1 **Problem: equating distributions** Determine the constants α, β, γ, η such that

2 $$\alpha\delta(t) + \beta\delta'(t) + \gamma\delta(t-2) + \eta\delta''(t) = 3\delta(t) + 4\delta'(t)$$

Solution This expression is an equality of distributions. It does not mean that for each t the left-hand side takes on the same value as the

[1] *Ibid.*, chap. 3. sec 3.

right-hand side, because distributions are not functions of t. This equality must be interpreted by *A.5.1*. In other words, *2* means that

3 $$\langle \alpha\delta(t),\varphi\rangle + \langle \beta\delta'(t),\varphi\rangle + \langle \gamma\delta(t-2),\varphi\rangle + \langle \eta\delta''(t),\varphi\rangle = \langle 3\delta(t),\varphi\rangle + \langle 4\delta'(t),\varphi\rangle$$

which is an equality between numbers and which must hold for all $\varphi \in \mathfrak{D}$. Replace $\varphi(t)$ in *3* by $\varphi_0(t)$ defined in *A.3.11*. Then in view of *A.4.5*, *A.5.3*, *A.5.4*, and *A.3.10*, we obtain successively

$$\begin{aligned}\langle \alpha\delta(t),\varphi_0\rangle &+ \langle \beta\delta'(t),\varphi_0\rangle + \langle \gamma\delta(t-2),\varphi_0\rangle + \langle \eta\delta''(t),\varphi_0\rangle \\ &= \alpha\langle \delta(t),\varphi_0\rangle + \beta\langle \delta'(t),\varphi_0\rangle + \gamma\langle \delta(t-2),\varphi_0\rangle + \eta\langle \delta''(t),\varphi_0\rangle \\ &= \alpha\varphi_0(0) + \beta(-\varphi_0'(0)) + \gamma\varphi_0(2) + \eta\varphi_0''(0) \\ &= \alpha\end{aligned}$$

Similarly, the right-hand side of *3* with φ replaced by φ_0 is equal to 3. Thus $\alpha = 3$. Replacing $\varphi(t)$ in *3* by $\varphi_1(t)$ defined in *A.3.11* gives $\beta = 4$. Replacing $\varphi(t)$ by $\varphi_0(t-2)$ leads to $\gamma = 0$, and replacing $\varphi(t)$ by $\varphi_2(t)$ leads to $\eta = 0$. Thus we have

$$3\delta(t) + 4\delta'(t) = 3\delta(t) + 4\delta'(t)$$

which is obviously an equality between distributions according to *A.5.1*. Thus we have the

4 **Assertion** Two linear combinations of $\delta, \delta', \ldots, \delta^{(k)}$ with *constant* coefficients are equal if and only if the coefficients of derivatives of the same order are equal.

5 *Caveat* The reader should notice the importance of the assumption that α, β, γ are constants. Indeed, *A.5.18* implies that

$$(1 + \sin t)\delta'(t) \neq \delta'(t)$$

because, in fact,

$$(1 + \sin t)\delta'(t) = \delta'(t) - \delta(t)$$

6 **Problem Differentiating a discontinuous function** Find the first and second derivatives of the function f, illustrated by Fig. *A.7.1* and defined by

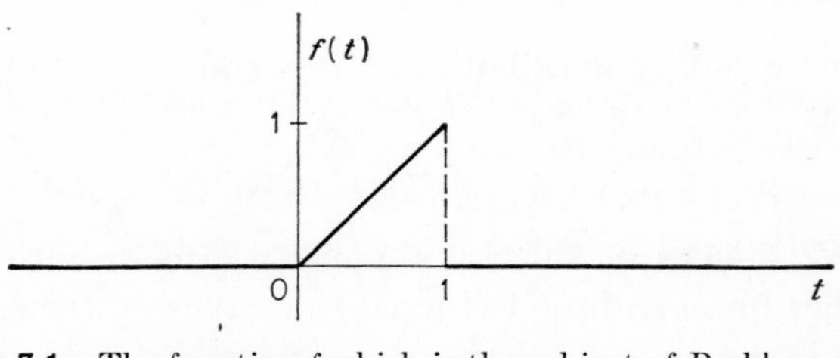

Fig. A.7.1 The function f which is the subject of Problem *A.7.6*.

7 $$f(t) = t1(t) - (t-1)1(t-1) - 1(t-1)$$

Solution f is obviously not differentiable at $t = 0$ and at $t = 1$. Consider f as a distribution; then its derivative, in the distribution sense, is obtained by differentiating term by term; thus

$$f' = t\delta(t) + 1(t) - (t-1)\delta(t-1) - 1(t-1) - \delta(t-1)$$

which, by *A.5.15*, reduces to

8 $$\begin{aligned} f' &= 1(t) - 1(t-1) - \delta(t-1) \\ f'' &= \delta(t) - \delta(t-1) - \delta'(t-1) \end{aligned}$$

Let us verify that *8* actually is the derivative of f. For all $\varphi \in \mathfrak{D}$, we have

$$\begin{aligned} \langle f',\varphi\rangle &= -\langle f,\varphi'\rangle && \text{by } A.5.4 \\ &= \int_{-\infty}^{+\infty} f(t)\varphi'(t)\,dt && \text{because } f \text{ is an integrable function } A.4.3 \\ &= -\int_0^1 t\varphi'(t)\,dt && \text{by } 7 \\ &= \int_0^1 \varphi(t)\,dt - \varphi(1) && \text{by integration by parts} \\ &= \langle (1(t) - 1(t-1) - \delta(t-1)), \varphi(t)\rangle \end{aligned}$$

Since this equality holds for all $\varphi \in \mathfrak{D}$, *8* is a valid equality between distributions (*A.5.1*).

9 **Problem Determining the impulse response of a time-invariant differential system** Consider the differential system defined by

10 $$\dot{y} + y = \ddot{u} + \dot{u} + u$$

By *4.5.50*, its impulse response is the solution of the differential equation such that $y(0-) = u(0-) = \dot{u}(0-) = 0$ and $u = \delta(t)$.
Solution $\delta(t) = 0$ for all $t \neq 0$ in the sense that $\langle\delta(t),\varphi\rangle = 0$ for any testing function φ whose support does not include 0. Hence for $t \neq 0$, $\dot{y} + y = 0$. That is, y satisfies the homogeneous equation $\dot{y} + y = 0$; therefore

$$\begin{aligned} y(t) &= y(0+)e^{-t} && \forall t > 0 \\ y(t) &= 0 && \forall t < 0 \end{aligned}$$

since $y(0-) = 0$.

The problem, then, is to evaluate $y(0+)$ and determine the behavior (in the distribution sense) of y at 0.

In view of *4*, since the right-hand side of *10* is $\ddot{\delta} + \dot{\delta} + \delta$, y must include both δ and $\dot{\delta}$. By *4*, it does not include any higher derivative of δ. Hence, put

$$y = \alpha\delta'(t) + \beta\delta(t) + \gamma 1(t)e^{-t} \qquad \forall t$$

where α, β, γ are unknown *constants*. Taking derivatives in the distribution sense, we have (using *A.5.10*),

$$y + \dot{y} = \alpha\delta'' + (\beta + \alpha)\delta'(t) + \beta\delta(t) + \gamma e^{-t}\Big|_{t=0}\delta(t) + \gamma 1(t)(e^{-t} - e^{-t})$$
$$= \delta'' + \delta' + \delta$$

Noting that the coefficients of the δ, δ', δ'' are constants, we invoke *4* and get

$$\alpha = 1 \qquad \beta + \alpha = 1 \qquad \beta + \gamma = 1$$

that is, $$y(t) = \delta'(t) + 1(t)e^{-t} \qquad \forall t$$

11 **Problem Determining the impulse response of a time-varying differential system** Consider the time-varying differential system defined by

12 $$(1 + e^{-t})\dot{y} + \cos ty = 2\dot{u} + u$$

By *4.5.58*, its impulse response is the solution of *12* such that

$$y(0-) = u(0-) = 0 \qquad u = \delta(t)$$

Solution Let $\psi(t)$ be the solution of the homogeneous equation such that $\psi(0) = 1$. Since the right-hand side of *12* has only δ and δ', let us try

$$y = \alpha\delta(t) + \gamma 1(t)\psi(t)$$

where α and γ are unknown constants. By direct substitution we have

$$\alpha(1 + e^{-t})\dot{\delta}(t) + [\gamma(1 + e^{-t}) + \alpha\cos t]\delta(t)$$
$$+ \gamma 1(t)[(1 + e^{-t})\dot{\psi} + \cos t\psi] = 2\dot{\delta} + \delta$$

The last brackets are identical to zero from the definition of ψ. Using *A.5.10* and *A.5.13*, we have

$$2\alpha\dot{\delta}(t) + (2\gamma + 2\alpha)\delta(t) = 2\dot{\delta} + \delta$$

Hence, since α, γ are constants, by *4* we get

$$\alpha = 1 \qquad \gamma = -\tfrac{1}{2} \qquad \text{and} \qquad y(t) = \delta(t) - \tfrac{1}{2}1(t)\psi(t)$$

13 *Comment* Consider the system described by $L(p,t)y = M(p,t)u$, where L and M are differential operators of order n and m, respectively. Then, it follows immediately from the method of solution of Problem *11* that $n < m$ implies that the impulse response will contain derivatives of δ; in other words, for $n < m$, the system is improper (see *3.6.27*).

14 **Problem** Let $g(t)$ be a real-valued function of t having a continuous derivative for all t. Let $g(t) \neq 0$ for all $t \neq t_0$ and $g(t_0) = 0$ with $g'(t_0) \neq 0$. Find a convenient expression for $\delta[g(t)]$.

Solution Let us give an interpretation to the distribution $\delta[g(t)]$ by considering the integral

$$\int_{-\infty}^{+\infty} \delta[g(t)]\varphi(t)\,dt \triangleq \langle \delta[g(t)],\varphi(t)\rangle$$

From the properties of the distribution δ and of g, the integral depends only on the behavior of φ in an arbitrarily small neighborhood of t_0. Pick $\varepsilon > 0$ small enough that g' does not change sign in the interval $[t_0 - \varepsilon, t_0 + \varepsilon]$. Hence g defines a one-one mapping of $[t_0 - \varepsilon, t_0 + \varepsilon]$ onto $[\eta_1,\eta_2]$, where $\eta_1 = g(t_0 - \varepsilon)$, $\eta_2 = g(t_0 + \varepsilon)$. Let $u = g^{-1}$ be the inverse mapping, that is, u maps $[\eta_1,\eta_2]$ onto $[t_0 - \varepsilon, t_0 + \varepsilon]$ and

$$u[g(t)] = t \qquad \forall\, t \in [t_0 - \varepsilon, t_0 + \varepsilon]$$

and

$$u(0) = t_0$$

For convenience set $y = g(t)$. We obtain successively

$$\begin{aligned}\langle \delta(g(t)),\varphi(t)\rangle &= \int_{t_0-\epsilon}^{t_0+\epsilon} \delta(g(t))\varphi(t)\,dt \\ &= \int_{\eta_1}^{\eta_2} \delta(y)\varphi(u(y))u'(y)\,dy\end{aligned}$$

Note that $\varphi(u(y))u'(y)$ is a continuous function of y at $y = 0$ because the continuity of g' implies that of u' by the implicit-function theorem. If $g' > 0$ in $[t_0 - \varepsilon, t_0 + \varepsilon]$, then $\eta_2 > \eta_1$ and

$$\langle \delta(g(t)),\varphi(t)\rangle = \varphi(u(0))u'(0) = \frac{\varphi(t_0)}{g'(t_0)}$$

If $g' < 0$ in $[t_0 - \varepsilon, t_0 + \varepsilon]$, then $\eta_2 < \eta_1$ and

$$\langle \delta(g(t)),\varphi(t)\rangle = -\varphi(u(0))u'(0) = \frac{-\varphi(t_0)}{g'(t_0)}$$

Hence, in both cases,

$$\langle \delta(g(t)),\varphi(t)\rangle = \frac{\varphi(t_0)}{|g'(t_0)|}$$

or, equivalently,

$$\delta(g(t)) = \frac{\delta(t - t_0)}{|g'(t_0)|}$$

REFERENCES AND SUGGESTED READING

1 Van der Pol, B., and H. Bremmer: "Operational Calculus," Cambridge University Press, New York, 1955.

2 Schwartz, L.: "Théorie des distributions," vols. 1 and 2, Hermann & Cie., Paris, 1951, 1957.
3 Schwartz, L.: "Méthodes mathématiques pour les sciences physiques," Hermann & Cie., Paris, 1961.
4 Beckenbach, E. F. (ed.): "Modern Mathematics for the Engineer," Second Series, chap. 1, From Delta Functions to Distributions, by A. Erdelyi, McGraw-Hill Book Company, Inc., New York, 1961.
5 Gelfand, I. M., and G. E. Schilow: "Verallgemeinerte Funktionen und das Rechnen mit Ihnen," vols. 1 and 2, Deutscher Verlag der Wissenschaften, Berlin, 1960, 1962.

Laplace transformation and z transformation

B

1 *Introduction*

This appendix starts with a brief exposition of the Laplace transformation and is concerned primarily with those aspects of this vast subject which are relevant to the material in the main body of the text. Since there are many readily available books on the Laplace transformation, ranging all the way from exhaustive and rigorous treatments to cookbook-type presentations, we shall merely state the principal definitions and some of the main results and add, when necessary, a few clarifying comments. For proofs the reader is referred to the texts listed at the end of this appendix. The last section gives the definition and the main properties of the z transformation.

2 *Basic concepts and definitions of the Laplace transformation*

1 **Remark** In the following discussion, s stands for a complex variable ranging over the complex s plane. The real and imaginary parts of s are denoted by $\text{Re } s \triangleq \sigma$ and $\text{Im } s \triangleq \omega$, respectively. A time function is denoted by $f(t)$, or f for short, and its Laplace transform is written as $F(s)$ or $\mathcal{L}\{f(t)\}$. Note that we do not adhere to the convention *1.3.3* for reasons explained in *1.3.3*. Integrals are understood in the Lebesgue sense unless otherwise indicated.

Stated informally, the basic idea behind the Laplace transformation is that of resolution of a time function $f(t)$ into a continuum of "elementary" time functions $\{e^{st}\}$, where s is a complex variable taking values on a line parallel to the axis of imaginaries in the s plane. Thus, informally, the Laplace transform of $f(t)$ is a function $F(s)$ such that $F(s)\,ds$ represents the content in $f(t)$ of elementary time functions $e^{\lambda t}$ whose λ lies in the interval $(s, s + ds)$.

This idea underlies the definitions of the unilateral (one-sided) and the bilateral (two-sided) Laplace transforms given below.

2 **Definition** The *unilateral Laplace transform* of a time function $f(t)$ defined on the interval $[0, \infty)$ is denoted by $F(s)$ or $\mathfrak{L}\{f(t)\}$ and is defined by the integral

3
$$F(s) = \int_0^\infty f(t)e^{-st}\,dt$$

for all values of s for which *3* exists (converges).

A basic result concerning the existence of $F(s)$ is contained in the following

4 **Theorem** If $F(s)$ exists for some s, say, $s_0 \triangleq \sigma_0 + j\omega_0$, then it exists for all s such that $\text{Re } s > \text{Re } s_0$. Furthermore, $F(s)$ is analytic in the domain defined by $\text{Re } s > \text{Re } s_0$. (See Ref. *1*, vol. 1, page 35 *et seq.*)

5 *Comment* The theorem makes no assertion concerning the convergence of *3* for s such that $\text{Re } s = \text{Re } s_0$. The reason for it is that, in general, *3* may converge for some points on the vertical line passing through the point s_0 and may diverge for other points on this line.

The greatest lower bound on $\text{Re } s_0$ for which *3* converges is denoted by α and is called the *abscissa of convergence* for f. More compactly, we have the

6 **Definition** Abscissa of convergence for $f \triangleq \alpha \triangleq$ infimum of σ over all s for which *3* converges. The domain defined by $\text{Re } s > \alpha$ constitutes the *domain of existence* (or *convergence*) of $F(s)$. The infimum of σ over all s for which *3* converges *absolutely* [i.e., with the integrand taken as $|f(t)e^{-st}|$] is the *abscissa of absolute convergence* for f and is denoted by α_a.

7 *Example* The abscissa of convergence for the exponential function e^{at}, where a is a real constant, is a. The abscissa of convergence for e^{-t^2} is $-\infty$. The function e^{t^2} is an example of a function which is not Laplace transformable since it has no finite abscissa of convergence.

8 **Remark** In many of the applications that are of interest to us the function $f(t)$ may contain delta functions at $t = 0$. In such cases, there are two alternative ways of resolving the ambiguity at $t = 0$. One is to extend the lower limit of integration to $0-$ in order to include the delta functions in question within the limits of integration, and the other is to leave out the delta functions by starting the integration at $0+$. Thus, under these two alternatives we have, respectively,

9
$$F(s) = \int_{0-}^\infty f(t)e^{-st}\,dt$$

and

10
$$F_+(s) = \int_{0+}^\infty f(t)e^{-st}\,dt$$

We use the symbol $F_+(s)$ to identify the latter because we shall be using for the most part *9* rather than *10*. Thus, when we speak of the unilateral Laplace transform of $f(t)$, *9* will be understood unless explicitly stated to the contrary.

We turn next to bilateral Laplace transforms.

11 **Definition** The *bilateral Laplace transform* of a time function $f(t)$ defined on $(-\infty, \infty)$ is denoted by $\bar{F}(s) = \mathfrak{L}_{\mathrm{II}}\{f(t)\}$ [or simply $F(s)$ where no confusion with the unilateral Laplace transform is likely to arise] and is defined by the integral

12 $$\bar{F}(s) = \mathfrak{L}_{\mathrm{II}}\{f(t)\} = \int_{-\infty}^{\infty} f(t)e^{-st}\,dt$$

for all values of s for which *12* exists (converges). ◁

By considering the two halves of $f(t)$ separately, it is easy to verify the truth of the following

13 **Assertion** If the abscissae of convergence for $1(t)f(t)$ and $1(t)f(-t)$ are α and β, respectively, and if $\beta \geq \alpha$, then $\bar{F}(s)$ exists and is analytic throughout the region (called the *strip of convergence*) defined by $\alpha < \operatorname{Re} s < \beta$.

14 *Example* For the function $f(t)$ defined by

$$f(t) = 1(-t)e^{t} + 1(t)e^{-2t}$$

the strip of convergence is given by $-2 < \operatorname{Re} s < 1$.

It is easy to show that a sufficient condition for the existence of a strip of convergence is that $f(t)$ be of *exponential class* in the sense that $|f(t)| \leq Ce^{\alpha t}$ for $t \geq 0$ and $|f(t)| \leq Ce^{\beta t}$ for $t < 0$, with $\alpha < \beta$ and C a finite constant (see Ref. *1*, vol. 1, page 407).

The *Fourier transform* of $f(t)$ may be regarded as a special case of the bilateral transform of $f(t)$. Specifically, if the axis of imaginaries falls within the strip of convergence, then we can set $s = j\omega$ and define

15 $$\mathfrak{F}\{f(t)\} \triangleq \text{Fourier transform of } f(t) \triangleq \int_{-\infty}^{\infty} f(t)e^{-j\omega t}\,dt$$

For simplicity, $\bar{F}(j\omega)$ will usually be written as $F(j\omega)$.

3 *Basic properties of Laplace transforms*

In what follows, we list without proof some of the main properties of unilateral and bilateral Laplace transforms. Whenever we do not differentiate between them, the implication is that the property in question is possessed by both. It is understood that the equalities involving time functions hold for all t (more strictly, *almost* all t) over which the functions are defined and that the equalities involving Laplace transforms hold for s which fall within their common domain of existence.

1 **Property: linearity** The Laplace transformation is a linear operation in the sense that, for all constants a, b and all time functions f_1, f_2

2 $$\mathfrak{L}\{af_1(t) + bf_2(t)\} = a\mathfrak{L}\{f_1(t)\} + b\mathfrak{L}\{f_2(t)\}$$

over the range of definition of f_1 and f_2, provided the Laplace transforms on the left-hand side and the right-hand side of *2* exist. [This condition implies that the strip of convergence for $af_1 + bf_2$ is $\max(\alpha_1,\alpha_2) < \operatorname{Re} s < \min(\beta_1,\beta_2)$, where α_1, β_1 and α_2, β_2 define the strips of convergence for f_1 and f_2, respectively.]

3 **Property: translation theorem for time functions** For all real nonnegative constants a

4 $$\mathfrak{L}\{f(t-a)\} = e^{-as}\mathfrak{L}\{f(t)\}$$

Note that for bilateral transforms, the restriction $a > 0$ is unnecessary. If $a < 0$, then for unilateral transforms *4* should be replaced by

5 $$\mathfrak{L}\{f(t-a)\} = e^{-as}\left[\mathfrak{L}\{f(t)\} - \int_0^{-a} f(t)e^{-st}\,dt\right]$$

6 **Property: translation theorem for unilateral Laplace transforms** Let $F(s)$ be the unilateral Laplace transform of $f(t)$. Then for any constant a (real or complex)

7 $$\mathfrak{L}\{e^{-at}f(t)\} = F(s+a)$$

The same result holds for bilateral transforms, with the strip of convergence for $e^{-at}f(t)$ being that for $f(t)$ shifted to the left by amount $\operatorname{Re} a$. (See Ref. *2*, page 39.)

A key property of the Laplace transform involves the convolution of two time functions, defined as follows.

8 **Definition** Let f_1 and f_2 be defined on $(-\infty,\infty)$. Then the *convolution* of f_1 and f_2 is a time function denoted by $f_1 * f_2$, with the value of $f_1 * f_2$ at time t given by the integral

9 $$f_1 * f_2(t) = \int_{-\infty}^{\infty} f_1(t)f_2(t-\xi)\,d\xi$$

if it exists for all t. The convolution of f_1 and f_2 is a commutative operation in the sense that $f_1 * f_2 = f_2 * f_1$ for all t. ◁

If f_1 and f_2 are one-sided, i.e., vanish for $t < 0$, then their convolution is given by

10 $$f_1 * f_2(t) = \int_0^t f_1(\xi) f_2(t - \xi)\, d\xi$$

For the convolution of one-sided f_1 and f_2 we have the following

11 **Property: convolution theorem for time functions** The unilateral Laplace transform of the convolution of $f_1(t)$ and $f_2(t)$ is given by

12 $$\mathcal{L}\{f_1 * f_2\} = F_1(s)F_2(s)$$

More specifically, let $\mathcal{L}\{f_1(t)\}$ and $\mathcal{L}\{f_2(t)\}$ converge absolutely for some s, say s_0. Then (I) $f_1 * f_2$ exists for almost all $t \geq 0$, (II) $\mathcal{L}\{f_1 * f_2\}$ converges for s_0, and (III) *12* holds for s_0 and all s such that $\text{Re}\, s > \text{Re}\, s_0$. (See Ref. *1*, vol. 1, p. 124.)

The same result holds for bilateral transforms, provided $f_1 * f_2$ exists and there is a common strip of convergence defined by $\max(\alpha_1,\alpha_2) < \text{Re}\, s < \min(\beta_1,\beta_2)$ (see Ref. *2*, page 39).

13 **Property: convolution theorem for Laplace and Fourier transforms** The unilateral Laplace transform of the product of $f_1(t)$ and $f_2(t)$ is given by the following integral in the s plane:

14 $$\mathcal{L}\{f_1(t)f_2(t)\} = \frac{1}{2\pi j} \int_{\sigma_1 - j\infty}^{\sigma_1 + j\infty} F_1(\lambda) F_2(s - \lambda)\, d\lambda$$

where the integration is carried out along the vertical line $\text{Re}\, s = \sigma_1$, with σ_1 and s in *14* constrained by two conditions: (I) $\sigma_1 > \alpha_1$ (abscissa of convergence for f_1) and (II) $\text{Re}\, s - \sigma_1 > \alpha_2$ (abscissa of convergence for f_2). (See Ref. *1*, vol. 1, page 414.)

The same result holds for bilateral transforms, with the strip of convergence for $f_1(t)f_2(t)$ defined by $\alpha_2 + \sigma_1 < \text{Re}\, s < \beta_2 + \sigma_1$, $\alpha_1 < \sigma_1 < \beta_1$, where α_1, β_1 and α_2, β_2 define the strips of convergence for f_1 and f_2, respectively. (See Ref. *2*, page 47.) An immediate consequence of this property of bilateral transforms is the following: If $f_1(t)$ and $f_2(t)$ have Fourier transforms $F_1(j\omega)$ and $F_2(j\omega)$, respectively, then the Fourier transform of the product $f_1(t)f_2(t)$ is given by the convolution of $F_1(j\omega)$ and $F_2(j\omega)$; that is,

15 $$\mathcal{F}\{f_1(t)f_2(t)\} = \frac{1}{2\pi} \int_{-\infty}^{\infty} F_1(j\omega') F_2(j\omega - j\omega')\, d\omega'$$

From this relation it readily follows that f_1, f_2 and their respective Fourier transforms have the

16 **Property: Parseval's formula** If f_1 and f_2 are square integrable, that is,

$$\int_{-\infty}^{\infty} |f_i(t)|^2 \, dt < \infty \qquad i = 1, 2$$

then
$$\int_{-\infty}^{\infty} f_1(t) f_2(t) \, dt = \frac{1}{2\pi} \int_{-\infty}^{\infty} F_1^*(j\omega) F_2(j\omega) \, d\omega$$

where $F_1^*(j\omega)$ is the complex conjugate of $F_1(j\omega)$. (See Ref. *3*, page 48, and Ref. *4*, page 27.)

Laplace transforms of derivatives and integrals

17 **Remark** In what follows, $F(s)$ stands for the unilateral Laplace transform defined by *9* and p denotes the derivative operator in the distribution sense (see *A.2.3* and *A.5.4*). $f^{(n)}(0-)$ stands for the nth derivative of $f(t)$ evaluated at $0-$ and analogously for $f^{(n)}(0+)$.

The following formulae summarize those properties of the Laplace transforms which are of frequent use in the solution of differential and integrodifferential equations.

18 **Property: formula for the Laplace transform of nth derivative** We have

19 $$\mathcal{L}\{p^n f(t)\} = s^n F(s) - s^{n-1} f(0-) - \cdots - f^{(n-1)}(0-) \qquad n = 0, 1, 2, \ldots$$

which reduces to

20 $$\mathcal{L}\{p^n f(t)\} = s^n F(s)$$

if $f(t)$ and its derivatives vanish for $t < 0$. It should be noted that in terms of $F_+(s)$ (see *B.2.10*), we have

21 $$\mathcal{L}\{p^n f(t)\} = s^n F_+(s) - s^{n-1} f(0+) - \cdots - f^{(n-1)}(0+) \qquad n = 0, 1, 2, \ldots$$

Note that it is this expression rather than *19* that is found in most classical texts on the Laplace transformation. We use for the most part *19* because it is better adapted to the needs of system analysis.

22 **Remark** Equation *19* can be expressed in a more compact form by using the initial-value derivative operator p_0 defined by

$$p_0^n f(t) = f^{(n)}(0-) \qquad n = 0, 1, 2, \ldots$$

Then *19* becomes simply

$$\mathcal{L}\{p^n f(t)\} = s^n F(s) - \left(\frac{s^n - p_0^n}{s - p_0}\right) f(t)$$

This relation easily generalizes to differential operators of the form

$$L(p) = a_n p^n + \cdots + a_0$$

Thus

23 $$\mathcal{L}\{L(p)f(t)\} = L(s)F(s) - \left(\frac{L(s) - L(p_0)}{s - p_0}\right) f(t)$$

24 **Remark** A special case of *18* which is of frequent use in dealing with linear time-invariant systems is the following: Suppose that $f(t)$ is given by the convolution of one-sided functions h and u,

$$f(t) = \int_0^t h(t - \xi)u(\xi)\, d\xi$$

and $L(p)$ is a differential operator. Then

25 $$\mathcal{L}\{L(p)f(t)\} = L(s)U(s)H(s)$$

where $U(s) \triangleq \mathcal{L}\{u(t)\}$ and $H(s) \triangleq \mathcal{L}\{h(t)\}$. This follows at once from *20* and *11*.

26 **Property: Laplace transform of nth-order integral** Let $\frac{1}{p^n} f(t)$, $n \geq 0$, denote the nth-order indefinite integral of $f(t)$, with $f^{(-n)}(0-)$ denoting the initial value of $\frac{1}{p^n} f(t)$ at $0-$. Then, if the Laplace transform of $\frac{1}{p^n} f(t)$ exists, we have

27 $$\mathcal{L}\left\{\frac{1}{p^n} f(t)\right\} = s^{-n}F(s) + s^{-n}f^{(-1)}(0-) + \cdots + s^{-1}f^{(-n)}(0-)$$

28 **Property** For all points within the domain of existence of $F(s)$ (unilateral or bilateral) we have

29 $$\mathcal{L}\{t^n f(t)\} = (-1)^n \frac{d^n}{ds^n} F(s) \qquad n = 0, 1, 2, \ldots$$

Initial- and final-value theorems for unilateral transforms

30 **Theorem** If $\lim_{t \to 0} f(t)$ exists as t approaches zero from the right, then

31 $$f(0+) = \lim_{s \to \infty} sF(s)$$

Comment It should be noted that the right-hand member of *31* may exist without the existence of $f(0+)$. For this reason it is important to know that $f(0+)$ exists before using *31*.

32 **Theorem** If $\lim_{t\to\infty} f(t)$ exists, then

33 $$\lim_{t\to\infty} f(t) = \lim_{s\to 0} sF(s)$$

Comment The comment for *30* applies to this theorem also.

Inversion formulae for Laplace transforms

Of basic importance in the theory of the Laplace transformation is the so-called inversion formula which yields the expression for $f(t)$ in terms of $F(s)$. For the one-sided Laplace transform we have the

34 **Theorem** Let $F(s) = \mathfrak{L}\{f(t)\}$, with $f(t) = 0$ for $t < 0$, and let α_a be the abscissa of absolute convergence of f. If f is of bounded variation in the neighborhood of t, then,

35 $$\frac{f(t+0) + f(t-0)}{2} = \frac{1}{2\pi j}\int_{c-j\infty}^{c+j\infty} F(s)e^{st}\,ds \quad \forall c > \alpha_a$$

where the integral is to be interpreted as $\lim_{\Omega\to\infty} \int_{c-j\Omega}^{c+j\Omega}$. ◁

In the case of the two-sided Laplace transformation, formula *35* holds for all $\alpha < c < \beta$, where α and β are the abscissae of absolute convergence of $1(t)f(t)$ and $1(t)f(-t)$, respectively.

In many instances, the inversion formula *35* can be calculated by contour integration provided the open path of integration can be closed. The *Jordan lemma* gives a set of sufficient conditions for closing the integration path (see Ref. *1*, vol. 1, page 224).

36 **Theorem** Let C_l be the left-half-plane semicircle of radius R centered on the origin: $C_l = \left\{s \,\middle|\, |s| = R \text{ and } \frac{\pi}{2} \le \measuredangle s \le \frac{3\pi}{2}\right\}$.

If, as $R \to \infty$, $F(s) \to 0$ uniformly on C_l, then

37 $$\lim_{R\to\infty} \int_{C_l} F(s)e^{st}\,ds = 0 \qquad \forall t > 0$$

A similar statement holds for $C_r = \left\{s \,\middle|\, |s| = R, -\frac{\pi}{2} \le \measuredangle s \le \frac{\pi}{2}\right\}$, but then *37* holds for all $t < 0$.

38 *Exercise* Let $P(s)$ and $Q(s)$ be polynomials such that the degree of Q is larger than the degree of P; let $t_0 > 0$. Show that

$$\mathfrak{L}^{-1}\left(\frac{P(s)}{Q(s)}\,e^{-st_0}\right) = 0 \qquad \text{for all } t < t_0$$

This concludes our résumé of those properties of the Laplace transforms which are of relevance to the material in the main body of the text.

4 *z transforms*

In the case of time-invariant discrete-time systems, the z transform plays a role similar to that of the Laplace transform. In this section we define the z transform and cite its principal properties.

1 **Definition** Given a sequence of scalars $\{f_n\}_0^\infty$, the z transform of this sequence is the function of the complex variable z defined by

2 $$\tilde{F}(z) = \sum_{n=0}^{\infty} f_n z^{-n}$$

3 *Comment* The z transform can be considered as an operator mapping sequences of scalars into functions of the complex variable.

4 *Comment* In most engineering applications, one considers a function f which satisfies $f(t) = 0$ for $t < 0$ and which is either continuous at $t = nT$, $n = 0, 1, \ldots$, or is such that $f(nT-)$ and $f(nT+)$ both exist for all nonnegative integers n. To the function f one associates "by sampling with period T" the sequence $\{f_n\}$, where $f_n = f(nT+)$. One refers to the z transform of the sequence $\{f_n\}$ as the "z transform of the function f." In symbols, $\tilde{F}(z) \triangleq \mathrm{Z}\{f(t)\}$, with

5 $$\tilde{F}(z) \triangleq \sum_{k=0}^{\infty} f(kT+)z^{-k} \quad \triangleleft$$

The following properties of the z transform follow directly from the fact that $\tilde{F}(z)$ is a power series in z^{-1}.

6 **Property**[1] (I) The radius of convergence R_f of the power series *2* is given by

$$R_f = \limsup_{n\to\infty} \sqrt[n]{|f_n|}$$

(II) The power series *2* converges absolutely for all $z \ni |z| > R_f$ and uniformly for all $z \ni |z| > R$, where R is any radius larger than R_f.

(III) $\tilde{F}(z)$ is an analytic function of z in the domain $|z| > R_f$.

(IV) Derivatives of $\tilde{F}$ of any order can be obtained by differentiating the series term by term provided $|z| > R_f$.

[1] E. Hille, "Analytic Function Theory," vol. 1, secs. 5.4 and 5.5, Ginn and Company, Boston, 1959.

Properties of the z transform

We shall state the properties of the z transform by using the engineering terminology indicated in *4*. We *assume* throughout that the functions that we consider satisfy the conditions stated in *4* and have a z transform with a finite radius of convergence.

7 **Linearity theorem**

$$\mathcal{Z}(\alpha f) = \alpha \mathcal{Z}(f) \qquad \forall \text{ complex numbers } \alpha, \forall |z| > R_f$$
$$\mathcal{Z}(f + g) = \mathcal{Z}(f) + \mathcal{Z}(g) \qquad \forall |z| > \max(R_f, R_g)$$

Proof Refer to Definition *1* and *5*.

8 **Inversion theorem**

9 $$f(nT) = \frac{1}{2\pi j} \int_\Gamma \tilde{F}(z) z^{n-1}\, dz \qquad n = 0, 1, \ldots$$

where Γ is any simple closed rectifiable curve enclosing the origin and lying outside the circle $|z| = R > R_f$. The integration is performed in the counterclockwise direction.

10 *Comment* This theorem implies that, provided $R_f < \infty$, the z transform is a one-one mapping of the space of sequences into the set of functions which are analytic in some neighborhood of infinity.

Proof Start from the R.H.S. of *9*. Replace $\tilde{F}$ by its defining series *2*. Integrate term by term, which is legitimate by *6*(II). Finally, use the residue theorem to obtain *9*.

From definition *5* we immediately obtain

11 **Initial-value theorem**

$$f(0+) = \lim_{z \to \infty} \tilde{F}(z)$$

12 **Final-value theorem** If the sequence $\{f(nT+)\}_0^\infty$ tends to a limit, say, f_∞, then

(I) $R_f = 1$ and $\tilde{F}(z)$ is analytic outside the circle $|z| = 1$.

(II) $\lim_{z \to 1} (z - 1)\tilde{F}(z) = f_\infty$, z real and $z > 1$.

Proof To prove (I), use *6*(I) and observe that $f_n \to f_\infty$ implies that $\limsup_{n \to \infty} \sqrt[n]{|f_n|} = 1$.

To prove (II), observe that $f_n \to f_\infty$ means that for any $\varepsilon > 0$ there is a number N (which depends on ε) such that $n \geq N$ implies $|f_n - f_\infty| < \varepsilon$. Therefore,

$$\sum_{k=0}^{\infty} f_{N+k} z^{-(N+k)} = z^{-N} \sum_{k=0}^{\infty} f_{N+k} z^{-k}$$
$$= z^{-N} \left\{ \sum_{k=0}^{\infty} (f_{N+k} - f_\infty) z^{-k} + \sum_{k=0}^{\infty} f_\infty z^{-k} \right\} \qquad |z| > 1$$

Since $|z| > 1$, the second sum is $f_\infty(1 - z^{-1})^{-1}$. Let the first sum be called $R(\varepsilon,z)$, i.e.,

13 $$R(\varepsilon,z) \triangleq \sum_{k=0}^{\infty} (f_{N+k} - f_\infty)z^{-k}$$

Thus

$$\sum_{k=0}^{\infty} f_{N+k}z^{-(N+k)} = \frac{z^{-N}}{1 - z^{-1}} f_\infty + z^{-N}R(\varepsilon,z)$$

Now

$$\begin{aligned}\tilde{F}(z) &= \sum_{n=0}^{N-1} f_n z^{-n} + \sum_{k=0}^{\infty} f_{N+k}z^{-(N+k)} \\ &= \sum_{n=0}^{N-1} f_n z^{-n} + \frac{z^{-N}}{1 - z^{-1}} f_\infty + z^{-N}R(\varepsilon,z) \qquad |z| > 1\end{aligned}$$

Therefore,

14 $$(z-1)\tilde{F} = (z-1)\sum_{n=0}^{N-1} f_n z^{-n} + z^{-N+1}f_\infty + (z-1)z^{-N}R(\varepsilon,z) \qquad |z| > 1$$

Now, restricting z to be real, we obtain from *13*

$$\begin{aligned}|(z-1)z^{-N}R(\varepsilon,z)| &= \left|(z-1)z^{-N}\sum_{k=0}^{\infty}(f_{N+k} - f_\infty)z^{-k}\right| \qquad |z| > 1 \\ &< (z-1)z^{-N}\sum_{k=0}^{\infty}\varepsilon z^{-k} \qquad z \text{ real}, z > 1\end{aligned}$$

and

15 $$|(z-1)z^{-N}R(\varepsilon,z)| < \varepsilon z^{(1-N)} \qquad z \text{ real}, z > 1$$

Now let $z \to 1$, with z real and $z > 1$. The first term of *14* tends to zero; the second tends to f_∞; and, by *15*, the last one is smaller in absolute value than any ε. Hence, (II) follows.

16 **Shifting theorem** If $\tilde{F}(z)$ is the z transform of the sequence $\{f_0,f_1, f_2, \ldots\}$, then $z^{-1}\tilde{F}(z)$ is the z transform of sequence $\{0,f_0,f_1,f_2, \ldots\}$.
Proof Immediate from Definition *1*.

REFERENCES AND SUGGESTED READING

1 Doetsch, G.: "Handbuch der Laplace Transformation," vols. 1 to 3, Verlag Birkhauser, Basel, 1950.
2 Van der Pol, B., and H. Bremmer: "Operational Calculus," Cambridge University Press, New York, 1955.
3 Goldberg, R. R.: "Fourier Transforms," Cambridge University Press, New York, 1961.

4 Papoulis, A.: "The Fourier Integral and Its Applications," McGraw-Hill Book Company, Inc., New York, 1962.

5 Jury, E. I.: "Sampled Data Control Systems," John Wiley & Sons, Inc., New York, 1958.

6 Ragazzini, J. R., and G. F. Franklin: "Sampled-data Control Systems," McGraw-Hill Book Company, Inc., New York, 1958.

7 Tou, J. T.: "Digital and Sampled-data Control Systems," McGraw-Hill Book Company, Inc., New York, 1959.

8 Bridgland, T. F., Jr.: A Linear Algebraic Formulation of the Theory of Sampled Data Control, *J. Soc. Indust. Appl. Math.*, vol. 7, no. 4, pp. 431–446, 1959.

9 Doetsch, G.: "Guide to the Applications of Laplace Transforms," D. Van Nostrand Company, Inc., Princeton, N.J., 1961.

Vectors and linear transformations

C

1 Introduction

The purpose of this appendix is twofold: first, to collect a number of results necessary for developments in the text and, second, to give a rapid, yet logical, derivation of results of interest in the theory and the applications of linear systems. In order to keep the size of this appendix within reason, we have assumed that the reader has some knowledge of vector and matrix algebra; more specifically, we have assumed that he knows the basic properties of determinants (including Cramer's rule) and the basic facts of matrix algebra (addition, multiplication, and inversion). This allows us to shorten our presentation, to leave a number of derivations as exercises, and, for example, to mention in a comment the inverse of a matrix before we encounter the definition of the inverse in formal presentation.

The next thirteen sections of the appendix are devoted to the definition of the basic concepts and the derivation of the associated fundamental facts. The final six sections make full use of the preceding ones and are devoted to the derivation of those results that are used most frequently in the text. Since the text itself provides ample motivation for this appendix (and the large number of cross references from the text to this appendix proves this point) we have eliminated almost all motivational introductions. We have, however, added a last section which reviews the reasons for the appearance of the adjoint in so many applications.

Most of the material presented here is well known and is available in numerous books, a number of which are listed as references. On the other hand, the section on pseudo inverses is new.

2 Linear vector space

1 **Definition** A (*linear*) *vector space* $\mathfrak{X}$ is a set of elements called *vectors* satisfying the following conditions:

(I) For every pair of vectors $\mathbf{x}$ and $\mathbf{y}$ in $\mathfrak{X}$ there corresponds a unique vector $\mathbf{x} + \mathbf{y}$ in $\mathfrak{X}$, called the sum of $\mathbf{x}$ and $\mathbf{y}$; this operation of addition has the following properties:

(*a*) $\mathbf{x} + \mathbf{y} = \mathbf{y} + \mathbf{x}$

(*b*) $\mathbf{x} + (\mathbf{y} + \mathbf{z}) = (\mathbf{x} + \mathbf{y}) + \mathbf{z}$

(*c*) There is a unique vector $\mathbf{0}$ such that $\mathbf{x} + \mathbf{0} = \mathbf{x}$ for all $\mathbf{x} \in \mathfrak{X}$.

(*d*) For every vector $\mathbf{x} \in \mathfrak{X}$ there is a vector $-\mathbf{x} \in \mathfrak{X}$ such that

$$\mathbf{x} + (-\mathbf{x}) = \mathbf{0}$$

(II) To every scalar α and vector $\mathbf{x} \in \mathfrak{X}$ there is a vector $\alpha\mathbf{x} \in \mathfrak{X}$, called the *product* of α and $\mathbf{x}$. It has the following properties:

(*a*) $\alpha(\beta\mathbf{x}) = (\alpha\beta)\mathbf{x}$ (*b*) $1\mathbf{x} = \mathbf{x}$ for every $\mathbf{x}$

(*c*) $\alpha(\mathbf{x} + \mathbf{y}) = \alpha\mathbf{x} + \alpha\mathbf{y}$ (*d*) $(\alpha + \beta)\mathbf{x} = \alpha\mathbf{x} + \beta\mathbf{x}$

In applications, α will usually be a real number; however, there are always instances where α is complex. For this reason we shall henceforth develop the theory under the assumption that the scalars are complex numbers. Technically, such linear vector spaces are called linear vector spaces over the field of complex numbers.

2 *Example* In physics all the forces applied at a point constitute a vector space: the vectors are ordered triples of real numbers, which are their components with respect to a system of coordinates; the scalars are real numbers. They may be complex when the phasor notation is used. The ith component is then $f_i(t) = \text{Re}\,[F_i \exp(j\omega t)]$, where $|F_i|$ is the amplitude and $\measuredangle F_i$ is the phase of the sinusoidal component $f_i(t)$.

3 *Example* In most of our applications, we shall consider vectors in n-dimensional space. These vectors may be considered as defined by an ordered n-tuple of complex numbers, e.g., $\mathbf{x} = (\xi_1,\xi_2, \ldots ,\xi_n)$, where the ξ_i's are called the components of $\mathbf{x}$ with respect to a set of basis vectors. We shall henceforth call this space $\mathcal{C}^n$. Let

$$\mathbf{y} = (\eta_1,\eta_2, \ldots ,\eta_n)$$

The sum will be defined as $\mathbf{x} + \mathbf{y} = (\xi_1 + \eta_1, \ldots , \xi_n + \eta_n)$ and the product as $\alpha\mathbf{x} = (\alpha\xi_1,\alpha\xi_2, \ldots ,\alpha\xi_n)$. The zero vector is

$$\mathbf{0} = (0,0, \ldots ,0)$$

4 *Example* In signal analysis, the vectors are "signals," i.e., functions of time f subject to $\int_{-\infty}^{+\infty} |f(t)|^2\, dt < \infty$. The class of all such functions of time constitutes a vector space. The scalars are either real or complex numbers.

5 *Example* All the solutions of the linear homogeneous differential equation

$$\frac{d^2y}{dt^2} + 3\frac{dy}{dt} + 2y = 0$$

are of the form $\alpha e^{-t} + \beta e^{-2t}$, where α and β are scalars (possibly complex). They constitute a linear vector space.

6 *Example* If $\mathbf{a}$ and $\mathbf{b}$ are two vectors in the plane, the set of all vectors of the form $\alpha\mathbf{a} + \beta\mathbf{b}$, with $|\alpha| \leq 1$ and $|\beta| \leq 1$, is not a vector space. (State why.)

7 *Example* The set of all complex-valued continuous functions over the interval [0,1] is a linear vector space.

8 *Example* The set of all solutions $\mathbf{E}(x,y,z,t)$, $\mathbf{H}(x,y,z,t)$ of Maxwell's equations for a cavity resonator with perfectly conducting walls constitutes a linear vector space. (*Hint:* $\nabla \times \mathbf{E} = -\mu\, \partial\mathbf{H}/\partial t, \nabla \times \mathbf{H} = \varepsilon\, \partial\mathbf{E}/\partial t$, and, on the boundary, $\mathbf{n} \times \mathbf{E} = \mathbf{0}$ and $\mathbf{n} \cdot \mathbf{H} = \mathbf{0}$.)

3 *Linear dependence*

1 **Definition** The vectors $\mathbf{a}_1, \mathbf{a}_2, \ldots, \mathbf{a}_k$ are said to be *linearly independent* if any relation of the form

2 $$\sum_{i=1}^{k} \alpha_i\mathbf{a}_i = \mathbf{0}$$

implies that $\alpha_i = 0$ for $i = 1, 2, \ldots, k$.

The vectors $\mathbf{a}_1, \mathbf{a}_2, \ldots, \mathbf{a}_k$ are *linearly dependent* if there is a set of scalars $\{\alpha_i\}$ not all zero, such that

3 $$\sum_{i=1}^{k} \alpha_i\mathbf{a}_i = \mathbf{0} \qquad \text{with } \sum_{i=1}^{n} |\alpha_i| > 0$$

4 *Example* In $\mathcal{C}^3$ $\mathbf{a}_1 \triangleq (1,0,0)$, $\mathbf{a}_2 \triangleq (0,1,0)$, $\mathbf{a}_3 \triangleq (0,0,1)$ are linearly independent. If $\mathbf{a}_4 \triangleq (1,3,0)$, then $\mathbf{a}_1$, $\mathbf{a}_2$, and $\mathbf{a}_4$ are linearly dependent.

5 *Exercise* Let $\mathfrak{X}$ be the linear vector space of all complex-valued functions of t, $-\infty < t < \infty$, with the usual definitions of addition and multiplication. Show that the vectors ϕ_i, $i = 1, 2, \ldots, N$, defined by $\phi_i(t) = e^{\lambda_i t}$ are linearly independent if and only if the exponents λ_i are pairwise distinct, that is, $\lambda_i \neq \lambda_j$ for all i, j.

6 **Theorem** The vectors $\mathbf{a}_1, \mathbf{a}_2, \ldots, \mathbf{a}_n$ are linearly dependent if and only if one of them, say, $\mathbf{a}_k$, $1 \leq k \leq n$, can be expressed as a linear combination of the others.

Proof Follows directly from the definitions.

7 **Theorem** The vectors $\mathbf{a}_1, \mathbf{a}_2, \ldots, \mathbf{a}_n$ of $\mathcal{C}^n$ are linearly independent if and only if

$$\det \mathbf{A} = 0$$

where $\mathbf{A}$ is the matrix whose ith column is made of the components of $\mathbf{a}_i$.

If the vectors $\mathbf{a}_1, \mathbf{a}_2, \ldots, \mathbf{a}_r$ of $\mathcal{C}^n$, where $r < n$, are linearly independent, then

$$\text{rank } (\mathbf{A}) = r$$

i.e., at least one $(r \times r)$ minor of $\mathbf{A}$ is not zero and all minors of higher order are zero.

Proof These statements follow directly from a well-known property of determinants: a determinant is equal to zero if and only if there is a linear combination of its column vectors that is equal to the zero vector.

4 *Bases*

1 **Definition** A set $\mathcal{B}$ of vectors of a linear vector space $\mathcal{X}$ is said to be a *basis* of $\mathcal{X}$ if (I) the vectors of $\mathcal{B}$ are linearly independent and (II) every vector of $\mathcal{X}$ can be expressed as a linear combination of the vectors of $\mathcal{B}$.

2 **Definition** A set of vectors is said to *span* a vector space $\mathcal{X}$ if any vector in $\mathcal{X}$ can be expressed as a linear combination of vectors of that set.

Given any set of vectors $\mathbf{x}_1, \mathbf{x}_2, \ldots, \mathbf{x}_m$, the set of all vectors of the form

$$\sum_{i=1}^{m} \alpha_i \mathbf{x}_i$$

is itself a vector space: it is the vector space spanned by $\mathbf{x}_1, \mathbf{x}_2, \ldots, \mathbf{x}_m$. We denote it by $\mathcal{S}[\mathbf{x}_1, \mathbf{x}_2, \ldots, \mathbf{x}_m]$.

3 *Example* The vectors $\mathbf{x}_1 = (1,0,0)$, $\mathbf{x}_2 = (0,1,0)$, $\mathbf{x}_3 = (0,0,1)$, and $\mathbf{x}_4 = (1,1,0)$ span the three-dimensional euclidean space, but they do not constitute a basis. The first three vectors constitute a basis. In fact, $\mathbf{x}_3$ with any two of the remaining vectors constitutes a basis.

4 **Theorem** If $\mathbf{a}_1, \mathbf{a}_2, \ldots, \mathbf{a}_n$ form a basis of the vector space $\mathcal{X}$, then every vector $\mathbf{x} \in \mathcal{X}$ has a *unique* representation of the form

5 $$\mathbf{x} = \sum_{i=1}^{n} \xi_i \mathbf{a}_i$$

The numbers $\xi_1, \xi_2, \ldots, \xi_n$ are called the *components* of $\mathbf{x}$ with respect to the basis $\mathbf{a}_1, \mathbf{a}_2, \ldots, \mathbf{a}_n$.

Proof By definition of the basis, for any $\mathbf{x}$ there exists a representation such as *5*. It is unique because if there were two distinct representations of that form, then by subtraction we would get

$$\sum_{i=1}^{n} (\xi_i - \xi_i')\mathbf{a}_i = \mathbf{0}$$

where the ξ_i''s are the coefficients of the assumed second representation. Now, the linear independence of the set $\{\mathbf{a}_1,\mathbf{a}_2, \ldots ,\mathbf{a}_n\}$ implies that $\xi_i - \xi_i' = 0$ for $i = 1, 2, \ldots, n$. In other words, the representations are identical.

6 **Corollary** If $\mathcal{A} = \{\mathbf{a}_1,\mathbf{a}_2, \ldots ,\mathbf{a}_n\}$ constitutes a basis of $\mathfrak{X}$, if $\mathbf{x} \in \mathfrak{X}$, and if $\mathbf{x} \neq \mathbf{0}$, then $\{\mathbf{x},\mathbf{a}_1, \ldots ,\mathbf{a}_n\}$ are linearly dependent and for some k, $1 \leq k \leq n$, the set $\mathcal{B} = \{\mathbf{x},\mathbf{a}_1, \ldots ,\mathbf{a}_{k-1},\mathbf{a}_{k+1}, \ldots ,\mathbf{a}_n\}$ is a basis of $\mathfrak{X}$.

Proof Since $\mathcal{A}$ is a basis, we have, for any $\mathbf{x} \in \mathfrak{X}$,

7 $$\mathbf{x} = \sum_{i=1}^{n} \xi_i\mathbf{a}_i \qquad \text{or} \qquad \mathbf{x} - \sum_{1}^{n} \xi_i\mathbf{a}_i = \mathbf{0}$$

where $\sum_{1}^{n} |\xi_i| > 0$. From the last equality, it follows that $\mathbf{x}, \mathbf{a}_1, \ldots, \mathbf{a}_n$ are linearly dependent.

Now to show that $\mathcal{B}$ is a basis of $\mathfrak{X}$, let k, $1 \leq k \leq n$, be an index such that $\xi_k \neq 0$; then

8 $$\mathbf{a}_k = \frac{1}{\xi_k}\mathbf{x} - \sum_{i=1}^{n} \left(\frac{\xi_i}{\xi_k} - \delta_{ik}\right) \mathbf{a}_i$$

Now since $\mathcal{A}$ is a basis, for any $\mathbf{y} \in \mathfrak{X}$,

$$\mathbf{y} = \sum_{i=1}^{n} \eta_i\mathbf{a}_i$$

and, upon substituting *8* for $\mathbf{a}_k$, we get a relation of the form

$$\mathbf{y} = \xi\mathbf{x} + \sum_{\substack{j=1\\ j\neq k}}^{n} \xi_j'\mathbf{a}_j$$

In other words, the set $\mathcal{B} = \{\mathbf{x},\mathbf{a}_1, \ldots ,\mathbf{a}_{k-1},\mathbf{a}_{k+1}, \ldots ,\mathbf{a}_n\}$ spans $\mathfrak{X}$. To show that this set of vectors is linearly independent, we use contradiction. We suppose they are not independent; then we use *7* to show that this would imply that the set $\mathcal{A}$ would be linearly dependent. Thus, the set $\mathcal{B}$ spans $\mathfrak{X}$ and is linearly independent. Therefore, it is a basis.

9 **Definition** A vector space $\mathfrak{X}$ is said to be *a finite-dimensional vector space* if it has a finite basis. If the number of elements in its basis is n, it is designated by $\mathcal{C}^n$.

10 **Theorem** Any two bases of a finite-dimensional vector space have the same number of elements. This theorem justifies the definition of the *dimension*.

11 **Definition** The number of elements in a basis of the vector space $\mathfrak{X}$ is called the *dimension* of $\mathfrak{X}$.

Proof The theorem is proved by contradiction. Let

$$\mathcal{A} = \{\mathbf{a}_1, \ldots, \mathbf{a}_n\} \qquad \text{and} \qquad \mathcal{B} = \{\mathbf{b}_1, \mathbf{b}_2, \ldots, \mathbf{b}_m\}$$

be bases of $\mathfrak{X}$. Suppose that $n < m$. By the corollary, for some k, $1 \leq k \leq n$, $\mathcal{A}_1 = \{\mathbf{b}_1, \mathbf{a}_1, \ldots, \mathbf{a}_{k-1}, \mathbf{a}_{k+1}, \ldots, \mathbf{a}_n\}$ is a basis of $\mathfrak{X}$. Applying it once more for some j, $1 \leq j \leq n$ and $j \neq k$,

$$\mathcal{A}_2 = \{\mathbf{b}_1, \mathbf{b}_2, \mathbf{a}_1, \ldots, \mathbf{a}_{j-1}, \mathbf{a}_{j+1}, \ldots, \mathbf{a}_{k-1}, \mathbf{a}_{k+1}, \ldots, \mathbf{a}_n\}$$

is a basis of $\mathfrak{X}$. Note that since $\mathbf{b}_2$ and $\mathbf{b}_1$ are elements of the same basis $\mathcal{B}$, when $\mathbf{b}_2$ is expressed as a linear combination of the elements of $\mathcal{A}_1$, at least one of the $\mathbf{a}_i$'s appears in the linear combination with a coefficient $\neq 0$; for otherwise the elements of $\mathcal{B}$ would be linearly dependent, which would contradict the assumption that $\mathcal{B}$ is a basis. After n applications of Corollary *6*, we arrive at the conclusion that $\mathcal{A}_n = \{\mathbf{b}_1, \mathbf{b}_2, \ldots, \mathbf{b}_n\}$ is a basis of $\mathfrak{X}$. Therefore, $\mathbf{b}_m$ can be expressed as a linear combination of $\mathbf{b}_1, \mathbf{b}_2, \ldots, \mathbf{b}_n$, that is, the vectors $\mathbf{b}_1, \mathbf{b}_2, \ldots, \mathbf{b}_n, \mathbf{b}_m$ are linearly dependent. This contradicts the fact that $\mathcal{B}$ is a basis. Therefore, $n = m$.

12 *Example* In Example *C.2.3* the vectors $\mathbf{u}_i = (\delta_{i1}, \delta_{i2}, \ldots, \delta_{in})$ constitute a basis for $\mathcal{C}^n$. (The Kronecker symbol $\delta_{ij} \triangleq 0$ whenever $i \neq j$ and $\delta_{ij} \triangleq 1$ when $i = j$.)

13 *Example* In Example *C.2.5*, the solutions e^{-t} and e^{-3t} constitute a basis for the space of solutions.

14 *Exercise* Consider the space of all band-limited functions f: that is, the functions whose Fourier transform vanishes outside the interval $(-W,W)$, where W is the bandwidth, in cycles per second. Interpret the sampling theorem to conclude that (I) these band-limited functions form a linear vector space $\mathfrak{X}$ and (II) a basis of $\mathfrak{X}$ is the denumerable set of functions

$$\phi_n(t) = \frac{\sin(2\pi Wt - n\pi)}{2\pi Wt - n\pi} \qquad n = \ldots, -1, 0, 1 \ldots$$

15 *Exercise* In $\mathcal{C}^n$ any set of n linearly independent nonzero vectors is a basis.

5 *Scalar product*

1 **Definition** The *scalar product* of two vectors $\mathbf{x}$ and $\mathbf{y} \in \mathfrak{X}$ is a complex number, denoted by $\langle \mathbf{x},\mathbf{y} \rangle$, having the properties that for all $\mathbf{x}$, $\mathbf{y}$ in $\mathfrak{X}$ and all complex numbers α_1, α_2

(I) $\langle \mathbf{x},\mathbf{y} \rangle^* = \langle \mathbf{y},\mathbf{x} \rangle$

(II) $\langle \alpha_1\mathbf{x}_1 + \alpha_2\mathbf{x}_2, \mathbf{y} \rangle = \alpha_1^*\langle \mathbf{x}_1,\mathbf{y} \rangle + \alpha_2^*\langle \mathbf{x}_2,\mathbf{y} \rangle$

(III) $\langle \mathbf{x},\mathbf{x} \rangle > 0$ for all $\mathbf{x} \neq \mathbf{0}$

2 *Comment* First, (I) implies that $\langle \mathbf{x},\mathbf{x} \rangle$ is real. Second, (I) and (II) imply that $\langle \mathbf{x},\mathbf{0} \rangle = \langle \mathbf{0},\mathbf{x} \rangle^* = 0\langle \mathbf{x},\mathbf{x} \rangle^* = 0$. Third, (I) and (II) imply that $\langle \mathbf{x},\alpha\mathbf{y} \rangle = \alpha\langle \mathbf{x},\mathbf{y} \rangle$.

3 *Example* In Example *C.2.7* show that $\int_0^1 x(t)^*y(t)\,dt$ satisfies the three requirements for being called a scalar product.

4 *Example* In $\mathcal{C}^n$ let $\mathbf{x} = (\xi_1,\xi_2, \ldots ,\xi_n)$ and $\mathbf{y} = (\eta_1,\eta_2, \ldots ,\eta_n)$; then $\langle \mathbf{x},\mathbf{y} \rangle = \sum_{i=1}^{n} \xi_i^*\eta_i$. This choice of scalar product is equivalent to the assumption that the ξ_i's and the η_i's are the coefficients of the representation of $\mathbf{x}$ and $\mathbf{y}$, respectively, in terms of an *orthonormal basis* $(\mathbf{u}_1,\mathbf{u}_2, \ldots ,\mathbf{u}_n)$, that is, a basis such that

$$\langle \mathbf{u}_i,\mathbf{u}_j \rangle = \delta_{ij} \qquad i,j = 1, 2, \ldots , n$$

This scalar product is called the *complex scalar product* in $\mathcal{C}^n$.

The scalar product gives a natural norm on the vector space: the *norm* of $\mathbf{x}$ is defined by

5 $$\|\mathbf{x}\| = \sqrt{\langle \mathbf{x},\mathbf{x} \rangle}$$

A more complete discussion of norms is to be found in Sec. *16*.

6 *Comment* If the vector $\mathbf{x}$ in $\mathcal{C}^n$ has real components ξ_i, with respect to an orthonormal basis, its norm is given by

7 $$\|\mathbf{x}\| = \sqrt{\sum_{i=1}^{n} \xi_i^2}$$

which is the *euclidean length* of the vector. The term "length" is justified because for $n = 3$, $\|\mathbf{x}\|$ is actually the length of $\mathbf{x}$.

8 **Schwarz inequality** For all $\mathbf{x},\mathbf{y} \in \mathfrak{X}$,

9 $$|\langle \mathbf{x},\mathbf{y} \rangle| \leq \|\mathbf{x}\| \; \|\mathbf{y}\|$$

where the equality holds if and only if $\mathbf{x} = \mu\mathbf{y}$ for some scalar μ.

Proof For $\mathbf{x},\mathbf{y} \in \mathfrak{X}$ and any scalar λ, (II) and (III) of Definition *1* imply that

$$\langle \mathbf{x} + \lambda\mathbf{y}, \mathbf{x} + \lambda\mathbf{y} \rangle = \langle \mathbf{x},\mathbf{x} \rangle + \lambda^*\langle \mathbf{y},\mathbf{x} \rangle + \lambda\langle \mathbf{x},\mathbf{y} \rangle + \lambda\lambda^*\langle \mathbf{y},\mathbf{y} \rangle \geq 0$$

where the equals sign holds if and only if $\mathbf{x} + \lambda\mathbf{y} = \mathbf{0}$. Since for $\mathbf{y} = \mathbf{0}$, *8* is obviously true, let us consider the case where $\mathbf{y} \neq \mathbf{0}$. Picking $\lambda = -\langle\mathbf{y},\mathbf{x}\rangle/\langle\mathbf{y},\mathbf{y}\rangle$, we get, using (I),

$$\langle\mathbf{x},\mathbf{x}\rangle\langle\mathbf{y},\mathbf{y}\rangle \geq \langle\mathbf{x},\mathbf{y}\rangle\langle\mathbf{y},\mathbf{x}\rangle = |\langle\mathbf{x},\mathbf{y}\rangle|^2$$

Finally, *9* follows from the definition of the norm *5*.

10 **Definition** $\mathbf{x}$ is said to be *orthogonal to* $\mathbf{y}$ if $\langle\mathbf{x},\mathbf{y}\rangle = 0$.

11 *Exercise* If $\mathbf{x} \in \mathcal{C}^n$ is orthogonal to all vectors of some basis of $\mathcal{C}^n$, then $\mathbf{x} = \mathbf{0}$. (*Hint:* Let $\{\mathbf{u}_i\}$ be a basis of $\mathcal{C}^n$ and let $\mathbf{x} = \sum_{i=1}^{n} \xi_i\mathbf{u}_i$. Take the scalar product of both sides by $\mathbf{u}_k$, $k = 1, \ldots, n$.)

12 **Definition** A *subspace* $\mathcal{B}$ of a finite dimensional space $\mathcal{X}$ is a set of vectors of $\mathcal{C}^n$ such that if $\mathbf{x}$ and $\mathbf{y}$ are in $\mathcal{B}$, then for all α and β, $\alpha\mathbf{x} + \beta\mathbf{y} \in \mathcal{B}$.

13 *Example* In the ordinary three-dimensional space with $\mathbf{u}_1$, $\mathbf{u}_2$, $\mathbf{u}_3$ as a basis, the plane which contains $\mathbf{u}_1$ and $\mathbf{u}_2$ is a subspace of the whole space. Also, $\mathbf{u}_1$ and $\mathbf{u}_2$ span that subspace.

14 *Example* If e^{-t}, e^{-2t}, e^{-3t} are three solutions of a linear differential equation $Ly = 0$, then all solutions of the form $\alpha e^{-t} + \beta e^{-et}$ constitute a subspace of the vector space of solutions.

6 *The Schmidt orthonormalization procedure*

The Schmidt orthonormalization procedure solves the following problem: given a basis $\{\mathbf{a}_1,\mathbf{a}_2, \ldots ,\mathbf{a}_n\}$ of $\mathcal{C}^n$, find an orthonormal basis of $\mathcal{C}^n$, that is, a basis $\{\mathbf{v}_1,\mathbf{v}_2, \ldots ,\mathbf{v}_n\}$ such that $\langle\mathbf{v}_i,\mathbf{v}_j\rangle = \delta_{ij}$, $i,j = 1, 2, \ldots, n$.

Let us first describe the mechanics of the solution: at each step we construct a basis vector $\mathbf{u}_k$ of an intermediate basis and by normalization of $\mathbf{u}_k$ we get $\mathbf{v}_k$, the vector of the desired orthonormal basis.

1

$$\begin{array}{ll}
\mathbf{u}_1 = \mathbf{a}_1 & \mathbf{v}_1 = \mathbf{u}_1/\|\mathbf{u}_1\| \\
\mathbf{u}_2 = \mathbf{a}_2 - \langle\mathbf{v}_1,\mathbf{a}_2\rangle\mathbf{v}_1 & \mathbf{v}_2 = \mathbf{u}_2/\|\mathbf{u}_2\| \\
\mathbf{u}_3 = \mathbf{a}_3 - \langle\mathbf{v}_1,\mathbf{a}_3\rangle\mathbf{v}_1 - \langle\mathbf{v}_2,\mathbf{a}_3\rangle\mathbf{v}_2 & \mathbf{v}_3 = \mathbf{u}_3/\|\mathbf{u}_3\| \\
\cdots\cdots\cdots & \cdots\cdots \\
\mathbf{u}_r = \mathbf{a}_r - \sum_{k=1}^{r-1} \langle\mathbf{v}_k,\mathbf{a}_r\rangle\mathbf{v}_k & \mathbf{v}_r = \mathbf{u}_r/\|\mathbf{u}_r\| \\
\cdots\cdots\cdots & \cdots\cdots \\
\mathbf{u}_n = \mathbf{a}_n - \sum_{k=1}^{n-1} \langle\mathbf{v}_k,\mathbf{a}_n\rangle\mathbf{v}_k & \mathbf{v}_n = \mathbf{u}_n/\|\mathbf{u}_n\|
\end{array}$$

It is obvious that the construction guarantees that $\|\mathbf{v}_k\| = 1$ for all k's. Direct verification shows that $\langle \mathbf{v}_k, \mathbf{u}_r \rangle = 0$ for all $k < r$. Since this is true for all r, we have $\langle \mathbf{v}_i, \mathbf{v}_j \rangle = 0$ for all $i \neq j$. Therefore, the basis $\{\mathbf{v}_1, \mathbf{v}_2, \ldots, \mathbf{v}_n\}$ is *orthonormal* since

2 $$\langle \mathbf{v}_i, \mathbf{v}_j \rangle = \delta_{ij} \qquad i,j = 1, 2, \ldots, n$$

Let us consider the geometric aspect of the process: $\mathbf{v}_1$ is the unit vector along $\mathbf{a}_1$; $\mathbf{u}_2$ is the vector perpendicular to $\mathbf{a}_1$ whose length is the distance from the tip of $\mathbf{a}_2$ to the line supporting $\mathbf{v}_1$ (Fig. *C.6.1*); $\mathbf{u}_3$ is

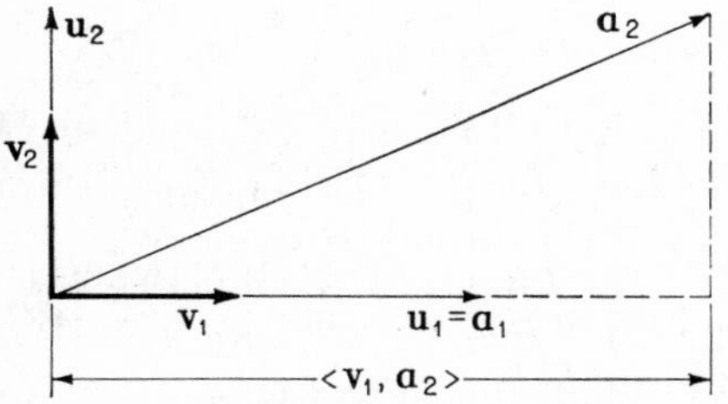

Fig. C.6.1 Schmidt orthonormalization. Relation between the vectors $\mathbf{a}_1$ and $\mathbf{a}_2$ of the original basis and the vectors $\mathbf{v}_1$ and $\mathbf{v}_2$ of the new orthonormal basis.

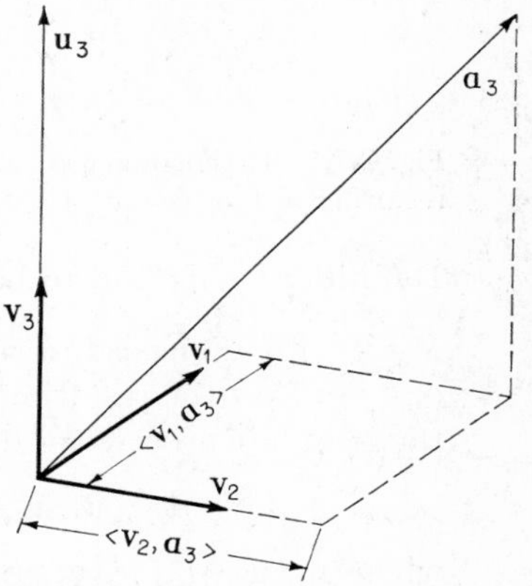

Fig. C.6.2 Schmidt orthonormalization; the figure illustrates the projection of $\mathbf{a}_3$ on the plane supported by $\mathbf{v}_1$ and $\mathbf{v}_2$ and the resulting definition of $\mathbf{u}_3$. The vectors $\mathbf{v}_1$, $\mathbf{v}_2$, and $\mathbf{v}_3$ belong to the new orthonormal basis.

parallel to the perpendicular dropped from the tip of $\mathbf{a}_3$ on the plane spanned by $\mathbf{a}_1$, $\mathbf{a}_2$ (Fig. *C.6.2*, where the process is shown in perspective); $\mathbf{u}_r$ is parallel to the perpendicular dropped from the tip of $\mathbf{a}_r$ to the subspace spanned by $\mathbf{a}_1, \mathbf{a}_2, \ldots, \mathbf{a}_{r-1}$. Observe that this subspace is also spanned by $\mathbf{v}_1, \mathbf{v}_2, \ldots, \mathbf{v}_{r-1}$; hence, any vector in that subspace is of the form $\sum_{i=1}^{r-1} \alpha_i \mathbf{v}_i$ and any such vector is also orthogonal to $\mathbf{u}_r$ since $\langle \mathbf{u}_r, \mathbf{v}_i \rangle = 0$ for $i = 1, 2, \ldots, r-1$.

7 *Orthogonal projections*

1 **Theorem** Let $\mathfrak{M}$ be a subspace of $\mathbb{C}^n$. Then any vector $\mathbf{x}$ not in $\mathfrak{M}$ can be represented in one and only one way as

2 $$\mathbf{x} = \mathbf{y} + \mathbf{y}_p$$

where $\mathbf{y} \in \mathfrak{M}$ and $\mathbf{y}_p = \mathbf{x} - \mathbf{y}$ is orthogonal to all vectors of $\mathfrak{M}$. (See Fig. *C.7.1*.)

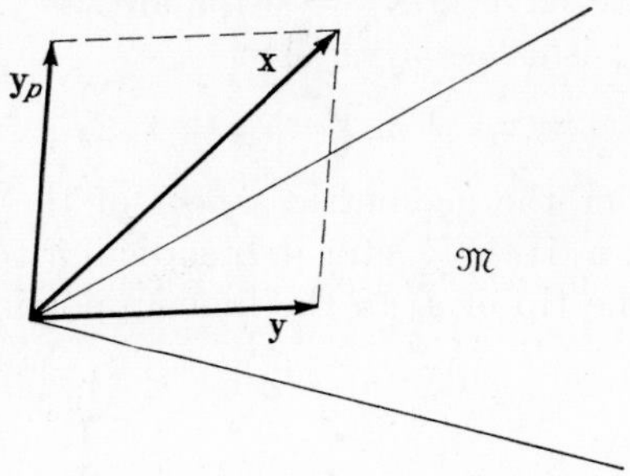

Fig. C.7.1 Orthogonal projection of **x** on the subspace $\mathfrak{M}$ (shown here as a plane), resulting in two vectors $\mathbf{y} \in \mathfrak{M}$ and $\mathbf{y}_p \perp \mathfrak{M}$.

3 **Definition** **y** is said to be the *orthogonal projection of* **x** *on* $\mathfrak{M}$.

Proof Pick a basis for $\mathfrak{M}$ and adjoin to it linearly independent vectors of $\mathcal{C}^n$ so that the resulting set is a basis for $\mathcal{C}^n$. Using these vectors, by the Schmidt process we obtain an orthonormal basis for $\mathcal{C}^n$:

4 $$\mathbf{u}_1, \mathbf{u}_2, \ldots, \mathbf{u}_s, \mathbf{u}_{s+1}, \ldots, \mathbf{u}_n$$

where $\mathbf{u}_1, \mathbf{u}_2, \ldots, \mathbf{u}_s$ span $\mathfrak{M}$. Thus, for any $\mathbf{x} \in \mathcal{C}^n$

5 $$\mathbf{x} = \sum_{i=1}^{s} \xi_i \mathbf{u}_i + \sum_{k=s+1}^{n} \xi_k \mathbf{u}_k$$

Let the first sum be **y** and the second be $\mathbf{y}_p$. Clearly, $\mathbf{y} \in \mathfrak{M}$. Since $\mathbf{y}_p = \mathbf{x} - \mathbf{y}$ is a linear combination of $\mathbf{u}_{s+1}, \ldots, \mathbf{u}_n$, and since the basis $\{\mathbf{u}_i\}$ is an orthonormal basis, $\mathbf{y}_p$ is orthogonal to $\mathbf{u}_1, \mathbf{u}_2, \ldots, \mathbf{u}_s$ and hence to every vector of $\mathfrak{M}$, because $\mathfrak{M} = \mathcal{S}[\mathbf{u}_1, \ldots, \mathbf{u}_s]$. It remains to show that the representation is unique. Suppose it were not, i.e., suppose there is another representation of **x** such that $\mathbf{x} = \mathbf{y}' + \mathbf{y}_p'$, where $\mathbf{y}' \in \mathfrak{M}$ and $\mathbf{y}_p'$ is orthogonal to all the vectors of $\mathfrak{M}$. Then $\mathbf{x} = \mathbf{y}' + \mathbf{y}_p'$ with $\mathbf{y} \neq \mathbf{y}'$. By subtracting this second representation from *2*, we have

6 $$(\mathbf{y} - \mathbf{y}') + (\mathbf{y}_p - \mathbf{y}_p') = \mathbf{0}$$

and, by scalar multiplication,[1]

$$\langle \mathbf{y} - \mathbf{y}', \mathbf{y} - \mathbf{y}' \rangle + \langle \mathbf{y} - \mathbf{y}', \mathbf{y}_p - \mathbf{y}_p' \rangle = 0$$

[1] Since we are using the complex scalar product (see *C.5.4*), the order of the factors in a scalar product is important. In the case at hand we have to have $\mathbf{y} - \mathbf{y}'$ as the left-hand member in both scalar products. To see the point, imagine Eq. *6* written out as n scalar equations relative to some orthonormal basis. Now multiply each scalar equation by the complex conjugate of the corresponding component of $\mathbf{y} - \mathbf{y}'$ (relative to the same basis!). Add the results and observe that they amount to the sum of the two scalar products with their factors in the order shown above.

Now $\mathbf{y}_p$ and $\mathbf{y}'_p$ are orthogonal to all vectors of $\mathfrak{M}$ and hence to $\mathbf{y} - \mathbf{y}'$; therefore, the second term is zero and the above equality then implies $\mathbf{y} = \mathbf{y}'$. Hence, the representation is unique.

Let $\mathfrak{M}_0 = \mathcal{S}[\mathbf{u}_{s+1},\mathbf{u}_{s+2}, \ldots ,\mathbf{u}_n]$. Then, every vector of $\mathfrak{M}_0$ is orthogonal to every vector of $\mathfrak{M}$. Furthermore, any vector in $\mathcal{C}^n$ orthogonal to every vector in $\mathfrak{M}$ is a vector of $\mathfrak{M}_0$. Hence $\mathfrak{M}_0$ is the set of all vectors of $\mathcal{C}^n$ that are orthogonal to all vectors of $\mathfrak{M}$. $\mathfrak{M}_0$ is said to be the *orthogonal complement* of $\mathfrak{M}$. It is denoted by $\mathfrak{M}^\perp$.

In order to further exhibit the relation between the subspaces $\mathfrak{M}$ and $\mathfrak{M}_0$, we need to introduce a concept that will be of great usefulness later on.

7 **Definition** Let $\mathfrak{M}$ and $\mathfrak{N}$ be two subspaces of a vector space $\mathfrak{X}$. $\mathfrak{X}$ is said to be the *direct sum of* $\mathfrak{M}$ *and* $\mathfrak{N}$, written $\mathfrak{M} \oplus \mathfrak{N} = \mathfrak{X}$, if any $\mathbf{x} \in \mathfrak{X}$ may be written in one and only one way as $\mathbf{x} = \mathbf{y} + \mathbf{z}$, where $\mathbf{y} \in \mathfrak{M}$ and $\mathbf{z} \in \mathfrak{N}$.

8 *Example* Let $\mathbf{e}_1$, $\mathbf{e}_2$, and $\mathbf{e}_3$ be a basis for $\mathcal{C}^3$. Let $\mathfrak{M} = \mathcal{S}[\mathbf{e}_1,\mathbf{e}_2]$ and $\mathfrak{N} = \mathcal{S}[\mathbf{e}_3]$, that is, $\mathfrak{M}$ is the plane spanned by $\mathbf{e}_1$ and $\mathbf{e}_2$ and $\mathfrak{N}$ is the straight line spanned by $\mathbf{e}_3$. Clearly, $\mathcal{C}^3 = \mathfrak{M} \oplus \mathfrak{N}$. ◁

Going back to the subspaces $\mathfrak{M}$ and $\mathfrak{M}_0$ of $\mathcal{C}^n$ defined in Theorem *1*, we see that their relation can be expressed by

$$\mathcal{C}^n = \mathfrak{M} \oplus \mathfrak{M}_0 \qquad \mathfrak{M} \perp \mathfrak{M}_0$$

By the second expression, $\mathbf{y} \in \mathfrak{M} \Rightarrow \langle \mathbf{y},\mathbf{y}_0\rangle = 0,\ \forall \mathbf{y}_0 \in \mathfrak{M}_0$.

9 **Corollary** With the notation of Theorem *1*, we have

10 $$\dim \mathcal{C}^n = \dim \mathfrak{M} + \dim \mathfrak{M}_0$$

Proof Exercise for the reader. (*Hint:* Look at the proof of *1*.)

11 **Theorem** Let $\mathfrak{M}$ be a subspace of $\mathcal{C}^n$; then $\mathbf{y}$ is the orthogonal projection of $\mathbf{x}$ on $\mathfrak{M}$ if and only if

12 $$\|\mathbf{x} - \mathbf{y}\| = \min_{\mathbf{z} \in \mathfrak{M}} \|\mathbf{x} - \mathbf{z}\|$$

Proof Use the orthonormal basis *4* and the representation *5*. For any $\mathbf{z}$ in $\mathfrak{M}$, let $\mathbf{z} = \sum_{i=1}^{s} \zeta_i \mathbf{u}_i$. Hence

$$\mathbf{x} - \mathbf{z} = \sum_{i=1}^{s} (\xi_i - \zeta_i)\mathbf{u}_i + \sum_{k=s+1}^{s} \xi_k \mathbf{u}_k$$

and

$$\|\mathbf{x} - \mathbf{z}\|^2 = \sum_{i=1}^{s} |\xi_i - \zeta_i|^2 + \sum_{k=s+1}^{n} |\xi_k|^2$$

Clearly, $\|\mathbf{x} - \mathbf{z}\|$ is minimum if and only if $\xi_i = \zeta_i$, $i = 1, 2, \ldots, s$; that is, $\mathbf{z} = \mathbf{y}$.

8 *Reciprocal basis*

1 **Definition** Let $\mathcal{B} = \{\mathbf{u}_1, \mathbf{u}_2, \ldots, \mathbf{u}_n\}$ be a basis of $\mathbb{C}^n$. The reciprocal basis to $\mathcal{B}$ is the set of vectors $\{\mathbf{v}_1, \mathbf{v}_2 \ldots, \mathbf{v}_n\}$ such that

2 $$\langle \mathbf{v}_i, \mathbf{u}_j \rangle = \delta_{ij} \qquad i,j = 1, 2, \ldots, n \quad \triangleleft$$

In other words, $\langle \mathbf{v}_1, \mathbf{u}_1 \rangle = 1$ and $\mathbf{v}_1$ is orthogonal to $\mathbf{u}_2, \mathbf{u}_3, \ldots, \mathbf{u}_n$. The vectors $\mathbf{v}_1, \ldots, \mathbf{v}_n$ constitute a basis because (I) they are linearly independent and (II) they span the space $\mathbb{C}^n$. To establish (I) suppose they were not linearly independent; then $\Sigma_k \alpha_k \mathbf{v}_k = \mathbf{0}$ for some α_k's not all zero. From *2* we get, by taking the scalar product of the last vector equation with $\mathbf{u}_i$, $i = 1, 2, \ldots, n$,

$$\sum_{k=1}^{n} \alpha_k \langle \mathbf{u}_i, \mathbf{v}_k \rangle = \alpha_i \langle \mathbf{u}_i, \mathbf{v}_i \rangle = \alpha_i = 0 \qquad i = 1, 2, \ldots, n$$

Hence, $\alpha_i = 0$ for all i's, which contradicts the assumption that the $\mathbf{v}_i$'s were linearly dependent. (II) Any vector $\mathbf{x} \in \mathbb{C}^n$ can be expressed as a linear combination of the $\mathbf{v}_i$'s, viz.,

$$\mathbf{x} = \sum_{i=1}^{n} \langle \mathbf{u}_i, \mathbf{x} \rangle \mathbf{v}_i$$

To establish this relationship, let $\mathbf{y} \triangleq \mathbf{x} - \sum_{i=1}^{n} \langle \mathbf{u}_i, \mathbf{x} \rangle \mathbf{v}_i$. Taking the scalar product with $\mathbf{u}_k$ and using *2*, we get, as above, $\langle \mathbf{u}_k, \mathbf{y} \rangle = 0$, $k = 1, 2, \ldots, n$; hence, $\mathbf{y} = \mathbf{0}$ by Exercise *C.5.11*. The reciprocal basis to $\mathbf{u}_1$, $\mathbf{u}_2$ is illustrated in Fig. *C.8.1*.

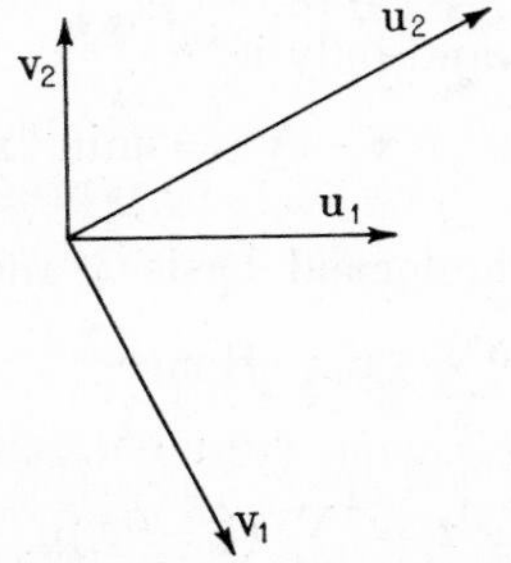

Fig. C.8.1 Relation between a basis $\{\mathbf{u}_1, \mathbf{u}_2\}$ for the plane and its reciprocal basis.

The main use of the reciprocal basis is the convenient expression for the components of any $\mathbf{x}$ in $\mathbb{C}^n$ relative to the basis $\{\mathbf{u}_1, \mathbf{u}_2, \ldots, \mathbf{u}_n\}$:

3 $$\mathbf{x} = \sum_{i=1}^{n} \langle \mathbf{v}_i, \mathbf{x} \rangle \mathbf{u}_i \qquad \forall \mathbf{x} \in \mathbb{C}^n$$

4 *Exercise* Let $\{\mathbf{u}_1,\mathbf{u}_2, \ldots ,\mathbf{u}_n\}$ be an arbitrary basis of $\mathcal{C}^n$. Let u_{ij}, $j = 1, 2, \ldots, n$, be the n components of $\mathbf{u}_i$. The matrix $\mathbf{U} = (u_{ij})$ has as its ith column the components of $\mathbf{u}_i$. Let $\mathbf{V}$ be the matrix whose jth row consists of the complex conjugate of the components of $\mathbf{v}_j$, where $\{\mathbf{v}_1, \ldots ,\mathbf{v}_n\}$ is the reciprocal basis of $\{\mathbf{u}_1, \ldots ,\mathbf{u}_n\}$. Show that

$$\mathbf{VU} = \mathbf{I} \qquad \text{or equivalently} \qquad \mathbf{V} = \mathbf{U}^{-1}$$

In other words, the computation of a reciprocal basis amounts to a matrix inversion.

5 *Exercise* Let $\{\mathbf{v}_1,\mathbf{v}_2, \ldots ,\mathbf{v}\}$ be a basis for $\mathcal{C}^n$. Show that the n scalars $\langle \mathbf{v}_i,\mathbf{x}\rangle$ uniquely define $\mathbf{x}$. (*Hint:* Use *3*.)

9 *Linear transformation*

The principal reason for learning the basic facts and the terminology of linear vector spaces is to provide a framework to discuss the linear transformations, or linear operators as they are often called. We shall give a very general definition of linear transformations in order to emphasize the fact that they appear in almost all branches of engineering. Very soon, however, we shall restrict ourselves to linear transformations whose domain and whose range are an n-dimensional linear vector space.

1 **Definition** A *linear transformation* (or a linear operator) $\mathcal{L}$ is a function whose domain is a linear vector space $\mathfrak{X}$ and whose range is in a linear vector space $\mathcal{Y}$ such that for any $\mathbf{x}_1$ and $\mathbf{x}_2$ in $\mathfrak{X}$ and any scalar α

(I) $\quad \mathbf{y}_1 = \mathcal{L}\mathbf{x}_1 \Rightarrow \alpha\mathbf{y}_1 = \mathcal{L}(\alpha\mathbf{x}_1)$

(II) $\quad \mathbf{y}_i = \mathcal{L}\mathbf{x}_i, i = 1, 2 \Rightarrow \mathcal{L}(\mathbf{x}_1 + \mathbf{x}_2) = \mathbf{y}_1 + \mathbf{y}_2$

2 *Example* Let $\mathbf{x}$ be an n-rowed column vector whose elements are complex numbers and let $\mathcal{L}$ be represented by $\mathbf{A}$, an $m \times n$ matrix of complex numbers; $\mathbf{y}$ is the m-rowed column vector

$$\mathbf{Ax} = \mathbf{y}$$

Here $\mathfrak{X} = \mathcal{C}^n$ is the usual n-dimensional vector space and $\mathcal{Y}$ an m-dimensional vector space. If $m = n$, $\mathcal{Y}$ is usually identified with $\mathfrak{X}$. In many applications where $m < n$, $\mathcal{Y}$ is considered to be a subspace of $\mathfrak{X}$.

3 *Example* Let $\mathfrak{X}$ be the set of all bounded integrable functions over $(-\infty,+\infty)$; let $\mathcal{Y}$ be identical to $\mathfrak{X}$. The transformation is defined in terms of a function $h(t)$ such that $\int_{-\infty}^{+\infty} |h(\tau)|\, d\tau < \infty$:

$$y(t) = \int_{-\infty}^{+\infty} h(t - \tau)x(\tau)\, d\tau \qquad -\infty < t < \infty$$

x is the input and y is the zero-state response of a linear time-invariant system whose impulse response is $h(t)$.

4 *Example* $\mathfrak{X}$ is the set of all functions having continuous derivatives in $(-\infty,+\infty)$. $\mathcal{Y}$ is the set of continuous functions in $(-\infty,\infty)$. The linear transformation is defined by

$$y = \frac{d}{dt}x$$

5 *Example* $\mathfrak{X}$ is the set of all periodic functions with the same period $T = 2\pi/\omega_0$, with continuous derivative. Thus for any $x \in \mathfrak{X}$,

$$x(t) = \sum_{-\infty}^{+\infty} \xi_n \exp(jn\omega_0 t) \qquad -\frac{\pi}{\omega_0} \leq t \leq \frac{\pi}{\omega_0}$$

where the ξ_n's are the components of x with respect to the orthogonal basis $\{\exp(jn\omega_0 t)\}_{-\infty}^{+\infty}$. Let y be the steady-state output of a given linear time-invariant system when x is the input; then, we know that (see *9.4.17*)

$$y(t) = \sum_{-\infty}^{+\infty} H(jn\omega_0)\xi_n \exp(jn\omega_0 t)$$

where $H(j\omega)$ is the transfer function of the system and H is assumed to be strictly stable. As x ranges over $\mathfrak{X}$, y will range over a linear vector space $\mathcal{Y}$. Thus, the linear system defines a linear transformation $\mathfrak{N}$ on the inputs x to obtain the outputs y.

6 **Definition** The *range of a linear transformation* $\mathcal{A}$ is the set $\mathcal{R}(\mathcal{A})$ defined by

$$\mathcal{R}(\mathcal{A}) = \{\mathbf{y} \in \mathcal{Y} | \mathbf{y} = \mathcal{A}\mathbf{x} \text{ for some } \mathbf{x} \in \mathfrak{X}\}$$

In other words, $\mathcal{R}(\mathcal{A})$ is the image of the vector space $\mathfrak{X}$ under the linear transformation $\mathcal{A}$.

7 **Definition** The *null space of an L.T.*[1] $\mathcal{A}$ is the set $\mathfrak{N}(\mathcal{A})$ defined by

$$\mathfrak{N}(\mathcal{A}) = \{\mathbf{x} \in \mathfrak{X} | \mathcal{A}\mathbf{x} = \mathbf{0}\}$$

That is, $\mathfrak{N}(\mathcal{A})$ is the set of all vectors of $\mathfrak{X}$ that $\mathcal{A}$ maps into the zero vector of $\mathcal{Y}$.

8 **Remark** It is very important to realize that *in general* $\mathcal{R}(\mathcal{A})$ and $\mathfrak{N}(\mathcal{A})$ *may have nonzero vectors in common.* Take $\mathbb{C}^2$ and $\mathbf{A} = \begin{bmatrix} 0 & 1 \\ 0 & 0 \end{bmatrix}$: since $\mathbf{A}^2 = \begin{bmatrix} 0 & 0 \\ 0 & 0 \end{bmatrix}$, any vector $\mathbf{x} = (\alpha,0)$ is in both $\mathcal{R}(\mathbf{A})$ and $\mathfrak{N}(\mathbf{A})$. Indeed, $\mathbf{x}$ is the image of $\mathbf{z} = (0,\alpha)$ under $\mathbf{A}$ (that is, $\mathbf{x} = \mathbf{A}\mathbf{z}$) and $\mathbf{A}\mathbf{x} = \mathbf{0}$.

[1] L.T. is an abbreviation for linear transformation.

9 *Exercise* Show that $\mathcal{R}(\mathcal{A})$ and $\mathcal{N}(\mathcal{A})$ are linear vector spaces.

10 **Definition** The dimension of the subspace $\mathcal{R}(\mathcal{A})$ is called the *rank* of the linear transformation $\mathcal{A}$. The dimension of $\mathcal{N}(\mathcal{A})$ is called the *nullity* of the linear transformation $\mathcal{A}$.

10 *Representation of an linear transformation in* $\mathcal{C}^n$

Let $\mathcal{L}$ be an L.T. mapping of the n-dimensional space $\mathcal{C}^n$ into the m-dimensional space $\mathcal{C}^m$. We shall show that with respect to a specified basis in $\mathcal{C}^n$ and a specified basis in $\mathcal{C}^m$ the linear transformation $\mathcal{L}$ is represented by a matrix $\mathbf{L}$. The matrix $\mathbf{L}$ representing the L.T. depends on the particular bases chosen. This dependence of the representation of the L.T. on the basis is analogous to the dependence of the components of a vector on the basis. For example, a vector $\mathbf{a}$ in a plane is represented by the ordered pair (0,1) with respect to a first basis and is represented by $(1/\sqrt{2}, 1/\sqrt{2})$ with respect to another basis.

Let $\{\mathbf{u}_1,\mathbf{u}_2, \ldots ,\mathbf{u}_n\}$ be a basis for $\mathcal{C}^n$ and $\{\mathbf{v}_1, \ldots ,\mathbf{v}_m\}$ be a basis for $\mathcal{C}^m$. Consider the arbitrary vector $\mathbf{x} \in \mathcal{C}^n$; then $\mathbf{x}$ has a unique representation in terms of the basis $\{\mathbf{u}_1, \mathbf{u}_2, \ldots ,\mathbf{u}_n\}$,

1 $$\mathbf{x} = \sum_{i=1}^{n} \xi_i \mathbf{u}_i$$

Consider the vector $\mathcal{L}\mathbf{u}_i$. It belongs to $\mathcal{C}^m$; hence, it has a unique representation in terms of the basis $\{\mathbf{v}_1,\mathbf{v}_2, \ldots ,\mathbf{v}_m\}$. Define the scalars λ_{ji} by

2 $$\mathcal{L}\mathbf{u}_i = \sum_{j=1}^{m} \lambda_{ji}\mathbf{v}_j \qquad i = 1, 2, \ldots , n$$

By direct application of the definition of an L.T.,

$$\mathbf{y} = \mathcal{L}\mathbf{x} = \mathcal{L}\left(\sum_{i=1}^{n} \xi_i\mathbf{u}_i\right) = \sum_{i=1}^{n} \xi_i\mathcal{L}\mathbf{u}_i = \sum_{i=1}^{n} \xi_i \left(\sum_{j=1}^{m} \lambda_{ji}\mathbf{v}_j\right)$$

where we have used *1*, the properties (I) and (II) of *C.9.1*, and *2*. Finally,

$$\mathbf{y} = \sum_{j=1}^{m} \left(\sum_{i=1}^{n} \lambda_{ji}\xi_i\right) \mathbf{v}_j$$

Thus the components η_j of $\mathbf{y}$ relative to the basis $\mathbf{v}_1, \mathbf{v}_2, \ldots , \mathbf{v}_m$ of $\mathcal{C}^m$ are obtained in terms of the components of $\mathbf{x}$ relative to the basis

$\mathbf{u}_1, \ldots, \mathbf{u}_n$ of $\mathcal{C}^n$ by the operation

3 $$\eta_j = \sum_{i=1}^{n} \lambda_{ji}\xi_i$$

Thus we are led to state the

4 **Theorem** Given a basis $\{\mathbf{u}_1,\mathbf{u}_2, \ldots ,\mathbf{u}_n\}$ of $\mathcal{C}^n$ and a basis $\{\mathbf{v}_1, \ldots ,\mathbf{v}_m\}$ of $\mathcal{C}^m$ the L.T. $\mathcal{L}$ mapping $\mathcal{C}^n$ into $\mathcal{C}^m$ is represented by a matrix $\mathbf{L} = (\lambda_{ji})$ whose ith column consists of the components of $\mathcal{L}\mathbf{u}_i$ relative to the basis $\{\mathbf{v}_1, \ldots ,\mathbf{v}_m\}$. ◁

Frequently we shall drop the distinction between the L.T. $\mathcal{L}$ and its matrix representation $\mathbf{L}$ when we are studying a specific problem in which the bases are fixed once and for all throughout the problem.

5 *Exercise* The purpose of this exercise is to show that the definitions of matrix addition and matrix multiplication follow naturally from the consideration of addition and composition of L.T. Let $\mathcal{C}^n$ be a vector space with basis $\{\mathbf{u}_1,\mathbf{u}_2, \ldots ,\mathbf{u}_n\}$. Let $\mathcal{A}$ and $\mathcal{B}$ be two L.T.'s on $\mathcal{C}^n$ into itself. *The sum* $\mathcal{A} + \mathcal{B}$ is defined as the L.T. which maps any vector $\mathbf{x} \in \mathcal{C}^n$ into the vector $\mathcal{A}\mathbf{x} + \mathcal{B}\mathbf{x}$. *The product* $\mathcal{A}\mathcal{B}$ is the L.T. which maps the vector $\mathbf{x} \in \mathcal{C}^n$ into the vector $\mathbf{z} \in \mathcal{C}^n$, where $\mathbf{z}$ is defined as follows: let $\mathbf{y} = \mathcal{B}\mathbf{x}$; then $\mathbf{z} = \mathcal{A}\mathbf{y}$. This may be written as $\mathbf{z} = \mathcal{A}(\mathcal{B}\mathbf{x})$. Show that if, with respect to the given basis of $\mathcal{C}^n$, the L.T. $\mathcal{A}$ and $\mathcal{B}$ are respectively represented by the matrices $\mathbf{A} = (\alpha_{ij})$ and $\mathbf{B} = (\beta_{ij})$, then

(I) $\mathcal{A} + \mathcal{B}$ is represented by the matrix $\mathbf{A} + \mathbf{B} = (\alpha_{ij} + \beta_{ij})$.

(II) $\mathcal{A}\mathcal{B}$ is represented by the matrix $\mathbf{AB} = \left(\sum_{k=1}^{n} \alpha_{ik}\beta_{kj}\right)$.

6 *Exercise* Using the notation of Exercise *5*, construct an example in $\mathcal{C}^2$ showing that

(I) $\mathbf{AB} \neq \mathbf{BA}$.

(II) $\mathbf{CD} = \mathbf{0}$, where $\mathbf{C} \neq \mathbf{0}$, $\mathbf{D} \neq \mathbf{0}$, and $\mathbf{0}$ is the zero matrix, namely, the matrix all of whose elements are zero.

7 **Remark** (I) of Exercise *6* shows that matrix multiplication is not commutative; (II) shows that in matrix algebra there are divisors of zero and consequently the cancellation law of ordinary algebra does not apply to matrices. In other words, $\mathbf{AB} = \mathbf{AC}$ and $\mathbf{A} \neq \mathbf{0}$ do not imply $\mathbf{B} = \mathbf{C}$.

8 *Exercise* Let $\mathbf{A} = \begin{bmatrix} 0 & 1 & 0 \\ 0 & 0 & 1 \\ 0 & 0 & 0 \end{bmatrix}$. Show that $\mathbf{A}^3$ is the zero matrix.

(Again, $\mathbf{A}$ is a nonzero matrix and $\mathbf{A} \cdot \mathbf{A} \cdot \mathbf{A}$ is the zero matrix.)

9 **Theorem** Let $\mathcal{A}$ be an L.T. of $\mathcal{C}^n$ into $\mathcal{C}^n$. Let the $n \times n$ matrix $\mathbf{A}$ be the representation of $\mathcal{A}$ with respect to some basis of $\mathcal{C}^n$. Then

$$\text{rank of } \mathcal{A} \triangleq \dim \mathcal{R}(\mathcal{A}) = \text{rank } (\mathbf{A})$$

That is, the rank of the linear transformation $\mathcal{A}$ is the rank of the matrix **A** which represents the linear transformation with respect to some basis.

Proof This assertion follows directly from Theorem *4*, the definition of the rank of $\mathcal{A}$, and standard properties of determinants. It is therefore left as an exercise for the reader.

11 *Matrix representation of an L.T. and changes of bases*

Let, for simplicity, $\mathcal{L}$ be an L.T. of $\mathcal{C}^n$ into $\mathcal{C}^n$. Let $\{\mathbf{u}_1,\mathbf{u}_2, \ldots ,\mathbf{u}_n\}$ be a basis of $\mathcal{C}^n$ and $\mathbf{L} = (\lambda_{ij})$ be the corresponding representation of $\mathcal{L}$; that is, from *C.10.2*,

1
$$\mathcal{L}\mathbf{u}_i = \sum_{j=1}^{n} \lambda_{ji}\mathbf{u}_j$$

Let $\{\hat{\mathbf{u}}_1,\hat{\mathbf{u}}_2, \ldots ,\hat{\mathbf{u}}_n\}$ be a new basis of $\mathcal{C}^n$. The problem is to find $\hat{\mathbf{L}}$, the matrix representation of $\mathcal{L}$ with respect to the new basis.

Expand the new basis vectors in terms of the old:

2
$$\hat{\mathbf{u}}_i = \sum_{\alpha=1}^{n} c_{\alpha i}\mathbf{u}_\alpha$$

That is, the ith column of the matrix $(c_{\alpha i})$ consists of the components of $\hat{\mathbf{u}}_i$ relative to the old basis.

Now consider an arbitrary vector $\mathbf{x} \in \mathcal{C}^n$. The components of $\mathbf{x}$ are defined as

$$\mathbf{x} = \sum_{\alpha} \xi_\alpha \mathbf{u}_\alpha = \sum_{\beta} \hat{\xi}_\beta \hat{\mathbf{u}}_\beta$$

Hence, from *2*,

$$\mathbf{x} = \sum_{\beta} \hat{\xi}_\beta \sum_{\alpha} c_{\alpha\beta}\mathbf{u}_\alpha = \sum_{\alpha} \Big(\sum_{\beta} c_{\alpha\beta}\hat{\xi}_\beta\Big) \mathbf{u}_\alpha$$

and by the uniqueness of the representation (see *C.4.4*)

$$\xi_\alpha = \sum_{\beta=1}^{n} c_{\alpha\beta}\hat{\xi}_\beta \qquad \alpha = 1, 2, \ldots, n$$

Hence, we conclude:

3 The column vector of the old components (ξ_α) of $\mathbf{x}$ is the product of the matrix $\mathbf{C} = (c_{\alpha\beta})$ and the column vector of the new components $(\hat{\xi}_\beta)$ of $\mathbf{x}$, where $\mathbf{C}$ is the matrix defined in *2*.

Let us now compute the relation between $\mathbf{L}$ and $\hat{\mathbf{L}}$. From the definition of $\hat{\mathbf{L}}$ (by analogy with *1*) we get, using *2*,

4
$$\begin{aligned}\mathcal{L}\hat{\mathbf{u}}_\alpha &= \sum_{\beta} \hat{\lambda}_{\beta\alpha}\hat{\mathbf{u}}_\beta = \sum_{\beta} \hat{\lambda}_{\beta\alpha} \Big(\sum_{\gamma} c_{\gamma\beta}\mathbf{u}_\gamma\Big) \\ &= \sum_{\gamma} \Big(\sum_{\beta} \hat{\lambda}_{\beta\alpha}c_{\gamma\beta}\Big) \mathbf{u}_\gamma\end{aligned}$$

Using *2*, rewrite $\mathcal{L}\hat{\mathbf{u}}_\alpha$ in a different way and use *1* to get

5 $$\mathcal{L}\hat{\mathbf{u}}_\alpha = \mathcal{L}\left(\sum_\eta c_{\eta\alpha}\mathbf{u}_\eta\right) = \sum_\eta c_{\eta\alpha}\left(\sum_\gamma \lambda_{\gamma\eta}\mathbf{u}_\gamma\right) = \sum_\gamma\left(\sum_\eta c_{\eta\alpha}\lambda_{\gamma\eta}\right)\mathbf{u}_\gamma$$

Comparing *4* and *5*,

$$\sum_\eta c_{\eta\alpha}\lambda_{\gamma\eta} = \sum_\beta \hat{\lambda}_{\beta\alpha}c_{\gamma\beta} \qquad \alpha,\gamma = 1, 2, \ldots, n$$

Let $\mathbf{C}$ be the matrix $(c_{\alpha\beta})$; then

$$\mathbf{LC} = \mathbf{C\hat{L}}$$

These results can be condensed in the following

6 **Theorem** Let $\mathcal{L}$ be a linear transformation of $\mathcal{C}^n$ into $\mathcal{C}^n$. Let $\{\mathbf{u}_1, \ldots, \mathbf{u}_n\}$ and $\{\hat{\mathbf{u}}_1, \ldots, \hat{\mathbf{u}}_n\}$ be respectively the old and the new bases of $\mathcal{C}^n$. Let $\mathbf{C}$ be the matrix $(c_{\alpha\beta})$ expressing the new basis vectors in terms of the old ones:

$$\hat{\mathbf{u}}_i = \sum_{k=1}^n c_{ki}\mathbf{u}_k$$

If $\mathbf{L}$ and $\hat{\mathbf{L}}$ are the matrix representations of $\mathcal{L}$ with respect to the corresponding bases, then

7 $$\hat{\mathbf{L}} = \mathbf{C}^{-1}\mathbf{LC}$$

If $\mathbf{x} \in \mathcal{C}^n$ and if

8 $$\mathbf{x} = \sum_{k=1}^n \xi_k\mathbf{u}_k = \sum_{i=1}^n \hat{\xi}_i\hat{\mathbf{u}}_i$$

then

9 $$\xi_k = \sum_{j=1}^n c_{kj}\hat{\xi}_j \qquad k = 1, 2, \ldots, n$$

10 *Exercise* Show that $\mathbf{C}$ is nonsingular.

12 *Direct sums and projections*

Let us recall (see *C.5.12*) that a *subspace* $\mathcal{B}$ of a finite dimensional space $\mathcal{C}^n$ is a set of vectors in $\mathcal{C}^n$ such that if $\mathbf{x} \in \mathcal{B}$ and $\mathbf{y} \in \mathcal{B}$, then for all α's and β's, $\alpha\mathbf{x} + \beta\mathbf{y} \in \mathcal{B}$. Also recall that (see *C.7.7*) the space $\mathcal{C}^n$ is said to be the *direct sum* of two subspaces $\mathfrak{M}_1$ and $\mathfrak{M}_2$ if $\mathfrak{M}_1$ and $\mathfrak{M}_2$ are subspaces of $\mathcal{C}^n$ and if every $\mathbf{x} \in \mathcal{C}^n$ has one and only one representation as the sum of a vector in $\mathfrak{M}_1$ and a vector in $\mathfrak{M}_2$. This is written as

1 $$\mathcal{C}^n = \mathfrak{M}_1 \oplus \mathfrak{M}_2$$

From the definition we have for every $\mathbf{x}$ a unique representation of the form

2 $$\mathbf{x} = \mathbf{x}_1 + \mathbf{x}_2 \qquad \text{with } \mathbf{x}_i \in \mathfrak{M}_i \quad i = 1, 2$$

3 **Theorem** $\mathcal{C}^n = \mathfrak{M}_1 \oplus \mathfrak{M}_2 \Leftrightarrow \mathfrak{M}_1$ and $\mathfrak{M}_2$ have only the zero vector in common and any vector $\mathbf{x}$ in $\mathcal{C}^n$ can be represented as the sum of a vector in $\mathfrak{M}_1$ and a vector in $\mathfrak{M}_2$.

Proof Exercise for the reader.

4 **Definition** Let $\mathcal{C}^n = \mathfrak{M}_1 \oplus \mathfrak{M}_2$ and, $\forall \mathbf{x} \in \mathcal{C}^n$, let $\mathbf{x} = \mathbf{x}_1 + \mathbf{x}_2$, where $\mathbf{x}_i \in \mathfrak{M}_i$, $i = 1, 2$; then the transformation $\mathbf{E}$ such that

5 $$\mathbf{E}\mathbf{x} = \mathbf{x}_1$$

is called the *projection on* $\mathfrak{M}_1$ *along* $\mathfrak{M}_2$.

6 *Exercise* Verify that $\mathbf{E}$ is a *linear* transformation.

7 *Comment* It is important to be aware of two subtle points: (I) the projection just defined is not necessarily an orthogonal projection as was the case in Sec. *7*; (II) in order to completely define the projection, we must say the projection on $\mathfrak{M}_1$ *along* $\mathfrak{M}_2$. This point is illustrated in Fig. *C.12.1a*, where $\mathcal{C}^n$ is the plane and $\mathfrak{M}_1$ is the ξ axis. Figure *C.12.1a* shows a possible choice for $\mathfrak{M}_2$ and Fig. *C.12.1b* shows another. Note the difference between the projections of $\mathbf{x}$ on $\mathfrak{M}_1$ in the two cases.

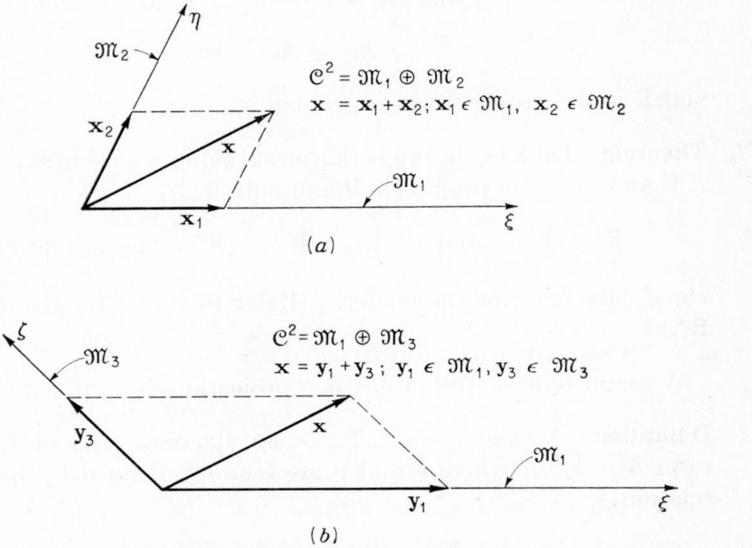

Fig. C.12.1 (*a*) If the vector $\mathbf{x}$ is decomposed according to the direct sum $\mathfrak{M}_1 \oplus \mathfrak{M}_2$, the result is $\mathbf{x}_1 + \mathbf{x}_2$. (*b*) If the decomposition is done according to $\mathfrak{M}_1 \oplus \mathfrak{M}_3$, the result is $\mathbf{y}_1 + \mathbf{y}_3$.

8 *Exercise* Let $\mathbf{E}$ be the projection on $\mathfrak{M}_1$ along $\mathfrak{M}_2$. Show that

$$\mathfrak{M}_1 = \mathcal{R}(\mathbf{E}) \triangleq \{\mathbf{x} | \mathbf{E}\mathbf{x} = \mathbf{x}\}$$
$$\mathfrak{M}_2 = \mathfrak{N}(\mathbf{E}) \triangleq \{\mathbf{y} | \mathbf{E}\mathbf{y} = \mathbf{0}\}$$

9 **Theorem** The L.T. $\mathbf{E}$ is the projection on $\mathfrak{M}_1$ along $\mathfrak{M}_2$ if and only if

10 $$\mathbf{E} = \mathbf{E}^2$$

where $\mathfrak{M}_1 = \mathcal{R}(\mathbf{E})$ and $\mathfrak{M}_2 = \mathfrak{N}(\mathbf{E})$.

Proof $\Rightarrow$ By Definition *4*, $\mathcal{C}^n = \mathfrak{M}_1 \oplus \mathfrak{M}_2$. Therefore, for any $\mathbf{x}$ in $\mathcal{C}^n$ there is a unique decomposition $\mathbf{x} = \mathbf{x}_1 + \mathbf{x}_2$, with $\mathbf{x}_i \in \mathfrak{M}_i$. The decomposition of $\mathbf{x}_1$ is $\mathbf{x}_1 + \mathbf{0}$. Therefore, by the definition of $\mathbf{E}$,

$$\mathbf{E}^2\mathbf{x} = \mathbf{E}(\mathbf{E}\mathbf{x}) = \mathbf{E}\mathbf{x}_1 = \mathbf{x}_1 = \mathbf{E}\mathbf{x} \qquad \forall \mathbf{x} \in \mathcal{C}^n$$

and *10* follows.

$\Leftarrow$ We have the algebraic fact that

$$\mathbf{x} = \mathbf{E}\mathbf{x} + (\mathbf{I} - \mathbf{E})\mathbf{x}$$

Clearly $\mathbf{E}\mathbf{x} \in \mathfrak{M}_1$. We assert that $(\mathbf{I} - \mathbf{E})\mathbf{x} \in \mathfrak{M}_2$; indeed, the assumption $\mathbf{E} = \mathbf{E}^2$ implies that $\mathbf{E}(\mathbf{I} - \mathbf{E})\mathbf{x} = (\mathbf{E} - \mathbf{E}^2)\mathbf{x} = \mathbf{0}$, that is, $(\mathbf{I} - \mathbf{E})\mathbf{x} \in \mathfrak{N}(\mathbf{E}) \triangleq \mathfrak{M}_2$. Thus any $\mathbf{x}$ in $\mathcal{C}^n$ can be written as a sum of a vector in $\mathfrak{M}_1$ and a vector in $\mathfrak{M}_2$. By *3* it remains to show that $\mathfrak{M}_1$ and $\mathfrak{M}_2$ have only the vector $\mathbf{0}$ in common. Suppose $\mathbf{y} \in \mathfrak{M}_1$ and $\mathbf{y} \in \mathfrak{M}_2$. Then, by *8*, $\mathbf{E}\mathbf{y} = \mathbf{y}$ and $\mathbf{E}\mathbf{y} = \mathbf{0}$; hence, $\mathbf{y} = \mathbf{0}$. Therefore,

$$\mathfrak{M}_1 \oplus \mathfrak{M}_2 = \mathcal{C}^n$$

and $\mathbf{E}$ is the projection on $\mathfrak{M}_1$ along $\mathfrak{M}_2$.

11 **Theorem** Let $\mathbf{E}$ be the projection on $\mathfrak{M}_1$ along $\mathfrak{M}_2$ where $\mathfrak{M}_1 \oplus \mathfrak{M}_2 = \mathcal{C}^n$. E is an *orthogonal* projection if and only if

$$\mathbf{E}^2 = \mathbf{E} \quad \text{and} \quad \mathbf{E}^* = \mathbf{E} \quad (\mathbf{E}^* \text{ is the adjoint of } \mathbf{E})$$

Proof Exercise for the reader. (Refer to *C.14.1* for the definition of $\mathbf{E}^*$.)

A useful representation of some projections is obtained by the *dyad*.

12 **Definition** A *dyad* is an L.T., or an algebraic sum of L.T.[1] of the form $\mathbf{A} = \mathbf{a}\rangle\langle\mathbf{b}$ (where $\mathbf{a}$ and $\mathbf{b}$ are vectors), defined by the following relation:

13 $$\mathbf{A}\mathbf{x} = \langle\mathbf{b},\mathbf{x}\rangle\mathbf{a} \qquad \text{for all } \mathbf{x} \in \mathcal{C}^n$$

[1] In cases where the dyad consists of only one such term, it is sometimes referred to as a "one-term dyad."

In other words, **A** maps any vector **x** into a vector proportional to **a**; clearly, then, $\mathcal{R}(\mathbf{a}\rangle\langle\mathbf{b}) = \mathcal{S}[\mathbf{a}]$. The rank of $\mathbf{a}\rangle\langle\mathbf{b}$ is unity and its nullity is $n - 1$ because $\mathfrak{N}(\mathbf{a}\rangle\langle\mathbf{b})$ is the hyperplane orthogonal to **b**, that is, $\{\mathbf{x}|\langle\mathbf{b},\mathbf{x}\rangle = 0\}$.

14 *Exercise* Establish that the matrix representation of a one-term dyad $\mathbf{a}\rangle\langle\mathbf{b}$ may be described as follows. Consider an arbitrary orthonormal basis $\mathcal{B}$: let (α_i) and (β_j) be the components of **a** and **b** with respect to the basis $\mathcal{B}$; then the (i,k) element of the matrix representing $\mathbf{a}\rangle\langle\mathbf{b}$ is $\alpha_i\beta_k^*$.

15 *Exercise* Consider two dyads $\mathbf{A} = \mathbf{a}\rangle\langle\mathbf{b}$, $\mathbf{B} = \mathbf{c}\rangle\langle\mathbf{d}$. Show that $\mathbf{AB} = \langle\mathbf{b},\mathbf{c}\rangle\,\mathbf{C}$, where $\mathbf{C} = \mathbf{a}\rangle\langle\mathbf{d}$.

16 **Theorem** Let $\mathcal{B} = \{\mathbf{u}_1,\mathbf{u}_2, \ldots ,\mathbf{u}_n\}$ be a basis and $\{\mathbf{v}_1, \ldots ,\mathbf{v}_n\}$ be the reciprocal basis of $\mathcal{B}$. For $i = 1, 2, \ldots, n$ let

$$\mathfrak{M}_i = \mathcal{S}[\mathbf{u}_i] \qquad \text{and} \qquad \mathfrak{M}_i' = \mathcal{S}[\mathbf{u}_1,\mathbf{u}_2, \ldots ,\mathbf{u}_{i-1},\mathbf{u}_{i+1}, \ldots ,\mathbf{u}_n]$$

Then

$$\mathbf{E}_i = \mathbf{u}_i\rangle\langle\mathbf{v}_i \qquad i = 1, 2, \ldots, n$$

is the projection on $\mathfrak{M}_i$ along $\mathfrak{M}_i'$.

Proof By direct computation, using Exercise *15* and $\langle\mathbf{u}_i,\mathbf{v}_i\rangle = 1$, we get $\mathbf{E}_i^2 = \mathbf{E}_i$; hence, $\mathbf{E}_i$ is a projection. We also have $\mathcal{R}(\mathbf{E}_i) = \mathcal{S}[\mathbf{u}_i] = \mathfrak{M}_i$ and $\mathfrak{N}(\mathbf{E}_i) = \{\mathbf{y}|\langle\mathbf{v}_i,\mathbf{y}\rangle = 0\}$. Now, from the definition of the reciprocal basis, that set is spanned by $\mathbf{u}_1, \ldots, \mathbf{u}_{i-1}, \mathbf{u}_{i+1}, \ldots, \mathbf{u}_n$; hence $\mathfrak{N}(\mathbf{E}_i) = \mathfrak{M}_i'$. Therefore, $\mathbf{E}_i$ is the projection on $\mathfrak{M}_i$ along $\mathfrak{M}_i'$.

17 **Corollary** With the same notation as above, with **I** being the identity transformation

18 $$\mathbf{I} = \sum_{i=1}^{n} \mathbf{u}_i\rangle\langle\mathbf{v}_i$$

and, for all $\mathbf{x} \in \mathcal{C}^n$,

19 $$\mathbf{x} = \Big(\sum_{i=1}^{n} \mathbf{u}_i\rangle\langle\mathbf{v}_i\Big)\,\mathbf{x} = \sum_{i=1}^{n} \langle\mathbf{v}_i,\mathbf{x}\rangle\mathbf{u}_i$$

Proof Exercise for the reader.

20 **Corollary** The projections $\mathbf{E}_i$ defined in Theorem *16* are such that

$$\mathbf{E}_i\mathbf{E}_k = \delta_{ik}\mathbf{E}_i \qquad i,k = 1, 2, \ldots, n$$

$$\sum_{i=1}^{n} \mathbf{E}_i = \mathbf{I}$$

21 **Corollary** Let $\mathbf{A} = (a_{ij})$ be the matrix representation of an L.T. $\mathcal{A}$ relative to the basis $\mathcal{B} \triangleq \{\mathbf{u}_1,\mathbf{u}_2, \ldots ,\mathbf{u}_n\}$. Let $\mathbf{v}_1, \ldots, \mathbf{v}_n$ be the reciprocal basis to $\mathcal{B}$. Then a dyad representation of $\mathcal{A}$ is

22 $$\sum_{i=1}^{n} \Big(\mathbf{u}_i\rangle\langle\sum_{j=1}^{n} a_{ij}^*\mathbf{v}_j\Big)$$

Proof Clearly *22* is a dyad representation, Call it **B**. It remains to show that **B** represents the L.T. $\mathcal{A}$. In particular, we need only show that

$$\mathbf{B}\mathbf{u}_k = \mathbf{A}\mathbf{u}_k \qquad k = 1, 2, \ldots, n$$

By *22*, and since $\langle \mathbf{v}_j, \mathbf{u}_k \rangle = \delta_{jk}$ by definition of a reciprocal basis, we have

$$\mathbf{B}\mathbf{u}_k = \sum_{i=1}^{n} a_{ik}\mathbf{u}_i \qquad k = 1, 2, \ldots, n$$

That is, $\mathbf{B}\mathbf{u}_k$ has $(a_{1k}, a_{2k}, \ldots, a_{nk})$ as components with respect to the basis $\mathcal{B}$.

By *C.10.4* we also have

$$\mathbf{A}\mathbf{u}_k = \sum_{i=1}^{n} a_{ik}\mathbf{u}_i \qquad k = 1, 2, \ldots, n$$

Hence the corollary is established.

13 *Invariant subspaces*

1 **Definition** $\mathfrak{M}$ is said to be an *invariant subspace under the L.T.* **A** if $\mathbf{x} \in \mathfrak{M} \Rightarrow \mathbf{A}\mathbf{x} \in \mathfrak{M}$.

2 *Exercise* Show that the sets $\mathcal{C}^n$, $\mathcal{R}(\mathbf{A})$, $\mathfrak{N}(\mathbf{A})$, $\left\{\mathbf{x} \mid \sum_{k=0}^{N} \alpha_k \mathbf{A}^k \mathbf{x} = \mathbf{0}\right.$, where the α_k's are numbers and N is an arbitrary integer$\left.\right\}$ are invariant subspaces under **A**.

3 **Theorem** Let $\mathcal{C}^n = \mathfrak{M} \oplus \mathfrak{N}$. Let $\mathfrak{M}$ be invariant under **A** and have dimension k; then the L.T. **A** has a matrix representation of the form

4
$$\begin{array}{c} \\ k\{ \\ \\ \end{array} \overbrace{\left[\begin{array}{c|c} \mathbf{P} & \mathbf{R} \\ \hline \mathbf{0} & \mathbf{Q} \end{array}\right]}^{k} \begin{array}{c} \\ \\ \} \; n-k \end{array}$$
$$\underbrace{\qquad\qquad}_{n-k}$$

provided a suitable basis of $\mathcal{C}^n$ is used.

Proof Let $\{\mathbf{u}_1, \mathbf{u}_2, \ldots, \mathbf{u}_k\}$ be a basis for $\mathfrak{M}$ and $\{\mathbf{u}_{k+1}, \mathbf{u}_{k+2}, \ldots, \mathbf{u}_n\}$ be a basis for $\mathfrak{N}$. Then $\{\mathbf{u}_1, \mathbf{u}_2, \ldots, \mathbf{u}_n\}$ is a basis for $\mathcal{C}^n$. The zero submatrix in *4* follows immediately from the fact that for any

$$\mathbf{x} \in \mathfrak{M} \rightarrow \mathbf{x} = \sum_{1}^{k} \xi_i \mathbf{u}_i$$

for some ξ_i's and $\mathbf{Ax} = \sum_1^k \eta_i \mathbf{u}_i$, since $\mathfrak{M}$ is invariant under **A**. (The η_i's are appropriate linear combinations of the ξ_k's.)

5 **Corollary** If $\mathcal{C}^n = \mathfrak{M} \oplus \mathfrak{N}$ and both $\mathfrak{M}$ and $\mathfrak{N}$ are invariant under **A**, then the L.T. **A** has a representation of the form

$$\left[\begin{array}{c|c} \mathbf{P} & \mathbf{0} \\ \hline \mathbf{0} & \mathbf{Q} \end{array}\right]$$

6 *Comment* These two results form the basis for the diagonalization of matrices. (See also *D.5.21*.)

14 *Adjoint transformation*

The concept of the adjoint of an L.T. plays a very important role in many problems. It is used throughout the text and is basic to the developments of the rest of this appendix. Section *20* is, in fact, devoted to the review of those problems in which the adjoint is important.

1 **Definition** Let **A** be an L.T. on $\mathcal{C}^n$.[1] The adjoint transformation $\mathbf{A}^*$ of **A** is a transformation such that

2 $$\langle \mathbf{Ax},\mathbf{y}\rangle = \langle \mathbf{x},\mathbf{A}^*\mathbf{y}\rangle \qquad \forall \mathbf{x},\mathbf{y} \in \mathcal{C}^n$$

3 *Exercise* Verify that the transformation $\mathbf{A}^*$ defined by *2* is linear. [*Hint:* Consider $\langle \mathbf{x},\mathbf{A}(\mathbf{y}_1 + \mathbf{y}_2)\rangle$ $\forall \mathbf{x},\mathbf{y}_1,\mathbf{y}_2$; use *1* and the linearity of the scalar product (see *C.5.1*).]

4 *Exercise* Show that $(\mathbf{AB})^* = \mathbf{B}^*\mathbf{A}^*$; $(\mathbf{A}+\mathbf{B})^* = \mathbf{A}^* + \mathbf{B}^*$; $(\alpha\mathbf{A})^* = \alpha^*\mathbf{A}^*$, where α is any scalar.

5 **Theorem** $(\mathbf{A}^*)^* = \mathbf{A}$.

Proof Interchange the order of the factors in the scalar products of *2*:

$$\langle \mathbf{y},\mathbf{Ax}\rangle = \langle \mathbf{A}^*\mathbf{y},\mathbf{x}\rangle \qquad \forall \mathbf{x},\mathbf{y} \in \mathcal{C}^n$$

Apply the property defined by *2* to the right-hand side of the above relation and get

$$\langle \mathbf{y},\mathbf{Ax}\rangle = \langle \mathbf{y},(\mathbf{A}^*)^*\mathbf{x}\rangle \qquad \forall \mathbf{x},\mathbf{y} \in \mathcal{C}^n$$

Hence

$$\langle \mathbf{y},[\mathbf{A} - (\mathbf{A}^*)^*]\mathbf{x}\rangle = 0 \qquad \forall \mathbf{x},\mathbf{y} \in \mathcal{C}^n$$

[1] Strictly speaking, we should use the notation $\mathfrak{A}$ for the L.T. and **A** for its matrix representation with respect to some basis. However, to adhere strictly to this notation becomes very cumbersome. In the following we shall often use the same notation for an L.T. and its matrix representation.

Since this equality holds for all **y**'s and **x**'s, it holds in particular if **y** is successively taken to be the vectors of a basis of $\mathcal{C}^n$. Consequently, by *C.5.11*,

$$[\mathbf{A} - (\mathbf{A}^*)^*]\mathbf{x} = \mathbf{0} \qquad \forall \mathbf{x} \in \mathcal{C}^n$$

Therefore, the L.T. $\mathbf{A} - (\mathbf{A}^*)^*$ is the L.T. that maps any **x** into **0**; in other words, $\mathbf{A} = (\mathbf{A}^*)^*$.

6 **Theorem** Let $\mathcal{A}$ be an L.T. in $\mathcal{C}^n$ and **A** its matrix representation relative to an orthonormal basis. The matrix representation of the adjoint transformation $\mathcal{A}^*$ (relative to the same basis) is the conjugate transpose of the matrix **A**.

Proof By definition, $\langle \mathcal{A}\mathbf{x},\mathbf{y}\rangle = \langle \mathbf{x},\mathcal{A}^*\mathbf{y}\rangle$ for all $\mathbf{x},\mathbf{y} \in \mathcal{C}^n$. Let $\mathbf{u}_1, \ldots, \mathbf{u}_n$ be the orthonormal basis. Let $\mathbf{x} = \sum_j \xi_j \mathbf{u}_j$ and $\mathbf{y} = \sum_i \eta_i \mathbf{u}_i$. Then, by the linearity of the scalar product, we have

$$\left\langle \sum_j \mathcal{A}\xi_j \mathbf{u}_j, \sum_i \eta_i \mathbf{u}_i \right\rangle = \sum_{ij} \xi_j^* \eta_i \langle \mathcal{A}\mathbf{u}_j, \mathbf{u}_i\rangle$$

$$\left\langle \sum_j \xi_j \mathbf{u}_j, \sum_i \mathcal{A}^* \eta_i \mathbf{u}_i \right\rangle = \sum_{i,j} \xi_j^* \eta_i \langle \mathbf{u}_j, \mathcal{A}^*\mathbf{u}_i\rangle$$

From the definition of $\mathcal{A}^*$, the right-hand sides of these two equations are equal for all possible choices of ξ_j and η_i. Hence

$$\langle \mathbf{u}_j, \mathcal{A}^*\mathbf{u}_i\rangle = \langle \mathbf{u}_i, \mathcal{A}\mathbf{u}_j\rangle^* \qquad i,j = 1, 2, \ldots, n$$

Since the $\mathbf{u}_i$'s are orthonormal, the basis coincides with its reciprocal basis and the left-hand side is the *j*th component of $\mathcal{A}^*\mathbf{u}_i$, that is, it is the element of the *j*th row and *i*th column of the matrix $\mathbf{A}^*$. The right-hand side is the complex conjugate of the (i,j) element of the matrix **A**. Therefore, if $\mathbf{A} = (a_{ij})$ and $\mathbf{A}^* = (b_{ij})$,

$$b_{ij} = a_{ji}^* \qquad i,j = 1, 2, \ldots, n$$

7 **Definition** Let $\mathcal{A}$ be an L.T. on $\mathcal{C}^n$. If $\mathcal{A} = \mathcal{A}^*$, then $\mathcal{A}$ is said to be *self-adjoint*.

8 *Comment* Let **A** be the matrix representing the self-adjoint L.T. $\mathcal{A}$ with respect to an orthonormal basis. Then, by *6*, $a_{ij} = a_{ji}^*$ for

$$i,j = 1, 2, \ldots, n$$

The matrix **A** is said to be *hermitian*.

9 *Exercise* Show that if **A** is self-adjoint, $\langle \mathbf{x},\mathbf{A}\mathbf{x}\rangle$ is real, $\forall \mathbf{x} \in \mathcal{C}^n$.

10 *Exercise* Let **A** be an arbitrary $n \times n$ matrix. Show that $\mathbf{A}^*\mathbf{A}$ is hermitian. Show that it is a nonnegative definite hermitian matrix. (A hermitian matrix **H** is said to be nonnegative definite if $\langle \mathbf{x},\mathbf{H}\mathbf{x}\rangle \geq 0$, $\forall \mathbf{x} \in \mathcal{C}^n$.)

15 *Systems of linear equations*

Consider the system of linear equations

1 $$\sum_{j=1}^{n} a_{ij}x_j = b_i \qquad i = 1, 2, \ldots, n$$

where the matrix $\mathbf{A} = (a_{ij})$ and the column vector $\mathbf{b}$ are given.[1] The problem is to settle the following questions: When does the system have a solution, and if it has a solution, is it unique? If it is not, how does one obtain all of its solutions? To settle these questions, it is expedient to first consider a theorem listing relevant properties of $\mathbf{A}$ and then deduce their consequences relative to the system *1*.

The reader might be astonished that we shall not go into the usual long-detailed study of determinants, minors, etc. The reason is that in the solution of systems of equations involving more than, say, five equations, determinants are very seldom used. In fact, their principal use is as a tool to prove theorems. The main drawback of determinants is that the determinant of an $n \times n$ matrix consists of an algebraic sum of $n!$ terms and that each term is a product of n elements of the determinant. If $n = 20$, this is 2.4329×10^{18} terms, and if the computation of one term requires one microsecond, the $n!$ terms require about 10^5 years! For this reason modern computer programs solve systems of linear equations either by the Gauss elimination procedure or by iteration.

To proceed further, we must recall the

2 **Definition** The *rank of an L.T.* is the dimension of its range space $\mathcal{R}(\mathbf{A})$; that is, it is the maximum number of linearly independent vectors $\mathbf{y}_1, \mathbf{y}_2, \ldots, \mathbf{y}_r$ that can be written as $\mathbf{y}_i = \mathbf{A}\mathbf{x}_i$ for some $\mathbf{x}_i \in \mathcal{C}^n$. The *nullity of an L.T.* is the dimension of its null space; i.e., it is the maximum number of linearly independent vectors $\mathbf{x}_1, \mathbf{x}_2, \ldots, \mathbf{x}_\nu$ such that $\mathbf{A}\mathbf{x}_i = \mathbf{0}$, $i = 1, 2, \ldots, \nu$.

3 *Exercise* Let $\mathbf{A}$ be a matrix representing an L.T. $\mathcal{A}$ in $\mathcal{C}^n$. Show that the rank of the L.T. $\mathcal{A}$ just defined is equal to the rank of the matrix $\mathbf{A}$ representing $\mathcal{A}$. (An $n \times n$ matrix $\mathbf{A}$ is of rank r if and only if it has at least one minor of order r which is not zero and all its minors of order greater than r are zero.)

Theorems *4* and *6* below have two interpretations: (I) in abstract language, $\mathbf{A}$ is an L.T. of $\mathcal{C}^n$ into itself, $\mathbf{x}$ and $\mathbf{b}$ are elements of $\mathcal{C}^n$. (II) In the language of linear algebraic equations, $\mathbf{A}$ is an $n \times n$ matrix of complex numbers, and $\mathbf{x}$ and $\mathbf{b}$ are n-tuples of complex numbers. The matrix $\mathbf{A}$ is the representation of some L.T. relative to some (usually unspecified) orthonormal basis.

[1] *1* might suggest that we assumed as many equations as unknowns. This is not so, because we may always write a matrix with some of its rows or columns filled with zeros. Therefore, the following discussion is completely general.

4 **Theorem** Let $\mathbf{A}$ be a linear transformation in $\mathcal{C}^n$; then

(I) $\mathcal{C}^n = \mathcal{R}(\mathbf{A}) \oplus \mathcal{N}(\mathbf{A}^*)$.

(II) $\mathcal{N}(\mathbf{A}^*)$ is the orthogonal complement of $\mathcal{R}(\mathbf{A})$.

(III) $\dim \mathcal{R}(\mathbf{A}) + \dim \mathcal{N}(\mathbf{A}^*) = n$.

(IV) $\dim \mathcal{R}(\mathbf{A}) = \dim \mathcal{R}(\mathbf{A}^*)$ and $\dim \mathcal{N}(\mathbf{A}) = \dim \mathcal{N}(\mathbf{A}^*)$: that is, $\mathbf{A}$ and $\mathbf{A}^*$ have the same rank and nullity.

(V) $\mathbf{A}$ is a one-one mapping of $\mathcal{R}(\mathbf{A}^*)$ onto $\mathcal{R}(\mathbf{A})$.

Proof To prove (I) and (II) let $\mathbf{y} \in \mathcal{R}(\mathbf{A})^\perp$ [that is, the orthogonal complement of $\mathcal{R}(\mathbf{A})$; *C.7.6 et seq.*]. Since $\mathbf{A}(\mathbf{A}^*\mathbf{y}) \in \mathcal{R}(\mathbf{A})$ and since $\mathbf{y} \in \mathcal{R}(\mathbf{A})^\perp$, we have $0 = \langle \mathbf{y},\mathbf{AA}^*\mathbf{y}\rangle = \langle \mathbf{A}^*\mathbf{y},\mathbf{A}^*\mathbf{y}\rangle = \|\mathbf{A}^*\mathbf{y}\|^2 = 0$; thus $\mathbf{A}^*\mathbf{y} = \mathbf{0}$ and $\mathbf{y} \in \mathcal{N}(\mathbf{A}^*)$. Thus we have proved that $\mathbf{y} \in \mathcal{R}(\mathbf{A})^\perp \Rightarrow \mathbf{y} \in \mathcal{N}(\mathbf{A}^*)$. Suppose that $\mathbf{z} \in \mathcal{N}(\mathbf{A}^*)$; then, for all $\mathbf{x}$, $0 = \langle \mathbf{A}^*\mathbf{z},\mathbf{x}\rangle = \langle \mathbf{z},\mathbf{Ax}\rangle$, that is, $\mathbf{z}$ is orthogonal to all vectors in $\mathcal{R}(\mathbf{A})$. Hence we have proved that $\mathbf{z} \in \mathcal{N}(\mathbf{A}^*) \Rightarrow \mathbf{z} \in \mathcal{R}(\mathbf{A})^\perp$. Therefore, $\mathcal{N}(\mathbf{A}^*) = \mathcal{R}(\mathbf{A})^\perp$; i.e., (II) is proved, and (I) follows from the fact that $\mathcal{C}^n = \mathcal{R}(\mathbf{A}) \oplus \mathcal{R}(\mathbf{A})^\perp$.

(III) From (I) it follows that any basis of $\mathcal{R}(\mathbf{A})$ together with any basis of $\mathcal{N}(\mathbf{A}^*)$ constitutes a basis for $\mathcal{C}^n$. Since the dimension of a subspace is the number of vectors in any of its bases, (III) follows.

(IV) Let $\{\mathbf{u}_1,\mathbf{u}_2, \ldots ,\mathbf{u}_n\}$ be a basis of $\mathcal{C}^n$ such that $\{\mathbf{u}_{r+1}, \ldots ,\mathbf{u}_n\}$ is a basis for $\mathcal{N}(\mathbf{A})$; then for any $\mathbf{x} = \sum_{i=1}^{n} \xi_i\mathbf{u}_i$,

$$\mathbf{Ax} = \sum_1^n \xi_i\mathbf{Au}_i = \sum_1^r \xi_k\mathbf{Au}_k$$

Therefore, $\mathcal{R}(\mathbf{A})$ is spanned by $\{\mathbf{Au}_1,\mathbf{Au}_2, \ldots ,\mathbf{Au}_r\}$; hence, $\dim \mathcal{R}(\mathbf{A}) \leq r$ and $\dim \mathcal{R}(\mathbf{A}) \leq n - \dim \mathcal{N}(\mathbf{A})$. By applying this inequality to $\mathbf{A}^*$, we get $\dim \mathcal{R}(\mathbf{A}^*) \leq n - \dim \mathcal{N}(\mathbf{A}^*)$, which together with (III) gives

$$\dim \mathcal{R}(\mathbf{A}^*) \leq \dim \mathcal{R}(\mathbf{A})$$

We again apply this inequality to $\mathbf{A}^*$ and use the fact that $(\mathbf{A}^*)^* = \mathbf{A}$ to get

$$\dim \mathcal{R}(\mathbf{A}) \leq \dim \mathcal{R}(\mathbf{A}^*)$$

Therefore, $\dim \mathcal{R}(\mathbf{A}) = \dim \mathcal{R}(\mathbf{A}^*)$; hence, by *2*, $\mathbf{A}$ and $\mathbf{A}^*$ have the same rank. This fact together with (III) implies that they also have the same nullity. (V) Apply (I) to $\mathbf{A}^*$; thus $\mathcal{C}^n = \mathcal{R}(\mathbf{A}^*) \oplus \mathcal{N}(\mathbf{A})$. Therefore, if $\{\mathbf{u}_1,\mathbf{u}_2, \ldots ,\mathbf{u}_r\}$ is a basis for $\mathcal{R}(\mathbf{A}^*)$ and $\{\mathbf{u}_{r+1}, \ldots ,\mathbf{u}_n\}$ is a basis for $\mathcal{N}(\mathbf{A})$, $\{\mathbf{u}_1, \ldots ,\mathbf{u}_n\}$ is a basis for $\mathcal{C}^n$. For any $\mathbf{x} \in \mathcal{C}^n$ we have a unique decomposition

5 $$\mathbf{x} = \sum_{i=1}^{n} \xi_i\mathbf{u}_i = \mathbf{y} + \mathbf{z}$$

where $\mathbf{y} = \sum_1^r \xi_i\mathbf{u}_i$ and $\mathbf{z} = \sum_{r+1}^n \xi_i\mathbf{u}_i$, $\mathbf{y} \in \mathcal{R}(\mathbf{A}^*)$ and $\mathbf{z} \in \mathcal{N}(\mathbf{A})$, and also $\mathbf{Ax} = \mathbf{Ay}$. Thus, any vector $\mathbf{Ax}$ in $\mathcal{R}(\mathbf{A})$ is the mapping of a vector

$\mathbf{y} \in \mathcal{R}(\mathbf{A}^*)$, that is, $\mathbf{A}$ maps $\mathcal{R}(\mathbf{A}^*)$ *onto* $\mathcal{R}(\mathbf{A})$. Now, r is by assumption the dimension of $\mathcal{R}(\mathbf{A}^*)$, but by (IV) it is also that of $\mathcal{R}(\mathbf{A})$; hence, the r vectors $\{\mathbf{Au}_1, \ldots, \mathbf{Au}_r\}$ spanning $\mathcal{R}(\mathbf{A})$ constitute a basis for $\mathcal{R}(\mathbf{A})$. For any $\mathbf{x} \in \mathcal{C}^n$ the relation between $\mathbf{Ax}$ and the vector $\mathbf{y}$ defined in *5* is one-one, since they both have $(\xi_1, \xi_2, \ldots, \xi_r)$ as components relative to the basis $\{\mathbf{Au}_1, \ldots, \mathbf{Au}_r\}$ and $\{\mathbf{u}_1, \ldots, \mathbf{u}_r\}$, respectively. Hence $\mathbf{A}$ is a one-one mapping of $\mathcal{R}(\mathbf{A}^*)$ onto $\mathcal{R}(\mathbf{A})$. Q.E.D.

With these properties of $\mathbf{A}$ at our fingertips, we return to our equations and state the pertinent results in the form of a

6 **Theorem** Let $\mathbf{A}$ be a linear transformation on $\mathcal{C}^n$ and $\mathbf{b} \in \mathcal{C}^n$. Then we assert that

(I) The system of equations

7
$$\mathbf{Ax} = \mathbf{b}$$

has a solution if and only if $\mathbf{b}$ is orthogonal to all solutions of $\mathbf{A}^*\mathbf{y} = \mathbf{0}$, that is, if $\mathbf{b} \in \mathfrak{N}(\mathbf{A}^*)^\perp = \mathcal{R}(\mathbf{A})$.

(II) The system *7* has a *unique solution* if and only if

8
$$\mathbf{Ay} = \mathbf{0}$$

has no nontrivial solutions.

(III) For all $\mathbf{b} \in \mathcal{C}^n$ the system *7* has a *unique solution* if and only if the rank of $\mathbf{A}$ is n.

(IV) If the rank of $\mathbf{A}$ is r and $r < n$ and if $\mathbf{b} \in \mathcal{R}(\mathbf{A})$, then the *most general solution* of *7* is

9
$$\mathbf{x} = \mathbf{x}_0 + \mathbf{y}$$

where $\mathbf{x}_0 \in \mathcal{R}(\mathbf{A}^*)$ and $\mathbf{y}$ is any vector of $\mathfrak{N}(\mathbf{A})$. Furthermore,

10
$$\|\mathbf{x}\|^2 = \|\mathbf{x}_0\|^2 + \|\mathbf{y}\|^2$$

where the norm is defined by the scalar product (see *C.5.5*).

11 *Comment* In case (IV), among all the solutions of *7*, $\mathbf{x}_0$ is that which has the minimum length.

Proof (I) By the definition of $\mathcal{R}(\mathbf{A})$ (see *C.9.6*), *7* has a solution if and only if $\mathbf{b} \in \mathcal{R}(\mathbf{A})$. By conclusion (I) of Theorem *4*, this is equivalent to $\mathbf{b}$ belonging to the orthogonal complement of $\mathfrak{N}(\mathbf{A}^*)$, that is, $\mathbf{b}$ is orthogonal to every solution of $\mathbf{A}^*\mathbf{y} = \mathbf{0}$. (II) Use contradiction. To prove $\Rightarrow$, suppose *8* has a nonzero solution $\mathbf{y}_0$. If *7* has a solution, say, $\mathbf{x}_0$, then $\mathbf{x}_0 + \mathbf{y}_0$ is also a solution of *7*. That is, the solution of *7* is not unique. Therefore, if *7* has a unique solution, *8* cannot have a nontrivial solution. To prove $\Leftarrow$, suppose the solution of *7* were not unique; then the difference $\mathbf{x}_0 - \mathbf{x}_0'$ between two solutions would be a nontrivial solution of *8*.

(III) By conclusion (III) of Theorem *4*, "rank of $\mathbf{A}$ is equal to n" is equivalent to "dimension of $\mathfrak{N}(\mathbf{A}^*)$ is zero"; hence, by Theorem

4, conclusion (IV), dim $\mathfrak{N}(\mathbf{A}) = 0$. Therefore, "rank of $\mathbf{A}$ is n" is equivalent to "$\mathbf{y} = \mathbf{0}$ is the only solution of *8*." (IV) By Theorem *4*, conclusion (V), if $\mathbf{b} \in \mathfrak{R}(\mathbf{A})$, there is a unique $\mathbf{x}_0 \in \mathfrak{R}(\mathbf{A}^*)$ such that

$$\mathbf{A}\mathbf{x}_0 = \mathbf{b}$$

For any $\mathbf{y} \in \mathfrak{N}(\mathbf{A})$, we have $\mathbf{A}(\mathbf{x}_0 + \mathbf{y}) = \mathbf{b}$. Finally, by Theorem *4*, conclusion (II), $\mathfrak{R}(\mathbf{A}^*)$ is the orthogonal complement of $\mathfrak{N}(\mathbf{A})$; hence, $\langle \mathbf{x}_0,\mathbf{y}\rangle = 0$. Let $\mathbf{x} = \mathbf{x}_0 + \mathbf{y}$; then upon expanding the equality $\langle \mathbf{x}_0 + \mathbf{y}, \mathbf{x}_0 + \mathbf{y}\rangle = \langle \mathbf{x},\mathbf{x}\rangle = \|\mathbf{x}\|^2$ we get *10*. Q.E.D.

12 *Exercise* Let $\mathbf{A}$ be an L.T. on $\mathcal{C}^n$ defined by its matrix representation (a_{ij}). For all $i,j = 1, 2, \ldots, n$, let $\mathbf{a}_j$ be the vector whose elements are $(a_{1j},a_{2j}, \ldots ,a_{nj})$ and let $\boldsymbol{\alpha}_i$ be the vector whose elements are $(a_{i1},a_{i2}, \ldots ,a_{in})$: $\mathbf{a}_j$ is the jth column vector of $\mathbf{A}$ and $\boldsymbol{\alpha}_i$ is the ith row vector of $\mathbf{A}$. Show that (I) $\mathfrak{R}(\mathbf{A}) = \mathcal{S}[\mathbf{a}_1,\mathbf{a}_2, \ldots ,\mathbf{a}_n]$, that is, the range of $\mathbf{A}$ is spanned by its columns; (II) $\mathfrak{R}(\mathbf{A}^*) = \mathcal{S}[\boldsymbol{\alpha}_1^*,\boldsymbol{\alpha}_2^*, \ldots ,\boldsymbol{\alpha}_n^*]$, where $\boldsymbol{\alpha}_i^*$ is the vector whose components are $(a_{i1}^*,a_{i2}^*, \ldots ,a_{in}^*)$; (III) the system of n linear homogeneous equations $\mathbf{A}\mathbf{x} = \mathbf{0}$ is equivalent to $\langle \boldsymbol{\alpha}_i^*,\mathbf{x}\rangle = 0$, $i = 1, 2, \ldots, n$. (IV) Use (II) and (III) to show that $\mathfrak{N}(\mathbf{A}) = \{\mathbf{x}|\mathbf{A}\mathbf{x} = \mathbf{0}\}$ is the orthogonal complement of $\mathfrak{R}(\mathbf{A}^*)$.

Let the rank of $\mathbf{A}$ be n. Then from (III), Theorem *6*, the L.T. $\mathbf{A}$ defines for each $\mathbf{b}$ in $\mathcal{C}^n$ one and only one $\mathbf{x}$ such that $\mathbf{A}\mathbf{x} = \mathbf{b}$. In other words, $\mathbf{A}$ is a one-one mapping of $\mathcal{C}^n$ onto itself. Hence an inverse mapping exists. This inverse mapping is itself a linear transformation called the *inverse transformation* and is denoted $\mathbf{A}^{-1}$. We write $\mathbf{x} = \mathbf{A}^{-1}\mathbf{b}$.

13 **Definition** Any L.T. that has an inverse is called *nonsingular*. A *singular* L.T. is one that has no inverse. By *6*, any singular L.T. has a rank $<n$.

14 *Exercise* Apply Theorem *4* to a hermitian matrix $\mathbf{H}$ (see *C.14.8*). Show, in particular, that $\mathcal{C}^n = \mathfrak{R}(\mathbf{H}) \oplus \mathfrak{N}(\mathbf{H})$ and $\mathfrak{R}(\mathbf{H}) \perp \mathfrak{N}(\mathbf{H})$. [This implies that $\mathbf{H}$ is a one-one mapping of $\mathfrak{R}(\mathbf{H})$ onto itself.]

16 *Norms*

Norm of a vector

Given a linear vector space, the idea of the norm of a vector $\mathbf{x}$ is a generalization of the idea of length. There are, however, several ways in which a norm may be defined, but in any case the norm of $\mathbf{x}$ is a real number, denoted by $\|\mathbf{x}\|$, which must satisfy the following postulates.

1 $\|\mathbf{x}\| \geq 0$ for all $\mathbf{x} \in \mathfrak{X}$

2 $\|\mathbf{x}\| = 0 \Leftrightarrow \mathbf{x} = \mathbf{0}$

3 $\|a\mathbf{x}\| = |a| \, \|\mathbf{x}\|$ for all numbers a and vectors $\mathbf{x} \in \mathfrak{X}$

4 $\|\mathbf{x} + \mathbf{y}\| \leq \|\mathbf{x}\| + \|\mathbf{y}\|$ for all pairs $\mathbf{x},\mathbf{y} \in \mathfrak{X}$

This last requirement is called the *triangle inequality.*

Examples of norms in $\mathcal{C}^n$[1]

Let $\mathbf{x}$ have components $\xi_1, \xi_2, \ldots, \xi_n$ with respect to some orthonormal basis $\mathbf{u}_1, \mathbf{u}_2, \ldots, \mathbf{u}_n$.

5 $$\|\mathbf{x}\|_2 = \sqrt{\langle \mathbf{x},\mathbf{x} \rangle} = \sum_{i=1}^{n} |\xi_i|^2$$

Let $\mathbf{x}$ have components $\zeta_1, \zeta_2, \ldots, \zeta_n$ with respect to some arbitrary basis $\mathbf{v}_1, \mathbf{v}_2, \ldots, \mathbf{v}_n$.

6 $$\|\mathbf{x}\|_\infty = \max_i |\zeta_i|$$

7 $$\|\mathbf{x}\|_1 = \sum_{i=1}^{n} |\zeta_i|$$

8 *Exercise* Show that the norms *5* to *7* satisfy the four postulates.

The principal use of norms is to define the concept of convergence. Given a norm $\|\cdot\|$, the sequence of vectors $\{\mathbf{x}_n\}$ is said to converge to some vector $\mathbf{x}$ if the sequence of numbers $\|\mathbf{x}_n - \mathbf{x}\| \to 0$. Thus the norm ties back the concept of convergence of vectors to that of numbers. This type of convergence is referred to as "convergence in the norm topology" or "convergence in the strong topology."

It can be shown that, in the n-dimensional space $\mathcal{C}^n$, the three norms defined by *5* to *7* are *equivalent;* i.e., any sequence which converges in the sense of any one of these norms converges in the sense of the others.

Norm of a linear transformation

The concept of norm can be extended to linear transformations. Consider an L.T. $\mathbf{A}$ of $\mathcal{C}^n$ into $\mathcal{C}^n$ and a norm $\|\cdot\|$ on $\mathcal{C}^n$. For any $\mathbf{x}$, we may consider the numbers $\|\mathbf{Ax}\|$ and $\|\mathbf{x}\|$. It is obvious that $\|\mathbf{Ax}\|$ will usually depend on the direction of $\mathbf{x}$ and will always depend on its "length" $\|\mathbf{x}\|$; thus, a natural way to define the norm of $\mathbf{A}$, denoted by $\|\mathbf{A}\|$, is

9 $$\|\mathbf{A}\| = \inf \{k \mid \|\mathbf{Ax}\| \leq k\|\mathbf{x}\| \quad \forall \mathbf{x} \in \mathcal{C}^n\}$$

[1] The subscripts 2, ∞, and 1 are used to distinguish the several norms.

It is immediately apparent that

10 $$\|\mathbf{Ax}\| \leq \|\mathbf{A}\| \; \|\mathbf{x}\| \qquad \forall \mathbf{x} \in \mathcal{C}^n$$

and

11 $$\|\mathbf{A}\| = \sup_{\|\mathbf{x}\|=1} \|\mathbf{Ax}\|$$

In other words, $\|\mathbf{A}\|$ is the maximum "length" of the vectors $\mathbf{Ax}$ when $\mathbf{x}$ ranges over the unit sphere S in $\mathcal{C}^n$. The unit sphere is defined by $S = \{\mathbf{x}:\|\mathbf{x}\| = 1\}$.

The norms of L.T. of $\mathcal{C}^n$ into $\mathcal{C}^n$ have the following properties:

12 $$\|\mathbf{A} + \mathbf{B}\| \leq \|\mathbf{A}\| + \|\mathbf{B}\|$$

13 $$\|\mathbf{AB}\| \leq \|\mathbf{A}\| \; \|\mathbf{B}\|$$

The proof of *12* and *13* follow from the following observations: $\forall \mathbf{x}$ in $\mathcal{C}^n$,

$$\|(\mathbf{A} + \mathbf{B})\mathbf{x}\| = \|\mathbf{Ax} + \mathbf{Bx}\| \leq \|\mathbf{Ax}\| + \|\mathbf{Bx}\| \leq (\|\mathbf{A}\| + \|\mathbf{B}\|) \; \|\mathbf{x}\|$$
$$\|\mathbf{ABx}\| \leq \|\mathbf{A}\| \; \|\mathbf{Bx}\| \leq \|\mathbf{A}\| \; \|\mathbf{B}\| \; \|\mathbf{x}\|$$

The convergence of a sequence of L.T. is defined as follows: the sequence of L.T. $\{\mathbf{A}_n\}$ converges to an L.T. $\mathbf{A}$ if the sequence of numbers $\|\mathbf{A}_n - \mathbf{A}\| \to 0$.

14 *Exercise* Prove that if $\|\mathbf{A}\| < 1$, then $\sum_{k=0}^{\infty} \mathbf{A}^k$ converges to $(\mathbf{I} - \mathbf{A})^{-1}$. (*Hint:* Consider the sequence $\mathbf{B}_n$, where $\mathbf{B}_n = \sum_{k=0}^{n} \mathbf{A}^k$. Use *12* and *13* to establish convergence. Then use $\mathbf{B}_n - \mathbf{AB}_n = \mathbf{I} - \mathbf{A}^{n+1}$ and $\mathbf{A}^k \to \mathbf{0}$ as $k \to \infty$.)

15 *Exercise* Prove that for any $\mathbf{A}$, $\sum_{k=0}^{\infty} \frac{1}{k!} \mathbf{A}^k$ converges.

16 *Exercise* Let $\{\mathbf{u}_i\}^n$ be an orthonormal basis. Let (a_{ij}) represent $\mathbf{A}$ in that basis. With norm *5* show that

$$\|\mathbf{A}\|_2 \leq \Big(\sum_{i,j=1}^{n} |a_{ij}|^2\Big)^{\frac{1}{2}}$$

17 *Exercise* Let $\{\mathbf{u}_i\}$ be a basis and (a_{ij}) represent $\mathbf{A}$ in that basis. With norm *6*, show that $\|\mathbf{A}\|_\infty = \max_i \Big(\sum_{j=1}^{n} |a_{ij}|\Big)$. With norm *7*, show that $\|\mathbf{A}\|_1 = \max_j \Big(\sum_{i=1}^{n} |a_{ij}|\Big)$.

17 *Pseudo inverse of a matrix*

The pseudo inverse of a matrix is a generalization of the notion of inverse that has already found numerous applications. Let us recall that if the $n \times n$ matrix $\mathbf{A}$ is nonsingular, then for any $\mathbf{y} \in \mathcal{C}^n$ there is one and only one $\mathbf{x} \in \mathcal{C}^n$ such that $\mathbf{Ax} = \mathbf{y}$. Furthermore, the relationship between $\mathbf{y}$ and $\mathbf{x}$ is linear and defines the inverse of $\mathbf{A}$: $\mathbf{x} = \mathbf{A}^{-1}\mathbf{y}$.

Let $\mathbf{A}$ be singular (that is, its null space contains nonzero vectors and the rank of $\mathbf{A}$ is smaller than n). Given any $\mathbf{y} \in \mathcal{C}^n$, the equation $\mathbf{Ax} = \mathbf{y}$ either has no solutions [when $\mathbf{y} \notin \mathcal{R}(\mathbf{A})$; see *C.15.6*] or has an infinite number of solutions [because to any solution we may add a nonzero vector of $\mathfrak{N}(\mathbf{A})$ and obtain another solution]. These two features of the problem suggest that we should reformulate the problem in order that it will always have one and only one solution. First, we should not ask for $\mathbf{Ax}$ to be equal to $\mathbf{y}$ and, second, among all the solutions, we should pick the one having the least norm. A possible reformulation is the following: given $\mathbf{A}$ (possibly singular), for any $\mathbf{y} \in \mathcal{C}^n$, find the vector $\mathbf{x}_0$ of least norm[1] which minimizes $\|\mathbf{Ax} - \mathbf{y}\|$. We can describe $\mathbf{x}_0$ as follows. Project $\mathbf{y}$ orthogonally on $\mathcal{R}(\mathbf{A})$; let $\mathbf{y}_p$ be its projection; then $\mathbf{y}_p \in \mathcal{R}(\mathbf{A})$ (see *C.7.1*). There is one and only one vector in $\mathcal{R}(\mathbf{A}^*)$, say, $\mathbf{x}_0$, such that $\mathbf{Ax}_0 = \mathbf{y}_p$ (see *C.15.4*). Finally, from *C.7.11* and *C.15.10* it follows that $\|\mathbf{Ax}_0 - \mathbf{y}\| = \min_{\mathbf{x} \in \mathcal{C}^n} \|\mathbf{Ax} - \mathbf{y}\|$. It can further be shown that the relation between the solution $\mathbf{x}_0$ of the modified problem and $\mathbf{y}$ is linear: $\mathbf{x}_0 = \mathbf{A}^\dagger\mathbf{y}$, where $\mathbf{A}^\dagger$ is said to be the pseudo inverse of $\mathbf{A}$. Obviously, if $\mathbf{A}$ is nonsingular, $\mathbf{A}^\dagger = \mathbf{A}^{-1}$. Note that $\mathbf{A}^\dagger$ maps $\mathcal{C}^n$ onto $\mathcal{R}(\mathbf{A}^*)$ and that the null space of $\mathbf{A}^\dagger$ is $\mathcal{R}(\mathbf{A})^\perp = \mathfrak{N}(\mathbf{A}^*)$.

Definition of the pseudo inverse

We could develop the theory from this point of view. It is, however, more efficient to use the insight of the above discussion to set up a formal definition of the pseudo inverse and easily derive its properties.

1 **Definition** Let $\mathbf{A}$ be an L.T. mapping $\mathcal{C}^n$ into $\mathcal{C}^n$. The pseudo inverse of $\mathbf{A}$ is denoted by $\mathbf{A}^\dagger$ and satisfies the conditions

$$
\begin{array}{lll}
\text{(I)} & \mathbf{A}^\dagger\mathbf{Ax} = \mathbf{x} & \forall \mathbf{x} \in \mathfrak{N}(\mathbf{A})^\perp = \mathcal{R}(\mathbf{A}^*) \\
\text{(II)} & \mathbf{A}^\dagger\mathbf{z} = 0 & \forall \mathbf{z} \in \mathcal{R}(\mathbf{A})^\perp = \mathfrak{N}(\mathbf{A}^*) \\
\text{(III)} & \mathbf{A}^\dagger(\mathbf{y} + \mathbf{z}) = \mathbf{A}^\dagger\mathbf{y} + \mathbf{A}^\dagger\mathbf{z} & \forall \mathbf{y} \in \mathcal{R}(\mathbf{A}),\ \forall \mathbf{z} \in \mathcal{R}(\mathbf{A})^\perp
\end{array}
$$

2 *Comment* (I) implies that the L.T. $\mathbf{A}^\dagger\mathbf{A}$ restricted to $\mathcal{R}(\mathbf{A}^*) = \mathfrak{N}(\mathbf{A})^\perp$ is the identity mapping. Conditions (I), (II), and (III) define $\mathbf{A}^\dagger$

[1] We use here the norm defined by the scalar product $\|\mathbf{x}\|^2 = \langle \mathbf{x},\mathbf{x} \rangle$.

completely: (I) specifies the values of $\mathbf{A}^\dagger$ on $\mathcal{R}(\mathbf{A})$, (II) specifies them on $\mathcal{R}(\mathbf{A})^\perp$, and (III) specifies them on $\mathcal{R}(\mathbf{A}) \oplus \mathcal{R}(\mathbf{A})^\perp = \mathcal{C}^n$.

3 **Corollary** $\mathbf{A}^\dagger$ defined by *1* is a linear transformation.

Proof The corollary follows immediately from the computation $\mathbf{A}^\dagger\mathbf{u}$, where $\mathbf{u}$ is an arbitrary vector of $\mathcal{C}^n$. Since $\mathcal{C}^n = \mathcal{R}(\mathbf{A}) \oplus \mathcal{R}(\mathbf{A})^\perp$, let $\mathbf{u} = \mathbf{y} + \mathbf{z}$, where $\mathbf{y} \in \mathcal{R}(\mathbf{A})$, $\mathbf{z} \in \mathcal{R}(\mathbf{A})^\perp$. By (III) and (II) we get

$$\mathbf{A}^\dagger\mathbf{u} = \mathbf{A}^\dagger\mathbf{y} + \mathbf{A}^\dagger\mathbf{z} = \mathbf{A}^\dagger\mathbf{y}$$

Now from *C.15.4*, there is one and only one $\mathbf{x}_1 \in \mathcal{R}(\mathbf{A}^*)$ such that $\mathbf{A}\mathbf{x}_1 = \mathbf{y}$. Finally, from (I) $\mathbf{A}^\dagger\mathbf{A}\mathbf{x}_1 = \mathbf{x}_1$; that is, $\mathbf{A}^\dagger\mathbf{u} = \mathbf{x}_1$. It is obvious from the above constructions that this relation between $\mathbf{u}$ and $\mathbf{x}_1$ is homogeneous and additive. Hence $\mathbf{A}^\dagger$ is an L.T. ◁

From these considerations the following result is obvious.

4 **Corollary**

$$\mathcal{R}(\mathbf{A}^\dagger) = \mathcal{R}(\mathbf{A}^*) = \mathcal{N}(\mathbf{A})^\perp$$
$$\mathcal{N}(\mathbf{A}^\dagger) = \mathcal{N}(\mathbf{A}^*) = \mathcal{R}(\mathbf{A})^\perp$$

Definition *1* and Corollaries *3* and *4* are illustrated in Fig. *C.17.1*. The two sets on the left of this figure represent the orthogonal decomposition of $\mathcal{C}^n$ in $\mathcal{N}(\mathbf{A}) \oplus \mathcal{N}(\mathbf{A})^\perp$, and the two sets on the right represent

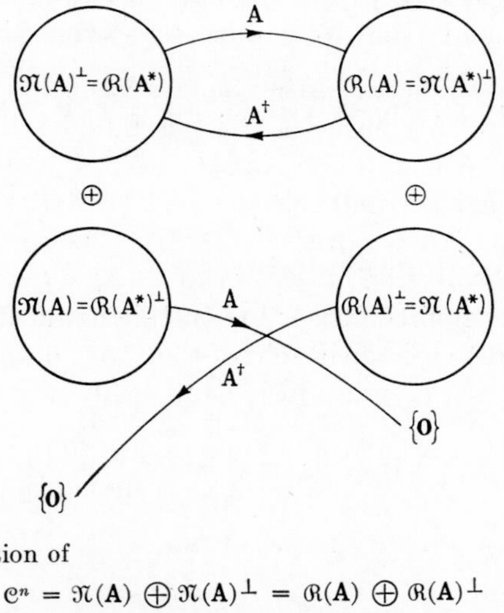

Fig. C.17.1 Illustration of

$$\mathcal{C}^n = \mathcal{N}(\mathbf{A}) \oplus \mathcal{N}(\mathbf{A})^\perp = \mathcal{R}(\mathbf{A}) \oplus \mathcal{R}(\mathbf{A})^\perp$$

and the corresponding mapping properties of $\mathbf{A}$ and its pseudo inverse $\mathbf{A}^\dagger$.

the decomposition of $\mathcal{C}^n$ in $\mathcal{R}(\mathbf{A}) \oplus \mathcal{R}(\mathbf{A})^\perp$. By definition, $\mathbf{A}$ maps $\mathcal{N}(\mathbf{A})$ into $\{\mathbf{0}\}$ and $\mathbf{A}^\dagger$ maps $\mathcal{N}(\mathbf{A}^*) = \mathcal{R}(\mathbf{A})^\perp$ into $\{\mathbf{0}\}$. Also, $\mathbf{A}^\dagger$ restricted to $\mathcal{R}(\mathbf{A})$ [which is a mapping denoted by $\mathbf{A}^\dagger/\mathcal{R}(\mathbf{A})$] is the inverse of $\mathbf{B}$, where by definition, $\mathbf{B}$ is the one-one linear mapping which is $\mathbf{A}$ restricted to $\mathcal{R}(\mathbf{A}^*) = \mathcal{N}(\mathbf{A})^\perp$.

Properties of the pseudo inverse

5 **Theorem**

(I) $\mathbf{A}^\dagger\mathbf{A}$ is the orthogonal projection of $\mathcal{C}^n$ onto $\mathcal{R}(\mathbf{A}^*) = \mathcal{N}(\mathbf{A})^\perp$

(II) $(\mathbf{A}^\dagger)^\dagger = \mathbf{A}$

(III) $\mathbf{A}^\dagger\mathbf{A}\mathbf{A}^\dagger = \mathbf{A}^\dagger$

(IV) $\mathbf{A}\mathbf{A}^\dagger\mathbf{A} = \mathbf{A}$

(V) $\mathbf{A}\mathbf{A}^\dagger$ is the orthogonal projection of $\mathcal{C}^n$ onto $\mathcal{R}(\mathbf{A}) = \mathcal{N}(\mathbf{A}^*)^\perp$

6 *Comment* (I) and (V) imply that $(\mathbf{A}^\dagger\mathbf{A})^* = \mathbf{A}^\dagger\mathbf{A}$ and $(\mathbf{A}\mathbf{A}^\dagger)^* = \mathbf{A}\mathbf{A}^\dagger$. Penrose[1] has shown that these two relations, together with (III) and (IV), considered as matric equations in $\mathbf{A}^\dagger$, define a unique matrix which he calls the pseudo inverse of $\mathbf{A}$.

Proof (I) For any $\mathbf{x}$ in $\mathcal{C}^n$ consider the orthogonal decomposition $\mathbf{x} = \mathbf{x}_1 + \mathbf{x}_2$ with $\mathbf{x}_1 \in \mathcal{N}(\mathbf{A})^\perp$ and $\mathbf{x}_2 \in \mathcal{N}(\mathbf{A})$. Then, by the definition of $\mathcal{N}(\mathbf{A})$ and *1*, $\mathbf{A}^\dagger\mathbf{A}\mathbf{x} = \mathbf{A}^\dagger\mathbf{A}\mathbf{x}_1 = \mathbf{x}_1$ and the assertion follows.

(II) This fact is obvious from the symmetry of the definition and of Fig. *C.17.1*. It is easily proved with the help of *1* and *4*.

(III) Let $\mathbf{y} \in \mathcal{C}^n$ and $\mathbf{y} = \mathbf{y}_1 + \mathbf{y}_2$, with $\mathbf{y}_1 \in \mathcal{R}(\mathbf{A})$ and $\mathbf{y}_2 \in \mathcal{R}(\mathbf{A})^\perp$. From *1*, $\mathbf{A}^\dagger\mathbf{y} = \mathbf{A}^\dagger\mathbf{y}_1 \in \mathcal{N}(\mathbf{A})^\perp$. From (I),

$$\mathbf{A}^\dagger\mathbf{A}(\mathbf{A}^\dagger\mathbf{y}) = \mathbf{A}^\dagger\mathbf{A}(\mathbf{A}^\dagger\mathbf{y}_1) = \mathbf{A}^\dagger\mathbf{y}_1 = \mathbf{A}^\dagger\mathbf{y}$$

Thus $\mathbf{A}^\dagger\mathbf{A}\mathbf{A}^\dagger\mathbf{y} = \mathbf{A}^\dagger\mathbf{y}$ for all $\mathbf{y} \in \mathcal{C}^n$.

(IV) Put $\mathbf{A}^\dagger = \mathbf{B}$. Use (II) and (III) to get (IV).

(V) Let $\mathbf{y} \in \mathcal{C}^n$ and let $\mathbf{y} = \mathbf{y}_1 + \mathbf{y}_2$, with $\mathbf{y}_1 \in \mathcal{R}(\mathbf{A})$ and $\mathbf{y}_2 \in \mathcal{R}(\mathbf{A})^\perp$; then $\mathbf{A}\mathbf{A}^\dagger\mathbf{y} = \mathbf{A}\mathbf{A}^\dagger\mathbf{y}_1 = \mathbf{y}_1$, where the last equality follows from (IV). Thus, for any $\mathbf{y} \in \mathcal{C}^n$, $\mathbf{A}\mathbf{A}^\dagger\mathbf{y} = \mathbf{y}_1$, where $\mathbf{y}_1$ is the orthogonal projection of $\mathbf{y}$ on $\mathcal{R}(\mathbf{A})$.

7 **Theorem** $(\mathbf{A}^*)^\dagger = (\mathbf{A}^\dagger)^*$.

Proof By *5*, $\mathbf{A}\mathbf{A}^\dagger = (\mathbf{A}\mathbf{A}^\dagger)^* = \mathbf{A}^{\dagger *}\mathbf{A}^*$; hence $\mathbf{A}^{\dagger *}\mathbf{A}^*$ is by *5*(V) the orthogonal projection of $\mathcal{C}^n$ onto $\mathcal{R}(\mathbf{A})$. On the other hand, *5*(I) applied to $\mathbf{A}^*$ asserts that $\mathbf{A}^{*\dagger}\mathbf{A}^*$ is the orthogonal projection of $\mathcal{C}^n$ onto $\mathcal{R}(\mathbf{A}^{**}) = \mathcal{R}(\mathbf{A})$. Hence, $\mathbf{A}^{*\dagger}\mathbf{A}^* = \mathbf{A}^{\dagger *}\mathbf{A}^*$, or, equivalently,

$$\mathbf{A}^{*\dagger}\mathbf{x} = \mathbf{A}^{\dagger *}\mathbf{x}$$

for all $\mathbf{x} \in \mathcal{R}(\mathbf{A}^*)$. It remains to show that the same relation holds for all $\mathbf{x} \in \mathcal{N}(\mathbf{A})$. Applying *1* to $\mathbf{A}^\dagger$, we have $\mathcal{N}(\mathbf{A}^{\dagger *}) = \mathcal{N}(\mathbf{A}^{\dagger\dagger}) = \mathcal{N}(\mathbf{A})$, where the last equality follows from *5*(II). But

$$\mathcal{N}(\mathbf{A}^{*\dagger}) = \mathcal{N}(\mathbf{A}^{**}) = \mathcal{N}(\mathbf{A})$$

Hence $\mathbf{A}^{*\dagger}\mathbf{x} = \mathbf{A}^{\dagger *}\mathbf{x} = \mathbf{0}$ for all $\mathbf{x} \in \mathcal{N}(\mathbf{A})$. ◁

The approximating property of $\mathbf{A}^\dagger$ mentioned in the introduction can be derived from the definition.

[1] R. Penrose, A Generalized Inverse for Matrices, *Proc. Cambridge Phil. Soc.*, vol. 51, part 3, pp. 406–413, 1955.

8 **Theorem** Let $\mathbf{y} \in \mathcal{C}^n$ and $\mathbf{x}_0 = \mathbf{A}^\dagger\mathbf{y}$. Then

9 $$\|\mathbf{A}\mathbf{x}_0 - \mathbf{y}\| \leq \|\mathbf{A}\mathbf{x} - \mathbf{y}\| \qquad \forall \mathbf{x} \in \mathcal{C}^n$$

and $\mathbf{x}_0$ is the vector of least norm which satisfies *9*. (The norm is defined by $\|\mathbf{y}\|^2 = \langle \mathbf{y},\mathbf{y}\rangle$.)

Proof Let $\mathbf{y} = \mathbf{y}_1 + \mathbf{y}_2$, with $\mathbf{y}_1 \in \mathcal{R}(\mathbf{A})$ and $\mathbf{y}_2 \in \mathcal{R}(\mathbf{A})^\perp$. Then

$$\|\mathbf{A}\mathbf{x}_0 - \mathbf{y}\| = \|\mathbf{A}\mathbf{A}^\dagger\mathbf{y} - \mathbf{y}\| = \|\mathbf{y}_1 - (\mathbf{y}_1 + \mathbf{y}_2)\| = \|\mathbf{y}_2\|$$

For any $\mathbf{x} \in \mathcal{C}^n$; $\mathbf{A}\mathbf{x} \in \mathcal{R}(\mathbf{A})$, hence

$$\|\mathbf{A}\mathbf{x} - \mathbf{y}\|^2 = \|\mathbf{A}\mathbf{x} - \mathbf{y}_1 - \mathbf{y}_2\|^2 = \|\mathbf{A}\mathbf{x} - \mathbf{y}_1\|^2 + \|\mathbf{y}_2\|^2$$

Hence *9* follows from these two equalities. Finally, to show that $\mathbf{x}_0$ is the vector of least norm satisfying *9*, observe the following. If $\mathbf{x}_1 \in \mathfrak{N}(\mathbf{A})$, $\mathbf{A}\mathbf{x}_0 = \mathbf{A}(\mathbf{x}_0 + \mathbf{x}_1)$. And, since $\mathbf{x}_0 \in \mathcal{R}(\mathbf{A}^\dagger) = \mathcal{R}(\mathbf{A}^*) = \mathfrak{N}(\mathbf{A})^\perp$, $\|\mathbf{x}_0 + \mathbf{x}_1\|^2 = \|\mathbf{x}_0\|^2 + \|\mathbf{x}_1\|^2$; hence, $\|\mathbf{x}_0\| \leq \|\mathbf{x}_0 + \mathbf{x}_1\|$.

10 *Comment* In the language of linear algebraic equations, Theorem *8* may be rephrased as follows.

(I) If $\mathbf{y} \in \mathcal{R}(\mathbf{A})$, $\mathbf{A}\mathbf{x} = \mathbf{y}$ has a solution and any of its solutions is of the form

$$\mathbf{x} = \mathbf{A}^\dagger\mathbf{y} + (\mathbf{I} - \mathbf{A}^\dagger\mathbf{A})\mathbf{z}$$

where $\mathbf{z}$ is an arbitrary vector of $\mathcal{C}^n$. [Note that *5*(I) implies that $\mathbf{I} - \mathbf{A}^\dagger\mathbf{A}$ is the orthogonal projection of $\mathcal{C}^n$ on $\mathfrak{N}(\mathbf{A})$; hence, $(\mathbf{I} - \mathbf{A}^\dagger\mathbf{A})\mathbf{z}$ is an arbitrary vector of $\mathfrak{N}(\mathbf{A})$.]

(II) If $\mathbf{y} \notin \mathcal{R}(\mathbf{A})$, the equation $\mathbf{A}\mathbf{x} = \mathbf{y}$ has no solutions. The vector $\mathbf{x}_0 = \mathbf{A}^\dagger\mathbf{y}$ is the vector of least norm which when reinserted into the equation gives the least error $\mathbf{e} \triangleq \mathbf{A}\mathbf{x} - \mathbf{y}$ (in the sense of *9*). ◁

Now we prove a polar decomposition theorem which is useful in getting a geometric insight into the effect of a general L.T. mapping $\mathcal{C}^n$ into $\mathcal{C}^n$.

11 **Theorem** If $\mathbf{A}$ is a nonsingular L.T. of $\mathcal{C}^n$ into $\mathcal{C}^n$, there is a unique decomposition of $\mathbf{A}$,

12 $$\mathbf{A} = \mathbf{U}\mathbf{H}$$

where $\mathbf{H}$ is positive definite hermitian and $\mathbf{U}$ is unitary, that is, $\mathbf{U}^* = \mathbf{U}^{-1}$. If $\mathbf{A}$ is singular, then we have a decomposition

13 $$\mathbf{A} = \mathbf{U}\mathbf{H}$$

where both $\mathbf{H}$ and $\mathbf{U}$ are singular, $\mathbf{H}$ is hermitian nonnegative definite, and

14 $$\mathbf{H}^2 = \mathbf{A}^*\mathbf{A} \qquad \mathbf{U} = \mathbf{A}\mathbf{H}^\dagger \qquad \mathbf{U}^* = \mathbf{U}^\dagger$$

Proof Let us prove the second statement. We anticipate a little and use *C.19.1*, *C.19.2*, and *C.19.7*. Since $\mathbf{A}^*\mathbf{A}$ is hermitian (self-adjoint) and nonnegative definite (see *C.14.10*), $\mathbf{A}^*\mathbf{A} = \sum_{i=1}^{n} \lambda_i \mathbf{E}_i$, with $\lambda_i \geq 0$. Define the matrix $\mathbf{H}$ by $\mathbf{H} \triangleq \Sigma \sqrt{\lambda_i}\, \mathbf{E}_i$. $\mathbf{H}$ is then hermitian and is such that $\mathbf{A}^*\mathbf{A} = \mathbf{H}^2$; thus $\mathcal{R}(\mathbf{H}) = \mathcal{R}(\mathbf{H}^*)$ and $\mathbf{H}\mathbf{H}^\dagger = \mathbf{H}^\dagger\mathbf{H}$. Since $\mathbf{H}^\dagger$ maps $\mathcal{C}^n$ onto $\mathcal{R}(\mathbf{H})$, we have $\mathbf{H}^\dagger = \sum_{\lambda_i > 0} \lambda_i^{-1/2}\mathbf{E}_i$. Now define $\mathbf{U}$ by $\mathbf{U} = \mathbf{A}\mathbf{H}^\dagger$. Since $\mathbf{H}^\dagger$ commutes with $\mathbf{H}$ and since $\mathbf{H}$ is hermitian, we have

$$\mathbf{U}^*\mathbf{U} = (\mathbf{A}\mathbf{H}^\dagger)^*(\mathbf{A}\mathbf{H}^\dagger) = \mathbf{H}^{\dagger *}\mathbf{A}^*\mathbf{A}\mathbf{H}^\dagger = \mathbf{H}^{\dagger *}\mathbf{H}\mathbf{H}\mathbf{H}^\dagger = \mathbf{H}^\dagger\mathbf{H}\mathbf{H}^\dagger\mathbf{H} = \mathbf{H}^\dagger\mathbf{H}$$

By *5*(I), $\mathbf{U}^*\mathbf{U} = \mathbf{H}^\dagger\mathbf{H}$ is the orthogonal projection of $\mathcal{C}^n$ onto $\mathcal{R}(\mathbf{H})$: $\mathbf{U}^*\mathbf{U}\mathbf{x} = \mathbf{x}$ for all $\mathbf{x} \in \mathcal{R}(\mathbf{H})$. However, by considering Fig. *C.17.1*, it is easy to show that $\mathcal{R}(\mathbf{H}) = \mathcal{R}(\mathbf{A}^*) = \mathcal{R}(\mathbf{U}^*)$; thus $\mathbf{U}^*\mathbf{U}\mathbf{x} = \mathbf{x}$ for all $\mathbf{x}$ in $\mathcal{R}(\mathbf{U}^*)$. Finally, for all $\mathbf{y} \in \mathcal{R}(\mathbf{U})^\perp = \mathcal{N}(\mathbf{U}^*)$, $\mathbf{U}^*\mathbf{y} = \mathbf{0}$; and by *1*, $\mathbf{U}^* = \mathbf{U}^\dagger$. The decomposition *12* follows directly from the definition of $\mathbf{U}$: $\mathbf{U}\mathbf{H} = \mathbf{A}\mathbf{H}^\dagger\mathbf{H} = \mathbf{A}$ because $\mathbf{H}^\dagger\mathbf{H}$ is the orthogonal projection of $\mathcal{C}^n$ on $\mathcal{R}(\mathbf{A}^*)$.

The proof for the case where $\mathbf{A}$ is nonsingular is a special case of the preceding one.

The calculation of $\mathbf{A}^\dagger$

15 **Theorem** Let $\mathbf{S}$ be the hermitian nonnegative definite matrix defined by

16 $$\mathbf{S} = \mathbf{A}^*\mathbf{A}$$

Then

17 $$\mathbf{A}^\dagger = \mathbf{S}^\dagger\mathbf{A}^*$$

Comment This theorem implies that the computation of the pseudo inverse of any $n \times n$ matrix $\mathbf{A}$ reduces to the computation of the pseudo inverse of a hermitian nonnegative definite $n \times n$ matrix $\mathbf{S}$.

Proof If $\mathbf{x} \in \mathcal{N}(\mathbf{A}^*)$, then, by *1*, $\mathbf{A}^\dagger\mathbf{x} = \mathbf{0}$ and also $\mathbf{S}^\dagger\mathbf{A}^*\mathbf{x} = \mathbf{0}$. Now let $\mathbf{y} \in \mathcal{R}(\mathbf{A})$. By *C.15.4* there is a unique $\mathbf{x} \in \mathcal{R}(\mathbf{A}^*)$ such that $\mathbf{A}\mathbf{x} = \mathbf{y}$. On the one hand, $\mathbf{A}^\dagger\mathbf{y} = \mathbf{A}^\dagger\mathbf{A}\mathbf{x} = \mathbf{x}$ by (I) of Definition *1*. On the other hand, from *C.15.4*, $\mathbf{A}^*\mathbf{A}$ is a one-one map of $\mathcal{R}(\mathbf{A}^*)$ onto itself and, by *1*, for any $\mathbf{x} \in \mathcal{R}(\mathbf{A}^*)$, $(\mathbf{A}^*\mathbf{A})^\dagger\mathbf{A}^*\mathbf{A}\mathbf{x} = \mathbf{x}$, or $(\mathbf{A}^*\mathbf{A})^\dagger\mathbf{A}^*\mathbf{y} = \mathbf{x} = \mathbf{A}^\dagger\mathbf{y}$. Thus for all $\mathbf{y} \in \mathcal{R}(\mathbf{A})$, $(\mathbf{A}^*\mathbf{A})^\dagger\mathbf{A}^*\mathbf{y} = \mathbf{A}^\dagger\mathbf{y}$. Thus the linear operators on both sides of *17* give the same result when they operate on vectors of $\mathcal{R}(\mathbf{A})$ and $\mathcal{N}(\mathbf{A}^*)$. Since $\mathcal{C}^n = \mathcal{R}(\mathbf{A}) \oplus \mathcal{R}(\mathbf{A})^\perp$ and $\mathcal{N}(\mathbf{A}^*) = \mathcal{R}(\mathbf{A})^\perp$, *17* is established.

18 *Exercise* Let $\mathbf{A} = \operatorname{diag}(a_{11}, a_{22}, \ldots, a_{nn})$. Show that

$$\mathbf{A}^{\dagger} = \operatorname{diag}(\alpha_{11}, \alpha_{22}, \ldots, \alpha_{nn})$$

where $\alpha_{ii} = a_{ii}^{-1}$ if $a_{ii} \neq 0$ and $\alpha_{ii} = 0$ if $a_{ii} = 0$. Give the geometric interpretation.

19 *Exercise* Let $\mathbf{B}$ be hermitian. Let $\mathbf{U}$ be the matrix whose ith column is the normalized ith eigenvector of $\mathbf{B}$. Then $\mathbf{U}$ is unitary; that is, $\mathbf{U}^*\mathbf{U} = \mathbf{I}$. Let $\mathbf{B} = \mathbf{U}\mathbf{\Lambda}\mathbf{U}^*$, where $\mathbf{\Lambda} = \operatorname{diag}(\lambda_1, \lambda_2, \ldots, \lambda_n)$, and then show that $\mathbf{B}^{\dagger} = \mathbf{U}\mathbf{\Lambda}^{\dagger}\mathbf{U}^*$.

20 *Exercise*[1] Suppose $\mathbf{A}$ is of rank $r < n$. Suppose we know the $n \times r$ matrix $\mathbf{B}$ and $r \times n$ matrix $\mathbf{C}$, both of rank r, which have the property that

$$\mathbf{A} = \mathbf{BC}$$

Show that

$$\mathbf{A}^{\dagger} = \mathbf{C}^*(\mathbf{CC}^*)^{-1}(\mathbf{B}^*\mathbf{B})^{-1}\mathbf{B}^*$$

21 *Exercise*[2] Suppose $\mathbf{A}$ has its last $n - r$ columns identical to zero and that its first r columns are linearly independent. Let $\mathbf{N}$ be the $n \times r$ matrix consisting of these r columns. Then

$$\mathbf{A}^{\dagger} = \mathbf{K}(\mathbf{N}^*\mathbf{N})^{-1}\mathbf{N}^*$$

where $\mathbf{K}$ is an $n \times r$ matrix whose first r rows constitute a unit matrix and all other rows are identical to zero.

18 *Simple L.T.*

1 **Definition** Let $\mathbf{A}$ be an $n \times n$ matrix whose elements are real or complex numbers. An *eigenvalue of* $\mathbf{A}$ is a number λ, possibly complex, such that the polynomial $\Delta(\lambda) \equiv \det(\mathbf{A} - \lambda\mathbf{I}) = 0$. The polynomial $\Delta(\lambda)$ is called the *characteristic polynomial.* We may also define the eigenvalues in terms of L.T. without recourse to any matrix representation: an eigenvalue of an L.T. $\mathbf{A}$ is a number λ such that the L.T. $\mathbf{A} - \lambda\mathbf{I}$ is singular, i.e., there is at least one vector $\mathbf{x} \neq \mathbf{0}$ such that $(\mathbf{A} - \lambda\mathbf{I})\mathbf{x} = \mathbf{0}$.

2 *Exercise* Show that, in $\mathcal{C}^n$, the two definitions are equivalent.

3 *Exercise* Show directly that the zeros of $\Delta(\lambda)$ are independent of the basis used to obtain the matrix representation of the L.T. (*Hint:* Use

[1] T. N. E. Greville, Some Applications of the Pseudo Inverse of a Matrix, *Soc. Indust. Appl. Math. Rev.*, vol. 2, no. 1, pp. 15–22, 1960.

[2] J. B. Rosen, The Gradient Projection Method for Nonlinear Programming, *J. Soc. Indust. Appl. Math.*, vol. 8, no. 1, pp. 181–217, 1960.

C.11.7) and the fact that the determinant of a product of $n \times n$ matrices is the product of their respective determinants.)

4 **Definition** An *eigenvector* of $\mathbf{A}$ is a nonzero vector $\mathbf{x}$ such that $\mathbf{Ax} = \lambda\mathbf{x}$. Clearly, since $(\mathbf{A} - \lambda\mathbf{I})\mathbf{x} = \mathbf{0}$ is implied, with $\mathbf{x} \neq \mathbf{0}$, the number λ is necessarily an eigenvalue. $\mathbf{x}$ is said to be an eigenvector associated with the eigenvalue λ. This is equivalent to saying $\mathbf{x}$ is in the null space of the L.T. $\mathbf{A} - \lambda\mathbf{I}$.

Note that if $\mathbf{x}$ is an eigenvector, then for any scalar $k \neq 0$, $k\mathbf{x}$ is also an eigenvector. Eigenvectors will usually be so scaled that $\|\mathbf{x}\| = 1$; in such case the eigenvector is said to be *normalized.*

5 *Exercise* Show that $\mathfrak{N}(\mathbf{A} - \lambda_i\mathbf{I}) \triangleq \{\mathbf{x}|(\mathbf{A} - \lambda_i\mathbf{I})\mathbf{x} = \mathbf{0}\}$ is an invariant subspace under $\mathbf{A}$.

6 **Definition** A *simple L.T.* is one whose eigenvectors span the space.

7 *Comment* Not all L.T. are simple; for example, let

8 $$\mathbf{A} = \begin{bmatrix} 1 & 1 \\ 0 & 1 \end{bmatrix}$$

Then $\det(\mathbf{A} - \lambda\mathbf{I}) = (\lambda - 1)^2$ and $\lambda = 1$ is the only eigenvalue. There is only one (normalized) eigenvector, namely, $\mathbf{u}_1 = \begin{bmatrix} 1 \\ 0 \end{bmatrix}$. Obviously, it cannot span $\mathcal{C}^2$.

It should be stressed that the eigenvectors spanning the space need not correspond to distinct eigenvalues. For example, let $\mathbf{A} = \begin{bmatrix} 1 & 0 \\ 0 & 1 \end{bmatrix}$. Its eigenvalues are both equal to 1 and the eigenvectors are $\mathbf{u}_1 = \begin{bmatrix} 1 \\ 0 \end{bmatrix}$ and $\mathbf{u}_2 = \begin{bmatrix} 0 \\ 1 \end{bmatrix}$. $\mathbf{u}_1$ and $\mathbf{u}_2$ span $\mathcal{C}^2$; hence, $\mathbf{A}$ is simple. In *5.4.6* we have shown that if $\mathbf{A}$ has distinct eigenvalues, then the eigenvectors of $\mathbf{A}$ span the space $\mathcal{C}^n$. Consequently, the class of all simple L.T. is larger than the class of all L.T. that have distinct eigenvalues.

9 **Corollary** $\mathbf{A}$ is a simple L.T. if and only if there is a basis with respect to which matrix representation of $\mathbf{A}$ is diagonal.

Proof $\Rightarrow$ $\mathbf{A}$ is simple; then there are n eigenvectors $\mathbf{u}_1, \mathbf{u}_2, \ldots, \mathbf{u}_n$ (with associated eigenvalues $\lambda_1, \lambda_2, \ldots, \lambda_n$) which constitute a basis $\mathcal{B}$ for $\mathcal{C}^n$. Hence $\mathbf{Au}_i = \lambda_i\mathbf{u}_i$, $i = 1, 2, \ldots, n$. Therefore, by *C.10.4*, the representation of $\mathbf{A}$ in that basis is a matrix whose ith column has all its components equal to zero except the ith, which is λ_i. Thus, $\mathbf{A} = \text{diag}(\lambda_1,\lambda_2, \ldots ,\lambda_n)$.

⇐ By assumption, **A** is diagonal; let $\mathbf{A} = \text{diag}(\lambda_1, \lambda_2, \ldots, \lambda_n)$. If $\mathbf{u}_i$ is the ith basis vector for this matrix representation, we have

$$\mathbf{A}\mathbf{u}_i = \lambda_i \mathbf{u}_i \qquad i = 1, 2, \ldots, n$$

Hence, $\mathbf{u}_1, \mathbf{u}_2, \ldots, \mathbf{u}_n$ are eigenvectors and they span the space. Therefore, by definition **A** is a simple L.T.

The effect of a simple L.T. **A** on a vector **x** is illustrated in Fig. *C.18.1*.

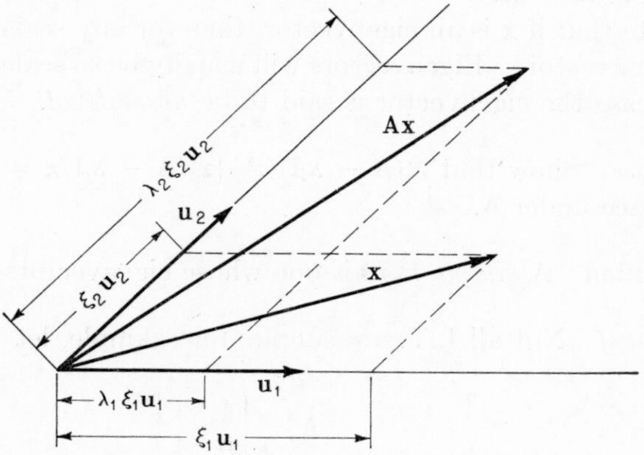

Fig. C.18.1 Relation between **x** and **Ax** through the spectral representation of **A**.

10 *Exercise* Let **A** be an L.T. on $\mathcal{C}^n$. Then λ_i is an eigenvalue of **A** if and only if λ_i^* is an eigenvalue of $\mathbf{A}^*$. (*Hint:* Use an orthonormal basis and take the conjugate transpose of the matrix $\mathbf{A} - \lambda\mathbf{I}$.)

11 **Theorem** Let **A** be a simple L.T. on $\mathcal{C}^n$. Let $\mathbf{u}_1, \mathbf{u}_2, \ldots, \mathbf{u}_n$ be a set of eigenvectors of **A** which constitutes a basis $\mathcal{B}$ of $\mathcal{C}^n$. Then, the reciprocal basis of $\mathcal{B}$ $\{\mathbf{v}_1, \ldots, \mathbf{v}_n\}$ is constituted by eigenvectors of $\mathbf{A}^*$; and if the eigenvalue associated with $\mathbf{u}_i$ is λ_i, that associated with $\mathbf{v}_i$ is λ_i^*.

Proof By definition of a reciprocal basis: $\langle \mathbf{u}_i, \mathbf{v}_j \rangle = \delta_{ij}$, $i,j = 1, \ldots, n$. Now on the one hand, for all i, j's

$$\langle \mathbf{v}_j, \mathbf{A}\mathbf{u}_i \rangle = \langle \mathbf{v}_j, \lambda_i \mathbf{u}_i \rangle = \lambda_i \langle \mathbf{v}_j, \mathbf{u}_i \rangle = \lambda_i \delta_{ij} = \lambda_j \delta_{ij}$$

and on the other hand, using the definition of the adjoint (see *C.14.1*)

$$\lambda_j \delta_{ij} = \langle \mathbf{v}_j, \mathbf{A}\mathbf{u}_i \rangle = \langle \mathbf{A}^*\mathbf{v}_j, \mathbf{u}_i \rangle = \langle \mathbf{u}_i, \mathbf{A}^*\mathbf{v}_j \rangle^*$$

Hence, for all i, j's

$$\langle \mathbf{u}_i, \mathbf{A}^*\mathbf{v}_j \rangle = \lambda_j^* \delta_{ij}$$

Since the $\mathbf{u}_i$'s constitute a reciprocal basis of the $\mathbf{v}_j$'s, we see that

$$\mathbf{A}^*\mathbf{v}_j = \lambda_j^* \mathbf{v}_j \qquad j = 1, 2, \ldots, n$$

12 **Corollary** If **A** is a simple L.T. on $\mathcal{C}^n$, $\mathbf{A}^*$ is also a simple L.T. on $\mathcal{C}^n$.

13 **Theorem** Let $\mathbf{A}$ be a simple L.T. on $\mathcal{C}^n$. Let $\{\mathbf{u}_1, \ldots, \mathbf{u}_n\}$ be a set of eigenvectors of $\mathbf{A}$ constituting a basis $\mathcal{B}$ of $\mathcal{C}^n$. Let the $\mathbf{v}_j$'s be the reciprocal basis to $\mathcal{B}$. If $\mathbf{E}_i = \mathbf{u}_i\rangle\langle\mathbf{v}_i$, $i = 1, 2, \ldots, n$, then

14 $$\mathbf{A} = \sum_{i=1}^{n} \lambda_i \mathbf{E}_i = \sum_{i=1}^{n} \lambda_i \mathbf{u}_i\rangle\langle\mathbf{v}_i$$

and

15 $$\mathbf{A}^* = \sum_{i=1}^{n} \lambda_i^* \mathbf{E}_i^* = \sum_{i=1}^{n} \lambda_i^* \mathbf{v}_i\rangle\langle\mathbf{u}_i$$

Proof $\forall \mathbf{x} \in \mathcal{C}^n$ we have a unique representation by *C.4.4* and *C.8.3*:

$$\mathbf{x} = \sum_{i=1}^{n} \zeta_i \mathbf{u}_i = \sum_{i=1}^{n} \langle\mathbf{v}_i,\mathbf{x}\rangle\mathbf{u}_i$$

Hence

$$\mathbf{Ax} = \sum_{i=1}^{n} \langle\mathbf{v}_i,\mathbf{x}\rangle\mathbf{A}\mathbf{u}_i = \sum_{i=1}^{n} \lambda_i\langle\mathbf{v}_i,\mathbf{x}\rangle\mathbf{u}_i$$

from which *14* follows. The proof of *15* follows a similar computation.

16 *Comment* The formulae *14* and *15* are the main reason for introducing simple L.T. These formulae give an easily visualized interpretation of the relation between $\mathbf{x}$ and $\mathbf{Ax}$. Indeed, *14* shows that the simple L.T. $\mathbf{A}$ is completely described by a basis made up of its eigenvectors $\{\mathbf{u}_1, \ldots, \mathbf{u}_n\}$ and the corresponding eigenvalues λ_i. For any $\mathbf{x}$ consider the expansion of $\mathbf{x}$ along the eigenvectors $\mathbf{u}_1, \ldots, \mathbf{u}_n$ together with the corresponding components (see Fig. *C.18.1*). $\mathbf{Ax}$ is the vector having each one of its components multiplied by the corresponding eigenvalue. This very simple visualization of the effect of operating on $\mathbf{x}$ by $\mathbf{A}$ is the geometrical equivalent to choosing $\{\mathbf{u}_1,\mathbf{u}_2, \ldots, \mathbf{u}_n\}$ as basis vectors and observing that with respect to that basis $\mathbf{A}$ is represented by the diagonal matrix, diag $(\lambda_1,\lambda_2, \ldots, \lambda_n)$. An analogous interpretation holds for *15*.

Anticipating a bit what is to follow (*D.4.1* in particular), let us observe that if the function f is analytic in an open set containing the eigenvalues λ_i of $\mathbf{A}$, then $f(\mathbf{A})$ is *defined* by

17 $$f(\mathbf{A}) = \sum_{i=1}^{n} f(\lambda_i)\mathbf{E}_i = \sum_{i=1}^{n} f(\lambda_i)\mathbf{u}_i\rangle\langle\mathbf{v}_i$$

In particular,

18 $$\mathbf{A}^k = \sum_{i=1}^{n} \lambda_i^k \mathbf{u}_i\rangle\langle\mathbf{v}_i$$

19 $$e^{\mathbf{A}t} = \sum_{i=1}^{n} e^{\lambda_i t}\mathbf{u}_i\rangle\langle\mathbf{v}_i$$

20 **Corollary** If f is an analytic function in an open set containing the eigenvalues λ_i of a simple L.T. $\mathbf{A}$ on $\mathcal{C}^n$ then the L.T. $f(\mathbf{A})$ has the same eigenvectors as $\mathbf{A}$ and its corresponding eigenvalues are $f(\lambda_i)$.

21 *Exercise* Let $\mathbf{A}$ be simple. Show that $\mathcal{C}^n = \mathcal{R}(\mathbf{A}) \oplus \mathfrak{N}(\mathbf{A})$. Compare with *C.15.4*.

19 *Normal L.T.*

In this section we shall consider a subclass of simple L.T., the normal transformation. It will show that for any normal matrix there is an *orthonormal* set of eigenvectors which span the space.

1 **Definition** An L.T. $\mathcal{A}$ is called *normal* if $\mathcal{A}^*\mathcal{A} = \mathcal{A}\mathcal{A}^*$. If $\mathbf{A}$ is the matrix representation of a normal L.T. $\mathcal{A}$ relative to any basis, then $\mathbf{A}^*\mathbf{A} = \mathbf{A}\mathbf{A}^*$. If the basis is orthonormal, then the matrix $\mathbf{A}$ commutes with its *conjugate transpose* $\mathbf{A}^*$.

In order to visualize the scope of normal L.T., consider the following

2 *Exercise* A matrix is normal if it belongs to one of the following classes: (I) hermitian ($\mathbf{A}^* = \mathbf{A}$), (II) skew hermitian ($\mathbf{A}^* = -\mathbf{A}$), (III) real symmetric ($a_{ij} = a_{ji} = a_{ij}^*$), (IV) real skew symmetric ($a_{ij} = -a_{ji} = a_{ij}^*$),

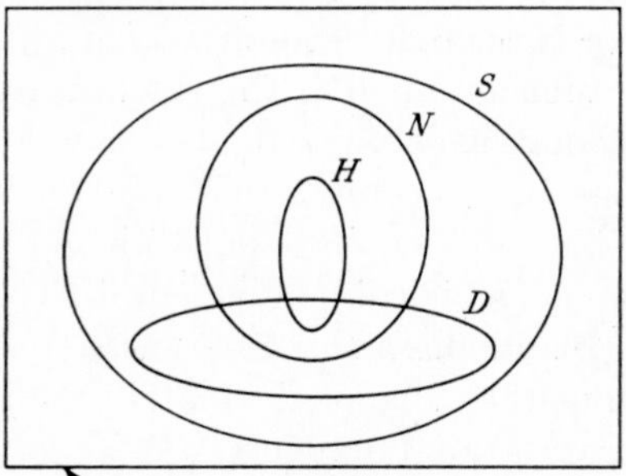

Fig. C.19.1 Inclusion relations between the set of all L.T. in $\mathcal{C}^n$; the set of all simple (S), normal (N), and hermitian (H), L.T.; and the L.T. that have distinct eigenvalues (D).

(V) unitary ($\mathbf{AA}^* = \mathbf{I}$), (VI) orthogonal (all a_{ij}'s real, and $\mathbf{AA}^* = \mathbf{I}$), and (VII) diagonal ($a_{ij} = 0$, if $i \neq j$). We therefore arrive at the following classification of L.T. in $\mathcal{C}^n$. Consider Fig. *C.19.1*. The rectangle represents the set of all L.T. in $\mathcal{C}^n$. The set S is the set of all simple L.T., and the sets D, N, H respectively represent the set of all L.T. with distinct eigenvalues, the set of all normal L.T., and the set of all hermitian L.T. We have $H \subset N \subset S$ and $D \subset S$. However, there are L.T. in D that are not in N, for example, the matrix

$$\begin{bmatrix} 1 & 2 \\ 0 & 3 \end{bmatrix}$$

3 **Theorem** Let $\mathbf{A}$ be normal, $\mathbf{Au} = \lambda\mathbf{u} \Leftrightarrow \mathbf{A}^*\mathbf{u} = \lambda^*\mathbf{u}$.
Proof By assumption, $(\mathbf{A} - \lambda\mathbf{I})\mathbf{u} = \mathbf{0}$. Since $\mathbf{A}$ is normal and since λ is a number, $\mathbf{A} - \lambda\mathbf{I} \triangleq \mathbf{B}$ is also normal (note that $\mathbf{B}^* = \mathbf{A}^* - \lambda^*\mathbf{I}$). Hence,

$$\|\mathbf{Bu}\|^2 = \langle\mathbf{Bu},\mathbf{Bu}\rangle = \langle\mathbf{u},\mathbf{B}^*\mathbf{Bu}\rangle = \langle\mathbf{u},\mathbf{BB}^*\mathbf{u}\rangle$$
$$= \langle\mathbf{B}^*\mathbf{u},\mathbf{B}^*\mathbf{u}\rangle = \|\mathbf{B}^*\mathbf{u}\|^2$$

Hence $\mathbf{Bu} = \mathbf{0}$ if and only if $\mathbf{B}^*\mathbf{u} = \mathbf{0}$.

4 **Corollary** The eigenvalues of a hermitian matrix are real.

5 *Exercise* Prove Corollary *4* directly from $\mathbf{A} = \mathbf{A}^*$. (*Hint*: Consider $\langle\mathbf{u},\mathbf{Au}\rangle = \lambda\langle\mathbf{u},\mathbf{u}\rangle$ and its conjugate. Use the properties of the scalar product and the definitions of $\mathbf{A}^*$ and of a hermitian matrix.)

6 **Theorem** Let $\mathbf{A}$ be normal; then the eigenvectors corresponding to distinct eigenvalues are orthogonal. That is, if $\mathbf{Au}_1 = \lambda_1\mathbf{u}_1$ and $\mathbf{Au}_2 = \lambda_2\mathbf{u}_2$ with $\lambda_1 \neq \lambda_2$, then $\langle\mathbf{u}_1,\mathbf{u}_2\rangle = 0$.
Proof From the assumption and Theorem *3*, $\mathbf{u}_1$ is also an eigenvector of $\mathbf{A}^*$ and $\mathbf{A}^*\mathbf{u}_1 = \lambda_1^*\mathbf{u}_1$. Therefore, $\langle\mathbf{u}_2,\mathbf{A}^*\mathbf{u}_1\rangle = \lambda_1^*\langle\mathbf{u}_2,\mathbf{u}_1\rangle$. Hence, taking the complex conjugate of this relation and using the definition of $\mathbf{A}^*$, $\langle\mathbf{u}_1,\mathbf{Au}_2\rangle = \lambda_1\langle\mathbf{u}_1,\mathbf{u}_2\rangle$. From the assumption, $\langle\mathbf{u}_1,\mathbf{Au}_2\rangle = \lambda_2\langle\mathbf{u}_1,\mathbf{u}_2\rangle$. Therefore, by subtraction $0 = (\lambda_1 - \lambda_2)\langle\mathbf{u}_1,\mathbf{u}_2\rangle$, from which the conclusion follows, since $\lambda_1 \neq \lambda_2$. ◁

The most important result concerning normal L.T. is their *spectral representation*, which may be stated in the form of

7 **Theorem** Let $\mathbf{A}$ be *normal*. Let $\lambda_1, \lambda_2, \ldots, \lambda_\sigma$ be its distinct eigenvalues. Then

(I) $\mathcal{C}^n = \mathfrak{N}(\mathbf{A} - \lambda_1\mathbf{I}) \oplus \mathfrak{N}(\mathbf{A} - \lambda_2\mathbf{I}) \oplus \cdots \oplus \mathfrak{N}(\mathbf{A} - \lambda_\sigma\mathbf{I})$ with

$$\mathfrak{N}(\mathbf{A} - \lambda_i\mathbf{I}) \perp \mathfrak{N}(\mathbf{A} - \lambda_j\mathbf{I})$$

whenever $i \neq j$.

(II) Let $\mathbf{E}_i$ be the orthogonal projection of $\mathcal{C}^n$ on $\mathfrak{N}(\mathbf{A} - \lambda_i\mathbf{I})$,

$$i = 1, 2, \ldots, \sigma$$

Then

8
$$\mathbf{E}_i^2 = \mathbf{E}_i = \mathbf{E}_i^* \qquad i = 1, 2, \ldots$$
$$\mathbf{E}_i\mathbf{E}_j = \mathbf{0} \qquad i \neq j$$

and

9
$$\mathbf{A} = \sum_{i=1}^{\sigma} \lambda_i\mathbf{E}_i$$

(III) There exists a set of *orthonormal* eigenvectors which span the space; hence

10 $$\mathbf{A} = \sum_{i=1}^{n} \lambda_{\nu_i} \mathbf{u}_i\rangle\langle\mathbf{u}_i$$

where λ_{ν_i} is the eigenvalue associated with the eigenvector $\mathbf{u}_i$ and the integers $\nu_i, \ldots, \nu_n$ belong to the set $\{1,2, \ldots, \sigma\}$.

11 *Comment* (I) implies that the eigenvectors (associated with possibly multiple eigenvalues of **A**) span the space $\mathcal{C}^n$; hence, any normal transformation is a simple transformation. Furthermore, if in each

$$\mathfrak{N}(\mathbf{A} - \lambda_i \mathbf{I})$$

one picks an orthonormal basis (whose elements are of necessity eigenvectors associated with the same eigenvalue λ_i), then the union of all these bases constitutes an orthonormal basis for $\mathcal{C}^n$ made up of eigenvectors of **A**. With respect to such an orthonormal basis the matrix representation of the L.T. $\mathfrak{A}$ is diagonal.

12 *Comment* Equations *9* and *10* should be compared with *C.18.14* and *C.18.15*. For the special class of normal transformations, the projections $\mathbf{E}_i$ are now *orthogonal projections;* and since the basis $\{\mathbf{u}_1,\mathbf{u}_2, \ldots ,\mathbf{u}_n\}$ is orthonormal, one need not in *10* use the reciprocal basis as one had to in *C.18.14*.

13 *Comment* Equations *9* and *10* are applicable in the case of self-adjoint L.T. in more general spaces with the only modification that the summation is over an infinite, not necessarily denumerable, set. (See, e.g., Refs. *2*, *10*, *12*, and *14*.) ◁

Before proving Theorem *7*, let us deduce two important consequences.

14 **Theorem** If **A** is normal and if R, r respectively denote the largest and smallest real parts of the eigenvalues of **A**, then

$$2r \leq \frac{\langle \mathbf{x},\mathbf{A}\mathbf{x}\rangle + \langle \mathbf{x},\mathbf{A}^*\mathbf{x}\rangle}{\langle \mathbf{x},\mathbf{x}\rangle} \leq 2R \qquad \forall \mathbf{x} \in \mathfrak{X}$$

Proof Exercise for the reader. (*Hint:* Use *8* and *9*.)

15 **Corollary** If **A** is hermitian, then

$$\lambda \leq \frac{\langle \mathbf{x},\mathbf{A}\mathbf{x}\rangle}{\langle \mathbf{x},\mathbf{x}\rangle} \leq \Lambda$$

where Λ, λ are the largest and the smallest eigenvalues of **A**, respectively.

Proof **A** is hermitian and hence is normal. However, by *4*, all its eigenvalues are real. Hence *14* ⇒ *15*.

16 *Exercise* Let $\mathbf{A}$ be any $n \times n$ matrix. Using the norm defined by $\|\mathbf{x}\|^2 = \langle \mathbf{x},\mathbf{x} \rangle$, show that $\|\mathbf{A}\| \leq \text{tr}\,(\mathbf{A}^*\mathbf{A})$. [*Hint:* Observe that $\mathbf{A}^*\mathbf{A}$ is hermitian and nonnegative; also $\text{tr}\,(\mathbf{A}^*\mathbf{A})$ is the sum of the eigenvalues of $\mathbf{A}^*\mathbf{A}$.]

17 *Exercise* Let the n-tuples $\mathbf{a}_i = (a_{1i}, a_{2i}, \ldots, a_{ni})$ be the components of n linearly independent vectors with respect to some orthonormal basis. Show that $\mathbf{A} = (\alpha_{ij})$, where $\alpha_{ij} = \langle \mathbf{a}_i, \mathbf{a}_j \rangle$, is hermitian and positive definite (that is, $\langle \mathbf{x},\mathbf{A}\mathbf{x} \rangle > 0$ for all $\mathbf{x} \neq \mathbf{0}$). *Hint:* For all $\boldsymbol{\xi} \neq \mathbf{0}$,

$$\Big\| \sum_i \xi_i \mathbf{a}_i \Big\|^2 = \sum_{i,j} \xi_i^* \xi_j \alpha_{ij} > 0$$

18 *Exercise* A hermitian matrix is positive definite if and only if all its eigenvalues are positive (>0). (*Hint:* Use *15* and the definition of an eigenvector.)

19 *Exercise* If $\mathbf{A}$ is a positive definite hermitian matrix, then $\mathbf{A}$ is nonsingular (that is, $\det \mathbf{A} \neq 0$). Furthermore, using the representation *10*, show that the inverse of $\mathbf{A}$ is given by

$$\mathbf{A}^{-1} = \sum_{i=1}^{n} \lambda_{\nu_i}^{-1} \mathbf{u}_i\rangle \langle \mathbf{u}_i$$

Let us leave the proof of Theorem *7* as a graded set of exercises.

20 *Exercise* Prove that $\mathfrak{N}(\mathbf{A} - \lambda_i\mathbf{I}) \perp \mathfrak{N}(\mathbf{A} - \lambda_j\mathbf{I})$ for $i \neq j$ follows directly from Theorem *6*. Show that this also implies $\mathbf{E}_i\mathbf{E}_j = \mathbf{0}$ for $i \neq j$, since $\mathfrak{R}(\mathbf{E}_k) = \mathfrak{N}(\mathbf{A} - \lambda_k\mathbf{I})$ for all k's.

21 *Exercise* Let $\mathbf{A}$ be normal; let λ_i be an eigenvalue of $\mathbf{A}$; then $\mathfrak{N}(\mathbf{A} - \lambda_i\mathbf{I})$ and its orthogonal complement are invariant subspaces under $\mathbf{A}$. *Hint:* Observe that $\mathbf{A}$ commutes with $\mathbf{A} - \lambda_i\mathbf{I}$ and that

$$\mathbf{A}^*(\mathbf{A} - \lambda_i\mathbf{I}) = \mathbf{A}\mathbf{A}^* - \lambda_i\mathbf{A}^* = (\mathbf{A} - \lambda_i\mathbf{I})\mathbf{A}^*$$

22 *Exercise* Show that the dimension of $\mathfrak{N}(\mathbf{A} - \lambda_i\mathbf{I})$ is equal to the multiplicity of λ_i as a zero of $\Delta(\lambda)$. (*Hint:* For conciseness let

$$\mathfrak{N} \triangleq \mathfrak{N}(\mathbf{A} - \lambda_i\mathbf{I})$$

and $\mathfrak{N}^\perp$ be its orthogonal complement. Both $\mathfrak{N}$ and $\mathfrak{N}^\perp$ are invariant under $\mathbf{A}$. Let $\mathbf{A}_1$ (and $\mathbf{A}_2$) be the L.T. a restricted to the domain $\mathfrak{N}$ (and $\mathfrak{N}^\perp$), respectively. Let d be the dimension of $\mathfrak{N}$. Then $\mathbf{A}_1$ ($\mathbf{A}_2$, respectively) is representable by a $d \times d$ matrix [respectively, $(n - d) \times (n - d)$ matrix]. Since $\mathfrak{N}$ and $\mathfrak{N}^\perp$ are invariant,

$$\Delta(\lambda) \triangleq \det\,(\mathbf{A} - \lambda\mathbf{I}) = \det\,(\mathbf{A}_1 - \lambda\mathbf{I}) \det\,(\mathbf{A}_2 - \lambda\mathbf{I})$$

Since $\mathbf{A}_1$ is restricted to $\mathfrak{N}$, each vector of any basis of $\mathfrak{N}$ is an eigenvector of $\mathbf{A}$ associated with the same eigenvalue λ_i; hence,

$$\det\,(\mathbf{A}_1 - \lambda_i\mathbf{I}) = (\lambda_i - \lambda)^d$$

From the definition of $\mathfrak{N}^\perp$, det $(\mathbf{A}_2 - \lambda_i\mathbf{I}) \neq 0$; hence λ_i is a root of multiplicity d of $\Delta(\lambda)$.)

23 *Exercise* Use Theorem *6* and Exercise *20* to show that

$$\mathfrak{N}(\mathbf{A} - \lambda_1\mathbf{I}) \oplus \mathfrak{N}(\mathbf{A} - \lambda_2\mathbf{I}) \oplus \cdots \oplus \mathfrak{N}(\mathbf{A} - \lambda_\sigma\mathbf{I}) = \mathcal{C}^n$$

20 *Comment on the adjoint*

The adjoint of an L.T. **A** is a concept that has appeared repeatedly throughout the text and throughout this appendix. We propose here to exhibit together some of the facts concerning the adjoint that cause it to appear in so many apparently unrelated instances.

Looking at **A** as a mapping of $\mathcal{C}^n$ into $\mathcal{C}^n$, we have the following facts[1] (see *C.15.4*):

1 $$\mathcal{C}^n = \mathcal{R}(\mathbf{A}^*) \overset{\perp}{\oplus} \mathfrak{N}(\mathbf{A}) = \mathcal{R}(\mathbf{A}) \overset{\perp}{\oplus} \mathfrak{N}(\mathbf{A}^*)$$

2 **A** is a one-one mapping of $\mathcal{R}(\mathbf{A}^*)$ onto $\mathcal{R}(\mathbf{A})$

These facts are illustrated by Fig. *C.17.1* and are basic to the understanding of the problems involved in the solution of a set of linear algebraic equations and in the definition of the pseudo inverse of **A**.

If, in addition, **A** is a simple L.T., then we have the spectral representation (see *C.18.13*)

3 $$\mathbf{A} = \sum_{i=1}^{n} \lambda_i \mathbf{u}_i\rangle\langle\mathbf{v}_i$$

where $\mathbf{u}_i$ is an eigenvector of **A** associated with the eigenvalue λ_i; $\mathbf{v}_i$ is the ith vector of the basis reciprocal to the basis $\{\mathbf{u}_1,\mathbf{u}_2, \ldots ,\mathbf{u}_n\}$; and $\mathbf{v}_i$ is an eigenvector of $\mathbf{A}^*$ associated with the eigenvalue λ_i^* (see *C.18.11*).

Considering now differential equations of the form $\dot{\mathbf{x}} = \mathbf{Ax} + \mathbf{a}$, we assume that **A** is constant. If **A** is a simple L.T., the Green dyadic is given by (see *5.2.24*)

4 $$\mathbf{G}(t,\xi) = 1(t - \xi) \sum_{i=1}^{n} e^{\lambda_i(t-\xi)}\mathbf{u}_i\rangle\langle\mathbf{v}_i$$

$$= 1(t - \xi) \sum_{i=1}^{n} e^{\lambda_i t}\mathbf{u}_i\rangle\langle e^{-\lambda_i^*\xi}\mathbf{v}_i$$

Let us recall that t is the instant of observation and ξ is the instant at which the input is applied. (t and ξ play along the time axis the

[1] The notation $\overset{\perp}{\oplus}$ is used to indicate at the same time that the direct sum of $\mathcal{R}(\mathbf{A}^*)$ and $\mathfrak{N}(\mathbf{A})$ is $\mathcal{C}^n$ and that $\mathfrak{N}(\mathbf{A})$ is the orthogonal complement of $\mathcal{R}(\mathbf{A}^*)$.

same role as the observation point and the source point in the Green function of problems involving, for example, the Laplace or Helmholtz partial differential equation.) The behavior of **G** with respect to t is determined by the dynamics of the free system $\dot{\mathbf{x}} = \mathbf{A}\mathbf{x}$. Indeed, $e^{\lambda_i t}\mathbf{u}_i$ is one of its solutions; it is, in fact, a rather special one, since $\mathbf{u}_i$ is an eigenvector of **A** associated with the eigenvalue λ_i. The behavior of **G** with respect to ξ is determined by the dynamics of the adjoint system $d\mathbf{z}/d\xi = -\mathbf{A}^*\mathbf{z}$; indeed, $e^{-\lambda_i^* t}\mathbf{v}_i$ is one of its solutions and $\mathbf{v}_i$ is an eigenvector of $\mathbf{A}^*$ associated with the eigenvalue λ_i^* (of $\mathbf{A}^*$).

In the time-varying case, the Green dyadic becomes (see *6.2.44*)

$$\mathbf{G}(t,\xi) = -1(t-\xi) \sum_{i=1}^{n} \boldsymbol{\phi}_i(t,t_0)\rangle \langle \boldsymbol{\psi}_i(\xi,t_0)$$

Let us recall that $\boldsymbol{\phi}_i(t,t_0)$ is the ith column of the state transition matrix $\boldsymbol{\Phi}(t,t_0)$ and, hence, is a solution of $\dot{\mathbf{x}} = \mathbf{A}(t)\mathbf{x}$. $\boldsymbol{\psi}_i(\xi,t_0)$ is the ith column vector of the state transition matrix $\boldsymbol{\Psi}(\xi,t_0)$ of the adjoint problem $d\mathbf{z}/d\xi = -\mathbf{A}^*(\xi)\mathbf{z}$. So again the behavior of the Green dyadic **G** with respect to its first argument, the instant of observation t, is governed by the dynamics of the free system. The behavior of **G** with respect to its second argument ξ, the instant at which the input is applied, is governed by the dynamics of the adjoint system. Since in many engineering problems it is the second behavior that is of interest, it is natural that the adjoint system plays a key role in the solution of the problem. (See, for example, Remark *6.2.45*.)

REFERENCES AND SUGGESTED READING

1 Bellman, R.: "Introduction to Matrix Analysis," McGraw-Hill Book Company, Inc., New York, 1960.

2 Dunford, N., and J. T. Schwartz: "Linear Operators. Part I: General Theory," Interscience Publishers, Inc., New York, 1958.

3 Finkbeiner, D. T.: "Introduction to Matrices and Linear Transformations," W. H. Freeman and Company, San Francisco, 1960.

4 Frazer, R. A., W. J. Duncan, and A. R. Collar: "Elementary Matrices," Cambridge University Press, New York, 1938.

5 Gantmacher, F. R.: "The Theory of Matrices," vols. 1 and 2, Chelsea Publishing Company, New York, 1959.

6 Halmos, P. R.: "Finite Dimensional Vector Spaces," 2d ed., D. Van Nostrand Company, Inc., Princeton, N.J., 1950.

7 Hamburger, H. L., and M. E. Grimshaw: "Linear Transformations in n Dimensional Space," Cambridge University Press, New York, 1951.

8 Hoffman, K., and R. Kunze: "Linear Algebra," Prentice-Hall, Inc., Englewood Cliffs, N.J., 1961.

9 MacDuffee, C. C.: "The Theory of Matrices," Chelsea Publishing Company, New York, 1956.

10 Morse, P. M., and H. Feshbach: "Methods of Theoretical Physics," vols. 1 and 2, McGraw-Hill Book Company, Inc., New York, 1953.
11 Perlis, S.: "Theory of Matrices," Addison-Wesley Publishing Company, Inc., Reading, Mass., 1952.
12 Riesz, F., and B. Sz.-Nagy: "Functional Analysis," Frederick Ungar Publishing Co., New York, 1955.
13 Stewart, F. M.: "Introduction to Linear Algebra," D. Van Nostrand Company, Inc., Princeton, N.J., 1963.
14 Taylor, A. E.: "Introduction to Functional Analysis," John Wiley & Sons, Inc., New York, 1958.

Function of a matrix

D

1 *Introduction*

The purpose of this appendix is to present the definition of a function of a matrix and to derive computational techniques. In Sec. *2* we introduce the concept of the multiplicity of an eigenvalue (i.e., the order of the eigenvalue as a zero of the minimal polynomial). In Sec. *3* we define the index of an eigenvalue and show that the multiplicity of an eigenvalue is always equal to its index. With these results at hand, the definition of a function of a matrix follows quite naturally. In the next two sections we develop and use the geometric insight built up previously to obtain the fundamental formula for a function of a matrix. Section *8* is devoted to methods of computation.

2 *Minimal polynomial and multiplicity of an eigenvalue*

We know that the polynomial $\Delta(\lambda) = \det(\mathbf{A} - \lambda\mathbf{I})$ is called the *characteristic polynomial of* **A** and that its zeros are the *eigenvalues.* We shall denote them by $\lambda_1, \lambda_2, \ldots$. Given the polynomial

$$p(\lambda) = \sum_{k=0}^{N} a_k \lambda^k$$

we *define* $p(\mathbf{A})$ as the matrix equal to the polynomial $\sum_{k=0}^{N} a_k \mathbf{A}^k$, where $\mathbf{A}^0 = \mathbf{I}$. This definition implies that if two polynomials p and q are equal, that is, $p(\lambda) = q(\lambda)$ for all λ, then $p(\mathbf{A}) = q(\mathbf{A})$.

1 **Definition** The minimal polynomial of the matrix **A** is the polynomial $\psi(\lambda)$ of least degree such that $\psi(\mathbf{A}) = \mathbf{0}$ and the coefficient of the highest power of λ is unity.

2 **Assertion** If λ_i is an eigenvalue of $\mathbf{A}$, then $\psi(\lambda_i) = 0$.
Proof Exercise for the reader. [*Hint:* Let $\mathbf{u}_i \neq \mathbf{0}$ be an eigenvector of $\mathbf{A}$ associated with the eigenvalue λ_i; compute $\psi(\mathbf{A})\mathbf{u}_i$.] ◁

Consequently, we shall use throughout the notation

$$\psi(\lambda) = \prod_{i=1}^{\sigma} (\lambda - \lambda_i)^{m_i}$$

where the product is carried over the σ distinct eigenvalues of $\mathbf{A}$. The exponent m_i is called the *multiplicity of the eigenvalue* λ_i.[1]

3 *Example*

$$\text{For } \mathbf{A} = \begin{bmatrix} 2 & 0 \\ 0 & 2 \end{bmatrix}, \Delta(\lambda) = (\lambda - 2)^2, \psi(\lambda) = \lambda - 2$$

$$\text{For } \mathbf{A} = \begin{bmatrix} 1 & 1 & 0 \\ 0 & 1 & 0 \\ 0 & 0 & 1 \end{bmatrix}, \Delta(\lambda) = -(\lambda - 1)^3, \psi(\lambda) = (\lambda - 1)^2$$

4 *Example* The matrices

$$\begin{bmatrix} 2 & 0 & 0 & 0 \\ 0 & 2 & 0 & 0 \\ 0 & 0 & 2 & 0 \\ 0 & 0 & 0 & 2 \end{bmatrix}, \begin{bmatrix} 2 & 1 & 0 & 0 \\ 0 & 2 & 0 & 0 \\ 0 & 0 & 2 & 1 \\ 0 & 0 & 0 & 2 \end{bmatrix}, \begin{bmatrix} 2 & 0 & 0 & 0 \\ 0 & 2 & 1 & 0 \\ 0 & 0 & 2 & 1 \\ 0 & 0 & 0 & 2 \end{bmatrix}, \begin{bmatrix} 2 & 1 & 0 & 0 \\ 0 & 2 & 1 & 0 \\ 0 & 0 & 2 & 1 \\ 0 & 0 & 0 & 2 \end{bmatrix}$$

all have a common characteristic polynomial $(\lambda - 2)^4$ but have, respectively, $\lambda - 2$, $(\lambda - 2)^2$, $(\lambda - 2)^3$, $(\lambda - 2)^4$ as minimal polynomials.

5 *Exercise* If $\mathbf{T}$ is a nonsingular matrix and if ψ is the minimal polynomial of $\mathbf{A}$, then ψ is also the minimal polynomial of $\mathbf{T}^{-1}\mathbf{A}\mathbf{T}$. [*Hint:* For any integer k, $\mathbf{T}^{-1}\mathbf{A}^k\mathbf{T} = (\mathbf{T}^{-1}\mathbf{A}\mathbf{T})^k$.]

6 *Exercise* Show that $\Delta(\lambda) = \psi(\lambda) \cdot$ [greatest common divisor of all minors of order $(n - 1)$ of $(\mathbf{A} - \lambda\mathbf{I})$]. [*Hint:* Consider the matrix $\mathbf{B}(\lambda)$ such that $b_{ik}(\lambda) =$ cofactor of the (k,i) element of $\mathbf{A} - \lambda\mathbf{I}$. Observe that $\mathbf{B}(\lambda)(\mathbf{A} - \lambda\mathbf{I}) = \Delta(\lambda)\mathbf{I}$. Cancel common factors, etc.]

7 *Exercise* Let $1(t)$ be the unit step function; let $\mathbf{f}$ be an arbitrary constant vector. Assume $\mathbf{x}(0) = \mathbf{0}$, and use Laplace transforms to compute the response of the system S defined by

$$S: \qquad \dot{\mathbf{x}}(t) = \mathbf{A}\mathbf{x}(t) + 1(t)\mathbf{f}$$

Show that, irrespective of what $\mathbf{f}$ might be, if degree $\psi <$ degree Δ, then the time dependence of $\mathbf{x}(t)$ involves only terms of the form $e^{\lambda_k t}$, $te^{\lambda_k t}$, . . . , $t^{m_k - 1}e^{\lambda_k t}$, where m_k is the multiplicity of the root λ_k of $\psi(\lambda)$. Therefore, it is the minimal polynomial ψ (and not the characteristic polynomial Δ) which characterizes the dynamics of S. (*Hint:* Use *6*.)

[1] This definition of multiplicity of an eigenvalue does not agree with that of all authors. The reader is cautioned to ascertain what each author means by the expression.

8 **Theorem** Let $\psi(\lambda) = \prod_{i=1}^{\sigma} (\lambda - \lambda_i)^{m_i}$ be the minimal polynomial of the matrix $\mathbf{A}$. Let p and q be two arbitrary polynomials. Then

$$p(\mathbf{A}) = q(\mathbf{A}) \Leftrightarrow p \equiv q \qquad \mathrm{mod}\ \psi$$

That is, the matrices $p(\mathbf{A})$ and $q(\mathbf{A})$ are equal if and only if the polynomials p and q have the same remainder when divided by the polynomial ψ.

Proof $\Leftarrow$ Divide p and q by ψ and let q_1 and q_2 be the quotients. Then, by assumption, the remainders are identical, say, r_1. Thus

$$p = q_1\psi + r_1$$
$$q = q_2\psi + r_1$$

Hence, since the two equations above are identities in λ, we may substitute $\mathbf{A}$ for λ and get

$$p(\mathbf{A}) = q_1(\mathbf{A})\psi(\mathbf{A}) + r_1(\mathbf{A}) = r_1(\mathbf{A})$$
$$q(\mathbf{A}) = q_2(\mathbf{A})\psi(\mathbf{A}) + r_1(\mathbf{A}) = r_1(\mathbf{A})$$

Hence $p(\mathbf{A}) = q(\mathbf{A})$.

$\Rightarrow$ By assumption, $(p - q)(\mathbf{A}) = \mathbf{0}$. Hence from the definition of ψ the polynomial $p - q$ is a multiple of ψ; hence, $p \equiv q \pmod{\psi}$.

9 **Corollary** With the notation of *8*,

$$p(\mathbf{A}) = q(\mathbf{A}) \Leftrightarrow p^{(l)}(\lambda_k) = q^{(l)}(\lambda_k) \qquad \text{for } l = 0, 1, \ldots, m_k - 1 \quad k = 1, 2, \ldots, \sigma$$

Proof $\Rightarrow$ By Theorem *8*, $p(\mathbf{A}) = q(\mathbf{A})$ implies that, for all λ's,

10 $$p(\lambda) = q_1(\lambda)\psi(\lambda) + r_1(\lambda)$$

11 $$q(\lambda) = q_2(\lambda)\psi(\lambda) + r_1(\lambda)$$

Since, for $k = 1, 2, \ldots, \sigma$, λ_k is a zero of order m_k of ψ, we have

$$(q_i\psi)^{(l)}\Big|_{\lambda=\lambda_k} = \sum_{\alpha=0}^{l} \binom{l}{\alpha} q_i^{(\alpha)}\psi^{(l-\alpha)}\Big|_{\lambda=\lambda_k} = 0 \qquad i = 1, 2$$

Therefore, from *10* and *11* we have

$$p^{(l)}(\lambda_k) = q^{(l)}(\lambda_k) \qquad k = 1, 2, \ldots, \sigma \quad l = 0, 1, \ldots, m_k - 1$$

since they are both equal to $r_1^{(l)}(\lambda_k)$.

$\Leftarrow$ Since $p^{(l)}(\lambda_k) = q^{(l)}(\lambda_k)$ for $k = 1, 2, \ldots, \sigma$ and

$$l = 0, 1, \ldots, m_k - 1$$

and since p and q are polynomials, the polynomial $p - q$ is a multiple of $\prod_{k=1}^{\sigma} (\lambda - \lambda_k)^{m_k}$, hence of ψ. Therefore, $p - q = b\psi$, where b is a polynomial. Hence, $p(\mathbf{A}) - q(\mathbf{A}) = b(\mathbf{A})\psi(\mathbf{A})$ and

$$p(\mathbf{A}) = q(\mathbf{A}) \qquad \text{since } \psi(\mathbf{A}) = \mathbf{0}$$

3 *The index of an eigenvalue*

Now consider $\mathbf{A}$ as a linear transformation. From this point of view we have defined *an eigenvalue of* $\mathbf{A}$ as a value of λ for which the L.T. $\mathbf{A} - \lambda\mathbf{I}$ on $\mathcal{C}^n$ to $\mathcal{C}^n$ is not one-one. An eigenvalue thus defined is necessarily a zero of $\Delta(\lambda) = \det(\mathbf{A} - \lambda\mathbf{I})$.

1 **Definition** Let us denote by $\mathfrak{N}_i^k$ the null space of the L.T. $(\mathbf{A} - \lambda_i\mathbf{I})^k$. In symbols,

$$\mathfrak{N}_i^k \triangleq \{\mathbf{x} | (\mathbf{A} - \lambda_i\mathbf{I})^k\mathbf{x} = \mathbf{0}\}$$

Clearly,

$$\mathfrak{N}_i^1 \subset \mathfrak{N}_i^2 \subset \mathfrak{N}_i^3 \subset \cdots$$

2 **Definition** The *index of the eigenvalue* λ_i is the least integer such that

$$\mathfrak{N}_i^k = \mathfrak{N}_i^{k+1}$$

The index of λ_i will be denoted by ν_i. $\mathfrak{N}_i^{\nu_i}$, which we write $\mathfrak{N}_i$, is called the *generalized null space of* $\mathbf{A}$ *associated with the ith eigenvalue.*

3 *Example* Let $\mathbf{A} = \begin{bmatrix} 1 & 1 & 0 \\ 0 & 1 & 1 \\ 0 & 0 & 2 \end{bmatrix} \qquad \Delta(\lambda) = -(\lambda - 1)^2(\lambda - 2)$

Consider the eigenvalue $\lambda_1 = 1$. Since

$$\mathbf{A} - \mathbf{I} = \begin{bmatrix} 0 & 1 & 0 \\ 0 & 0 & 1 \\ 0 & 0 & 1 \end{bmatrix} \qquad (\mathbf{A} - \mathbf{I})^2 = \begin{bmatrix} 0 & 0 & 1 \\ 0 & 0 & 1 \\ 0 & 0 & 1 \end{bmatrix} = (\mathbf{A} - \mathbf{I})^3$$

and

$$\mathfrak{N}_1^1 = \{\mathbf{x} | (\mathbf{A} - \mathbf{I})\mathbf{x} = \mathbf{0}\} = \{\mathbf{x} | x_2 = x_3 = 0\}$$
$$\mathfrak{N}_1^2 = \{\mathbf{x} | (\mathbf{A} - \mathbf{I})^2\mathbf{x} = \mathbf{0}\} = \{\mathbf{x} | x_3 = 0\}$$
$$\mathfrak{N}_1^3 = \mathfrak{N}_1^2$$

hence, $\nu_1 = 2$. Similarly, the index of $\lambda_2 = 2$ is $\nu_2 = 1$ with

$$\mathfrak{N}_2 = \{\mathbf{x} | x_1 = x_2 = x_3\}$$

4 *Exercise* For any integer k, $\mathfrak{N}_i^k$ is an *invariant subspace* of $\mathbf{A}$, that is,

$$\mathbf{x} \in \mathfrak{N}_i^k \text{ implies } \mathbf{Ax} \in \mathfrak{N}_i^k$$

Hint: Observe that $\mathbf{A}$ and $(\mathbf{A} - \lambda_i\mathbf{I})^k$ commute; hence,

$$(\mathbf{A} - \lambda_i\mathbf{I})^k\mathbf{Ax} = \mathbf{A}(\mathbf{A} - \lambda_i\mathbf{I})^k\mathbf{x}$$

5 *Exercise* If ν_i is the index of the eigenvalue λ_i, then for $l = 1, 2, \ldots,$

$$\mathfrak{N}_i^{\nu_i+l} = \mathfrak{N}_i^{\nu_i}$$

Hint: By definition it is true for $l = 1$. Next use induction, i.e., assume $\mathfrak{N}_i^{\nu_i+l-1} = \mathfrak{N}_i^{\nu_i}$ and show that $\mathfrak{N}_i^{\nu_i+l} = \mathfrak{N}_i^{\nu_i}$. Use the relation

$$(\mathbf{A} - \lambda_i\mathbf{I})^{\nu_i+l} = (\mathbf{A} - \lambda_i\mathbf{I})^{\nu_i+l-1}(\mathbf{A} - \lambda_i\mathbf{I}) \quad \triangleleft$$

The interesting fact is that the multiplicity m_i of λ_i is equal to the index ν_i of λ_i. In order to prove this fact, we establish the necessary and sufficient conditions for two polynomials in the L.T. $\mathbf{A}$ to be equal.

6 **Theorem** Let the L.T. $\mathbf{A}$ have the eigenvalues $\lambda_1, \lambda_2, \ldots, \lambda_\sigma$ with indices $\nu_1, \nu_2, \ldots, \nu_\sigma$, respectively. Let p and q be two polynomials. Then $p(\mathbf{A}) = q(\mathbf{A})$ if and only if, for $k = 1, 2, \ldots, \sigma$,

7 $$p^{(l)}(\lambda_k) = q^{(l)}(\lambda_k) \qquad l = 0, 1, 2, \ldots, \nu_k - 1$$

Proof Let z be the polynomial $p - q$. Then the theorem is equivalent to

$$z(\mathbf{A}) = \mathbf{0} \Leftrightarrow z^{(l)}(\lambda_k) = 0 \qquad l = 0, 1, \ldots, \nu_k - 1; k = 1, \ldots, \sigma$$

$\Rightarrow$ We may delete from $z(\lambda)$ any factor of the form $(\lambda - \mu)$, where μ is not an eigenvalue because the operator $(\mathbf{A} - \mu\mathbf{I})$ is one-one; hence, for any $\mathbf{y}$, $(\mathbf{A} - \mu\mathbf{I})\mathbf{y}$ is zero if and only if $\mathbf{y} = \mathbf{0}$. Let the resulting polynomial be r_1; then $r_1(\mathbf{A}) = \mathbf{0}$ by assumption. Let $r_1(\lambda) = \prod_{i=1}^{\sigma} (\lambda - \lambda_i)^{\gamma_i}$.

If λ_i is any eigenvalue of $\mathbf{A}$, there is a $\mathbf{y} \neq \mathbf{0}$ such that $\mathbf{Ay} = \lambda_i\mathbf{y}$; hence, $r_1(\mathbf{A})\mathbf{y} = r_1(\lambda_i)\mathbf{y} = \mathbf{0}$ because $r_1(\mathbf{A}) = \mathbf{0}$. Therefore, $r_1(\lambda_i) = 0$, that is, r_1 has a zero at each eigenvalue of $\mathbf{A}$. In other words, $\gamma_i \geq 1$ for each i. It remains to show that the multiplicity γ_i of each zero λ_i is at least as great as the index ν_i. Suppose it were not; that is, $\gamma_i < \nu_i$. Then there would be a vector $\mathbf{v}$ such that $\mathbf{0} \neq \mathbf{v} \in \mathfrak{N}_i^{\gamma_i+1}$ but $\mathbf{v} \notin \mathfrak{N}_i^{\gamma_i}$; thus, $(\mathbf{A} - \lambda_i\mathbf{I})^{\gamma_i+1}\mathbf{v} = \mathbf{0}$ and the vector $\mathbf{w}$ defined by $\mathbf{w} = (\mathbf{A} - \lambda_i\mathbf{I})^{\gamma_i}\mathbf{v}$ is nonzero. Let $r_1(\lambda) = (\lambda - \lambda_i)^{\gamma_i}t(\lambda)$; clearly the polynomial $t(\lambda)$ is such that $t(\lambda_i) \neq 0$, since γ_i is the multiplicity of the zero λ_i of r_1. Observe that $\mathbf{Aw} = \lambda_i\mathbf{w}$; hence,

$$\mathbf{0} = r(\mathbf{A})\mathbf{v} = t(\mathbf{A})(\mathbf{A} - \lambda_i\mathbf{I})^{\gamma_i}\mathbf{v} = t(\mathbf{A})\mathbf{w} = t(\lambda_i)\mathbf{w}$$

which is a contradiction since $t(\lambda_i) \neq 0$ and $\mathbf{w} \neq \mathbf{0}$. Therefore, $\gamma_i \geq \nu_i$ for each i, that is, $r_i(\lambda)$ has at λ_i a zero of multiplicity at least equal to ν_i. Hence $z(\lambda)$, which is a multiple of $r_i(\lambda)$, has the same property.

$\Leftarrow$ Let $\mathbf{u}_1, \mathbf{u}_2, \ldots, \mathbf{u}_n$ be a basis for the space For each $i = 1, 2, \ldots, n$, $\mathbf{u}_i, \mathbf{A}\mathbf{u}_i, \mathbf{A}^2\mathbf{u}_i, \ldots, \mathbf{A}^n\mathbf{u}_i$, being $n + 1$ vectors in an n-dimensional space, are linearly dependent. Hence, for

$$i = 1, 2, \ldots, n$$

there exists a polynomial $p_i(\lambda)$ such that $p_i(\mathbf{A})\mathbf{u}_i = \mathbf{0}$. Let $m(\lambda)$ be the least common multiple of the n polynomials $p_1, p_2, \ldots, p_n$. $m(\mathbf{A}) = \mathbf{0}$ because, for any vector $\mathbf{x}$, $m(\mathbf{A})\mathbf{x} = \mathbf{0}$, since $m(\mathbf{A})\mathbf{u}_i = \mathbf{0}$ for $i = 1, 2, \ldots, n$. As in the first part of the proof, if we may delete from $m(\lambda)$ all factors of the form $(\lambda - \mu)$, where μ is not an eigenvalue of $\mathbf{A}$, we get a new polynomial m_1 such that $m_1(\mathbf{A}) = \mathbf{0}$. Again as above, the last equality implies that $m_1(\lambda) = \prod_{i=1}^{\sigma} (\lambda - \lambda_i)^{\gamma_i}$ with $\gamma_i \geq \nu_i$ for each i. Let $m_2(\lambda) = \prod_{i=1}^{\sigma} (\lambda - \lambda_i)^{\nu_i}$. We still have $m_2(\mathbf{A}) = \mathbf{0}$ because the fact that $\mathfrak{N}_i^{\nu_i+k} = \mathfrak{N}_i^{\nu_i}$, $k = 1, 2, \ldots$, implies that the null space of $(\mathbf{A} - \lambda_i\mathbf{I})^{\nu_i+k}$ is the same as that of $(\mathbf{A} - \lambda_i\mathbf{I})^{\nu_i}$. Hence the null space of $m_2(\mathbf{A})$ is the same as that of $m_1(\mathbf{A})$, namely, the whole space. By assumption, the polynomial $z(\lambda)$ has a zero of order ν_k at λ_k for $k = 1, 2, \ldots \sigma$ and $m_2(\lambda) = \prod_{i=1}^{\sigma} (\lambda - \lambda_i)^{\nu_i}$. Therefore, $z(\lambda)$ is a multiple of $m_2(\lambda)$ and $m_2(\mathbf{A}) = \mathbf{0}$ implies $z(\mathbf{A}) = \mathbf{0}$. Q.E.D.

8 **Corollary** Let $\mathbf{A}$ be an L.T. in the n-dimensional space with eigenvalues $\lambda_1, \lambda_2, \ldots, \lambda_\sigma$ with respective multiplicities $m_1, m_2, \ldots, m_\sigma$ and indices $\nu_1, \nu_2, \ldots, \nu_s$. Then

$$m_i = \nu_i \qquad i = 1, 2, \ldots, \sigma$$

In other words, the multiplicity of an eigenvalue is equal to its index.

4 *Definition of a function of a matrix*[1]

1 **Definition** Let $\mathbf{A}$ be a matrix with eigenvalues $\lambda_1, \lambda_2, \ldots, \lambda_\sigma$. Let f be a function analytic in an open set containing $\lambda_1, \lambda_2, \ldots, \lambda_\sigma$. Let $p(\lambda)$ be a polynomial such that

[1] In the following we may interchangeably replace the word *matrix* by *linear transformation on* $\mathcal{C}^n$.

2 $$p^{(l)}(\lambda_k) = f^{(l)}(\lambda_k) \qquad l = 0, 1, 2, \ldots, m_k - 1; k = 1, 2, \ldots, \sigma$$

Then we define the function f of the matrix **A** as

$$f(\mathbf{A}) = p(\mathbf{A})$$

3 *Comment* This definition makes sense, since Theorem *D.2.8* guarantees that the result is independent of the choice of the polynomial p.

4 **Corollary** Let f, g be two functions analytic in an open set containing the λ_i's; then

$$f(\mathbf{A}) + g(\mathbf{A}) = h(\mathbf{A}) \qquad \text{where } h = f + g$$
$$f(\mathbf{A})g(\mathbf{A}) = k(\mathbf{A}) \qquad \text{where } k = fg$$

5 **Corollary** If $f(\lambda) = \sum_{k=0}^{N} a_k \lambda^k$, then $f(\mathbf{A}) = \sum_{k=0}^{N} a_k \mathbf{A}^k$.

6 **Corollary** $f(\mathbf{A}) = \mathbf{0}$ if and only if $f^{(l)}(\lambda_k) = 0$, $l = 0, 1, 2, \ldots, m_k - 1$; $k = 1, 2, \ldots, \sigma$.

7 *Exercise* Prove Corollaries *4* to *6*. (*Hint:* Refer to the definition.)

8 *Exercise* Show that for any matrix **A**

$$e^{j\mathbf{A}} = \cos \mathbf{A} + j \sin \mathbf{A}$$
$$\sin 2\mathbf{A} = 2 \sin \mathbf{A} \cos \mathbf{A}$$
$$\cos^2 \mathbf{A} + \sin^2 \mathbf{A} = \mathbf{I}$$
$$\exp [\mathbf{A}(t_1 + t_2)] = [\exp (\mathbf{A}t_1)][\exp (\mathbf{A}t_2)] \qquad \forall t_1, t_2$$
$$\sin \mathbf{A}(t_1 + t_2) = \sin \mathbf{A}t_1 \cos \mathbf{A}t_2 + \cos \mathbf{A}t_1 \sin \mathbf{A}t_2 \qquad \forall t_1, t_2$$

5 *Geometric structure of the L.T.* A

Let **A** have $\lambda_1, \lambda_2, \ldots, \lambda_\sigma$ as eigenvalues with multiplicities $m_1, m_2, \ldots, m_\sigma$, respectively. Consider the polynomials $\varphi_k(\lambda)$ defined as follows: for each k, $1 \le k \le \sigma$,

1 $$\varphi_k(\lambda_k) = 1$$
$$\varphi_k^{(l)}(\lambda_k) = 0 \qquad l = 1, 2, \ldots, m_k - 1$$
$$\varphi_k^{(l)}(\lambda_j) = 0 \qquad l = 0, 1, 2, \ldots, m_j - 1; \; j = 1, 2, \ldots, k - 1, k + 1, \ldots \sigma$$

These polynomials are easily obtained from the partial-fraction expansion of $1/\psi(\lambda)$, where $\psi(\lambda)$ is the minimal polynomial of **A**. Let us first expand in partial fractions and then collect terms:

2 $$\frac{1}{\psi(\lambda)} = \sum_{k=1}^{\sigma} \sum_{l=0}^{m_k - 1} \frac{c_{kl}}{(\lambda - \lambda_k)^{l+1}} = \sum_{k=1}^{\sigma} \frac{n_k(\lambda)}{(\lambda - \lambda_k)^{m_k}}$$

Here the $n_k(\lambda)$ are polynomials in λ and of degree $[n_k(\lambda)] < m_k$. Then it is easy to show that

3 $$\varphi_k(\lambda) = \frac{\psi(\lambda) n_k(\lambda)}{(\lambda - \lambda_k)^{m_k}}$$

The polynomials $\varphi_k(\lambda)$ given by *3* satisfy the above conditions because

4 $$\sum_{k=1}^{\sigma} \varphi_k(\lambda) = 1 \qquad \text{for all } \lambda\text{'s}$$

5 $\varphi_k(\lambda)$ contains the factors $(\lambda - \lambda_j)^{m_j}$ for $j \neq k$ and $1 \leq j \leq \sigma$.

6 **Theorem** Let the polynomials φ_k, $k = 1, 2, \ldots, \sigma$, be defined by *3* and let $\varphi_k(\mathbf{A}) \triangleq \mathbf{E}_k$; then

(I) $\mathbf{E}_k \cdot \mathbf{E}_k = \mathbf{E}_k$ that is, $\mathbf{E}_k$ is a projection (*C.12.9*)

(II) $\mathbf{E}_k \cdot \mathbf{E}_j = \mathbf{0}$ $j \neq k;\ j,k = 1, 2, \ldots, \sigma$

(III) $\sum_{k=1}^{\sigma} \mathbf{E}_k = \mathbf{I}$

(IV) $\mathcal{C}^n = \mathcal{R}(\mathbf{E}_1) \oplus \mathbf{R}(\mathbf{E}_2) \oplus \cdots \oplus \mathbf{R}(\mathbf{E}_\sigma)$ that is, the whole space $\mathcal{C}^n$ is the direct sum of the ranges of $\mathbf{E}_1, \mathbf{E}_2, \ldots, \mathbf{E}_\sigma$

Proof (I) follows from $\varphi_k^2(\mathbf{A}) = \varphi_k(\mathbf{A})$ by Theorem *D.2.8*. (II) follows from Corollary *D.4.6* and the fact that the polynomial $\varphi_k(\lambda)\varphi_j(\lambda)$ has a zero of order $\geq m_i$ at each λ_i. (III) follows from *4*. (IV) Since $\varphi_k(\mathbf{A}) = \mathbf{E}_k$ is a polynomial in $\mathbf{A}$, $\mathbf{E}_k$ and $\mathbf{A}$ commute; therefore, $\mathcal{R}(\mathbf{E}_k)$, the range of $\mathbf{E}_k$, is an invariant subspace of $\mathbf{A}$. Therefore by (II) and (III), we conclude that the whole space is the direct sum of the ranges of $\mathbf{E}_1, \mathbf{E}_2, \ldots, \mathbf{E}_\sigma$; hence (IV).

7 *Comment* The decomposition of any $\mathbf{x}$ in components $\mathbf{x}_k$ such that $\mathbf{x}_k \in \mathcal{R}(\mathbf{E}_k)$ is given by

8 $$\mathbf{x} = \sum_{k=1}^{\sigma} \mathbf{E}_k \mathbf{x} = \sum_{k=1}^{\sigma} \mathbf{x}_k \qquad \text{where } \mathbf{x}_k \triangleq \mathbf{E}_k \mathbf{x}$$

The decomposition is unique because of (IV).

9 *Exercise* Show that (I) $\sum_{k=1}^{\sigma} \varphi_k(\lambda) = 1$ for all λ's, (II) $\varphi_j(\lambda)\varphi_k(\lambda)$ is a multiple of $\psi(\lambda)$ if $j \neq k$, and (III) $[\varphi_k(\lambda)]^2 \equiv \varphi_k(\lambda) \pmod{\psi}$.

10 *Exercise* Use the results of *9* to prove Theorem *6* by invoking only the definition of $\psi(\lambda)$ and Theorem *D.2.8*.

11 *Exercise* Show that the range of $\mathbf{E}_k$ is an invariant subspace of $\mathbf{A}$.

12 **Theorem** The range of $\mathbf{E}_k$ is the generalized null space $\mathfrak{N}_k$ associated with the eigenvalue λ_k. Symbolically, for $k = 1, 2, \ldots, \sigma$,

13 $$\mathcal{R}(\mathbf{E}_k) = \mathfrak{N}_k = \{\mathbf{x} | (\mathbf{A} - \lambda_k\mathbf{I})^{m_k}\mathbf{x} = \mathbf{0}\}$$

14 *Comment* From (II) and (III) of Theorem *6* the whole space $\mathcal{C}^n$ may be considered as the direct sum of the ranges of $\mathbf{E}_1, \mathbf{E}_2, \ldots, \mathbf{E}_\sigma$. With the present theorem the whole space $\mathcal{C}^n$ is the direct sum of the generalized null spaces[1]

15 $$\mathcal{C}^n = \mathcal{R}(\mathbf{E}_1) \oplus \cdots \oplus \mathcal{R}(\mathbf{E}_\sigma)$$

and

$$\mathcal{C}^n = \mathfrak{N}_1 \oplus \mathfrak{N}_2 \oplus \cdots \oplus \mathfrak{N}_\sigma$$

Proof (I) We prove that

16 $$\mathcal{R}(\mathbf{E}_k) \subset \mathfrak{N}_k$$

Suppose $\mathbf{0} \neq \mathbf{x} \in \mathcal{R}(\mathbf{E}_k)$; then, for some $\mathbf{y} \neq \mathbf{0}$,

$$\mathbf{x} = \mathbf{E}_k\mathbf{y} = \varphi_k(\mathbf{A})\mathbf{y}$$

and $$(\mathbf{A} - \lambda_k\mathbf{I})^{m_k}\mathbf{x} = (\mathbf{A} - \lambda_k\mathbf{I})^{m_k}\varphi_k(\mathbf{A})\mathbf{y} = n_k(\mathbf{A})\psi(\mathbf{A})\mathbf{y} = \mathbf{0}$$

where in the last step we used *3*. Therefore, $\mathbf{x} \in \mathfrak{N}_k$.

(II) We prove next that $j \neq k$ implies $\mathfrak{N}_j \cap \mathfrak{N}_k = \{\mathbf{0}\}$.[2] This result, together with *6*(IV) and *16*, implies that $\mathcal{R}(\mathbf{E}_k) = \mathfrak{N}_k$. Let $\mathbf{x} \in \mathfrak{N}_k \cap \mathfrak{N}_j$. Let $\rho_k(\lambda) = (\lambda - \lambda_k)^{m_k}$ and $\rho_j(\lambda) = (\lambda - \lambda_j)^{m_j}$. Hence, $\rho_k(\mathbf{A})\mathbf{x} = \mathbf{0}$ and $\rho_j(\mathbf{A})\mathbf{x} = \mathbf{0}$. Since ρ_k and ρ_j are relatively prime polynomials, there exist polynomials g_j and g_k such that, for all λ's,

$$g_k(\lambda)\rho_k(\lambda) + g_j(\lambda)\rho_j(\lambda) = 1$$

Hence $$g_k(\mathbf{A})\rho_k(\mathbf{A})\mathbf{x} + g_j(\mathbf{A})\rho_j(\mathbf{A})\mathbf{x} = \mathbf{x}$$

Since the left-hand side is equal to zero, $\mathbf{x} = \mathbf{0}$. Hence the only vector common to both $\mathfrak{N}_k$ and $\mathfrak{N}_j$ is the zero vector. Q.E.D.

17 **Corollary** The dimension of $\mathcal{R}(\mathbf{E}_k)$ (and of $\mathfrak{N}_k$ by Theorem *12*) is r_k, the order of λ_k as a zero of $\Delta(\lambda)$. [The proof follows directly from considering the system of n homogeneous equations $(\mathbf{A} - \lambda_k\mathbf{I})\mathbf{x} = \mathbf{0}$. The number of linearly independent solutions is equal to the order of the zero λ_k of det $(\mathbf{A} - \lambda\mathbf{I})$.] ◁

[1] Compare this result with Theorem *C.19.7*.

[2] That is, the only vector common to $\mathfrak{N}_j$ and $\mathfrak{N}_k$ is the zero vector $\mathbf{0}$.

The partition of the whole space $\mathcal{C}^n$ into invariant subspaces in Eq. *15* is of great importance. From *C.13.5* it follows that if we take as a basis for the whole space the union of bases of these invariant subspaces, the matrix representation of **A** will consist of diagonal blocks:

18
$$\begin{bmatrix} \mathbf{M}_1 & \mathbf{0} & \cdot & \cdot & \mathbf{0} \\ \mathbf{0} & \mathbf{M}_2 & & & \cdot \\ \cdot & & \mathbf{M}_3 & & \cdot \\ \cdot & & & \ddots & \cdot \\ \mathbf{0} & \cdots & \cdots & \cdots & \mathbf{M}_k \end{bmatrix}$$

The submatrix $\mathbf{M}_i$ represents **A** in the subspace $\mathfrak{N}_i$. The Jordan canonical form is obtained by picking in each $\mathfrak{N}_i$ a special basis. It can be shown that each $\mathbf{M}_i$ is then such that its only nonzero elements are on the main diagonal and on the diagonal next to the main one (either above it or below it).

19 *Exercise* Show that

$$\mathcal{C}^n = \mathfrak{N}_k \oplus \mathcal{R}[(\mathbf{A} - \lambda_k\mathbf{I})^{m_k}]$$

(*Hint:* Observe that $\mathfrak{N}_k = \mathcal{R}[\varphi_k(\mathbf{A})]$ and that, in the notation of the proof of *12*, φ_k and ρ_k are relatively prime.)

20 *Exercise* By a suitable choice of basis, **A** may be diagonalized if and only if all roots of $\psi(\lambda)$ are simple. This is equivalent to saying **A** is a simple L.T. if and only if all roots of $\psi(\lambda)$ are simple (see *C.18.9*).

21 *Exercise* The Jordan canonical form can be expressed as follows: there is a basis $\{\mathbf{e}_1,\mathbf{e}_2, \ldots ,\mathbf{e}_n\}$ for the space $\mathcal{C}^n$, a set of integers

$$1 = n_1 < n_2 < \cdots < n_k \leq n$$

and an enumeration (with possible repetitions) $\mu_1, \mu_2, \ldots, \mu_k$ of the σ eigenvalues[1] of **A** such that

$$\mathbf{A}\mathbf{e}_i = \mu_j\mathbf{e}_i + \mathbf{e}_{i-1} \qquad \text{for } n_j < i < n_{j+1}$$

and
$$\mathbf{A}\mathbf{e}_{n_j} = \mu_j\mathbf{e}_{n_j}$$

The diagonal blocks will be of order $n_2 - n_1, n_3 - n_2, \ldots, n - n_k$. By *C.10.4*, this description of the Jordan form corresponds to that which has the 1's just above the main diagonal. The reason for this rather cryptic statement is the large number of cases covered by the description. Let us illustrate it by examples:

[1] That is, each one of the μ_i is a member of the set $\{\lambda_1,\lambda_2, \ldots ,\lambda_\sigma\}$. Furthermore, repetitions may occur in the enumeration because k may be larger than σ.

$$\begin{bmatrix} \lambda_1 & 0 & 0 \\ 0 & \lambda_1 & 0 \\ 0 & 0 & \lambda_1 \end{bmatrix} \qquad \begin{aligned} &\mathcal{C}^3 = \mathcal{N}(\mathbf{A} - \lambda_1\mathbf{I});\ \nu_1 = 1,\ \dim \mathcal{N}(\mathbf{A} - \lambda_1\mathbf{I}) = 3 \\ &n_i = i,\ i = 1, 2, 3;\ \mu_1 = \lambda_1,\ \mu_2 = \lambda_1,\ \mu_3 = \lambda_1 \end{aligned}$$

This case illustrates the parenthetical statement "with possible repetitions."

$$\left[\begin{array}{cc|c} \lambda_1 & 0 & 0 \\ 0 & \lambda_1 & 0 \\ \hline 0 & 0 & \lambda_2 \end{array}\right] \qquad \begin{aligned} &\mathcal{C}^3 = \mathcal{N}(\mathbf{A} - \lambda_1\mathbf{I}) \oplus \mathcal{N}(\mathbf{A} - \lambda_2\mathbf{I});\ \nu_1 = 1,\ \nu_2 = 1 \\ &\dim \mathcal{N}(\mathbf{A} - \lambda_1\mathbf{I}) = 2,\ \dim \mathcal{N}(\mathbf{A} - \lambda_2\mathbf{I}) = 1 \\ &n_i = i,\ i = 1, 2, 3;\ \mu_1 = \lambda_1,\ \mu_2 = \lambda_1,\ \mu_3 = \lambda_2 \end{aligned}$$

$$\left[\begin{array}{cc|c} \lambda_1 & 1 & 0 \\ 0 & \lambda_1 & 0 \\ \hline 0 & 0 & \lambda_2 \end{array}\right] \qquad \begin{aligned} &\mathcal{C}^3 = \mathcal{N}_1^2 \oplus \mathcal{N}(\mathbf{A} - \lambda_2\mathbf{I});\ \nu_1 = 2,\ \nu_2 = 1 \\ &\dim \mathcal{N}_1^2 = 2;\ \dim \mathcal{N}(\mathbf{A} - \lambda_2\mathbf{I}) = 1,\ n_1 = 1,\ n_2 = 3 \\ &\mu_1 = \lambda_1,\ \mu_2 = \lambda_2 \end{aligned}$$

$$\left[\begin{array}{cc|cc} \lambda_1 & 1 & 0 & 0 \\ 0 & \lambda_1 & 0 & 0 \\ \hline 0 & 0 & \lambda_1 & 1 \\ 0 & 0 & 0 & \lambda_1 \end{array}\right] \qquad \begin{aligned} &\mathcal{C}^4 = \mathcal{N}_1^2;\ \nu_1 = 2;\ \dim \mathcal{N}_1^2 = 4 \\ &n_1 = 1,\ n_2 = 3;\ \mu_1 = \lambda_1,\ \mu_2 = \lambda_1 \end{aligned}$$

$$\left[\begin{array}{ccc|c|cc} \lambda_1 & 1 & 0 & 0 & 0 & 0 \\ 0 & \lambda_1 & 1 & 0 & 0 & 0 \\ 0 & 0 & \lambda_1 & 0 & 0 & 0 \\ \hline 0 & 0 & 0 & \lambda_1 & 0 & 0 \\ \hline 0 & 0 & 0 & 0 & \lambda_2 & 1 \\ 0 & 0 & 0 & 0 & 0 & \lambda_2 \end{array}\right] \qquad \begin{aligned} &\mathcal{C}^6 = \mathcal{N}_1^3 \oplus \mathcal{N}_2^2;\ \nu_1 = 3,\ \nu_2 = 2 \\ &\dim \mathcal{N}_1 = 4,\ \dim \mathcal{N}_2 = 2 \\ &n_1 = 3,\ n_2 = 4,\ n_3 = 6;\ \mu_1 = \lambda_1, \\ &\mu_2 = \lambda_1,\ \mu_3 = \lambda_2 \end{aligned}$$

22 *Exercise* (*Cayley-Hamilton theorem*) Let $\mathbf{A}$ be a matrix and Δ its characteristic polynomial. Then $\Delta(\mathbf{A}) = \mathbf{0}$. (*Hint:* Observe that each basis vector used in the representation *18* belongs to one of the $\mathcal{N}_k$'s.)

6 *The fundamental formula*

1 **Theorem** If f is analytic in an open set containing $\lambda_1, \lambda_2, \ldots, \lambda_\sigma$, then

2 $$f(\mathbf{A}) = \sum_{k=1}^{\sigma} \sum_{l=0}^{m_k-1} \frac{(\mathbf{A} - \lambda_k\mathbf{I})^l}{l!} f^{(l)}(\lambda_k)\mathbf{E}_k$$

where $f(\mathbf{A})$ is defined by *D.4.1* and $\mathbf{E}_k$ is defined in *D.5.3* and *D.5.6*.
Proof Consider the interpolating polynomial

$$q(\mu) = \sum_{k=1}^{\sigma} \sum_{l=0}^{m_k-1} \frac{(\mu - \lambda_k)^l}{l!} f^{(l)}(\lambda_k)\varphi_k(\mu)$$

Making use of the properties *D.5.1* of the polynomials φ_k, it is easy to see that the conditions *D.4.2* are satisfied, namely,

$$q^{(l)}(\lambda_k) = f^{(l)}(\lambda_k) \qquad l = 0, 1, \ldots, m_k - 1; k = 1, 2, \ldots, \sigma$$

Hence, by Definition *D.4.1*,

$$q(\mathbf{A}) = f(\mathbf{A})$$

and *2* follows.

3 **Corollary: the fundamental formula for $f(\mathbf{A})$** Let

4 $$\mathbf{Z}_{kl} = (1/l!)(\mathbf{A} - \lambda_k\mathbf{I})^l\mathbf{E}_k$$

where $\mathbf{E}_k \triangleq \varphi_k(\mathbf{A})$ and the polynomial φ_k is defined by *D.5.3*. Then

5 $$f(\mathbf{A}) = \sum_{k=1}^{\sigma} \sum_{l=0}^{m_k-1} f^{(l)}(\lambda_k)\mathbf{Z}_{kl}$$

6 *Comment* Observe that the $\mathbf{Z}_{kl}$, called the *components* of the matrix **A**, depend only on **A** and not on f. This formula exhibits the fact that $f(\mathbf{A})$ depends only on the behavior of f at the eigenvalues of **A**. If λ_k is a simple root of $\psi(\lambda) = 0$, then $f(\mathbf{A})$ depends only on the value of f at λ_k. If λ_k is a zero of order m_k of ψ, then $f(\mathbf{A})$ depends only on the value of f and its $(m_k - 1)$ first derivatives at λ_k.

7 *Exercise* Show directly from *4* that $\mathbf{Z}_{k0} = \varphi_k(\mathbf{A})$, where φ_k is the polynomial defined by *D.5.3*.

8 *Exercise* If $j \neq k$, then for any $0 \leq l \leq m_k - 1$, $0 \leq m \leq m_j - 1$,

$$\mathbf{Z}_{kl}\mathbf{Z}_{jm} = \mathbf{0}$$

9 *Exercise* Show that

$$\mathbf{A} = \sum_{k=1}^{\sigma} (\lambda_k\mathbf{E}_k + \mathbf{Z}_{k1})$$

10 *Exercise* For any $k = 1, 2, \ldots$, if $j \geq m_k$, then

$$\mathbf{Z}_{kj} = \mathbf{0}$$

11 *Exercise* Let **A** have n distinct real eigenvalues. Let $\varepsilon_1, \varepsilon_2, \ldots, \varepsilon_n$ be an arbitrary sequence of 1 and -1's. Show that $\mathbf{X} \triangleq \sum_{i=1}^{n} \epsilon_i \sqrt{\lambda_i}\, \mathbf{E}_i$ satisfies the equation $\mathbf{X}^2 = \mathbf{A}$. In other words, any such **X** is a possible choice for $\sqrt{\mathbf{A}}$.

12 *Exercise* Show that

$$\exp(\mathbf{A}t) = \sum_{k=1}^{\sigma} \sum_{l=0}^{m_k-1} t^l e^{\lambda_k t}\mathbf{Z}_{kl}$$

13 *Exercise* Let f be an entire function (i.e., analytic in the whole complex plane). Show that

$$\frac{d}{dt} f(\mathbf{A}t) = \mathbf{A}f'(\mathbf{A}t) \qquad \forall t$$

where **A** is a matrix of constant elements and f' is the derivative of f. In particular, show that

$$\frac{d}{dt}[\exp(\mathbf{A}t)] = \mathbf{A}\exp(\mathbf{A}t)$$

14 *Exercise* Show that if **A** is skew symmetric (i.e., the transpose of **A**, say, $\mathbf{A}'$, is $-\mathbf{A}$) then $\exp(\mathbf{A}t)$ is orthogonal (that is, $[\exp(\mathbf{A}t)]'[\exp(\mathbf{A}t)] = \mathbf{I}$). Give an interpretation of this fact by considering the differential equation $\dot{\mathbf{x}} = \mathbf{A}\mathbf{x}$ and studying the properties of its solutions.

15 *Exercise* If $\mathbf{Z}_{kl}\mathbf{x} \neq \mathbf{0}$, then $\mathbf{Z}_{kj}\mathbf{x} \neq \mathbf{0}$ for all $j < l$.

16 *Exercise* Application to Markov chains. Let $\mathbf{P} = (p_{ij})$ be a Markov matrix: $p_{ij} \geq 0$, $\forall i, j$; $\sum_{j=1}^{\infty} p_{ij} = 1$, $\forall i$. p_{ij} is the probability of going from state i to state j in one transition.

(I) Let $\mathbf{p} = (p_1, p_2, \ldots, p_n)$ and $\mathbf{q} = (q_1, q_2, \ldots, q_n)$, where $\mathbf{q} = \mathbf{pP}$. (Interpretation: p_i is the probability of being in state i; q_j is the probability of being in state j after one transition.) Use the fact that $p_i \geq 0$ and $\sum_{i=1}^{n} p_i = 1$ to prove that all eigenvalues of **P** are in the circle $|\lambda| \leq 1$ and that those which are on the boundary have index 1. (II) Show that $\lim_{N\to\infty} \sum_{0}^{N} \mathbf{P}^k/(N+1)$ converges to a matrix **E**. (III) $\mathbf{E}^2 = \mathbf{E} = \mathbf{EP} = \mathbf{PE}$. (IV) $\mathcal{R}(\mathbf{E})$ is an invariant subspace of **P**, in fact the null space associated with the eigenvalue 1.

(V) $$\mathcal{C}^n = \mathcal{R}(\mathbf{E}) \oplus \mathcal{R}(\mathbf{I} - \mathbf{P})$$

(VI) For every **a** in $\mathcal{R}(\mathbf{E})$, there is a unique **x** such that $\mathbf{Px} = \mathbf{x}$ and $\mathbf{Ex} = \mathbf{a}$.

17 *Exercise* Show that

$$\mathbf{A}^N = \sum_{k=1}^{\sigma} \sum_{l=0}^{m_k-1} N(N-1) \cdots (N-l+1)\lambda_k^{N-l}\mathbf{Z}_{kl}$$

7 *Alternative expressions for* $f(\mathbf{A})$

Frequently, a function of a matrix is defined as follows. Let f be analytic in the disk $|\lambda| < R$, where $R > \max_{1\leq k\leq\sigma} |\lambda_k|$. Let the power-series representation of f over this disk be

$$f(\lambda) = \sum_{k=0}^{\infty} a_k\lambda^k$$

Then,

1 $$\sum_{k=0}^{\infty} a_k \mathbf{A}^k$$

is often taken as the meaning of $f(\mathbf{A})$.

This definition leads to exactly the same matrix $f(\mathbf{A})$ as the preceding one because of the following

2 **Theorem** Let f and each member of the sequence $\{f_N\}$ be analytic functions in an open set containing $\lambda_1, \lambda_2, \ldots, \lambda_\sigma$. Then, as $N \to \infty$

$$f_N(\mathbf{A}) \to f(\mathbf{A}) \Leftrightarrow f_N^{(l)}(\lambda_k) \to f^{(l)}(\lambda_k) \qquad 0 \le l \le m_k - 1$$

and $k = 1, 2, \ldots, \sigma$.

3 *Comment* If we take $f_N(\lambda) = \sum_{k=0}^{N} a_k \lambda^k$, then the above condition is fulfilled and Definition *D.4.1* gives the same result as *1*. Definition *D.4.1* has the advantage that it will suggest a computational procedure and that it is closely related to the geometrical structure of the L.T. **A**.

Proof $\Leftarrow$ This follows immediately from *D.6.5* once it is observed that the $\mathbf{Z}_{kl}$'s depend only on **A** and not on f.

$\Rightarrow$ Suppose now that $f_N(\mathbf{A}) \to f(\mathbf{A})$; we shall prove that $f_N^{(l)}(\lambda_k) \to f^{(l)}(\lambda_k)$. Pick an arbitrary eigenvalue, say, λ_k. Then pick $\mathbf{0} \ne \mathbf{x} \in \mathfrak{N}_k$ such that $\mathbf{x} \notin \mathfrak{N}_k^{m_k-1}$. Hence $\mathbf{E}_k\mathbf{x} = \mathbf{x}$ and $\mathbf{E}_j\mathbf{x} = \mathbf{0}$ if $j \ne k$. Let $\mathbf{y}_\beta = (\mathbf{A} - \lambda_k\mathbf{I})^\beta \mathbf{x}$, $\beta = 0, 1, 2, \ldots, m_k - 1$. To simplify the notation, let us put $\mu_k \triangleq m_k - 1$. From *D.6.2*, $f_N(\mathbf{A})\mathbf{y}_{\mu_k} = f_N(\lambda_k)\mathbf{y}_{\mu_k}$. Hence, since $f_N(\mathbf{A}) \to f(\mathbf{A})$, $f_N(\lambda_k) \to f(\lambda_k)$. Similarly, from *D.5.2*, $f_N(\mathbf{A})\mathbf{y}_{\mu_k-1} = f_N(\lambda_k)\mathbf{y}_{\mu_k-1} + f_N'(\lambda_k)\mathbf{y}_{\mu_k}$; consequently $f_N'(\lambda_k) \to f'(\lambda_k)$. Proceeding in this way, we establish $f_N^{(l)}(\lambda_k) \to f^{(l)}(\lambda_k)$ for

$$l = 2, 3, \ldots, m_k - 1 \quad \text{Q.E.D.}$$

4 **Theorem** Let f be analytic in a domain D containing the eigenvalues λ_i of **A**. Let C, the boundary of D, consist of a finite number of closed rectifiable Jordan curves; then

5 $$f(\mathbf{A}) = \frac{1}{2\pi j} \oint_C f(\lambda)(\lambda\mathbf{I} - \mathbf{A})^{-1}\, d\lambda$$

Proof Let $\rho(x) = 1/(\lambda - x)$. From *D.6.2* applied to the function ρ

$$(\lambda\mathbf{I} - \mathbf{A})^{-1} = \rho(\mathbf{A}) = \sum_{k=1}^{\sigma} \sum_{l=1}^{m_k-1} \frac{(\mathbf{A} - \lambda_k\mathbf{I})^l}{(\lambda - \lambda_k)^{l+1}} \mathbf{E}_k$$

Hence, in view of the analyticity of $f(\lambda)$ in the domain D,

$$\frac{1}{2\mu j}\oint_C f(\lambda)(\lambda\mathbf{I} - \mathbf{A})^{-1}\,d\lambda = \sum_{k=1}^{\sigma}\sum_{l=0}^{m_k-1}\frac{(\mathbf{A} - \lambda_k\mathbf{I})^l}{l!}f^{(l)}(\lambda_k)\mathbf{E}_k$$

The right-hand side according to *D.6.2* is the matrix $f(\mathbf{A})$; hence the theorem is established.

8 *Practical computation of* $f(\mathbf{A})$

The problem is the following: given an $n \times n$ matrix $\mathbf{A}$ whose elements are real or complex numbers and given a function, say, $f(x)$, find a convenient way for computing $f(\mathbf{A})$. This is an important problem in practice, as is shown by the following examples.

1 *Example* In the theory of linear time-invariant systems described by the system of differential equations $\dot{\mathbf{x}} = \mathbf{A}\mathbf{x} + \mathbf{a}(t)$, one is led to consider the matrix $e^{\mathbf{A}t}$. In this case $f(x) = e^{xt}$.

2 *Example* In the theory of linear time-invariant discrete systems described by $\mathbf{x}_{k+1} = \mathbf{A}\mathbf{x}_k + \mathbf{a}_k$, one is led to consider $\mathbf{A}^N$. In this case $f(x) = x^N$.

3 *Example* In the theory of stationary Markov chains one is particularly interested in the limiting behavior of $\mathbf{P}^N$ as $N \to \infty$, where $\mathbf{P}$ is the transition probability matrix of the chain.

Let $\lambda_1, \lambda_2, \ldots, \lambda_\sigma$ be the eigenvalues of $\mathbf{A}$: different eigenvalues are given a different label, so that $i \neq j$ implies $\lambda_i \neq \lambda_j$. If all the n eigenvalues of $\mathbf{A}$ are distinct, then $\sigma = n$; otherwise, $\sigma < n$.

Let $m_1, m_2, \ldots, m_\sigma$ be the multiplicity of the eigenvalues; that is, λ_i is a zero of order m_i of the *minimal* polynomial of $\mathbf{A}$.[1]

The interpolation method

This method is based directly on the definition of $f(\mathbf{A})$. We recall that if $p(\lambda) = \sum_{k=0}^{N} a_k\lambda^k$ is a polynomial, we define $p(\mathbf{A})$ as the matrix $\sum_{k=0}^{N} a_k\mathbf{A}^k$ with $\mathbf{A}^0 = \mathbf{I}$. Now, by Definition *D.4.1*,

4 $$f(\mathbf{A}) = p(\mathbf{A})$$

[1] As will be pointed out later, no error will be caused if one takes m_i to be the order of λ_i as a zero of the *characteristic* polynomial $\Delta(\lambda) = \det(\mathbf{A} - \lambda\mathbf{I})$. The computations, however, may be more complicated than they need be (see Remark *27*).

provided the interpolating polynomial p satisfies the following conditions:

5 $$f(\lambda_k) = p(\lambda_k) \qquad k = 1, 2, \ldots, \sigma$$

6 $$f^{(l)}(\lambda_k) = p^{(l)}(\lambda_k) \qquad k = 1, 2, \ldots, \sigma \qquad l = 1, 2, \ldots, m_k - 1$$

Thus, the computation of $f(\mathbf{A})$ consists of two steps: (I) the determination of an interpolating polynomial p satisfying conditions *5* and *6*, and (II) the evaluation of $p(\mathbf{A})$.

7 *Comment* Note the following special case: If the minimal polynomial $\psi(\lambda)$ has distinct roots, the interpolating polynomial is the well-known Lagrange interpolating polynomial

8 $$p(\lambda) = \sum_{k=1}^{\sigma} \frac{(\lambda - \lambda_1)(\lambda - \lambda_2) \cdots (\lambda - \lambda_{k-1})(\lambda - \lambda_{k+1}) \cdots (\lambda - \lambda_\sigma)}{(\lambda_k - \lambda_1)(\lambda_k - \lambda_2) \cdots (\lambda_k - \lambda_{k-1})(\lambda_k - \lambda_{k+1}) \cdots (\lambda_k - \lambda_\sigma)} f(\lambda_k)$$

Consequently

9 $$f(\mathbf{A}) = \sum_{k=1}^{\sigma} \left[\frac{f(\lambda_k)}{\prod_{\substack{i=1 \\ i \neq k}}^{\sigma} (\lambda_k - \lambda_i)} \prod_{\substack{i=1 \\ i \neq k}}^{\sigma} (\mathbf{A} - \lambda_i \mathbf{I}) \right]$$

10 *Example* Compute $\exp(\mathbf{A}t)$ for $\mathbf{A} = \begin{bmatrix} 1 & 1 & 0 \\ 0 & 1 & 0 \\ 0 & 0 & 2 \end{bmatrix}$.

Here $\lambda_1 = 1$, $m_1 = 2$; $\lambda_2 = 2$, $m_2 = 1$.

$$f(x) = \exp(xt) \qquad f'(x) = t \exp(xt)$$

Let $p(\lambda) = \alpha_0 + \alpha_1\lambda + \alpha_2\lambda^2$. Then $p'(\lambda) = \alpha_1 + 2\alpha_2\lambda$. The conditions *5* and *6* read

$$\begin{aligned} p(1) &= f(1) & \alpha_0 + \alpha_1 + \alpha_2 &= e^t \\ p'(1) &= f'(1) & \alpha_1 + 2\alpha_2 &= te^t \\ p(2) &= f(2) & \alpha_0 + 2\alpha_1 + 4\alpha_2 &= e^{2t} \end{aligned}$$

Solving the system, we get

$$\begin{aligned} \alpha_0 &= -2te^t + e^{2t} \\ \alpha_1 &= 2e^t + 3te^t - 2e^{2t} \\ \alpha_2 &= -e^t - te^t + e^{2t} \end{aligned}$$

With $\mathbf{A}^2 = \begin{bmatrix} 1 & 2 & 0 \\ 0 & 1 & 0 \\ 0 & 0 & 4 \end{bmatrix}$ we get

$$f(\mathbf{A}) = \alpha_0 \begin{bmatrix} 1 & 0 & 0 \\ 0 & 1 & 0 \\ 0 & 0 & 1 \end{bmatrix} + \alpha_1 \begin{bmatrix} 1 & 1 & 0 \\ 0 & 1 & 0 \\ 0 & 0 & 2 \end{bmatrix} + \alpha_2 \begin{bmatrix} 1 & 2 & 0 \\ 0 & 1 & 0 \\ 0 & 0 & 4 \end{bmatrix}$$

$$= \begin{bmatrix} e^t & te^t & 0 \\ 0 & e^t & 0 \\ 0 & 0 & e^{2t} \end{bmatrix} = e^{\mathbf{A}t}$$

11 *Comment* In general, we have

12 $$\exp(\mathbf{A}t) = \sum_{k=0}^{m-1} \alpha_k(t)\mathbf{A}^k$$

where m is the degree of the minimal polynomial of $\mathbf{A}$. The algebraic equations which determine the α_k's are of the form

$$\mathbf{M}\boldsymbol{\alpha} = \boldsymbol{\phi}(t)$$

where $\boldsymbol{\alpha} = (\alpha_0, \ldots, \alpha_{m-1})$; $\boldsymbol{\phi}$ is a vector whose elements are of the form $t^l e^{\lambda_k t}$, $k = 1, 2, \ldots, \sigma$; $l = 0, \ldots, m_k - 1$. The components of $\boldsymbol{\phi}$ form a set of functions of t which are linearly independent over any interval of positive length. Since the matrix $\mathbf{M}$ is a Vandermonde determinant in the case of simple eigenvalues and is closely related to a Vandermonde determinant when the eigenvalues are multiple, it is easy to show that $\mathbf{M}$ is always nonsingular. Therefore, the vector $\boldsymbol{\alpha}$ has components that are linearly independent linear combinations of the components of $\boldsymbol{\phi}$. Hence the

13 **Assertion** The components $\alpha_k(t)$ of $\boldsymbol{\alpha}$ form a set of functions of time that are linearly independent over any interval of positive length.

Method based on the fundamental formula

The second method is based on the fundamental formula, *D.6.5*, which states that, for any function f which is analytic at the eigenvalues $\lambda_1, \lambda_2, \ldots, \lambda_\sigma$ of $\mathbf{A}$,

14 $$f(\mathbf{A}) = \sum_{k=1}^{\sigma} \sum_{l=0}^{m_k-1} f^{(l)}(\lambda_k)\mathbf{Z}_{kl}$$

where the matrices $\mathbf{Z}_{kl}$, called the *components* of $\mathbf{A}$, depend exclusively on $\mathbf{A}$.

The matrices $\mathbf{Z}_{kl}$, although expressible as polynomials in $\mathbf{A}$, may be computed directly by inserting in the fundamental formula *14* appropriate trial functions f. The technique is best illustrated by an example.

15 *Example* Consider $\mathbf{A} = \begin{bmatrix} 1 & 1 & 0 \\ 0 & 1 & 1 \\ 0 & 0 & 2 \end{bmatrix}$, $\psi(\lambda) = (\lambda - 1)^2(\lambda - 2)$.

For any f analytic at $\lambda = 1$ and $\lambda = 2$, *14* states that

$$f(\mathbf{A}) = f(1)\mathbf{Z}_{10} + f'(1)\mathbf{Z}_{11} + f(2)\mathbf{Z}_{20}$$

The component matrices will be determined by taking special cases for f.

(I) Let $f(\lambda) = 1$ for all λ

16
$$\mathbf{Z}_{10} + \mathbf{Z}_{20} = \mathbf{I}$$

(II) Let $f(\lambda) = \lambda - 1$; hence

17
$$\mathbf{Z}_{11} + \mathbf{Z}_{20} = \mathbf{A} - \mathbf{I}$$

(III) Let $f(\lambda) = (\lambda - 1)^2$; hence

18
$$\mathbf{Z}_{20} = (\mathbf{A} - \mathbf{I})^2 = \begin{bmatrix} 0 & 0 & 1 \\ 0 & 0 & 1 \\ 0 & 0 & 1 \end{bmatrix}$$

16 to *18* constitute a system of equations in the $\mathbf{Z}_{ki}$. Observe that the coefficient matrix of the system of equations that has to be solved to find the $\mathbf{Z}_{ki}$ is in the triangular form; hence, the solution is obtained by successive substitutions from the bottom up.

$$f(\mathbf{A}) = f(1)\begin{bmatrix} 1 & 0 & -1 \\ 0 & 1 & -1 \\ 0 & 0 & 0 \end{bmatrix} + f'(1)\begin{bmatrix} 0 & 1 & -1 \\ 0 & 0 & 0 \\ 0 & 0 & 0 \end{bmatrix} + f(2)\begin{bmatrix} 0 & 0 & 1 \\ 0 & 0 & 1 \\ 0 & 0 & 1 \end{bmatrix}$$

In particular, if $f(\lambda) = e^{\lambda t}$, then $f'(\lambda) = te^{\lambda t}$ and

$$e^{\mathbf{A}t} = e^t\begin{bmatrix} 1 & 0 & -1 \\ 0 & 1 & -1 \\ 0 & 0 & 0 \end{bmatrix} + te^t\begin{bmatrix} 0 & 1 & -1 \\ 0 & 0 & 0 \\ 0 & 0 & 0 \end{bmatrix} + e^{2t}\begin{bmatrix} 0 & 0 & 1 \\ 0 & 0 & 1 \\ 0 & 0 & 1 \end{bmatrix}$$
$$= \begin{bmatrix} e^t & te^t & -e^t - te^t + e^{2t} \\ 0 & e^t & -e^t + e^{2t} \\ 0 & 0 & e^{2t} \end{bmatrix}$$

19 *Comment* The trial functions, written in the reverse of the order in which they appear above, are $(\lambda - 1)^2$, $(\lambda - 1)$, 1. It is easily recognized that they may be obtained by taking the minimum polynomial ψ and successively canceling one factor from ψ, then another from the resulting quotient, etc. It is clear that this technique will work in

general and will always result in a linear system of matrix equations for the $\mathbf{Z}_{ki}$ in which the matrix of the coefficients is triangular.

20 **Remark** If $\mathbf{A}$ has real elements, then both the characteristic and the minimal polynomial have real coefficients. Let the roots of the minimal polynomial be ordered so that $\lambda_1, \lambda_2, \ldots, \lambda_r$ are the real roots and $\lambda_{r+1}, \lambda_{r+1}^*, \ldots, \lambda_\sigma, \lambda_\sigma^*$ are the complex root pairs.

If the function $f(\cdot)$ has the property that $f(\lambda^*) = f(\lambda)^*$ for all λ, then cancellations occur and the fundamental formula *14* becomes

21 $$f(\mathbf{A}) = \sum_{k=1}^{r} \sum_{i=0}^{m_i-1} f^{(i)}(\lambda_k)\mathbf{Z}_{ki} + \sum_{k=r+1}^{\sigma} \sum_{i=0}^{m_i-1} \{\text{Re}\,[f^{(i)}(\lambda_k)]\mathbf{R}_{ki} + \text{Im}\,[f^{(i)}(\lambda_k)]\mathbf{X}_{ki}\}$$

where, for each complex root λ_k, we split $2\mathbf{Z}_{ki}$ into its real and imaginary parts,

$$2\mathbf{Z}_{ki} = \mathbf{R}_{ki} - j\mathbf{X}_{ki}$$

Consequently, *21* involves only real numbers with the corresponding increased convenience of the numerical work.

22 *Example* Evaluate $e^{\mathbf{A}t}$, where $\mathbf{A}$ is a 3×3 matrix with a real eigenvalue λ_1 and two complex conjugate eigenvalues λ_2 and λ_2^*. Let $\lambda_2 = \sigma_2 + j\omega_2$. Then from *21*

$$\exp(\mathbf{A}t) = e^{\lambda_1 t}\mathbf{Z}_{10} + e^{\sigma_2 t}[\mathbf{R}_{20}\cos\omega_{20}t + \mathbf{X}_{20}\sin\omega_2 t]$$

Apply *14* to $\varphi(\lambda) \triangleq (\lambda - \lambda_2)(\lambda - \lambda_2^*) = \lambda^2 - 2\sigma_2\lambda + |\lambda_2|^2$; hence

23 $$(\lambda_1^2 - 2\sigma_2\lambda_1 + |\lambda_2|^2)\mathbf{Z}_{10} = \mathbf{A}^2 - 2\sigma_2\mathbf{A} + |\lambda_2|^2\mathbf{I}$$

This equation determines $\mathbf{Z}_{10}$. The remaining unknown matrices $\mathbf{R}_{20}$ and $\mathbf{X}_{20}$ are obtained by substituting for f the functions $\varphi_1(\lambda) = \lambda - \sigma_2$, $\varphi_2(\lambda) = 1$ for all λ's in *21*:

24 $$(\lambda_1 - \sigma_2)\mathbf{Z}_{10} + \omega_2\mathbf{X}_{20} = \mathbf{A} - \sigma_2\mathbf{I}$$

25 $$\mathbf{Z}_{10} + \mathbf{R}_{20} = \mathbf{I}$$

The set of equations *23* to *25* can easily be solved for the three matrices $\mathbf{Z}_{10}, \mathbf{R}_{20}, \mathbf{X}_{20}$.

26 **Remark** There are convenient *numerical checks* on the evaluation of the $\mathbf{Z}_{kl}$'s:

(I) Put $f(\lambda) = \lambda$ in *14*. The right-hand side should give $\mathbf{A}$.

(II) Put $f(\lambda) \equiv 1$ in *14*; then $\sum_{k=1}^{\sigma} \mathbf{Z}_{k0} = \mathbf{I}$.

(III) For $k = 1, 2, \ldots, \sigma$, $\mathbf{Z}_{k0}^2 = \mathbf{Z}_{k0}$.

(IV) If $k \neq j$, $\mathbf{Z}_{k0}\mathbf{Z}_{j0} = \mathbf{0}$.

$$\mathbf{Z}_{kl}\mathbf{Z}_{jm} = \mathbf{0} \qquad 0 \le l \le m_k - 1;\ 0 \le m \le m_j - 1$$

27 **Remark** It may happen that we know only the characteristic polynomial Δ and not the minimal polynomial ψ. We assert that if we apply the fundamental formula *14* in which we use for the m_k's the order of the λ_k's as zeros of Δ (instead of their order as zeros of ψ), the same matrix $f(\mathbf{A})$ will be obtained.

This assertion follows from two considerations. First, the order of λ_k as a zero of Δ is never smaller than its order as a zero of ψ; second, $\mathbf{Z}_{kl}$ for $l \geq m_k$ is the zero matrix. This is immediate since by *D.6.4* and *D.6.2* it is implied that $\mathbf{Z}_{kl} = q_{kl}(\mathbf{A})$, where the polynomial q_{kl} is given by

$$q_{kl}(\lambda) = \frac{1}{l!}(\lambda - \lambda_k)^l \varphi_k(\lambda) = \frac{\psi(\lambda)n_k(\lambda)}{l!}(\lambda - \lambda_k)^{l-m_k}$$

Thus q_{kl} is a multiple of ψ whenever $l \geq m_k$. Hence from the definition of the minimum polynomial, $\mathbf{Z}_{kl} = \mathbf{0}$ for $l \geq m_k$.

Therefore, when the system of equations for the $\mathbf{Z}_{kl}$'s is solved, one may find some of them to be identically zero.

REFERENCES AND SUGGESTED READING

1 Dunford, N., and J. T. Schwarz: "Linear Operators. Part I: General Theory," Interscience Publishers, Inc., New York, 1958.

2 Fantappie: Sulle Funzioni di Una Matriza, *Anais Acad. Brasil. Cienc.*, vol. 26, no. 1, pp. 25–33, 1954.

3 Frazer, R. A., W. J. Duncan, and A. R. Collar: "Elementary Matrices," Cambridge University Press, New York, 1938.

4 Gantmacher, F. R.: "The Theory of Matrices," vols. 1 and 2, Chelsea Publishing Company, New York, 1959.

5 Hamburger, H. L., and M. E. Grimshaw: "Linear Transformations in n Dimensional Space," Cambridge University Press, New York, 1951.

6 Wedderburn, J. H. M.: Lectures on Matrices, 1934, *Amer. Math. Soc. Colloq. Publ.*, vol. 17.

Glossary of Symbols

Following is a list of principal symbols appearing in the book. For convenience, the symbols are grouped into three categories; each symbol is followed by a brief description and, where necessary, the location of its first use or formal definition.

I. General conventions

1. Lowercase boldface letters denote vectors, e.g., $\boldsymbol{\alpha}$, $\mathbf{u}$, $\mathbf{x}$.
2. Capital boldface letters denote matrices, e.g., $\mathbf{A}$, $\mathbf{B}$, $\mathbf{M}$.
3. Greek and italic type are used for scalar-valued variables, functions and operators, e.g., α, $u(t)$, L.
4. Capital script letters denote systems and sets (spaces), e.g., $\mathcal{A}$, $\mathcal{R}$.
5. Capital letters are used to denote the Laplace transforms; e.g., $H(s)$ is the Laplace transform of $h(t)$.
6. f or $f(\cdot)$ denotes a function, with the dot standing for an undesignated variable; $f(t)$ denotes the value of f at time t. The latter convention is not adhered to strictly, so that in many instances $f(t)$ is used in the same sense as f or $f(\cdot)$ (*1.3.3*).
7. $f_{[t_0,t_1]}$ denotes a segment of f over the closed interval $[t_0,t_1]$, that is, the set of pairs $\{(t,f(t)),\ t_0 \leq t \leq t_1\}$. Likewise for open and semi-closed intervals (*1.3.3*).
8. Braces denote a set or a family; e.g., $\{\mathbf{x}\}$ is a set with generic element $\mathbf{x}$. $\{\mathbf{x}|P\}$ is a set of $\mathbf{x}$'s having property P. $\{u_i\}^n$ is the sequence $u_0, \ldots, u_n$.
9. A bar over a function indicates that its range is a function space, e.g., $\bar{\mathbf{A}}(\boldsymbol{\alpha};\mathbf{u})$ (*1.6.2*).
10. A dot over a time function indicates its time derivative; e.g., $\dot{\mathbf{x}}$. $\mathbf{x}^{(n)}$ or $\mathbf{x}^{(n)}(t)$ stands for the nth derivative of $\mathbf{x}(t)$.
11. Superscript asterisk (*) denotes (I) the complex conjugate of a number, e.g., ξ^*; (II) the adjoint of an operator, e.g., L^*; (III) the conjugate transpose of a matrix, e.g., $\mathbf{A}^*$; or (IV) the terminal state, e.g., $\boldsymbol{\alpha}^*$.
12. Superscript minus one ($^{-1}$) denotes the inverse of a system or a transformation or a matrix, e.g., $\mathcal{A}^{-1}$, L^{-1}, $\mathbf{A}^{-1}$.
13. Superscript dagger (†) denotes the pseudo inverse of a matrix, e.g., $\mathbf{A}^\dagger$.
14. Superscript perpendicular ($^\perp$) denotes the orthogonal complement of a subspace, e.g., $\mathcal{M}^\perp$.

15. Superscript tilde (˜) denotes (I) the z transform, e.g., $\tilde{F}(z)$, or (II) the suppressed output vector, e.g., $\tilde{\mathbf{y}}$.

II. General symbols and abbreviations

$\triangleq$	equals by definition; denotes
$\Rightarrow$	implies (*2.1.11*)
$\Leftarrow$	is implied by (*2.1.11*)
$\Leftrightarrow$	implies and is implied by; if and only if (*2.1.13*)
$\ni$	such that (*B.4.6 et seq.*)
$\forall$	for all (*1.3.2*)
$\exists$	there exists (*1.3.2*)
$\supset$	contains (*2.5.1*)
$\subset$	is a subset of; is contained in
$\in$	is an element of
$\notin$	does not belong to
$\cup$	union
$\cap$	intersection
$\{x\|P\}$	set of x's having property P
$\simeq$	state equivalent (*2.2.1*)
	approximately equals
$\sim$	asymptotically equals
$\not\simeq$	not state equivalent (*2.2.3*)
$\equiv$	system equivalence (*2.5.8*)
$\doteq$	zero-state equivalent (*2.9.1*)
$\overset{*}{=}$	conditionally equivalent (*2.7.5*)
$\times$	cartesian product (*1.4.17*)
	direct product (*1.10.2*)
$+$	parallel combination (*1.10.30*)
$\oplus$	direct sum (*C.7.7*)
$\overset{\perp}{\oplus}$	direct sum of orthogonal subspaces
$*$	convolution (*B.3.9*)
$\langle\cdot,\cdot\rangle$	scalar product (dots stand for undesignated variables) (*C.5.1*)
$\cdot\rangle\langle\cdot$	dyad (*5.4.15*)
(a,b)	open interval $a < t < b$
$(a,b]$	semiclosed interval $a < t \leq b$
$[a,b]$	closed interval $a \leq t \leq b$
$t-$	instant of time immediately preceding t
$t+$	instant of time immediately following t
$\|\cdot\|$	norm (*C.16.1, C.16.9, C.16.11*)
$\|\cdot\|_1$	l_1 norm (*C.16.7*)
$\|\cdot\|_2$	l_2 norm (*C.16.5, C.16.16*)
$\|\cdot\|_\infty$	l_∞ norm (*C.16.16*)
$\measuredangle\, s$	argument of the complex number s

$\mathfrak{F}$	Fourier transform (*B.2.15*)
$\mathfrak{L}$	Laplace transform (*B.2.2*)
$\mathfrak{L}_{II}$	bilateral Laplace transform (*B.2.11*)
$\mathcal{C}^n$	space of ordered n-tuples of complex numbers
$\mathcal{R}^n$	space of ordered n-tuples of real numbers
C^n	space of functions possessing continuous derivatives of order n
$\inf_x$	infimum over x (greatest lower bound)
$\sup_x$	supremum over x (least upper bound) (p. 401 n)
lim inf	limit inferior
lim sup	limit superior
sgn	signum function: $\operatorname{sgn} x = 1$ for $x > 0$, $\operatorname{sgn} x = -1$ for $x < 0$, $\operatorname{sgn} x = 0$ for $x = 0$ (*7.7.10 et seq.*)
$\max(m,n)$	$\max(m,n) = m$ if $m \leq n$, $\max(m,n) = n$ if $n > m$ (*3.8.22*)
$\max_i$	maximum over i
det	determinant
tr	trace
diag	diagonal matrix
L.T.	linear transformation
i.s.L.	in the sense of Lyapunov
b.i.b.o	bounded-input bounded-output
R.H.S.	right-hand side
L.H.S.	left-hand side
Q.E.D.	*quod erat demonstrandum*
et seq.	*et sequens*
$\triangleleft$	end of discussion

III. Symbols with special meaning (arranged in alphabetical order)

$\mathcal{A}$	system, abstract object (*1.4.17*)
$\mathcal{A}\mathcal{B}$	tandem combination (product) of $\mathcal{A}$ and $\mathcal{B}$, with $\mathcal{B}$ followed by $\mathcal{A}$ (*1.10.23*)
$\mathbf{A}(\boldsymbol{\alpha};\mathbf{u}_{(t_0,t]})$	response of $\mathcal{A}$ at time t to input $\mathbf{u}_{(t_0,t]}$, with $\mathcal{A}$ in state $\boldsymbol{\alpha}$ at time t_0 (*1.6.2*)
$\mathbf{A}(\boldsymbol{\alpha};\mathbf{u})$	abbreviation of above (*1.6.2*)
$\bar{\mathbf{A}}(\boldsymbol{\alpha};\mathbf{u}_{(t_0,t]})$	response segment of $\mathcal{A}$ to input $\mathbf{u}_{(t_0,t]}$, with $\mathcal{A}$ in state $\boldsymbol{\alpha}$ at time t_0 (*1.6.2*)
$\bar{\mathbf{A}}(\boldsymbol{\alpha};\mathbf{u})$	abbreviation of above (*1.6.2*)
$\mathbf{A}(\boldsymbol{\theta};\mathbf{u})$	zero-state response of $\mathcal{A}$ to input $\mathbf{u}$ (*2.8.18*)
$\mathbf{A}(\mathbf{u})$	abbreviation of above (*2.8.18*)
$\mathbf{A}(\boldsymbol{\alpha};\mathbf{0})$	zero-input response of $\mathcal{A}$ starting in state $\boldsymbol{\alpha}$ (*2.8.23*)

$\mathcal{A}(\mathbf{u},\mathbf{y})$ input-output relation (*1.4.17*)
$\mathcal{A}^{-1}$ inverse of $\mathcal{A}$ (*2.10.6*)
$\mathcal{A}_l^{-1}$ left-constrained inverse of $\mathcal{A}$ (*2.10.20*)
$\mathbf{a}(t)$ equivalent input (*5.2.20*)
$\mathcal{C}^n$ space of ordered n-tuples of complex numbers
C^n space of functions possessing continuous derivatives of order n
$\mathfrak{D}$ space of testing functions (p. 522)
$\mathfrak{D}_K$ space of testing functions whose support is contained in the finite interval K (p. 523)
$\mathfrak{D}$ system of the differential operator type (*3.3.1*)
D unit delay operator (*3.8.36*)
δ_{ij} Kronecker delta: $\delta_{ij} = 1$ for $i \neq j$, $\delta_{ii} = 0$ (*C.4.12*)
$\delta(t)$ delta function (unit impulse) occurring at $t = 0$ (*A.2.1*)
$\delta^{(n)}(t)$ delta function of order n (*A.2.5*)
$\mathbf{E}$ projection (*C.12.14*)
$\mathbf{E}_k$ projection on $\mathfrak{N}_k$ (*D.5.6, D.5.13*)
$\exp \mathbf{A}t$ exponential of the matrix $\mathbf{A}t$ (*5.2.3, D.6.12*)
$\mathfrak{F}$ Fourier transform (*B.2.15*)
$\mathbf{G}(t,\tau)$ Green's dyadic (*5.2.24*)
$\mathbf{\Gamma}$ matrix relating two sets of basis functions (*3.2.9*)
$h(t,\xi)$ impulse response [zero-state response at time t to $\delta(t - \xi)$] (*3.6.5, 6.3.2*)
$h(t)$ impulse response of a time-invariant system with $\xi = 0$ (*3.6.5*)
$\mathbf{h}(t)$ state impulse response (*3.7.31*)
$H(s)$ transfer function (*3.6.17, 9.2.1*)
$\mathbf{I}$ identity matrix, unitor (*1.9.8*)
$L(p)$ constant-coefficient differential operator (*3.8.11*)
$L(p,t)$ variable-coefficient differential operator (*4.5.58, 6.2.47*)
$\dfrac{1}{L(p)}$ system characterized by $L(p)y = u$ ($u \triangleq$ input, $y \triangleq$ output) (*4.3.1 et seq.*)
$\dfrac{1}{L(p)} \cdot M(p)$ system characterized by $L(p)y = M(p)u$ (*4.5.9 et seq.*)
$\mathfrak{L}$ Laplace transform
$\mathfrak{L}^{-1}$ inverse Laplace transform
$\mathfrak{L}_{\mathrm{II}}$ bilateral Laplace transform
λ_i ith eigenvalue of $\mathbf{A}$ (*5.4.5*)
$\mathfrak{M}$ subspace of a linear vector space (*C.5.12*)
$\mathfrak{N}(\mathcal{A})$ null space of the linear transformation $\mathcal{A}$ (*C.9.7*)
$\mathfrak{N}(\mathbf{A})$ null space of the linear transformation represented by matrix $\mathbf{A}$ (*C.9.7*)

$\mathfrak{N}_k^l$ null space of $(\mathbf{A} - \lambda_k\mathbf{I})^l$ (*5.5.2, D.3.1*)

$\mathfrak{N}_k$ generalized null space of $\mathbf{A}$ associated with its kth eigenvalue (*5.5.5, D.3.2*)

$\mathbf{0}$ zero vector, zero matrix, null function (*2.8.1*)

o of the order of (*7.4.1 et seq.*)

$1(t)$ unit step function (*A.2.1 et seq.*)

p derivative in the distribution sense (*3.8.3, A.2.3, A.5.4 et seq.*)

$\phi_i(t,t_0)$ ith basis function (zero-input response) starting at t_0 (*3.6.32*)

$\phi_i(t)$ ith basis function starting at $t_0 = 0$ (*3.6.39*)

$\mathbf{\Phi}(t,t_0)$ state transition matrix (*6.2.8*)

$\mathbf{\Phi}(t)$ state transition matrix with $t = 0$ (*3.7.7, 5.2.8*)

$\hat{\mathbf{\Phi}}(s)$ Laplace transform of $\mathbf{\Phi}(t)$ (*5.3.2 et seq.*)

$\mathcal{R}$ system of the reciprocal differential operator type (*3.3.1*)

$\mathcal{R}(\mathcal{A})$ range of the linear transformation $\mathcal{A}$ (*C.9.6*)

$\mathcal{R}(\mathbf{A})$ range of the linear transformation represented by the matrix $\mathbf{A}$ (*C.9.6*)

$R[\mathbf{u}(t)]$ range of the variable $\mathbf{u}(t)$ (at fixed t) (*1.4.3, 1.4.17*)

$R[\mathbf{u}]$ range of the time function $\mathbf{u}$ (*1.4.3, 1.4.17*)

$R_{[t_0,t_1]}$ space of input-output pairs over $[t_0,t_1]$ (*1.4.17*)

Re real part of

Σ state space (*1.6.2*)

$\Sigma(t,t_0)$ state space of a free interconnection at time t (*1.10.15*)

$\Sigma(t)$ state space of an interconnection at time t (*1.10.21*)

$\mathbf{s}(t)$ state at time t (*1.7.1*)

$\mathbf{s}(\mathbf{s}(t_0);\mathbf{u}_{(t_0,t]})$ state at time t when the input $\mathbf{u}_{(t_0,t]}$ is applied, with the system initially in state $\mathbf{s}(t_0)$ (*1.8.2*)

$\mathcal{S}[\mathbf{x}_1, \ldots, \mathbf{x}_n]$ subspace spanned by $\mathbf{x}_1, \ldots, \mathbf{x}_n$ (*A.4.2 et seq.*)

T range of t (*1.3.1*)

T_δ translation operator (*3.2.2*)

$\langle T,\phi \rangle$ value of the distribution T at ϕ (*A.4.1*)

$\mathbf{\theta}$ zero state (*2.8.2*)

$\mathbf{u}$ input vector (*1.4.17*)

$\mathbf{uu}'$ $\mathbf{u}$ followed by $\mathbf{u}'$ (*1.6.16*)

u_j^i jth component of input to $\mathcal{A}_i$ (*2.6.1*)

$1(t)$ unit step function starting at $t = 0$ [$1(t) = 0$ for $t < 0$, $1(t) = 1$ for $t \geq 0$] (*A.2.1 et seq.*)

$(\mathbf{u},\mathbf{y})$ input-output pair (*1.4.17*)

$\mathbf{x}(t)$ state at time t of a differential system (*3.6.2 et seq., 5.2.1*)

$\mathbf{x}(t;\mathbf{x}_0,t_0)$ state at time t given that the state at t_0 is $\mathbf{x}_0$ and no input is applied during $(t_0,t]$ (*5.2.11*)

$\mathbf{x}(t;\mathbf{x}_0,t_0;\mathbf{a}_{(t_0,t]})$ state at time t when the input $\mathbf{a}_{(t_0,t]}$ is applied and the initial state (at t_0) is $\mathbf{x}_0$ (*5.2.21*)

$\mathbf{y}$ output vector (*1.4.17*)

$\tilde{\mathbf{y}}$ suppressed output vector (p. 11)

$\mathbf{Z}_{kl}$ components of the matrix $\mathbf{A}$ (*5.3.1*)

$Z(s,\boldsymbol{\alpha})$ Laplace transform of the zero-input response starting in state $\boldsymbol{\alpha}$ (*4.7.6*)

Index

Page references in **boldface** type indicate definitions